FATTY ACIDS

AND

THEIR DERIVATIVES

FATTY ACIDS

AND

THEIR DERIVATIVES

A. W. RALSTON

Assistant Director of Research
Armour and Company

JOHN WILEY & SONS, INC., NEW YORK

CHAPMAN & HALL, LTD., LONDON

PRINTED IN THE UNITED STATES OF AMERICA

PREFACE

SEVERAL GENERATIONS HAVE passed since Chevreul first isolated the fatty acids, and during this period the labors of many investigators have advanced our knowledge of the physical and chemical properties of these compounds. Progress in our understanding of the fatty acids has been highlighted by certain notable contributions, some of which have compelled us to modify our earlier, simpler concepts. The structures of the acids as revealed by x rays, the behavior of acid mixtures, the role of polymorphism, the colloidal behavior of many of the fatty acid derivatives testify to the unexpected complexities of which the casual observer is unaware. Perchance some master craftsman will arise with the ability to weave together the phenomena associated with this field. More probably, this task will be accomplished only by the tireless and unceasing toil of many present and future scientists. It is to this latter group that this book is primarily directed. It will have served its purpose if it helps those who are to write that which is yet unwritten concerning this interesting group of organic compounds.

The subject matter of this book logically divides itself into two sections. The first embraces a description of the fatty acids, their occurrence in nature, their synthesis, and their physical properties. The second is concerned with the synthesis, properties, and uses of the various fatty acid derivatives.

This writing has been confined to those acids which contain six or more carbon atoms and the derivatives of these acids. The term derivative is employed in its broader sense and includes those compounds which can be obtained by employing the fatty acids as the starting material. Any group of compounds which can be prepared from the acids either directly or indirectly is, therefore, considered as a fatty acid derivative. Those acids and derivatives which contain less than six carbon atoms have been

v

mentioned only where their inclusion has served to complete a series or has been deemed essential for purposes of orientation. The naturally occurring fats, oils, and waxes have been considered only as sources of the fatty acids, and no attempt has been made to include the configuration of the naturally occurring glycerides or to discuss in any detail the generalizations pertaining to the structural differences which characterize the glycerides from different sources. The synthetic glycerides, on the other hand, have been discussed at some length since they can rightly be considered as derivatives of the acids. The preparation of the fatty acids from their natural esters has been considered as pertinent subject matter, as have the various processes for the separation and purification of the acids.

The preparation, physical and chemical properties, and certain uses of the major derivatives of the fatty acids are discussed in detail. In considering these various derivatives an attempt has also been made to throw light upon their historical background and to estimate their relative importance. Where a voluminous patent literature has been built around a specific type of derivative that material which best illustrates the synthesis and characteristic properties of the class has been chosen.

This book has been a number of years in preparation, a period through which I have enjoyed the advice and encouragement of my friend and former teacher, Dr. Henry Gilman. The transition from a crude manuscript to a finished book demands many hours of tiresome and tedious work. A number of my associates have cooperated with me in this phase of the undertaking, and to them goes my sincere gratitude. This humble acknowledgment combines my deep appreciation and my recognition of the importance of such contributions. I am indebted to Dr. E. J. Hoffman and Mr. R. J. Drozda for checking the references and to Miss Helen Peterson and Miss Catherine O'Connor for the several typings of the manuscript. Miss O'Connor also assisted in the proofreading and in the preparation of the index. Mr. C. McCann aided in the translation of many articles from the German literature. The drawings were prepared by Mr. C. W. Hoerr and Mr. D. N. Eggenberger. The original manuscript was critically reviewed by Dr. F. K. Broome, who has also assisted in the reading of the proof and in the preparation of the index. His careful surveys of the several phases of the manuscript and his many suggestions have been of great value. I am indebted to the many workers in this

field who have permitted me to quote from their publications and
to those editors of scientific journals who have allowed the use of
printed material. I thank Esther for her unfailing patience and
encouragement.

In closing, I am mindful of the loyal cooperation of my fellow
workers in this laboratory and of the enthusiastic support and
encouragement of my superiors in Armour and Company, without
which certain portions of the experimental work recorded herein
would not have been brought to materialization.

A. W. R.

Chicago, Illinois
January, 1948

CONTENTS

ix

THE SATURATED FATTY ACIDS

The fatty acids are a large group of aliphatic carboxylic acids, so termed because of their widespread occurrence in the natural fats, oils, and allied substances. In view of the common origin of all fatty acids, their structural similarities, and their mutual association in nature, one should keep in mind that the various series have many properties in common. Thus, a number of the generalizations which pertain to the saturated series will be found to embrace the entire group of fatty acids. We cannot, therefore, consider such series as the saturated acids, the various unsaturated acids, the hydroxy acids, and other series of fatty acids in a strictly isolated sense. These groups simply represent a classification based upon certain differences in chemical structure, which differences permit of a comparatively logical grouping of a large number of closely related chemical individuals.

The saturated acids are a homologous series of compounds of the general formula RCO_2H, in which the R group is a straight-chain radical broadly characterized as $CH_3(CH_2)_x$ or C_nH_{2n+1}. The acids range from volatile liquids to waxy solids as the series is ascended and the intermediate members show all gradations between these two extremes. Those acids which contain from six to nine carbon atoms are oily liquids, whereas those having ten or more carbon atoms are solids which increase in waxlike properties with increase in molecular weight. Strictly speaking, the term saturated fatty acid is descriptive only of the higher members of the series, the properties of which are essentially dependent upon the presence of the long-chain alkyl group. The lower members of this homologous series are extremely water soluble; however, water solubility decreases rapidly with increase in the number of carbon atoms. The boiling points increase with each successive addition of a CH_2 group. The same may be said of the melting points subject to the consideration of alternation between the melting points of odd and even members.

1

Our knowledge of the fatty acids dates back to a time previous to the establishment of a rational chemical nomenclature for organic compounds. As a consequence, the various members of the series are not usually designated by their true systematic names, but rather by their common names, which in most cases have a historical significance and are retained largely because of common usage and convenience. For example, the names lauric, palmitic, and stearic acids are descriptive of the sources of the acids. Although the continued use of these common names, particularly when carried over to a derivative, frequently leads to confusion, these acids will probably always be so designated. It appears desirable, therefore, in order to avoid any confusion as to nomenclature, to present at the beginning of this chapter a list of the various members of the saturated fatty acid series, including the chemical names, formulas, and also the present accepted common names of the more important members. Table I contains this information for the more important saturated fatty acids which contain five or more carbon atoms.

TABLE I
Names and Formulas of Saturated Fatty Acids

Chemical Name	Formula	Common Name
Pentanoic	$CH_3(CH_2)_3CO_2H$	Valeric
Hexanoic	$CH_3(CH_2)_4CO_2H$	Caproic
Heptanoic	$CH_3(CH_2)_5CO_2H$	Enanthic
Octanoic	$CH_3(CH_2)_6CO_2H$	Caprylic
Nonanoic	$CH_3(CH_2)_7CO_2H$	Pelargonic
Decanoic	$CH_3(CH_2)_8CO_2H$	Capric
Undecanoic	$CH_3(CH_2)_9CO_2H$	....
Dodecanoic	$CH_3(CH_2)_{10}CO_2H$	Lauric
Tridecanoic	$CH_3(CH_2)_{11}CO_2H$	....
Tetradecanoic	$CH_3(CH_2)_{12}CO_2H$	Myristic
Pentadecanoic	$CH_3(CH_2)_{13}CO_2H$	....
Hexadecanoic	$CH_3(CH_2)_{14}CO_2H$	Palmitic
Heptadecanoic	$CH_3(CH_2)_{15}CO_2H$	{ Margaric { (Daturic)
Octadecanoic	$CH_3(CH_2)_{16}CO_2H$	Stearic
Nonadecanoic	$CH_3(CH_2)_{17}CO_2H$	....
Eicosanoic	$CH_3(CH_2)_{18}CO_2H$	Arachidic
Docosanoic	$CH_3(CH_2)_{20}CO_2H$	Behenic
Tetracosanoic	$CH_3(CH_2)_{22}CO_2H$	Lignoceric
Hexacosanoic	$CH_3(CH_2)_{24}CO_2H$	Cerotic
Octacosanoic	$CH_3(CH_2)_{26}CO_2H$	Montanic
Triacontanoic	$CH_3(CH_2)_{28}CO_2H$	Melissic
Dotriacontanoic	$CH_3(CH_2)_{30}CO_2H$	Lacceroic

Historical Considerations

For a critical evaluation of our knowledge of the saturated fatty acids it is necessary to go far back into chemical history and retrace the various contributions which have culminated in our present ideas concerning them. In view of the facts that the saturated fatty acids present an excellent example of homology and are of comparatively simple structure, and since certain members of the series occur abundantly, one might expect that their study has offered few difficult problems. That this is not the case is testified to by the fact that it has been only within comparatively recent years that the true chemical structure of the higher members has been determined and that generalizations with regard to the series as a whole have been formulated and proved. In a historical review of this series there are several facts which must be borne in mind. Our earliest knowledge of these acids was essentially confined to those members which occur naturally. Acids such as enanthic or pelargonic, which are obtained only synthetically, were not known to earlier workers. Of still more importance is the fact that the naturally occurring saturated acids are invariably associated with unsaturated acids and oftentimes hydroxy acids. Thus, our earlier information concerning the fatty acids was not confined exclusively to any particular series of acids. The saturated fatty acids were the first of the fatty acids recognized as chemical individuals and most of the pioneer discoveries and theories embraced only the members of this series. That other types of acids existed, however, was recognized at the outset.

Our ancestors developed many specific uses for fats in addition to their use as foods, and it is evident that they must have had a considerable familiarity with the properties of the various fatty substances. Burning oils, drying oils, waxes, tallows, and other types were recognized as having distinctive properties and specific uses at a very early stage in our civilization. Somewhat later the cultivation of various oil-bearing trees and plants was developed, along with methods for the extraction and purification of the oils so obtained.

Saponification was the first chemical reaction to which oils and fats were subjected, and the early chemical history of these substances actually constitutes a study of this process. The study of the products of saponification offered the initial clue to the actual structure of the fats. Soaps were first prepared by boiling fats with wood ashes and were considered to be a combination of the fats with the ash constituents. Later, caustic was substituted for the wood ashes, but it was not until the middle of the seventeenth century that it was suggested that soap consisted of a combination of acid with alkali. As early as 1666 Tachenium stated, in his paper entitled "Hippocrates Chimicas," that saponification represents such a process.

Our present views concerning the structure of the fats and fatty acids were formulated during the first quarter of the nineteenth century. The father of our modern conception of fatty substances was a French chemist, Chevreul, whose contributions upon this subject were made between the years 1813 and 1825. Chevreul's work was presented in a series of papers before the French Academy and was later summarized in a book entitled *Recherches chimiques sur les corps gras d'origine animal*, which was published by G. Levrault in Paris during the year 1823. His classical work on fatty substances was of importance not only because he first established the structure of the fats and isolated a number of the more important saturated acids, but also because he succeeded in liberating this field from many of the erroneous theories and fanciful ideas of his day.

Both of the constituents of fats, glycerol and the fatty acids, had been isolated many years before Chevreul's time. In 1741, Geoffroy ascertained that the products obtained from the neutralization of soap differed from the original fat in that such substances were soluble in alcohol, whereas the fats themselves were insoluble. There can be no question but that Geoffroy actually had isolated the fatty acids, but the significance of his discovery was not apparent at that time. In 1779, Scheele discovered that one of the products of the action of lead oxide on olive oil was a sweet substance which he termed "olsuss." Four years later he obtained this substance from a number of other oils and stated that it was apparently a constituent of all oils and fats. The discovery of glycerol occurred at perhaps the most chaotic period in all chemical history. Lavoisier's researches upon combustion had been announced just a few years previously. The phlogiston theory, which considered fire as a material element, had dominated chemical thinking since its proposal by Becher and its advancement by Stahl. This theory, although under severe attack by Lavoisier, still had many adherents, one of the most ardent of whom was Scheele. Because of Scheele's interpretation of all his experiments and discoveries in the light of the phlogiston theory, their true significance was not fully appreciated until many years later. Thus, as late as 1787 Abbé Rozier, in commenting upon oils in his work entitled *A Complete Agricultural Course*, stated that fats and oils were composed of phlogiston, water, and earth. Oils offered many complex problems, one of which was concerned with the so-called oil principle. Fourcroy comments in detail in his *Elements of Natural History and Chemistry* on this oil principle, which he considered to be identical with the distillate obtained during the pyrolysis of fatty substances.

The isolation of fatty acids by Geoffroy and of glycerol by Scheele were discoveries of extreme importance; however, their interpretation and actual significance were only apparent after the work of Chevreul. Although Braconnot,[1] * whose investigations were contemporary with those of Chevreul, did much to advance the technology of fats, he apparently never recognized the true nature of the fats or the meaning of many of his observations. Chevreul's work on the fats was initiated by a study of the products of saponification of pork fat, which confirmed the presence of glycerol in the saponification products. Treatment of the resulting soaps with hydrochloric acid yielded a solid fatty substance which he named "margarine" and a liquid which he described as "fluid grease." Chevreul determined that both the "margarine" and the "fluid grease" are acidic substances, and a short time later he named the former margaric acid. He also stated that the fats are ester-like substances in which the alcohol is glycerol. The "fluid grease" was undoubtedly oleic acid, but its identity was not established until some time later. The name margaric acid, which Chevreul gave to the solid acid, was retained until 1857, when Heintz[2] proved it to be identical with the acid obtained from palm oil by Frémy[3] which was termed palmitic acid. Very early in his work Chevreul observed that the solid acid isolated from mutton tallow had a higher melting point than that obtained from pork fat, and this observation culminated in Chevreul's discovery of stearic acid in 1816. In 1819, Chevreul obtained from dolphin oil an acid which he named "phocenic acid," later found to be identical with valeric acid, and in the same year he separated butyric, caproic, and capric acids from butter fat by fractional crystallization of their barium salts.

Very few important scientific contributions go unchallenged, and Chevreul's findings were no exception. His statement that

* Bibliographical notes will be found at end of each chapter.

the fats are ester-like bodies which combine glycerol and the fatty acids was in conflict with the then accepted theory of Lavoisier. This theory held that the essential element of all acids is oxygen and that the amount of oxygen in compounds is a measure of their acidic properties. Since the percentage of oxygen in glycerol is substantially greater than that in the fatty acids, it was quite difficult to see how glycerol could function as a base. Lavoisier's views concerning acids were first seriously challenged by the investigations of Gay-Lussac, Thenard, and Davy upon the constitution of hydrochloric acid and also by Gay-Lussac's observations that hydrocyanic acid contains only hydrogen, carbon, and nitrogen. Several of Chevreul's contemporaries, particularly Fourcroy, argued that the acidic nature of the products obtained by Chevreul were due to the fixation of oxygen during the saponification. Chevreul then showed that similar products were obtained when the saponification was conducted *in vacuo* and later proved that water was involved in all processes of fat splitting. He did not, however, assign formulas to the fatty acids which he isolated, but confined his disclosure to a description of their general properties.

In 1819, six of the more important saturated fatty acids had been isolated; namely, butyric, valeric, caproic, capric, palmitic, and stearic acids. A period of twenty years elapsed after the discovery of these acids by Chevreul until any further additions were made to this list. Playfair [4] in 1841 announced the isolation of myristic acid from nutmeg butter, and the next year Marsson [5] discovered lauric acid in laurel kernel oil. The existence of lauric acid was later confirmed by its isolation from coconut oil by Görgey.[6] Caprylic acid, which was apparently overlooked by Chevreul, was discovered by Lerch [7] in 1844 during an examination of the fatty acids of butter fat. The first saturated fatty acid containing more than eighteen carbon atoms to be described was behenic acid, which was isolated from behen oil by Völcker [8] in 1848, and in the same year Brodie [9] established the presence of cerotic acid in beeswax. Six years later Gösmann [10] announced the discovery of arachidic acid in peanut oil, and a number of years later Kreiling [11] restudied the acids of peanut oil and observed the presence of lignoceric acid, which had been previously discovered by Hell and Hermanns [12] in their investigation of the fatty acids of beech tar paraffin. A study of the fatty acids of beeswax by Nafzger,[13] Marie,[14] and others led to the isolation of montanic and melissic acids, but their identity as individuals was not proved until a comparatively recent date.

Occurrence of the Saturated Fatty Acids

The saturated fatty acids occur in association with the unsaturated fatty acids [15] and hydroxy acids in the various oils, fats, and waxes. Such fatty substances are essential components of animal, marine, and vegetable life, and the fatty acids are undoubtedly a necessary factor in the life cycle of every living thing. We are, at present, quite ignorant of the laws which govern the natural occurrence of the fatty acids and can only offer certain generalizations based upon observation.

The fatty acids occur almost exclusively in nature in the form of esters. They are seldom found in the free state. Although free fatty acids have been frequently reported in the fats of ripe seeds and in the waxes, there is considerable question as to whether they were originally present as such or were formed by the action of the various seed lipases or by refining processes to which the waxes were subjected. The glycerides constitute, by far, the most important source of the fatty acids. These glycerides are esters of the trihydric alcohol glycerol with the fatty acids and are represented in nature by the many oils, fats, and phosphatides. It is beyond the scope or intention of this book to discuss the naturally occurring glycerides in detail since this subject has been adequately treated by others.[16] However, the glycerides are, by far, the most abundant source of the fatty acids and it is advisable to consider in some detail several of the generalizations concerning them.

The glycerides occur widely distributed as normal constituents of all forms of animal, vegetable, and marine life. The particular acids present depend very largely on the source of the glyceride, although the relative amounts of the various acids have been shown to be influenced by the environment under which they are formed. Thus, the fats of sea life are characterized by the presence of high molecular weight, highly unsaturated acids associated with only minor amounts of saturated acids. Fats of land animals contain large amounts of C_{16} and C_{18} saturated and unsaturated acids, whereas fats of vegetable origin contain substantial amounts of one or more closely related acids which are characteristic of the particular source. Thus, coconut oil contains a large amount of lauric acid and closely related acids, ricinoleic acid is found in castor oil, eleostearic acid characterizes tung oil, and palmitic acid constitutes a major component of palm oil.

A marked correlation exists between the fats produced by the various members of the animal kingdom, particularly as regards their depot fats and the fats contained in their normal food. Sea algae and other marine plants contain many of the characteristic acids present in fish oils,[17] and the work of Klem [18] indicates that the fats of whales and those of the crustacea upon which they feed are of quite similar composition. This correlation appears, however, to be confined essentially to the depot fats since the same author has shown that rats fed on coconut oil and whale oil contained similar body fats on starvation. An interesting example of the influence of diet fat on the composition of depot fats has been reported recently by Hilditch and Murti.[19] The depot fat of the land crab *Birgus latro*, L., commonly known as the coconut crab, contains 66.5% of fully saturated glycerides and shows a remarkable similarity in composition to coconut oil; however, the remainder of the fat is typical of that of marine animals. This unusual composition of the depot fat is attributed to the fact that this crab is known to feed on coconuts. The influence of the composition of fats in feeds on the structure of the body fats of hogs has been studied by a number of investigators, among whom may be mentioned Ellis and Isbell [20] and Ellis and Zeller.[21] Similar studies on rats have been made by Anderson and Mendel [22] and also by Eckstein.[23] This work has shown conclusively that the composition of the body fats of animals is influenced by the composition of the fatty foods ingested.

There is considerable evidence to support the generalization that the colder and more vigorous the climate in which a plant is grown the greater the unsaturation of the fatty acids produced by it. Many examples of plants containing highly unsaturated glycerides and thriving only in comparatively hot climates can be cited as refuting this belief. The work of Ivanov,[24] Pigulevskiĭ,[25] and others has, however, shown rather conclusively that fats of plants of the same species are more saturated the warmer the climate in which they are grown. The following conclusions were drawn by Pigulevskiĭ.

The nature of the oil in a plant depends upon climate conditions, a given plant growing in a cold climate producing acids of a lower degree of saturation and, therefore, of greater chemical activity than the same plant growing in a warm climate. Cultivated plants growing under more favorable conditions lose the ability to produce acids as unsaturated as those produced by plants in the wild state. While there is a difference in the relative amounts of different acids and different oils, there seems to be little difference in the nature of these acids, these usually being oleic, linoleic, and linolenic acids.

Since animals are primarily dependent upon the vegetable kingdom for their foods, it follows that the more saturated fats should be found in animals which live in the warmer climates. This generalization may also apply to the actual formation of the animal fats, as indicated by the observations that animals fed similar foods, but maintained under different temperature conditions, possess body fats of varying degrees of saturation.

The naturally occurring glyceride mixtures generally contain at least five, and frequently more, different fatty acids, and cannot be, therefore, rightly considered as simple esters. The earlier workers in the field of the fats and fatty acids assumed the fats to be mixtures of simple triglycerides. For example, it was thought for some time that a fat which contained equimolecular proportions of palmitic, oleic, and linoleic acids would consist essentially of a mixture of tripalmitin, triolein, and trilinolein. It is now known that this is not the case and that a fat of the above composition would contain only a small percentage of simple triglycerides. Nature shows a very decided preference toward the formation of mixed triglycerides, and in practically every case the naturally occurring glycerides will show as heterogeneous a structure as theoretically possible. Thus, the amount of any individual fatty acid in a fat will be found evenly distributed throughout the various glycerides. No completely satisfactory explanation of this observation has been offered; however, it is interesting to note that minimum-melting-point systems result from this heterogeneous arrangement. By reason of this preference for the formation of mixed triglycerides, the fats, in most cases, present a rather complicated mixture of glycerides and it is usually necessary to saponify or otherwise split the fats completely before pure compounds can be obtained from them.

The fatty acids are also found widely distributed in the various plant, animal, and insect waxes. Although these waxes comprise only a relatively small percentage of the total amount of fatty substances found in nature, they are of interest from both a chemical and a biological standpoint. The waxes differ from the fats in that in the latter the alcohol is always glycerol, whereas in the former the alcohol is generally a monohydric alcohol. The waxes possess a somewhat less complicated structure than the glycerides and, indeed, it is frequently possible to separate pure esters from them. Thus, ceryl cerotate may be readily isolated from Chinese wax, or cetyl palmitate from spermaceti or opium wax by repeated crystallization. Many examples can be cited in which pure esters can be obtained by crystallization of the natural waxes. Esters of the cyclic alcohols, or sterols, are examples of waxes which are found widely distributed throughout both the animal and the vegetable kingdoms. Cholesterol esters are found in significant amounts in wool wax and other animal waxes, and their presence in various portions of the animal body, such as the spinal cord, brain, and nervous system, suggests that they are intimately connected with life processes. The esters of the phytosterols which characterize plant waxes are of appreciable biological interest.

Significant facts regarding the fatty acids found in the waxes are that they are usually of high molecular weight and belong to the saturated series. Another point of interest is that these waxes generally contain very appreciable amounts of high molecular weight hydrocarbons which partially account for their high percentage of unsaponifiable matter. Waxes also contain some free fatty acids, although there is a question as to whether these are present originally or formed during various processes of extraction and refining. The waxes may be either liquids or solids and are found in both the animal and the vegetable kingdoms. Among the important animal waxes may be mentioned sperm oil, wool wax, and the various cholesterol esters present in the animal body. Vegetable waxes are usually obtained from the leaves of plants or as exudates from plant tissue. One of the most important vegetable waxes, carnauba wax, is obtained from the leaves of a tropical palm, *Copernicia cerifera;* candelilla wax is obtained from a shrub, *Pedilanthus pavonis,* cottonseed wax from raw cotton, and palm wax as an exudate of the palm tree. The various insect waxes, such as beeswax, Chinese wax, and many others, are formed by the insects at some period during the life cycle and resemble the plant waxes in many important respects. Bacterial waxes, such as those formed by tubercle or leprosy bacilli, have been the subject of considerable investigation as regards their constitution and properties. The peat waxes, such as montan wax, are rather closely related to the vegetable waxes, owing perhaps to a common origin.

From the foregoing, it is apparent that since the saturated fatty acids occur associated with unsaturated acids and with acids of other series, any comments with reference to the occurrence of the saturated acids can generally be applied to the entire group of fatty acids. There are, however, several important observations and generalizations which pertain rather specifically to members of one or the other series. Those which apply to the saturated series can be considered at this time and those which concern the other series will be discussed under their proper headings. Palmitic acid is the most abundant and widely distributed of the saturated fatty acids. This acid is the major component of many of the fats and waxes and has been found in practically every fatty substance so far investigated. Stearic acid is also an important constituent of all animal fats and of many of the vegetable fats and waxes. It is, however, not so abundant in nature as its lower homolog palmitic acid. This is quite contrary to the popular belief, since stearic acid is generally considered to be the most characteristic and prevalent of all the saturated acids. Saturated acids which contain more than eighteen carbon atoms are usually present only as minor components in the animal and vegetable fats; however, such acids frequently constitute major components of many of the plant and insect waxes. Acids containing less than sixteen carbon atoms are frequently encountered in the vegetable oils, but, with the exception of the milk fats, they do not form major components of the animal fats.

An interesting observation which applies specifically to the saturated acids is that when one member of the series is present in large amount in a fat, the next lower and the next higher homologs will also be found. Thus, if an oil contains lauric acid as a major component it will invariably contain capric acid and smaller amounts of acids lower than capric acid, and it will also contain myristic acid together with smaller amounts of the higher molecular weight acids. This mutual association of the saturated acids has been universally recognized. It presents one of the reasons why the separation of the higher acids has been so difficult and the final determination of their structures so long delayed.

Several generalizations concerning the structure and configuration of the naturally occurring saturated acids have been the subject of considerable controversy. It is now rather universally accepted that the naturally occurring acids contain a normal, unbranched chain of carbon atoms and that only those which have an even number of carbon atoms exist in the natural fats. An apparent exception to both of these statements is the presence of isovaleric acid in certain dolphin and porpoise oils, and in the oil from valerian roots. The presence of isovaleric acid in dolphin jaw and head oils was first noted by Chevreul, and later André [26] compared the acids obtained from dolphin jaw oil and from valerian root with synthetic isovaleric acid and showed the three acids to be identical. The more recent work of Klein and Stigol [27] and of Gill and Tucker [28] has conclusively shown that isovaleric acid must be considered as an exception to the general rule. The occurrence of isovaleric acid as a normal constituent of certain fats has been a subject of speculation, and several explanations have been offered to account for its presence. Holde and Bleyberg [29] have suggested that it is produced by the degradation of albumin, while others have pointed out the similarity of the carbon structures of isovaleric acid and isoprene as indicating a possible biological relationship between these two compounds.

The question concerning the non-occurrence in natural fats of fatty acids having an uneven number of carbon atoms was not easily answered. Since the saturated acids form a series of closely related compounds, the adjacent members of which differ by only one CH_2 group, it is evident that the higher members are so similar that their separation one from another is extremely difficult. Because of the difficulty in separating and purifying the higher acids and because of the tendency of the saturated acids to form binary mixtures which exhibit many of the properties of pure compounds, practically every acid containing an odd number of carbon atoms up to tritriacontanoic acid has at some time been reported as a component of a naturally occurring fatty substance. Thus, such acids as neocerotic, ceroplastic, cluytinic, ibotocerotic, margaric, tachardiaceric, dorosomic, daturic, and many others have been shown to be difficultly separable acid mixtures and not chemical individuals. Since palmitic and stearic acids are the most abundant of the saturated acids and are common components of many fatty substances, it is not surprising that the acid having their mean molecular weight, heptadecanoic acid, is the uneven acid most frequently reported as present in natural products. Acids described as heptadecanoic acid have been designated by such names as margaric, daturic, and dorosomic acids, and in several instances the question of their identity has cast considerable doubt upon the theory of the non-existence in natural products of acids with an odd number of carbon atoms. All such reported cases have, after further investigation, been shown to be equi-molecular mixtures of palmitic and stearic acids, and it is now conclusively established that heptadecanoic acid does not occur in the natural fats which have so far been examined.

The formulas first assigned to the saturated fatty acids by earlier workers in this field showed them to contain a normal chain of carbon atoms. In the case of the lower members of the series, it was soon conclusively proved that they possess an unbranched carbon chain. Thus, Lieben and Rossi [30] and Linnemann [31] compared a number of the lower members with normal synthetic acids and found them to be identical. Krafft [32] proved the normal structure of lauric acid by showing that it formed normal undec-anoic acid by degradation. A similar method of proof was employed by Krafft [33] to establish the normal configuration of myris-tic, palmitic, and stearic acids. Thus, the normal structure of the acids containing eighteen carbon atoms or less was proved at a comparatively early date. In recent years, several acids which offer possible exceptions to this generalization have been described. An isopalmitic acid has been reported in egg yolk oil by Suzuki, [34] in shark egg oil by Ono, [35] in egg oil of *Bombyx mori* by Ozaki and Kasai, [36] and in chrysalis oil by Kawase, Suda, and Fukuzawa. [37] Its existence in the latter has been questioned by Ueno and Ikuta. [38] A branched stearic acid, termed tuberculostearic acid, has been isolated from the wax of the tubercle bacillus by Anderson and Chargaff, [39] and by Anderson and Uyei, [40] from the fat of the leprosy bacillus. Various saturated acids present in wool wax have been stated to possess an iso-structure; however, there is some doubt as to their actual identity.

Although the higher saturated acids, those with more than eighteen carbon atoms, were at first considered to contain a normal carbon chain, it is interesting to note that it has been only within the last few years that they have been definitely assigned a normal structure. Gösmann [10] considered arachidic acid to be eicosanoic, and the higher acids were assumed for many years to contain an unbranched chain of carbon atoms. Doubt was cast upon this supposition, however, when it was shown by many workers that the acids of high molecular weight which were isolated from natural sources possessed much lower melting points than the normal acids prepared by synthetic means. Thus, Ehrenstein and Stuewer [41] stated that arachidic acid was not eicosanoic acid but an isobehenic acid. Levene and Taylor [42] prepared a number of the higher saturated acids and found that they possessed much higher melting points than those isolated from natural sources. Levene, West, and van der Scheer [43] had previously found that the hydrocarbons formed from the natural acids possessed lower melting points than the synthetic normal hydrocarbons and thus questioned the normal structures assigned to these acids. These discrepancies between the melting points of the synthetic and naturally occurring acids led to an increased effort to purify the naturally occurring acids in an endeavor to ascertain their true configurations. Francis, Piper, and Malkin,[44] Holde and Bleyberg,[29] and others have concluded from a study of x-ray measurements on highly purified, naturally occurring, saturated acids that the spacings conform to a normal and not an iso-structure. Later work has resulted in a verification of these findings.

Synthesis of the Saturated Fatty Acids

Many of the acids shown in Table I occur in abundant quantities in the oils, fats, and waxes while others have been shown to be entirely absent. There is, consequently, a great difference in the relative importance of the various members of this series. Those which occur naturally can, in most cases, be readily obtained from such sources, while the availability of the other members is limited to their synthetic preparation. All the acids of this series, including some of quite high molecular weight, have been prepared synthetically, and a short description of the general methods employed follows.

The synthesis of the saturated fatty acids has been accomplished by a number of procedures, some of which can be advantageously employed for the preparation of any of the members whereas others are of limited adaptability. Such synthetic methods involve one of two general procedures. Either shorter-chain acids can be subjected to a series of reactions, the final product of which is a longer-chain acid, or the higher molecular weight acids may be degraded to acids of lower molecular weight.

Among the first methods employed is one which is highly satisfactory and still frequently used. This consists of the reduction of an acid or its alkyl ester to the corresponding alcohol, conversion of this alcohol to the alkyl iodide and then to the corresponding cyanide, which is hydrolyzed to give an acid containing one carbon atom more than the original acid. For example, pentadecanoic acid can be synthesized from myristic acid by the following steps:

$C_{13}H_{27}CO_2H \rightarrow C_{13}H_{27}CH_2OH \rightarrow C_{13}H_{27}CH_2I \rightarrow C_{13}H_{27}CH_2CN \rightarrow$

$$C_{13}H_{27}CH_2CO_2H$$

Lieben and Rossi [30] and Linnemann [31] used this method for the preparation of several of the lower acids, and the procedure has since been adopted by Levene and Taylor [42] and by many others for the synthesis of various higher saturated acids.

The malonic acid synthesis offers one of the most convenient procedures for the synthesis of the higher saturated acids. This reaction involves the following steps:

$RCO_2H \rightarrow RCH_2OH \rightarrow RCH_2I \rightarrow RCH_2CH(CO_2Et)_2 \rightarrow$

$$RCH_2CH(CO_2H)_2 \rightarrow RCH_2CH_2CO_2H$$

This method is especially useful for the preparation of acids of quite high molecular weight, Bleyberg and Ulrich [45] having used it for the preparation of the saturated acids from eicosanoic to triacontanoic acid. It was also employed by Francis, Collins, and Piper [46] and by Shiina [47] for the preparation of a number of saturated acids.

An interesting method for the synthesis of the higher members of this acid series consists of the preparation of the higher keto acids, the Clemmensen [48] reduction of which yields the normal acids. The keto acid is obtained by the reaction of an ω-bromo acid with the sodium derivative of ethyl acetoacetate and the condensation of the resulting product with a high molecular weight acid chloride, followed by the hydrolysis of this condensation product. This method was proposed by Robinson,[49] who prepared triacontanoic acid by condensing the ethyl ester of 11-bromoundecanoic acid with ethyl sodioacetoacetate and treating the product with stearoyl chloride. Hydrolysis of the resulting ethyl 2-acetyl-2-stearoylbrassylate gives 13-ketotriacontanoic acid, the reduction of which yields triacontanoic acid. Francis, Collins, and Piper [46] prepared tetratriacontanoic and pentatetracosanoic acids by a similar procedure.

The Grignard reaction has frequently been employed for the synthesis of acids of the saturated series. The alkyl halide of the parent acid is prepared and converted to the alkylmagnesium halide by the usual procedure. When this Grignard reagent is treated with carbon dioxide in acid solution, an acid is obtained which contains one carbon atom more than the parent acid. Thus, palmitic acid may be converted to heptadecanoic acid as follows:

$$C_{15}H_{31}CO_2H \rightarrow C_{15}H_{31}CH_2OH \rightarrow C_{15}H_{31}CH_2I \rightarrow C_{15}H_{31}CH_2MgI \rightarrow$$

$$C_{15}H_{31}CH_2CO_2H$$

Ruttan [50] has used this method for the preparation of several high molecular weight acids. Lukeš [51] has prepared the acids from hexanoic to decanoic by treating Grignard reagents with N-methylsuccinimide. The resulting 1-methyl-5-alkylpyrrol-2-one yields a γ-keto acid on hydrolysis which contains four carbon atoms more than the original acid. The saturated fatty acid is obtained by reduction of this keto acid.

By the methods described above it is possible to start with any acid in this series and prepare from it any other acid having a greater number of carbon atoms. Another general type of procedure, which is perhaps of equal importance, consists of the stepwise degradation of an acid to its next lower homolog. One of the earliest methods of this type was employed by Krafft [32] for the preparation of undecanoic acid from lauric acid. The process consists of the preparation of a methyl ketone by heating the barium salt of the higher acid with barium acetate and the oxidation of this ketone by means of potassium permanganate and sulfuric acid. Krafft [33] also prepared tridecanoic, pentadecanoic, and heptadecanoic acids by this procedure. The method results in the synthesis of an acid which contains one carbon atom less than the original acid. Because of the comparatively poor yields which result, it is used infrequently as a means of obtaining the saturated acids.

Another early method for the conversion of a higher acid to its next lower homolog consists of the action of excess bromine in alkaline solution on amides. The reaction of bromine with amides was first proposed by Hofmann [52] for the preparation of amines and substituted ureas, and three years later he stated [53] that by the use of excess bromine the nitrile of the lower homolog is obtained in appreciable yields. Thus, heptadecanoic acid is prepared from stearic acid by the following reactions:

$$C_{17}H_{35}CO_2H \rightarrow C_{17}H_{35}CONH_2 \rightarrow (C_{17}H_{35}NH_2) \rightarrow C_{16}H_{33}CN \rightarrow$$

$$C_{16}H_{33}CONH_2 \rightarrow C_{16}H_{33}CO_2H$$

This method has since been employed by Lutz [54] for the degradation of myristic acid to tridecanoic acid and thence to lauric acid.

The degradation of an acid to its next lower homolog may be accomplished by its conversion to an aldehyde containing one carbon atom less than the original acid, followed by the oxidation of this aldehyde to its corresponding acid. Le Sueur [55] prepared the aldehydes by conversion of the acids to their α-bromo derivatives which were then treated with potassium hydroxide to form α-hydroxy acids. The aldehydes result from the heating of these α-hydroxy acids for one hour at 270–280°. Le Sueur accomplished the preparation of margaric acid from stearic acid by this procedure. During the same year Blaise [56] developed a similar process; however, his interpretation of the various steps involved differed somewhat from that of his contemporary. In a later paper, Le Sueur [57] extended his investigations to include several other members of the series. A number of years later, Lapworth [58] introduced a modification of the original method, the modification consisting of the direct oxidation of 2-hydroxymyristic acid in acetone solution by means of potassium permanganate, and this procedure was employed subsequently by Levene and West,[59] who reported substantial yields of margaric and pentadecanoic acids from stearic and palmitic acids, respectively. Oxidation of the α-hydroxy acid in acetone solution eliminates the necessity for the isolation and purification of the intermediate aldehyde and consequently results in higher yields.

The fusion of α-chloro or α-bromo acids with potassium hydroxide at about 300° has been proposed by Rochussen [60] as a satisfactory means of acid degradation. Capric acid has been obtained from 2-chloroundecanoic acid, enanthic acid from 2-bromocaprylic acid, and capric and undecanoic acids from 2-bromolauric acid by this reaction.

The various methods of synthesis or degradation described above are of general application inasmuch as they may be used for the conversion of any acid to a lower or higher homolog by a stepwise process. In addition to such methods there are also a number of quite specific processes which can be employed advantageously for the preparation of certain members of the saturated acid series. One of the most important of these is the catalytic hydrogenation of an unsaturated acid or ester to the corresponding saturated compound. In a number of cases highly purified unsaturated acids or esters can be prepared and their catalytic hydrogenation offers an excellent source of saturated acids. Thus, stearic acid, entirely free from palmitic acid, can be obtained by the hydrogenation of ethyl oleate or oleic acid. Recently, Kass and Keyser [61] have suggested the hydrogenation of purified elaidic acid, linoleic acid, or eleostearic acid as a means of preparing pure stearic acid. The hydrogenation of erucic acid or its esters offers the best source of behenic acid. If the pure unsaturated acid can be obtained easily, hydrogenation presents an extremely satisfactory means of preparing the corresponding saturated acid.

The oxidation of unsaturated acids is frequently used for the production of certain saturated acids. The method, which is essentially limited to monoölefinic acids, depends on the oxidative cleavage of the double bond to produce a fatty acid and a dicarboxylic acid. An outstanding example of this method is the preparation of pelargonic and azelaic acids by the oxidation of oleic acid.

The destructive distillation of the hydroxy acids or their soaps is sometimes employed for the production of shorter-chain saturated acids. For example, 10-undecenoic acid may be prepared easily by the destructive distillation of ricinoleic acid or its salts, which yields enanthaldehyde and undecenoic acid according to the following equation:

$$CH_3(CH_2)_5CH(OH)CH_2CH:CH(CH_2)_7CO_2H \rightarrow$$
$$CH_3(CH_2)_5CHO + CH_2:CH(CH_2)_8CO_2H$$

The resulting aldehyde can be oxidized to enanthic acid or the undecenoic acid hydrogenated to undecanoic acid. This decomposition was extensively studied by Krafft,[62] who later [63] described the reduction of the resulting 10-undecenoic acid to undecanoic acid by means of hydriodic acid and red phosphorus.

Mixtures of fatty acids may be prepared by oxidation of paraffins, and although this method has received considerable commercial prominence it is not easily adapted to the preparation of individual acids. Several other specific methods for the preparation of saturated acids may be mentioned. Among these are the fusion of unsaturated acids with alkali, and the pyrolysis of nitriles followed by hydrolysis of the resulting products. The latter procedure offers a source of many shorter-chain acids.

Fatty Acids of the Saturated Series

The following summary of the individual members of the series of saturated fatty acids is concerned with their historical background, occurrence, synthesis, and their more important physical constants. Their physical properties are discussed in detail in a separate chapter, as are also their esters and other derivatives. Readers interested in a specific acid should consult these later chapters in addition to the following.

BUTANOIC ACID (n-BUTYRIC ACID)

n-Butyric acid is a colorless, unpleasant-smelling liquid, soluble in water (5.62 g. in 100 cc. at $-1.1°$), miscible with ethanol and ether, and soluble in most organic solvents. The acid melts at $-7.9°$ and boils at 162–162.5° at 768.8 mm.[64] Its density and refractive index have been reported to be as follows: d_4^{20} 0.9587, n_D^{20} 1.33906, and n_D^{70} 1.3775.

n-Butyric acid was first recognized as a constituent of the natural fats by Chevreul. It occurs, in association with caproic, caprylic, and higher acids, in the milk fats of mammals, the amount varying with the type of animal, its diet, and its environment. Dhingra [65] reported 3.0, 3.3, and 2.1% in goat, sheep, and camel milk fats, respectively, and Bhattacharya and Hilditch [66] found 4.1% in buffalo milk fat. It is a common component of all butter fats in amounts varying from 2 to 4%. n-Butyric acid has been observed as its hexyl ester in the oil of the fruit of *Heracleum giganteum* by Zincke and collaborators.[67]

n-Butyric acid is formed by the "butyric fermentation" of carbohydrates and in certain fermentations of glycerol. It has been reported by Neuberg and Rosenberg [68] to be a product of the putrefaction of casein, by Neuberg and Arinstein [69] to be produced in fermentation of certain sugars, and by Scala [70] to be formed during rancidity production in oils. Schutze, Shive, and Lochte [71] have identified n-butyric acid in certain petroleum distillates, and Kumamoto [72] reported its presence in Kaoliang fusel oil. It has been observed in the products formed during the dry distillation of wood, and Schmid [73] has recently shown it to be produced during the distillation of amber.

PENTANOIC ACID (n-VALERIC ACID); ISOVALERIC ACID

Isovaleric acid is the only known exception to the generalization that only even-carbon acids exist in natural products. Chevreul isolated an acid which he termed "phocenic acid" from dolphin jaw oil, and this acid was subsequently shown to be isovaleric acid.

Both n-valeric acid and isovaleric acid are colorless liquids which possess a characteristic putrid odor. The normal acid melts at

$-34.5°$ and boils at $186.35°$ at 760 mm., $96°$ at 23 mm., and $86°$ at 15 mm.; the iso-acid (3-methylbutanoic acid) melts at $-51°$ and boils at $176.7°$ at 760 mm. Both acids are appreciably soluble in water (100 g. of water dissolves 3.7 g. of n-valeric acid at $16°$ and 4.2 g. of isovaleric at $20°$). Other constants for these acids are: n-valeric, d_4^{20} 0.9387, d_4^{15} 0.9435, n_D^{20} 1.4086; isovaleric, d_4^{15} 0.937, $n_D^{22.4}$ 1.40178.

These acids have been synthesized by a number of different methods. Lieben and Rossi [30] and Adams and Marvel [74] prepared n-valeric acid by the hydrolysis of n-butyl cyanide, and Gilman and Parker [75] have described its synthesis by the action of carbon dioxide on butylmagnesium bromide. A satisfactory method for the preparation of n-valeric acid is the decomposition of n-propyl-malonic acid.[76] Isovaleric acid can be prepared by a similar procedure. Valeric acids have been reported to be formed by the action of carbon dioxide and water on olefins,[77] or by the action of formic acid on butene.[78] The formation of isovaleric acid during the high-pressure synthesis of alcohols from carbon monoxide and hydrogen has been observed by Strada.[79] Zelinskii and Przheval'skii [80] have prepared n-valeric acid by the oxidation of hexane, and Koizumi [81] has described its preparation by the electrolytic oxidation of 1-pentanol. The formation of valeric acids during putrefactive changes in carbohydrates and proteins has been frequently observed.[68, 82, 83]

The presence of a valeric acid in natural products has been the subject of considerable controversy. It has frequently been claimed that the "phocenic acid" of Chevreul and the valeric acid isolated from valerian root were mixtures of butyric and caproic acids, and there has also been some question as to whether the reported valeric acid had a normal or iso configuration. These questions were answered by the work of André [26] which showed conclusively that the valeric acid found in valerian root and in dolphin and porpoise oils was actually isovaleric acid and not an equimolecular mixture of butyric and caproic acids. André compared the valeric acid obtained from natural sources with synthetic isovaleric acid, prepared from isobutylmagnesium bromide and carbon dioxide, and found them to be identical. The later work of Klein and Stigol [27] and of Gill and Tucker [28] upon porpoise jaw oil has confirmed the natural occurrence of isovaleric acid. More recently, cetyl isovalerate has been isolated from the products of distillation of pilot-whale head oil by Tsujimoto and Koyanagi.[84]

Bullock [85] has confirmed the presence of valeric acid in oil of valerian root; Schutze, Shive, and Lochte [71] have isolated it from petroleum distillates; and Kumamoto [72] has reported that it comprises 53% of a Kaoliang fusel oil. Apparently the valeric acid present in natural oils is isovaleric acid and not the normal acid. Several observers have attributed its presence to the decomposition of albumins. The resemblance of the carbon structure of isovaleric acid to isoprene has also been the subject of considerable speculation.

Hexanoic Acid (Caproic Acid)

This acid was first isolated by Chevreul during his investigations upon the composition of butter fat. It has since been reported as a minor component of many animal and vegetable oils, particularly the milk fats, coconut oil, and various palm oils.

Caproic acid is a colorless, oily liquid of unpleasant odor. It melts at $-3.9°$ and boils at $205.35°$ at 760 mm., $146°$ at 100 mm., and $100°$ at 10 mm. The melting point of $-3.9°$ for this acid, which was reported by Simon,[86] should replace the value of $-1.5°$ observed by Fittig [87] and by Gartenmeister [88] and frequently reported in the literature. Other physical constants which have been reported for caproic acid are: d_4^0 0.94423, d_4^{15} 0.93136, d_4^{30} 0.91832, n_D^{20} 1.41635. Its solubility in water, 0.8859 g. per 100 cc., is much less than that of valeric acid. It is soluble in ether, both cold and hot ethanol, and other organic solvents.

Caproic acid can be readily prepared by the hydrolysis of n-pentyl cyanide,[30] by the decomposition of n-butylmalonic acid,[74, 89] by the oxidation of 1-hexanol,[90] or by the oxidation of castor oil with nitric acid.[91] It can also be prepared by the action of carbon dioxide on n-pentylmagnesium bromide, according to the method employed by Gilman and Parker [75] for the synthesis of n-valeric acid. The formation of small amounts of caproic acid has been noted by Strada [79] during the high-pressure synthesis of alcohols from carbon monoxide and hydrogen. Caproic acid is formed in small amounts during the putrefaction of casein,[68] by the action of bacteria upon carbohydrates,[83] and during rancidity production in oils and fats.[70]

Caproic acid is found in a number of vegetable oils and fats. It is never present in large amounts and is always associated with caprylic acid and higher saturated acids. All milk fats contain caproic acid; however, the amount present seldom exceeds 3%.

Polonovski, Cuvelier, and Avenard [92] have reported 0.35% caproic acid in human milk; Hilditch and Paul [93] found 2.0% in the fat of cow's milk; Dhingra [65] reported 3.0, 2.8, and 0.9% in the milk fats of goats, sheep, and camels, and Bhattacharya and Hilditch [66] observed 1.4% in buffalo milk fat. Riemenschneider and Ellis [94] have confirmed the presence of this acid in goat's milk fat. The butter fats contain caproic acid in varying amounts depending upon the source and method of treatment of the fat. The distillation of the fatty acids of butter fat offers a commercial source of caproic acid.

Coconut oils contain caproic acid, the amount reported by various investigators varying from a fraction of 1% to approximately 5%, disagreements which are largely occasioned by different methods of isolation. Birosel and others [95] have reported 0.38% of caproic acid in the fat of fresh coconut milk; Lepkovsky, Feskov, and Evans [96] found 0.5% in coconut oil, whereas Taylor and Clarke [97] reported 0.46%. Elsdon,[98] however, found 2% by alcoholysis of the coconut oil with methanol followed by fractionation. Caproic acid also occurs in small amounts in various other oils, mainly those of the palm family. Babassu fat [99] contains 0.1% of caproic acid and palm kernel oil (Brazil) [100] 1.66%. Its presence has been reported in the fat of barley rootlets [101] and in the algae fats.[102] Substantial amounts of caproic acid appear to be present in the various fusel oils. Kumamoto [72] found 17.2% in sweet potato fusel oil and 25.5% in cane molasses fusel oil, and Shoruigin and others [103] have noted its presence in potato fusel oil.

Apparently the normal acid is the only hexanoic acid which is found in natural products. Its normal structure was proved at an early date by Lieben and Rossi,[30] and although isocaproic acids have been reported in natural products from time to time their presence has never been confirmed.

HEPTANOIC ACID (ENANTHIC ACID)

Enanthic acid was first described by Bussy,[104] who obtained it by the oxidation of enanthaldehyde. Enanthic acid is a colorless, oily liquid which possesses a disagreeable, rancid odor. The melting point of $-8.9°$ as recorded by Deffet [105] has been redetermined by Bilterys and Gisseleire,[106] who reported it to be $-7.46°$. Enanthic acid boils at 223.01° at 760 mm., and at 124–125.5° at 0.8 mm. The other accepted constants for this acid are: d_4^0 0.93454, d_4^{15} 0.92215, d_4^{30} 0.90989, and n_D^{70} 1.4130. Enanthic acid is only slightly soluble in water, 0.2419 g. dissolving in 100 cc. at 15°. It is soluble in ethanol and ether.

Enanthic acid is not found in the natural oils, fats, and waxes, although it has been reported in several of the floral waxes and Ruzicka and Schinz [107] have stated that it is present in violet leaf oil. It has also been identified in the pyrolytic products of shark oils; [108] however, it was not believed to be present in the original oil.

A number of methods have been proposed for the synthesis of enanthic acid, the most satisfactory of which is the oxidation of heptanal by potassium permanganate in acid solution.[109] It has also been prepared from heptanal by oxidation with dilute nitric acid [110, 111, 112] or with potassium dichromate and sulfuric acid.[113] An alkaline solution of potassium permanganate was employed by Fournier,[114] and an acetone solution by Rogers.[115] Wahlfors [116] has described the preparation of enanthic acid by the action of nitric acid upon castor oil. The acid has also been prepared by the oxidation of 1-heptanol,[117] and by heating 1-heptanol with dry potassium hydroxide at 200–230°.[118] The oxidation of stigmasterol [119] has been observed to yield enanthic acid, and Strada [79] reported its presence in the products produced by the high-pressure synthesis of alcohols from carbon monoxide and hydrogen. Smit [120] has stated that enanthic acid is produced by the ozonization of castor oil. The presence of enanthic acid has been observed in rancid oils,[70] and it is evidently found in various fusel oils in appreciable amounts. Kumamoto [72] reported 58.3% in molasses fusel oil and 26.9% in sweet potato fusel oil.

OCTANOIC ACID (CAPRYLIC ACID)

Caprylic acid was first described by Lerch,[7] who isolated it during his study of the fatty acids of butter fat. It is a colorless liquid which possesses an unpleasant, persistent, rancid odor. Holde and Gentner [121] reported a melting point of 16.3° for caprylic acid, a value which was later confirmed by Deffet.[105] The acid boils at 239.3° at 760 mm., and at 124° at 10 mm. Other physical constants for caprylic acid are: d_4^{20} 0.90884, d_4^{70} 0.8708, n_D^{20} 1.4285, n_D^{70} 1.4085. Caprylic acid is very slightly soluble in water, 0.079 g. dissolving in 100 cc. of water at 15°. It is soluble in ethanol, ether, benzene, and other organic solvents.

Caprylic acid has been synthesized by several methods, two of the most important of which are the hydrolysis of octanenitrile,[31] and the decomposition of hexylmalonic acid according to the procedure employed by v. Braun and others [122] for the preparation of 2-bromocaprylic acid. The acid can also be prepared by the oxidation of 1-octanol. Rochussen [60] has synthesized caprylic acid by heating 2-chloroundecanoic acid with potassium hydroxide at 300°, and Truchet [123] has described its formation by the action of potassium hydroxide upon 1-chlorooctyne.

Caprylic acid is found widely distributed in nature in the various milk and butter fats, coconut and similar oils, and in the various palm oils. It has also been reported to be present in small amounts in many of the lesser-known oils, such as grapefruit seed oil,[124] oil of sweet oranges,[125] oil of lemongrass,[126] fat of the seeds of the bay tree,[127] grape seed oil,[128] violet leaf oil,[107] and the fat of nux vomica.[129]

One of the best-known sources of caprylic acid is coconut oil, in which it is found associated with both lower and higher saturated acids and from which it can be obtained by distillation of the acids or their alkyl esters. The literature contains many conflicting statements relative to the amount of caprylic acid present in this oil, and although some variations between various samples are to be expected it is believed that many of the low values reported for caprylic acid are due to its loss during separation and identification. Elsdon [98] reported 9% of çaprylic acid in coconut oil by fractionation of the methyl esters, a value which, as shown by later work, is evidently approximately correct. Taylor and Clarke [97] found 8.7% in this oil, Nobori [130] reported 8.73%, and Lepkovsky, Feskov, and Evans [96] reported 9%. Armstrong, Allan, and Moore [131] in their investigation of African coconut oil have observed that the oil from the parings contained 2% of caprylic acid and that from the kernels 9.5%. Many lower values have been reported for the caprylic acid content of the coconut oils, but it is surprising that Bömer and Baumann [132] have stated that caprylic acid is not present in coconut oil. Caprylic acid also occurs in substantial amounts in several of the palm oils, particularly palm kernel oil. Armstrong, Allan, and Moore [133] found 3% of caprylic acid in palm kernel oil, and recently McKinney and Jamieson [100] have reported 9.10% in a Brazilian palm kernel oil. Heiduschka and Agsten [99] found 5% of caprylic acid in babassu fat, and Hilditch and Vidyarthi [134] reported 7.5% in cohune nut oil.

Small amounts of caprylic acid have also been observed in several fats of marine origin. Nobori has recently observed it to be present in Japanese sardine oil [135] and also in herring oil.[130]

Tsujimoto [136] had previously reported its presence in the head oil of the sperm whale. Takahashi and others [102] have stated that caprylic acid is found in algae fat.

Caprylic acid occurs along with other saturated acids in the various milk fats. Dhingra [65, 137] reported 3.9, 3.8, and 0.6% in the milk fats of goats, sheep, and camels, respectively, and its presence in the fat of sow's milk has been observed by Laxa.[138] The amount found in the various milk fats apparently varies with the type, diet, and environment of the animal from which the milk is obtained. Butter fat contains varying amounts of caprylic acid, Libbert [139] having reported 0.8% in this fat, a value which is probably considerably below the average.

Caprylic acid has been reported to be a component of fusel oils. Kumamoto [72] found 23.7% in potato fusel oil, and Shoruigin and others [103] have confirmed its presence in this oil. Raper [140] has reported the presence of caprylic acid in the products formed during the butyric fermentation of sugar.

It is apparent that caprylic acid is rather widely distributed in the animal and vegetable fats, where it occurs generally as a minor component. It is invariably associated with the lower saturated acids such as caproic, and with the higher acids such as capric and lauric. The naturally occurring acid has a normal structure and no reports of the existence of isocaprylic acids in natural products have been substantiated.

NONANOIC ACID (PELARGONIC ACID)

Since pelargonic acid is one of the oxidation products of oleic acid it was probably first encountered during a study of the oxidation of this acid. Among the earlier descriptions of pelargonic acid is that given by Zincke and Franchimont,[141, 142] who prepared it from 1-octanol by conversion of the alcohol to the iodide and thence to the cyanide, which was hydrolyzed to the corresponding acid.

Pelargonic acid is a colorless fatty liquid which possesses a very heavy rancid odor. Franchimont and Zincke reported the melting point of pelargonic acid to be 12–12.5°, which is in good agreement with the value of 12.30° determined many years later by Deffet.[105] Pelargonic acid boils at 254.4° at 760 mm., and at 180° at 100 mm. Other physical constants for this acid are as follows: $d_4^{12.5}$ 0.9109, $d_4^{17.5}$ 0.9068, d_4^{20} 0.90552, and n_D^{20} 1.43057. The acid is very slightly soluble in water, soluble in ethanol, ether, acetic acid, and many other organic solvents.

One of the most satisfactory methods for the preparation of pelargonic acid is the oxidative cleavage of oleic acid. Lapworth and Mottram [143] reported 70% of the theoretical yield of this acid by the oxidation of dihydroxystearic acid with potassium permanganate, a reaction which has lately been studied in detail by Bougault and Schuster.[144] Molinari and Soncini,[145] Harries and Türk,[146] and Thieme [147] have described the preparation of pelargonic acid by the decomposition of oleic acid ozonide. The decomposition of erucic acid ozonide also results in a high yield of pelargonic acid.[148] It is one of the products of the oxidative cleavage of stearolic acid.[149, 150] The oxidation of methyl or ethyl oleate in acetone or acetic acid solution has been shown by Armstrong and Hilditch [151] to result in high yields of pelargonic acid. The fusion of unsaturated acids or of dihydroxy acids with alkalies brings about a cleavage of the alkylene or alkyl chain, with the formation of lower molecular weight acids, and this method has been successfully used for the preparation of pelargonic acid from various unsaturated and dihydroxy acids. Eckert [152] has obtained pelargonic acid by the fusion of dihydroxystearic acid with potassium hydroxide and potassium iodate, and Nicolet and Jurist [153] have studied its formation by the fusion of dihydroxystearic acid with potassium hydroxide. The fusion of 10-undecenoic acid [154] and of 2-bromoundecanoic acid [60] with potassium hydroxide has also been shown to result in good yields of pelargonic acid. Pelargonic acid can be readily prepared by the oxidation of various octyl ketones according to the method employed by Krafft.[32, 33] St. Pfau [155] has described the preparation of this acid by the oxidation of methyl octyl ketone with sodium hypoiodite. The synthesis of pelargonic acid from heptyl bromide by means of the malonic acid method has been recently described by Reid and Ruhoff.[89] Other reported methods for the synthesis of this acid are: the oxidation of pelargonaldehyde by means of silver oxide; [156] the oxidation of castor oil with nitric acid; [157] and the heating of barium stearate with sodium methylate.[158]

Pelargonic acid is not present in the naturally occurring oils and fats, although it has frequently been reported in oil of rue, and Tassilly [159] has stated that it occurs in Japan wax. It is, however, formed during various oxidative and rancidity changes in fats,[70, 160] and is a common constituent of many fusel oils.[72, 161] Those cases in which its presence has been reported in the naturally occurring oils can probably be explained by its formation during an oxidative cleavage of the acids of the original oils.

DECANOIC ACID (CAPRIC ACID)

Chevreul first identified capric acid during his investigation of the composition of butter fat. It has since been shown to be a common component of many of the naturally occurring fats and oils.

Capric acid is a low-melting solid. It possesses a heavy, somewhat rancid odor which is much less penetrating and less disagreeable than that of its lower homologs. The accepted value for the melting point of capric acid, 31.3°, was established by Deffet [105] and is in agreement with the value of 31.3–31.4° previously found by Görgey.[6] Other values which have been reported are 31° [121] and 35°.[162] Capric acid boils at 268.7° at 760 mm., at 200° at 100 mm., and at 149° at 11 mm. Other physical constants for this acid are: d_4^{40} 0.8858, n_D^{40} 1.42855, and $n_D^{60.6}$ 1.4201. It is very slightly soluble in water and easily soluble in ethanol, ether, and in most organic solvents.

The naturally occurring oils and fats, such as coconut oil and palm kernel oil, offer the best sources of capric acid. The acid has, however, been synthesized by a number of methods, several of which may be conveniently employed for its preparation. The oxidation of 1-decanol with potassium permanganate and sulfuric acid,[163] or with silver oxide,[164] results in substantial yields of capric acid. The acid may be prepared from 1-nonanol by conversion to the iodide and thence to the cyanide, which is then hydrolyzed with alcoholic potassium hydroxide.[165] Among the earlier methods employed for the preparation of capric acid is that proposed by Krafft,[32, 33] which consists of the degradation of higher acids by their conversion to methyl ketones followed by oxidation of these ketones to the lower acids. Capric acid has been prepared from methyl decyl ketone by this method.[166] Houben [162] has studied the preparation of capric acid by the rearrangement of methyl nonyl ketoxime to N-methylcapramide, followed by hydrolysis of the amide to capric acid. Rochussen [60] has prepared the acid by the fusion of 2-bromolauric acid with potassium hydroxide at 300°, and recently Kao and Ma [167] have reported a good yield of capric acid by heating 2-dodecenoic acid with potassium hydroxide and a small amount of water at 300°.

Capric acid occurs in various vegetable oils, particularly coconut oils and oils of the palm family. It is also found in the milk fats, and is present in small quantities in a number of other fats of both vegetable and animal origin. Other saturated acids, such as caprylic and lauric, always accompany capric acid in the natural glycerides. The presence of capric acid in coconut oil was first established by Görgey.[6] Many values have since been reported for the capric acid content of this oil, but it appears that the amount present roughly approximates that of caprylic acid. Nobori [130] has recently reported 8.05% of capric acid in coconut oil; Elsdon [98] found 10%; Lepkovsky [96] reported 6.8%; Taylor and Clarke,[97] 5.6%; and Börner and Baumann [132] failed to establish its presence in this oil. Armstrong, Allan, and Moore [131] have stated that the paring oil from African coconuts contains 2% of capric acid and the kernel oil 4.5%. The fat of the milk of fresh coconuts has recently been reported to contain 8.95% of capric acid.[95] The great range of values reported for the percentage of capric acid in coconut oil is largely due to different methods of isolation and analysis; however, it appears that the average value for the capric acid content of coconut oil is approximately 9%. Capric acid occurs in substantial quantities in many oils of the palm family. Babassu fat [99] has been reported to contain 2.7% of this acid, cohune nut fat,[134] 6.5%, and palm kernel oil (Brazil),[100] 7.64%. Many of the lesser-known oils contain small quantities of capric acid, its presence having been reported in grapefruit seed oil,[124] oil of lemongrass,[126] and coffee bean fat.[168]

Although capric acid, like caprylic acid, does not generally constitute a major percentage of the fatty acids present in an oil, several oils appear to be outstanding exceptions to this generalization, since elm seed oil has been reported by Pawlenko [169] and later by Schuette and Lunde,[170] to contain 50% of this acid. The seed oil of the California bay tree has been recognized as an excellent source of capric acid, having been stated to contain 37%.[127] Several of the marine oils have been reported to contain capric acid, notably sperm-whale blubber oil,[171] herring oil,[172] sardine oil,[135] and the head oil of the sperm whale.[136]

Capric acid occurs in appreciable amounts in the milk fats, the percentage present being somewhat greater than that of caprylic acid. Dhingra [65] found 8.6% in goat milk fat, 7.8% in sheep milk fat, and 1.4% in camel milk fat, and Longenecker [173] reported 2.7% in cow milk fat. It also occurs in the various butter fats in amounts varying from a fraction of 1% to several per cent.

Capric acid has been reported in various fusel oils by several investigators,[72,103,161] but the amount present is considerably less than that of caprylic acid. Its occurrence has also been observed in the various products formed by the putrefaction of proteins.[68]

Undecanoic Acid

This acid was first described by Krafft,[63] who prepared it by the reduction of 10-undecenoic acid with red phosphorus and hydrogen iodide.

Undecanoic acid is a low-melting, crystalline solid possessing a rather pleasant odor which distinguishes it from the lower members of the series. The acid melts at 28.5° and boils at 228° at 160 mm., 212.5° at 100 mm., and 164° at 15 mm. Other physical constants for this acid are: d_4^{25} 0.9905, d_4^{30} 0.8889, and n_D^{70} 1.4203. Undecanoic acid is very slightly soluble in water and is soluble in ethanol, ether, acetone, and other organic solvents.

Undecanoic acid has been prepared by the reduction of 10-undecenoic acid by red phosphorus and hydrogen iodide.[63] It can also be obtained by the catalytic hydrogenation of this acid. 10-Undecenoic acid is formed during the destructive distillation of ricinoleic acid or its salts, a process which results in a mixture of enanthaldehyde and 10-undecenoic acid. The first description of the preparation of 10-undecenoic acid from this source was given by Krafft [62] during his studies upon the pyrolysis of castor oil, and the pyrolysis of ricinoleic acid has since been extensively studied by Goldsobel.[174] The decomposition of castor oil has more recently been investigated in detail.[175,176] In view of the availability of the castor oil acids, 10-undecenoic acid offers an excellent source of undecanoic acid.

Undecanoic acid has been prepared by the oxidation of methyl undecyl ketone,[33] a reaction which results in a substantial yield of this acid. Rochussen [60] has described the preparation of undecanoic acid by the fusion of 2-bromolauric acid with potassium hydroxide. Undecanoic acid has been prepared by the ozonolysis of gadoleic acid,[177] and it has also been identified as one of the oxidation products of paraffin.[178] It can be prepared from capric acid by reduction of this acid or its esters to 1-decanol, followed by the conversion of this alcohol to 1-iododecane and thence to undecanenitrile, which is then hydrolyzed. Since undecanoic acid does not occur in the natural fats and oils, its availability is limited to the various synthetic methods which can be employed for its preparation.

DODECANOIC ACID (LAURIC ACID)

Lauric acid was first described by Marsson [5] during an investigation of the fatty acids of laurel kernel oil. It is the lowest molecular weight acid of the saturated series that is found abundantly in nature and it constitutes a major proportion of the component acids of several oils, particularly those of the palm family.

Lauric acid is a crystalline solid which possesses a faint, fatty odor. It melts at 44° and boils at 225° at 100 mm., 176° at 15 mm., and 141–142° at 0.7 mm. Other constants for lauric acid are: [121, 179] d_4^{50} 0.8690, d_4^{75} 0.8573, $n_D^{60.1}$ 1.4261, and n_D^{70} 1.4225. Lauric acid is very slightly soluble in boiling water and appreciably soluble in acetone, ethanol, and ether.

A number of methods have been proposed for the synthesis of lauric acid. However, since it can be readily obtained from those oils in which it constitutes a major percentage of the mixed acids, the various synthetic means are generally used for purposes of identification rather than as a source of the acid. In order to prepare lauric acid from such an oil, it is customary to fractionally distil the acid mixture obtained by saponification and acidification of the oil, or to fractionate the methyl or ethyl esters. Alcoholysis has frequently been employed as a means of separating lauric acid from oils. [98, 127, 180, 181, 182] Fractionation may be preceded by a separation of lauric acid and lower acids from the higher acids by means of the solubilities of their lithium or magnesium salts in aqueous ethanol. [183]

Lauric acid may be prepared from undecanoic acid by conversion to the alcohol and thence to the cyanide, which is then hydrolyzed. Lutz [54] has described the preparation of lauric acid from N-dodecyl-N'-tridecanoylurea by means of the Hofmann degradation. Vongerichten and Köhler [184] have studied the preparation of lauric acid by the Beckmann rearrangement of the oxime of the keto acid prepared from 6,7-dihydroxystearic acid. Rochussen [60] has prepared lauric acid by the action of potassium hydroxide at 300° on 2-bromomyristic acid. The reduction of 12-iodolauric acid to lauric acid by zinc and acetic acid has been described by Bougault. [185] 12-Iodolauric acid may be readily obtained from 10-undecenoic acid. [186]

Lauric acid constitutes approximately 50% of the component acids of coconut oil and this oil has long been considered an excellent source of lauric acid. Elsdon [98] has reported the lauric acid content of coconut oil to be 45%; Lepkovsky [96] has isolated 46.4%;

Nobori [130] found 51.34%; and Taylor and Clarke [97] reported 45%. Armstrong, Allan, and Moore [131] found 28.9% lauric acid in the oil of African coconut parings and 51.0% in the kernel oil. The fat from the milk of fresh coconuts has been reported to contain 55.06% of this acid.[95] Many seed oils of the palm family contain large amounts of lauric acid. For example, babassu fat [99] contains 45.8%, dika fat [187] 58.6%, palmiche nut oil (Cuban) [188] 32.0%, and palm kernel oil [133] 52%. Lauric acid has frequently been observed in a number of the lesser-known oils, such as the fat of the Virginia creeper,[189] pine needle wax,[190] pear seed oil,[191] and oil of niger seed.[192] The acid is also found in small quantities in several of the animal depot fats, among which may be mentioned horse fat,[193] goat fat,[194] and the fat of human subcutaneous tissue.[195] The animal milk fats contain lauric acid in association with other saturated acids, the amount generally being somewhat less than that of capric acid and appreciably less than that of myristic or palmitic acid. Lauric acid is also present in butter fats, the percentage varying with the source of the fat.

Some marine oils [196] contain small amounts of lauric acid; however, in several of the marine oils it apparently constitutes a major component. Toyama [197] first reported the presence of lauric acid in the head oil of the sperm whale. Hilditch and Lovern [171] stated later that the amount is 16%, and recently Tsujimoto and Koyanagi [198] have observed that the lauric acid is present in this oil as cetyl laurate. Its presence has also been established in Japanese sardine oil [135] (1.6%) and in the fat of marine algae [199] (0.3%). The presence of lauric acid has also been reported in various fusel oils.[72, 103]

TRIDECANOIC ACID

Tridecanoic acid was first prepared by Krafft [33] by the oxidation of methyl tridecyl ketone. The acid is a low-melting, crystalline solid which possesses a faint, rather pleasant odor. It melts at 44.5° and boils at 236° at 100 mm. The refractive index of tridecanoic acid is n_D^{70} 1.4249.[179] The acid is insoluble in water and soluble in ethanol, acetone, ether, and other organic solvents.

A number of methods have been used for the preparation of tridecanoic acid from both its lower and its higher homologs. One of the better procedures is the hydrolysis of tridecanenitrile, which can be prepared from lauric acid. Ruzicka, Stoll, and Schinz [200] have described the preparation of 1-bromododecane, from which tridecanenitrile can be readily synthesized. Reid, Ruhoff, and Burnett [201] have recently suggested some modifications of the original procedure. 1-Dodecanol, the alcohol used for the preparation of 1-bromododecane, can be obtained by the reduction of ethyl laurate with sodium and ethanol,[202] or by the catalytic hydrogenation of ethyl laurate or lauric acid.[203, 204, 205, 206]

The synthesis of tridecanoic acid by the oxidation of 1-tridecanol with potassium permanganate in aqueous acetone has been described by Le Sueur,[57] and Blau [207] has also studied the oxidation of this alcohol with potassium dichromate and concentrated sulfuric acid. Tridecanoic acid has been prepared from myristic acid by conversion of the latter to 2-bromomyristic acid and thence to 2-hydroxymyristic acid, which is then oxidized to tridecanoic acid with potassium permanganate.[58] This procedure was later studied and somewhat modified by Levene and West.[208] The preparation of tridecanoic acid from 1-iodoundecane by the malonic acid synthesis has been described,[209] and Robinson [210] has studied its formation by the reaction between 1-iodoundecane and ethyl cyanoacetate. Tridecanoic acid results from the oxidation of methyl tridecyl ketone with potassium dichromate and sulfuric acid.[33] Lutz [54] has studied the formation of tridecanoic acid by the Hofmann reaction, and has also synthesized this acid by saponification of the nitrile obtained by the action of excess bromine in alkaline solution on N-tridecyl-N'-tetradecanoylurea. He also studied the saponification of N-dodecyl-N'-tridecanoylurea to dodecylamine and potassium tridecanoate. Fischer and Schneider [211] have stated that tridecanoic acid is among the products resulting from the oxidation of paraffin.

Tridecanoic acid is not present in the natural oils, fats, and waxes. A saturated acid, which was termed "Cocinsäure," was formerly stated to occur in natural products; however, Krafft [33] proved this acid to be a mixture and not a chemical individual.

Tetradecanoic Acid (Myristic Acid)

Myristic acid was first isolated by Playfair [4] in the course of an investigation of the fatty acids of nutmeg fat. The acid is found widely distributed in the animal and vegetable fats and forms a major component of the fatty acids of the *Myristicaceae* and the seed fats of the palm family.

Myristic acid is an odorless, crystalline solid which possesses a somewhat waxy feel. It melts at 54.4°,[212] a value which is higher than that previously reported by Krafft,[33] 53.5°, but is considerably lower than that observed by Levene and West,[208] 58.0°. The acid boils at 250.5° at 100 mm. and at 199° at 16 mm. Other physical constants for myristic acid are: d_4^{54} 0.8622, d_4^{70} 0.8533, and n_D^{70} 1.4273.[121] Myristic acid is insoluble in water, soluble in ethanol to the extent of 44 g. in 100 cc., and soluble in ether, acetone, glacial acetic acid, and chloroform.

Myristic acid has been prepared synthetically from both its higher and its lower homologs. Since it is present as the principal saturated acid in several of the well-known oils, particularly ucuhuba tallow and dika nut oil, and to a smaller extent in coconut oil, it is generally obtained from such sources rather than by synthetic procedures. Marasse[213] and later Bodenstein[214] prepared myristic acid by the fusion of stearolic acid with potassium hydroxide. Brown and Farmer[215] have recently described its synthesis by the oxidation of 4-ketostearic acid with chromium trioxide.

Myristic acid is the principal acid in many of the nut oils of the *Myristicaceae*. Steger and van Loon[216] found 66.6% in ucuhuba nut fat, and Ramos and de Nascimento[217] reported this fat to contain 73% of myristic acid. Other fats of this family possess large amounts of myristic acid; for example, nutmeg fat contains 76.7%[218] and otobo nut fat, 73.4%.[219] The preparation of myristic acid from nutmeg butter has been described by Verkade and Coops.[220] Many of the other seed fats have been observed to have large amounts of this acid. For example, dika fat has been reported[182] to contain 50.6% of myristic acid, jaboty kernel oil, 28%,[221] and Khakan kernel oil, 52.9%.[222] Myristic acid is always accompanied by smaller amounts of other saturated acids in those seed oils in which it constitutes the principal acid. The preparation of myristic acid from bayberry wax has recently been described.[223] Myristic acid also occurs in appreciable amounts in those oils which contain lauric acid as the principal component acid, for example, palm kernel oil and babassu fat. Elsdon[98] has reported 20% of myristic acid in coconut oil, Taylor and Clarke[97] and Lepkovsky[96] found 18%, and more recently Nobori[130] reported 13.06%. Armstrong, Allan, and Moore[131] have found 22.0% in the paring oil of African coconuts and 18.5% in the kernel oil. Hilditch and Vidyarthi[134] have stated that cohune nut fat contains 16% myristic acid and palm kernel oil[133] has been reported to contain 15% of this acid.

Myristic acid has also been observed to be a minor component of many vegetable oils, such as cottonseed oil,[224] rice bean oil,[225] olive oil,[226] mustard seed oil,[227] tobacco seed oil,[228] poke root oil,[229] black walnut oil,[230] and Brazil nut oil.[231]

A number of animal depot fats have been found to contain small amounts of myristic acid. Among the depot fats in which this acid has been observed are goat fat,[194] horse fat,[193] rat fat,[232, 233] duck fat,[234] and mink fat,[235] as well as in the phosphatides of beef suprarenals.[236]

The percentage of myristic acid in the animal milk fats is generally greater than that of any other saturated fatty acid with the exception of palmitic acid.[66, 93, 94, 137, 138, 237] Myristic acid is also present in appreciable amounts in the various butter fats.[238]

The marine oils frequently contain small quantities of myristic acid, and in a few of these oils it appears to be present in rather appreciable amounts.[239, 240] Small percentages of myristic acid have also been isolated from shark liver oil,[241, 242] and it is present in whale oil to the extent of from 4 to 5%.[243, 244] Hilditch and Lovern[171] have reported 14% of myristic acid in sperm-whale blubber oil, and Bonnevie-Svendsen[245] has found 10.8% present in a hydrogenated whale oil. It has been reported to be the principal saturated acid of herring oil,[246, 247] to be present in eel oil,[248] and to constitute 9.2% of the fatty acids of menhaden oil.[136] Myristic acid occurs in appreciable amounts in the head oil of the sperm whale.[171] Its presence in whale oil may be partially ascribed to its occurrence in the fats of marine algae, in certain specimens of which it has been found to constitute as much as 9.2% of the fatty acids.[102, 199] Myristic acid has also been observed to be present in wool grease[249, 250] and the various egg oils.[36, 251]

PENTADECANOIC ACID

Since pentadecanoic acid does not occur in the natural fats and oils, our knowledge of it is confined to the properties of the synthetic acid and to the various methods which have been used for its preparation. The acid was first prepared by Krafft[33] by the oxidation of methyl pentadecyl ketone, and since this time it has been obtained by a variety of procedures most of which involve either its synthesis from a lower acid or the degradation of a higher acid.

Pentadecanoic acid is an odorless, crystalline solid with a somewhat waxy texture. Francis, Piper, and Malkin[44] reported the melting point to be 52.1°, which is somewhat higher than the value of 51° found by Krafft [33] but lower than that observed by Levene and West.[59] The acid boils at 257° at 100 mm., and its refractive index and density are n_D^{70} 1.4339 [179] and d_4^{80} 0.8423. It is insoluble in water and easily soluble in ether, ethanol, chloroform, benzene, and petroleum ether.

Pentadecanoic acid has been prepared by heating 1-pentadecanol with a mixture of potassium and calcium oxides at 250°,[252] and by oxidizing this alcohol with potassium permanganate.[57] Its preparation by the oxidation of cetene with aqueous potassium permanganate has been described by Landa.[253] The oxidation of methyl pentadecyl ketone with potassium dichromate and sulfuric acid has been studied by Krafft.[33] Pentadecanoic acid has been prepared from palmitic acid by conversion of the latter to 2-hydroxypalmitic acid and oxidation of this acid by means of potassium permanganate in acetone.[59] The hydrolysis of pentadecanenitrile with five parts of concentrated hydrochloric acid at 150° for three hours results in its conversion to pentadecanoic acid.[254] The synthesis of pentadecanoic acid from myristic acid has recently been described by Krewson,[255] who reduced butyl myristate to 1-tetradecanol and then converted it to the nitrile through the bromide. The pentadecanenitrile was then hydrolyzed to the corresponding acid. Fischer and Schneider [211] have stated that pentadecanoic acid is present in the products formed by the oxidation of paraffin.

Although it is believed that pentadecanoic acid does not occur in natural products, several investigators have reported the presence of this acid or its isomers. Hinsberg and Roos [256] have observed a pentadecylic acid in the saponification products of yeast fat; Abraham and Hilditch [250] have stated that a pentadecylic acid is present in wool grease; and Dieterle, Haubold, and Meyer [257] have reported its presence in the fat of the bark of *Xanthoxylum carolinianum*.

Hexadecanoic Acid (Palmitic Acid)

Palmitic acid occurs more abundantly than any of the other acids of the saturated series and is present in essentially all the oils and fats of animal, vegetable, or marine origin. It constitutes the principal acid in a large number of fats. The acid was isolated in 1816 by Chevreul, who termed it "margaric acid." This acid was subsequently shown to be identical with palmitic acid isolated from palm oil by Frémy.[3]

Palmitic acid is an odorless, waxy, crystalline solid which melts to an oily liquid at 62.85°.[46] Other melting points which have been reported for palmitic acid are: 62.62°,[258] 62.6°,[259] 62.50°,[260] 63.10°,[44] and 62.67°.[261] The acid boils at 268.0° at 100 mm., at 219° at 20 mm., and at 139° at 1 mm.[180] Other constants for palmitic acid are: d_4^{62} 0.8527 (liquid), d_4^{70} 0.8487, $d_4^{75.8}$ 0.8465, d_4^{90} 0.8347, n_D^{60} 1.4339, n_D^{70} 1.4303, $n_D^{74.5}$ 1.4284,[262] and n_D^{80} 1.42691.[263] Palmitic acid is insoluble in water, sparingly soluble in cold ethanol, soluble in hot ethanol and in ether, and sparingly soluble in petroleum ether. Ruttan [50] determined its solubility in ethanol to be as follows: 1.449 g. dissolve in 100 g. ethanol at 0°, 3.087 g. at 7.4°, 7.523 g. at 16.2°, 15.577 g. at 24.6°, 29.879 g. at 28.8°, and 81.110 g. at 36.8°.

Palmitic acid can easily be obtained from many of the fats and waxes in which it occurs. Its preparation from Japan wax has been described by Krafft,[264] from Chinese vegetable tallow (*Stillingia*) by Dubovitz,[265] and from bayberry wax by Sauer, Hain, and Boutwell.[223] Hell and Jordanoff [266] have studied the preparation of palmitic acid from palm oil and have stated that the yield was not so high as that obtained from Japan wax.

Palmitic acid can be prepared synthetically by the hydrolysis of hexadecanenitrile, by the oxidation of 1-hexadecanol,[267] or by any of the methods generally applicable to the preparation of acids of the saturated series. Such methods, however, are not frequently employed as a source of palmitic acid, because of the ease with which it can be obtained from natural products.

Palmitic acid occurs as a major component in many of the vegetable oils and particularly in the fruit fats, in some of which it is present to the extent of 70% of the fatty acids. It has been reported to occur in palm oils to the extent of from 30 to 43%,[268,269] and in palm kernel oils from 7 to 9%.[100,133] Japan wax consists principally of palmitin and free palmitic acid,[159] Tsuji-moto [270] having reported the palmitic acid content to be 77%. It occurs in large amounts in *Stillingia* tallow,[271] and is the chief saturated acid of chrysalis oil.[272,273] Palmitic acid occurs in coconut oil together with other saturated acids, the amount being considerably less than that of myristic acid. Elsdon [98] reported 7% of palmitic acid in coconut oil and Lepkovsky [96] found 9%. The percentage of palmitic acid has been determined in a large number of vegetable oils, fats, and waxes, some of the results being as follows: babassu fat,[99] 6.9%; Brazil nut oil,[274] 13.55%; beechnut oil,[275] 4.88%; oil of niger seeds,[192] 8.4%; kapok seed oil,[276] 10.2%; poke root oil,[230] 8.63%; oat oil,[277] 9.45%; ucuhuba fat,[278] 8.4%; corn oil,[279] 7.7%; cohune nut fat,[134] 9.5%; avocado oil,[280] 6.9%; tomato seed oil,[281] 12.47%; tobacco seed oil,[282] 3.1%; pumpkin seed oil,[283] 6.2%; grape seed oil,[284] 6.17%; coffee bean oil,[285, 286] 20.17% and 28–29%; cashew kernel oil,[287] 6.4%; fat of wheat starch,[288] 35%; and cottonseed oil,[289] 20.04%. Palmitic acid has been found to comprise 60% of the fatty acids of the oil of the blessed thistle.[290] The presence of palmitic acid has also been reported in many of the floral waxes,[291] and in a large number of the essential oils, such as parsley seed oil,[292] oil of slash-pine tips,[293] and oil of sweet orange.[125]

Several of the bacterial waxes contain palmitic acid,[40, 294, 295, 296] and it has also been isolated in large quantities from many of the insect waxes. It is present in beeswax as cetyl palmitate[297] and melissyl palmitate.[298]

Palmitic acid is found in appreciable amounts in all the animal fats, where in most cases it is the chief saturated acid present. It is the principal saturated acid of lard, the amount present varying somewhat with the source;[299] it is also the chief saturated acid of beef tallow,[300] and its presence in substantial amounts has been reported in various other animal depot fats, such as rat body fat,[233] horse fat,[193, 301] goose fat,[302] goat fat,[194] pig liver fat,[303] mink fat,[235] alligator fat,[304] and many others. Palmitic acid has been stated to comprise 10% of the fatty acids of ox blood.[305] Palmitic acid is the chief saturated acid of the animal milk fats, the amount usually being from 20 to 30% of the mixed fatty acids. Arnold[237] has observed that the palmitic acid in human milk fat varies from 25 to 35%. It also occurs in the various butter fats in substantial amounts.

Palmitic acid is an important component of most of the marine oils and has been reported to be the principal saturated acid of whale oil,[306] constituting approximately 5% of the fatty acids present.[243] It comprises 20% of the fatty acids of hydrogenated herring oil and 17.4% of the fatty acids of hydrogenated sardine oil.[307] It is present in large percentages in the various fish liver oils,[308, 309] Ueno and Ikuta[310] reporting that it comprises 60% of the fatty acids of blue shark liver oil. The fats of the various marine algae contain appreciable amounts of palmitic acid,[311, 312, 313]

Lovern [199] reporting 7.3% in the fat of a certain marine alga. This acid has been reported in various egg oils such as shark egg oil,[35] hen egg yolk oil,[251, 314] and several other egg oils which have been examined.[34] It has been observed in certain fusel oils,[315] and has been isolated from several petroleum distillates.[316]

ISOPALMITIC ACID

An isopalmitic acid which melts at 57–58° has been isolated from shark egg oil [35] and also from the egg oil of *Bombyx mori*.[36] This acid was formerly reported by Suzuki [34] to be present in substantial quantities in egg yolk oil. An isopalmitic acid has also been reported in Japanese chrysalis oil,[37] but the later work by Ueno and Ikuta [317] has cast considerable doubt upon this observation. There is appreciable evidence to support the belief that isopalmitic acids are present in wool wax; [250, 318] however, proof of the identity of these acids requires further confirmation.

HEPTADECANOIC ACID (MARGARIC ACID, DATURIC ACID)

Heptadecanoic acid does not occur in the natural fats and oils, although its presence has often been reported, and it has been only within recent years that such names as margaric acid and daturic acid have ceased to be the subjects of scientific controversies. All the naturally occurring heptadecanoic acids which have been described and subsequently investigated have been shown to consist of mixtures of palmitic and stearic acids. Because of the frequent mutual occurrence of palmitic and stearic acids in fats, and since they are often the chief saturated acids, it is not surprising that a mixture of them has frequently been identified as a pure compound.

Heptadecanoic acid is a waxy, crystalline solid which melts to an oily, odorless liquid at 61.3°.[212] Other physical constants for heptadecanoic acid are: d_4^{60} 0.8579, d_4^{80} 0.8396, and n_D^{60} 1.4319.[179] The acid is insoluble in water and soluble in ethanol, ether, and glacial acetic acid. Its solubility in ethanol is as follows: 1.15 g. dissolve in 100 g. of ethanol at 0°, 2.42 g. at 5.4°, 4.0 g. at 10°, 6.72 g. at 15°, 13.4 g. at 21°, and 32.14 g. at 28°.[50]

Heptadecanoic acid was first synthesized by Heintz,[2, 319] who started with ethanol and finally prepared heptadecanoic acid stepwise by the cyanide method. Krafft [33] remarked that the procedure used by Heintz owed its final success more to the perseverance of the author than to the method itself. Le Sueur [55] has prepared heptadecanoic acid by the oxidation of the corresponding aldehyde with potassium permanganate. The oxidation of 2-hydroxystearic acid by potassium permanganate produces heptadecanoic acid.[59] The acid has also been obtained by Ruttan [50] from the action of carbon dioxide on hexadecylmagnesium iodide. Heptadecanoic acid is produced by the reaction of silver stearate and iodine followed by saponification of the resulting heptadecyl stearate and oxidation of the 1-heptadecanol.[320] The preparation of heptadecanoic acid from palmitic acid by the cyanide method has been described by Levene and Taylor.[42] This latter method is frequently employed for its preparation and is, perhaps, the most satisfactory procedure.

The term "margaric acid" was first employed by Chevreul in 1816 to describe an acid isolated from pork fat. Heintz [319] was unable to obtain heptadecanoic acid from this source and found that Chevreul's margaric acid was identical with palmitic acid previously isolated by Frémy.[3] The name "margaric acid" was then dropped from the literature. However, in 1890 Gérard [321] isolated an acid from datura oil, to which he gave the name daturic acid, which appeared to be heptadecanoic acid. In defining daturic acid in Wurtz' *Chemical Dictionary*, Arnaud [322] described it as a mixture of palmitic and stearic acids, which prompted Gérard to repeat his work upon datura oil. Gérard [323] then stated that a daturic acid melting at 54.5° was isolated from datura oil, and that this acid was not a mixture of palmitic and stearic acids but a chemical individual. In the meantime, Noerdlinger [324] stated that daturic acid was present in palm oil, and later Holde and Strange [325] reported a daturic acid in olive oil and Kreis and Hafner [326] found a heptadecanoic acid melting at 55.5–56.5° in lard. Holde [327] then reexamined the acid found in olive oil and reported that it was a mixture of palmitic and stearic acids. He further stated that, in his opinion, the acids isolated by Gérard, Noerdlinger, and Kreis and Hafner were also mixtures. Bömer and Limprich [328] later showed that heptadecanoic acid does not occur in lard. Meyer and Beer [329] isolated a daturic acid melting at 55.5° from datura oil and reaffirmed the presence of this acid in natural products, but the more recent work of Walden,[330] Verkade and Coops,[331] and Manjunath and Siddappa [332] has shown the reported daturic acid in this oil to be a mixture. Klimont and Mayer [333] have isolated an acid melting at 57.5–58° from goose fat which they claimed to be heptadecanoic acid, but Bömer and Merten [302] have stated that this acid is not found in goose fat. Heptadecanoic acid has been reported to occur in fish oils,[334] and Marcelet [335] has given the name "dorosomic acid" to an acid isolated from this source. Heptadecanoic acid has also been reported in Gedda wax,[298, 336] in lumbang oil,[337] in poke root fat,[229] and in alfalfa seed oil.[338] Recently, Schuette and Vogel [339] have shown that heptadecanoic acid is not present in alfalfa seed oil.

In spite of the fact that some of the arguments for the existence of heptadecanoic acid in natural products have not as yet been refuted, it is reasonably safe to conclude that this acid is not present in the naturally occurring fats and oils.

OCTADECANOIC ACID (STEARIC ACID)

Stearic acid was discovered by Chevreul in 1816 during his investigation of the fatty acids of mutton tallow. Although it does not occur as abundantly in nature as its next lower homolog, palmitic acid, it is generally referred to as the "characteristic fatty acid." It occurs as the principal saturated acid in comparatively few fats. However, it is found quite widely distributed in the animal and vegetable fats, and its ease of preparation by the reduction of its numerous unsaturated counterparts makes it perhaps the best known and most important of the acids of the saturated series.

Stearic acid is a waxy solid which can be crystallized, usually in the form of leaflets, from a number of organic solvents. It melts to an oily liquid at $69.6°$.[212, 340] A number of somewhat lower values for the melting point of this acid have been reported, such as $69.4–69.5°$,[341] $69.32°$,[258] $69.4°$,[121] $69.3°$,[259] and $69.45°$.[46] Several higher values have also been observed, for example, $70.1°$,[44] $70.5–71.5°$,[42] and $70.5°$.[262] The highest melting point recorded is that given by Saytzeff, $71–71.5°$.[342] Stearic acid boils at $291°$ at 100 mm., at $238°$ at 17 mm., at $232°$ at 15 mm., and at $158–160°$ at 0.25 mm. Other physical constants for stearic acid are: d_4^{20} 0.9408, $d_4^{69.2}$ 0.8454 (liquid), d_4^{80} 0.8386, n_D^{70} 1.4332, and n_D^{80} 1.4300. Stearic acid is quite insoluble in water, a saturated solution having been found to contain 1.2×10^{-6} mole per liter at $37°$.[343] The solubility of stearic acid in ethanol at various temperatures is as follows: [50] 0.393 g. dissolves in 100 g. ethanol at $0°$, 0.770 g. at $7.4°$, 1.832 g. at $16.2°$, 4.073 g. at $24.6°$, 5.971 g. at $28.8°$, and 22.51 g. at $38.6°$. Its solubilities in 95.7, 95.5, 95.1, 94.5, and 94.3% ethanol at $0°$ have been found to be: 0.1246, 0.1223, 0.1139,

0.1035, and 0.0996 g. per 100 cc.[344] The solubility of stearic acid in 91.53% ethanol in grams per hundred grams of solution is 0.113 g. at 0°, 0.396 g. at 10°, and 1.803 g. at 25°; in 86.16% ethanol, 0.061 g. at 0°, 0.232 g. at 10°, and 1.014 g. at 25°; and in 63.07% ethanol, 0.031 g. at 10° and 0.087 g. at 25°.[345, 346] It is easily soluble in ether, soluble in benzene and carbon disulfide, and slightly soluble in petroleum ether.

Stearic acid can be obtained from any of the glycerides in which it occurs; however, because of the difficulty of completely separating it from palmitic acid, it is generally prepared by reduction of the more easily purified unsaturated acids, such as oleic acid, linoleic acid, and elaidic acid. Many synthetic methods have been proposed for the preparation of stearic acid, a number of which are of academic interest only. Stearic acid has been produced from cetyl iodide and malonic acid by the malonic acid synthesis,[347] or by heating cetylacetoacetic ester with concentrated alcoholic potassium hydroxide.[348] Wilde and Reychler[349] have reported a 70% yield of stearic acid when oleic acid was heated with 1% of iodine at 270–280°. The synthesis of stearic acid by the reduction of 10-iodostearic acid with zinc and hydrochloric acid in ethanol solution has been described.[350] The reduction of oleic or elaidic acid with hydrogen iodide and red phosphorus at 200° gives stearic acid,[351] as does the catalytic reduction of these acids in the presence of nickel,[352] copper,[353, 354] or colloidal palladium.[355] The preparation of stearic acid by the reduction of dihydroxystearic acid,[356, 357] iodoelaidic acid,[358] and of ricinoleic acid[359] has also been reported. The electrolytic reduction of oleic acid to stearic acid has been the subject of several investigations.[360, 361, 362] The catalytic hydrogenation of the octadecenoic acids or their alkyl esters is one of the most satisfactory methods for the preparation of pure stearic acid, owing mainly to the ease of purification of the starting materials. Levene and Taylor[42] have studied the preparation of stearic acid by the hydrogenation of ethyl oleate, and recently Kass and Keyser[61] have described the preparation of stearic acid, free from palmitic acid, by the hydrogenation of purified elaidic acid, α-eleostearic acid, or β-eleostearic acid.

Stearic acid can be obtained from several of the naturally occurring glycerides in which it comprises the chief saturated acid. Its preparation from cocoa butter,[363] and from Chinese tallow and shea butter,[265] has been described.

Stearic acid appears in all the animal body fats, the amount depending upon the type of animal, its diet, and its environment. With the exception of palmitic acid, it is the most prominent of the saturated fatty acids in the animal fats. Hilditch and Longenecker [364] have reported a stearic acid content varying from 21.0 to 26.5% in the several ox depot fats which they examined. The amount present in the pig depot fats is quite variable and is generally somewhat less than half that of the palmitic acid. The percentage of stearic acid has been determined in a large number of animal depot fats, examples of which are rat fat,[365] 4.0–6.2%; mink fat,[235] 26.7%; reindeer fat,[366] 20.5%; and goose fat,[302] 3.8%. Stearic acid occurs in large amounts in the hydrogenated animal fats, 73.3% having been found in hydrogenated lard, 64.5% in hydrogenated tallow, and 60.7% in hydrogenated horse fat.[367] The various animal milk fats contain stearic acid in amounts ranging from approximately 5 to 15%.[65, 94, 368] It is also present in the various butter fats in appreciable amounts.[238, 369]

The vegetable fats and oils generally contain stearic acid in small amounts, varying from a fraction of 1% to approximately 10%; however, in a few of these fats stearic acid is present as a major component. Shea butter,[370] which contains 30 to 35% of stearic acid, and cocoa butter,[371] which has been reported to contain 34% of this acid, are examples of this latter type. Considerable work has been reported in the literature upon the stearic acid content of vegetable oils, some of the results which have been obtained being as follows: soybean oil,[372] 7%; corn oil,[279] 3.5%; cottonseed oil,[224] 2%; peanut oil,[373] 6.2 and 4.9%; coconut oil,[96] 1%; sesame oil,[374] 4.6%; palm kernel oil,[133] 2.5%; barley fat,[375] 2.6%; tomato seed oil,[281] 5.89%; rubber seed oil,[376] 9.1%; chrysalis oil,[273] 4%; kapok seed oil,[276] 8.4%; black walnut oil,[230] 1.8%; hazelnut oil,[231] 1.59%; beechnut oil,[275] 3.45%; cantaloupe seed oil,[377] 4.5%; sunflower seed oil,[378] 2.9%; cashew kernel oil,[287] 11.24%; cohune nut fat,[134] 3%; and oiticica fat,[379] 1.4%. Stearic acid constitutes a major percentage of the fatty acids of hydrogenated vegetable oils; for instance, hydrogenated cottonseed oil has been reported to contain 76% of this acid.[380]

Oils and fats of marine origin contain stearic acid only as a minor component. Its presence has been reported in dolphin oil,[27] herring oil,[381, 382] whale oil,[243, 244] menhaden oil,[248] sardine oil,[383] and in the various fish liver oils.[384, 385] Stearic acid has also been observed in the various marine algae fats.[199, 311, 386] The hydrogenated fish oils contain considerable amounts of stearic acid, hydrogenated whale oil [245] having been reported to contain 10.8%, and hydrogenated sardine oil,[307] 27.6%.

The presence of stearic acid has also been observed in several bacterial waxes, such as the wax of B. *leprae* [296] and the wax of the tubercle bacillus.[39]

NONADECANOIC ACID

Nonadecanoic acid is not found in the naturally occurring oils, fats, or waxes. The acid has, however, been prepared synthetically by several investigators and its properties have been reported. It is a waxy, crystalline solid which melts to an oily liquid at 68.65° [212] and boils at 297–298° at 100 mm. The acid has been synthesized by Schweizer [387] by heating nonadecanenitrile with alcoholic potassium hydroxide. Levene and Taylor [42] and Francis, Piper, and Malkin [44] have also reported the preparation of the acid by this method. The acid has been claimed to be one of the products of the oxidation of paraffin.[211]

An acid, stated to be isomeric with nonadecanoic acid, has been reported to be present in the wax of the tubercle bacillus. The acid was first isolated from this source by Anderson and Chargaff [39] during the fractional distillation of the methyl esters of the liquid saturated acids from this wax, and the name tuberculostearic acid was employed, since it was considered to be isomeric with stearic acid. Sometime later a similar acid was isolated from bovine tubercular wax [294] and from the wax of the leprosy bacillus.[40] Tuberculostearic acid is a liquid at ordinary temperatures, melting at 10–11°. Its density and refractive index have been reported as d_4^{24} 0.8771 and n_D^{25} 1.4512. The work of Spielman [388] has indicated this acid to be 10-methylstearic acid, and consequently it should be considered as an isomer of nonadecanoic acid. The fact that synthetic 10-methylstearic acid melts ten degrees higher than the naturally occurring tuberculostearic acid casts some doubt upon the actual structure of the acid.

EICOSANOIC ACID (ARACHIDIC ACID)

Arachidic acid was discovered in 1854 by Gösmann,[10] who considered it to be eicosanoic acid. The presence of arachidic acid in the natural products, and its normal structure, were accepted for seventy years, after which time certain questions arose concerning its identity. These questions have only recently been answered.

Eicosanoic acid is a waxy solid which melts at $75.35°$ [212] to a liquid whose constants are: d_4^{100} 0.8240 and n_D^{100} 1.4250.[45] The acid boils at 203–205° at 1 mm. It is sparingly soluble in cold ethanol, 0.022 part dissolving in 100 parts of 90% ethanol at 15°, and 0.045 part at 20°. It is readily soluble in chloroform, ether, and benzene.

A number of procedures have been employed for the synthesis of eicosanoic acid. Schweizer [387] prepared the acid by heating octadecylacetoacetic ester with potassium hydroxide, and a similar treatment of brassidic acid [389] or erucic acid [363, 390] has been reported to result in substantial yields of eicosanoic acid. The acid has also been prepared by the action of fuming nitric acid upon behenolic acid.[391] The hydrolysis of eicosanenitrile [42] is one of the most satisfactory procedures for the synthesis of eicosanoic acid. The preparation of this acid by the malonic acid synthesis has been described by Adam and Dyer [392] and also by Bleyberg and Ulrich.[45] The procedure followed in this synthesis is to reduce stearic acid or its esters to 1-octadecanol, convert this alcohol to 1-iodoöctadecane and then to octadecylmalonic acid. Eicosanoic acid results from the pyrolysis of the octadecylmalonic acid.

Eicosanoic acid is found widely distributed in nature, although the amount present in any specific fat or oil is small, generally of the order of 1%. In a few of the fats it occurs to the extent of several per cent of the mixed acids, and in rare instances it constitutes a major component. Examples of the latter type are: rambutan tallow, in which Morgan and Holmes [393] have found 20.6% and Hilditch and Stainsby [394] have reported 34.7%; pulasan tallow, which the latter authors have found to contain 22.3% of arachidic acid; and macassar nut fat, from which Dhingra, Hilditch, and Vickery [395] have isolated 22.6%.

The vegetable oils generally contain less than 1% of eicosanoic acid. Baughman and Jamieson [396] have reported 0.6% of arachidic acid in sunflower seed oil, 0.7% in soybean oil, 0.4% in corn oil, and 0.58% in cottonseed oil. Rubber seed oil [377] has been found to contain 0.3% of eicosanoic acid; rice oil,[397] 0.5%; and olive oil,[398] 0.2%. Eicosanoic acid occurs in somewhat larger amounts in a few of the vegetable oils. Coffee bean oil contains 2.11% of eicosanoic acid, poke root oil [229] 5.91%, and peanut oils [373] from 3 to 4%.

Arachidic acid has been observed in small amounts in the various animal depot fats and also in the milk fats. Bosworth [399] has reported 0.8% in human milk fat.

The various fish oils contain arachidic acid, its presence having been reported in sardine oil,[400] whale oil,[242, 306] and shark liver oil.[241, 308] Certain hydrogenated oils, particularly hydrogenated fish oils such as menhaden oil,[248] whale oil,[401] and sardine oil,[402] contain appreciable amounts of arachidic acid. Ueno and Matsuda [307] found 28% of arachidic acid in hydrogenated herring oil and 23% in hydrogenated cod liver oil. Hydrogenated cottonseed oil has been reported to contain 7% of this acid.[403]

It was accepted without question for a number of years that the arachidic acid obtained from peanut oil and from other oils and fats was eicosanoic acid. Gösmann [10] assumed the naturally occurring acid to be eicosanoic acid, and Caldwell [404] and later Tassinari [405] likewise stated that arachidic acid and eicosanoic acid are similar. Their identity appeared to be completely established when Schweizer [387] compared arachidic acid with synthetic eicosanoic acid. Further confirmation was given at a much later date by Cohen,[406] who stated that the arachidic acid isolated from peanut oil was actually eicosanoic acid. However, three years earlier Ehrenstein and Stuewer [41] had claimed that the arachidic acid from peanut oil was not eicosanoic acid, but an isobehenic acid. Many investigators believed that arachidic and eicosanoic acids were not identical, owing to the much lower melting point of the acid obtained from peanut oil. Since arachidic acid is present in large amounts in rambutan tallow, and consequently is easily separated and purified, Ehrenstein and Stuewer and others considered the arachidic acid from this source to be eicosanoic acid. Morgan and his collaborators [363, 407] then confirmed the presence of eicosanoic acid in rambutan tallow, but questioned its existence in peanut oil. Kreiling [11] had previously observed the presence of higher acids in the arachidic acid obtained from peanut oil, and this observation was confirmed by Holde and Godbole.[408] There is little question, therefore, that some of the arachidic acids prepared from peanut oil contained impurities. Holde and others [409] stated that the arachidic acid from peanut oil contained lignoceric and higher acids and that, in their opinion, the acids of peanut oil possess a normal structure. These authors, however, considered the "arachidic" acid from peanut oil to be docosanoic acid. The studies of Francis, Piper, and Malkin [44] upon the x-ray spacings of the arachidic acid from peanut oil have called attention to the fact that previous confusion regarding the structure of arachidic acid from this source has been brought about by the difficulty in separating pure eicosanoic acid from its higher homologs. The x-ray investigation of Morgan and Holmes [410] upon arachidic acid from peanut oil also indicated that the acid under observation was not a pure compound. Proof of the normal structure of arachidic acid from peanut oil, and of its identity with eicosanoic acid, has been presented by Jantzen and Tiedcke, [411] who fractionated the methyl esters of the high molecular weight acids of peanut oil and conclusively established the presence of eicosanoic acid.

HENEICOSANOIC ACID

Heneicosanoic acid is a waxy, crystalline solid which melts at 74.3°.[212] Levene and Taylor [42] have reported the melting point to be 75–76°, and Francis, Piper, and Malkin,[44] 75.2°.

Heneicosanoic acid was first synthesized by Le Sueur and Withers [412] by the reduction of 13-ketoheneicosanoic acid with amalgamated zinc and hydrochloric acid. The acid obtained by these authors melted at 73–74°, and was reported to be readily soluble in ether, chloroform, cold benzene, and hot ethyl acetate or acetone. The 13-ketoheneicosanoic acid employed in this synthesis was prepared from dihydroxybehenic acid according to a method previously described.[413] Fusion of dihydroxybehenic acid with excess potassium hydroxide at 240–245° resulted in the formation of 2-hydroxy-2-octyltetradecanedioic acid. The oxidation of this dicarboxylic acid with potassium permanganate in aqueous acetone gave a substantial yield of 13-ketoheneicosanoic acid. Levene and Taylor [42] have reported the preparation of heneicosanoic acid from arachidic acid by the nitrile method, and Morgan and Holmes [414] have synthesized this acid by the oxidation of methyl heneicosyl ketone.

An acid, stated to be heneicosanoic acid, has been isolated from beef marrow by Eylerts,[415] who gave it the name medullic acid. Later, Mohr [416] and also Thümmel [417] stated that medullic acid is actually a mixture of palmitic and stearic acids. Much later, Tutin and Clewer [418] isolated from *Cluytia similis* an acid, termed cluytinic acid, which melted at 69°, and stated that they considered this acid to be heneicosanoic acid. Morgan and Holmes [410] studied the x-ray spacings of cluytinic acid and stated that it is a mixture of tetracosanoic and hexacosanoic acids. Two years later, Francis, Piper, and Malkin [44] compared the x-ray spacings of synthetic heneicosanoic acid with those of a sample of cluytinic acid given to them by Tutin and stated that they were clearly not identical. Arachidic acid obtained from peanut oil has frequently been confused with heneicosanoic acid. Flaschenträger and Halle [419] have also reported 0.06% of heneicosanoic acid in the fatty acids of Japan wax. However, the evidence which has been presented to date rather clearly indicates that heneicosanoic acid is not present in the natural fats and waxes.

DOCOSANOIC ACID (BEHENIC ACID)

Behenic acid was discovered in 1848 by Völcker [8] during an investigation of the fatty acids of behen oil. The acid has since been recognized as a minor component of many seed fats and has been reported to occur in traces in several animal milk fats and in the marine oils. Although behenic acid is not found abundantly in nature, its unsaturated counterparts occur in large amounts in some of the seed oils and in the marine oils. The monoölefinic acid erucic acid is the principal acid present in rape oil, and the marine oils contain substantial amounts of highly unsaturated acids having twenty-two carbon atoms. The saturated acid can easily be prepared from any of these acids by catalytic hydrogenation.

Behenic acid is a waxy solid melting at 79.95° [212] to an oily liquid (d_4^{100} 0.8221 and n_D^{100} 1.4270), which boils at 306° at 60 mm.[420] Talanzeff [421] reported a melting point of 83–84°, and Morgan and Holmes [414] a melting point of 83° for behenic acid. One hundred grams of 90% ethanol dissolve 0.102 g. of behenic acid at 17°, and at 25° 0.218 g. of the acid dissolves in 100 cc. of 91.53% ethanol, 0.116 g. in 100 cc. of 86.16% ethanol, and 0.011 g. in 100 cc. of 63.07% ethanol.[346] One hundred grams of ether dissolve 0.1922 g. of behenic acid at 16°.[421]

Behenic acid has been obtained by the hydrolysis of docosanenitrile.[42] Bleyberg and Ulrich [45] have described its preparation from eicosanoic acid by the malonic acid synthesis. The best method, by far, for the preparation of behenic acid is the reduction of normal unsaturated acids containing twenty-two carbon atoms, or their halogen substitution products. Such acids are easily obtained from natural products and their reduction results in essentially quantitative yields of behenic acid. The acid has been prepared by shaking erucic acid in ether solution with platinum black in a hydrogen atmosphere.[422] Morgan and Holmes [414] have described its preparation from erucic acid by reduction with hydrogen in the presence of colloidal palladium, and Yokoyama and Kotake [423] have studied its formation by the reduction of erucic acid with selenium. Behenic acid has also been obtained by the catalytic hydrogenation of erucic acid, brassidic acid, and trierucin in the presence of metallic nickel.[424] The electrolytic reduction of erucic acid to behenic acid by means of a platinum cathode has been described.[362] Stohmann and Langbein [420] have reported the formation of behenic acid by heating erucic acid with iodine at 270°, followed by treatment of the reaction product with zinc and hydrochloric acid. The reduction of iodobehenic acid with zinc and hydrochloric acid has been studied by Talanzeff.[421]

Behenic acid has been reported in small quantities in several of the seed fats, such as rape oil,[227,425] peanut oil,[411,426] mustard seed oil,[427] and rice bean oil.[225] It has been found in large amounts in several hydrogenated oils such as jamba oil, mustard seed oil, and rape oil, which have been reported to contain 50.8, 46.3, and 57.6%, respectively.[227] Behenic acid has been observed in small amounts in human milk fat [399] and in butter fats.[428] The marine oils contain small amounts of behenic acid, its presence having been reported in sardine oil,[400] whale oil,[306,429] and shark liver oils.[241,310,430] Hydrogenated herring oil has been found to contain 7% of behenic acid, hydrogenated sardine oil 18%, and hydrogenated cod liver oil 13%.[307] Behenic acid has also been reported in montan wax [431] and in the wax of slash pine.[293]

TRICOSANOIC ACID

Tricosanoic acid is not present in the naturally occurring fats and waxes; however, it has been synthesized by several methods, and its properties have been described. Various melting points have been reported for the synthetic acid, probably the most accurate of which is 79.1°, recently reported by Francis and Piper.[212] At one time, the acid was thought to occur in the wax of olive leaves,[432] and there has been some speculation as to its presence in peanut oil.

Tricosanoic acid, melting at 80–81°, has been prepared by Levene and Taylor [42] by the hydrolysis of tricosanenitrile, which was synthesized from behenic acid. Robinson [49] has reported the preparation of tricosanoic acid by the reduction of 13-ketotricosanoic acid, the latter compound resulting from the condensation of the sodium derivative of ethyl 2-acetylbrassylate with stearoyl chloride. Its formation by the reduction of 13-ketotricosanoic acid has been further studied by Ashton, Robinson, and Smith.[433] Taylor and Levene [434] obtained tricosanoic acid, melting at

76.5–77.5°, by the oxidation of 2-hydroxylignoceric acid with potassium permanganate. Klenk [435] has reported tricosanoic acid to be the main product formed by the oxidation of cerebronic acid.

TETRACOSANOIC ACID (LIGNOCERIC ACID)

Lignoceric acid was first described by Hell and Hermanns,[12] who isolated the acid from beech-tar paraffin. Later, Kreiling [11] observed the presence of a higher acid in the arachidic acid obtained from peanut oil and obtained a small amount of lignoceric acid which he believed to be similar to that previously found in beech tar. These investigators considered lignoceric acid to be identical with tetracosanoic acid. Later work indicated that the lignoceric acids obtained from different sources did not have similar melting points, and these observations, combined with the failure of the naturally occurring acids to agree in melting point with the synthetic acid, cast doubt upon the normal structure of lignoceric acid. It has now been conclusively established, however, that lignoceric acid is tetracosanoic acid.

Francis and Piper [212] reported the melting point of highly purified tetracosanoic acid to be 84.15°, a value which is similar to that formerly reported by Francis, Collins, and Piper,[46] and somewhat higher than those previously reported.[44, 262] The refractive index of the liquid acid is n_D^{100} 1.4287.[45] The solubilities of tetracosanoic acid in 91.53, 86.16, and 63.07% ethanol at 25° have been found to be 0.182, 0.092, and 0.011 g. per 100 cc., respectively.[345]

Tetracosanoic acid can be prepared synthetically by a number of methods. The hydrolysis of tetracosanenitrile results in an essentially quantitative yield of the corresponding acid.[42] Brigl [436] has described the preparation of tetracosanoic acid by the decomposition of docosylmalonic acid, a method which was employed at a later date by Bleyberg and Ulrich.[45] The action of ethyl acetoacetate and lauroyl chloride upon 11-bromoundecanoic acid results in 13-ketotetracosanoic acid, from which tetracosanoic acid can be prepared by the Clemmensen reduction.[433] Sullivan[437] has reported the formation of tetracosanoic acid by the distillation of rotten oak wood.

Lignoceric acid is found in many of the vegetable oils, particularly the seed fats; however, the amount observed is generally quite small. Corn oil [279] has been reported to contain 0.2% of lignoceric acid, sunflower seed oil [378] 0.4%, soybean oil [438] 0.1%, sesame oil [374] 0.04%, coffee bean oil [286] 1.8%, black walnut oil [230] 0.04%, mustard oil [277] 1.1%, and rape oil [227] 2.4%. Seed fats in general contain only small percentages of lignoceric acid, although the fat of the seeds of the deciduous tree *Adenanthera pavonina* offers an interesting exception, having been reported to contain 25.5% of this acid.[439] Ayyar [440] has obtained from this source a 1.5% yield, based on the weight of the seeds, of lignoceric acid melting at 80–81°.

The fish oils contain small amounts of lignoceric acid.[241, 310, 400, 430] It is also present in appreciable amounts in several hydrogenated marine oils, since Ueno and Matsuda [307] have reported 4.0% in hydrogenated sardine oil and 6.0% in hydrogenated herring oil. It has been observed in several of the animal oils, particularly in the phosphatide fractions. Rosenheim and Maclean [441] have noted its presence in kidney fat, and Bosworth and Brown [428] have established its presence in butter fat. The fat of the mold *Aspergillus niger* contains 11.8% of lignoceric acid.[442] The various insect waxes such as Chinese wax [443] and beeswax,[444] the mineral waxes such as montan wax,[431] and the bacterial waxes [296] have been reported to contain lignoceric acid.

The structure of the naturally occurring lignoceric acid has been the subject of considerable disagreement. It was considered for many years to be tetracosanoic acid. However, in 1913 Meyer and others [445] pointed out that the lignoceric acid isolated from peanut oil or beechwood tar was not identical with synthetic tetracosanoic acid, since it did not yield behenic acid upon acid degradation. These authors concluded that naturally occurring lignoceric acid possessed a branched chain of carbon atoms. In the same year, Levene and West [446] had concluded from an examination of the hydrocarbon prepared from lignoceric acid that the acid did possess a normal carbon chain. Later,[208] however, these authors stated that a reexamination of the hydrocarbon prepared from lignoceric acid and the normal hydrocarbon showed them to differ and, consequently, that lignoceric acid did not contain a straight chain of carbon atoms. An examination of the lignoceric acid obtained from beechwood tar convinced Brigl and Fuchs [447] that two isomeric lignoceric acids were present and that one of them was the normal acid, a statement which was challenged by Levene, Taylor, and Haller.[448] Somewhat later, Cohen [406] claimed that the lignoceric acid isolated from peanut oil was a straight-chain acid. A comparison of the x-ray spacings of synthetic tetracosanoic acid with the lignoceric acids obtained from peanut oil and beechwood tar led Francis, Piper, and Malkin [44] to state that lignoceric acid and tetracosanoic acid are identical, and that the so-called isotetracosanoic acid is a mixture. This conclusion was strengthened by a fractionation of the higher saturated acids of peanut oil by Jantzen and Tiedcke,[411] and later by Taylor.[449] Meanwhile, Holde and others [431] isolated an acid from montan wax which they considered to be tetracosanoic acid, and they stated that the lignoceric acid from peanut oil was tetracosanoic acid containing other acids as impurities.[29] The question of the normal structure of the lignoceric acids from various sources undoubtedly arose from the difficulty of obtaining a pure acid from the oils and fats in which it is present.

An isomeric lignoceric acid, carnaubic acid, has been reported to occur in several waxes. The acid derives its name from its association with carnauba wax, in which it was first observed by Stürcke.[450] Darmstaedter and Lifschütz [451] later claimed to have isolated a similar acid from wool wax, and still later Röhmann [452] reported it to be contained in coffee wax. It has also been observed in the phosphatide fraction of kidney fat.[453] Röhmann [454] later denied the existence of carnaubic acid in wool wax; however, Salomone [249] has again reported its presence in this wax. It has also been claimed that this acid has been isolated from cotton wax [455] and millet oil.[456]

Carnaubic acid melts at 72.5° and is soluble in ether, acetone, methanol, benzene, and hot ethanol. It is found associated with the higher alcohols, with which it is undoubtedly combined as an ester. It appears in millet oil as a triglyceride. The question as to whether this acid is actually an isomeric lignoceric acid or merely a difficultly separable acid mixture has not been satisfactorily answered. On the basis of the data so far presented, one would certainly not be justified in assuming that carnaubic acid is a chemical individual.

PENTACOSANOIC ACID

Pentacosanoic acid is not found in the naturally occurring fats or waxes. It has been reported to be contained in several of the waxes and also in peanut oil, but a reexamination of such acids has shown them to be mixtures of even-carbon acids and not pentacosanoic acid as reported.

The melting point of highly purified pentacosanoic acid has been found to be 83.0°.[212] This value is somewhat lower than the melting point of 84–85° previously reported by Levene and

Taylor,[42] but is in fair agreement with the value of 82.8° observed by Francis, Piper, and Malkin.[44]

Pentacosanoic acid has been prepared from lignoceric acid by conversion of this acid to pentacosanenitrile, followed by hydrolysis of this compound to the corresponding acid.[42]

Owing to the difficulty of separating the higher acids from fats or waxes in which they occur in small amounts, it is not surprising that acid mixtures have been considered, in several instances, to be pentacosanoic acid. Gascard and Damoy [457] and later Damoy [458] have reported the isolation of a pentacosanoic acid, melting at 77.8°, from beeswax, designating the acid as neocerotic acid, and Holde and Bleyberg [426] also claimed the presence of neocerotic acid in this wax. Tropsch and Koch [459] have stated that pentacosanoic acid is present in montan wax, and Holde and others [409] have claimed its isolation from peanut oil. Somewhat later, Holde, Bleyberg, and Vohrer [431] found that the reported pentacosanoic acid of montan wax was a mixture of even acids, and Jantzen and Tiedcke [411] stated that they could find no evidence of the presence of acids containing an odd number of carbon atoms in peanut oil.

HEXACOSANOIC ACID (CEROTIC ACID)

Cerotic acid and its higher homologs occur principally in the various animal, vegetable, and insect waxes as esters of the higher fatty alcohols. They are found only in traces in the vegetable fats. Owing to the difficulty of separating the higher aliphatic acids from one another, considerable uncertainty has existed regarding the identity and structure of cerotic acid. Many of the cerotic acids described in the literature are actually acid mixtures, and the failure of investigators to recognize them as such has resulted in much speculation regarding the actual structure of this acid. The weight of evidence certainly indicates that hexacosanoic acid, to which the name cerotic acid can properly be applied, is present in the natural waxes.

Hexacosanoic acid is a waxy solid which melts at 87.7°,[45, 212] giving an oily liquid of d_4^{100} 0.8198 and n_D^{100} 1.4301. The acid is easily soluble in boiling methanol, ethanol, acetone, benzene, or chloroform. It is only slightly soluble in cold ethanol.

Hexacosanoic acid melting at 88–89° has been prepared synthetically by the hydrolysis of hexacosanenitrile.[42] Gascard [340, 460] has studied the synthesis of hexacosanoic acid by the oxidation of ceryl alcohol, the melting point of the product being reported as

82–82.5°. Bleyberg and Ulrich [45] have described the preparation of hexacosanoic acid by the decomposition of tetracosylmalonic acid, which can be obtained from lignoceric acid by the malonic acid synthesis. Cerotic acid can be prepared from Chinese wax,[14] montan wax,[431] or beeswax [457] by saponification and fractionation of their mixed acids.

The presence of cerotic acid in the various vegetable, insect, and mineral waxes has been established for many years. It was first observed in Chinese wax by Brodie,[9] where it exists chiefly in the form of ceryl cerotate. Cerotic acid is the principal acid of beeswax, and it has been stated to occur in this wax both in the free state and as esters of the higher alcohols.[13, 297, 426, 458, 461, 462] Cerotic acid has been isolated from montan wax.[431] It has frequently been claimed to be the principal acid of wool wax,[249, 454, 463] and Lipp and Kovacs [336] have established its presence in Gedda wax. Jakobsen [464] has reported that flax wax contains 32.5% of cerotic acid, and Fargher and Probert [455] have separated the acid from cotton wax. Practically every wax which has been examined has been found to contain cerotic acid. Its presence has been reported in floral waxes,[291] bamboo wax,[465] carnauba wax,[450] and the wax of stick-lac.[466] The acid isolated from the latter source has been named tachardiaceric acid, but it is considered to be cerotic acid.

Anderson and coworkers [39, 295, 467, 468] have reported the isolation of an isomeric cerotic acid from the acetone-soluble fraction of the wax of tubercle bacilli. This acid, which has been termed phthioic acid, is stated to be biologically active and is apparently associated with the phosphatide portion of the wax. More recently, Spielman and Anderson [469] have described phthioic acid as a branched-chain, polymethylated hexacosanoic acid.

Although cerotic acid is found principally in the waxes, its presence in traces has been observed in many of the vegetable fats. Examples of such fats are peanut oil,[470, 471] spinach fat,[472] pumpkin seed oil,[473] and the fat of rice polishings.[474] The fat of fern spores has been shown to contain appreciable amounts of cerotic acid.[475]

Owing to the difficulty of separating pure cerotic acid from its naturally occurring sources, the question of its identity has been a subject of controversy for many years. The cerotic acid which Brodie [9] first isolated from Chinese wax melted at 78° and was considered by him to have the formula $C_{27}H_{54}O_2$. Somewhat later, Schalfeieff [476] studied cerotic acid from this source and stated that two acids were present, one of which had the formula previously assigned to cerotic acid, the other being a tetracosanoic acid. Nafzger [13] later announced that the cerotic acid from this source was a mixture of acids, and that cerotic acid itself contained either twenty-six or twenty-seven carbon atoms. The formula which Brodie assigned to cerotic acid was questioned by Hell and Hermanns.[12] Marie [14] then undertook a detailed study of the cerotic acid obtained from beeswax and assigned the formula $C_{25}H_{50}O_2$ to the acid which melted at 77.9°. He also stated that this acid was mixed with a triacontanoic acid which melted at 90°. Henriques [477] restudied the acid isolated from Chinese tallow and stated that the cerotic acid obtained from this source was identical with hexacosanoic acid. Lewkowitsch [478] had previously observed that the neutralization value of the cerotic acid isolated from beeswax agreed with that of hexacosanoic acid. In 1921 Gascard [340] stated that the cerotic acid from Chinese wax had the formula $C_{27}H_{54}O_2$, and three years later Grassow [479] announced the isolation of a cerotic acid from wool fat which he stated to be identical with that obtained from beeswax by Marie. In the same year, Damoy [458] separated from beeswax an acid melting at 82–82.5° and assigned to it the formula $C_{27}H_{54}O_2$.

The isolation of a cerotic acid melting at 85–85.5° from the fat of fern spores [480] was an event of considerable importance. The melting points of the cerotic acids previously obtained from other sources were much lower than that of the synthetic hexacosanoic acid. These authors believed that these low melting points were due to impurities, and they succeeded in obtaining from beeswax an acid, melting at 83–84°, which did not depress the melting point of the acid isolated from the fern spores. The next year, Morgan and Holmes [470] separated from peanut oil a cerotic acid which melted at 77°, and stated that on the basis of its x-ray spacings it contained a straight chain of twenty-six carbon atoms. The x-ray spacings of the cerotic acids from beeswax and from Chinese wax were investigated later by Francis, Piper, and Malkin,[44] who concluded that the one from beeswax was hexacosanoic acid containing octacosanoic acid as an impurity, and that the one from Chinese wax was hexacosanoic acid. More recently, Mattissohn [444] has stated that the acids obtained from beeswax which have been identified as odd-carbon acids are probably mixtures of hexacosanoic acid with its higher homologs. The cerotic acid present in montan wax is identical with hexacosanoic acid.[431] The question of the composition or structure of the cerotic acid found in wool grease has not been answered. Abraham and Hilditch [250] have stated that the acid melting at 73–75° obtained from this source is not hexacosanoic acid.

There can be no question but that many of the cerotic acids reported in the literature are not individual acids but acid mixtures. It has, however, been conclusively shown that hexacosanoic acid is present in many of the waxes and fats, and the term cerotic acid should refer to this acid irrespective of its source.

HEPTACOSANOIC ACID

Heptacosanoic acid has been synthesized from 1-hexacosanol by conversion of the alcohol to the nitrile and hydrolysis of the latter to the corresponding acid.[481] The acid obtained in this manner melted at 87.5–87.7°.

Acids designated as heptacosanoic acid have frequently been reported to be contained in the fats and waxes. Brodie,[9] Schalfeieff,[476] and others [241,482] considered the cerotic acid present in Chinese wax to be heptacosanoic acid. Koyama [483] has more recently given the name ibotoceric acid to an acid, considered to be heptacosanoic acid, obtained from Chinese wax. This acid has been reported to have been found in beeswax.[297,426,484,485] Tropsch and Kreutzer [486] have separated an acid from montan wax to which they gave the name carboceric acid, assigning the formula $C_{27}H_{54}O_2$. Peanut oil,[458] wool fat,[454] and several other oils have been reported to contain heptacosanoic acid.

In spite of the numerous reports of the occurrence of heptacosanoic acid in natural products, sufficient evidence has been offered to make it extremely unlikely that this acid is actually present. Lewkowitsch,[478] Henriques,[477] Holde, Bleyberg, and Vohrer,[431] Mattissohn,[444] and others have stated that the naturally occurring acids previously supposed to contain twenty-seven carbon atoms are actually mixtures of even-carbon acids. The x-ray investigations of Morgan and Holmes,[470] and of Francis, Piper, and Malkin [44] later, have given further support to this contention.

OCTACOSANOIC ACID (MONTANIC ACID)

Montanic acid is found almost exclusively in the vegetable, insect, and mineral waxes. Its name is derived from the lignite wax, montan wax.

The history of montanic acid is quite interesting. The acid was probably first described by Nafzger,[13] who reported its presence in the high molecular weight acids of beeswax. Somewhat later, von Boyen [487] obtained this acid from montan wax and considered its formula to be $C_{29}H_{58}O_2$. A number of investigators [488, 489, 490] likewise held the opinion that montanic acid contained twenty-nine carbon atoms. Detailed studies [491, 492] have shown, however, that montanic acid is octacosanoic acid, and that the acids described previously were mixtures of this acid with its lower and higher homologs. This contention has received further confirmation from studies of the x-ray spacings of both naturally occurring and synthetic montanic acid. When the name montanic acid is employed, it should, therefore, be considered as synonymous with octacosanoic acid.

Octacosanoic acid has been prepared synthetically by several methods. The pure acid is a waxlike solid which melts at 90.9°.[212] Bleyberg and Ulrich [45] have reported the following constants: m.p. 90.3–90.5°, d_4^{100} 0.8191, and n_D^{100} 1.4313. It is soluble in petroleum ether, hot ethanol, and glacial acetic acid. The acid has been obtained [45] by the decomposition of hexacosylmalonic acid. Damoy,[458] and later Piper, Chibnall, and Williams,[481] described the synthesis of octacosanoic acid by the oxidation of 1-octacosanol. It has also been obtained by the hydrolysis of octacosanenitrile. The separation of montanic acid from montan wax has been described by several investigators.[431, 493, 494] Gascard and Damoy [457] have prepared montanic acid from beeswax, and Koyama [483] has obtained it from Chinese wax. Montan wax is generally prepared by the steam distillation of crude bitumen extracts. The acids obtained from this wax are accompanied by large amounts of high molecular weight hydrocarbons. Marcusson and Smelkus [495] have claimed that these hydrocarbons are largely formed by the decomposition of the wax esters. High molecular weight hydrocarbons, however, are common components of many of the waxes, such as Chinese wax,[443] beeswax,[496] and candelilla wax,[497] and they are apparently present originally in the lignite waxes in appreciable amounts.

Montanic acid has been reported to be contained in most of the waxes which have been investigated; however, it is either absent or present only in traces in the glycerides. Besides being found in montan wax and beeswax, it is apparently present in cotton wax,[455] bamboo wax,[465] Chinese wax,[483] and a number of the bitumen waxes of peat.[484] Ryan and Dillon [494] have reported the montanic acid content of montan wax to be 41.33%. The acid obtained from this source generally melts considerably lower than the synthetic acid, owing to the difficulties encountered in separating it from its homologs and other impurities.[498, 499]

NONACOSANOIC ACID

Nonacosanoic acid has frequently been reported to be a component of the naturally occurring wax esters.[487, 488, 489, 493] However, a large number of observations have been presented which show that the nonacosanoic acids so reported are actually mixtures of even-carbon acids.[44, 431, 491, 492, 498, 499]

Nonacosanoic acid is a waxlike solid which melts at 90.3°.[46] The acid has been synthesized from octacosanoic acid by the nitrile method.[481, 500] Recently, Stadler [484] has reported the presence of nonacosanoic acid in Bohemian montan wax, and Roginskaya [485] has claimed its separation from a bitumen wax of peat. Both of these observations require substantial confirmation before they can be accepted.

TRIACONTANOIC ACID (MELISSIC ACID)

Nafzger [13] first described melissic acid during his examination of the higher fatty acids of beeswax. As with most of the higher fatty acids, considerable uncertainty has existed concerning the identity of the various melissic acids obtained from the wax esters. It is now believed that melissic acid is identical with triacontanoic acid and that speculation regarding its structure has been occasioned by the difficulty of separating it from its lower homologs.

Francis, Collins, and Piper [46] have determined the melting point of synthetic triacontanoic acid to be 93.6°, a value which was later verified by Francis and Piper.[212] Bleyberg and Ulrich [45] reported a melting point of 91.9–92.1° for the synthetic acid and a refractive index of n_D^{100} 1.4323 for the liquid. The acid is soluble in hot ethanol, carbon disulfide, and chloroform, and sparingly soluble in ether.

Triacontanoic acid melting at 93.6° has been synthesized by the oxidation of myricyl alcohol.[241, 481, 501] Its preparation by the action of the mixed oxides of potassium and calcium upon myricyl alcohol in the presence of hydrogen has also been described.[450, 502] Bleyberg and Ulrich [45] obtained triacontanoic acid by the decomposition of octacosylmalonic acid, which was prepared from octacosanoic acid by the malonic acid synthesis. Robinson [49] has prepared triacontanoic acid by the reduction of 13-ketotriacontanoic acid with zinc amalgam in a mixture of hydrochloric and acetic acids.

Melissic acid occurs almost exclusively in the various vegetable, insect, and mineral waxes. Its presence in beeswax was first indicated by the work of Schalfeieff, [476] was later established by Nafzger, [13] and has since been verified by a number of investigators. [457, 458, 480, 503, 504] Melissic acid has also been found in a number of other insect waxes, such as coccid waxes, [505, 506] Chinese wax, [443] the wax of cocoon fibers, [507] and the wax of the scale insect *Ceroplastes rubens*. [508] An acid, probably isomeric with triacontanoic acid, has been separated from human tubercle wax. [509] Melissic acid has also been found in sugar cane wax, [510] clematis wax, [511] the wax of slash pine, [293] bayberry wax, [501] and cotton wax. [512] It has been stated by Marie [503] to be present in carnauba wax, and Jamieson and McKinney [513] have observed its presence in traces in palm oil. Melissic acid is found in bitumen waxes such as montan wax. [514]

Ever since melissic acid was first isolated by Nafzger, [13] there has been speculation regarding its identity. Schwalb [515] considered the melissic acid prepared from beeswax to be $C_{31}H_{62}O_2$, and this formula has been restated by several investigators. [241, 426, 457, 458] Marie, [503] however, claimed that melissic acid is triacontanoic acid. Morgan and Bowen [363] have pointed out the difficulties in separating the higher fatty acids by fractional crystallization, and have stated that this fact should be borne in mind in identifying the naturally occurring higher fatty acids.

ACIDS HIGHER THAN TRIACONTANOIC ACID

Several of the higher saturated acids have been prepared synthetically, and a few of them have been reported to be present in the natural waxes. The higher members of the saturated series of aliphatic acids are waxy solids, those of quite high molecular weight resembling paraffin in many respects. The relative differences which are brought about by successive additions of methylene groups are much less with the higher acids than with their lower homologs, and consequently such acids exhibit little change in properties from member to member. Owing to their similarity in physical properties and the absence of marked solubility differences, the separation of these acids from one another is extremely difficult. It was to be expected, therefore, that there would be considerable lack of agreement concerning the identity of the higher acids which have been isolated from the natural sources.

Hentriacontanoic Acid. $C_{30}H_{61}CO_2H$

This acid has been prepared by Piper, Chibnall, and Williams [481] by the hydrolysis of hentriacontanenitrile, which was obtained from 1-triacontanol. These authors reported a melting point of 93.0–93.2° for the acid prepared in this manner.

Hentriacontanoic acid has been reported to be present in several wax esters.[340, 426, 457, 458] However, it is probable that the acids investigated were mixtures of even-carbon-membered acids.

Dotriacontanoic Acid (Lacceroic Acid). $C_{31}H_{63}CO_2H$

Piper, Chibnall, and Williams [481] synthesized this acid by the oxidation of 1-dotriacontanol, reporting its melting point to be 96.1–96.3°. This is in agreement with the melting points of 96.2°, observed by Francis, Collins, and Piper,[46] and 96.0°, found by Francis and Piper.[212] Francis, King, and Willis [500] have described the preparation of dotriacontanoic acid from 1-iodotriacontane and malonic acid by the malonic acid synthesis.

This acid probably occurs in the higher acid fractions of the natural waxes. Gascard [516] has isolated from the wax of stick-lac an acid having the formula $C_{32}H_{64}O_2$, to which he gave the name lacceroic acid.

Tritriacontanoic Acid (Psyllic Acid, Ceromelissic Acid).
$C_{32}H_{65}CO_2H$

Psyllic acid, melting at 94–95°, was reported obtained by the saponification of psylla wax with hydrogen bromide.[517] Kono [430] has claimed the isolation of a similar acid from the wax of *Ceroplastes ceriferus.* Koyama [508] has given the name ceromelissic acid to an acid, melting at 94°, which he obtained from the wax of the scale insect *Ceroplastes rubens.* The occurrence of tritriacontanoic acid in natural products, however, is extremely doubtful, and confirmation will be required before such observations can be accepted.

Tetratriacontanoic Acid (Geddic Acid). $C_{33}H_{67}CO_2H$

Tetratriacontanoic acid, melting at 98.3–98.5°, has been synthesized by the oxidation of 1-tetracontanol.[481] Francis, King, and Willis [500] have also described the preparation of this acid by the Clemmensen reduction of 13-ketotetratriacontanoic acid, which was prepared by the method proposed by Robinson.[49] A melting point of 98.2° for tetratriacontanoic acid has recently been reported.[46, 212] Lipp and Kovacs [336] have succeeded in separating tetratriacontanoic acid, melting at 94.5–95.0°, from Gedda wax. The acid was named geddic acid by these authors.

Pentatriacontanoic Acid (Ceroplastic Acid). $C_{34}H_{69}CO_2H$

Pentatriacontanoic acid, melting at 98.3–98.5°, has been prepared from 1-tetratriacontanol by the cyanide method.[481] Ceroplastic acid, melting at 92°, was reported to have been separated from olive wax,[432] and an acid melting at 96–98°, claimed to be pentatriacontanoic acid, has been isolated from the wax of *Ceroplastes rubens*.[508]

Hexatriacontanoic Acid. $C_{35}H_{71}CO_2H$

This acid has been prepared by the oxidation of 1-hexatriacontanol by Piper, Chibnall, and Williams,[481] who reported a melting point of 100.1–100.3°. Hexatriacontanoic acid obtained from tetratriacontanoic acid [500] melts at 99.9°. The melting point of 99.9° for this acid has recently been confirmed.[46, 212]

Octatriacontanoic Acid. $C_{37}H_{75}CO_2H$

Melting points of 101.1° [46] and of 101.6° [212] have been reported for the synthetic acid.

Hexatetracontanoic Acid. $C_{45}H_{91}CO_2H$

This acid has been synthesized by the Clemmensen reduction of 13-ketohexatetracontanoic acid.[500] This latter acid was prepared by the saponification of ethyl 2-acetyl-2-tetratriacontanoyl-brassylate, which was obtained from the reaction of tetratriacontanoyl chloride with ethyl sodio-2-acetylbrassylate by the method previously described by Robinson.[49]

Melting points of 107.1° [46] and of 106.85° [212] have been reported for synthetic hexatetracontanoic acid.

References

1. Braconnot, *Ann. chim.* [1], **93**, 225 (1815).
2. Heintz, *Ann. Physik* [4], **102**, 257 (1857).
3. Frémy, *J. pharm. chim.* [2], **26**, 757 (1840).

4. Playfair, *Ann.*, **37**, 152 (1841).
5. Marsson, *ibid.*, **41**, 329 (1842).
6. Görgey, *ibid.*, **66**, 290 (1848).
7. Lerch, *ibid.*, **49**, 212 (1844).
8. Völcker, *ibid.*, **64**, 342 (1848).
9. Brodie, *ibid.*, **67**, 180 (1848).
10. Gösmann, *ibid.*, **89**, 1 (1854).
11. Kreiling, *Ber.*, **21**, 880 (1888).
12. Hell and Hermanns, *ibid.*, **13**, 1713 (1880).
13. Nafzger, *Ann.*, **224**, 225 (1884).
14. Marie, *Ann. chim. phys.* [7], **7**, 145 (1896).
15. The unsaturated fatty acids are often termed fat acids to distinguish them from the members of the saturated series.
16. The reader is referred to the following: Lewkowitsch, *Chemical Technology and Analysis of Oils, Fats and Waxes*, 6th ed., 3 vols., Macmillan and Co., London (1921–23); Elsdon, *Edible Oils and Fats*, D. Van Nostrand Co., New York (1926); Hefter and Schönfeld, *Chemie und Technologie der Fette und Fettprodukte*, Julius Springer, Vienna (1936); Hilditch, *The Chemical Constitution of Natural Fats*, John Wiley & Sons, New York (1940); Hilditch, *The Industrial Chemistry of Fats and Waxes*, Baillière, Tindall, and Cox, London (1941); Jamieson, *Vegetable Fats and Oils*, 2nd ed., Reinhold Publishing Corp., New York (1943); Bailey, *Industrial Oil and Fat Products*, Interscience Publishers, New York (1945).
17. Tsujimoto, *Chem. Umschau*, **32**, 125 (1925).
18. Klem, *Norske Videnskaps-Akad. Oslo, Hvalradets Skrifter* No. **11**, 49 (1935).
19. Hilditch and Murti, *J. Soc. Chem. Ind.*, **58**, 351 (1939).
20. Ellis and Isbell, *J. Biol. Chem.*, **69**, 219 (1926).
21. Ellis and Zeller, *ibid.*, **89**, 185 (1930).
22. Anderson and Mendel, *ibid.*, **76**, 729 (1928).
23. Eckstein, *ibid.*, **81**, 613 (1929).
24. Ivanov, *Bull. univ. Asie centrale*, No. **12**, 21 (1926).
25. Pigulevskiĭ, *J. Russ. Phys. Chem. Soc.*, **47**, 203, 2032, *Proc.* (1915); **47**, 393 (1915).
26. André, *Compt. rend.*, **178**, 1188 (1924).
27. Klein and Stigol, *Pharm. Zentralhalle*, **71**, 497 (1930).
28. Gill and Tucker, *Oil & Fat Industries*, **7**, 101 (1930).
29. Holde and Bleyberg, *Metallbörse*, **20**, 1855 (1930).
30. Lieben and Rossi, *Ann.*, **159**, 58 (1871).
31. Linnemann, *ibid.*, **161**, 175 (1872).
32. Krafft, *Ber.*, **12**, 1664 (1879).
33. Krafft, *ibid.*, **12**, 1668 (1879).
34. Suzuki, *Bull. Agr. Chem. Soc. Japan*, **3**, 54 (1927).
35. Ono, *J. Agr. Chem. Soc. Japan*, **8**, 788 (1932).
36. Ozaki and Kasai, *ibid.*, **10**, 745 (1934).
37. Kawase, Suda, and Fukuzawa, *J. Chem. Soc. Japan*, **24**, 181 (1921).
38. Ueno and Ikuta, *J. Soc. Chem. Ind., Japan*, **37**, S.b. 124 (1934).
39. Anderson and Chargaff, *J. Biol. Chem.*, **85**, 77 (1930).
40. Anderson and Uyei, *ibid.*, **97**, 617 (1932).

41. Ehrenstein and Stuewer, *J. prakt. Chem.* [2], **105,** 199 (1922).
42. Levene and Taylor, *J. Biol. Chem.*, **59,** 905 (1924).
43. Levene, West, and van der Scheer, *ibid.*, **20,** 521 (1915).
44. Francis, Piper, and Malkin, *Proc. Roy. Soc.* (*London*), **128A,** 214 (1930).
45. Bleyberg and Ulrich, *Ber.*, **64,** 2504 (1931).
46. Francis, Collins, and Piper, *Proc. Roy. Soc.* (*London*), **158A,** 691 (1937).
47. Shiina, *J. Soc. Chem. Ind., Japan*, **39,** S.b. 180 (1936).
48. Clemmensen, *Ber.*, **46,** 1837 (1913).
49. Robinson, *J. Chem. Soc.*, 1543 (1934).
50. Ruttan, *Eighth Intern. Congr. Appl. Chem.*, **25,** 431 (1912).
51. Lukeš, *Chem. Listy*, **24,** 197 (1930).
52. Hofmann, *Ber.*, **14,** 2725 (1881).
53. Hofmann, *ibid.*, **17,** 1406 (1884).
54. Lutz, *ibid.*, **19,** 1433 (1886).
55. Le Sueur, *J. Chem. Soc.*, **85,** 827 (1904).
56. Blaise, *Compt. rend.*, **138,** 697 (1904); *Bull. soc. chim.* [3], **31,** 483 (1904).
57. Le Sueur, *J. Chem. Soc.*, **87,** 1888 (1905).
58. Lapworth, *ibid.*, **103,** 1029 (1913).
59. Levene and West, *J. Biol. Chem.*, **16,** 475 (1914).
60. Rochussen, *Ber. Schimmel & Co. Akt.-Ges.*, 181 (1929).
61. Kass and Keyser, *J. Am. Chem. Soc.*, **62,** 230 (1940).
62. Krafft, *Ber.*, **10,** 2034 (1877).
63. Krafft, *ibid.*, **11,** 2218 (1878).
64. Dippy, *J. Chem. Soc.*, 1222 (1938).
65. Dhingra, *Biochem. J.*, **27,** 851 (1933).
66. Bhattacharya and Hilditch, *Analyst*, **56,** 161 (1931).
67. Zincke, *Ann.*, **152,** 1 (1869); Franchimont and Zincke, *Ber.*, **4,** 822 (1871); Franchimont, *ibid.*, **5,** 786 (1872); Möslinger, *ibid.*, **9,** 998 (1876).
68. Neuberg and Rosenberg, *Biochem. Z.*, **7,** 178 (1907).
69. Neuberg and Arinstein, *ibid.*, **117,** 269 (1921).
70. Scala, *Gazz. chim. ital.*, **38,** I, 307 (1908).
71. Schutze, Shive, and Lochte, *Ind. Eng. Chem.*, *Anal. Ed.*, **12,** 262 (1940).
72. Kumamoto, *J. Chem. Soc. Japan*, **53,** 30 (1932).
73. Schmid, *Oesterr. Chem.-Ztg.*, **39,** 96 (1936).
74. Adams and Marvel, *J. Am. Chem. Soc.*, **42,** 310 (1920).
75. Gilman and Parker, *ibid.*, **46,** 2816 (1924).
76. Fürth, *Monatsh.*, **9,** 308 (1888).
77. Larson, U. S. Patent 2,020,689 (1935).
78. Carpenter, U. S. Patent 2,013,338 (1934).
79. Strada, *Giorn. chim. ind. applicata*, **16,** 62 (1934).
80. Zelinskii and Przheval'skii, *J. Russ. Phys. Chem. Soc.*, **40,** 1105 (1908).
81. Koizumi and Nippon Shinyaku K.K., Japan. Patent 113,554 (1935).
82. Neuberg, *Biochem. Z.*, **37,** 490 (1911).
83. Lefranc, Brit. Patent 17,776 (1918).
84. Tsujimoto and Koyanagi, *J. Soc. Chem. Ind., Japan*, **40,** S.b. 272 (1937).
85. Bullock, *Pharm. J.*, **117,** 152 (1926).
86. Simon, *Bull. soc. chim. Belg.*, **38,** 47 (1929).
87. Fittig, *Ann.*, **200,** 21 (1880).
88. Gartenmeister, *ibid.*, **233,** 249 (1886).

89. Reid and Ruhoff, *Organic Syntheses*, Coll. Vol. 2, Blatt, editor, p. 474, John Wiley & Sons, New York (1943).

90. Franchimont and Zincke, *Ann.*, **163**, 193 (1872).

91. Tripier, *Bull. soc. chim.* [3], **11**, 98 (1894).

92. Polonovski, Cuvelier, and Avenard, *Compt. rend. soc. biol.*, **111**, 6 (1932).

93. Hilditch and Paul, *Biochem. J.*, **30**, 1905 (1936).

94. Riemenschneider and Ellis, *J. Biol. Chem.*, **113**, 219 (1936).

95. Birosel, Millar, Nessia, and Tagorda, *Univ. Philippines Nat. and Applied Sci. Bull.*, **7**, 39 (1939).

96. Lepkovsky, Feskov, and Evans, *J. Am. Chem. Soc.*, **58**, 978 (1936).

97. Taylor and Clarke, *ibid.*, **49**, 2829 (1927).

98. Elsdon, *Analyst*, **38**, 8 (1913).

99. Heiduschka and Agsten, *J. prakt. Chem.* [2], **126**, 53 (1930).

100. McKinney and Jamieson, *Oil & Soap*, **15**, 172 (1938).

101. Smeets and Ruppol, *Bull. soc. chim. biol.*, **16**, 865 (1934).

102. Takahashi, Shirahama, and Tase, *J. Chem. Soc. Japan*, **54**, 619 (1933).

103. Shoruigin, Isagulyantz, Belov, and Aleksandrova, *J. Gen. Chem. (U.S.S.R.)*, **4**, 372 (1934).

104. Bussy, *Ann.*, **60**, 246 (1846).

105. Deffet, *Bull. soc. chim. Belg.*, **40**, 385 (1931).

106. Bilterys and Gisseleire, *ibid.*, **44**, 567 (1935).

107. Ruzicka and Schinz, *Helv. Chim. Acta*, **18**, 381 (1935).

108. Mailhe, *Bull. soc. chim.* [4], **31**, 249 (1922); *Ann. chim.* [9], **17**, 304 (1922).

109. Ruhoff, *Organic Syntheses*, Coll. Vol. 2, Blatt, editor, p. 315, John Wiley & Sons, New York (1943).

110. Tilley, *Ann.*, **67**, 105 (1848).

111. Mehlis, *ibid.*, **185**, 358 (1877).

112. Krafft, *Ber.*, **15**, 1711 (1882).

113. Grimshaw and Schorlemmer, *Ann.*, **170**, 137 (1873).

114. Fournier, *Bull. soc. chim.* [4], **5**, 920 (1909).

115. Rogers, *J. Am. Pharm. Assoc.*, **12**, 503 (1923).

116. Wahlfors, *Oefvers. af finska Vet. Soc. förh.*, XXX [*Ber.*, **21**, 711R (1888)].

117. Schorlemmer and Thorpe, *Ann.*, **217**, 149 (1883).

118. Guerbet, *Compt. rend.*, **153**, 1487 (1911).

119. Guiteras, *Z. physiol. Chem.*, **214**, 89 (1933).

120. Smit, *Rec. trav. chim.*, **49**, 539 (1930).

121. Holde and Gentner, *Ber.*, **58B**, 1418 (1925).

122. v. Braun, Anton, Fischer, Keller, and Manz, *ibid.*, **67B**, 218 (1934).

123. Truchet, *Ann. chim.* [10], **16**, 309 (1931).

124. Nelson and Mottern, *Ind. Eng. Chem.*, **26**, 634 (1934).

125. Naves, *Parfums France*, **10**, 160 (1932).

126. Naves, *ibid.*, **9**, 60 (1931).

127. Noller, Millner, and Gordon, *J. Am. Chem. Soc.*, **55**, 1227 (1933).

128. Darner, *N. Dakota Expt. Sta. Record*, **30**, 617 (1913).

129. Watt and Angus, *J. Soc. Chem. Ind.*, **35**, 201 (1916).

130. Nobori, *J. Soc. Chem. Ind., Japan*, **43**, S.b. 199 (1940).

131. Armstrong, Allan, and Moore, *J. Soc. Chem. Ind.*, **44**, 63T (1925).

132. Bömer and Baumann, *Z. Untersuch. Nahr.- u. Genussm.*, **40**, 97 (1920).

133. Armstrong, Allan, and Moore, *J. Soc. Chem. Ind.*, **44**, 143T (1925).

134. Hilditch and Vidyarthi, *ibid.*, **47**, 35T (1928).
135. Nobori, *J. Soc. Chem. Ind., Japan*, **43**, S.b. 59 (1940).
136. Tsujimoto, *ibid.*, **24**, 41 (1920).
137. Dhingra, *Biochem. J.*, **28**, 73 (1934).
138. Laxa, *Ann. fals.*, **24**, 87 (1931).
139. Libbert, *Arkansas Agr. Expt. Sta. Bull.*, No. **280**, 40 (1932).
140. Raper, *J. Physiol., Proc.*, **35**, xxiv (1907).
141. Zincke and Franchimont, *Ann.*, **164**, 333 (1872).
142. Franchimont and Zincke, *Ber.*, **5**, 19 (1872).
143. Lapworth and Mottram, *J. Chem. Soc.*, **127**, 1987 (1925).
144. Bougault and Schuster, *J. pharm. chim.* [8], **15**, 5 (1932).
145. Molinari and Soncini, *Ber.*, **39**, 2735 (1906).
146. Harries and Türk, *ibid.*, **38**, 1630 (1905); **39**, 3732 (1906); Harries, *ibid.*, **39**, 3728 (1906).
147. Thieme, *Ann.*, **343**, 354 (1905).
148. Fahrion, *Z. angew. Chem.*, **21**, 1219 (1908).
149. Arnaud and Hasenfratz, *Compt. rend.*, **152**, 1603 (1911).
150. Grün and Wittka, *Chem. Umschau*, **32**, 257 (1925).
151. Armstrong and Hilditch, *J. Soc. Chem. Ind.*, **44**, 43T (1925).
152. Eckert, *Monatsh.*, **38**, 1 (1917).
153. Nicolet and Jurist, *J. Am. Chem. Soc.*, **44**, 1136 (1922).
154. Shagalova, *Masloboïno Zhirovoe Delo*, **11**, 452 (1935).
155. St. Pfau, *Helv. Chim. Acta*, **15**, 1267 (1932).
156. Wolbaum and Stephan, *Ber.*, **33**, 2302 (1900).
157. Gerhardt, *Ann.*, **67**, 235 (1848).
158. Mai, *Ber.*, **22**, 2133 (1889).
159. Tassilly, *Bull. soc. chim.* [4], **9**, 608 (1911).
160. Fierz-David, *Z. angew. Chem.*, **38**, 6 (1925).
161. Luce, *J. pharm. chim.* [7], **22**, 136 (1920).
162. Houben, *Ber.*, **35**, 3587 (1902).
163. Schulz, *ibid.*, **42**, 3613 (1909).
164. Stephan, *J. prakt. Chem.* [2], **62**, 523 (1900).
165. Bagard, *Bull. soc. chim.* [4], **1**, 346 (1907).
166. Krafft, *Ber.*, **15**, 1687 (1882).
167. Kao and Ma, *J. Chem. Soc.*, 2046 (1931).
168. Heiduschka and Kuhn, *J. prakt. Chem.* [2], **139**, 269 (1934).
169. Pawlenko, *Chem. Rev. Fett- u. Harz-Ind.*, **19**, 43 (1912).
170. Schuette and Lunde, *Oil & Soap*, **13**, 12 (1936).
171. Hilditch and Lovern, *J. Soc. Chem. Ind.*, **47**, 105T (1928).
172. Nobori, *J. Soc. Chem. Ind., Japan*, **43**, S.b. 110 (1940).
173. Longenecker, *J. Soc. Chem. Ind.*, **56**, 199T (1937).
174. Goldsobel, *Ber.*, **27**, 3121 (1894).
175. Horel, *Chem. Obzor*, **6**, 236 (1931).
176. Vernon and Ross, *J. Am. Chem. Soc.*, **58**, 2430 (1936).
177. Toyama and Tsuchiya, *J. Soc. Chem. Ind., Japan*, **37**, S.b. 14 (1934).
178. Bergmann, *Z. angew. Chem.*, **31**, I, 69 (1918).
179. Waterman and Bertram, *Rec. trav. chim.*, **46**, 699 (1927).
180. Krafft and Wielandt, *Ber.*, **29**, 1316 (1896).
181. Fahrion, *Z. angew. Chem.*, **21**, 1125 (1908).

182. Collin and Hilditch, *J. Soc. Chem. Ind.*, **49**, 138T (1930).
183. Jacobson and Holmes, *J. Biol. Chem.*, **25**, 55 (1916).
184. Vongerichten and Köhler, *Ber.*, **42**, 1638 (1909).
185. Bougault, *Compt. rend.*, **150**, 874 (1910).
186. Bhattacharya and Simonsen, *Proc. 15th Indian Sci. Congress*, **153** (1928).
187. Bushell and Hilditch, *J. Soc. Chem. Ind.*, **58**, 24 (1939).
188. Stillman and Reed, *Oil & Soap*, **11**, 208 (1934).
189. Beal and Glenz, *J. Ind. Eng. Chem.*, **11**, 959 (1919).
190. Sakurai, *J. Pharm. Soc. Japan*, **53**, 579 (1933).
191. Bureš, *Chimie & industrie Special No.*, p. 1056 (June, 1933).
192. Sahasrabuddhe and Kale, *J. Univ. Bombay*, **1**, pt. 2, 37 (1932).
193. Heiduschka and Steinruck, *J. prakt. Chem.* [2], **102**, 241 (1921).
194. Dhingra and Haneef, *J. Soc. Chem. Ind.*, **58**, 292 (1939).
195. Eckstein, *J. Biol. Chem.*, **64**, 797 (1925).
196. Rees, *Analyst*, **58**, 222 (1933).
197. Toyama, *J. Soc. Chem. Ind.*, *Japan*, **30**, 519 (1927).
198. Tsujimoto and Koyanagi, *ibid.*, **40**, S.b. 191 (1937).
199. Lovern, *Dept. Sci. Ind. Research, Rept. Food Investigation Board*, **1934**, 89 (1935) [*C.A.*, **30**, 314 (1936)].
200. Ruzicka, Stoll, and Schinz, *Helv. Chim. Acta*, **11**, 670 (1928).
201. Reid, Ruhoff, and Burnett, *Organic Syntheses*, Coll. Vol. 2, Blatt, editor, p. 246, John Wiley & Sons, New York (1943).
202. Ford and Marvel, *ibid.*, p. 372.
203. Adkins and Folkers, *J. Am. Chem. Soc.*, **53**, 1095 (1931).
204. Normann, *Z. angew. Chem.*, **44**, 714 (1931).
205. Schrauth, Schenck, and Stickdorn, *Ber.*, **64**, 1314 (1931).
206. Lazier, U. S. Patent 1,839,974 (1932).
207. Blau, *Monatsh.*, **26**, 89 (1905).
208. Levene and West, *J. Biol. Chem.*, **18**, 463 (1914).
209. Levene, West, Allen, and van der Scheer, *ibid.*, **23**, 71 (1915).
210. Robinson, *J. Chem. Soc.*, **125**, 226 (1924).
211. Fischer and Schneider, *Ber.*, **53**, 922 (1920).
212. Francis and Piper, *J. Am. Chem. Soc.*, **61**, 577 (1939).
213. Marasse, *Ber.*, **2**, 359 (1869).
214. Bodenstein, *ibid.*, **27**, 3397 (1894).
215. Brown and Farmer, *Biochem. J.*, **29**, 631 (1935).
216. Steger and van Loon, *Rec. trav. chim.*, **54**, 149 (1935).
217. Ramos and de Nascimento, *Rev. chim. ind. Rio de Janeiro*, **7**, 186 (1938).
218. Collin and Hilditch, *Biochem. J.*, **23**, 1273 (1929).
219. Baughman, Jamieson, and Brauns, *J. Am. Chem. Soc.*, **43**, 199 (1921).
220. Verkade and Coops, *Rec. trav. chim.*, **46**, 528 (1927).
221. Jumelle, *Mat. grasses*, **18**, 7639 (1926).
222. Gunde and Hilditch, *J. Chem. Soc.*, 1015 (1939).
223. Sauer, Hain, and Boutwell, *Organic Syntheses*, **20**, 67 (1940).
224. Jamieson and Baughman, *J. Am. Chem. Soc.*, **42**, 1197 (1920).
225. Takahashi, *J. Tokyo Chem. Soc.*, **40**, 191 (1919).
226. Jamieson, *Oil & Fat Industries*, **4**, 426 (1927).
227. Sudborough, Watson, and Ayyar, *J. Indian Inst. Sci.*, **9A**, 25 (1926).
228. Cruz and West, *Philippine J. Sci.*, **61**, 161 (1936).

229. Goldstein and Jenkins, *J. Am. Pharm. Assoc.*, **25**, 636 (1936).
230. Jamieson and McKinney, *Oil & Soap*, **13**, 202 (1936).
231. Schuette and Chang, *J. Am. Chem. Soc.*, **55**, 3333 (1933).
232. Banks, Hilditch, and Jones, *Biochem. J.*, **27**, 1375 (1933).
233. Spadola and Ellis, *J. Biol. Chem.*, **113**, 205 (1936).
234. Hirose, *J. Soc. Chem. Ind.*, *Japan*, **29**, 17 (1926).
235. Lode, *Fettchem. Umschau*, **42**, 205 (1935).
236. Ault and Brown, *J. Biol. Chem.*, **107**, 607 (1934).
237. Arnold, *Z. Untersuch. Nahr.- u. Genussm.*, **23**, 433 (1912).
238. Holland, Garvey, Pierce, Messer, Archibald, and Dunbar, *J. Agr. Research*, **24**, 365·(1923).
239. Barnicoat, *Dept. Sci. Ind. Research, Rept. Food Investigation Board*, **1930**, 38 [*C.A.*, **25**, 5050 (1931)].
240. Ueno and Yamasaki, *J. Soc. Chem. Ind.*, *Japan*, **35**, S.b. 492 (1932).
241. Toyama and Tsuchiya, *ibid.*, **30**, 63, 207 (1927).
242. Toyama, *Chem. Umschau*, **34**, 19 (1927).
243. Greitemann, *ibid.*, **32**, 226 (1925).
244. Milligan, Knuth, and Richardson, *J. Am. Chem. Soc.*, **46**, 157 (1924).
245. Bonnevie-Svendsen, *Tids. Kemi, Farm. Terapi*, **13**, 285 (1916).
246. Bonnevie-Svendsen, *ibid.*, **13**, 212 (1916).
247. Ono, *J. Agr. Chem. Soc. Japan*, **11**, 773 (1935).
248. Twitchell, *J. Ind. Eng. Chem.*, **9**, 581 (1917).
249. Salomone, *Boll. laniera*, **44**, 199 (1930).
250. Abraham and Hilditch, *J. Soc. Chem. Ind.*, **54**, 398T (1935).
251. Trost and Doro, *Ann. chim. applicata*, **27**, 233 (1937).
252. Panics, *Monatsh.*, **15**, 9 (1894).
253. Landa, *Chem. Listy*, **22**, 361 (1928).
254. Majima and Nakamura, *Ber.*, **46**, 4089 (1913).
255. Krewson, *Pharm. Arch.*, **10**, 88 (1939).
256. Hinsberg and Roos, *Z. physiol. Chem.*, **38**, 1 (1903).
257. Dieterle, Haubold, and Meyer, *Arch. Pharm.*, **269**, 384 (1931).
258. De Visser, *Rec. trav. chim.*, **17**, 182 (1898).
259. Eisenstein, *Chem. Umschau*, **27**, 3 (1920).
260. Müller, *J. Chem. Soc.*, **123**, 2043 (1923).
261. Smith, *ibid.*, 625 (1936).
262. Partheil and Ferié, *Arch. Pharm.*, **241**, 545 (1903).
263. Scheij, *Rec. trav. chim.*, **18**, 169 (1899).
264. Krafft, *Ber.*, **21**, 2265 (1888).
265. Dubovitz, *Chem.-Ztg.*, **54**, 814 (1930).
266. Hell and Jordanoff, *Ber.*, **24**, 936 (1891).
267. Claus and von Dreden, *J. prakt. Chem.* [2], **43**, 148 (1891).
268. Dean and Hilditch, *J. Soc. Chem. Ind.*, **52**, 165T (1933).
269. Steger and van Loon, *Rec. trav. chim.*, **54**, 284 (1935).
270. Tsujimoto, *Bull. Chem. Soc. Japan*, **10**, 212 (1935).
271. Koyama, *J. Chem. Soc. Japan*, **54**, 1233 (1933).
272. Ueno and Ikuta, *J. Soc. Chem. Ind.*, *Japan*, **37**, S.b. 124 (1934).
273. Bergmann, *J. Biol. Chem.*, **114**, 27 (1936).
274. Schuette, Thomas, and Duthey, *J. Am. Chem. Soc.*, **52**, 4114 (1930).
275. Heiduschka and Roser, *J. prakt. Chem.* [2], **104**, 137 (1922).
276. Jamieson and McKinney, *Oil & Soap*, **13**, 233 (1936).

277. Takahashi, Tase, and Saegi, *J. Agr. Chem. Soc. Japan*, **11**, 199 (1935).
278. Langton, *Food*, **4**, 279 (1935).
279. Baughman and Jamieson, *J. Am. Chem. Soc.*, **43**, 2696 (1921).
280. Jamieson, Baughman, and Hann, *Oil & Fat Industries*, **5**, 202 (1928).
281. Sorgès, *Chim. ind. agr. biol.*, **5**, 232 (1929).
282. Roberts and Schuette, *J. Am. Chem. Soc.*, **56**, 207 (1934).
283. Riebsomer and Nesty, *ibid.*, **56**, 1784 (1934).
284. Otin and Dima, *Allgem. Oel- u. Fett-Ztg.*, **31**, 107 (1934).
285. Schuette, Cowley, and Chang, *J. Am. Chem. Soc.*, **56**, 2085 (1934).
286. Bengis and Anderson, *J. Biol. Chem.*, **105**, 139 (1934).
287. Patel, Sudborough, and Watson, *J. Indian Inst. Sci.*, **6**, 111 (1923).
288. Lehrman, *J. Am. Chem. Soc.*, **52**, 808 (1930).
289. Jamieson and Baughman, *Cotton Oil Press*, **4**, No. 3, 61 (1920).
290. Ferenez, *Arch. Pharm.*, **257**, 180 (1919).
291. Straman, *Pharm. Weekblad*, **64**, 52 (1927).
292. Hilditch and Vidyarthi, *J. Soc. Chem. Ind.*, **46**, 172T (1927).
293. Hall and Gisvold, *J. Biol. Chem.*, **113**, 487 (1936).
294. Anderson and Roberts, *ibid.*, **89**, 599 (1930).
295. Burt and Anderson, *ibid.*, **94**, 451 (1931).
296. Anderson, Crowder, Newman, and Stodola, *ibid.*, **113**, 637 (1936).
297. Brodie, *Ann.*, **71**, 144 (1849).
298. Buchner, *Fette u. Seifen*, **44**, 205 (1937).
299. Amberger and Wiesehahn, *Z. Untersuch. Nahr.- u. Genussm.*, **46**, 276 (1923).
300. Banks and Hilditch, *Biochem. J.*, **25**, 1168 (1931).
301. Schuette, Garvin, and Schwoegler, *J. Biol. Chem.*, **107**, 635 (1934).
302. Bomer and Merten, *Z. Untersuch. Nahr.- u. Genussm.*, **43**, 101 (1922).
303. Irving and Smith, *Biochem. J.*, **29**, 1358 (1935).
304. Kobayashi, *J. Soc. Chem. Ind., Japan*, **25**, 691 (1922).
305. Parry and Smith, *Biochem. J.*, **30**, 592 (1936).
306. Toyama, *J. Soc. Chem. Ind., Japan*, **29**, 531 (1926).
307. Ueno and Matsuda, *ibid.*, **38**, S.b. 398 (1935).
308. Toyama and Tsuchiya, *ibid.*, **30**, 116, 207 (1927).
309. Hilditch and Houlbrooke, *Analyst*, **53**, 246 (1928).
310. Ueno and Ikuta, *J. Soc. Chem. Ind., Japan*, **37**, S.b. 506 (1934).
311. Takahashi, Shirahama, and Tase, *J. Chem. Soc. Japan*, **56**, 1250 (1935).
312. Takahashi and Shirahama, *ibid.*, **57**, 411 (1936).
313. Takahashi, Shirahama, and Ito, *ibid.*, **59**, 662 (1938).
314. Paladino, *Biochem. Z.*, **17**, 356 (1909).
315. Kino, *J. Soc. Chem. Ind., Japan*, **31**, 749 (1928).
316. Tanaka and Kuwata, *J. Faculty Eng. Tokyo Imp. Univ.*, **17**, 293 (1928).
317. Ueno and Ikuta, *Analyst*, **59**, 745 (1934).
318. Kuwata and Ishii, *J. Soc. Chem. Ind., Japan*, **39**, 317 (1936).
319. Heintz, *J. prakt. Chem.* [1], **66**, 1 (1855).
320. Heiduschka and Ripper, *Ber.*, **56**, 1736 (1923).
321. Gérard, *Compt. rend.*, **111**, 305 (1890); *Ann. chim. phys.* [6], **27**, 549 (1892).
322. Arnaud in Wurtz, *Dictionnaire de Chimie Pure et Appliquée*, 2nd Supplement, pt. 3, p. 4, Librairie Hachette et Cie., Paris (1897).
323. Gérard, *Compt. rend.*, **120**, 565 (1895).
324. Noerdlinger, *Z. angew. Chem.*, **5**, 110 (1892).

325. Holde and Strange, *Ber.*, **34**, 2402 (1901).
326. Kreis and Hafner, *ibid.*, **36**, 2766 (1903).
327. Holde, *ibid.*, **38**, 1247 (1905).
328. Bömer and Limprich, *Z. Untersuch. Nahr.- u. Genussm.*, **23**, 641 (1912).
329. Meyer and Beer, *Monatsh.*, **33**, 311 (1912).
330. Walden, *Chem. Umschau*, **32**, 275 (1925).
331. Verkade and Coops, *Biochem. Z.*, **206**, 468 (1928).
332. Manjunath and Siddappa, *J. Indian Chem. Soc.*, **12**, 400 (1935).
333. Klimont and Mayer, *Monatsh.*, **36**, 281 (1915).
334. Fahrion, *Chem. Umschau*, **24**, 57 (1917).
335. Marcelet, *Compt. rend.*, **187**, 145 (1928).
336. Lipp and Kovacs, *J. prakt. Chem.* [2], **99**, 243 (1919).
337. Birosel, *Philippine J. Sci.*, **45**, 251 (1931).
338. Jacobson and Holmes, *J. Am. Chem. Soc.*, **38**, 480 (1916).
339. Schuette and Vogel, *Oil & Soap*, **16**, 16 (1939).
340. Gascard, *Ann. chim.* [9], **15**, 332 (1921).
341. Schiff, *Ann.*, **223**, 247 (1884).
342. Saytzeff, *J. Russ. Phys. Chem. Soc.*, **17**, 417 (1885).
343. Mukherjee and Datta, *J. Indian Chem. Soc.*, **16**, 573 (1939).
344. Emerson, *J. Am. Chem. Soc.*, **29**, 1750 (1907).
345. Thomas and Yu, *ibid.*, **45**, 113 (1923).
346. Thomas and Mattikow, *ibid.*, **48**, 968 (1926).
347. Krafft, *Ber.*, **17**, 1627 (1884).
348. Guthzeit, *Ann.*, **206**, 351 (1881).
349. Wilde and Reychler, *Bull. soc. chim.* [3], **1**, 295 (1889).
350. M. Saytzeff, C. Saytzeff, and A. Saytzeff, *J. prakt. Chem.* [2], **35**, 369 (1887).
351. Goldschmiedt, *Jahresber. Fortschr. Chem.*, 579 (1876).
352. Sabatier and Mailhe, *Ann. chim. phys.* [8], **16**, 70 (1909).
353. Erdmann and Bedford, *Ber.*, **42**, 1324 (1909).
354. Erdmann, Ger. Patent 211,669 (1907).
355. Paal and Roth, *Ber.*, **41**, 2282 (1908).
356. Chonowsky, *ibid.*, **42**, 3339 (1909).
357. Crowder and Anderson, *J. Biol. Chem.*, **97**, 393 (1932).
358. Arnaud and Posternak, *Compt. rend.*, **150**, 1245 (1910).
359. Sigmund and Haas, *Monatsh.*, **50**, 357 (1928).
360. de Hemptinne, Ger. Patent 167,107 (1904).
361. Petersen, *Z. Elektrochem.*, **11**, 549 (1905).
362. Boehringer and Sons, Ger. Patents 187,788, 189,332 (1906).
363. Morgan and Bowen, *J. Soc. Chem. Ind.*, **43**, 346T (1924).
364. Hilditch and Longenecker, *Biochem. J.*, **31**, 1805 (1937).
365. Channon, Jenkins, and Smith, *ibid.*, **31**, 41 (1937).
366. Baughman, Jamieson, and McKinney, *Oil & Fat Industries*, **6**, 11 (Aug., 1929).
367. Ueno and Takeuchi, *J. Soc. Chem. Ind., Japan*, **38**, S.b. 740 (1935).
368. Smith and Dastur, *Biochem. J.*, **32**, 1868 (1938).
369. Bosworth and Sisson, *J. Biol. Chem.*, **107**, 489 (1934).
370. Southcombe, *J. Soc. Chem. Ind.*, **28**, 499 (1909).
371. Hilditch and Stainsby, *ibid.*, **55**, 95T (1936).
372. Pfahler, *Chem. Umschau*, **33**, 65 (1926).

373. Jamieson, Baughman, and Brauns, *J. Am. Chem. Soc.*, **43**, 1372 (1921).
374. Jamieson and Baughman, *ibid.*, **46**, 775 (1924).
375. Täufel and Rusch, *Z. Untersuch. Lebensm.*, **57**, 422 (1929).
376. Jamieson and Baughman, *Oil & Fat Industries*, **7**, 419 (1930).
377. Baughman, Brauns, and Jamieson, *J. Am. Chem. Soc.*, **42**, 2398 (1920).
378. Jamieson and Baughman, *ibid.*, **44**, 2952 (1922).
379. Farmer and Paice, *J. Chem. Soc.*, 1630 (1935).
380. Ueno and Iwai, *J. Soc. Chem. Ind., Japan*, **38**, S.b. 602 (1935).
381. Lexow, *Tids. Kemi*, **15**, 309 (1918).
382. Svendsen, *J. Soc. Chem. Ind.*, **36**, 657 (1917).
383. Eibner and Semmelbauer, *Chem. Umschau*, **31**, 189 (1924).
384. Klenk, *Z. physiol. Chem.*, **217**, 228 (1933).
385. Ueno and Komori, *J. Soc. Chem. Ind., Japan*, **38**, S.b. 352 (1935).
386. Takahashi and Shirahama, *J. Chem. Soc. Japan*, **57**, 411 (1936).
387. Schweizer, *Arch. Pharm.*, **222**, 753 (1884).
388. Spielman, *J. Biol. Chem.*, **106**, 87 (1934).
389. Goldschmiedt, *Jahresber. Fortschr. Chem.*, 728 (1877).
390. Fitz, *Ber.*, **4**, 442 (1871).
391. Grossmann, *ibid.*, **26**, 639 (1893).
392. Adam and Dyer, *J. Chem. Soc.*, **127**, 70 (1925).
393. Morgan and Holmes, *J. Soc. Chem. Ind.*, **44**, 219T (1925).
394. Hilditch and Stainsby, *ibid.*, **53**, 197T (1934).
395. Dhingra, Hilditch, and Vickery, *ibid.*, **48**, 281T (1929).
396. Baughman and Jamieson, *J. Am. Chem. Soc.*, **43**, 2696 (1921); **44**, 2947 (1922); *Cotton Oil Press*, **4**, No. 3, 61 (1920).
397. Cruz, West, and Aragon, *Philippine J. Sci.*, **48**, 5 (1932).
398. Baughman and Jamieson, *J. Oil & Fat Ind.*, **2**, 110 (1925).
399. Bosworth, *J. Biol. Chem.*, **106**, 235 (1934).
400. Ikuta and Ueno, *J. Soc. Chem. Ind., Japan*, **33**, S.b. 245 (1930).
401. Armstrong and Hilditch, *J. Soc. Chem. Ind.*, **44**, 180T (1925).
402. Toyama and Tsuchiya, *Bull. Chem. Soc. Japan*, **10**, 192 (1935).
403. Ueno and Iwai, *J. Soc. Chem. Ind., Japan*, **38**, S.b. 602 (1935).
404. Caldwell, *Ann.*, **101**, 97 (1857).
405. Tassinari, *Gazz. chim. ital.*, **8**, 305 (1878).
406. Cohen, *Verslag Akad. Wetenschappen Amsterdam*, **34**, 462 (1925).
407. Morgan and Holmes, *J. Soc. Chem. Ind.*, **44**, 219T (1925).
408. Holde and Godbole, *Ber.*, **59**, 36 (1926).
409. Holde, Bleyberg, and Rabinowitsch, *ibid.*, **62**, 177 (1929).
410. Morgan and Holmes, *J. Soc. Chem. Ind.*, **47**, 309T (1928).
411. Jantzen and Tiedcke, *J. prakt. Chem.* [2], **127**, 277 (1930).
412. Le Sueur and Withers, *J. Chem. Soc.*, **107**, 736 (1915).
413. Le Sueur and Withers, *ibid.*, **105**, 2800 (1914).
414. Morgan and Holmes, *J. Soc. Chem. Ind.*, **44**, 491T (1925).
415. Eylerts, *Vierteljahresschr. prakt. Pharm.*, **9**, 330 (1860).
416. Mohr, *Z. physiol. Chem.*, **14**, 390 (1890).
417. Thümmel, *Arch. Pharm.*, **228**, 280 (1890).
418. Tutin and Clewer, *J. Chem. Soc.*, **101**, 2221 (1912).
419. Flaschenträger and Halle, *Z. physiol. Chem.*, **190**, 120 (1930).
420. Stohmann and Langbein, *J. prakt. Chem.* [2], **42**, 361 (1890).
421. Talanzeff, *ibid.* [2], **50**, 71 (1894).

422. Vavon, *Compt. rend.*, **149**, 997 (1909).
423. Yokoyama and Kotake, *J. Chem. Soc. Japan*, **56**, 336 (1935).
424. Sudborough, Watson, Ayyar, and Damle, *J. Indian Inst. Sci.*, **9A**, 67 (1926).
425. Yamasaki and Ichihara, *J. Chem. Soc. Japan*, **56**, 1332 (1935).
426. Holde and Bleyberg, *Z. angew. Chem.*, **43**, 897 (1930).
427. Sudborough, Watson, Ayyar, and Muscarenhas, *J. Indian Inst. Sci.*, **9A**, 43 (1926).
428. Bosworth and Brown, *J. Biol. Chem.*, **103**, 115 (1933).
429. Toyama, *Chem. Umschau*, **31**, 221 (1924); **33**, 293 (1926).
430. Kono, *J. Agr. Chem. Soc. Japan*, **9**, 458 (1933).
431. Holde, Bleyberg, and Vohrer, *Brennstoff-Chem.*, **11**, 128 (1930).
432. Power and Tutin, *J. Chem. Soc.*, **93**, 891 (1908).
433. Ashton, Robinson, and Smith, *ibid.*, 283 (1936).
434. Taylor and Levene, *J. Biol. Chem.*, **80**, 609 (1928).
435. Klenk, *ibid.*, **105**, 467 (1934).
436. Brigl, *Z. physiol. Chem.*, **95**, 161 (1915).
437. Sullivan, *J. Ind. Eng. Chem.*, **8**, 1027 (1916).
438. Baughman and Jamieson, *J. Am. Chem. Soc.*, **44**, 2947 (1922).
439. Mudbidri, Ayyar, and Watson, *J. Indian Inst. Sci.*, **11A**, pt. 14, 173 (1928).
440. Ayyar, *Proc. 15th Indian Sci. Congr.*, 161 (1928).
441. Rosenheim and Maclean, *Biochem. J.*, **9**, 103 (1915).
442. Bernhauer and Posselt, *Biochem. Z.*, **294**, 215 (1937).
443. Collins, *J. Soc. Chem. Ind.*, **54**, 33T (1935).
444. Mattissohn, *Fettchem. Umschau*, **41**, 235 (1934).
445. Meyer, Brod, and Soyka, *Monatsh.*, **34**, 1113 (1913).
446. Levene and West, *J. Biol. Chem.*, **15**, 193 (1913).
447. Brigl and Fuchs, *Z. physiol. Chem.*, **119**, 280 (1922).
448. Levene, Taylor, and Haller, *J. Biol. Chem.*, **61**, 157 (1924).
449. Taylor, *ibid.*, **91**, 541 (1931).
450. Stürcke, *Ann.*, **223**, 283 (1884).
451. Darmstaedter and Lifschütz, *Ber.*, **29**, 618 (1896); **31**, 97 (1898).
452. Röhmann, *Zentr. Physiol.*, **19**, 317 (1905).
453. Dunham and Jacobson, *Z. physiol. Chem.*, **64**, 302 (1910).
454. Röhmann, *Biochem. Z.*, **77**, 298 (1916).
455. Fargher and Probert, *J. Textile Inst.*, **14**, 49T (1923).
456. Ito, *J. Faculty Agr., Hokkaido Imp. Univ.*, **37**, 1 (1934).
457. Gascard and Damoy, *Compt. rend.*, **177**, 1222 (1923).
458. Damoy, *J. pharm. chim.* [7], **29**, 148 (1924).
459. Tropsch and Koch, *Brennstoff-Chem.*, **10**, 82 (1929).
460. Gascard, *Compt. rend.*, **170**, 1326 (1920).
461. Schalfeieff, *Ber.*, **9**, 278 (1876).
462. Marie, *J. Soc. Chem. Ind.*, **13**, 1207 (1894); **14**, 599 (1895); **15**, 362 (1896).
463. Heiduschka and Nier, *J. prakt. Chem.* [2], **149**, 98 (1937).
464. Jakobsen, *Cotton Oil Press*, **6**, No. 1, 43 (1922).
465. Tsujimoto, *J. Soc. Chem. Ind., Japan*, **42**, S.b. 396 (1939).
466. Tschirch and Schaefer, *Pharm. Acta Helv.*, **1**, 9 (1926).
467. Anderson and Chargaff, *J. Biol. Chem.*, **85**, 77 (1929).
468. Anderson and Chargaff, *Z. physiol. Chem.*, **191**, 166 (1930).

469. Spielman and Anderson, *J. Biol. Chem.*, **112**, 759 (1936).
470. Morgan and Holmes, *Nature*, **117**, 624 (1926).
471. Holde and Godbole, *Z. deut. Öl- u. Fett-Ind.*, **46**, 129, 145, 163, 179 (1926).
472. Speer, Wise, and Hart, *J. Biol. Chem.*, **82**, 105 (1929).
473. Power and Salway, *J. Am. Chem. Soc.*, **32**, 346 (1910).
474. Tange, *Sci. Papers Inst. Phys. Chem. Research Tokyo*, **14**, 275 (1930).
475. Kiesel, *Z. physiol. Chem.*, **149**, 231 (1925).
476. Schalfeieff, *Bull. soc. chim.* [2], **26**, 450 (1876).
477. Henriques, *Ber.*, **30**, 1415 (1897).
478. Lewkowitsch, *Proc. Chem. Soc.*, **6**, 91 (1890).
479. Grassow, *Biochem. Z.*, **148**, 61 (1924).
480. Dietzel and Krug, *Ber.*, **58**, 1307 (1925).
481. Piper, Chibnall, and Williams, *Biochem. J.*, **28**, 2175 (1934).
482. Huminski, *Roczniki Chem.*, **15**, 53 (1935).
483. Koyama, *J. Chem. Soc. Japan*, **55**, 348 (1934).
484. Stadler, *Mitt. Kohlenforsch. Inst. Prag.*, 445 (1933).
485. Roginskaya, *J. Applied Chem. U.S.S.R.*, **9**, 108 (1936).
486. Tropsch and Kreutzer, *Brennstoff-Chem.*, **3**, 49 (1922).
487. von Boyen, *Z. angew. Chem.*, **14**, 1110 (1901).
488. Hell, *ibid.*, **13**, 556 (1900).
489. Kraemer and Spilker, *Ber.*, **35**, 1212 (1902).
490. Eisenreich, *Chem. Rev. Fett- u. Harz-Ind.*, **16**, 211 (1909).
491. Rigg, *Trans. Proc. New Zealand Inst.*, **44**, 270 (1911).
492. Ryan and Algar, *Proc. Roy. Irish Acad.*, **30B**, 97 (1913).
493. Meyer and Brod, *Monatsh.*, **34**, 1143 (1913).
494. Ryan and Dillon, *Proc. Roy. Dublin Soc.*, **12**, 202 (1909).
495. Marcusson and Smelkus, *Chem.-Ztg.*, **41**, 129 (1917).
496. Mangold, *J. Soc. Chem. Ind.*, **10**, 860 (1891).
497. Meyer and Soyka, *Monatsh.*, **34**, 1159 (1913).
498. Wood and Nicholas, *J. Inst. Pet. Tech.*, **14**, 493 (1928).
499. Holde, Bleyberg, and Vohrer, *Brennstoff-Chem.*, **10**, 101 (1929).
500. Francis, King, and Willis, *J. Chem. Soc.*, 999 (1937).
501. Matthes and Sander, *Arch. Pharm.*, **246**, 165 (1908).
502. Pieverling, *Ann.*, **183**, 344 (1876).
503. Marie, *Bull. soc. chim.* [3], **15**, 565 (1896).
504. Hata, *J. Chem. Soc. Japan*, **58**, 1188 (1937).
505. Kono, *J. Agr. Chem. Soc. Japan*, **8**, 1150 (1932).
506. Kono and Maruyama, *ibid.*, **12**, 523 (1936).
507. Masami, *Bull. Agr. Chem. Soc. Japan*, **4**, 123 (1928).
508. Koyama, *J. Chem. Soc. Japan*, **56**, 365 (1935).
509. Anderson, *J. Biol. Chem.*, **97**, 639 (1932).
510. Lüdecke, *Seifensieder-Ztg.*, **53**, 316 (1926).
511. Tutin and Clewer, *J. Chem. Soc.*, **105**, 1845 (1914).
512. Knecht and Allan, *J. Soc. Dyers Colourists*, **27**, 142 (1911).
513. Jamieson and McKinney, *Oil & Soap*, **11**, 207 (1934).
514. Brodie, *Ann.*, **71**, 144 (1849).
515. Schwalb, *ibid.*, **235**, 106 (1886).
516. Gascard, *Compt. rend.*, **159**, 260 (1914).
517. Sundwik, *Z. physiol. Chem.*, **32**, 355 (1901).

II

THE ETHYLENIC FATTY ACIDS

Of all the classes of chemical compounds which are found in nature few offer more interest both to the chemist and to the biologist than the group known as the ethylenic fatty acids. Whereas the saturated fatty acids constitute a perfect example of a homologous series, the chemical and physical properties of the individual members of which are essentially dependent upon the presence of long, saturated hydrocarbon chains, the ethylenic acids offer a somewhat more complex chemical study. The presence of one or more unsaturated bonds in the hydrocarbon chains of these acids distinguishes them from those of the saturated series. The properties of the ethylenic acids, therefore, not only embrace those of their saturated counterparts but also include those reactions typical of unsaturated carbon-to-carbon linkages. Thus, the direct addition of halogens or halogen halides, hydroxylation, oxidative cleavage, hydrogenation, and many other reactions characterize the unsaturated acids. In this group of compounds we also encounter the phenomena of both position and geometrical isomerisms, so that even those acids of comparatively simple empirical formulas represent not one, but a number of possible chemical individuals. It can, therefore, be said that the chemistry of the ethylenic acids is appreciably more involved than that of the saturated acids, and although our knowledge of the latter group is comparatively far advanced many of the generalizations pertaining to the former require further experimentation and confirmation.

The ethylenic fatty acids are found widely distributed as esters in the various natural oils, fats, and waxes. They constitute a major percentage of the acids of the vegetable oils and also occur in large amounts in the various animal fats. The fish oils are characterized by large percentages of unsaturated acids and particularly by acids containing three or more ethylenic bonds. The unsaturated fatty acids which are present in the naturally occurring

72

fats are found associated with the saturated acids, most generally in the form of mixed triglycerides. The constitution of these naturally occurring glycerides is a subject of rather unusual interest, and a very definite plan appears to have been followed governing the distribution of the fatty acids in the various naturally occurring fatty substances. In general, it is evident that the so-called law of even distribution regulates the molecular constitution of fatty materials. According to this generalization the amount of any acid in a fatty mixture will be found evenly distributed throughout the various glycerides present. Thus, it is only when the percentage of any individual acid is quite high that simple triglycerides are encountered.

Pure unsaturated fatty acids can only rarely be obtained by fractionation of the glycerides themselves, and they are prepared from the fatty acid mixtures only by long and tedious processes. The saturated acids can be prepared by complete hydrogenation of acid mixtures followed by ester fractionation; however, such methods are not, in general, applicable to the ethylenic acids.

Classification and General Considerations

In our discussion of the saturated acids we observed that they are all characterized by the presence of a saturated hydrocarbon chain, and that the essential difference between the various members is the number of carbon atoms in the alkyl group. When we consider the ethylenic fatty acids it must be realized that, although the individual members have many properties in common, the increased complexity occasioned by the presence of one or more ethylenic bonds must be recognized. This requires a subdivision of the ethylenic acids into several acid series before any logical discussion is possible. The accepted manner of subdivision, and the one which appears to be the most reasonable, is to classify the ethylenic acids according to the number of unsaturated bonds in the chain. Thus the ethylenic acids are classed as mono-, di-, tri-, and polyethylenic acids depending upon the number of unsaturated carbon-to-carbon bonds present in their molecules. Although such a classification presents several objections it does utilize their most important chemical differences as the basis of division, and the fact that this means of classification has successfully passed the test of time cannot be denied. In considering the ethylenic fatty acids we will, therefore, divide them into four major series which are as follows: the monoethylenic acids, the diethylenic acids, the triethylenic acids, and the polyethylenic acids.

As we study the ethylenic fatty acids it becomes apparent that nature has certainly not fashioned them in any haphazard manner, but rather according to certain very definite procedures. These procedures are evidently associated with the various biological processes by which the fatty acids are formed and utilized in life processes. Man is, unfortunately, ignorant of many of the factors which influence the structure and configuration or govern the occurrence of these acids. We must, therefore, content ourselves by recording the various observations which have been made in the hope that future studies will throw further light upon this subject. Before we discuss any specific series of ethylenic acids it should be of interest to consider some of the generalizations which pertain to this large class of compounds.

The ethylenic fatty acids are found widely distributed, generally as glycerides, in the animal, vegetable, and marine oils. The animal fats usually do not contain large amounts of acids possessing more than one double bond, so that large sources of the highly unsaturated acids are essentially confined to the vegetable and marine oils. The composition of the animal depot fats is, of course, somewhat dependent upon the food consumed by the animal. The diet, however, is not the only controlling factor, since animals possess certain typical fats, the composition of which is largely dependent upon the type of animal. Several other factors, such as climate and environment, are known to influence the composition of the animal fats. No clear-cut generalizations can be drawn, at this time, regarding the influence of these factors, and until the various metabolic processes are better understood, it must suffice simply to present those observations which have been recorded. When we consider the vegetable fats and oils we find that many of them, particularly those found in the colder climates, contain large amounts of highly unsaturated acids. Oils of plant origin are generally classified as non-drying, semi-drying, and drying oils, depending upon the relative amounts of unsaturated acids in their respective glycerides. The unsaturated acids in the semi-drying oils are represented by substantial percentages of monoölefinic acids together with lesser amounts of more highly unsaturated acids, whereas the drying oils contain large percentages of diolefinic and triolefinic acids. No clear line of demarkation can be drawn between the semi-drying and drying oils and many examples of borderline cases can be cited. There is, however, one common feature concerning the various vegetable oils which is highly significant. This is the fact that, by far, the greater proportion of the acids present in these oils contain eighteen carbon atoms. While certain notable exceptions to this observation can be cited, it is apparent that the chemistry of such acids as oleic, linoleic, linolenic, and eleostearic essentially comprises the chemistry of the fatty acids of vegetable origin.

The fats of marine life contain acids which differ materially in structure from those obtained from other sources. These fats are characterized by the presence of substantial quantities of highly unsaturated acids containing twenty or more carbon atoms, which contain as basic structural units the groups $:CHCH_2CH:$ and $:CH(CH_2)_2CH:$. However, appreciable amounts of acids containing less than eighteen carbon atoms are frequently found in some of the fish oils, and such acids generally possess the group $:CH(CH_2)_7CO_2H$ observed in oleic acid. Fats of fresh water fish and of marine mammals contain smaller percentages of highly unsaturated acids with twenty or more carbon atoms, and larger amounts of unsaturated acids having eighteen or less carbon atoms, than the fats of salt water origin. An examination of the fatty matter present in the plants which fish utilize for food shows a significant similarity in composition with that of the fish oils themselves. This raises the question as to the origin of these highly unsaturated acids which are so characteristic of the marine oils.

One of the most interesting facts relative to the occurrence of the unsaturated fatty acids is the tendency of certain plant species to synthesize specific unsaturated acids to such an extent that the presence of these acids definitely characterizes oils from these sources. Thus, linseed oil contains a large percentage of linolenic acid together with linoleic acid; eleostearic acid distinguishes tung oil; erucic acid characterizes rape seed oil; oleic acid constitutes the major proportion of the acids of olive oil; and the principal acid of parsley seed oil is an isomer of oleic acid, petroselinic acid. While the relative proportions of the various acids in the oils obtained from certain plants may differ according to the conditions of growth, climate, or other factors, the ability to synthesize these characteristic acids is apparently an inherent property of the plant itself.

The effect of climate and of other environmental conditions upon the relative amounts of the various unsaturated acids found in the fats has long been a quite controversial issue. Certainly, it is a subject which is not devoid of interest, and one which is so closely associated with life processes as to offer an important field for biological investigations. A large number of observations, most of which have been made upon the vegetable oils, indicate that cold climates favor the production of highly unsaturated fatty acids. That is, a plant of the same species will produce a more unsaturated oil the cooler the climate in which it is grown. Pigulevskiĭ,[1] after a study of numerous plant oils obtained from plants grown in various parts of Russia, arrived at the conclusion that the nature of the oil produced in a plant is influenced by climatic conditions. The lowered melting point attending increased unsaturation offers a partial explanation of this phenomenon. Later,[2] this author cited further examples in support of this contention and stated that the difference was not that one oil contains more unsaturated acids than another oil but rather that the relative proportions of the various unsaturated acids differ. This raises a very important point and one which should be borne clearly in mind. Temperature and other factors do not bring about a fundamental change in the type of acids produced by a given plant species, but affect only the relative percentages of such acids. Primitive plants, which possess the ability to produce unsaturated acids of a certain configuration, will retain this ability irrespective of their environment. Ivanov [3] has commented upon the sensitivity of the linolenic acid content of plants to temperature conditions. It must be admitted that some exceptions to the above generalization can be cited and that specific instances exist of highly unsaturated oils which are produced by plants grown in warm climates. These exceptions, however, are not impressive unless they involve differences in the types of acids produced rather than in relative amounts. That certain semi-tropical plants produce conjugated unsaturated acids of a high degree of unsaturation, whereas closely related plants grown in northern climates produce unconjugated acids, refers to factors more fundamental than the temperature conditions of growth. A high degree of unsaturation is generally accompanied by fluidity at lower temperatures and also by a relatively high chemical and perhaps biological activity. Comparatively recent work [4] has indicated that the linolenic acid content of linseed oil increases materially during the ripening of the seeds, and Bauer [5] has observed a decided increase in the oleic acid content of sunflower seed oil during this ripening period. It would appear, therefore, that there are certain critical periods in the life cycle of plants during which temperature effects are critical and exert their maximum influence upon the composition of the seed fats.

Quite a number of observations have been reported which indicate that temperature conditions exert an influence upon the degree of unsaturation of the various animal fats. The classical experiments of Henriques and Hansen [6] would appear to support the contention that the higher the external temperature the greater the tendency towards the formation of unsaturated acids. These authors examined the body fats of three pigs which had been fed identical diets, but which were held at different temperatures during the course of the experiment. The most saturated fat was obtained from the pig held at 0°, but covered with a sheepskin; the fat from the animal held at 0° without external covering was the most unsaturated, while that from the animal held at 30–35° was found to be of intermediate composition. It is also generally accepted that the more saturated fats are present in the warmer portions of an animal. That body temperature, however, is not a fundamental factor in determining the degree of unsaturation of the various animal fats is shown by the fact that when one compares the composition of animal fats with the body temperatures of the animals from which they are obtained no decided correlation is evidenced. It must be remembered, however, that the natural tendency of animal types to synthesize or assimilate certain acids is probably an inherent characteristic. Thus, Isaachsen [7] failed to observe highly unsaturated acids with twenty or more carbon atoms in swine which had been fed material containing herring oil; and Ellis and Zeller [8] reported that hogs raised on a low-fat diet apparently synthesized fat at a normal rate.

It has been frequently stated that the large amount of highly unsaturated acids in the fish oils is a manifestation of a temperature effect. That this cannot be accepted without reservation is apparent when one compares the fats of marine animals with the fish oils and also considers the difference in composition between marine and fresh water fish oils. Lovern [9] has commented upon the reduced amount of highly unsaturated C_{20} and C_{22} acids found in the oils of fresh water fish as compared with the oils of salt water fish. Klenk, Ditt, and Diebold [10] have, however, recently stated that the content of highly unsaturated C_{20} and C_{22} acids in the depot fats is related to the body temperature, and they believe that the differences observed cannot be attributed to the food consumed, since herbivorous and carnivorous reptile fats showed similar compositions. In general, it is fairly well established that cold temperatures and severe conditions favor the formation of unsaturated acids in the various plants and animals. The specific type of plant or animal and the primitive tendency to synthesize fatty mixtures of characteristic composition are factors of primary consideration. All these variables must be carefully considered in discussing any specific cases which are cited either in support or in refutation of this generalization.

The unsaturated fatty acids found in vegetable and animal fats show certain structural similarities which are probably related to their formation in nature. Oleic acid is, by far, the most abundant of the naturally occurring fatty acids. Oleic acid, 9-octadecenoic acid, possesses the groups $CH_3(CH_2)_7CH$: and :$CH(CH_2)_7CO_2H$. A large number of the naturally occurring fatty acids, particularly those which are found in substantial quantities, show structural relationships with this acid. Thus, linoleic acid, or 9,12-octadecadienoic acid, contains the group :$CH(CH_2)_7CO_2H$, similar to that found in oleic acid, and linolenic acid, or 9,12,15-octadecatrienoic acid, also possesses this group. Both of these acids are found widely distributed in the vegetable fats and are major components of most of the drying and semi-drying oils. The group :$CH(CH_2)_7CO_2H$ is also present in eleostearic acid, the characteristic acid of tung oil. The structural similarity of these unsaturated acids is quite interesting. When we observe, however, that the principal monoethenoic acids which contain ten, twelve, fourteen, and sixteen carbon atoms also have a double bond in the 9-position and thus possess the group :$CH(CH_2)_7CO_2H$, we realize the very close relationship which exists between many of these unsaturated acids. Of the monoölefinic acids which contain more than eighteen carbon atoms, gadoleic acid shows 9- unsaturation and erucic acid (13-docosenoic acid) contains the group $CH_3(CH_2)_7CH$: which is present in oleic acid.

The Monoethylenic Acids

The monoethylenic fatty acids constitute a large group of chemically similar individuals all of which possess the general formula $C_nH_{2n-2}O_2$. The large number of possible representatives of this series is occasioned not only by reason of the difference in the number of carbon atoms in their hydrocarbon chains, but also by virtue of both position and geometrical isomerism of their unsaturated bonds. Thus even the simplest members of this group, such as the hexenoic acids, occur in several isomeric forms. As the length of the hydrocarbon chain increases, the number of possible position isomers likewise increases. Position isomerism allows of four isomeric hexenoic acids, three of which permit of *cis-trans* isomerism, while the octadecenoic acids are represented by sixteen possible position isomers, fifteen of which exhibit geometrical isomerism. The number of theoretically possible monoethylenic fatty acids is, therefore, quite large. Many representatives of this group are found in the naturally occurring fatty substances, and several of them occur in very large amounts. Oleic acid is the most abundant of all the naturally occurring fatty acids and is invariably considered as the typical acid of this group. Because of the historical significance of this acid and its wide occurrence, this series is frequently referred to as the oleic acid series. Although no other monoethylenic acid rivals oleic acid in importance, many members of this group, such as palmitoleic acid, are found widely distributed throughout the animal and vegetable fats.

The oleic acid series constitutes a large group of naturally occurring compounds, many representatives of which have been isolated from the fats and oils. In considering the series as a whole, however, we should not lose sight of the fact that many of the members of this group either do not occur in natural products or have not, as yet, been isolated. As a consequence, our knowledge of some of the members of the oleic acid series is confined to the preparation and properties of the synthetic acids. Since all the high molecular weight monoethylenic acids have not been prepared, our knowledge of this important group of compounds is, even today, somewhat limited.

The question of the nomenclature of these acids is quite important. Any rational system for naming the monoethylenic acids must designate the chain length of any particular acid and must also distinguish it from its possible isomers. In other words, the name given to any particular acid must convey not only the chain length but also the position and configuration of the double bond in the alkylene chain. It is quite regrettable that considerable confusion exists in the earlier literature concerning the unsaturated fatty acids owing to the absence of a uniform system of nomenclature. The present accepted method of naming the unsaturated acids is undoubtedly quite familiar to most chemists; however, a short review of the principles involved will serve to eliminate any possible confusion in our later discussion of the specific members of this series. The unsaturated fatty acids, like the hydrocarbons and many other aliphatic compounds, derive their names from either the Greek or the Latin numerals which designate the number of carbon atoms in the acid chain. The carbon atom of the carboxyl group is considered to be a part of the chain, and the presence of an olefinic linkage is designated by a contraction of the suffix "ene." The carbon atoms of the acid chain are numbered beginning with the carbon atom of the carboxyl group and the position of the ethylenic bond is established by the appropriate numerical prefix. Thus, the prefix 9,10- is used to designate that the double bond lies between the ninth and tenth carbon atoms, the prefix 6,7-, between the sixth and seventh carbon atoms, and so on. Frequently only the number of the carbon atom nearest to the carboxyl group is used as a prefix. Thus 9,10-decenoic acid can be correctly called 9-decenoic acid or 2,3-dodecenoic acid, 2-dodecenoic acid. This latter nomenclature will be generally followed throughout this writing. The following examples are illustrative:

$$-\overset{|}{\underset{10}{C}}=\overset{|}{\underset{9}{C}}-\overset{|}{\underset{8}{C}}-\overset{|}{\underset{7}{C}}-\overset{|}{\underset{6}{C}}-\overset{|}{\underset{5}{C}}-\overset{|}{\underset{4}{C}}-\overset{|}{\underset{3}{C}}-\overset{|}{\underset{2}{C}}-\overset{1}{C}\overset{\textstyle O}{\underset{\textstyle OH}{\Big\langle}}$$

9-Decenoic acid

$$-\overset{|}{\underset{12}{C}}-\overset{|}{\underset{11}{C}}-\overset{|}{\underset{10}{C}}-\overset{|}{\underset{9}{C}}-\overset{|}{\underset{8}{C}}-\overset{|}{\underset{7}{C}}-\overset{|}{\underset{6}{C}}-\overset{|}{\underset{5}{C}}-\overset{|}{\underset{4}{C}}-\overset{|}{\underset{3}{C}}=\overset{|}{\underset{2}{C}}-\overset{1}{C}\overset{\textstyle O}{\underset{\textstyle OH}{\Big\langle}}$$

2-Dodecenoic acid

An alternative system of nomenclature, which is frequently employed in the early literature, is to designate the carbon atoms by the letters of the Greek alphabet. The carbon atom adjacent to the carboxyl group is termed α, the next β, the next γ, and so on along the chain. This method is often used, particularly in naming the substituted acids, although numerals appear preferable.

All monoethylenic fatty acids, with the exception of those which contain a double bond in the terminal position, are capable of existing in two geometrical forms, *cis* and *trans*. When the structure of an acid permits of both a *cis* and a *trans* modification, the name should bear this distinction. This is accomplished by prefixing either of the above terms to the name of the acid. Thus, *cis*-9-octadecenoic acid can refer only to the *cis* form of an acid which contains eighteen carbon atoms and a double bond between the ninth and tenth carbon atoms. Since it is rather generally accepted, however, that all naturally occurring acids have a *cis* structure it is usually not customary to employ the prefix *cis* when discussing such acids.

The above system of nomenclature is quite rational and should be employed wherever possible. We must realize, however, that our familiarity with many of these acids preceded by many years the establishment of a uniform method of nomenclature. As a consequence of this, many of the important naturally occurring acids and many of their geometrical isomerides are designated by common names, such as oleic, palmitoleic, erucic, elaidic, or brassidic acid. Such names generally have a historical background and either refer to the origins of the acids, their structural similarities to other acids, or are simply names given to them at the time of their discovery. Since these names have frequently been adopted before the actual configuration of the acid was known, many of them will undoubtedly be retained and will continue to be widely used. Names such as oleic acid or elaidic acid are so intimately interwoven in the literature of the fatty substances that to suggest their modification or disuse would be akin to sacrilege.

The following paragraphs contain brief descriptions of the synthesis, properties, and occurrence of many of the monoethylenic fatty acids. It should be borne in mind that, from a practical standpoint, those acids which occur in large amounts in nature or which can be easily prepared from available acids are of much greater economic and perhaps scientific interest than those which occur in only minute amounts or are synthesized only by difficult and involved procedures.

PENTENOIC ACIDS

The pentenoic acids are not found in the naturally occurring fats and oils; however, the synthetic acids have been known for many years. Three pentenoic acids are possible, two of which are capable of existing as *cis-trans* isomers.

4-Pentenoic Acid. $CH_2:CHCH_2CH_2CO_2H$

The preparation of this acid by the action of sodium ethylate upon the ethyl ester of allylacetoacetic acid has been described by Zeidler.[11] Messerschmidt [12] employed aqueous potassium hydroxide to effect the hydrolysis. The decarboxylation of allylmalonic acid has been shown by Conrad and Bischoff [13] to result in substantial yields of 4-pentenoic acid. Allylmalonic acid can be obtained by the action of allyl bromide upon ethyl sodiomalonate. Perkin and Simonsen [14] have reported the formation of ethyl 4-pentenoate by the reduction of ethyl 4-pentynoate by means of sodium and absolute ethanol. The reduction of 3-vinylacrylic acid by means of sodium amalgam and water has been observed by Doebner [15] to yield 4-pentenoic acid with no shift in the position of the double bond. This claim has since been disputed by several authors who have stated that the only product formed by this reduction is 3-pentenoic acid. Fittig [16] has shown that the treatment of 4-pentenoic acid with aqueous sodium hydroxide does not result in a shift in the position of the double bond.

4-Pentenoic acid is a colorless liquid for which the following physical constants have been reported: b_{745} 186–187°,[17] b_{760} 187–189°,[12] d_4^0 0.9987, d_4^{18} 0.9843, $n_D^{7.5}$ 1.4341. It is slightly soluble in water and easily soluble in ethanol and ether. The p-toluidide boils at 205° at 16 mm. and melts at 81.5°.[18]

3-Pentenoic Acid. $CH_3CH:CHCH_2CO_2H$

3-Pentenoic acid has been shown by Fittig and MacKenzie [19] to be formed in subordinate amounts to its 2-isomer by the decarboxylation of the reaction product of propanal and malonic acid. Thiele and Jehl [20] have studied the reduction of vinylacrylic acid with sodium amalgam and stated that it proceeds in the expected manner to form 3-pentenoic acid rather than the 4-isomer as reported by Doebner.[15] Goldberg and Linstead [21] have also reported that 3-pentenoic acid is the major product formed by the reduction of vinylacrylic acid. 3-Pentenoic acid is one of the products formed during the dry distillation of 3-hydroxyvaleric acid and also by the heating of sodium 3-hydroxyvalerate with aqueous sodium hydroxide.[22] Methylparaconic acid has been shown to yield 3-pentenoic acid, together with other products, when heated.[22, 23] Methylparaconic acid can be obtained by the reduction of the ethyl ester of acetosuccinic acid according to the method of Fichter and Pfister.[18] Zincke and Küster [24] have claimed the formation of 3-pentenoic acid by the reduction of pentachloropentadienoic acid, $CCl_2:CClCCl:CClCO_2H$.

3-Pentenoic acid is a colorless liquid which boils at 193–194° at atmospheric pressure and at 98° at 19 mm.[21] The acid is moderately soluble in water and easily soluble in ethanol and ether. Its *p*-toluidide melts at 106°.

2-Pentenoic Acid. $CH_2CH_2CH:CHCO_2H$

2-Pentenoic acid is formed, together with its 3-isomer, when propanal is condensed with malonic acid and the product decarboxylated.[22, 25, 26] The two acids may be easily separated owing to the fact that the latter readily forms a lactone. Fittig and Spenzer [22] showed that the double bond of 3-pentenoic acid migrates towards the carboxyl group under the influence of caustic alkalies. The equilibrium involved in the migration of the double bonds of the 3- and 2-pentenoic acids in the presence of bases has been extensively studied by Goldberg and Linstead.[21] If pyridine containing 0.5% of piperidine is used as the condensing agent in the malonic acid synthesis, only the 2-isomer is formed. This effect is quite specific and cannot be correlated to the basicity of the condensing agent, as shown by later work.[27] Treatment of 2-bromovaleric acid with quinoline has been shown to result almost completely in the formation of 2-pentenoic acid.[28] Rupe, Ronus, and Lotz [29] have made a further study of this method for the preparation of 2-pentenoic acid. The dehydration of 3-hydroxyvaleric acid or its salts forms a mixture of 2- and 3-pentenoic acids. Bourguel [30] has studied the hydrogenation of 2-acetylenic acids to 2-ethylenic acids in the presence of platinum.

Trans-2-pentenoic acid has been reported by Bourguel [30] to be formed by treatment of the *cis* acid with iodine. The *trans* acid was reported to boil at 106° under 15 mm. pressure, whereas the corresponding *cis* isomer boiled at 88°. Bourguel reported d_4^{15} 1.454 for the *trans* and d_4^{15} 0.992 and n_D^{15} 1.450 for the *cis* isomer. *Cis*-2-pentenoic acid melts at 8°.[21] Several boiling points have been observed: 195–197°,[19] 200–201°,[27] 105° at 19 mm.,[21] 99° at 10 mm., and 71° at 2 mm.[26] The following densities have been reported: d_4^0 1.0074, d_4^{15} 0.9921, and d_4^{50} 0.9550. All the above constants refer to the *cis* modification. The acid has been stated to be soluble in water to the extent of one part in 15.89 parts.[31] It is very soluble in ethanol and ether. Its *p*-toluidide melts at 110°.

HEXENOIC ACIDS

Four hexenoic acids are theoretically possible, three of which can exhibit *cis-trans* isomerism. One of the hexenoic acids has been reported to be a component of peppermint oil.

5-Hexenoic Acid. $CH_2:CH(CH_2)_3CO_2H$

5-Hexenoic acid is formed when 6-aminocaproic acid is treated with nitrous acid.[18, 32, 33]   The reaction product also contains a small amount of 4-hexenoic acid. The distillation of 2-hydroxy-2-methyladipic acid has been shown by Fichter and Langguth [34] to yield a mixture of 5- and 4-hexenoic acids. Letch and Linstead [35] have studied the synthesis of this acid by the above two methods and also by the action of 1-bromo-3-butene upon ethyl sodiomalonate. Linstead and Rydon [36] have also described the preparation of 5-hexenoic acid by the malonic acid synthesis. The electrolysis of potassium ethyl pimelate has been shown to yield 5-hexenoic acid as one of the products.[37] Ciamician and Silber [38] have prepared 5-hexenal from cyclohexanone and have converted this aldehyde to the corresponding hydroxamic acid, which yielded 5-hexenoic acid upon treatment with sulfuric acid.

5-Hexenoic acid boils at 203° at 760 mm. and at 107° at 17 mm. Other physical constants have been reported to be as follows: $d_4^{19.2}$ 0.9639, d_4^{20} 0.9610, $n_D^{19.1}$ 1.4375, and n_D^{20} 1.4343. Fichter and Pfister [18] reported the melting point of the *p*-toluidide to be 75° whereas Letch and Linstead [35] have reported 58°.

4-Hexenoic Acid. $CH_3CH:CH(CH_2)_2CO_2H$

4-Hexenoic acid has been shown by Fichter [39] to be formed by the distillation of the lactone of 5-hydroxy-4-carboxyhexanoic acid by the following reaction:

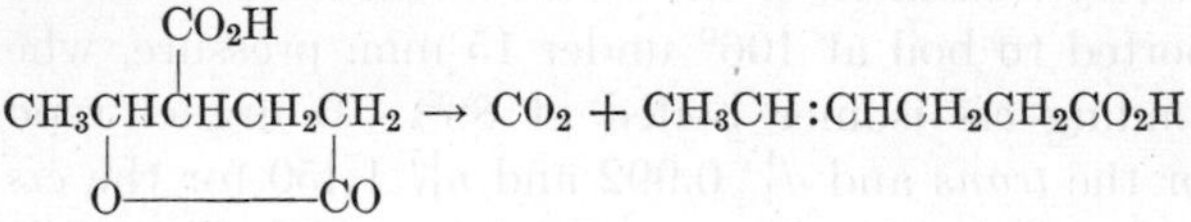

$$\underset{\underset{\displaystyle O\text{————}CO}{\displaystyle |\qquad\quad\ \ |}}{CH_3CHCHCH_2CH_2} \rightarrow CO_2 + CH_3CH:CHCH_2CH_2CO_2H$$

overscript: CO$_2$H

The structure of the reaction product was later confirmed [18] by its oxidation to acetic and succinic acids by means of potassium permanganate. 5-Hydroxy-4-carboxyhexanoic acid can be prepared by the reduction of diethyl 2-acetylglutarate with sodium amalgam. The distillation of 2-hydroxy-2-methyladipic acid yields a mixture of 4- and 5-hexenoic acids,[34] as does also the action of nitrous acid upon 6-aminohexanoic acid.[18, 32] The reduction of sorbic acid, $CH_3CH:CHCH:CHCO_2H$, was formerly considered to yield only 3-hexenoic acid (hydrosorbic acid); however, recent work has shown that substantial quantities of 4-hexenoic acid are also formed during this process. Decarboxylation of the product formed by the action of 1-bromo-2-butene upon ethyl sodio-malonate yields 4-hexenoic acid.[35, 40] The following physical constants have been reported for this acid: m.p. 0°, b_{760} 206.5°, b_{12} 102°, d_4^{20} 0.9658, n_D^{20} 1.4367. Its p-toluidide melts at 103°.[18]

3-Hexenoic Acid (Hydrosorbic Acid). $CH_3CH_2CH:CHCH_2CO_2H$

The reduction of sorbic acid, $CH_3CH:CHCH:CHCO_2H$, to hydrosorbic acid has been the subject of considerable study. Sorbic acid was first recognized by Hofmann,[41] who obtained it from the juice of the berries of the mountain ash. It has been synthesized by Doebner [42] by the action of 2-butenal and malonic acid. The presence of the conjugated unsaturated system in sorbic acid leads to the expectancy that its reduction product would consist essentially of 3-hexenoic acid. Earlier workers [43, 44, 45, 46] considered the reduction of sorbic acid to result exclusively in the formation of 3-hexenoic acid; however, the fact that a substantial amount of 4-hexenoic acid is also formed during this reduction has been subsequently established.[21, 47, 48] The relative proportion of the isomeric acids is somewhat dependent upon the reducing conditions, Evans and Farmer [47] having reported the formation of 35% of the 4-isomer by the reduction of sodium sorbate with aluminum amalgam, 40% with sodium amalgam in acetic acid, and 30% by the action of sodium amalgam upon sodium sorbate in the presence of carbon dioxide. Boxer and Linstead [27] have studied the preparation of 3-hexenoic acid by the condensation of butanal and malonic acid in the presence of various organic bases, and this condensation has been recently studied by Delaby and Lecomte.[49] The debromination of 3-bromocaproic acid results in a mixture of 3- and 2-hexenoic acids.[29] 3-Hexenoic acid is formed, together with 3-caprolactone, during the distillation of ethylparaconic acid.

The following physical constants have been reported for 3-hexenoic acid: m.p. 12°, b_{760} 208°, b_{12} 103°, d_4^{22} 0.9610, n_D^{20} 1.4255. Its p-toluidide melts at 95.5°.[18]

2-Hexenoic Acid. $CH_3CH_2CH_2CH:CHCO_2H$

This acid is formed, together with a smaller amount of its 3-isomer, by heating 3-hydroxycaproic acid with aqueous sodium hydroxide. The treatment of 2-bromocaproic acid with sodium hydroxide gives a mixture of 2- and 3-hexenoic acids with the former predominating.[29] The dehydrobromination of 2-bromocaproic acid has been suggested by Fichter and Pfister [18] as a means of obtaining pure 2-hexenoic acid. When 3-hexenoic acid is treated with strong alkalies the double bond shifts towards the carboxyl group with the formation of 2-hexenoic acid. The equilibrium conditions for this rearrangement have been extensively studied.[39, 50] Kon, Linstead, and Maclennan [51] have described the preparation of pure 2-hexenoic acid by the rearrangement of its 3-isomer and have developed a method for the separation of these two acids. 2-Hexenoic acid is formed by heating the condensation product of butanal and malonic acid,[26, 30] and Goldberg and Linstead [21] have also investigated the synthesis of this acid from butanal and malonic acid using pyridine containing 0.5% of piperidine as the condensing agent. An extensive investigation by Boxer and Linstead [27] of this condensation in the presence of various organic bases indicated that the formation of the 2-acid in the presence of pyridine and piperidine is an abnormal reaction, since in general such condensations result in the 3-isomer. This work somewhat refutes that of Zaar,[52] who stated that the strength of the base has a determining influence upon the configuration of the product. Isaacs and Wilson [53] have observed, however, that the above condensation reaction results mainly in 2-hexenoic acid together with smaller quantities of 3- and 4-hexenoic acids. Walbaum and Rosenthal [54] have reported 2-hexenoic acid to be present in Japanese peppermint oil.

2-Hexenoic acid melts at 32° and boils at 118° at 11 mm. The liquid acid has d_{40}^{40} 0.9627 and n_D^{40} 1.4601. The p-toluidide melts at 125°.[18]

HEPTENOIC ACIDS

Four of the possible heptenoic acids have been prepared and described. The 4-heptenoic acid has apparently not been synthesized although a number of its derivatives have been investigated. None of the heptenoic acids has been identified in the naturally occurring fats and oils.

6-Heptenoic Acid. $CH_2:CH(CH_2)_4CO_2H$

This acid has been prepared by Wallach [32] by the action of nitrous acid upon 7-aminoheptanoic acid. Gaubert, Linstead, and Rydon [55] have prepared 6-heptenoic acid by the malonic acid method. 6-Heptenoic acid has been shown by Fairweather [56] to be one of the products formed by the electrolysis of the half esters of suberic acid.

The physical constants of 6-heptenoic acid are: m.p. $-6.5°$, b_{760} 225–227°, b_{15} 125°, d_4^{17} 0.952, $d_4^{14.9}$ 0.9515, n_D^{17} 1.4425, $n_D^{14.9}$ 1.4404.[32, 55]

5-Heptenoic Acid. $CH_3CH\!:\!CH(CH_2)_3CO_2H$

Fichter and Gully [57] have prepared 5-heptenoic acid by the action of 4-chlorobutyric acid with the sodium or potassium derivative of acetoacetic ester.   Reduction of the resulting acetyladipic acid gives 2-(1-hydroxyethyl)adipic acid which yields 5-heptenoic acid upon distillation.   Ciamician and Silber [38] have prepared this acid from the corresponding aldehyde by conversion of the aldehyde to the hydroxamic acid, followed by treatment of the copper salt of this acid with sulfuric acid.   5-Heptenoic acid boils at 223° at 760 mm.

3-Heptenoic Acid. $CH_3CH_2CH_2CH\!:\!CHCH_2CO_2H$

3-Heptenoic acid has been prepared by Fittig and Schmidt [58] by the distillation of propylparaconic acid,

$$\overset{\displaystyle O\text{———}CO}{\underset{\displaystyle C_3H_7CHCH(CO_2H)CH_2}{\lfloor\qquad\qquad\rfloor}}$$

The acid has also been synthesized by Delaby and Lecomte [49] by the action of n-valeraldehyde and malonic acid.   The following boiling points have been reported for 3-heptenoic acid: b_{760} 226–228° and b_{10} 116.5–118°.

2-Heptenoic Acid. $CH_3(CH_2)_3CH\!:\!CHCO_2H$

2-Heptenoic acid has been prepared by Rupe, Ronus, and Lotz [29] by the action of quinoline upon 2-bromoheptenoic acid.   The acid was separated from the 3-isomer, which is also formed during the debromination, by the conversion of the latter into its lactone. Delaby and Guillot-Allègre [59] have described the preparation of 2-heptenoic acid by the oxidation of the corresponding aldehyde with silver oxide in alkaline solution.   The physical constants of 2-heptenoic acid are: $b_{11.5}$ 120–122°, b_{737} 225–228°, d_4^{20} 0.9576, and n_D^{20} 1.4488.

OCTENOIC ACIDS

Only two of the six possible octenoic acids have been described, although the remaining isomers appear in the literature either as substituted acids or acid derivatives.   The octenoic acids have not been found in the naturally occurring fatty substances.

7-Octenoic Acid. $CH_2:CH(CH_2)_5CO_2H$

The ethyl ester of this acid has been reported by Carmichael [60] to be formed during the electrolysis of potassium ethyl azelate. Ethyl 7-octenoate boils at 210°.

3-Octenoic Acid. $CH_3(CH_2)_3CH:CHCH_2CO_2H$

Delaby and Lecomte [49] have prepared 3-octenoic acid by the action of hexanal and malonic acid. The following physical constants were reported: b_{19} 140–142.5°, d_4^0 0.959, d_4^{20} 0.942, and n_D^{22} 1.4456.

2-Octenoic Acid. $CH_3(CH_2)_4CH:CHCO_2H$

This acid has been synthesized by Bachman [61] by the condensation of hexanal and malonic acid in the presence of pyridine. Bourguel [30] has reported that the hydrogenation of the corresponding acetylenic acid in the presence of platinum results in the formation of 2-octenoic acid.

The following physical constants have been reported for 2-octenoic acid: b_{15} 127°, b_{22} 154°, d_4^{20} 0.9807, and n_D^{20} 1.4587. The *p*-bromophenacyl ester melts at 92.5°. *Cis*-2-octenoic acid is transformed into its *trans* isomer by the action of iodine. The *trans* acid boils at 143° at 15 mm. and has d_4^{15} 0.945 and n_D^{20} 1.462.

NONENOIC ACIDS

Although the nonenoic acids have not been observed in the naturally occurring fats and oils, several of them have been synthesized and their properties described.

8-Nonenoic Acid. $CH_2:CH(CH_2)_6CO_2H$

This acid is known only as its ethyl ester. Brown and Walker [62] have reported that ethyl 8-nonenoate is one of the products formed during the electrolysis of monoethyl sebacate.

3-Nonenoic Acid. $CH_3(CH_2)_4CH:CHCH_2CO_2H$

The preparation of this acid by the condensation of heptanal and malonic acid in the presence of piperidine has been described by Zaar [52] and also by Delaby and Lecomte.[49] According to Zaar such condensations in the presence of ammonia or primary or secondary bases lead to the formation of 3-ethylenic acids, but condensations in the presence of tertiary bases result in 2-ethylenic acids. This is contrary to the opinion of Knoevenagel,[63] who considered the above reaction to result in the formation of the 2-acid if the condensation is conducted in piperidine.

The following physical constants have been reported for 3-nonenoic acid: b_2 114–115°, d_4^{20} 0.9290, d_4^{15} 0.9250, n_D^{20} 1.44842.

2-Nonenoic Acid. $CH_3(CH_2)_5CH:CHCO_2H$

This acid was first prepared by Fittig and Schneegans [64] by the Perkin reaction using heptanal, acetic anhydride, and sodium acetate. Its synthesis from heptanal and malonic acid in the presence of piperidine has been described,[65] although subsequent work has placed some doubt upon the identity of the acid obtained. The synthesis of 2-nonenoic acid by the action of heptanal and malonic acid in the presence of pyridine has been reported by Auwers,[26] Harding and Weizmann,[65] and also by Zaar.[52] In the opinion of Boxer and Linstead,[27] the effect of pyridine as a solvent in this condensation is unusual in its formation of 2-ethylenic acids, since its action is not common to the tertiary bases in general. 2-Nonenoic acid has been prepared by Delaby and Guillot-Allègre [59] by the oxidation of the corresponding 2-unsaturated aldehyde with silver oxide in alkaline solution. The following physical constants have been reported for 2-nonenoic acid: b_{13} 144°, b_2 130–132°, d_4^{15} 0.9316, d_4^{17} 0.9345, and n_D^{20} 1.45942. Bourguel [30] has reported the preparation of trans-2-nonenoic acid by treatment of the cis acid with iodine. The trans isomer boils at 154.5° at 15 mm. and has d_4^{15} 0.936 and n_D^{15} 1.4635.

DECENOIC ACIDS

Two of the decenoic acids have been reported to occur in the naturally occurring fats. These apparently represent the lowest molecular weight monoethylenic acids present in the natural fats, although lower acids have been reported in certain essential oils.

9-Decenoic Acid. $CH_2:CH(CH_2)_7CO_2H$

Smedley [66] was the first to observe the presence of a decenoic acid in butter fat, and ten years later Grün and Wirth [67] showed by the ozonization of its methyl ester that this acid is 9-decenoic acid. Its presence in milk fat was later confirmed by Bosworth and Brown,[68] in human milk fat by Bosworth,[69] and in goat milk fat by Riemenschneider and Ellis.[70] Toyama and Tsuchiya [71] have isolated an acid from sperm head oil which yielded formic and azelaic acids upon oxidation with potassium permanganate and is, apparently, 9-decenoic acid. These authors reported the following physical constants: b_{15} 143–148°, d_4^{15} 0.9238, n_D^{15} 1.4507, and n_D^{20} 1.4488. The presence of 9-decenoic acid in the natural fats is of interest because of its structural similarity to oleic acid.

4-Decenoic Acid (Obtusilic Acid). $CH_3(CH_2)_4CH:CH(CH_2)_2CO_2H$

Several investigators have reported the presence of this acid in the natural fats. Toyama [72] and Komori and Ueno [73] have claimed the isolation of 4-decenoic acid from the seed fat of *Lindera obtusiloba.* The last two reported the acid to yield capric acid upon hydrogenation and caproic and succinic acids when oxidized with potassium permanganate and suggested the name obtusilic acid. The following physical constants have been reported: b_{13} 148–150°, d_4^{15} 0.9222, d_4^{20} 0.9197, n_D^{15} 1.4519, and n_D^{20} 1.4497.

3-Decenoic Acid. $CH_3(CH_2)_5CH:CHCH_2CO_2H$

This acid has been prepared by Fittig and Schneegans [64] by the distillation of hexylparaconic acid. It melts at 10°.

2-Decenoic Acid. $CH_3(CH_2)_6CH:CHCO_2H$

Zaar [52] has described the preparation of 2-decenoic acid by the condensation of octanal and malonic acid in the presence of pyridine. The following constants were observed: $b_{4.5}$ 148–149°, d_4^{15} 0.9280, and n_D^{20} 1.4616.

UNDECENOIC ACIDS

The undecenoic acids have not been found in the naturally occurring fats and oils, and only a few members of this series have been synthesized. The terminally unsaturated member, 10-undecenoic acid, is of considerable interest since it is one of the products of the pyrolysis of ricinoleic acid, the principal acid of castor oil.

10-Undecenoic Acid. $CH_2:CH(CH_2)_8CO_2H$

10-Undecenoic acid results from the pyrolysis of ricinoleic acid and its derivatives by the following reaction:

$$CH_3(CH_2)_5CH(OH)CH_2CH:CH(CH_2)_7CO_2H \rightarrow$$

$$CH_3(CH_2)_5CHO + CH_2:CH(CH_2)_8CO_2H$$

The cleavage occurs between the eleventh and twelfth carbon atoms and is evidently accompanied by a migration of hydrogen from the hydroxyl group and by a shift in the position of the olefinic bond. The pyrolysis of castor oil was studied at an early date by Bussy and Lecanu,[74] who observed that it undergoes destructive distillation at 275–300° to give a liquid and a spongy residue. Some years later, Bussy[75] identified heptanal in the liquid product, and Krafft[76] distilled castor oil under a vacuum and identified not only heptanal but also an undecenoic acid in the distillation products. This undecenoic acid was shown by Becker[77] to yield nonanoic acid by fusion with potassium hydroxide and to give sebacic acid upon oxidation with fuming nitric acid, and the identity of this acid as 10-undecenoic acid was later confirmed by Perkin[78] and also by Brunner.[79] The insoluble residue resulting from the vacuum distillation of castor oil was investigated by Leeds[80] and also by Brunner,[79] and the latter reported that it yields 10-undecenoic acid upon treatment with alcoholic potassium hydroxide. The work of Goldsobel[81] established the structure of ricinoleic acid as 12-hydroxy-9-octadecenoic acid and suggested that the undecenoic acid resulting from its decomposition is 9-undecenoic acid and not the 10- acid. A study of the sulfochromic oxidation products of these acids led Simon[82] to a similar conclusion. Perkins and Cruz[83] have verified the formation of 10-undecenoic acid from the pyrolysis of ricinoleic acid and, more recently, Vernon and Ross[84] and also Barbot[85] have proposed a mechanism for this cleavage and suggest that it is accompanied by a molecular rearrangement which takes place under the influence of heat. 10-Undecenoic acid has been synthesized by Gaubert, Linstead, and Rydon[55] by the malonic acid method.

The physical constants which have been reported for 10-undecenoic acid are as follows: m.p. 22–23°,[55] 24.5°,[79] b_{760} 275°, b_{130} 230–235°, b_{100} 213.5°, b_{90} 198–200°, b_{15} 165°, b_{1} 131°, and d_{4}^{24} 0.9072.

9-Undecenoic Acid. $CH_3CH:CH(CH_2)_7CO_2H$

This acid has been prepared by Krafft and Seldis[86] by the reduction of 9-bromo-9-undecenoic acid by means of sodium and ethanol. The bromo acid was obtained by the action of hydrogen bromide upon 9-undecynoic acid, obtained from the 10-ethylenic acid. The debromination of 9-bromo-9-undecenoic acid by zinc and propionic acid has been shown by Harris and Smith[87] to yield 9-undecenoic acid. The acid melts at 11.4° and boils at 129–130° under 1 mm.

DODECENOIC ACIDS

Three of the dodecenoic acids have been shown to occur in the natural fats. The 4- acid occurs in small amounts in the oils of some tropical plants, where it is accompanied by its lower and higher homologs. Such oils generally contain lauric acid as the principal acid. The 5- isomer has been observed in certain marine oils, particularly the head and blubber oils of whales, and is also accompanied by its lower and higher homologs. The 9- acid has been reported to be present in certain milk fats. In addition to the naturally occurring dodecenoic acids, several others have been synthesized and their properties described.

11-Dodecenoic Acid. $CH_2:CH(CH_2)_9CO_2H$

This acid has been prepared by Tomecko and Adams [88] from 1-bromo-10-undecene by conversion to 11-dodecenenitrile, the hydrolysis of which yields 11-dodecenoic acid. The following physical constants were reported: b_3 143–144°, d_{20}^{20} 0.9030, and n_D^{20} 1.4510.

9-Dodecenoic Acid. $CH_3CH_2CH:CH(CH_2)_7CO_2H$

The presence of a dodecenoic acid in cochineal fat has been observed by Raimann.[89] Recently Kono and Maruyama [90] have obtained a dodecenoic acid from Japanese coccid wax and have suggested that this acid is 9-dodecenoic acid. The constitution of this acid has, however, not been definitely established. 9-Dodecenoic acid apparently occurs in the milk fats, in which it was first observed by Grün;[91] however, several later investigations have failed to establish its presence in this fat.[68, 70] Hilditch and collaborators,[92, 93] however, have definitely identified a dodecenoic acid in cow milk fat and have determined it to be 9-dodecenoic acid.

5-Dodecenoic Acid (Lauroleic Acid).
$CH_3(CH_2)_5CH:CH(CH_2)_3CO_2H$

Hilditch and Lovern [94] have isolated a dodecenoic acid from the head oil of the sperm whale and have stated that this acid appeared to differ from the dodecenoic acid found in the vegetable oils. The presence of a dodecenoic acid in herring oil had been previously indicated by Lexow,[95] and the structure of this acid has been determined to be 5-dodecenoic acid by Toyama and Tsuchiya,[96] who isolated it from both sperm blubber oil and sperm head oil.

The following physical constants were observed: d_4^{15} 0.9130 and n_D^{15} 1.4535.

4-Dodecenoic Acid (Linderic Acid).

$CH_3(CH_2)_6CH:CH(CH_2)_2CO_2H$

Several seed oils of tropical and subtropical plants have been shown to contain 4-dodecenoic acid, in which oils it is accompanied by both its lower and higher homologs 4-decenoic acid and 4-tetradecenoic acid. These seed oils generally contain lauric acid as the principal acid. A dodecenoic acid observed in Tsuzu and Kuromoji seed oils by Tsujimoto [97] was believed to be similar to an acid previously isolated from Tohaku oil by Iwamoto [98] and termed linderic acid. Later, Toyama [72] and Komori and Ueno [73] obtained linderic acid from the seed oil of Lindera obtusiloba and determined its structure to be 4-dodecenoic acid. Recently, Hata [99] has obtained linderic acid from several Formosan seed oils. Komori and Ueno have reported the physical properties of linderic acid to be b_{13} 170–172°, m.p. 1.0–1.3°, d_4^{15} 0.9106, d_4^{20} 0.9081, n_D^{15} 1.4545, and n_D^{20} 1.4529.

2-Dodecenoic Acid. $CH_3(CH_2)_8CH:CHCO_2H$

The synthesis of 2-dodecenoic acid has been reported by Zaar,[52] who prepared it by the action of decanal upon malonic acid in the presence of pyridine. The acid has b_2 164–165°, d_4^{20} 0.9130, and n_D^{20} 1.46390.

TRIDECENOIC ACIDS

Only a limited amount of information is available upon the tridecenoic acids. They are not found in the naturally occurring fats and oils and, apparently, only two representatives of this series have been synthesized.

12-Tridecenoic Acid. $CH_2:CH(CH_2)_{10}CO_2H$

This acid has been prepared by the action of 1-bromo-10-undecene and diethyl malonate in the presence of sodium.[100] Tomecko and Adams [88] have synthesized the acid by a similar procedure. The acid melts at 38–38.2° and has b_{25} 192°, b_{15} 185°, and b_3 162°.

2-Tridecenoic Acid. $CH_3(CH_2)_9CH:CHCO_2H$

Zaar [52] has described the preparation of 2-tridecenoic acid by the action of undecanal upon malonic acid in the presence of pyridine. The following physical constants were observed: b_2 169–171°, d_4^{30} 0.8995, and n_D^{20} 1.46121.

TETRADECENOIC ACIDS

Although the tetradecenoic acids are not found in large amounts in the naturally occurring fatty substances, they appear to be rather widely distributed, and at least three of them have been identified in the natural fats. 9-Tetradecenoic acid is present in small amounts in various animal depot fats and in milk fats; 5-tetradecenoic acid is found in certain marine oils, and 4-tetra-decenoic acid in the oils from several tropical and semi-tropical plants. It is interesting to note that two of these acids contain structural groups similar to those present in oleic acid.

9-Tetradecenoic Acid (Myristoleic Acid).

$$CH_3(CH_2)_3CH:CH(CH_2)_7CO_2H$$

9-Tetradecenoic acid has been observed in animal milk fats, depot fats, and in some marine oils. Since it is present only in small amounts, its identity, for some time, was a subject of con-siderable controversy. This acid is frequently referred to as myristoleic acid, although this name is not uniformly employed. In 1925, Armstrong and Hilditch [101] stated that the myristoleic acid which occurs in whale oil to the extent of 1.4% was mainly 9-tetradecenoic acid together with another tetradecenoic acid which contained a double bond nearer the carboxyl group. Two years later, Wagner [102] obtained a similar acid, and the next year Hilditch and Lovern [94] confirmed the presence of 9-tetradecenoic acid in whale blubber oil. The acid has also been observed in shark liver oil,[103, 104] Antarctic whale oil,[105] eel oil,[106] and in turtle oil.[107] Grün [91] first suggested the presence of a tetradecenoic acid in milk fats, and this was later confirmed by Bosworth and Brown [68] and also by Riemenschneider and Ellis.[70] Subsequent work has shown this tetradecenoic acid to be 9-tetradecenoic acid.[92, 93, 108] This acid has also been reported in human milk fat [69] and in a number of the animal depot fats.[109] A tetradecenoic acid, believed to be 9-tetradecenoic acid, has been recently isolated from Japanese coccid wax.[90] 9-Tetradecenoic acid is a liquid with d_4^{20} 0.9018 and n_D^{20} 1.4549.

5-Tetradecenoic Acid. $CH_3(CH_2)_7CH:CH(CH_2)_3CO_2H$

In 1923, Tsujimoto [110] obtained from sperm and dolphin oils a tetradecenoic acid which yielded myristic acid upon hydrogenation and gave pelargonic and glutaric acids upon oxidation. The suggestion was made that this acid was 5-tetradecenoic acid and two years later its identity was confirmed by the same investigator.[111] Later work [92] has served to distinguish this acid from the myristoleic acid isolated by Armstrong and Hilditch.[101] 5-Tetradecenoic acid has been reported to be present in the whale head and blubber oils [112, 113] and it has also been isolated from sardine oil, pilot whale oil, and from sperm blubber oil.[91, 114]

The following physical constants have been observed for 5-tetradecenoic acid: d_4^{15} 0.9081, d_4^{20} 0.9046, n_D^{15} 1.4571, and $n_{D,}^{20}$ 1.4552.

4-Tetradecenoic Acid (Tsuzuic Acid).

$$CH_3(CH_2)_8CH:CH(CH_2)_2CO_2H$$

Tsujimoto [97] has obtained a tetradecenoic acid from the seeds of *Tetradenia glauca* and *L. hypglauca* which differed from the tetradecenoic acid previously isolated from dolphin oil. Sometime later he identified this acid as 4-tetradecenoic acid,[115] and proposed the name tsuzuic acid. A similar acid has been subsequently isolated [72, 73] from the seed oil of *Lindera obtusiloba* and identified as the 4- acid. 4-Tetradecenoic acid is, therefore, evidently a common component of many tropical plant oils and is generally found, together with its lower and higher homologs, in those oils which contain lauric acid as the principal component acid.

The following physical constants have been reported for 4-tetradecenoic acid: m.p. 18.0–18.5°, b_{13} 185–188°, d_4^{15} 0.9055, d_4^{20} 0.9024, n_D^{15} 1.4575, and n_D^{20} 1.4557. The p-phenylphenacyl ester melts at 61.3°.[74]

PENTADECENOIC ACIDS

Only two pentadecenoic acids have been synthesized, and since the pentadecenoic acids do not occur in the naturally occurring fats and oils our knowledge of this group is limited to these two individuals.

14-Pentadecenoic Acid. $CH_2:CH(CH_2)_{12}CO_2H$

This terminally unsaturated acid has been prepared by the malonic acid method from 1-bromo-12-tridecene and diethyl malonate in the presence of sodium ethylate.[100] The boiling point reported was 195° at 8 mm.

2-Pentadecenoic Acid. $CH_3(CH_2)_{11}CH:CHCO_2H$

This acid has been prepared from myristic acid by Lauer, Gensler, and Miller [116] by conversion of the myristic acid to the corresponding α-hydroxy acid and thence, by the action of lead tetraacetate, to tridecanal. The condensation of this aldehyde with malonic acid in the presence of pyridine yields 2-pentadecenoic acid. This method is similar to that employed by Zaar [52] for the syntheses of several of the lower homologs of 2-pentadecenoic acid. The p-bromoanilide melts at 114–114.5° and the amide at 111.5–112.5°.

HEXADECENOIC ACIDS

Several of the possible hexadecenoic acids have been described. One of these acids, 9-hexadecenoic acid, is found widely distributed in the natural fatty substances. Although it does not occur in large amounts in any particular oil, it is one of the most important of the naturally occurring monoethylenic acids. 9-Hexadecenoic acid is the lowest molecular weight monoethylenic acid which occurs in appreciable amounts in animal, vegetable, and marine oils.

9-Hexadecenoic Acid (Palmitoleic Acid).
   $CH_3(CH_2)_5CH:CH(CH_2)_7CO_2H$

9-Hexadecenoic acid occurs as a minor component in both the animal and vegetable fats and oils and as a major component in many of the marine oils. It appears to occur in the greatest amounts in those fats which are representative of the lower forms of animal and vegetable life, since fats derived from the higher forms contain lesser amounts of palmitoleic acid, although it is generally present in these substances as a minor component. The structural relationship of this acid to oleic acid is noteworthy. The first reported instance of the isolation of a hexadecenoic acid from natural sources was announced by Hofstädter [117] in 1854, who obtained an acid corresponding to this composition from the head oil of the sperm whale. The acid was named physetoleic acid, which name was retained for a considerable period of time. In 1855, Gössmann and Scheven [118] announced the presence of a hexadecenoic acid in peanut oil, an observation which was confirmed the next year by Caldwell and Gössmann [119] and later by Schröder.[120] The acid from peanut oil was termed hypogaeic acid and its melting point was reported to be 34–35°. At this period, therefore, two naturally occurring hexadecenoic acids had been described, which were considered to be separate individuals. Physetoleic acid has been obtained by Ljubarsky [121] and by Bauer and Neth [122] from seal oil, and in 1906 Bull [123] isolated a hexadecenoic acid which melted at −1° from cod liver oil. This latter acid was considered to differ from the two previously described hexadecenoic acids. This acid was frequently referred to as "Bull's C_{16} Acid"; however, shortly after its isolation, Lewkowitsch [124] suggested the name palmitoleic acid. Ten years later Bonnevie-Svendsen [125] stated that this acid is also obtainable from herring oil.

At least three hexadecenoic acids have been stated to occur in the natural oils, which raises the question as to whether they are structurally identical or are different acids. This question was soon answered by proving that hypogaeic acid does not occur in peanut oil and that the hexadecenoic acids of marine origin are identical. The existence of hypogaeic acid in peanut oil was severely questioned by a number of investigators.[126, 127, 128, 129, 130] In 1919, Heiduschka and Felser [131] expressed the view that it is present in peanut oil in appreciable amounts; however, the later work of Jamieson, Baughman, and Brauns,[132] followed by the extensive investigation of Hilditch and Vidyarthi,[133] has shown hypogaeic acid to be non-existent. In 1924, Toyama [134] obtained a hexadecenoic acid, which he termed zoömaric acid, from whale oil, which acid he considered to be identical with "Bull's C_{16} Acid." This acid was later identified in herring oil,[135] shark and ray liver oils, and in other marine oils.[103, 136, 137] Armstrong and Hilditch [101] later isolated a hexadecenoic acid from South Georgian whale oil and established its structure as 9-hexadecenoic acid, and two years later Toyama [138] announced a similar structure for zoömaric acid. The work of these several investigators did much to remove the confusion which existed relative to the hexadecenoic acids, since it conclusively showed that acids such as physetoleic acid, "Bull's C_{16} Acid," and zoömaric acid are identical with palmitoleic acid, which is 9-hexadecenoic acid. The names palmitoleic acid and zoömaric acid are still frequently employed although their use is confusing.

9-Hexadecenoic acid has been shown to occur as a major component in many of the marine oils. Hilditch and Lovern [94] observed its presence in substantial amounts in sperm-whale blubber oil. Antarctic whale oil was reported [105] to contain 17% of 9-

hexadecenoic acid, a value which is in agreement with one previously recorded.[139] It has been observed to be present in turtle oil [107] to the extent of 10.9%. The acid isolated from the marine oils has been shown, in all cases, to be 9-hexadecenoic acid. Until comparatively recently it was considered that 9-hexadecenoic acid was confined to the marine oils or to oils of aquatic plants and animals. In 1928 Kawai [140] observed the presence of a hexadecenoic acid in tung oil and in linseed oil. Ten years later, Hilditch and Jasperson [141] stated that 9-hexadecenoic acid is apparently a common component of most vegetable fats and oils. The amount of 9-hexadecenoic acid present in the vegetable oils generally does not exceed 1%. Among the many oils which have been reported to contain 9-hexadecenoic acid may be mentioned: olive oil, tea seed oil,[142] peanut oil,[143] cottonseed oil,[141] and palm oil.[142] Many of the animal depot fats have been reported to contain 9-hexadecenoic acid.[10,144] For example, small amounts of this acid have been observed in the depot fats of oxen, sheep, and pigs.[109,145] Hilditch and coworkers [146,147,148,149] have reported the presence of 9-hexadecenoic acid in the fats of various fowls, reptiles, and rodents. 9-Hexadecenoic acid has been observed to occur in milk fats.[98,99,150] Bosworth and Brown [68] have reported its presence in the fatty acids of butter fat. It has also been observed in egg yolk oil.[151] The vegetable phosphatides contain from 5 to 10% of 9-hexadecenoic acid,[152] and it is also found in the liver phosphatides.[153] Chargaff [154] has reported it to be present in the fat and phosphatide fractions of diphtheria bacteria. A hexadecenoic acid has been obtained from lycopodium oil by Rathje,[155] and it appears that this acid is one of the components of the lycopodiumoleic acid previously reported as present in this oil.[156] An exhaustive investigation of this oil by Riebsomer and Johnson [157] showed that the unsaturated portion of the oil of lycopodium spores contains 35% of 9-hexadecenoic acid.

It is apparent that 9-hexadecenoic acid is widely distributed in animal, vegetable, and marine oils. It forms a major component in various marine animal oils and also in oils from other forms of aquatic life. Fats of sea algae, for example, contain as much as 20% of this acid [158] while certain marine oils contain even larger amounts. The fats of fresh water fish contain somewhat less 9-hexadecenoic acid than those of marine origin, and the fats of amphibious animals, such as frogs, are intermediate between land and marine animals. The higher animal depot fats contain much smaller amounts of this acid, and it is unusual for a vegetable oil to possess over 1%. These observations have been summarized by Hilditch,[159] who has commented upon the progressive decrease in the amount of 9-hexadecenoic acid present in a fat and the position of its source in the evolutionary scale of development.

7-Hexadecenoic Acid. $CH_3(CH_2)_7CH:CH(CH_2)_5CO_2H$

A hexadecenoic acid which melts at 21° has been obtained by Marasse [160] by the action of fused potassium hydroxide upon stearolic acid. This work was later repeated by Bodenstein,[129] who found the acid to be 7-hexadecenoic acid.

2-Hexadecenoic Acid. $CH_3(CH_2)_{12}CH:CHCO_2H$

Ponzio [161] has prepared 2-hexadecenoic acid by the action of alcoholic potassium hydroxide upon 2-iodopalmitic acid. The acid melted at 45°.

Heptadecenoic Acids

Only one of the heptadecenoic acids has been synthesized, and our knowledge of this series of acids is, therefore, limited to this one member. The saturated counterpart of the heptadecenoic acids, margaric acid, was frequently reported to be present in the natural fats; however, no such claims have been made for the heptadecenoic acids.

2-Heptadecenoic Acid. $CH_3(CH_2)_{13}CH:CHCO_2H$

This acid has been prepared by Lauer, Gensler, and Miller [116] by the malonic acid synthesis employing pentadecanal and malonic acid in the presence of pyridine. The reported melting point of the acid is 57.5° and of its *p*-bromoanilide, 115–116°.

Octadecenoic Acids

The monoölefinic fatty acids containing eighteen carbon atoms constitute the most important group of the mono-unsaturated fatty acids. Interest in them is largely due to the presence in this series of oleic acid, 9-octadecenoic acid. This acid occurs more abundantly in nature than any other fatty acid and is so widely spread among fatty substances that it can be said to be of almost universal occurrence. Much of our very early knowledge concerning the fatty acids is associated with oleic acid, and work upon it has resulted in many of our present-day views regarding *cis-trans* isomerism, position isomerism, hydroxylation, oxidative cleavage, hydrogenation, and other characteristic behaviors. The structural resemblance of many of the more important fatty acids to oleic acid exemplifies its key position among the unsaturated acids. Because of the prominence of oleic acid the members of this group are frequently referred to as "the oleic acids." The name oleic acid designates the *cis* acid which contains a double bond between the ninth and tenth carbon atoms, and the name isoöleic applies to an acid with its double bond in any other position. The *trans* isomeride of oleic acid is termed elaidic acid, and the name isoelaidic acid is likewise frequently employed to designate the *trans* form of any other member of this group.

Thirty-one octadecenoic acids are theoretically possible, sixteen of which possess a *cis* and fifteen a *trans* structure. Oleic acid and petroselinic acid, 6-octadecenoic acid, are naturally occurring, and both of these acids possess a *cis* configuration. Many of the other octadecenoic acids have been prepared synthetically; however, several of the members of this group have not, as yet, been described. As a consequence, broad generalizations with reference to the effect of the position of the double bond upon the physical properties of the octadecenoic acids are rather hazardous. The configurations of many of the acids which have been obtained by synthetic methods have not been rigidly proved, so that some question exists as to whether the reported properties relate to the *cis* or the *trans* form or to a mixture of the two. This fact, combined with the absence of many of the members of this group, renders our knowledge of the series as a whole somewhat incomplete. Fokin [162] has stated that if the double bond is between an even and an odd carbon atom (beginning with the carbon atom of the carboxyl group) the acid is a solid, whereas if it is between an odd and an even carbon atom the acid is a liquid. This statement refers only to the *cis* forms, and considerable work would have to be done before it is proved or disproved. In line with the observations upon the geometrical isomers of other types of compounds, the *trans* forms of these acids possess higher melting points than the corresponding *cis* forms. Since the question of isomerism constitutes a separate chapter it will not be extensively discussed at this time.

2-Octadecenoic Acid. $CH_3(CH_2)_{14}CH:CHCO_2H$

Pure 2-octadecenoic acid was first prepared by Ponzio [163] by the action of alcoholic potassium hydroxide upon 2-iodostearic acid.

The latter compound was prepared from 2-bromostearic acid, which was obtained by the action of bromine and phosphorus upon stearic acid. Le Sueur [164] prepared 2-octadecenoic acid by the action of alcoholic potassium hydroxide upon 2-bromostearic acid and proved its structure by oxidation to palmitic acid. The decomposition of 2-hydroxystearic acid has been claimed by Saytzeff [165] to yield the 2-unsaturated acid. The fusion of oleic acid with molten potassium hydroxide results in a mixture of solid acids which Saytzeff considered to be essentially 2-octadecenoic acid. This observation led to the erroneous supposition that ordinary oleic acid is 3-octadecenoic acid. The structure of 2-octadecenoic acid has been extensively studied by Semeria,[166] who observed that it formed solid solutions with stearic acid. Since only the *trans* configuration of ethylenic acids gives solid solutions with saturated acids, he concluded that the synthetic acid is the *trans* form. This explains the high melting points reported, 59° by Ponzio and 58–59° by Le Sueur, and also the latter's observation that no isomerization was observed when the synthetic acid was treated with nitrous acid. 2-Octadecenoic acid has been frequently reported to be contained in the so-called isoöleic acids formed during the hydrogenation of unsaturated fats. Its presence is attributed either to the migration of the double bond or to the dehydrogenation of stearic acid under the influence of the various catalytic materials employed. It is frequently referred to as 2-oleic acid, although this name is particularly confusing especially in the light of the possible *trans* structure of the acids so far described. 2-Octadecenoic acid has not been reported in the naturally occurring fats.

3-Octadecenoic Acid. $CH_3(CH_2)_{13}CH:CHCH_2CO_2H$

3-Octadecenoic acid has been prepared by Eckert and Halla [167] by the action of alcoholic potassium hydroxide upon 3-iodostearic acid. The melting point was reported to be 56–57°. Saytzeff [165] considered oleic acid to be 3-octadecenoic acid; however, this supposition has since been shown to be erroneous. 3-Octadecenoic acid has not been found in the natural fats and oils.

4-Octadecenoic Acid. $CH_3(CH_2)_{12}CH:CH(CH_2)_2CO_2H$

Eckert and Halla [167] have reported the formation of this acid as a secondary product during the action of alcoholic potassium hydroxide upon 3-iodostearic acid. The position of the double bond was established by its oxidation to myristic acid. It melts at 52.5°, and has not been observed in the naturally occurring fats and oils.

5-Octadecenoic Acid. $CH_3(CH_2)_{11}CH:CH(CH_2)_3CO_2H$

The addition of hydrogen iodide to 5-stearolic acid followed by reduction of the product with zinc and acetic acid has been reported by Posternak [168] to yield the *trans* form of 5-octadecenoic acid, melting at 47.5°. Egorov [169] has claimed the preparation of 5-octadecenoic acid by fusing oleic acid with potassium hydroxide. The product melted at 42–43° and may be the *cis* form of this acid. 5-Octadecenoic acid is not present in the naturally occurring fats and oils.

6-Octadecenoic Acid (Petroselinic Acid).
   $CH_3(CH_2)_{10}CH:CH(CH_2)_4CO_2H$

6-Octadecenoic acid was first described by Vongerichten and Köhler,[170] who isolated this acid from parsley seed oil and named it petroselinic acid. These authors determined the position of the double bond by the isolation of lauric acid from its oxidation products. The following physical constants were reported: m.p. 33–34°, d_4^{40} 0.8681, and n_D^{40} 1.4533. The naturally occurring acid possesses a *cis* configuration since Vongerichten and Köhler observed that it yielded an acid melting at 54° when treated with nitrous acid. The resulting acid is the *trans* form of 6-octadecenoic acid. Several years later, Palazzo and Tamburello [171] obtained an acid identical with petroselinic acid from ivy seed oil. A careful analysis of parsley seed oil by Hilditch and Jones [172] showed that the acids contain 76% of petroselinic acid and established the structure of the acid as 6-octadecenoic acid. The acid so obtained melted at 30°, a value which was confirmed by van Loon.[173] Hilditch and others [174, 175] later reported petroselinic acid to be present in a number of umbellate fats. The constitution of petroselinic acid has been confirmed by several investigators.[172, 173, 176] An acid has been obtained from coriander seed oil in 36.1% yield,[177] and this acid has been shown to be identical with that obtained from parsley seed oil.[178] The following physical constants were reported for 6-octadecenoic acid: m.p. 32–33°, d_4^{35} 0.8824, d_4^{40} 0.8794, and n_D^{47} 1.4535. In 1912, Matthes and Boltze [179] isolated an acid, which they named cheiranthic acid, from wallflower seed oil. This acid was thought to be identical with petroselinic acid; however, subsequent work has indicated it to be a mixture rather than a chemical individual. Hartley [180] has described an acid, considered to be 6-octadecenoic acid, which he isolated from the fatty acids of liver lecithin. The structure of this acid is still in question.

7-Octadecenoic Acid. $CH_3(CH_2)_9CH\!:\!CH(CH_2)_5CO_2H$

Posternak [168] has claimed the formation of 7-octadecenoic acid by the addition of hydrogen iodide to 7-stearolic acid followed by reduction of the product with zinc and acetic acid. The resulting acid melted at 45.5° and was assumed to be trans-7-octadecenoic acid. An acid considered to be 7-octadecenoic acid has also been obtained [177] by the migration of the double bond of 6-octadecenoic acid when treated with nickel carbonate. The following physical constants were reported: m.p. 51–52°, d_4^{50} 0.873, and $n_D^{50.1}$ 1.4450. The removal of hydrogen bromide from 7-bromostearic acid by means of alcoholic potassium hydroxide has recently been shown by Pigulevskiĭ and Simonova [181] to result in a 13% yield of 7-octadecenoic acid melting at 52°. The acid has not been reported in the naturally occurring fats and oils.

8-Octadecenoic Acid. $CH_3(CH_2)_8CH\!:\!CH(CH_2)_6CO_2H$

Arnaud and Posternak [182] have reported the isolation of 8-octadecenoic acid from the product obtained by the action of alcoholic potassium hydroxide upon 9-iodostearic acid. These authors [183] have also studied the products of the dehydration of 10-hydroxystearic acid and have reported the presence of substantial amounts of 8-octadecenoic acid. Both the cis and trans forms of 8-octadecenoic acid are formed by dehydration or by dehydrohalogenation of 10-hydroxy- or 10-halostearic acid. These latter compounds are readily formed from oleic acid by hydration or hydrohalogenation of its ethylenic bond. Actually, however, such reactions generally yield a mixture of isomeric acids. Recent studies [184,185] of the action of sulfuric acid upon oleic acid followed by hydrolysis of the addition product show that both 9- and 10-hydroxystearic acids are present, the dehydration of which will result in a mixture of isomeric acids.

The migration of the double bond of oleic acid in the presence of catalysts at elevated temperatures has been the subject of appreciable study for a number of years. The formation of palmitic acid by the fusion of oleic acid with potassium hydroxide, which was observed as early as 1840 by Varrentrapp,[186] can best be explained by a shift in the position of the double bond under these conditions. It is, therefore, believed that the treatment of fatty acids with strong alkalies brings about a migration of the ethylenic bonds toward the carboxyl group. The advent of catalytic hydrogenation resulted in an increased interest in the study of ethylenic bond migration in an attempt to explain the formation of the so-called isoöleic acids during such processes. The formation of these isoöleic acids may be accounted for by several processes, such as dehydrogenation, selective hydrogenation, and ethylenic bond migration. All these processes may take place simultaneously, especially at high temperatures. Migration of the double bond in oleic acid in the presence of various metallic catalysts will result in the formation of appreciable amounts of both 8- and 10-octadecenoic acids. This subject is treated in detail in a later chapter; however, it is of interest at this time to call attention to some of the more recent work in this field. Moore,[187] Hilditch and Vidyarthi,[188] Steger and Scheffers,[189] and many others have shown that the 9-bond of oleic acid and also of elaidic acid shifts in both directions during catalytic hydrogenation, and it is well known that the partial hydrogenation of unsaturated fatty oils leads to the formation of isomeric oleic acids. Bauer and Krallis [190] have shown that heat alone in the presence of various metallic catalysts brings about a migration of the ethylenic bond in oleic acid, the main products being the *cis* and *trans* forms of 8- and 10-octadecenoic acids, the latter apparently predominating.

9-Octadecenoic Acids (*Oleic Acid, Elaidic Acid*).

$$CH_3(CH_2)_7CH:CH(CH_2)_7CO_2H$$

Oleic acid is found more abundantly in nature than any other fatty acid. It constitutes a major component in many of the fats and oils and is present in essentially all fatty substances. Its *trans* isomer, elaidic acid, has been known for many years. The isomerization of oleic acid to elaidic acid is of interest not only because of the importance of the compounds involved, but also because many of our present views concerning geometrical isomerism were developed from a study of this equilibrium.

Oleic Acid

Oleic acid was first described by Chevreul in 1815, who isolated it in an impure form during his investigations of the constitution of fatty substances. The position of the double bond in oleic acid was not definitely proved until many years after its discovery. Varrentrapp [186] reported in 1840 that the fusion of oleic acid with potassium hydroxide yields palmitic acid and considered that the ethylenic bond is between the second and third carbon atoms. It was reported at an early date by several investigators [191,192,193] that the oxidation of oleic acid with nitric acid yields a mixture of saturated acids. Saytzeff [194] observed that the oxidation of oleic acid with potassium permanganate produces a dihydroxystearic acid and that the use of an excess of permanganate yields azelaic acid together with other products. The presence of azelaic acid in the oxidation products was confirmed by Spiridonoff.[195] The first rigid proof of the position of the double bond in oleic acid was developed by Baruch [196] during the course of his investigations of the constitution of stearolic acid. Oleic acid was brominated to give dibromostearic acid, which was treated with alcoholic potassium hydroxide to give the acetylenic acid, stearolic acid. When this was treated with concentrated sulfuric acid it yielded a ketostearic acid which forms a ketoxime capable of existing as two stereoisomers. The rearrangement and decomposition of these ketoxime stearic acids by treatment with fuming hydrochloric acid at 180–200° proceeds as follows:

(I) $CH_3(CH_2)_7C(NOH)(CH_2)_8CO_2H \rightarrow CH_3(CH_2)_7CONH(CH_2)_8CO_2H$

$+ CH_3(CH_2)_7NHCO(CH_2)_8CO_2H$

(II) $CH_3(CH_2)_7CONH(CH_2)_8CO_2H \xrightarrow{H_2O} CH_3(CH_2)_7CO_2H + H_2N(CH_2)_8CO_2H$

Nonanoic acid   9-Aminononanoic acid

(III) $CH_3(CH_2)_7NHCO(CH_2)_8CO_2H \xrightarrow{H_2O}$

$CH_3(CH_2)_7NH_2 + HO_2C(CH_2)_8CO_2H$

Octylamine   Sebacic acid

Isolation of the above products showed that the acetylenic bond in stearolic acid is between the ninth and tenth carbon atoms and consequently that the starting acid, oleic acid, is 9-octadecenoic acid. Baruch assigned a *trans* structure to oleic acid and a *cis* structure to elaidic acid. Several years later, Edmed [197] obtained both azelaic acid and pelargonic acid by the oxidation of oleic acid with either potassium permanganate or chromic acid. The action of ozone upon oleic acid was investigated simultaneously by Molinari and collaborators [198] and by Harries and associates.[199] These essentially concurrent investigations resulted in a bitter controversy regarding the reaction mechanism. The production of azelaic and nonanoic acids together with nonanal and azelaic acid semi-aldehyde, the relative amounts of which are dependent upon the conditions employed for the decomposition of the ozonides, served to confirm the structure of oleic acid as 9-octadecenoic acid. The fact that the double bond in oleic acid is between the ninth and tenth carbon atoms has since been proved by several investigators, among whom may be mentioned Armstrong and Hilditch,[200] who obtained high yields of both azelaic and nonanoic acids by the oxidation of alkyl oleates with potassium permanganate in acetone solution.

All methods which depend upon cleavage of an ethylenic bond for establishing its position in an alkyl chain must assume that there has been no migration of the unsaturated bond either preceding or during the cleavage reactions. Since synthetic reactions are generally free from such objections, the structure of oleic acid was not absolutely proved until its synthesis had been successfully accomplished. This was completed in 1934 by Noller and Bannerot,[201] who employed the following series of reactions. 9-Chlorononanal was first treated with bromine in carbon tetrachloride and with hydrogen bromide in methanol to give 8,9-dibromo-9-methoxynonyl chloride, $Cl(CH_2)_7CHBrCHBr(OCH_3)$. The reaction of this compound with octylmagnesium bromide, followed by hydrolysis of the resulting product, yielded 8-bromo-9-methoxyheptadecyl chloride, $Cl(CH_2)_7CHBrCH(OCH_3)(CH_2)_7$-$CH_3$. The reduction of this compound by zinc and 1-butanol gave 8-heptadecenyl chloride, which upon treatment with potassium cyanide and subsequent hydrolysis of the nitrile yielded a mixture of cis- and trans-9-octadecenoic acids. The mixture contained 37% of the cis form and 63% of the trans form, and these compounds possessed the known properties of oleic and elaidic acids respectively. Although the work of Noller and Bannerot was the first complete synthesis of oleic and elaidic acids, the previous work of Robinson and Robinson [202] can be stated to have indirectly proved the structure of this acid by synthetic means. These authors prepared 10-ketostearic acid by treating ethyl 2-sodio-2-acetylnonanoate with 9-carbethoxynonanoyl chloride, the product of which condensation yielded 10-ketostearic acid upon decomposition and subsequent hydrolysis. The reactions are as follows:

$$CH_3(CH_2)_6CNa(COCH_3)(CO_2C_2H_5) + ClCO(CH_2)_8CO_2C_2H_5 \rightarrow$$

$$CH_3(CH_2)_6\underset{\underset{\displaystyle CO(CH_2)_8CO_2C_2H_5}{|}}{C}(COCH_3)(CO_2C_2H_5) \rightarrow CH_3(CH_2)_7CO(CH_2)_8CO_2H$$

The conversion of the 10-ketostearic acid to stearolic acid was not successfully accomplished. It is known, however, that 10-keto-stearic acid is produced from stearolic acid by the action of sulfuric acid and also that stearolic acid can be reduced to oleic acid. In view of the previous work of Baruch [196] upon the structure of stearolic acid, it can be considered that this synthesis by Robinson and Robinson constituted an indirect proof of the structure of oleic acid. The formation of methyl oleate by the vapor-phase dehydrogenation of methyl stearate in the presence of nickel and ethylene at 190–200° has recently been reported by Margaillan and Angeli.[203]

Oleic acid occurs in substantial amounts in all the animal, vegetable, and marine fats and oils. It constitutes the principal fatty acid in the animal depot fats, the amount present being dependent upon the species of animal, its diet, and its environment. For example, ox depot fats [109] have been found to contain about 40% of oleic acid, hog depot fats [8, 204] from 40 to more than 50%, and horse depot fats [205, 206] approximately 50%. All the vegetable fats contain oleic acid, in a number of which it occurs in quite high percentages. It is present in olive oil [142, 207, 208, 209, 210] to the extent of approximately 70 to 85%, in almond oil [211] to more than 75%, and in cashew kernel oil [212] in a slightly lower amount. Oils such as olive oil and almond oil are frequently used as a source of oleic acid. Other common oils of vegetable origin which contain substantial amounts of oleic acid are: palm oil,[213] 40–42%; pumpkin seed oil,[214] 25%; cottonseed oil,[215] 35%; peanut oil,[132] 53–61%; cantaloupe seed oil,[216] 27%; corn oil,[217] 45%; squash seed oil,[218] 37%; soybean oil,[219] 33%; sunflower seed oil,[220] 33%; and tobacco seed oil,[221] 26%. It is present in much smaller amounts in palm kernel oil,[222] coconut oil,[223, 224] and many other oils. The marine oils, particularly the marine animal oils such as whale oil,[225] contain appreciable amounts of oleic acid. From the above examples it is apparent that oleic acid is found quite abundantly in fatty substances, and that its distribution is in no wise confined to one type of fat.

Pure oleic acid is extremely difficult to prepare from the naturally occurring oils; however, it has been separated in a reasonably pure state from several of the oils in which it is present in large amounts. The separation of oleic acid from other acids is discussed later, and only several of the general methods for its preparation from the natural oils will be mentioned at this time. Oils such as olive oil or almond oil, which are quite high in oleic acid, are customarily employed for its laboratory preparation. They contain, in addition to oleic acid, significant amounts of saturated acids and of acids more unsaturated than oleic acid. The problem, therefore, is to separate oleic acid from both the saturated and the more highly unsaturated acids. Saturated acids, esters, and salts possess higher melting points, lower solubilities in organic solvents, higher boiling points, and more pronounced crystalline properties than unsaturated acids and their derivatives of comparable chain length. Advantage is, therefore, taken of one or more of these differences in characteristics in order to effect a separation. The separation of solid from liquid fatty acids was first accomplished by extracting their lead soaps with ether.[186, 226] Twitchell [227] later modified this method by crystallizing the lead salts from 95% ethanol. This procedure effects a rough separation of oleic acid from the saturated acids and can be employed as a preliminary step. In 1925, Lapworth, Pearson, and Mottram [228] described a method for the preparation of pure oleic acid which included the separation of the acids as lead salts, fractional distillation followed by repeated crystallization of the barium salts, and finally another fractional distillation. Scheffers [229] has claimed the preparation of pure oleic acid from olive oil by a preliminary crystallization of the acids as lead salts followed by repeated fractional crystallizations of the lithium salts from 50% ethanol. The preparation of oleic acid, completely free from linoleic acid and containing only a fraction of 1% of saturated fatty acids, was reported by Bertram.[230] The method depends upon the formation of a complex between the oleic acid and mercuric acetate, followed by a crystallization of the oleic acid from acetone solution. A modification of Bertram's method was later proposed by Raymond.[231] A method involving the fractional crystallization of the lead salts, barium salts, and finally the lithium salts has been investigated by Skellon,[232] and Keffler and McLean [233] have proposed the crystallization of the lead and lithium salts followed by fractional distillation. Hartsuch [234] has reported the preparation of a sample containing 97.8% oleic acid by several crystallizations of olive oil fatty acids from acetone at low temperatures, followed by the removal of the saturated acids as lead soaps, in ethanol, and a final fractional distillation. The method recently described by Brown and Shinowara [235] is one of the most satisfactory yet proposed for the preparation of oleic acid. This method involves the separation of oleic acid from saturated acids and linoleic acid by a series of crystallizations of the acid mixture from acetone at low temperatures. The procedure as described by Brown [236] is as follows:

A solution of 225 g. of olive oil fatty acids in 3450 cc. of acetone was cooled to −20°C. overnight and filtered. The filtrate was cooled to −60°C. in a dry ice-alcohol bath and again filtered. The resulting crystal fraction was subjected to three further crystallizations at −60°C., each time from 2000 cc. of acetone. By this procedure the more soluble linoleic acid was removed in the several filtrates. After these four crystallizations at −60°C., the product was made up to 1250 cc. with acetone and cooled slowly to the first appearance of crystals, about −35°C. Although this crystal crop was largely oleic acid, it contained some additional saturated acids which had not been removed by the first separation at −20°C. The product remaining in the filtrate was oleic acid, the analytical constants of which were identical for practical purposes with those of another specimen obtained by a similar procedure which included, however, six crystallizations at −60°C.

A method combining fractional distillation with crystallization from acetone for the separation of pure oleic acid has been studied by Smith,[237] and Wheeler and Riemenschneider [238] have prepared methyl oleate of 99.6% purity by a procedure combining crystallization and fractional distillation. Recently, very pure specimens of methyl oleate and oleic acid have been prepared from olive oil by Brown and coworkers,[239] the procedure differing from that previously described in that the C_{18} methyl esters were repeatedly crystallized from methanol. The procedure as described by Foreman and Brown is as follows:

The C_{18} esters of olive oil were especially purified by two distillations through the column mentioned above. Methyl linoleate was then removed by five to six recrystallizations from methyl alcohol at −60°. The four per cent methyl stearate remaining in the oleate was then cautiously removed by cooling dilute solutions in methyl alcohol to about −30 to −34°. The constants of the final oleic acid indicated it to be about 99.8 per cent pure.

Details for the preparation of pure oleic acid from a number of fats and oils of both animal and vegetable origin are described in the article by Millican and Brown.

Pure oleic acid has the following physical constants: m.p. 13°, $b_{1.2}$ 200–201°, b_5 215–216°, b_{10} 225–226°, b_{15} 234–235°, d_4^{15} 0.898, d_4^{20} 0.895, d_4^{30} 0.887, d_4^{50} 0.875, n_D^{20} 1.45823, and n_D^{70} 1.44179. Oleic acid apparently exhibits dimorphism,[230, 240] crystallizing in two forms one of which melts at 13° and the other at 16°.

Several octadecenoic acids described in the literature have been shown upon further investigation to be ordinary oleic acid. Among these may be mentioned rapic acid, which Reimer and Will [241] first obtained from rape oil and which Zellner [242] considered to be an isomer of oleic acid. A reexamination of this acid by Grabner,[243] and later by Hilditch, Riley, and Vidyarthi,[244] showed it to be identical with oleic acid, and consequently rapic acid has no separate existence.

Elaidic Acid

The treatment of oleic acid with isomerizing agents, such as nitrogen oxides, results in the formation of an equilibrium mixture of oleic acid and its higher-melting *trans* isomeride, elaidic acid. The equilibrium mixture contains approximately 66% of elaidic acid and 34% of oleic acid; and since this composition can be obtained by starting with either pure component, the reaction represents a true isomeric equilibrium. In spite of the fact that the physical properties of elaidic acid clearly indicate it to be the *trans* isomer, it was not so considered for many years. It has now been conclusively shown that oleic acid is *cis*-9-octadecenoic acid and that elaidic acid is its *trans* isomeride, the respective structures being as follows:

$$\begin{array}{ll} CH_3(CH_2)_7CH & CH_3(CH_2)_7CH \\ \parallel & \parallel \\ HO_2C(CH_2)_7CH & HC(CH_2)_7CO_2H \\ \text{Oleic acid—}cis & \text{Elaidic acid—}trans \end{array}$$

The *trans* structure of elaidic acid has been shown by the fact that it forms solid solutions with saturated fatty acids,[245, 246] by x-ray investigations,[247] and by monomolecular-film studies.[248, 249]

Elaidic acid does not occur in the natural fats and oils. Our familiarity with this acid dates back well over one hundred years to the observations of Poutet.[250] In studying a method proposed by Boyle in 1661 for the preparation of ointments, Poutet found that when olive oil was treated with a concentrated solution of mercurous nitrate its consistency became comparable to that of pork fat. Thirteen years later, Boudet [251] studied the action of nitrous acid upon oleic acid and succeeded in preparing elaidic acid, which he reported to melt at 51.5°. The action of nitrous acid upon oleic acid was then investigated by Meyer,[252] Gottlieb,[253] and Lidow,[254] and later Jegorow [255] showed that the action of nitrogen oxides is catalytic in nature and that large amounts of the reagent lead to the formation of complex addition products. In 1894, Saytzeff [256] observed that oleic acid was converted to elaidic acid by the action of sulfurous acid or a saturated solution of sodium bisulfate, and later Fokin [257] reported a similar change in the presence of phosphorous acid. Fokin suggested that only those substances which are capable of existing in two modifications will bring about this isomerization; however, Rankoff [258] has produced isomerization by the use of sulfur or phosphorus in the presence of water. In 1932, Griffiths and Hilditch [259] published a comprehensive study of the elaidin reaction in which they confirmed the fact that the conversion is an equilibrium reaction, the equilibrium mixture containing 66% of elaidic acid. These authors further stated that Poutet's reagent is preferable to nitrogen oxides because of the tendency of the latter to form addition products. Small amounts of the catalyst and low temperatures favor the formation of elaidic acid.

Of the large number of catalysts which have been investigated for the conversion of oleic to elaidic acid, selenium appears to be by far the most effective. Its use for the preparation of elaidic acid was first proposed by Bertram,[260] who reported it to be capable of bringing about isomerization at 150–220° when as little as 0.003–0.1% is employed. The heating of triolein for eight hours with 0.3% selenium yields the equilibrium mixture, and compounds of selenium such as hydrogen selenide, selenium dioxide, and selenium dibromide were also found to be effective. Tellurium and its compounds are capable of bringing about this conversion, but they have not been so extensively studied as selenium. Bertram is of the opinion that the isomerization is brought about by the addition and elimination of unstable hydrogen compounds.

Elaidic acid is a solid which melts at 44.5°.[182, 261] It distils without decomposition at reduced pressures, the following boiling points having been reported: b_{10} 225°, b_{15} 234°, b_{30} 251.5°, and b_{50} 266°.

10-Octadecenoic Acid. $CH_3(CH_2)_6CH:CH(CH_2)_8CO_2H$

This acid was first described by Saytzeff,[165] who obtained it by the action of alcoholic potassium hydroxide upon 10-iodostearic acid, and also by the distillation of 10-hydroxystearic acid. Isoöleic acid has been considered to consist essentially of 10-octadecenoic acid.[262] A study of the dehydration of 10-hydroxystearic acid [263] has shown that both *cis*- and *trans*-10-octadecenoic acids and also oleic acid are present in the reaction product. According to Bauer and Panagoulias,[264] 10-octadecenoic acid is formed when oleic acid is treated with zinc chloride. The heating of 10-chlorostearic acid with nickel carbonate has been observed [177] to yield 10-octadecenoic acid, indicating that the double bond is shifted towards the methyl group rather than towards the carboxyl group under these conditions. During the hydrogenation of both oleic and elaidic acids the double bond shifts from the 9-position to both the 8- and the 10-positions,[189, 265] and according to Bauer and Krallis [190] the double bond of oleic acid is shifted when this acid is heated alone in the presence of copper or nickel catalysts. Under these conditions, however, the shift is preferentially to the 10-position rather than to the 8-position. Hilditch and Vidyarthi [188] have reported the formation of methyl 10-octadecenoate during the hydrogenation of methyl oleate.

The question as to the natural occurrence of 10-octadecenoic acid has not been conclusively settled. It has been reported to be present in the fatty acids of pig liver,[266] although Hartley [267] believes this to be 6-octadecenoic acid.

10-Octadecenoic acid melts at 44–45°; its other physical constants are d_4^{50} 0.8757 and n_D^{51} 1.4494. These values are probably questionable, since they may refer to a mixture of the *cis* and *trans* isomers.

11-Octadecenoic Acid (Vaccenic Acid).

$$CH_3(CH_2)_5CH:CH(CH_2)_9CO_2H$$

Both the *cis* and *trans* forms of 11-octadecenoic acid have apparently been prepared. The *cis* modification was first described by Fokin,[162] who reported its preparation along with 12-octadecenoic acid by the action of alcoholic potassium hydroxide on 12-bromostearic acid. Later, Fokin [268] reported the formation of both 11- and 12-octadecenoic acids by the action of phosphoric anhydride upon 12-hydroxystearic acid. The 12-hydroxystearic acid was obtained by the hydrogenation of ricinoleic acid in the presence of platinum. He reported the melting point of *cis*-11-octadecenoic acid to be 6–8°. The dehydration of 12-hydroxystearic acid was subsequently studied by Grün and Czerny [269] who reported that it gave a mixture of *cis*- and *trans*-11-octadecenoic acids, the former melting at 9.8–10.4° and the latter at 39.5°. It is possible, however, that the latter acid is actually 12-

octadecenoic acid. The partial hydrogenation of eleostearic acid has been claimed by Böeseken and van Krimpen [270] to result in the formation of an acid which they considered to be 11-octadecenoic acid.

It is fairly well established that 11-octadecenoic acid occurs in several of the animal fats. An acid termed vaccenic acid has been isolated by Bertram [271] from beef fat and it was later observed by Grossfeld and Simmer [272] to be present in mutton fat (1–2%), beef fat (1.6%), hog fat (0.2%), and butter (1–4.7%). The structure of vaccenic acid, as 11-octadecenoic acid, was proved by its oxidation to heptanoic acid and undecanedioic acid, $HO_2C(CH_2)_9CO_2H$. The melting point of 39° reported by Bertram [271] for vaccenic acid is of interest owing to the much lower value observed for the synthetic 11-octadecenoic acid. Recent work has indicated that vaccenic acid possesses growth promoting properties,[273] and the biological function of this acid is the subject of several current investigations.

12-Octadecenoic Acid. $CH_3(CH_2)_4CH:CH(CH_2)_{10}CO_2H$

12-Octadecenoic acid is formed together with its 11-isomer by the action of alcoholic potassium hydroxide upon 12-bromostearic acid,[162] and also by the dehydration of 12-hydroxystearic acid in the presence of phosphoric anhydride.[268] Its melting point was reported to be 33–34°.

The presence of 12-octadecenoic acid has been observed in the glycerides of partially hydrogenated peanut oil by Bauer and Mitsotakis.[274] The formation of 12-octadecenoic acid under these conditions is due very probably to the selective hydrogenation of the 9-ethylenic bond of linoleic acid. Hilditch and Vidyarthi [275] have stated that an appreciable amount of methyl 12-octadecenoate is formed during the partial hydrogenation of methyl linolenate. More recently, Puzanov [276] has reported the formation of 12-octadecenoic acid during the partial hydrogenation of sunflower seed oil. It is generally assumed that when the polyethylenic acids or their esters are hydrogenated, the reduction takes place preferentially at those bonds furthermost from the carboxyl group; however, that there are exceptions to this generalization has been shown by the above-reported observations.

Other Octadecenoic Acids

The octadecenoic acids from 13- to 17-octadecenoic acid have not been synthesized, nor has their presence been observed in the naturally occurring fats and oils. Several octadecenoic acids have been reported to occur in whale oil; however, their constitution has not been established.[101, 277] 15-Octadecenoic acid has been stated by Bauer and Ermann [278] to be formed during the hydrogenation of linolenic acid.

NONADECENOIC ACIDS

The nonadecenoic acids are not found in the naturally occurring oils and fats. Two straight-chain, monoethylenic acids containing nineteen carbon atoms have been reported to be present in natural oils; however, both of these instances were subsequently shown to be cases of mistaken identity. In 1848, Scharling [279] described an acid obtained from Arctic sperm oil which he considered to be a nonadecenoic acid and to which he gave the name doeglic acid. Many years later Bull [123] showed doeglic acid to be a mixture of oleic acid and gadoleic acid (9-eicosenoic acid). The name doeglic acid, therefore, should be dropped from the literature. Another nonadecenoic acid, termed jecoleic acid, has been stated by Heyerdahl [280] to be present in cod liver oil. Its existence was postulated upon the observation that the oxidation of cod liver oil acids with potassium permanganate yielded a so-called dihydroxyjecoleic acid, $C_{19}H_{38}O_4$. Bull, however, considered jecoleic acid, like doeglic acid, to be a mixture of oleic and gadoleic acids.

2-Nonadecenoic Acid. $CH_3(CH_2)_{15}CH:CHCO_2H$

2-Nonadecenoic acid is apparently the only member of this series which has been synthesized, Oskerk [281] having described its preparation by the removal of hydrogen bromide from 2-bromononadecanoic acid. The latter acid was prepared by the action of bromine and phosphorus on nonadecanoic acid.

EICOSENOIC ACIDS

At least two eicosenoic acids occur in the natural fats and oils and one of these, 9-eicosenoic acid (gadoleic acid), is found rather widely distributed in the marine animal and fish oils.

9-Eicosenoic Acid (Gadoleic Acid).
   $CH_3(CH_2)_9CH:CH(CH_2)_7CO_2H$

Gadoleic acid was first described by Bull,[123] who isolated it during his investigation of the fatty acids of cod liver oil. Bull further observed that doeglic and jecoleic acids, which had previously been stated to be contained in cod liver oil, were actually mixtures of gadoleic acid with oleic acid. Gadoleic acid has subsequently been found to be a common component of the fish and marine animal oils, in some of which it is present in appreciable amounts. Lexow [95] reported 11.7% of gadoleic acid in herring oil, and Toyama and associates [282] have reported it in shark and ray liver oils and whale oil. It has been stated to be present in shark liver oil to the extent of 16.4%.[104] The structure of gadoleic acid was determined by Takano [283] to be 9-eicosenoic acid, which structure has since been confirmed.[284] Toyama and Ishikawa [285] have reported an isomer of gadoleic acid, to which they gave the name gondoic acid, in whale blubber oil.

11-Eicosenoic Acid. $CH_3(CH_2)_7CH:CH(CH_2)_9CO_2H$

The seeds of the evergreen shrub *Simmondsia californica*, which occurs in the southwestern part of the United States, were observed by Greene and Foster [286] to contain 46% of a liquid wax (jajoba oil). Investigations of this wax [287,288] have shown it to consist essentially of esters of eicosenoic and docosenoic acids with the corresponding alcohols. 11-Eicosenoic acid was shown to be present.

Docosenoic Acids

Two docosenoic acids have been observed in the natural fats, one—erucic acid (13-docosenoic acid)—in certain seed fats, and the other—cetoleic acid (11-docosenoic acid)—in the fish and marine animal oils.

13-Docosenoic Acids. $CH_3(CH_2)_7CH:CH(CH_2)_{11}CO_2H$

Erucic Acid. Erucic acid was first described by Darby,[289] who obtained it from mustard seed oil. It has since been observed to be the principal acid in many of the seed fats, particularly those belonging to the *Cruciferae* family. The position of the double bond in erucic acid was not proved for many years after the discovery of the acid. Holt,[290] for example, in 1892, considered erucic acid to be 2-docosenoic acid. The next year, however, Fileti [291] reported that erucic acid gave nonanoic and brassylic acids upon oxidation with nitric acid, thus establishing its structure as 13-docosenoic acid. The oxidation products contain, in addition to the above-named two acids, a nitrogen compound, $C_9H_{18}N_2O_4$, together with small amounts of arachidic acid.

Erucic acid was first observed in rape oil by Websky.[292] It constitutes the principal acid of this oil, having been reported to be present to the extent of from 43.5 to 57.2%.[293, 294, 295] A value as high as 65% has been reported [296] for the erucic acid content of this oil. The fractional distillation of the fatty acids of rape seed oil showed erucic acid to constitute 40% of the total acids present.[224] Erucic acid is also present in other cruciferous oils, such as wallflower seed oil,[297] 40.6%, mustard seed oil,[298] 41.5%, and jamba oil,[299] 46.3%. An excellent source of erucic acid has recently been found in nasturtium oil, the fatty acids of which, according to the recent work of Hilditch and Meara,[300] contain 82% of erucic acid. Grape seed oil has frequently been reported to contain erucic acid; [301, 302, 303] however, the more recent work of Täufel and others [304, 305] indicated that these observations are erroneous.

Erucic acid has been prepared from rape oil by several procedures, the earlier of which generally involve a saponification of the rape oil by litharge, followed by an extraction of the lead soaps with ether to remove other acids. Reimer and Will [306] recommend the saponification of rape oil with alcoholic potassium hydroxide, separation of the acids by sulfuric acid, and crystallization of the erucic acid at 0° from a threefold quantity of 95% ethanol. Recrystallization of the product from 95% ethanol at 9°, gave erucic acid melting at 34°. Noller and Talbot [307] have suggested crystallization from 95% ethanol followed by fractional distillation. A preliminary separation of the lead salts followed by crystallization of the erucic acid from 95% ethanol has been employed by Holde and Wilke.[308] A final purification of erucic acid by crystallization from ethanol as the magnesium salt has been recommended.[309, 310]

Erucic acid melts at 33.5°. Noller and Talbot [307] have reported the following boiling points: b_5 241–243° and b_{12} 252–254°; Krafft and Noerdlinger [311] found b_{10} 254.5°, b_{15} 264°, and b_{30} 281°.

Erucic acid has a *cis* configuration. Its *trans* isomer, brassidic acid, is well known, and the conversion of erucic acid to brassidic acid has been extensively studied.

Brassidic Acid. The treatment of erucic acid with nitrous acid, dilute nitric acid, or other isomerizing agents results in its conversion to the *trans* isomer, brassidic acid. This acid was first obtained by Haussknecht [312] by the action of dilute nitric acid, and this transformation in the presence of nitrous acid has since been extensively investigated.[301, 313, 314] Erucic acid, like oleic acid, is isomerized by treatment with aqueous solutions of sulfurous acid at 200° for twenty-four hours.[256] Rankoff [315] has studied the conversion of erucic acid to brassidic acid by means of sulfur. The preparation of brassidic acid by the isomerization of rape seed oil with dilute nitric acid and sodium nitrite, followed by saponification and acidification of the resulting acids, has recently been described by Keffler and Maiden.[316] The acid melted at 59.9° after ten recrystallizations from absolute ethanol. Brassidic acid melts at 60° and has the following boiling points: b_{10} 256°, b_{15} 265°, and b_{30} 282°.[311] Rankoff [315] has reported the refractive index to be n_D^{100} 1.4347.

A comparison of the physical constants of erucic and brassidic acids indicates that erucic acid possesses a *cis* and brassidic acid a *trans* structure. They thus correspond to oleic and elaidic acids. However, the geometrical structures of erucic and brassidic acids were a subject of controversy for many years. The work of Bruni and Gorni [317] showed that *trans* isomers form solid solutions with the corresponding saturated compound whereas *cis* isomers do not. The systems formed by erucic acid, brassidic acid, and a so-called isomeric acid have been studied by Mascarelli and associates,[246, 318] who showed that brassidic acid forms solid solutions with behenic acid whereas erucic acid does not. Consequently, erucic acid possesses a *cis* and brassidic acid a *trans* configuration. The iso-erucic acid appeared to possess a *trans* configuration; however, its structure was not determined.

11-Docosenoic Acid (Cetoleic Acid).

$$CH_3(CH_2)_9CH:CH(CH_2)_9CO_2H$$

The docosenoic acid, cetoleic acid, present in marine oils has been shown by Toyama [319] to be 11-docosenoic acid. Previous to the work of Toyama the docosenoic acid of marine oils was considered to be identical with the docosenoic acid of vegetable origin. Cetoleic acid has been shown to be present in whale oils,[282, 319] shark liver oils,[104, 136, 137, 320] herring oil,[135] sardine oil,[321] and pin-fish oil.[322] Cetoleic acid is, therefore, apparently common to marine oils, in which it is generally accompanied by gadoleic acid. The last-mentioned acid, however, is usually present in larger amounts.

Other Docosenoic Acids

Several isomeric docosenoic acids have been synthesized, the compositions of which have not been definitely determined.

Alexandroff and Saytzeff [323] have described an acid prepared by the action of alcoholic potassium hydroxide on iodobehenic acid. The acid melted at 54–56° and was considered to be 2-docosenoic acid. Ponzio [324] stated that the so-called isoerucic acid is identical with erucic acid, and Mascarelli and coworkers [318, 325] have agreed with this statement. The view which has been expressed [326] that ioserucic acid is a mixture and not a chemical individual appears to be correct, and the term isoerucic acid, like isoöleic acid, probably does not refer to a pure substance.

TETRACOSENOIC ACIDS

15-Tetracosenoic acid is the only one of the tetracosenoic acids which has been identified in natural fats.

15-Tetracosenoic Acid (Selacholeic Acid, Nervonic Acid).

$$CH_3(CH_2)_7CH:CH(CH_2)_{13}CO_2H$$

Selacholeic acid has been identified as a component in the various liver oils of marine origin. Tsujimoto [136] reported selacholeic acid to occur in shark and ray liver oils, and its presence in these oils has been confirmed.[103, 137, 320] Hilditch and Houlbrooke [104] have reported the amount of selacholeic acid in shark liver oil to be 12.0%. In 1927, Tsujimoto [327, 328] determined the constitution of selacholeic acid to be 15-tetracosenoic acid. Selacholeic acid melts at 42.5–43°.

An acid termed nervonic acid, apparently identical with selacholeic acid [105, 327] has been isolated from brain cerebrosides by Klenk.[329] 15-Tetracosenoic acid has been synthesized by the malonic acid method from 13-docosenyl bromide,[330] a reaction which results in the formation of both the *cis* and the *trans* forms. The latter melted at 61°; the former, which melted at 39°, was shown to be identical with the naturally occurring acid.

HEXACOSENOIC ACIDS

17-Hexacosenoic Acid (Ximenic Acid).

$$CH_3(CH_2)_7CH:CH(CH_2)_{15}CO_2H$$

This acid was first reported to be contained in ximenia oil,[331] and somewhat later was tentatively identified as 17-hexacosenoic acid.[332] It has been stated to constitute 25% of the fatty acids present in this oil.

TRIACONTENOIC ACIDS

An acid termed lumequeic acid has been stated by Boeken-oogen [332] to accompany ximenic acid in ximenia oil. Its constitution was reported to be 21-triacontenoic acid, $CH_3(CH_2)_7CH:CH-(CH_2)_{19}CO_2H$.

The Dienoic Acids

Acids which contain two ethylenic bonds in the hydrocarbon chain characterize the semi-drying and drying oils. Although they are present in the marine oils and to a lesser extent in the various animal oils, they appear to be distinctively associated with oils of vegetable origin. Dienoic acids have the general formula $C_nH_{2n-4}O_2$. This series of acids is frequently called the linoleic acid series, because linoleic acid, like oleic acid in the ethylenic series, is the most important acid of the group.

In acids which contain two or more double bonds the position of these bonds with reference to each other is often a determinative factor in their physical and chemical properties. This is particularly true if the ethylenic linkages form a conjugated system, since such compounds show chemical properties quite distinct from those displayed by unconjugated systems. Because of their higher degree of unsaturation, the dienoic acids are more susceptible to various oxidative reactions than the ethylenic acids.

The isolation and identification of those dienoic acids which occur in the natural fats and oils has presented a somewhat more difficult problem than that encountered with the ethylenic acids. Dienoic acids containing fewer than eighteen carbon atoms, with the exception of sorbic acid, either do not exist in the natural fats or are present in such small amounts that they have not as yet been isolated. The octadecadienoic acid linoleic acid is found in large amounts in the vegetable oils and has been definitely identified as 9,12-octadecadienoic acid. The relationship which exists between the linoleic acid present in the vegetable fats and that found in the marine and animal oils has not been definitely decided. Although small amounts of ordinary linoleic acid appear in such fats the presence of other octadecadienoic acids seems probable. It appears that the linoleic acid which occurs in the animal fats is entirely a product of assimilation. Very few attempts have been made to synthesize the higher dienoic acids. The increased number of possible geometric isomers occasioned by the presence of a second ethylenic bond, and the difficulty of obtaining pure dienoic acids from the natural oils, add to the task of obtaining exact information concerning these acids. The next few years will undoubtedly see material contributions to our knowledge of the various members of this group.

The following is a short description of the various dienoic acids which have been either synthesized or identified in the natural fats and oils. Only the pentadienoic, hexadienoic, and octadecadienoic acids have been extensively investigated.

PENTADIENOIC ACIDS

The pentadienoic acids are not found in the natural fats, and many of the reported syntheses of these acids are questionable because of failures to characterize the product. Only the 2,4-acid has been described in detail.

2,4-Pentadienoic Acid. $CH_2:CHCH:CHCO_2H$

The synthesis of this acid from acrolein and malonic acid in the presence of pyridine has been described by Doebner.[15] The acid melts at 80° and easily polymerizes to a syrupy liquid upon heating to 110–115°. When reduced with sodium amalgam it yields allyl-acetic acid.

HEXADIENOIC ACIDS

One of the hexadienoic acids, sorbic acid, occurs in the natural oils.

2,4-Hexadienoic Acid (Sorbic Acid). $CH_3CH:CHCH:CHCO_2H$

Sorbic acid was first obtained by Hofmann [41] from the berries of the mountain ash. The acid was later investigated by Fittig,[44, 333] and in 1900 Doebner [42] accomplished the synthesis of sorbic acid from 2-butenal and malonic acid in the presence of pyridine. Doebner [334] had previously shown the naturally occurring acid to be 2,4-hexadienoic acid. Attempts by Doebner [42] to prepare sorbic acid by the Perkin synthesis from 2-butenal and acetic acid were not successful. The dehydration of 3-hydroxy-4-hexenoic acid in the presence of alkalies results in an almost theoretical yield of sorbic acid.[335] The acid is best obtained from the juice of mountain ash berries. 2,4-Hexadienoic acid freezes at 134.5° and boils at 228° with decomposition. It is insoluble in cold water, moderately soluble in hot water, and very soluble in ethanol and ether. It is quite easily polymerized owing to the presence of the conjugated system of double bonds.

Octadecadienoic Acids

It can be considered that our knowledge of the dienoic fatty acids is essentially confined to the octadecadienoic acids. Only one of the many possible octadecadienoic acids has been definitely identified in the natural oils; however, recent work has indicated that isomers of linoleic acid may also occur in natural products. The following octadecadienoic acids have been described.

9,12-Octadecadienoic Acid (Linoleic Acid).

$$CH_3(CH_2)_4CH:CHCH_2CH:CH(CH_2)_7CO_2H$$

Linoleic acid is the characteristic acid of the semi-drying oils, and is found widely distributed throughout the vegetable kingdom. The structure of the naturally occurring linoleic acid was a controversial subject for many years. Linoleic acid was first described in 1844 by Sacc,[336] who separated the acid from linseed oil fatty acids. The great difficulty in obtaining linoleic acid free of other unsaturated fatty acids led to many uncertainties concerning its actual structure. Earlier views that linoleic acid contained sixteen carbon atoms were dispelled by its conversion into stearic acid through reduction of the iodostearic acid obtained by the reaction of linoleic acid with hydrogen iodide.[337, 338] The formula $C_{20}H_{30}O_2$, ascribed to linoleic acid by Norton and Richardson,[339] was shown to be in error by Hazura and coworkers.[340] Their work confirmed that of Dieff and Reformatzky [337] and also of Peters,[341] who established the formula of linoleic acid as $C_{18}H_{32}O_2$. All these earlier workers recognized the fact that the linoleic acid or so-called hemp oil acid which they investigated contained other acids as impurities.

Since linoleic acid contains two ethylenic bonds, four geometrical isomerides are possible: namely, *cis,cis*; *cis,trans*; *trans,cis*; and *trans,trans*. Much of the work which has culminated in our present-day views covering the structure of naturally occurring linoleic acid has been concerned with a study of these four isomers and their derivatives. Both the bromination and the oxidation of linoleic acid have been extensively studied. In the former case tetrabromostearic acids and in the latter case tetrahydroxystearic acids (sativic acids) result. The study of the bromine derivatives of linoleic acid has added materially to our knowledge of the structure of this acid. The bromination of linoleic acid gives a solid tetrabromide melting at 114–115°,[338, 340] together with an approximately equal amount of a liquid tetrabromide. The former is sparingly soluble in petroleum ether and may be separated from the latter by the use of this solvent. Treatment of this solid tetra-bromide with zinc, by a method initially proposed by Rollett,[342] yields the so-called α-linoleic acid, whereas treatment of the liquid tetrabromide gives β-linoleic acid. When α-linoleic acid is bromi-nated, approximately equal amounts of a solid and a liquid tetra-bromide are again formed. Bromination of the β-linoleic acid results in the formation of both a solid and a liquid tetrabromide; however, the amount of the liquid tetrabromide greatly predomi-nates. The structure of these tetrabromides and of their reduction products, together with the relationship which exists between the reconstituted acids and naturally occurring linoleic acid, has long been a subject of interest. In the following discussion we must bear in mind that the tetrabromostearic acids from linoleic acid possess four asymmetric carbon atoms which permit of sixteen optical isomers or eight racemic mixtures. Four stereoisomers are possible by the debromination of these tetrabromides. The addition and removal of bromine is not generally accompanied by isomerization and, since two tetrabromides are obtained upon the bromination of linoleic acid, Nicolet and Cox [343] supported a view previously suggested by Bedford,[344] that natural linoleic acid contains at least two geometrical isomerides. However, since Rollett [342] had previ-ously shown that both a liquid and a solid tetrabromide result from the bromination of regenerated α-linoleic acid, the formation of two tetrabromides from natural linoleic acid does not imply that it is a mixture. In a comparatively recent study Green and Hilditch [345] have concluded that only one form of linoleic acid is present in the seed fats and that this may undergo partial isomerization upon bromination. Naturally occurring linoleic acid probably has a cis,cis configuration, and it is apparently identical with regenerated α-linoleic acid since both yield the same hydroxy acids upon oxida-tion. In 1938, Brown and Frankel [346] compared the linoleic acid obtained by the debromination of the solid tetrabromide (m.p. 114°) with a relatively pure linoleic acid obtained from corn oil, and found the two to be identical. This work indicated that only one linoleic acid is present in the natural seed oils; however, in the same year a contrary opinion was expressed by McCutcheon.[347]

Although the configurations of the solid tetrabromide and the regenerated α-linoleic acid have been established, the same cannot be said for the liquid tetrabromide and β-linoleic acid. Matthes and Boltze [179] claimed to have obtained a crystalline tetrabromide melting at 57–58° from the liquid tetrabromide, although this has not been substantiated. Suzuki and coworkers [348] have studied the oxidation of the partially debrominated tetrabromo acids, and have stated that α-linoleic acid has a *cis,cis* structure and the β-acid a *trans,trans* structure. The latter was designated as isolinoleic acid. Takahashi [349] has reported that the bromination of α-linoleic acid yields three tetrabromides: α-, melting at 113.5–114°, β-, melting at 59–60° and soluble in petroleum ether, and γ-, a petroleum-ether-soluble liquid. Upon rebromination, each of the acids obtained from the above yielded three tetrabromides, the one from which it was derived appearing in the greatest amount. Smith and West [350] have reported the presence of three solid tetrabromides and a liquid tetrabromide in the product obtained by the bromination of linoleic acid from lumbang oil, and they stated that these apparently correspond to the four isomeric modifications of linoleic acid. Van der Veen [351] has attempted to effect a separation of the isomeric regenerated linoleic acids by means of their lithium salts. Birosel [352] showed that the β-linoleic acid tetrabromide obtained by Smith and West was actually the methyl ester of the tetrabromide, resulting from the use of methanol as a solvent for crystallization, and that the δ-linoleic acid tetrabromide was a mixture of the acid and ester. Later, Birosel [353] showed that only one solid tetrabromide is obtained from linoleic acid of soybean oil and also from regenerated α-linoleic acid. In 1939, Hilditch and Jasperson [354] reasserted that natural linoleic acid and α-linoleic acid are identical and have a *cis,cis* configuration, that bromination yields *cis,cis*- and *cis,trans*-tetrabromides, and that the liquid tetrabromide is a mixture of *cis,cis*- and *cis,trans*-tetrabromides. In the same year, Riemenschneider, Wheeler, and Sando [355] presented an explanation of the behavior of linoleic acid upon bromination which is worthy of consideration. These authors regard the two tetrabromides as racemic isomers which are both derived by the addition of bromine to a *cis,cis* acid, the bromination of this acid proceeding as follows:

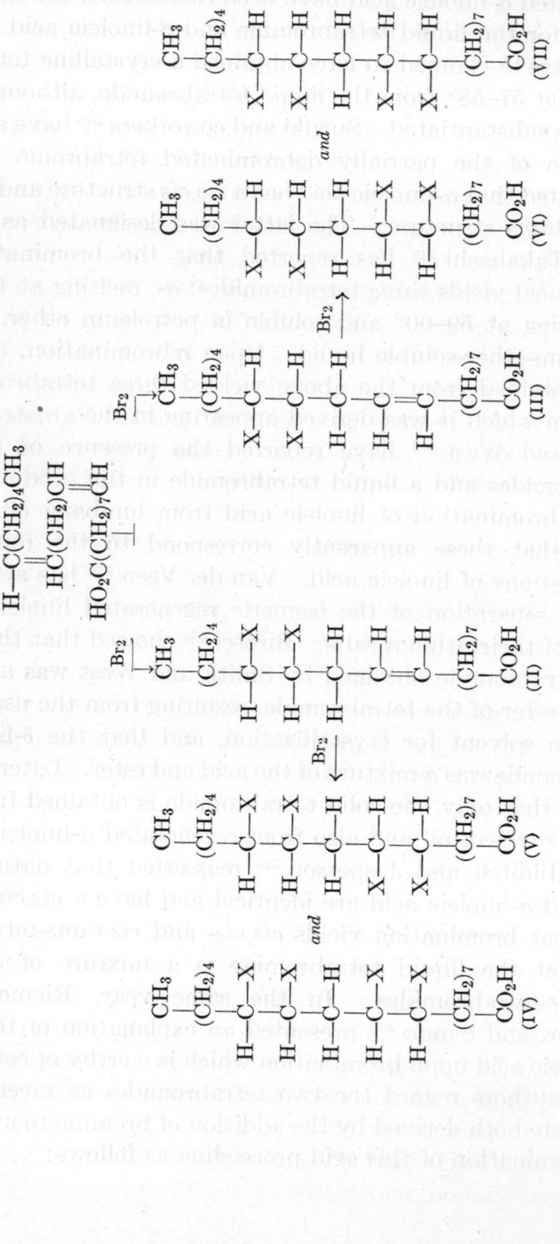

$$CH_3-(CH_2)_4-\underset{X}{\overset{H}{C}}-\underset{H}{\overset{X}{C}}-\underset{X}{\overset{H}{C}}-\underset{H}{\overset{X}{C}}-(CH_2)_7-CO_2H \quad (VII)$$

and

$$CH_3-(CH_2)_4-\underset{X}{\overset{H}{C}}-\underset{H}{\overset{X}{C}}-\underset{H}{\overset{X}{C}}-\underset{X}{\overset{H}{C}}-(CH_2)_7-CO_2H \quad (VI)$$

$\uparrow Br_2$

$$Br_2 \downarrow \quad CH_3-(CH_2)_4-\underset{X}{\overset{H}{C}}-\underset{X}{\overset{H}{C}}-\underset{H}{\overset{H}{C}}-\underset{H}{\overset{H}{C}}-(CH_2)_7-CO_2H \quad (III)$$

$$H-C(CH_2)_4CH_3 \\ HC(CH_2)CH \\ HO_2C(CH_2)_7CH$$

$$\overset{Br_2}{\rightarrow} CH_3-(CH_2)_4-\underset{X}{\overset{H}{C}}-\underset{H}{\overset{X}{C}}-\underset{}{\overset{}{C}}=\underset{}{\overset{}{C}}-\underset{H}{\overset{H}{C}}-(CH_2)_7-CO_2H \quad (II)$$

$\downarrow Br_2$

$$CH_3-(CH_2)_4-\underset{X}{\overset{H}{C}}-\underset{H}{\overset{X}{C}}-\underset{H}{\overset{H}{C}}-\underset{X}{\overset{H}{C}}-\underset{H}{\overset{X}{C}}-(CH_2)_7-CO_2H \quad (V)$$

and

$$CH_3-(CH_2)_4-\underset{H}{\overset{H}{C}}-\underset{H}{\overset{H}{C}}-\underset{X}{\overset{H}{C}}-\underset{X}{\overset{H}{C}}-\underset{H}{\overset{H}{C}}-(CH_2)_7-CO_2H \quad (IV)$$

It was pointed out that (IV) and (VII) are optical isomers forming a racemate and that (V) and (VI) are also optical isomers. This explanation accounts for the formation of a liquid and a solid tetrabromide by the bromination of a *cis,cis* acid, and suggests that α- and β-linoleic acids are identical. According to this explanation one would expect to obtain only two of the possible eight racemates. McCutcheon, Crawford, and Welch [356] have completed an infra-red and a Raman spectroscopic examination of linoleic acid and have stated that it contains only *cis* double bonds.

The above discussion has presented the various views which have been advanced regarding the structure of naturally occurring linoleic acid as determined by a study of its bromine derivatives. A study of the tetrabromides obtained from previously isomerized linoleic acid has also materially added to our knowledge of this subject and is worthy of mention. Owing to the fact that the drying and semi-drying oils do not yield solids when treated with isomerizing agents, such as nitrous acid, it was at first considered that such substances are without effect upon the dienoic acids. In 1892, Lidoff [357] pointed out that the treatment of linseed oil with isomerizing agents greatly increased its viscosity, which indicated that the oil had actually been isomerized during the process. The observation that linoleic acid is isomerized by nitrogen oxides was later confirmed by Green and Hilditch [345] and also by Noller and Girvin. [358] The elaidinization of linoleic acid, together with a study of the bromination and oxidation of the resulting product, has recently been made the subject of an investigation by Kass and Burr. [359] The treatment of linoleic acid with Poutet's reagent or with selenium gives both a liquid and a solid linolelaidic acid, the latter of which melts at 28–29°. Bromination of this solid linolelaidic acid gives a solid tetrabromide which melts at 78°, together with a liquid tetrabromide. The liquid linolelaidic acid gives no solid tetrabromide. A study of the oxidation products of these linolelaidic acids led to the conclusion that two isolinoleic acids had been formed; namely, *trans*-9,*trans*-12-linolelaidic acid and *trans*-9,*cis*-12-linolelaidic acid, an observation which is explainable upon the basis that the 12-bond cannot elaidinize without a previous or simultaneous elaidinization of the 9-bond. Failure to find ordinary linoleic acid, *cis*-9,*cis*-12-octadecadienoic acid, in the reaction mixture suggests that the elaidinization of linoleic acid does not yield an equilibrium mixture in which the original acid is one of the components. It will be recalled that oleic acid forms an equilibrium mixture of oleic and elaidic acids when treated with isomerizing agents. Hilditch and Jasperson [354] have stated that isomerized α-linoleic acid and isomerized β-linoleic acid do not yield a tetrabromostearic acid of melting point 114°. They consider that the isomerization of linoleic acid by selenium results almost exclusively in the formation of trans-9,trans-12-linolelaidic acid.

The oxidation of linoleic acid first yields tetrahydroxystearic acid which can then undergo further oxidation with the formation of cleavage products. A study of these cleavage products has conclusively shown that linoleic acid is 9,12-octadecadienoic acid.[360, 361, 362] Numerous investigations have been made on the intermediate oxidation products—the tetrahydroxystearic acids—from natural linoleic acid, α-linoleic acid, β-linoleic acid, and the various isomerized acids. In 1887, Hazura [363] observed that two sativic acids (tetrahydroxystearic acids), one melting at 171–173° and the other at 157–159°, result from the oxidation of natural linoleic acid or regenerated α-linoleic acid with potassium permanganate in alkaline solution. This observation has been confirmed by Reformatzky.[338] The formation of two tetrahydroxystearic acids upon oxidation, as well as the formation of two tetrabromostearic acids upon bromination, naturally brought up the question as to whether two stereoisomeric linoleic acids were originally present. Nicolet and Cox,[343] Bedford,[344] McCutcheon,[347] and others have subscribed to this opinion. However, the fact that both natural linoleic acid and regenerated α-linoleic acid yield the same two tetrahydroxystearic acids upon oxidation makes it extremely probable that natural linoleic acid is composed of only one isomeride,[345, 346, 353, 354, 364] which undergoes isomerization during oxidation or bromination. When Hilditch and Jasperson[354] oxidized β-linoleic acid, they obtained, among other products, 18.2% of the sativic acids (m.p. 173° and 157°), and they expressed the opinion that β-linoleic acid consists of a mixture of cis-9,cis-12- and cis-9,-trans-12-octadecadienoic acids. The same reasoning which led Riemenschneider, Wheeler, and Sando [355] to state that two tetrabromostearic acids would be expected from the bromination of cis-9,cis-12-octadecadienoic acid was also pointed out by them to apply with equal force to the oxidation products. It must be borne in mind that the conclusions of these authors should be applicable irrespective of which one of the four possible stereoisomeric acids was originally present. Birosel [352, 353] has stated that only two tetrahydroxystearic acids are obtained from the oxidation products of regenerated α-linoleic acid: an α-sativic acid melting at 164°, and a β-sativic acid melting at 174°. The lower-melting acids previously reported probably contained impurities, or were mixtures of these two acids. The sativic acid which melts at 164° was considered to be identical with one previously described by Meyer and Beer.[365] The oxidation of elaidinized linoleic acid with potassium permanganate produces a series of tetrahydroxystearic acids which differ from those obtained by the permanganate oxidation of natural or regenerated linoleic acids. These "elaidinized" tetra-hydroxystearic acids, however, appear to be similar to several acids previously obtained from natural linoleic acid by means other than permanganate oxidation. Kass and Burr [359] obtained two linol-elaidic acids by the action of nitrogen oxides or selenium on linoleic acid: a solid linolelaidic acid melting at 28–29°, and a liquid linolelaidic acid. Partial oxidation of the solid acid by means of potassium permanganate gave two tetrahydroxystearic acids, m.p. 122° and 146°, while partial oxidation of the liquid linolelaidic acid also gave two tetrahydroxystearic acids, melting at 126–127° and 156–158°. The probable identity of the former pair of tetrahydroxystearic acids with the two acids obtained by Burr and Burr [366] by the action of hydrogen peroxide on linoleic acid suggests that oxidation with this latter reagent may be accompanied by isomerization. The same may be said for the acids, m.p. 135° and 144°, obtained by Nicolet and Cox [343] by the saponification of linoleic chlorohydrin, and for the acids obtained by Green and Hilditch [345] by the peracetic acid oxidation of linoleic acid. The permanganate oxidation of isomerized α- or β-linoleic acid has been shown by Hilditch and Jasperson [354] to yield no tetrahydroxystearic acids similar to those obtained from the un-isomerized acids. The question of the stereochemical configurations of the bromo and hydroxy derivatives of linoleic acid together with the identity of the various regenerated acids is far from completely answered. Undoubtedly the greater weight of evidence supports the view that natural linoleic acid is composed of only one stereoisomeride. Oxidation under certain conditions is evidently accompanied by molecular rearrangement; however, isomerization does not necessarily accompany bromination and debromination.

Linoleic acid occurs abundantly in the drying and semi-drying oils of vegetable origin, particularly the seed oils, in the majority of which it constitutes a major component. Some of the percentages of linoleic acid which have been reported in various vegetable oils are as follows: cottonseed oil, 41.7%;[367] corn oil, 40.9%;[217] soybean oil, 51.5%,[368] 41.9–56.3%,[369] 53.0%;[370] sesame oil, 35.2%;[371] pumpkin seed oil, 40.4%;[372] sunflower seed oil, 57.5%;[220] lumbang oil, 39.62%;[373] linseed oil, 58.8%;[374] cantaloupe seed oil, 56.6%;[216] peanut oil, 7.4%,[131] 21.6–24.7%;[132] rice oil, 35%;[375] and squash seed oil, 44%.[218] Linoleic acid is present in small amounts in the animal depot fats. Hilditch and Longenecker[109] found 1.8% in ox depot fat and 4.9% in rat depot fat.[376] Bone greases contain approximately 5% of linoleic acid.[377] The amount of linoleic acid which has been reported in the pig depot fats varies between wide limits, 1 to 14%.[8, 204, 378, 379] In the case of the depot fats it is quite likely that the linoleic acid present is entirely a product of assimilation, and considerable doubt exists concerning the ability of animals to synthesize this acid. The liver fats generally contain significant amounts of linoleic acid, Irving and Smith[153] having reported 8% in pig liver fat. It is, however, a controversial question whether the linoleic acid found in the liver fats is identical with that obtained from vegetable sources. It appears that animals require small amounts of linoleic acid for the maintenance of proper growth,[380, 381, 382] and Williams and Anderson[383] have stated that the body either is incapable of synthesizing this acid or cannot synthesize it in the amounts demanded by the growing animal organism.

Small amounts of linoleic acid are present in the various animal milk fats; however, Hilditch and Jones[384] have found that this acid does not yield the tetrahydroxystearic acids which characterize ordinary linoleic acid. Later Bosworth and Brown[68] reported linoleic acid to be absent from butter fat. The possibility that the octadecadienoic acid which occurs in milk fat is a geometrical isomeride of seed-fat linoleic acid was suggested by Green and Hilditch;[345] however, a subsequent study by Hilditch and Jasperson[385] failed to establish its identity.

The configuration of the linoleic acid present in oils of marine origin has not been definitely determined. Isolinoleic acids have been reported in various oils, such as herring oil,[125] the fat of silk worm pupa,[386] and rice bran oil.[387] In the last instance, Haworth[388] showed the acid to be identical with ordinary linoleic acid.

Linoleic acid can be prepared by the reduction of its crystalline tetrabromide, m.p. 114–115°, by the method of Rollett.[342] The debromination is best accomplished by the use of zinc and has been conducted in boiling ethanol,[389] acidified ethanol,[342] pyridine,[390] and other solvents. Recently Matthews, Brode, and Brown [391] have subjected regenerated α-linoleic acid to low-temperature crystallization and have observed that it contains an appreciable percentage of isomeric linoleic acids. The separation of linoleic acid from vegetable oils by repeated low-temperature solvent crystallization has been accomplished by Brown and co-workers.[346, 392] The fatty acids of cottonseed oil or corn oil are first crystallized from several solvents to remove the saturated acids, a procedure which is followed by crystallization from acetone at −50° and then at −70°. The distillation of this final product yields a linoleic acid of 93.5% purity. A comparison of this acid with regenerated α-linoleic acid showed the two to be essentially identical.

The physical constants which have been reported for linoleic acid are as follows: m.p. −5.2 to −5.0°,[391] −6.8°,[392] −8 to −7°,[393] and −12 to −11°;[394] d_4^{18} 0.9038, $d_4^{22.8}$ 0.9007;[393] $n_D^{11.5}$ 1.4715, $n_D^{21.5}$ 1.4683,[393] n_D^{20} 1.4699;[392] and $b_{1.4}$ 202°.

9,11-Octadecadienoic Acid.

$CH_3(CH_2)_5CH:CHCH:CH(CH_2)_7CO_2H$

Although this acid has not been found in any of the natural fats, its ready availability by the dehydration of ricinoleic acid makes it of more than academic interest. 9,11-Octadecadienoic acid is isomeric with linoleic acid; however, since it possesses a conjugated system of double bonds, its chemical and physical properties differ quite materially from those of ordinary linoleic acid. Reactions such as heat gelation, 1:4-addition, and maleic anhydride addition distinguish acids containing conjugated systems from their unconjugated counterparts. Most of the work which has been reported on the preparation of 9,11-octadecadienoic acid by the dehydration of ricinoleic acid has not actually been accomplished with ricinoleic acid itself but with its glyceryl ester, castor oil.

When castor oil is distilled there results a large gelatinous residue which decomposes upon further heating. This observation was first made by Bussy and Lecanu [395] as early as 1825; however, the reason for this phenomenon was not understood for many years. When ricinoleic acid, 12-hydroxy-9-octadecenoic acid, is heated, the major decomposition products are representative of two general reactions. The ricinoleic acid may undergo scission into 10-undecenoic acid and heptanal according to the equation [76]

$$CH_3(CH_2)_5CHCH_2CH:CH(CH_2)_7CO_2H \rightarrow$$
$$\qquad\qquad |$$
$$\qquad\qquad OH$$

$$CH_2:CH(CH_2)_8CO_2H + CH_3(CH_2)_5CHO$$

10-Undecenoic acid   Heptanal

Or it may undergo dehydration with the formation of dienoic acids as follows:

$$CH_3(CH_2)_5CHCH_2CH:CH(CH_2)_7CO_2H$$
$$\qquad\qquad |$$
$$\qquad\qquad OH$$

$-H_2O$ $-H_2O$

$CH_3(CH_2)_4CH:CHCH_2CH:CH(CH_2)_7CO_2H$ $CH_3(CH_2)_4CH_2CH:CHCH:CH(CH_2)_7CO_2H$

9,12-Octadecadienoic acid   9,11-Octadecadienoic acid

These reactions may proceed simultaneously, or the conditions may be so adjusted that the reaction is predominantly one of scission or of dehydration. The dehydration reaction is materially favored by the presence of dehydrating catalysts such as aluminum oxide, sulfuric acid, phosphoric anhydride, or similar substances, while the scission reaction appears to be characteristic of high-temperature decompositions (250–300°). Various mechanisms, based on tautomeric forms, have been suggested for these several reactions.[85, 396] It will be noted that the dehydration of ricinoleic acid gives rise to two acids, namely, 9,12-octadecadienoic acid and 9,11-octadecadienoic acid. The former is linoleic acid and the latter is isomeric with linoleic acid and contains a conjugated system of double bonds. The dehydration of ricinoleic acid was studied in 1914 by Fokin,[397] who treated ricinoleic acid with phosphoric anhydride in the presence of benzene. The formation of both the conjugated and the unconjugated octadecadienoic acids was recognized; however, Fokin considered that the product consisted chiefly of the unconjugated acid. Two years later the dehydration of castor oil was extensively studied by Kronstein.[398] In 1930, Böeseken and Hoevers [399] studied the dehydration of ricinoleic acid in the presence of activated alumina, and several years later Scheiber [400] obtained patents for synthetic drying oils prepared from these conjugated acids. Several other catalysts have been proposed for this dehydration, among which may be mentioned non-oxidizing mineral acids,[401] Japanese acid earth,[402] sulfuric acid,[403] and metallic oxides.[404] The question as to the relative proportions of conjugated and unconjugated dienoic acids formed by the dehydration of ricinoleic acid has been the subject of some disagreement. Scheiber [405] stated that the 9,11-acid comprised 90% of the dienoic acids formed, a view which is quite contrary to that previously expressed by Fokin.[397] Recently, Forbes and Neville [406] and also Priest and von Mikusch [407] have stated that the dehydration of castor oil yields from 22 to 31% of conjugated dienoic acids. It seems quite probable, therefore, that this dehydration forms approximately equal amounts of ordinary linoleic acid and its conjugated isomer.

The conjugated acid, 9,11-octadecadienoic acid, when treated with nitrous acid, yields an acid which melts at 54°.[394] The bromination of this acid gives two tetrabromostearic acids, one melting at 130° and the other at 64–65°. Debromination of the former yields an acid melting at 54° and a liquid acid, whereas debromination of the latter gives only a liquid acid. The bromination of 9,11-octadecadienoic acid gives a tetrabromide melting at 124° which yields, upon debromination, an acid melting at 56°. All these acids showed an exaltation of the molecular refraction which indicated that they possess conjugated unsaturation. The acid melting at 54° was considered to be a stereoisomer of that melting at 56°, since a mixed melting point showed them to differ. 9,11-Octadecadienoic acid has been reported by Khonovskii [408] to be produced by the action of alcoholic potassium hydroxide on the diiodostearic acid formed by the action of hydrogen iodide on ricinoleic acid. Maruyama and Suzuki [409] have reported the presence of 9,11-octadecadienoic acid together with stearolic acid in the product formed by the action of alcoholic potassium hydroxide on 9,10-dichlorostearic acid.

Other Octadecadienoic Acids

The hydrogenation of polyethenoic fatty acids or their glycerides has been reported in several instances to yield octadecadienoic acids other than those described above. Bauer and Ermann [278] have stated that 12,15-octadecadienoic acid is present in the products formed during the partial hydrogenation of unsaturated acids. Since these dienoic acids have not been isolated or described, their existence is somewhat hypothetical.

The Trienoic Acids

Acids which contain three double bonds in the hydrocarbon chain are characteristic of the vegetable drying oils, to which they impart the property of forming hard films upon exposure to the atmosphere. Owing to the high degree of unsaturation of these acids they are quite easily polymerized or oxidized. They add six atoms of halogens to form hexahalo acids. The trienoic acids which occur in nature are essentially confined to those which possess eighteen carbon atoms, and, as in the case of the important naturally occurring dienoic acids, these acids show a remarkable structural similarity to oleic acid. Only two acids of this series are of major importance: linolenic acid, or 9,12,15-octadecatrienoic acid; and eleostearic acid, or 9,11,13-octadecatrienoic acid.

The specific properties of the trienoic acids are quite dependent upon the relative positions of the double bonds, the most important factor being whether these bonds form a conjugated or an isolated system of unsaturated linkages. The various considerations regarding geometrical isomerism of these acids and optical isomerism of their derivatives are somewhat more complex than is the case with the dienoic acids. Our present knowledge indicates that those generalizations which apply to the acids of lower unsaturation apply equally to these trienoic acids. Hydrogenation of the naturally occurring octadecatrienoic acids to stearic acid shows that they possess a straight chain of carbon atoms.

9,12,15-Octadecatrienoic Acid (Linolenic Acid).

$$CH_3CH_2CH:CHCH_2CH:CHCH_2CH:CH(CH_2)_7CO_2H$$

Linolenic acid occurs as a major component in the vegetable drying oils, the most important of which is linseed oil. It was first recognized as an individual acid by Hazura and Friedreich [410] during a study of the oxidation products of hemp oil acids. These authors isolated a hexahydroxystearic acid, melting at 203°, from the oxidation products, the formation of which indicated that a trienoic acid was present in the acid mixture. Later in the same year, Hazura [411] showed that hexabromostearic acid was not formed by the bromination of tetrabromostearic acid but by the bromination of a trienoic acid originally present, and he thus confirmed the existence of linolenic acid in the drying oils. Erdmann, Bedford, and Raspe [412] studied the products formed during the decomposition of the ozonides of ethyl α- and β-linolenates and stated that these acids are stereoisomerides, the structure of which is 9,12,15-octadecatrienoic acid. This formula for linolenic acid has been confirmed by subsequent workers.[188, 348, 413, 414]

When mixtures containing linolenic acid are brominated, one of the products is an ether-insoluble, solid hexabromide which melts at 179.5–180°. The reduction of this solid hexabromostearic acid by means of zinc yields a linolenic acid, the molecular weight and iodine number of which are close to the theoretical values. Until the preparation of natural linolenic acid by low-temperature solvent crystallization,[415] the debromination method offered the only source of reasonably pure linolenic acid. When this regenerated linolenic acid is rebrominated, it yields about 25% of the solid hexabromide melting at 179.5–180°, whereas the remainder is a liquid hexabromide which is soluble in ether. The acid resulting from the debromination of this solid hexabromide is known as α-linolenic acid, and that from the liquid hexabromide as β-linolenic acid. It can be seen, therefore, that the action of linolenic acid upon bromination and debromination is somewhat analogous to that of linoleic acid. As in the case of linoleic acid, therefore, we are faced with the questions as to whether these processes are accompanied by isomeric changes or whether the naturally occurring linolenic acid is actually a mixture of stereoisomeric acids. The number of isomeric possibilities inherent in linolenic acid and its derivatives, together with the difficulties of obtaining and working with pure natural linolenic acid, have made this question extremely difficult to answer. The formulation of any very definite views with relation to the stereochemical configurations of these various linolenic acids is certainly unwarranted until our present knowledge of them is materially increased. Erdmann and Bedford[389] considered α-linolenic acid to be identical with that found in seed fats, but believed that the linolenic acid obtained by the debromination of the solid hexabromide is a mixture of α- and β-linolenic acids. Since the bromination of regenerated linolenic acid yielded 23% of the solid hexabromide and 77% of the liquid hexabromide, they considered that these values represent the percentages of the two stereoisomers present in the debrominated acid. Later, Erdmann, Bedford, and Raspe[412] claimed to have obtained two ozonides from regenerated linolenic acid which they considered to correspond to the two isomeric acids originally present. Rollett[342] claimed the existence of two acids in regenerated linolenic acid and stated that bromination produces optical isomers of varying solubilities. These isomers would regenerate the original linolenic acid upon debromination. A study of the bromination of linolenic acid obtained from lumbang oil led Smith and West[350] to conclude that a molecular rearrangement occurs during the debromination but not during the bromination process.

Van der Veen [351] believes that there is an equilibrium between the isomers set up during the bromination process.

Shinowara and Brown [415] have compared the linolenic acid which they obtained by the low-temperature crystallization of the fatty acids of linseed and perilla oils with α-linolenic acid prepared by debromination of solid hexabromostearic acid. The crystallized acids showed hexabromide numbers [416] which averaged 92 (calculated as the free acid), while the hexabromide numbers of the debrominated α-acids ranged from 70 to 75. The purity of their crystallized acid was determined to be 88.0%, while that of the α-linolenic acid was assumed to be 100%. The former melted at $-11.2°$ and the latter at -14.5 to $-14.4°$. These authors concluded that the acids prepared by low-temperature crystallization and by debromination are not identical and that the latter are probably mixtures of either geometrical or position isomers. The possibility that the crystallized acids may be isomeric mixtures is also suggested. Recently, Matthews, Brode, and Brown [391] have subjected debrominated linolenic acid to low-temperature, fractional crystallization and have stated that the acid is apparently a mixture of at least two isomers. These isomers are of the cis-trans type and possess the same iodine numbers but different melting points. The lower-melting acid probably has a zero hexabromide number; the higher-melting acid showed a hexabromide number of 96.0 and was believed to be identical with natural linolenic acid. The isomerization is believed to be brought about during the process of debromination. A study of the bromination of elaidinized linolenic acid, however, has led Kass, Nichols, and Burr [417] to state that no significant isomerization occurs during the debromination process. Elaidolinolenic acid was prepared by the action of selenium on the ethyl esters of linseed oil fatty acids. The elaidolinolenic acid gives a hexabromide which melts at 169–170° and which shows a mixed melting point of 152–162° with α-hexabromostearic acid. Debromination of this elaidolinolenic acid hexabromide yields an acid melting at 29–30°, the bromination of which gives a 30.9–31.1% yield of the hexabromide melting at 169–170°. The average hexabromide number is thus 84.5. These results are not antagonistic to Rollett's view that the hexabromides of linolenic acid are racemic mixtures. It is of interest to note that Kass, Nichols, and Burr obtained both a solid and a liquid hexabromide from a completely elaidinized acid, assumed to be the stereoisomeride containing only traces of cis linkages. The formation of two or more hexabromides from natural linolenic acid or from α-linolenic acid does not, therefore, demand that such acids be composed of a mixture of stereoisomerides. Thus the terms β-linolenic acid and isolinolenic acid have little significance when applied to the naturally occurring acid. Somewhat previous to this work, McCutcheon [418] had stated that α- and β-linolenic acids are identical and that they are also identical with natural linolenic acid. Later, McCutcheon, Crawford, and Welch [356] reported that the infrared and Raman spectroscopic examinations of both linoleic and linolenic acids indicated that they possess only cis ethylenic linkages. The facts that pure linolenic acid has never been obtained directly from natural oils and that most of our views with regard to this acid are based upon a study of the acid prepared by debromination make definite standards of comparison very difficult to obtain. In view of the data pertaining to other unsaturated fatty acids, it is felt that linolenic acid should be considered as a homogeneous substance until definite proof has been offered to the contrary.

The oxidation of linolenic acid by means of potassium permanganate has been shown by Hazura and coworkers [340, 410, 411] to yield two hexahydroxystearic acids (linusic acids). These acids were termed linusic acid (m.p. 203°) and isolinusic acid (m.p. 173–175°) and can be separated by reason of the greater solubility of the latter in hot water. As shown in the case of the bromine derivatives, however, the formation of these two oxidation products does not require the previous existence of stereoisomerides in the original acid. A hexahydroxystearic acid melting at 178–179° was obtained by Kass, Nichols, and Burr [417] by the partial oxidation of elaidolinolenic acid by means of alkaline potassium permanganate. The presence or absence of a second hexadroxystearic acid in the reaction product was not conclusively shown.

Linolenic acid is generally associated with the drying oils of vegetable origin. Smaller amounts are also present in the semi-drying oils. Its presence in small percentages in certain animal fats is probably due to assimilation, and the inclusion of small amounts of linolenic acid in animal diets has been shown to cure certain fat-deficiency diseases.[419] Linolenic acid has been reported to occur in linseed oil in amounts ranging from 36 to 50%.[420, 421, 422] Jamieson and McKinney [423] have reported 7.4% of linolenic acid in American black walnut oil, and Ueno and Nishikawa [424] have observed 8.6% in a Japanese walnut oil. Various other values of this magnitude have been reported.[425, 426] Amounts of linolenic acid varying from 6 to 24% have been reported in hemp seed oil.[425, 427, 428] Among other oils in which linolenic acid is present as a major component may be mentioned: cedar nut oil,[429] chrysalis oil,[430] fig seed oil,[431] perilla oil,[432] pine seed oil,[433] and Para rubber seed oil.[434] It is present as a minor component in many of the semi-drying oils of vegetable origin, such as soybean oil,[371] 2.1%, and grape seed oil,[435] 2.4%. Small amounts have been reported in butter fat.[436]

Prior to the work of Shinowara and Brown,[415] the hexabromide reduction method [437] was generally employed for the preparation of linolenic acid. Although this method results in a linolenic acid having the theoretical iodine number and molecular weight, the yields are poor and the possibility of isomerization during the process has not been rigidly excluded. The fractional crystallization method eliminates the possibility of isomerization; however, it involves working at extremely low temperatures and does not produce a linolenic acid free from other unsaturated acids. The method is based on the fact that linolenic acid is more soluble in acetone and other organic solvents than the acids with which it is associated. Fractional crystallization of the fatty acids of either linseed or perilla oil from acetone at $-23°$, $-45°$, $-60°$, and finally at $-75°$ resulted in a filtrate which yielded a linolenic acid of 75% purity. Repeated crystallization of this product from petroleum ether at $-60°$ resulted in a linolenic acid of 88% purity. The contaminant was assumed to be linoleic acid.

Linolenic acid is a colorless liquid soluble in petroleum ether, acetone, ethanol, and ether. Shinowara and Brown [415] reported a melting point of -11.2 to $-11.0°$ and n_D^{20} 1.4780 for the acid prepared by the crystallization method, and -14.5 to $-14.4°$ and n_D^{20} 1.4795 for the purified debrominated acid. Linolenic acid can be distilled without material decomposition, $b_{0.001-0.002}$ 157–158°. Its density has been reported as d_4^{20} 0.9046.

6,9,12-Octadecatrienoic Acid.

$$CH_3(CH_2)_4CH:CHCH_2CH:CHCH_2CH:CH(CH_2)_4CO_2H$$

This acid was first observed by Heiduschka and Lüft,[438] along with ordinary linolenic acid, in the oil obtained from the seeds of the evening primrose. It yielded a hexabromostearic acid which melted at 195–196° and a hexahydroxystearic acid melting at 245°. Heiduschka and Lüft termed the acid γ-linolenic acid. In 1927,

Eibner, Widenmayer, and Schild [176] investigated the ozonization products of γ-linolenic acid and reported the acid to be 6,9,12-octadecatrienoic acid. They reported that its hexabromide melts without decomposition at 203°. The structural similarity of γ-linolenic acid to both petroselinic acid and oleic acid is noteworthy. It has been described as a bright yellow, pleasant-smelling liquid.

Other Non-conjugated Octadecatrienoic Acids

Fahrion [439] has described an acid, claimed to be an octadecatrienoic acid (jecoric acid), which is present in small amounts in sardine oil. The identity of jecoric acid has not been established and Lewkowitsch [440] has expressed the opinion that it is impure clupanodonic acid.

A supposedly non-conjugated octadecatrienoic acid has recently been reported [441] to be present in the oil from the seeds of *Santalum album*, and the name santalbic acid has been proposed. The acid melts at 41–42° and does not give a solid hexabromostearic acid upon bromination. The actual structure of this acid has not been determined.

9,11,13-Octadecatrienoic Acid (Eleostearic Acid).
$$CH_3(CH_2)_3CH:CHCH:CHCH:CH(CH_2)_7CO_2H$$

Eleostearic acid, the principal acid of Chinese wood oil or tung oil, possesses a conjugated system of three double bonds. Owing to the presence of this conjugated unsaturation, the chemical and physical properties of eleostearic acid differ greatly from those of linolenic acid.

Eleostearic acid readily adds two molecules of halogen; however, the third molecule is added only with great difficulty. Earlier workers, therefore, were of the opinion that eleostearic acid contained only two ethylenic linkages and was isomeric with linoleic acid. Two forms of eleostearic acid, designated as α- and β-, are known, the latter resulting from the former by the action of light, heat, or various catalysts. Both of these acids are solids, α-eleostearic acid melting at 48° and β-eleostearic acid at 71°. They are considered to be stereoisomers; however, we still have much to learn concerning the relationship which exists between them. Only α-eleostearic acid occurs in the natural oils, and this acid was at first termed eleomargaric acid.

Cloëz [442] considered eleostearic acid to be $C_{17}H_{30}O_2$; however, in 1902 Maquenne [443] proposed the formula $C_{18}H_{30}O_2$, and suggested the names α- and β-eleostearic acid to describe the lower- and higher-melting isomerides respectively. A study of the bromination of eleostearic acid led Kametaka [444] to state that it is a dienoic acid of the formula $C_{18}H_{32}O_2$, which opinion was accepted for many years. Majima [445] isolated valeraldehyde, valeric acid, azelaic acid semialdehyde, and azelaic acid from the products of decomposition of eleostearic acid ozonide, and thus placed the double bonds between the ninth and tenth and the thirteenth and fourteenth carbon atoms, as Maquenne [443] had previously assumed, the formula being $CH_3(CH_2)_3CH:CH(CH_2)_2CH:CH(CH_2)_7CO_2H$. This proposed formula found many adherents.[446, 447, 448] Both α- and β-eleostearic acids easily absorb two moles of bromine, with the formation of a solid tetrabromide melting at 115° and a liquid tetrabromide. The similarity in the melting point of this solid tetrabromide with that obtained from linoleic acid suggested that eleostearic acid is a stereoisomeride of linoleic acid. In 1921, Nicolet [449] showed that the tetrabromide from eleostearic acid, and that from linoleic acid are not identical, and in the next year Bauer and Herberts [447] pointed out that the debromination of α-eleostearic acid tetrabromide by means of zinc yields only β-eleostearic acid. These facts apparently confirmed the supposition that eleostearic acid is a position isomer of linoleic acid, and in 1924 Eibner, Merz, and Munzert [448] attributed the peculiar properties of eleostearic acid to the presence of two methylene groups massed between two ethylenic linkages. The fact that eleostearic acid contains three ethylenic linkages was suggested by the work of Böeseken and Ravenswaay,[450] who called attention to the high molecular refraction of this acid and observed that it reacted with more than two moles of hydrogen during hydrogenation. They considered that eleostearic acid contains three conjugated double bonds and proposed the formula $CH_3(CH_2)_3$-$CH:CHCH:CHCH:CH(CH_2)_7CO_2H$, which is the present accepted structure. This structure has been confirmed by Eibner and Rossmann [451] from a detailed study of the ozonide decomposition products. Fokin [452] had previously stated that eleostearic acid contained a conjugated system; however, he assumed the presence of only two double bonds. The action of conjugated systems upon halogenation explains why eleostearic acid readily forms a tetrabromide which resists further bromination. If the present accepted formula for eleostearic acid is correct, the tetrabromide should contain a double bond which can be further brominated or oxidized. The hexabromide of eleostearic acid has been prepared by Bauer and Rohrbach [453] and also by van Loon,[454] by bromination of eleostearic acid in the presence of ultraviolet light. The former of these reported a melting point of 139–141° and the latter, 157°. Debromination by means of zinc yielded β-eleostearic acid. The oxidation of eleostearic acid tetra-bromide by means of peracetic acid has shown that it contains an ethylenic bond.[455] Böeseken and van Krimpen [270] have stated that the hydrogenation of eleostearic acid with one mole of hydro-gen gives an acid which contains a conjugated system of two double bonds. The spectroscopic absorption studies of Manecke and Volbert,[456] together with the extended investigation of the oxidation products by Morrell and Marks,[457] have further con-firmed the belief that eleostearic acid is a conjugated isomer of linolenic acid.

The naturally occurring form of eleostearic acid, α-eleostearic acid, has been assumed to have a *cis* configuration.[458] The prepa-ration of this acid from Chinese wood oil has been described in detail by Thomas and Thomson.[459] Eleostearic acid is easily con-verted by light, heat, or catalysts such as iodine or sulfur into the higher-melting β-isomer. Debromination of the solid or liquid bromides resulting from the bromination of either α- or β-eleo-stearic acid results in the formation of β-eleostearic acid. All attempts to reconvert β-eleostearic acid into α-eleostearic acid have been unsuccessful. A study of the oxidation products of these acids indicates that they are *cis-trans* isomers. α-Eleostearic acid melts at 48° and distils at 235° under 12 mm. in the presence of carbon dioxide. It is easily soluble in ether, ethanol, carbon di-sulfide, and petroleum ether. β-Eleostearic acid melts at 71° and is also soluble in the above solvents.

Japanese tung oil [460] has been reported to contain 74.1% of eleostearic acid, Chinese tung oil [461, 462] 78.0 to 79.7%, and Florida tung oil [463] 94.1%. Eleostearic acid is a major component of bagilumbang nut oil [464] and essang seed oil,[465] and also occurs in smaller amounts in several other seed oils.

Conjugated unsaturated acids and their glycerides are quite easily polymerized and possess the property of forming elastic gels upon heating. Their chemical properties are characterized by 1,4-addition, and their physical properties by exaltation of the molecular refraction and characteristic ultraviolet absorptions. Among the distinguishing reactions of conjugated acids is their ability to combine with maleic anhydride, a reaction which is extensively employed for their quantitative estimation. In 1928, Diels and Alder [466] ascertained that compounds such as maleic anhydride form 1,4-addition products with conjugated diene hydrocarbons. Böeseken and Hoevers [399] have applied this reaction to 9,11-octadecadienoic acid obtained by the dehydration of ricinoleic acid, and Morrell and Samuels [467] have investigated the maleic anhydride addition products of α- and β-eleostearic acids. Both α- and β-eleostearic acids yield crystalline maleic anhydride addition products which melt at 62° and 77° respectively. Oxidation of these derivatives indicates that addition takes place at the eleventh and fourteenth carbon atoms in the former case and at the ninth and twelfth carbon atoms in the latter. The so-called diene value is a measure of the ability of fatty oils and acids to add maleic anhydride. In 1936–37, Kaufmann and coworkers [468] developed a laboratory method based upon maleic anhydride addition to determine the number of conjugated double bonds present in an acid or oil. The sample is treated with an excess of maleic anhydride in acetone, and, after completion of the reaction, the excess anhydride is removed by washing with water and is determined by titration with standard alkali. Simultaneously, Ellis and Jones [469] announced an essentially similar method in which toluene is employed as the solvent and the addition is catalyzed by a trace of iodine. These two methods have recently been compared by Pelikan and von Mikusch.[470] Bickford, Dollear, and Markley [471] and also Bruce and Denley [472] observed that hydroxylated compounds containing no conjugated bonds showed significant diene values. Lately, McKinney and Jamieson [473] have reported that eleostearic acid does not react quantitatively with maleic anhydride.

10,12,14-Octadecatrienoic Acid (Pseudo-eleostearic Acid).

$$CH_3(CH_2)_2CH:CHCH:CHCH:CH(CH_2)_8CO_2H$$

The treatment of linolenic acid or its glyceride with an excess of alkali was observed by Moore [474] to yield an acid which melts at 77° and which possesses a similarity to eleostearic acid. Two years later, Kass and Burr [475] subjected linseed oil fatty acids to the action of excess potassium hydroxide in anhydrous ethylene glycol and made an extended investigation of the resulting product. The oxidation products consisted of sebacic, oxalic, and n-butyric acids, indicating that the acid is 10,12,14-octadecatrienoic acid. It easily adds two moles of bromine to form a tetrabromide which melts at 104.5°. The bromination of pseudo-eleostearic acid in the presence of ultraviolet light results in the formation of the hexabromide, which melts at 152.5°. Kass and Burr suggested that this acid possesses a *trans,trans,trans* or a *trans,cis,trans* configuration, since it fails to yield clearly defined maleic anhydride addition products.

The Polyethenoic Acids

Acids which contain four or more ethylenic bonds are important components of the highly unsaturated oils of aquatic origin. They occur, to a much more limited extent, in certain animal fats, notably those of the liver and brain, and are probably also present in traces in the animal depot fats. The polyethenoic acids yield normal saturated acids upon hydrogenation, which shows them to possess straight hydrocarbon chains. The principal unsaturated acids of vegetable origin contain eighteen carbon atoms and show a structural similarity to oleic acid in that they possess a double bond between the ninth and tenth carbon atoms and contain the group $:CH(CH_2)_7CO_2H$. In the polyethenoic group, however, C_{20} and C_{22} acids appear to predominate, and these acids show little resemblance to the unsaturated fatty acids of the vegetable kingdom. Groups such as $:CHCH_2CH:$, $:CH(CH_2)_2CH:$, and $:CH(CH_2)_2CO_2H$ are characteristic of the polyethenoic acids of marine oils, and it is interesting to note that in spite of their high degree of unsaturation conjugation is apparently absent.[476] Owing to the difficulty of obtaining these acids in a state of purity and in view of their high chemical activity, the actual structures of many of the polyethenoic acids have not been definitely proved. The polyethenoic acids can be classified according to their origin into those which occur in the marine oils and those which are found in the animal and vegetable kingdoms. Although such an empirical classification leaves much to be desired, it is necessitated by the present uncertainties regarding the characterization of many of the individual acids of this group.

POLYETHENOIC ACIDS OF AQUATIC ORIGIN

The highly unsaturated acids present in fish oils, marine animal oils, algae fats, and other oils of aquatic origin were first investigated by Tsujimoto.[477] These acids may be separated from the more saturated acids by the fact that their lithium salts are exceedingly soluble in 95% acetone. The bromine derivatives of the more highly unsaturated acids are sparingly soluble in cold benzene. Fractional distillation of the ethyl esters of the acid mixtures obtained either by the lithium salt-acetone method or by the polybromide method has resulted in the isolation of acids which in many cases appear to be chemical individuals. In his initial work upon these highly unsaturated acids, Tsujimoto considered only one acid to be present, to which he gave the name clupanodonic acid and assigned the formula $C_{18}H_{28}O_2$. Subsequent work has shown that these acid mixtures contain highly unsaturated acids having from sixteen to twenty-four or more carbon atoms, and that C_{20} and C_{22} acids predominate. It has also been recognized that acids of different degrees of unsaturation are probably present in each of these series. In studying these acids it must be realized, therefore, that the structures assigned to them are still somewhat open to speculation and are subject to future revision.

The work of Tsujimoto was followed by a chemical examination of the highly unsaturated acids of herring oil [97, 125] which showed that approximately 7% of such acids are present and that in addition to the so-called clupanodonic acid the oil contained acids corresponding to the formulas $C_{20}H_{30}O_2$ and $C_{22}H_{34}O_2$. In a subsequent investigation, Tsujimoto [478] stated that clupanodonic acid has the formula $C_{22}H_{34}O_2$ and not $C_{18}H_{28}O_2$ as he had formerly suggested. Since this latter acid is also a recognized component of the highly unsaturated fish oils, this change in nomenclature was not without opposition.[479] The names moroctic [480] and stearidonic [481] acid have since been given to $C_{18}H_{28}O_2$. Tsujimoto [482] separated the acids of sardine oil by both the lithium salt-acetone and the polybromide methods, and the repeated fractional distillation of these products resulted in the preparation of nearly pure clupanodonic acid, which he described as a light yellow liquid with a fishy odor. This liquid became a semi-solid at $-78°$; its physical constants were reported to be: d_4^{15} 0.9385, d_4^{20} 0.9356, n_D^{15} 1.5039, and n_D^{20} 1.5020. Eibner and Semmelbauer [483] confirmed the presence of substantial amounts of docosapentaenoic acid in fish oils. A study of the decomposition products [484] of the ozonide of clupanodonic acid showed the following groups to be present in this acid: (1) $CH_3CH_2CH:$, (2) $:CHCH_2CH:$, (3) $:CH(CH_2)_2CH:$, and (4) $:CH(CH_2)_2CO_2H$. The later investigations of Toyama and Tsuchiya [485] upon the decomposition products of the ozonides both of amyl clupanodonate and of the di- and tetrabromides of clupanodonic acid indicated that clupanodonic acid is 4,8,12,15,19-docosapentaenoic acid. The evidence offered by Inoue and Kato [486] to the effect that clupanodonic acid contains an acetylenic linkage has not been confirmed.[487]

Although clupanodonic acid is the best known of the highly unsaturated acids occurring in oils of aquatic origin, it is, as previously stated, only one of perhaps many highly unsaturated acids present in such oils. Several of these acids have been isolated and structures tentatively assigned to them; however, their existence as chemical individuals requires further confirmation. It is quite certain that at least one highly unsaturated member of each of the C_{16}, C_{18}, C_{20}, C_{22}, and C_{24} series of acids occurs in these oils, and it is also probable that several of these series may be represented by more than one acid. In general, the number of ethylenic linkages increases with the number of carbon atoms. In the following description of the acids which have so far been identified as components of fish oils and various marine oils, it should be borne in mind that the assigned structures are still subject to revision.

Hexadecatrienoic Acid (Hiragonic Acid). $C_{16}H_{26}O_2$

Hiragonic acid has been described by Toyama and Tsuchiya,[488] who isolated the acid from sardine oil. The hexabromide is insoluble in ether but soluble in benzene, which permits of its separation from the other unsaturated acids of sardine oil. Hiragonic acid has been described as a yellow liquid of d_4^{15} 0.9324, d_4^{20} 0.9288, n_D^{15} 1.4876, n_D^{20} 1.4855, and iodine number 310.6. The hexabromide melts at 190°. Hydrogenation produces palmitic acid. The oxidation products of methyl hiragonate have been studied by Toyama and Tsuchiya,[480] and these authors are of the opinion that hiragonic acid is 6,10,14-hexadecatrienoic acid.

Octadecatetraenoic Acid (Moroctic Acid, Stearidonic Acid). $C_{18}H_{28}O_2$

The presence of an octadecatetraenoic acid in fish oils was first suggested by Tsujimoto [477] and was confirmed by Brown and Beal [479] and later by Suzuki and Masuda.[481] Its octabromide has been reported to melt at 104.5°.[489] Hydrogenation of this acid yields stearic acid. Toyama and Tsuchiya [480] prepared the acid by the debromination of the ether- and benzene-insoluble bromides of the highly unsaturated acids of sardine oil. The following physical constants were reported: d_4^{15} 0.9334, d_4^{20} 0.9297, n_D^{15} 1.4930, n_D^{20} 1.4911, mol. ref. 86.00, iodine number (Wijs) 372.6. Ozonolysis of both the methyl ester and the tetrathiocyanate indicated moroctic acid to be 4,8,12,15-octadecatetraenoic acid.

Eicosatetraenoic Acid. $C_{20}H_{32}O_2$

Eicosatetraenoic acid has frequently been reported to occur in fish and whale oils. Toyama and Tsuchiya [490] have claimed to have obtained this acid by subjecting a high-boiling fraction of the ethyl esters of sardine oil to a sodium soap-acetone separation. Hydrogenation of eicosatetraenoic acid produces arachidic acid. Ozonolysis of the amyl ester indicated the acid to be 4,8,12,16-eicosatetraenoic acid.

Eicosapentaenoic Acid (Timnodonic Acid). $C_{20}H_{30}O_2$

Eicosapentaenoic acid has been stated to occur along with eicosatetraenoic acids in the highly unsaturated acids of sardine oil. Toyama and Tsuchiya [490] obtained the acid from the high-boiling ethyl esters of sardine oil and subjected the amyl ester to ozonolysis. Their results indicated that this acid is 4,8,12,15,18-eicosapentaenoic acid. In 1937, Sanna [491] named this acid timnodonic acid.

Docosahexaenoic Acid. $C_{22}H_{32}O_2$

An acid claimed to be docosahexaenoic acid has been obtained, along with clupanodonic acid, from the high-boiling esters of sardine oil.[492] Ozonolysis of the amyl ester indicated the acid to be either 4,8,12,15,18,21- or 4,8,11,14,17,20-docosahexaenoic acid. The former structure was preferred by the discoverers.

Tetracosahexaenoic Acid (Nisinic Acid). $C_{24}H_{36}O_2$

Tetracosahexaenoic acid has been reported by Toyama and Tsuchiya [493] to be present as its methyl ester in the residue resulting from the distillation of the methyl esters of sardine oil. The acid was separated by the fractional precipitation of the sodium soaps from acetone. The amyl ester was ozonized and the decomposition products determined. A study of these products, with the assumption that the structure of nisinic acid is correlated with that of moroctic acid, indicated that nisinic acid is 3,8,12,15,18,21-tetracosahexaenoic acid.

Tetracosapentaenoic Acid (Scoliodonic Acid). $C_{24}H_{38}O_2$

Ueno and Iwai [494] have reported the presence of a tetracosapentaenoic acid, to which they gave the name scoliodonic acid, in fish liver oils. The acid was stated by Toyama and Tsuchiya [493] to accompany nisinic acid in the distillation residue obtained during the fractionation of the methyl esters of sardine oil acids. Ueno and Takase [495] oxidized tetracosapentaenoic acid by means of ozone, obtaining succinic and acetic acids, acetaldehyde, and carbon dioxide, thus indicating the presence of the following groups: $:CH(CH_2)_2CO_2H$, $:CHCH_2CH:$, and $CH_3CH_2CH:$.

Hexacosapentaenoic Acid (Shibic Acid). $C_{26}H_{42}O_2$

Hexacosapentaenoic acid has been observed by Ueno and Yonese [496] to be present in small amounts in tunny oil. It has also been reported to occur in other fish oils.[497]

Hexacosahexaenoic Acid (Thynnic Acid). $C_{26}H_{40}O_2$

Hexacosahexaenoic acid has been stated by Ueno and Yonese [498] to be present in small amounts in tunny oil. Its physical constants were reported to be: d_4^{20} 0.9433, n_D^{20} 1.5022, and iodine number 372.1.

The distribution of the highly unsaturated fatty acids which occur in the various types of aquatic life offers an unusually interesting biological and chemical study. Although the total amounts of polyethenoic acids in the fats of fresh water fish and of marine fish and marine mammals are comparable, there are some very significant differences in the relative proportions of the various types of acids contained in these fats. In general, the fats of fresh water fish are characterized by the presence of large amounts of unsaturated C_{18} acids with relatively small amounts of unsaturated C_{20} and C_{22} acids, whereas in the marine fats the unsaturated C_{20} and C_{22} acids predominate and the highly unsaturated C_{16} and C_{18} acids are present in much smaller proportions. Lovern [9] has suggested that this difference in composition may be attributable to differences in the food consumed and perhaps to environmental conditions. In 1937, Lovern [499] made a comparison of the fats of the migratory sea trout and of the non-migratory brown trout and found that they are definitely characteristic of the marine and fresh water types of fats respectively. The C_{18} unsaturated acids greatly predominated in the latter, whereas the former contained a relatively greater amount of unsaturated C_{20} and C_{22} acids. A comparison of the composition of the fats of grass- and mud-feeding carp with the food consumed showed that factors other than the food must play an important role in determining the composition of such fats.[500]

The compositions of the fats of marine mammals approach those of other marine species; however, highly unsaturated C_{18} acids are more abundant in such fats than in the fish fats of marine origin. Certain marine mammal oils are distinguished by relatively large amounts of unsaponifiable matter; the oil of the sperm whale, for example, contains appreciable quantities of wax esters, the presence of which may be due to some hydrogenation process which occurs during fat metabolism. Fish liver oils are, in general, more unsaturated than the body fats and are characterized by the presence of quite large amounts of highly unsaturated C_{20} and C_{22} acids. Fish and marine animal liver oils contain appreciable quantities of unsaponifiable materials which are present as higher alcohols or as the terpenoid hydrocarbon squalene. Hilditch and Houlbrooke [104] have commented upon the large amount of squalene present in shark liver oils and have suggested several possible mechanisms for its formation.

The fats of amphibians and reptiles are intermediate in composition between fats of aquatic and terrestrial origin. Tsujimoto [501] has shown that such fats contain highly unsaturated C_{20} and C_{22} acids, and Klenk [144, 502] has observed that frog fat resembles that of aquatic origin whereas lizard fat is of intermediate composition. Appreciable amounts of highly unsaturated C_{20} and C_{22} acids have been reported by Kobayashi [503] to be present in both crocodile and alligator fats.

The fats contained in aquatic plants do not appear to exhibit the characteristic constitutional differences between fresh water and marine types which have been observed in the fish fats. Tsujimoto [504] reported small amounts of highly unsaturated acids in algae fats, and later Lovern [505] investigated the composition of the fats of a number of marine and fresh water algae. The fat of green algae definitely resembles that of fresh water fish in that the percentage of highly unsaturated C_{16} and C_{18} acids is quite high while that of the C_{20} and C_{22} acids is low. Brown algae contain more unsaturated C_{20} and C_{22} acids and the fat of the red algae is distinctly marine in character. The differentiation of the fats of these aquatic plants is, therefore, apparently correlated to the color of the algae rather than to their environment.

A large amount of data have appeared in the literature relative to the presence or percentages of the various highly unsaturated acids which occur in specific oils of aquatic origin. Many of these data, particularly from the earlier work, are probably quite empirical. Some of the acids which have been reported may actually not exist, while others, assumed to be pure, may presumably contain quite high amounts of other acids. Thus, the percentages of clupanodonic acid reported in many of the fats may actually refer to the total amounts of high molecular weight unsaturated acids. It is, however, of some interest to review a few of the typical observations which have been made upon the various types of fats of aquatic origin. Herring oil [506] has been reported to contain 9% of clupanodonic acid. Large amounts of clupanodonic acid have been observed in sturgeon oil,[507] while whitefish oil [508] and pilchard oil [509] contain 6.71 and 16.87% respectively. A large number of observations have been made upon whale oil,[112, 134, 282, 322, 501, 510, 511] shark and ray liver oils,[103, 137, 320] cod liver oil,[481, 512] tunny liver oil,[513] seal oil,[122, 514] sea turtle fat,[515] and the fats of both marine and fresh water algae.[504, 516]

A comparison of the compositions of the various highly unsaturated fats of aquatic origin is best obtained by reporting the mean unsaturation of the acids of various chain lengths rather than attempting an actual identification of the acids themselves. For example, in the analysis of a North Sea cod liver oil Hilditch and Terleski [105] have reported 22% of C_{18} acids (mean unsaturation $-3.3H$), 25% C_{20} acids (mean unsaturation $-5.5H$), 20% C_{22} acids (mean unsaturation $-7.4H$), and less than 1% C_{24} unsaturated acids. This method of comparison has been employed by many investigators.[517] Recently, Farmer and Van den Heuvel [518] have made an extremely important contribution to the study of the constitution of these highly unsaturated acids, and it is quite probable that a continuation of their work will establish the structures of many of these acids. These authors subjected mixtures of high molecular weight unsaturated acids or their esters to molecular distillation at 10^{-4} mm., the time of contact of the substance with the heated surfaces being not more than sixty seconds. They pointed out that the ease of separation of two acids of different chain length is much greater the lower the temperature at which the distillation is conducted. It was also observed that ordinary vacuum distillation of the methyl esters of highly unsaturated acids is attended by appreciable polymerization or cyclization owing to the prolonged heating. It is highly probable, therefore, that much of the earlier work upon the structures of these acids is questionable because of this factor. In a later communication, Farmer and Van den Heuvel [519] subjected the unsaturated acids of cod liver oil to molecular distillation. These acids were first separated from the more saturated acids by the lithium soap-acetone method. The highest temperature recorded was 110° and the total time of contact approximately sixty seconds. The mean number of ethylenic groups of the acids of various chain length was found to be as follows: C_{16}, 1.3; C_{18}, 2.7; C_{20}, 4.9; and C_{22}, 6. The refractive index, n_D^{20} 1.49300, and the molecular refraction, 107.25, showed the C_{22} acid to be homogeneous. Oxidation of the so-obtained methyl docosahexaenoate by potassium permanganate and by ozone showed it to possess one of five possible structures, which are: 4,8,11,14,17,25-, 4,7,11,14,17,25-, 4,7,10,14,17,25-, 4,7,10,13,17,20-, and 4,7,10,13,16,25-docosahexaenoic acids. These observations raise considerable doubt as to the correctness of the structures previously assigned to clupanodonic acid. Farmer and Van den Heuvel stated that the structure of the fish oil acids is such that a C_{26} or C_{28} acid can have a maximum of 8 double linkages; a C_{24}, 7; a C_{20} or C_{22}, 6; a C_{18}, 5; and a C_{16}, 4. It has been suggested that possibly the polyethenoic acids may be limited to one member for each chain length. The polyethenoic acids of aquatic origin certainly merit further investigation, which would undoubtedly result in a clarification of many of these points.

POLYETHENOIC ACIDS OF ANIMAL ORIGIN

The occurrence of polyethenoic fatty acids in certain animal fats, mainly those of the kidney, liver, and brain, was first suggested by Hartley.[520] In 1909, Hartley [267] announced the presence of an eicosatetraenoic acid, $C_{20}H_{32}O_2$, in liver lipides, the evidence being based upon the separation of an octabromoarachidic acid and an octahydroxyarachidic acid from the bromination and oxidation products of the highly unsaturated acids of liver lipides. Lewkowitsch [440] has suggested the name arachidonic acid for this acid. Levene and coworkers [521] have confirmed the presence of arachidonic acid in liver lecithin and also in egg lecithin and brain cephalins and lecithins. The evidence for the occurrence of arachidonic acid was based upon the isolation and debromination of the octabromide and the subsequent hydrogenation of the resulting product to arachidic acid. The isolation of arachidonic acid from brain tissue has been described by Wesson,[522] who also established the presence of small amounts of arachidonic acid in rat liver, pancreas, kidney, lung, spleen, lymph gland, and muscle fats, and suggested that arachidonic acid may be an intermediate product in the metabolism of certain fatty acids containing less than twenty carbon atoms.[523]   Kimura [524] has identified arachidonic acid in ox liver oil, and Suzuki [525] has observed it to occur in very small amounts in Chinese egg yolk oil. Snider and Bloor [526] have reported arachidonic acid to be present in liver lecithin.

Although arachidonic acid appears in the greatest amount in the fatty substances of the brain, liver, and glandular organs, it is apparently present in small amounts in all the animal fats and is probably an essential acid for animal nutrition.[366] Arachidonic acid has been observed in small percentages in human depot fat,[527, 528] in pig and ox depot fats,[529, 530] in beef heart lipides,[531] and in butter fat.[532]   Brown [533] has isolated from liver lipides an arachidonic acid having n_D^{23} 1.5563, iodine number 316.2 (theory 334), mol. wt. 306.8 (theory 304), and a polybromide number of 80.4. The acid was described as a light-amber-colored oil possessing a distinctly fishy odor.   In 1934, Ault and Brown [534] prepared arachidonic acid from beef suprarenal phosphatides by both the lithium soap-acetone and the polybromide methods and obtained an acid melting at $-49.5°$ which had n_D^{20} 1.4824, iodine number 332.7, and a polybromide number of 84.2.   The phosphatides of beef suprarenals have been observed to contain 22% of arachidonic acid [535] and have been stated to be the best starting material for the preparation of this acid.   Recently, Shinowara and Brown [536] have prepared methyl arachidonate by low-temperature, fractional crystallization from acetone of the methyl esters of the fatty acids of beef suprarenal phosphatides.   A comparison of the ester so obtained with methyl arachidonate prepared by the debromination method has indicated the two to be similar.   Ozonolysis and also oxidation of the resulting acid with potassium permanganate in acetone has shown the arachidonic acid from this source to be 6,10,14,18-eicosatetraenoic acid.

There is considerable evidence to support the belief that acids more highly unsaturated than arachidonic acid, such as highly unsaturated C_{22} and C_{24} acids, may also be present in certain animal fats.   Brown [537] has suggested the occurrence of a tetracosapentaenoic acid in brain lipides, and later Brown and Ault [538] stated that this acid is present in both beef and sheep brain lipides, but is absent, or present only in traces, in the lipides of hog brain. Docosapentaenoic acid has been reported in beef brain fatty acids; [539] Irving and Smith [153] have stated that both C_{20} and C_{22}

unsaturated acids occur in pig liver acids; and Sueyoshi and Furukubo [540] have observed a docosapentaenoic acid in the fatty acids
of egg lecithin. The presence of both C_{20} and C_{22} unsaturated
acids has been reported in pig depot fats [541] and egg yolk fat.[542]
Small amounts of clupanodonic acid have been observed in lard
oils.[543]

POLYETHENOIC ACIDS OF VEGETABLE ORIGIN

The polyethenoic acids characteristic of fats of marine and fresh
water origin and of various animal fats apparently do not occur
in the vegetable kingdom. The only example of a polyethenoic
acid in the vegetable fats is parinaric acid, which was first described
by Tsujimoto and Koyanagi.[544] They obtained the acid from
"akarittom" (*Parinarium laurinum*) seed fat and considered it
to be an isomer of eleostearic acid. Parinaric acid melts at 85–86°
and was found by Tsujimoto [545] to yield a β-parinaric acid melting
at 95–96° when exposed to light or to various catalytic agents.
An earlier investigation of this acid by Farmer and Sunderland [546]
showed it to contain four conjugated ethylenic linkages and established its structure as 9,11,13,15-octadecatetraenoic acid. The
presence of the ethylenic bond in the 9,10-position definitely
distinguishes this acid from the polyethenoic acids of aquatic or
animal origin.

References

1. Pigulevskiĭ, *J. Russ. Phys. Chem. Soc.*, **47**, 393 (1915).
2. Pigulevskiĭ, *ibid.*, **47**, 2032 (1915); **48**, 324 (1916).
3. Ivanov, *Bull. univ. Asie centrale*, No. **12**, 21 (1926).
4. Ivanov and Klokov, *Allgem. Oel- u. Fett-Ztg.*, **30**, 149 (1933).
5. Bauer, *Fettchem. Umschau*, **41**, 1 (1934).
6. Henriques and Hansen, *Skand. Arch. Physiol.*, **11**, 151 (1901).
7. Isaachsen, *ibid.*, **55**, 273 (1929).
8. Ellis and Zeller, *J. Biol. Chem.*, **89**, 185 (1930).
9. Lovern, *Biochem. J.*, **26**, 1978 (1932).
10. Klenk, Ditt, and Diebold, *Z. physiol. Chem.*, **232**, 54 (1935).
11. Zeidler, *Ann.*, **187**, 30 (1877).
12. Messerschmidt, *ibid.*, **208**, 92 (1881).
13. Conrad and Bischoff, *ibid.*, **204**, 166 (1880).
14. Perkin and Simonsen, *J. Chem. Soc.*, **91**, 816 (1907).
15. Doebner, *Ber.*, **35**, 1136 (1902).
16. Fittig, *Ann.*, **283**, 47 (1894).
17. Marburg, *ibid.*, **294**, 89 (1897).
18. Fichter and Pfister, *Ber.*, **37**, 1997 (1904).
19. Fittig and MacKenzie, *Ann.*, **283**, 82 (1894).
20. Thiele and Jehl, *Ber.*, **35**, 2320 (1902).

21. Goldberg and Linstead, *J. Chem. Soc.*, 2343 (1928).
22. Fittig and Spenzer, *Ann.*, **283**, 66 (1894).
23. Fittig and Fränkel, *ibid.*, **255**, 18 (1889).
24. Zincke and Küster, *Ber.*, **22**, 486 (1889).
25. Vierhaus, *ibid.*, **26**, 915 (1893).
26. Auwers, *Ann.*, **432**, 46 (1923).
27. Boxer and Linstead, *J. Chem. Soc.*, 740 (1931).
28. Crossley and Le Sueur, *ibid.*, **77**, 83 (1900).
29. Rupe, Ronus, and Lotz, *Ber.*, **35**, 4265 (1902).
30. Bourguel, *Compt. rend.*, **188**, 1494 (1929).
31. Menozzi and Pantoli, *Gazz. chim. ital.*, **23**, II, 209 (1893).
32. Wallach, *Ann.*, **312**, 171 (1900); **343**, 40 (1905).
33. Helferich and Malkomes, *Ber.*, **55**, 702 (1922).
34. Fichter and Langguth, *ibid.*, **30**, 2050 (1897).
35. Letch and Linstead, *J. Chem. Soc.*, 1994 (1934).
36. Linstead and Rydon, *ibid.*, 1995 (1934).
37. Walker and Lumsden, *ibid.*, **79**, 1197 (1901).
38. Ciamician and Silber, *Ber.*, **41**, 1071 (1908).
39. Fichter, *ibid.*, **29**, 2367 (1896).
40. Eccott and Linstead, *J. Chem. Soc.*, 2153 (1929).
41. Hofmann, *Ann.*, **110**, 129 (1859).
42. Doebner, *Ber.*, **33**, 2140 (1900).
43. Fittig, *ibid.*, **24**, 82 (1891).
44. Fittig and Barringer, *Ann.*, **161**, 307 (1872).
45. Fittig and Baker, *ibid.*, **283**, 117 (1894).
46. Rupe, *ibid.*, **327**, 157 (1903).
47. Evans and Farmer, *J. Chem. Soc.*, 1644 (1928).
48. Burton and Ingold, *ibid.*, 2022 (1929).
49. Delaby and Lecomte, *Bull. soc. chim.* [5], **4**, 1007 (1937).
50. Linstead and Noble, *J. Chem. Soc.*, 610 (1934).
51. Kon, Linstead, and Maclennan, *ibid.*, 2454 (1932).
52. Zaar, *Ber. Schimmel & Co., Akt.-Ges.*, 299 (1929).
53. Isaacs and Wilson, *J. Chem. Soc.*, 574 (1936).
54. Walbaum and Rosenthal, *Ber. Schimmel & Co., Akt.-Ges.*, 205 (1929); *J. prakt. Chem.* [2], **124**, 63 (1930).
55. Gaubert, Linstead, and Rydon, *J. Chem. Soc.*, 1971 (1937).
56. Fairweather, *Proc. Roy. Soc. Edinburgh*, **46**, 71 (1926).
57. Fichter and Gully, *Ber.*, **30**, 2047 (1897).
58. Fittig and Schmidt, *Ann.*, **255**, 68 (1889).
59. Delaby and Guillot-Allègre, *Bull. soc. chim.* [4], **53**, 301 (1933).
60. Carmichael, *J. Chem. Soc.*, **121**, 2545 (1922).
61. Bachman, *J. Am. Chem. Soc.*, **55**, 4279 (1933).
62. Brown and Walker, *Ann.*, **274**, 41 (1893).
63. Knoevenagel, Ger. Patent 156,560 (1902).
64. Fittig and Schneegans, *Ann.*, **227**, 79 (1885).
65. Harding and Weizmann, *Proc. Chem. Soc.*, **26**, 24 (1910).
66. Smedley, *Biochem. J.*, **6**, 451 (1912).
67. Grün and Wirth, *Ber.*, **55**, 2197 (1922).
68. Bosworth and Brown, *J. Biol. Chem.*, **103**, 115 (1933).
69. Bosworth, *ibid.*, **106**, 235 (1934).

70. Riemenschneider and Ellis, *ibid.*, **113**, 219 (1936).
71. Toyama and Tsuchiya, *J. Chem. Soc. Japan*, **56**, 1313 (1935).
72. Toyama, *J. Soc. Chem. Ind., Japan*, **40**, S.b. 285 (1937).
73. Komori and Ueno, *Bull. Chem. Soc. Japan*, **12**, 226, 433 (1937).
74. Bussy and Lecanu, *J. pharm. chim.* [2], **13**, 57 (1827).
75. Bussy, *ibid.* [3], **8**, 321 (1845).
76. Krafft, *Ber.*, **10**, 2034 (1877).
77. Becker, *ibid.*, **11**, 1412 (1878).
78. Perkin, *J. Chem. Soc.*, **49**, 205 (1886).
79. Brunner, *Ber.*, **19**, 2224 (1886).
80. Leeds, *ibid.*, **16**, 290 (1883).
81. Goldsobel, *ibid.*, **27**, 3121 (1894).
82. Simon, *Compt. rend.*, **180**, 833 (1925).
83. Perkins and Cruz, *J. Am. Chem. Soc.*, **49**, 1070 (1927).
84. Vernon and Ross, *ibid.*, **58**, 2430 (1936).
85. Barbot, *Bull. soc. chim.* [5], **2**, 895 (1935).
86. Krafft and Seldis, *Ber.*, **33**, 3571 (1900).
87. Harris and Smith, *J. Chem. Soc.*, 1108 (1935).
88. Tomecko and Adams, *J. Am. Chem. Soc.*, **49**, 522 (1927).
89. Raimann, *Monatsh.*, **6**, 891 (1886).
90. Kono and Maruyama, *J. Agr. Chem. Soc. Japan*, **15**, 177 (1939).
91. Grün, *Z. angew. Chem.*, **37**, 228 (1924).
92. Hilditch and Paul, *Biochem. J.*, **30**, 1905 (1936).
93. Hilditch and Longenecker, *J. Biol. Chem.*, **122**, 497 (1938).
94. Hilditch and Lovern, *J. Soc. Chem. Ind.*, **47**, 105T (1928).
95. Lexow, *Tids. Kemi*, **15**, 309 (1918).
96. Toyama and Tsuchiya, *J. Chem. Soc. Japan*, **56**, 1050 (1935).
97. Tsujimoto, *J. Soc. Chem. Ind., Japan*, **29**, 105 (1926).
98. Iwamoto, *ibid.*, **24**, 1143 (1921).
99. Hata, *J. Chem. Soc. Japan*, **60**, 122 (1939).
100. Chuit, Boelsing, Hausser, and Malet, *Helv. Chim. Acta*, **10**, 113 (1927).
101. Armstrong and Hilditch, *J. Soc. Chem. Ind.*, **44**, 180T (1925).
102. Wagner, *Allgem. Oel- u. Fett-Ztg.*, **24**, 340 (1927).
103. Toyama and Tsuchiya, *J. Soc. Chem. Ind., Japan*, **30**, 207 (1927).
104. Hilditch and Houlbrooke, *Analyst*, **53**, 246 (1928).
105. Hilditch and Terleski, *J. Soc. Chem. Ind.*, **56**, 315T (1932).
106. Ono, *J. Agr. Chem. Soc. Japan*, **11**, 773 (1935).
107. Ogata and Minato, *J. Pharm. Soc. Japan*, **60**, 191 (1940).
108. Smith and Dastur, *Biochem. J.*, **32**, 1868 (1938).
109. Hilditch and Longenecker, *ibid.*, **31**, 1805 (1937); Longenecker and Hilditch, *ibid.*, **32**, 784 (1938).
110. Tsujimoto, *Chem. Umschau*, **30**, 33 (1923).
111. Tsujimoto, *ibid.*, **32**, 202 (1925).
112. Toyama, *ibid.*, **34**, 19 (1927).
113. Hilditch and Lovern, *J. Soc. Chem. Ind.*, **48**, 359T (1929).
114. Toyama and Tsuchiya, *J. Soc. Chem. Ind., Japan*, **38**, S.b. 680 (1935).
115. Tsujimoto, *Bull. Inst. Tokyo Ind. Research Lab.* [3], **23**, 53 (1928); *Chem. Umschau*, **35**, 225 (1928).
116. Lauer, Gensler, and Miller, *J. Am. Chem. Soc.*, **63**, 1153 (1941).
117. Hofstädter, *Ann.*, **91**, 177 (1854).

118. Gössmann and Scheven, *ibid.*, **94**, 230 (1855).
119. Caldwell and Gössmann, *ibid.*, **99**, 305 (1856).
120. Schröder, *ibid.*, **143**, 22 (1867).
121. Ljubarsky, *J. prakt. Chem.* [2], **57**, 19 (1898).
122. Bauer and Neth, *Chem. Umschau*, **31**, 5 (1924).
123. Bull, *Ber.*, **39**, 3570 (1906).
124. Lewkowitsch, *Jahrb. Chem.*, **16**, 402 (1906).
125. Bonnevie-Svendsen, *Tids Kemi Farm. Terapi*, **13**, 212 (1916).
126. Kreiling, *Ber.*, **21**, 880 (1888).
127. Schön, *Ann.*, **244**, 253 (1888).
128. Hazura and Grüssner, *Monatsh.*, **10**, 242 (1890)
129. Bodenstein, *Ber.*, **27**, 3397 (1894).
130. Meyer and Beer, *Monatsh.*, **34**, 1195 (1913).
131. Heiduschka and Felser, *Z. Untersuch. Nahr.- u. Genussm.*, **38**, 241 (1919).
132. Jamieson, Baughman, and Brauns, *J. Am. Chem. Soc.*, **43**, 1372 (1921).
133. Hilditch and Vidyarthi, *J. Soc. Chem. Ind.*, **46**, 172T (1927).
134. Toyama, *Chem. Umschau*, **31**, 221 (1924).
135. Tsujimoto, *J. Soc. Chem. Ind.*, *Japan*, **29**, 195 (1926).
136. Tsujimoto, *ibid.*, **29**, 67 (1926).
137. Toyama and Tsuchiya, *ibid.*, **30**, 63 (1927).
138. Toyama, *ibid.*, **30**, 603 (1927).
139. Milligan, Knuth, and Richardson, *J. Am. Chem. Soc.*, **46**, 157 (1924).
140. Kawai, *J. Chem. Soc. Japan*, **49**, 227 (1928).
141. Hilditch and Jasperson, *J. Soc. Chem. Ind.*, **57**, 84 (1938).
142. Hilditch and Thompson, *ibid.*, **56**, 434T (1937).
143. Longenecker, *ibid.*, **56**, 199T (1937).
144. Klenk, *Z. physiol. Chem.*, **221**, 67 (1933).
145. Hilditch, Lea, and Pedelty, *Biochem. J.*, **33**, 493 (1939).
146. Banks, Hilditch, and Jones, *ibid.*, **27**, 1375 (1933).
147. Hilditch, Jones, and Rhead, *ibid.*, **28**, 786 (1934).
148. Hilditch and Paul, *ibid.*, **31**, 227 (1937).
149. Green and Hilditch, *ibid.*, **32**, 681 (1938).
150. Riemenschneider and Ellis, *J. Biol. Chem.*, **114**, 441 (1936).
151. Trost and Doro, *Ann. chim. applicata*, **27**, 233 (1937).
152. Hilditch and Pedelty, *Biochem. J.*, **31**, 1964 (1937).
153. Irving and Smith, *ibid.*, **29**, 1358 (1935).
154. Chargaff, *Z. physiol. Chem.*, **218**, 223 (1933).
155. Rathje, *Arch. Pharm.*, **246**, 692 (1908).
156. Langer, *ibid.*, **227**, 241 (1889).
157. Riebsomer and Johnson, *J. Am. Chem. Soc.*, **55**, 3352 (1933).
158. Takahashi, Shirahama, and Ito, *J. Chem. Soc. Japan*, **59**, 662 (1938).
159. Hilditch, *Rec. trav. chim.*, **57**, 503 (1938).
160. Marasse, *Ber.*, **2**, 359 (1869).
161. Ponzio, *Gazz. chim. ital.*, **35**, II, 132 (1905).
162. Fokin, *J. Russ. Phys. Chem. Soc.*, **44**, 653 (1912).
163. Ponzio, *Gazz. chim. ital.*, **34**, II, 77 (1904); **35**, II, 569 (1905).
164. Le Sueur, *J. Chem. Soc.*, **85**, 1708 (1904).
165. M. Saytzeff, C. Saytzeff, and A. Saytzeff, *J. prakt. Chem.* [2], **35**, 369 (1887); [2], **37**, 269 (1888).
166. Semeria, *Atti accad. sci. Torino*, **59**, 700 (1924).

167. Eckert and Halla, *Monatsh.*, **34**, 1815 (1913).
168. Posternak, *Compt. rend.*, **162**, 944 (1916).
169. Egorov, *J. Russ. Phys. Chem. Soc.*, **46**, 975 (1914).
170. Vongerichten and Köhler, *Ber.*, **42**, 1638 (1909).
171. Palazzo and Tamburello, *Atti accad. Lincei* [5], **23**, II, 352 (1914).
172. Hilditch and Jones, *J. Soc. Chem. Ind.*, **46**, 174T (1927).
173. van Loon, *Rec. trav. chim.*, **46**, 492 (1927).
174. Hilditch and Jones, *Biochem. J.*, **22**, 326 (1928).
175. Christian and Hilditch, *ibid.*, **23**, 327 (1929).
176. Eibner, Widenmayer, and Schild, *Chem. Umschau*, **34**, 312 (1927).
177. Vanin and Chernoyarova, *J. Gen. Chem. (U.S.S.R.)*, **5**, 1537 (1935).
178. Chernoyarova, *ibid.*, **9**, 149 (1939).
179. Matthes and Boltze, *Arch. Pharm.*, **250**, 211 (1912).
180. Hartley, *J. Physiol.*, **38**, 353 (1909).
181. Pigulevskiĭ and Simonova, *J. Gen. Chem. (U.S.S.R.)*, **9**, 1928 (1939).
182. Arnaud and Posternak, *Compt. rend.*, **150**, 1130, 1245 (1910).
183. Arnaud and Posternak, *ibid.*, **150**, 1525 (1910).
184. Steger, van Loon, Vellenga, and Pennekamp, *Rec. trav. chim.*, **57**, 25 (1938).
185. Steger, van Loon, and Pennekamp, *ibid.*, **59**, 952 (1940).
186. Varrentrapp, *Ann.*, **35**, 196 (1840).
187. Moore, *J. Soc. Chem. Ind.*, **38**, 320T (1919).
188. Hilditch and Vidyarthi, *Proc. Roy. Soc. (London)*, **A122**, 552 (1929).
189. Steger and Scheffers, *Chem. Umschau*, **38**, 61 (1931).
190. Bauer and Krallis, *ibid.*, **38**, 201 (1931); **41**, 194 (1934).
191. Laurent, *Ann. chim. phys.* [2], **66**, 136 (1837).
192. Bromeis, *Ann.*, **35**, 86 (1840).
193. Redtenbacher, *ibid.*, **59**, 41 (1846).
194. Saytzeff, *J. Russ. Phys. Chem. Soc.*, **17**, 417 (1885); *J. prakt. Chem.* [2], **31**, 541 (1885); [2], **33**, 300 (1886).
195. Spiridonoff, *ibid.* [2], **40**, 243 (1889).
196. Baruch, *Ber.*, **27**, 172 (1894).
197. Edmed, *J. Chem. Soc.*, **73**, 627 (1898).
198. Molinari, *Ann. soc. chim. Milano*, **9**, 507 (1903); Molinari and Soncini, *Ber.*, **39**, 2735 (1906); Molinari and Barosi, *ibid.*, **41**, 2794 (1908).
199. Harries, *ibid.*, **36**, 1933 (1903); **39**, 3728 (1906); **42**, 446 (1909); *Ann.*, **374**, 288 (1910); Harries and Türk, *Ber.*, **38**, 1630 (1905); **39**, 3732 (1906); Harries and Thieme, *Ann.*, **343**, 354 (1905).
200. Armstrong and Hilditch, *J. Soc. Chem. Ind.*, **44**, 43T (1925).
201. Noller and Bannerot, *J. Am. Chem. Soc.*, **56**, 1563 (1934).
202. Robinson and Robinson, *J. Chem. Soc.*, **127**, 175 (1925).
203. Margaillan and Angeli, *Compt. rend.*, **206**, 1662 (1938); *Atti X° congr. intern. chim.*, **4**, 278 (1939).
204. Ellis and Isbell, *J. Biol. Chem.*, **69**, 239 (1926).
205. Lode, *Fettchem. Umschau*, **42**, 205 (1935).
206. Schuette, Garvin, and Schwoegler, *J. Biol. Chem.*, **107**, 635 (1934).
207. Jamieson and Baughman, *J. Oil & Fat Ind.*, **2**, 40 (1925); Baughman and Jamieson, *ibid.*, **2**, 110 (1925); Jamieson, Hann, and Baughman, *Oil & Fat Industries*, **4**, 63 (1927).

208. Jamieson, *ibid.*, **4**, 426 (1927).
209. Hilditch and Jones, *J. Chem. Soc.*, 805 (1932).
210. Brandonisio, *Chimica e industria Italy*, **18**, 14 (1936).
211. Heiduschka and Wiesemann, *J. prakt. Chem.* [2], **124**, 240 (1930).
212. Patel, Sudborough, and Watson, *J. Indian Inst. Sci.*, **6**, 111 (1923).
213. Dean and Hilditch, *J. Soc. Chem. Ind.*, **52**, 165T (1933).
214. Power and Salway, *J. Am. Chem. Soc.*, **32**, 346 (1910).
215. Jamieson and Baughman, *ibid.*, **42**, 1197 (1920).
216. Baughman, Brauns, and Jamieson, *ibid.*, **42**, 2398 (1920).
217. Baughman and Jamieson, *ibid.*, **43**, 2696 (1921).
218. Baughman and Jamieson, *ibid.*, **42**, 152 (1920).
219. Baughman and Jamieson, *ibid.*, **44**, 2947 (1922).
220. Jamieson and Baughman, *ibid.*, **44**, 2952 (1922).
221. Cruz and West, *Philippine J. Sci.*, **61**, 161 (1936).
222. Collin, *Biochem. J.*, **27**, 1366 (1933).
223. Taylor and Clarke, *J. Am. Chem. Soc.*, **49**, 2829 (1927).
224. Lepkovsky, Feskov, and Evans, *ibid.*, **58**, 978 (1936).
225. Williams and Maslov, *Schriften zentral. Forsch.-Inst. Lebensmittelchem.* (*U.S.S.R.*), **4**, 150 (1935).
226. Gusserow, *Arch. Pharm.*, **27**, 153 (1828).
227. Twitchell, *J. Ind. Eng. Chem.*, **13**, 806 (1921).
228. Lapworth, Pearson, and Mottram, *Biochem. J.*, **19**, 7 (1925).
229. Scheffers, *Rec. trav. chim.*, **46**, 293 (1927).
230. Bertram, *ibid.*, **46**, 397 (1927).
231. Raymond, *Chimie & industrie, Special No.*, p. 523 (February, 1929).
232. Skellon, *J. Soc. Chem. Ind.*, **50**, 131T (1931).
233. Keffler and McLean, *ibid.*, **54**, 362T (1935).
234. Hartsuch, *J. Am. Chem. Soc.*, **61**, 1142 (1939).
235. Brown and Shinowara, *ibid.*, **59**, 6 (1937).
236. Brown, *Chem. Rev.*, **29**, 333 (1941).
237. Smith, *J. Chem. Soc.*, 974 (1939).
238. Wheeler and Riemenschneider, *Oil & Soap*, **16**, 207 (1939).
239. Foreman and Brown, *Oil & Soap*, **21**, 183 (1944); Millican and Brown, *J. Biol. Chem.*, **154**, 437 (1944).
240. Kirschner, *Z. physik. Chem.*, **79**, 759 (1912).
241. Reimer and Will, *Ber.*, **20**, 2385 (1887).
242. Zellner, *Monatsh.*, **17**, 309 (1896).
243. Grabner, *Seife*, **7**, 167 (1921).
244. Hilditch, Riley, and Vidyarthi, *J. Soc. Chem. Ind.*, **46**, 462T (1927).
245. Bruni and Gorni, *Atti accad. Lincei* [5], **8**, II, 181 (1899).
246. Mascarelli, *ibid.* [5], **23**, II, 583 (1914); Mascarelli and Toschi, *ibid.* [5], **23**, II, 586 (1914); Mascarelli and Sanna, *ibid.* [5], **24**, II, 30 (1915).
247. Müller, *J. Chem. Soc.*, **123**, 2043 (1923); Müller and Shearer, *ibid.*, **123**, 3156 (1923).
248. Marsden and Rideal, *ibid.*, **1163** (1938).
249. Harkins and Florence, *Nature*, **142**, 913 (1938).
250. Poutet, *Ann. chim. phys.* [2], **12**, 58 (1819).
251. Boudet, *Ann.*, **4**, 1 (1832).
252. Meyer, *ibid.*, **35**, 174 (1840).

253. Gottlieb, *ibid.*, **57**, 33 (1846).
254. Lidow, *J. Russ. Phys. Chem. Soc.*, **24**, 515 (1892); **27**, 178 (1895).
255. Jegorow, *ibid.*, **35**, 973 (1903); *J. prakt. Chem.* [2], **86**, 521 (1912).
256. M. Saytzeff, C. Saytzeff, and A. Saytzeff, *J. prakt. Chem.* [2], **50, 73** (1894).
257. Fokin, *J. Russ. Phys. Chem. Soc.*, **42**, 1068 (1910).
258. Rankoff, *Ber.*, **62B**, 2712 (1929); **64B**, 619 (1931); **69B**, 1231 (1936).
259. Griffiths and Hilditch, *J. Chem. Soc.*, 2315 (1932).
260. Bertram, *Chem. Weekblad*, **33**, 3, 216 (1936); *Öle, Fette, Wachse, Seife, Kosmetik*, No. **7**, 1 (1938); U. S. Patent 2,165,530 (1939); *Rec. trav. chim.*, **59**, 650 (1940).
261. Holde and Rietz, *Ber.*, **57**, 99 (1924).
262. Shukoff and Schestakoff, *J. prakt. Chem.* [2], **67**, 414 (1903).
263. Veselý and Majtl, *Chem. Listy*, **19**, 345 (1925); *Bull. soc. chim.* [4], **39**, 230 (1936).
264. Bauer and Panagoulias, *Chem. Umschau*, **37**, 189 (1930).
265. Hilditch, *ibid.*, **37**, 354 (1930).
266. Channon, Irving, and Smith, *Biochem. J.*, **28**, 840 (1934).
267. Hartley, *J. Physiol.*, **38**, 353 (1909).
268. Fokin, *J. Russ. Phys. Chem. Soc.*, **46**, 1027 (1914).
269. Grün and Czerny, *Ber.*, **59B**, 54 (1926).
270. Böeseken and van Krimpen, *Verslag Akad. Wetenschappen Amsterdam*, **37**, 66 (1928); *Proc. Acad. Sci. Amsterdam*, **31**, 238 (1928).
271. Bertram, *Biochem. Z.*, **197**, 433 (1928).
272. Grossfeld and Simmer, *Z. Untersuch. Lebensm.*, **59**, 237 (1930).
273. Boer, Jansen, and Kentie, *Nature*, **158**, 201 (1946).
274. Bauer and Mitsotakis, *Chem. Umschau*, **35**, 137 (1928).
275. Hilditch and Vidyarthi, *Proc. Roy. Soc. (London)*, **122A**, 563 (1929).
276. Puzanov, *Masloboïno Zhirovoe Delo*, **12**, 444 (1936).
277. Moore, *J. Soc. Chem. Ind.*, **38**, 320T (1919).
278. Bauer and Ermann, *Chem. Umschau*, **37**, 241 (1930).
279. Scharling, *J. prakt. Chem.*, **43**, 257 (1848).
280. Heyerdahl, in *Cod-Liver Oil and Industry*, by Peter Möller, lxxxviii, London (1895).
281. Oskerk, *J. Russ. Phys. Chem. Soc.*, **46**, 411 (1914).
282. Toyama, *J. Soc. Chem. Ind., Japan*, **29**, 531 (1926); **30**, 519 (1927); Toyama and Tsuchiya, *ibid.*, **30**, 207 (1927).
283. Takano, *ibid.*, **36**, S.b. 549 (1933).
284. Toyama and Tsuchiya, *ibid.*, **37**, S.b. 14 (1934).
285. Toyama and Ishikawa, *ibid.*, **37**, S.b. 534 (1934).
286. Greene and Foster, *Botan. Gaz.*, **94**, 826 (1933).
287. McKinney and Jamieson, *Oil & Soap*, **13**, 289 (1936).
288. Green, Hilditch, and Stainsby, *J. Chem. Soc.*, 1750 (1936).
289. Darby, *Ann.*, **69**, 1 (1849).
290. Holt, *Ber.*, **25**, 961 (1892).
291. Fileti, *J. prakt. Chem.* [2], **48**, 72 (1893); Fileti and Ponzio, *ibid.* [2], **48**, 323 (1893).
292. Websky, *Jahresber. Fortschr. Chem.*, 443 (1853).
293. Täufel and Bauschinger, *Z. Untersuch. Lebensm.*, **56**, 253 (1928).
294. Sudborough, Watson, Ayyar, and Damle, *J. Indian Inst. Sci.*, **9A**, 26 (1926).

295. Hilditch, Riley, and Vidyarthi, *J. Soc. Chem. Ind.*, **46,** 457T (1927).
296. Toyama, *J. Soc. Chem. Ind., Japan,* **25,** 1044 (1922).
297. van Loon, *Rec. trav. chim.,* **49,** 745 (1930).
298. Sudborough, Watson, Ayyar, and Mascarenhas, *J. Indian Inst. Sci.,* **9A,** 43 (1926).
299. Sudborough, Watson, Ayyar, and Mirchandani, *ibid.,* **9A,** 52 (1926).
300. Hilditch and Meara, *J. Chem. Soc.,* 1608 (1938).
301. Fitz, *Ber.,* **4,** 442 (1871).
302. Carrière and Brunet, *Compt. rend.,* **185,** 1516 (1927).
303. Mikshich and Rezhek, *Bull. soc. chim. roy. Yougoslav.,* **1,** No. 2, 29 (1930).
304. Täufel, Fischler, and Jordan, *Allgem. Oel- u. Fett-Ztg.,* **28,** 119 (1931).
305. Täufel and Thaler, *Fettchem. Umschau,* **41,** 196 (1934).
306. Reimer and Will, *Ber.,* **19,** 3320 (1886).
307. Noller and Talbot, *Organic Syntheses,* Coll. Vol. 2, Blatt, editor, p. 258, John Wiley & Sons, New York (1943).
308. Holde and Wilke, *Z. angew. Chem.,* **35,** 289 (1922).
309. Thomas and Mattikow, *J. Am. Chem. Soc.,* **48,** 968 (1926).
310. Täufel and Bauschinger, *Z. angew. Chem.,* **41,** 157 (1928).
311. Krafft and Noerdlinger, *Ber.,* **22,** 816 (1889).
312. Haussknecht, *Ann.,* **143,** 40 (1867).
313. Sudborough and Gittins, *J. Chem. Soc.,* **95,** 315 (1909).
314. Rankoff, *J. prakt. Chem.* [2], **131,** 293 (1931).
315. Rankoff, *Ber.,* **63,** 2139 (1930).
316. Keffler and Maiden, *Bull. soc. chim. Belg.,* **44,** 467 (1935).
317. Bruni and Gorni, *Gazz. chim. ital.,* **30,** I, 55 (1900).
318. Mascarelli and Toschi, *ibid.,* **45,** I, 313 (1915); Mascarelli, *Atti accad. Lincei* [5], **26,** I, 71 (1917).
319. Toyama, *J. Soc. Chem. Ind., Japan,* **30,** 597 (1927).
320. Toyama and Tsuchiya, *ibid.,* **30,** 116 (1927).
321. Kino, *ibid.,* **37,** S.b. 442 (1934).
322. Toyama, *Chem. Umschau,* **33,** 293 (1926).
323. Alexandroff and Saytzeff, *J. prakt. Chem.* [2], **49,** 58 (1894); Saytzeff, *ibid.* [2], **50,** 65 (1894).
324. Ponzio, *Gazz. chim. ital.,* **34,** II, 50 (1904).
325. Mascarelli and Sanna, *ibid.,* **45,** II, 335 (1915); Mascarelli, *ibid.,* **47,** I, 160 (1917).
326. Mirchandani and Simonsen, *J. Chem. Soc.,* 371 (1927).
327. Tsujimoto, *J. Soc. Chem. Ind., Japan,* **30,** 868 (1927).
328. Tsujimoto, *J. Soc. Chem. Ind.,* **51,** 317T (1932).
329. Klenk, *Z. physiol. Chem.,* **166,** 287 (1927).
330. Hale, Lycan, and Adams, *J. Am. Chem. Soc.,* **52,** 4536 (1930).
331. Puntambekar and Krishna, *J. Indian Chem. Soc.,* **14,** 268 (1937).
332. Boekenoogen, *Fette u. Seifen,* **46,** 717 (1939).
333. Fittig, *Ann.,* **200,** 42 (1880).
334. Doebner, *Ber.,* **23,** 2377 (1890); **27,** 344 (1894).
335. Jaworsky and Reformatzky, *ibid.,* **35,** 3633 (1902).
336. Sacc, *Ann.,* **51,** 213 (1844).
337. Dieff and Reformatzky, *Ber.,* **20,** 1211 (1887).
338. Reformatzky, *J. prakt. Chem.* [2], **41,** 529 (1890).
339. Norton and Richardson, *Ber.,* **20,** 2735 (1887); *Am. Chem. J.,* **10,** 57 (1888).

340. Hazura, *Monatsh.*, **7**, 637 (1886); **8**, 147, 260 (1887); **9**, 180 (1888); Hazura and Friedreich, *ibid.*, **8**, 156 (1887); Hazura and Grüssner, *ibid.*, **9**, 198 (1888).
341. Peters, *ibid.*, **7**, 552 (1886).
342. Rollett, *Z. physiol. Chem.*, **62**, 410 (1909).
343. Nicolet and Cox, *J. Am. Chem. Soc.*, **44**, 144 (1922).
344. Bedford, *Dissertation, Halle* (1906).
345. Green and Hilditch, *Biochem. J.*, **29**, 1552 (1935).
346. Brown and Frankel, *J. Am. Chem. Soc.*, **60**, 54 (1938).
347. McCutcheon, *Can. J. Research*, **16B**, 158 (1938).
348. Inoue and Suzuki, *Proc. Imp. Acad. Tokyo*, **7**, 15 (1931); Maruyama and Suzuki, *ibid.*, **7**, 379 (1931); **8**, 186 (1932); Maruyama, *J. Chem. Soc. Japan*, **54**, 1082 (1933).
349. Takahashi, *J. Tokyo Chem. Soc.*, **40**, 233 (1919).
350. Smith and West, *Philippine J. Sci.*, **32**, 297 (1927).
351. van der Veen, *Chem. Umschau*, **38**, 117 (1931).
352. Birosel, *Univ. Philippines Nat. and Applied Sci. Bull.*, **2**, 103 (1932).
353. Birosel, *J. Am. Chem. Soc.*, **59**, 689 (1937).
354. Hilditch and Jasperson, *J. Soc. Chem. Ind.*, **58**, 233 (1939).
355. Riemenschneider, Wheeler, and Sando, *J. Biol. Chem.*, **127**, 391 (1939).
356. McCutcheon, Crawford, and Welch, *Oil & Soap*, **18**, 9 (1941).
357. Lidoff, *J. Russ. Phys. Chem. Soc.*, **24**, 515 (1892).
358. Noller and Girvin, *J. Am. Chem. Soc.*, **59**, 606 (1937).
359. Kass and Burr, *ibid.*, **61**, 1062 (1939).
360. Goldsobel, *J. Russ. Phys. Chem. Soc.*, **38**, 182 (1906).
361. Maruyama, *J. Chem. Soc. Japan*, **54**, 1073 (1933).
362. Nunn and Smedley-Maclean, *Biochem. J.*, **29**, 2742 (1935).
363. Hazura, *Monatsh.*, **8**, 147 (1887).
364. Kaufmann and Keller, *Chem. Umschau*, **38**, 203 (1931).
365. Meyer and Beer, *Monatsh.*, **33**, 311 (1912).
366. Burr and Burr, *J. Biol. Chem.*, **86**, 587 (1930).
367. Jamieson and Baughman, *J. Am. Chem. Soc.*, **42**, 1197 (1920).
368. Hashi, *J. Soc. Chem. Ind., Japan*, **30**, 849, S.b. 221 (1927).
369. Juschkewitsch, *Fettchem. Umschau*, **40**, 197 (1933).
370. Cruz and West, *Philippine J. Sci.*, **48**, 77 (1932).
371. Jamieson and Baughman, *J. Am. Chem. Soc.*, **46**, 775 (1924).
372. Riebsomer and Nesty, *ibid.*, **56**, 1784 (1934).
373. Jamieson and McKinney, *Oil & Soap*, **14**, 203 (1937).
374. Eibner and Schmidinger, *Chem. Umschau*, **30**, 293 (1923).
375. Jumelle, *Mat. grasses*, **12**, 5312 (1920).
376. Longenecker and Hilditch, *Biochem. J.*, **32**, 784 (1932).
377. Stadlinger and Tschirch, *Chem.-Ztg.*, **51**, 667 (1927).
378. Banks and Hilditch, *Biochem. J.*, **26**, 298 (1932).
379. Dean and Hilditch, *ibid.*, **27**, 1950 (1933).
380. Evans and Burr, *Proc. Soc. Exptl. Biol. Med.*, **25**, 41 (1927).
381. Burr and Burr, *J. Biol. Chem.*, **82**, 345 (1929).
382. Becker, *Mezőgazdasági Kutatások*, **6**, 363 (1933); *Z. Vitaminforsch.*, **4**, 241 (1935).
383. Williams and Anderson, *Oil & Soap*, **12**, 42 (1935).
384. Hilditch and Jones, *Analyst*, **54**, 75 (1929).

385. Hilditch and Jasperson, *J. Soc. Chem. Ind.*, **58**, 241 (1939).
386. Inoue and Suzuki, *Proc. Imp. Acad. Tokyo*, **7**, 15 (1931).
387. Takahashi, *J. Chem. Soc. Japan*, **42**, 130 (1921).
388. Haworth, *J. Chem. Soc.*, 1456 (1929).
389. Erdmann and Bedford, *Ber.*, **42**, 1324 (1909); *Z. physiol. Chem.*, **69**, 76 (1910).
390. Kaufmann, *Ber.*, **62**, 392 (1929).
391. Matthews, Brode, and Brown, *J. Am. Chem. Soc.*, **63**, 1064 (1941).
392. Brown and Stoner, *ibid.*, **59**, 3 (1937).
393. Holde and Gentner, *Ber.*, **58**, 1067 (1925).
394. Smit, *Rec. trav. chim.*, **49**, 539 (1930).
395. Bussy and Lecanu, *Ann. chim. phys.*, **30**, 5 (1825); **34**, 57 (1827).
396. Shuraev and Vasil'eva, *Masloboĭno Zhirovoe Delo*, No. **2**, 40 (1939).
397. Fokin, *J. Russ. Phys. Chem. Soc.*, **46**, 224 (1914).
398. Kronstein, *Ber.*, **49**, 722 (1916).
399. Böeseken and Hoevers, *Rec. trav. chim.*, **49**, 1165 (1930).
400. Scheiber, U. S. Patents 1,942,778, 1,979,495 (1934).
401. Ufer, U. S. Patent 1,892,258 (1932).
402. Yamada, *J. Soc. Chem. Ind.*, *Japan*, **38**, S.b. 120 (1935).
403. Schwarcman, U. S. Patent 2,140,271 (1938).
404. Münzel, Fr. Patent 830,494 (1938).
405. Scheiber, *Angew. Chem.*, **46**, 643 (1933).
406. Forbes and Neville, *Ind. Eng. Chem.*, **32**, 555 (1940).
407. Priest and von Mikusch, *ibid.*, **32**, 1314 (1940).
408. Khonovskii, *J. Russ. Phys. Chem. Soc.*, **43**, 1457 (1911).
409. Maruyama and Suzuki, *Proc. Imp. Acad. Tokyo*, **7**; 265 (1931).
410. Hazura and Friedreich, *Monatsh.*, **8**, 156 (1887).
411. Hazura, *ibid.*, **8**, 260 (1887).
412. Erdmann, Bedford, and Raspe, *Ber.*, **42**, 1334 (1909).
413. Eckert, *Monatsh.*, **38**, 1 (1917).
414. van der Veen, *Chem. Umschau*, **38**, 89 (1931).
415. Shinowara and Brown, *J. Am. Chem. Soc.*, **60**, 2734 (1938).
416. The hexabromide number is obtained by multiplying by 100 the weight of the solid, ether-insoluble hexabromostearic acid resulting from bromination and dividing this product by the weight of the sample brominated. The theoretical value for pure linolenic acid is 272. For a discussion of the hexabromide number see Steele and Washburn, *J. Ind. Eng. Chem.*, **12**, 52 (1920).
417. Kass, Nichols, and Burr, *J. Am. Chem. Soc.*, **63**, 1060 (1941).
418. McCutcheon, *Can. J. Research*, **18B**, 231 (1940).
419. Burr, Burr, and Miller, *J. Biol. Chem.*, **97**, 1 (1932).
420. Eibner and Brosel, *Chem. Umschau*, **35**, 157 (1928).
421. Kaufmann and Keller, *Z. angew. Chem.*, **42**, 73 (1929).
422. Gay, *J. Soc. Chem. Ind.*, **51**, 126T (1932).
423. Jamieson and McKinney, *Oil & Soap*, **13**, 202 (1936).
424. Ueno and Nishikawa, *J. Soc. Chem. Ind.*, *Japan*, **40**, S.b. 313 (1937).
425. Griffiths and Hilditch, *J. Soc. Chem. Ind.*, **53**, 75T (1934).
426. Ivanov and Berdichevskiĭ, *Schriften zentral. biochem. Forsch. Inst. Nahr. u. Genussmittelind.* (*U.S.S.R.*), **3**, 246 (1933).
427. Kaufmann and Juschkewitsch, *Z. angew. Chem.*, **43**, 90 (1930).

428. Heiduschka and Zwergal, *Pharm. Zentralhalle*, **77**, 551 (1936).
429. Ivanov and Resnikova, *Schriften zentral. biochem. Forsch. Inst. Nahr. u. Genussmittelind.* (*U.S.S.R.*), **3**, 239 (1933).
430. Bergmann, *J. Biol. Chem.*, **114**, 27 (1936).
431. Jamieson and McKinney, *Oil & Soap*, **12**, 88 (1935).
432. Kaufmann, *Allgem. Oel- u. Fett-Ztg.*, **27**, 39 (1930).
433. Eibner and Reitter, *Chem. Umschau*, **33**, 114 (1926).
434. Jamieson and Baughman, *Oil & Fat Industries*, **7**, 419 (1930).
435. Jamieson and McKinney, *Oil & Soap*, **12**, 241 (1935).
436. Eckstein, *J. Biol. Chem.*, **103**, 135 (1933).
437. For a description of this method see Rollett, *Z. physiol. Chem.*, **62**, 422 (1909); **70**, 404 (1910); Matthews, Brode, and Brown, *J. Am. Chem. Soc.*, **63**, 1064 (1941).
438. Heiduschka and Lüft, *Arch. Pharm.*, **257**, 33 (1919).
439. Fahrion, *J. Soc. Chem. Ind.*, **12**, 937 (1893).
440. Lewkowitsch, *Chemical Technology and Analysis of Oils, Fats and Waxes*, 6th ed., Vol. I, p. 214, Macmillan and Co., London (1921).
441. Madhuranath and Manjunath, *J. Indian Chem. Soc.*, **15**, 389 (1938).
442. Cloëz, *Compt. rend.*, **82**, 501 (1876).
443. Maquenne, *ibid.*, **135**, 696 (1902).
444. Kametaka, *J. Chem. Soc.*, **83**, 1042 (1903).
445. Majima, *Ber.*, **42**, 674 (1909).
446. Fahrion, *Farben-Ztg.*, **18**, 2418 (1913).
447. Bauer and Herberts, *Chem. Umschau*, **29**, 229 (1922).
448. Eibner, Merz, and Munzert, *ibid.*, **31**, 69 (1924).
449. Nicolet, *J. Am. Chem. Soc.*, **43**, 938 (1921).
450. Böeseken and Ravenswaay, *Rec. trav. chim.*, **44**, 241 (1925); K. Akad. *Wetenschappen Amsterdam*, **28**, 386 (1925).
451. Eibner and Rossmann, *Chem. Umschau*, **35**, 197 (1928).
452. Fokin, *J. Russ. Phys. Chem. Soc.*, **45**, 283 (1913).
453. Bauer and Rohrbach, *Chem. Umschau*, **35**, 53 (1928).
454. van Loon, *Rec. trav. chim.*, **50**, 32 (1931).
455. Böeseken, Smit, Hoogland, and van der Broek, *ibid.*, **46**, 619 (1927).
456. Manecke and Volbert, *Farben-Ztg.*, **32**, 2829, 2887 (1927).
457. Morrell and Marks, *J. Soc. Chem. Ind.*, **50**, 27T (1931).
458. Rossmann, *Chem. Umschau*, **39**, 220 (1932).
459. Thomas and Thomson, *J. Am. Chem. Soc.*, **56**, 898 (1934).
460. McKinney and Jamieson, *Oil & Soap*, **14**, 2 (1937).
461. Steger and van Loon, *J. Soc. Chem. Ind.*, **47**, 361T (1928).
462. Kaufmann and Baltes, *Ber.*, **69**, 2676 (1936).
463. McKinney and Jamieson, *Oil & Soap*, **12**, 92 (1935).
464. Jamieson and McKinney, *ibid.*, **12**, 146 (1935).
465. Steger and van Loon, *Rec. trav. chim.*, **54**, 988 (1935).
466. Diels and Alder, *Ann.*, **460**, 98 (1928).
467. Morrell and Samuels, *J. Chem. Soc.*, 2251 (1932).
468. Kaufmann and Baltes, *Fette u. Seifen*, **43**, 93 (1936); *Ber.*, **69**, 2676 (1936); Kaufmann, Baltes, and Büter, *ibid.*, **70**, 903 (1937).
469. Ellis and Jones, *Analyst*, **61**, 812 (1936).
470. Pelikan and von Mikusch, *Oil & Soap*, **14**, 209 (1937).

471. Bickford, Dollear, and Markley, *J. Am. Chem. Soc.*, **59**, 2744 (1937); *Oil & Soap*, **15**, 256 (1938).
472. Bruce and Denley, *Chemistry & Industry*, **56**, 937 (1937).
473. McKinney and Jamieson, *Oil & Soap*, **15**, 30 (1938).
474. Moore, *Biochem. J.*, **31**, 138 (1937).
475. Kass and Burr, *J. Am. Chem. Soc.*, **61**, 3292 (1939).
476. Morrell and Davis, *J. Soc. Chem. Ind.*, **55**, 101T (1936).
477. Tsujimoto, *J. Coll. Eng., Tokyo Imp. Univ.*, **4**, No. 1 (1906).
478. Tsujimoto, *J. Soc. Chem. Ind., Japan*, **23**, 1007 (1920).
479. Brown with Beal, *J. Am. Chem. Soc.*, **45**, 1289 (1923).
480. Toyama and Tsuchiya, *Bull. Chem. Soc. Japan*, **10**, 192 (1935).
481. Suzuki and Masuda, *Proc. Imp. Acad. Tokyo*, **4**, 165 (1928).
482. Tsujimoto, *Chem. Umschau*, **29**, 261 (1922); *J. Soc. Chem. Ind., Japan*, **26**, 1013 (1923).
483. Eibner and Semmelbauer, *Chem. Umschau*, **31**, 189 (1924).
484. Tsujimoto, *Bull. Chem. Soc. Japan*, **3**, 299 (1928).
485. Toyama and Tsuchiya, *ibid.*, **10**, 441 (1935).
486. Inoue and Kato, *Proc. Imp. Acad. Tokyo*, **10**, 463 (1934).
487. Toyama and Tsuchiya, *Bull. Chem. Soc. Japan*, **11**, 741, 751 (1936).
488. Toyama and Tsuchiya, *ibid.*, **4**, 83 (1929).
489. Suzuki and Yokoyama, *Proc. Imp. Acad. Tokyo*, **5**, 272 (1929).
490. Toyama and Tsuchiya, *Bull. Chem. Soc. Japan*, **10**, 241, 296 (1935).
491. Sanna, *Rend. seminar. facoltà sci. univ. Cagliari*, **7**, 53 (1937); *Chem. Zentr.*, II, 2616 (1937).
492. Toyama and Tsuchiya, *Bull. Chem. Soc. Japan*, **10**, 433 (1935).
493. Toyama and Tsuchiya, *ibid.*, **10**, 543, 547 (1935).
494. Ueno and Iwai, *J. Soc. Chem. Ind., Japan*, **37**, S.b. 251 (1934).
495. Ueno and Takase, *J. Chem. Soc. Japan*, **58**, 850 (1937).
496. Ueno and Yonese, *ibid.*, **57**, 322 (1936); *Bull. Chem. Soc. Japan*, **11**, 437 (1936).
497. Ueno and Iwai, *ibid.*, **11**, 643 (1936).
498. Ueno and Yonese, *J. Chem. Soc. Japan*, **57**, 180 (1936).
499. Lovern, *Dept. Sci. Ind. Research (Brit.) Food Invest. Board*, **1936**, 96 (1937).
500. Lovern, *Biochem. J.*, **29**, 1894 (1935).
501. Tsujimoto, *J. Soc. Chem. Ind., Japan*, **23**, 41, 1099 (1920).
502. Klenk, *Z. physiol. Chem.*, **221**, 259, 264 (1933).
503. Kobayashi, *J. Soc. Chem. Ind., Japan*, **25**, 691 (1922).
504. Tsujimoto, *Chem. Umschau*, **32**, 125 (1925).
505. Lovern, *Biochem. J.*, **30**, 387 (1936).
506. Grimme, *Chem. Umschau*, **28**, 17 (1921).
507. Williams and Burlachenko, *Schriften zentral. Forsch. Inst. Lebensmittelchem. (U.S.S.R.)*, **4**, 170 (1935).
508. Williams and Onishchenko, *ibid.*, **4**, 145 (1935).
509. Langton, *J. Soc. Chem. Ind.*, **42**, 47T (1923).
510. Toyama, *J. Soc. Chem. Ind., Japan*, **30**, 519 (1927).
511. Klein and Stigol, *Pharm. Zentralhalle*, **71**, 497 (1930).
512. Tsujimoto and Kimura, *J. Soc. Chem. Ind., Japan*, **26**, 1162 (1923).
513. Tomiyama, *Bull. Agr. Chem. Soc. Japan*, **9**, 141 (1933).

514. Ueno and Iwai, *J. Soc. Chem. Ind., Japan*, **42**, S.b. 371 (1939).
515. Pieraerts, *Mat. grasses*, **13**, 5733 (1921).
516. Takahashi, Shirahama, and Tase, *J. Chem. Soc. Japan*, **56**, 1250 (1935); Takahashi, Shirohama, and Togasawa, *ibid.*, **60**, 56 (1939).
517. For a comparison of the compositions of various fats of aquatic origin the reader is referred to Hilditch, *The Chemical Constitution of Natural Fats*, Chapter II, John Wiley & Sons, New York (1941).
518. Farmer and Van den Heuvel, *J. Soc. Chem. Ind.*, **57**, 24T (1938).
519. Farmer and Van den Heuvel, *J. Chem. Soc.*, 427 (1938).
520. Hartley, *J. Physiol.*, **36**, 17 (1907).
521. Levene and Simms, *J. Biol. Chem.*, **48**, 185 (1921); **51**, 285 (1922); Levene and Rolf, *ibid.*, **51**, 507 (1922); **54**, 91 (1922); **54**, 99 (1922); **67**, 659 (1926).
522. Wesson, *ibid.*, **60**, 183 (1924).
523. Wesson, *ibid.*, **65**, 235 (1925).
524. Kimura, *J. Soc. Chem. Ind., Japan*, **28**, 1366 (1925).
525. Suzuki, *Bull. Agr. Chem. Soc. Japan*, **3**, 54 (1927).
526. Snider and Bloor, *J. Biol. Chem.*, **99**, 555 (1933).
527. Eckstein, *ibid.*, **54**, 797 (1925).
528. Wagner, *Biochem. Z.*, **174**, 412 (1926).
529. Brown and Deck, *J. Am. Chem. Soc.*, **52**, 1135 (1930).
530. Brown and Sheldon, *ibid.*, **56**, 2149 (1934).
531. Bloor, *J. Biol. Chem.*, **68**, 33 (1926).
532. Bosworth and Sisson, *ibid.*, **107**, 489 (1934).
533. Brown, *ibid.*, **80**, 455 (1928).
534. Ault and Brown, *ibid.*, **107**, 615 (1934).
535. Ault and Brown, *ibid.*, **107**, 607 (1934).
536. Shinowara and Brown, *ibid.*, **134**, 331 (1940).
537. Brown, *ibid.*, **83**, 783 (1929).
538. Brown and Ault, *ibid.*, **89**, 167 (1930).
539. Brown, *ibid.*, **97**, 183 (1932).
540. Sueyoshi and Furukubo, *J. Biochem. Japan*, **13**, 155 (1931).
541. Hilditch, Lea, and Pedelty, *Biochem. J.*, **33**, 493 (1939).
542. Riemenschneider, Ellis, and Titus, *J. Biol. Chem.*, **126**, 255 (1938).
543. Marcusson and Böltger, *Chem. Rev. Fett- u. Harz-Ind.*, **21**, 180 (1914).
544. Tsujimoto and Koyanagi, *J. Soc. Chem. Ind., Japan*, **36**, S.b. 110 (1933).
545. Tsujimoto, *ibid.*, **39**, S.b. 116 (1936).
546. Farmer and Sunderland, *J. Chem. Soc.*, 759 (1935).

III

THE ACETYLENIC ACIDS, THE HYDROXY ACIDS, THE KETO ACIDS, THE CYCLIC ACIDS, AND THE DICARBOXYLIC ACIDS

PART 1 THE ACETYLENIC ACIDS

The acetylenic acids are a series of straight-chain carboxylic acids characterized by the presence of one or more triple carbon-to-carbon bonds in the hydrocarbon chain. Such acids show the chemical and physical properties of the fatty acids, plus those of acetylenic compounds. The mono-acetylenic acids are isomeric with the diethylenic acids; however, these two acid series differ quite materially in their chemical and physical properties. The acetylenic acids are much more resistant to oxidation than the corresponding dienoic acids.[1,2] The acetylenic acids, like the conjugated ethylenic acids, add one mole of halogen readily, the second mole being added only with difficulty. Upon oxidation acetylenic acids are converted into diketo acids, the further oxidation of which results in a cleavage with the formation of mono- and dicarboxylic acids. Treatment of acetylenic acids with concentrated sulfuric acid and other hydrolyzing agents results in the addition of a molecule of water with the formation of keto acids. Acetylenic acids are easily reduced to the corresponding saturated acids.

Acetylenic acids are very rarely found in the naturally occurring fats and oils, and they do not, therefore, possess the biological interest or the economic importance of the ethylenic acids. This should in no wise be interpreted as suggesting that these acids are devoid of interest or importance, since many of them can easily be prepared from the ethylenic acids and several representatives of this series have been known and studied for many years. A variety of methods have been employed for the preparation of the acetylenic acids, some of which are of limited applicability whereas several are of rather general utility. Among these latter methods may be mentioned the removal of halogen halides from either diiodo or dibromo acids by reaction with alcoholic potassium hydroxide. Since diiodo or dibromo acids can easily be prepared from the ethylenic acids, this method has been widely employed for the synthesis of acetylenic acids. This procedure has been employed by Overbeck,[3] Baruch,[4] and others for the preparation of stearolic acid (9-octadecynoic acid) from oleic acid, and by Haussknecht [5] for the synthesis of behenolic acid (13-docosynoic acid) from erucic acid. While alcoholic potassium hydroxide is the reagent most generally employed to effect dehydrohalogenations of this type, several other reagents may be used. Among these latter processes may be mentioned the treatment of a dihalo acid with sodium in liquid ammonia,[6] with sodamide,[7, 8] or with potassium xanthate.[9] Such dehydrohalogenations theoretically result in the formation of both acetylenic and dienoic acids; however, the latter reaction appears to be of secondary importance and is not frequently encountered when the above reagents are employed. A reaction which is frequently used for the preparation of 2-acetylenic acids is that between a substituted acetylide of the general formula $RC \vdots CNa$ and carbon dioxide in the presence of anhydrous ether. This procedure results in the formation of an acetylenic acid containing one more carbon atom than the original acetylide.

The following contains a description of the methods of preparation and reported physical properties of the normal acetylenic acids containing five or more carbon atoms. Their chemical properties and derivatives are discussed in a later chapter.

PENTYNOIC ACIDS

Three pentynoic acids are theoretically possible, none of which has been found in the naturally occurring fats and oils. Two of the pentynoic acids have been synthesized and their properties described.

4-Pentynoic Acid. $CH \vdots CCH_2CH_2CO_2H$

The synthesis of 4-pentynoic acid was first accomplished by Perkin and Simonsen [10] by the pyrolysis of 2-carboxy-4-pentynoic acid, $CH \vdots CCH_2CH(CO_2H)_2$. The latter acid was prepared by treating ethyl 2-carbethoxy-4-bromo-4-pentenoate with alcoholic potassium hydroxide. Gardner and Perkin [11] have prepared ethyl

2-acetyl-4-bromo-4-pentenoate by the action of ethyl acetoacetate on tribromopropane in the presence of sodium and ethanol. Treatment of this product with alcoholic potassium hydroxide yields 4-pentynoic acid.

4-Pentynoic acid is soluble in water, ethanol, ether, and other organic solvents. Its freezing point has been reported to be 57°, and its boiling point 203–204° at 766 mm.

2-Pentynoic Acid. $CH_3CH_2C \vdots CCO_2H$

This acid has been obtained by the action of carbon dioxide in dry ether on sodium ethylacetylide,[12] and also by the action of carbon dioxide on 1-butenylmagnesium bromide.[13]

HEXYNOIC, HEPTYNOIC, OCTYNOIC, NONYNOIC, AND DECYNOIC ACIDS

Only the 2-unsaturated members of this group of acids have been described. These have been prepared by the action of carbon dioxide in dry ether on the substituted sodium acetylides containing one less carbon atom than the desired acids.[14, 15] Thus 2-hexynoic acid was prepared by the action of carbon dioxide on sodium propylacetylide, or 2-heptynoic acid from sodium butylacetylide and carbon dioxide. These acids are very sparingly soluble in water and soluble in ethanol, ether, and other organic solvents. The following physical constants have been reported: 2-hexynoic acid, f.p. 27°, b_{20} 125°; 2-heptynoic acid, f.p. $< -20°$, b_{20} 135°; 2-octynoic acid, f.p. 2°, b_{19} 148–149°, $d_4^{12.6}$ 0.9623, $n_D^{12.6}$ 1.46335; 2-nonynoic acid, f.p. $-8°$, b_{19} 158–160°, $d_4^{12.5}$ 0.9525, $n_D^{12.5}$ 1.46429; 2-decynoic acid, f.p. 6–10°, b_{20} 164–168°, d_4^{17} 0.9408.

UNDECYNOIC ACIDS

The undecynoic acids have not been observed to occur in the natural fats and oils, but three of the nine possible isomeric acids have been described.

10-Undecynoic Acid. $CH \vdots C(CH_2)_8CO_2H$

The dehydrobromination of 10,11-dibromoundecanoic acid by means of concentrated alcoholic potassium hydroxide yields 9-undecynoic acid; however, Krafft[16] has reported that the treatment of bromoundecenoic acid with an alcoholic solution of potassium carbonate results in the formation of a product which consists largely of 10-undecynoic acid.

10-Undecynoic acid freezes at 42.7–42.9°, and boils at 175° under 15 mm.

9-Undecynoic Acid. $CH_3C \vdots C(CH_2)_7CO_2H$

The dehydrobromination of 10,11-dibromoundecanoic acid with highly concentrated, aqueous potassium hydroxide solution,[17] or with alcoholic potassium hydroxide,[16] has been observed to result in substantial yields of 9-undecynoic acid. Krafft[16] has shown that the dehydrobromination of bromoundecenoic acid with either concentrated aqueous or alcoholic potassium hydroxide yields the 9-acid and that treatment of the 10-acetylenic acid with these reagents results in a migration of the triple bond to the 9-position.

9-Undecynoic acid freezes at 59.5° and boils at 177° under 15 mm. It is difficultly soluble in water and easily soluble in ethanol, ether, and carbon disulfide.

2-Undecynoic Acid. $CH_3(CH_2)_7C \vdots CCO_2H$

Moureu and Delange[15] have prepared 2-undecynoic acid by the action of carbon dioxide in dry ether on sodium octylacetylide. The acid was observed to decompose into 1-decyne and carbon dioxide upon distillation at atmospheric pressure. 2-Undecynoic acid freezes at 30°.

HEXADECYNOIC ACIDS

The hexadecynoic acids are not found in the naturally occurring fatty substances. Of this group only 7-hexadecynoic acid has been described.

7-Hexadecynoic Acid. $CH_3(CH_2)_7C \vdots C(CH_2)_5CO_2H$

The preparation of 7-hexadecynoic acid by the dehydrobromination of 7,8-dibromopalmitic acid with alcoholic potassium hydroxide has been reported by Bodenstein.[18] The acid freezes at 47° and boils at 240° at 15 mm. 7-Hexadecynoic acid is insoluble in water and readily soluble in ethanol and ether.

HEPTADECYNOIC ACIDS

The heptadecynoic acids have not been reported to occur in the naturally occurring fats and oils. The 2-acid has been prepared and described.

2-Heptadecynoic Acid. $CH_3(CH_2)_{13}C \vdots CCO_2H$

Krafft and Heizmann [19] have described the synthesis of 2-heptadecynoic acid by the action of carbon dioxide in dry ether on sodium tetradecylacetylide. The acid freezes at 44–45° and is easily soluble in ethanol and ether but insoluble in water. Upon distillation at atmospheric pressure it decomposes into 1-hexadecyne and carbon dioxide.

OCTADECYNOIC ACIDS

The octadecynoic acids are frequently referred to as the stearolic acids, owing to the interest which has centered around the 9-member of this series, stearolic acid. This series also contains the only well-authenticated example of a naturally occurring mono-acetylenic acid, tariric acid (6-octadecynoic acid). Sixteen octadecynoic acids are theoretically possible, six of which are known. Most of our knowledge of the acetylenic acids has been derived from a study of 9-octadecynoic acid. Stearolic acid may be considered to be the characteristic high molecular weight acetylenic acid, since it occupies a place in the acetylenic acid series comparable to that of oleic acid among the ethylenic acids. Stearolic acid, however, has not been observed in the naturally occurring fats and oils, and therefore its importance is due to the ease of its preparation from oleic acid. The following octadecynoic acids have been described.

6-Octadecynoic Acid (Tariric Acid). $CH_3(CH_2)_{10}C \vdots C(CH_2)_4CO_2H$

The presence of tariric acid, in a *tariri* seed oil, was first observed by Arnaud.[20] Tariric acid yields lauric and adipic acids upon oxidation and was thus shown to be 6-octadecynoic acid. Grützner[21] has reported the freezing point of tariric acid to be 50.5°. The presence of tariric acid in the *Picramnia* seed fats has been confirmed by Grimme,[22] and more recently by Steger and van Loon,[23] who observed that it is essentially the only unsaturated acid present in the glycerides of the seed fat of *Picramnia sow*. These latter authors also obtained lauric acid and adipic acid by the ozonization of tariric acid and thus confirmed the previous work upon its structure. The structural relationship which exists between tariric acid and petroselinic acid (6-octadecenoic acid) is noteworthy. Vongerichten and Köhler[24] have prepared a 6-octadecynoic acid (petroselinolic acid), melting at 54°, by the action of potassium hydroxide in methanol upon 6,7-dibromostearic acid. The latter acid was obtained by the bromination of petroselinic acid.

9-Octadecynoic Acid (Stearolic Acid). $CH_3(CH_2)_7C \vdots C(CH_2)_7CO_2H$

Although stearolic acid has not been reported in the naturally occurring fats and oils, its structural similarity to oleic acid makes it the most important of the acetylenic acids. Stearolic acid was first obtained by Overbeck [3] by the action of alcoholic potassium hydroxide upon 9,10-dibromostearic acid (dibromoöleic acid). Stearolic acid results from the dehydrobromination of either oleic or elaidic acid dibromide.[25] The action of zinc and a mixture of hydrochloric and acetic acids on 9-keto-12-chlorostearic acid, prepared from ricinoleic acid, has been reported by Behrend [26] to give stearolic acid. A method for the preparation of stearolic acid from 9,10-dibromostearic acid by dehydrobromination with potassium hydroxide in 1-pentanol has been proposed by Kino [27] and has been employed by Kimura.[28]

The treatment of stearolic acid with fuming nitric acid first gives a diketostearic acid (9,10-diketostearic acid, stearoxylic acid), which undergoes further oxidation to pelargonic and azelaic acids, together with a small amount of 1,1-dinitrononane.[25, 29] The oxidation of stearolic acid with potassium permanganate yields pelargonic, suberic, azelaic, and caprylic acids.[30, 31] Fusion of stearolic acid with potassium hydroxide has been stated to yield myristic acid.[18] The work of Baruch [4] in 1894 has furnished a rigid proof that the triple bond in stearolic acid is between the ninth and tenth carbon atoms. This proof is as follows: stearolic acid forms a 10-ketostearic acid by treatment with concentrated sulfuric acid, thus:

$$CH_3(CH_2)_7C \vdots C(CH_2)_7CO_2H \xrightarrow[\text{H}_2\text{SO}_4]{\text{H}_2\text{O}} CH_3(CH_2)_7\underset{\underset{O}{\|}}{C}CH_2(CH_2)_7CO_2H$$

This forms two isomeric oximes upon reaction with hydroxylamine, as follows:

$$CH_3(CH_2)_7\underset{\underset{O}{\|}}{C}CH_2(CH_2)_7CO_2H \xrightarrow{\text{NH}_2\text{OH}} \begin{cases} CH_3(CH_2)_7\underset{\underset{NOH}{\|}}{C}(CH_2)_8CO_2H \quad (I) \\ \\ CH_3(CH_2)_7\underset{\underset{HON}{\|}}{C}(CH_2)_8CO_2H \quad (II) \end{cases}$$

Treatment with concentrated sulfuric acid results in a Beckmann [32] rearrangement, and when these rearranged products are treated with concentrated hydrochloric acid the following cleavage products result:

$$\text{(I)} \quad \underset{\underset{O}{\overset{\parallel}{}}}{CH_3(CH_2)_7\overset{\overset{H}{|}}{N}C}(CH_2)_8CO_2H \rightarrow CH_3(CH_2)_7NH_2 + HO\underset{\overset{\parallel}{O}}{C}(CH_2)_8CO_2H$$

$$\qquad\qquad\qquad\qquad\qquad\qquad\qquad \text{Octylamine} \qquad \text{Sebacic acid}$$

$$\text{(II)} \quad CH_3(CH_2)_7\overset{\overset{H}{|}}{\underset{\underset{O}{\overset{\parallel}{}}}{C}}N(CH_2)_8CO_2H \rightarrow CH_3(CH_2)_7CO_2H + H_2N(CH_2)_8CO_2H$$

$$\qquad\qquad\qquad\qquad\qquad\qquad \text{Pelargonic acid} \qquad \text{9-Aminopelargonic acid}$$

The isolation and identification of the above products showed that the acetylenic bond is between the ninth and tenth carbon atoms.

Stearolic acid has been reported to melt at 48°. It is insoluble in water, only slightly soluble in cold ethanol, and appreciably soluble in ether and hot ethanol.

8-Octadecynoic Acid. $CH_3(CH_2)_8C\vdots C(CH_2)_6CO_2H$
10-Octadecynoic Acid. $CH_3(CH_2)_6C\vdots C(CH_2)_8CO_2H$

The addition of hydrogen iodide to stearolic acid results in the formation of two isomeric iodoöctadecenoic acids: $CH_3(CH_2)_7\text{-}CH:CI(CH_2)_7CO_2H$, which melts at 23–24°; and $CH_3(CH_2)_7\text{-}CI:CH(CH_2)_7CO_2H$, which melts at 39°.[33] The addition of a second molecule of hydrogen iodide yields the isomeric diiodostearic acids. Arnaud and Posternak[34] have prepared 9,9-diiodostearic acid and 10,10-diiodostearic acid from stearolic acid and have treated these diiodo acids with alcoholic potassium hydroxide for the preparation of isomeric stearolic acids. By this process the former yields 8-octadecynoic acid, $CH_3(CH_2)_8C:C(CH_2)_6\text{-}CO_2H$, and the latter 10-octadecynoic acid, $CH_3(CH_2)_6C:C\text{-}(CH_2)_8CO_2H$. The 8-acid melts at 47.5° and the 10-acid at 47°. The oxidation of these acids with nitric acid yields suberic acid, $(CH_2)_6(CO_2H)_2$, in the case of 8-octadecynoic acid and sebacic acid, $(CH_2)_8(CO_2H)_2$, in the case of 10-octadecynoic acid.

5-Octadecynoic Acid. $CH_3(CH_2)_{11}C\vdots C(CH_2)_3CO_2H$
7-Octadecynoic Acid. $CH_3(CH_2)_9C\vdots C(CH_2)_5CO_2H$

The preparation of these acids from tariric acid has been described by Posternak.[35] The addition of two molecular equivalents of hydrogen iodide to tariric acid and the subsequent dehydroiodination of the product by means of alcoholic potassium hydroxide gives a mixture of at least three isomeric octadecynoic acids, one of which is tariric acid. When this tariric acid is removed from the reaction products and the remaining mixture is again successively treated with hydrogen iodide and alcoholic potassium hydroxide, there are obtained two new acids, 5-octadecynoic acid and 7-octadecynoic acid. The former acid forms 5,6-diketostearic acid, $CH_3(CH_2)_{11}COCO(CH_2)_3CO_2H$, melting at 94°, when oxidized with fuming nitric acid, from which tridecanoic acid is obtained upon further oxidation. The latter acid yields 7,8-diketostearic acid, $CH_3(CH_2)_9COCO(CH_2)_5CO_2H$, melting at 86.5°, one of the oxidative cleavage products of which is pimelic acid, $(CH_2)_5(CO_2H)_2$.

Naturally Occurring C_{18} Acids Containing Both Acetylenic and Ethylenic Bonds

The presence of acids in the natural fats containing both acetylenic and ethylenic bonds was suggested in 1937 by the work of Steger and van Loon,[36] who obtained an acid stated to be either 6-octadecen-9-ynoic acid or 9-octadecen-6-ynoic acid from the seed fat of *Onguekoa gore*. Oxidation showed this acid to possess unsaturated bonds between the sixth and seventh and the ninth and tenth carbon atoms; however, the actual position of the ethylenic and acetylenic bonds was not conclusively determined. An acid which melted at 38–39° and apparently contained one ethylenic and two acetylenic linkages was also isolated during this investigation. Three years later, Castille[37] also separated this latter acid, which he termed erythrogenic acid, from an *Ongokea* seed oil. The presence of one ethylenic and two acetylenic bonds was confirmed, and the acid was considered to have either the structure $CH_2\!:\!CHC\!:\!C(CH_2)_4C\!:\!C(CH_2)_7CO_2H$, or the structure $CH_2\!:\!CH(CH_2)_4C\!:\!CC\!:\!C(CH_2)_7CO_2H$. Steger and van Loon[38] have named this acid isamic acid and have presented evidence favoring the latter of the two structures proposed by Castille. The following physical constants have been reported for this acid: m.p. 39.5°, d_4^{45} 0.9309, d_4^{60} 0.91966, d_4^{78} 0.9095, n_D^{50} 1.49148, and n_D^{78} 1.4860.

DOCOSYNOIC ACIDS

13-Docosynoic Acid (Behenolic Acid).
$CH_3(CH_2)_7C\!:\!C(CH_2)_{11}CO_2H$

Behenolic acid has been prepared by the action of alcoholic potassium hydroxide upon 13,14-dibromobehenic acid (erucic acid dibromide).[5, 39, 40, 41] Behenolic acid stands in the same relation to erucic acid as stearolic acid does to oleic acid. It is not found in the naturally occurring fats and oils. Behenolic acid was shown by Baruch [42] to be 13-docosynoic acid, by the same procedure which he subsequently employed in establishing the position of the triple bond in stearolic acid. The oxime of ketobehenic acid, prepared from behenolic acid, was subjected to a Beckmann rearrangement, and the rearranged products were split with concentrated hydrochloric acid, separated, and identified. The presence of pelargonic acid and 13-aminotridecanoic acid, and of tetradecanedioic acid and octylamine, in the reaction products, established the structure of behenolic acid. The oxidation of behenolic acid with nitric acid yields behenoxylic acid (13,14-diketobehenic acid), the structure of which has been established by Spieckermann.[43] Pelargonic acid and tridecanedioic acid result from the oxidative cleavage of behenolic acid.

Behenolic acid freezes at 57.5°. It is easily soluble in absolute ethanol, ether, and other organic solvents, and is insoluble in water.

PART 2 THE HYDROXY ACIDS

The hydroxy fatty acids comprise a series of straight-chain carboxylic acids which contain one or more hydroxyl groups in the hydrocarbon portion of the molecule. They constitute a very large group of compounds, the individual members of which unquestionably merit considerable attention and study. Interest in these hydroxy acids arises not only from the many representatives of this class, but also from the wide variation in properties exhibited by these various acids. The hydroxy fatty acids may be saturated or they may contain one or more unsaturated bonds in the hydrocarbon chain. For example, 10-hydroxyoctadecanoic acid (10-hydroxystearic acid), $CH_3(CH_2)_7CH(OH)(CH_2)_8CO_2H$, is a saturated hydroxy fatty acid; 12-hydroxy-9-octadecenoic acid (ricinoleic acid), $CH_3(CH_2)_5CH(OH)CH_2CH:CH(CH_2)_7CO_2H$, is an ethylenic hydroxy acid; and 12-hydroxy-9-octadecynoic acid (ricinstearolic acid), $CH_3(CH_2)_5CH(OH)CH_2C:C(CH_2)_7CO_2H$, is an example of a hydroxy acetylenic acid. Since the hydroxy fatty acids possess at least one asymmetric carbon atom, they are capable of being resolved into their optical isomers, and most of the naturally occurring hydroxy acids are optically active. Those hydroxy acids which contain an ethylenic bond exhibit geometrical isomerism and can be obtained in either the *cis* or the *trans* form.

With the notable exception of ricinoleic acid, the principal acid of castor oil, the hydroxy acids do not occur in abundant quantities in the naturally occurring oils and fats. The waxy substances obtained from the leaves of certain coniferous plants contain significant amounts of saturated hydroxy acids, such as sabinic acid (12-hydroxylauric acid) and juniperic acid (16-hydroxy-palmitic acid). Hydroxy acids appear in certain animal fats, notably wool fat, and in the fatty acids of the brain. Their presence in such substances presents a subject of considerable biological interest. Hydroxy acids apparently occur in various bacterial waxes,[44, 45] and they have been observed to be formed by the action of molds on the oil in corn.[46] They are formed by the hydrolysis of suberin,[47] and by the oxidation of paraffin wax.[48, 49]

2-Hydroxy acids (β-hydroxy acids) are important intermediates in the biological oxidation of fatty acids [50] and are also apparently synthesized from unsaturated acids during the metabolism of insect and plant waxes, the unsaturated acids being built up from shorter-chain products.[51] Since the hydroxy fatty acids are intermediate products in many metabolic processes, it is not surprising that they are not generally present in large amounts. Due regard, however, must be given to the several notable exceptions to the above statement.

A large number of hydroxy fatty acids have been synthesized, several general methods being employed for their preparation. Perhaps the most common procedure is to treat halo-substituted acids with aqueous alkaline hydroxide solutions, a treatment which results in the substitution of a hydroxy group for the halogen. In the case of 4-hydroxy (γ-hydroxy) and 5-hydroxy (δ-hydroxy) acids, the lactone is frequently obtained rather than the free acid. The use of alcoholic alkaline hydroxide solutions results in the formation of unsaturated acids by the removal of hydrogen halide and consequently gives only small yields of hydroxy acids. The removal of hydrogen halides from 3-chloro acids generally yields γ-lactones, thus: $RCH_2CHClCH_2CO_2H \rightarrow RCHCH_2CH_2CO.$

$$\underset{O}{\underset{|\rule{3cm}{0.4pt}}{}}$$

The hydration of unsaturated acids under the catalytic influence of alkaline hydroxides has been employed for the preparation of the hydroxy acids or their lactones. A method frequently used for the synthesis of hydroxy acids is the treatment of an unsaturated acid with concentrated sulfuric acid followed by the hydrolysis of the sulfuric addition product, in which reaction the hydroxyl group is generally added to the carbon atom farther from the carboxyl group. As an example, Chernoyarova [52] has observed that the treatment of petroselinic acid (6-octadecenoic acid) with sulfuric acid, followed by hydrolysis of the resulting product, yields 7-hydroxystearic acid. Keto acids yield hydroxy acids upon reduction, and this method has been extensively employed for the preparation of the latter acids. Hydroxy acids which contain the hydroxyl group in a terminal position may be obtained by the partial reduction of dicarboxylic acids or their derivatives. The heating of the substituted paraconic acids [53] results in the formation of γ-lactones from which the hydroxy acids can be obtained, thus:

$$\begin{array}{ccc} \text{RCH}\!\!-\!\!-\!\!-\!\!\text{CHCO}_2\text{H} & \text{RCHCH}_2\text{CH}_2\text{CO} & \text{RCHCH}_2\text{CH}_2\text{CO}_2\text{H} \\ |\qquad\quad | & | \qquad\qquad | & | \\ \text{O}\!\!-\!\!-\!\!\text{COCH}_2 \!\!\to & \text{O}\!\!-\!\!-\!\!-\!\!-\!\! \!\!\to & \text{OH} \end{array}$$

The action of Grignard reagents upon aldehyde esters has frequently been employed for the preparation of hydroxy acids.[54, 55, 56, 57] The general reaction is as follows:

$$\begin{array}{c}\text{O} \\ \diagdown \\ \quad\ \text{C(CH}_2)_x\text{CO}_2\text{R} + \text{CH}_3(\text{CH}_2)_x\text{MgX} \to \\ \diagup \\ \text{H} \end{array} \quad \begin{array}{c} \text{MgXO} \diagdown \quad \diagup (\text{CH}_2)_x\text{CO}_2\text{R} \\ \text{C} \\ \diagup \quad \diagdown \\ \text{H} \quad (\text{CH}_2)_x\text{CH}_3 \end{array} \to$$

$$\text{CH}_3(\text{CH}_2)_x\text{CH(OH)(CH}_2)_x\text{CO}_2\text{R} + \text{MgX(OH)}$$

γ-Lactones are formed by the action of alkyl-substituted 2-propenyl bromides with alkylmalonic esters.[58] Hill [59] has recently proposed the preparation of hydroxy acids by the hydrogenation of polyesters. In addition to the above general procedures, there are a number of other methods which have been employed for the synthesis of specific hydroxy acids. Dihydroxy acids which contain hydroxyl groups upon adjacent carbon atoms result from the oxidation of ethylenic fatty acids or from the hydration of keto acids. The preparation and properties of these dihydroxy acids are discussed in detail in a later chapter.

Owing to the presence of a carboxyl group and one or more hydroxyl groups in the hydroxy acid molecule, such acids show the characteristic reactions not only of carboxylic acids but also of alcohols. Thus, the hydroxyl groups may be replaced by halogens, acylated, or otherwise esterified to give many of the typical reaction products of alcohols, while the carboxyl group may be converted into the usual carboxylic acid derivatives. The hydroxy acids show a progressive gradation in physical properties, and to a certain extent in chemical properties, with increase in the chain length of the molecule. This progressive change in properties is due essentially to increased molecular weight and is similar to that encountered in the other fatty acid series. The hydroxy acids are, in general, more soluble in water and ethanol and less soluble in petroleum ether and other hydrocarbon solvents than the non-hydroxy acids. The hydroxyl group can easily be acylated with acetic anhydride, and these acetyl groups can then be removed by treatment with potassium hydroxide. This method is the basis of the so-called acetyl value determination and constitutes a standard procedure for the determination of hydroxy acids in a fatty acid mixture.[60, 61] In addition to exhibiting the individual properties of alcohols and carboxylic acids, the hydroxy acids undergo several characteristic reactions which are dependent upon the presence of both a hydroxyl and a carboxyl group within one molecule. Such reactions are greatly influenced by the relative positions of these two groups. Thus, 2-hydroxy acids (α-hydroxy acids) when heated yield aldehydes, carbon monoxide, and water, as follows: $RCH(OH)CO_2H \rightarrow RCHO + CO + H_2O$. They also undergo esterification to form hemilactides or lactides as follows:

$$2RCH(OH)CO_2H \rightarrow \underset{\text{Hemilactide}}{\underset{|}{RCHCO_2H}} \rightarrow \underset{\text{Lactide}}{\underset{|}{RCHCOO}}$$

3-Hydroxy acids (β-hydroxy acids) lose water when heated, being converted into 3-ethylenic acids together with smaller amounts of other hydroxy acids. Dehydration to form ethylenic acids is also encountered with those acids in which the hydroxyl group is far removed from the carboxyl group and lactone formation or cyclization is not favored. The formation of an ethylenic acid is not generally encountered if the hydroxyl group occupies a terminal position. If the hydroxyl group is in close proximity to an ethylenic linkage, as in ricinoleic acid, dehydration and scission reactions predominate.

Perhaps the most characteristic reaction of hydroxy acids is that of lactone formation, which is a cyclization or intraesterification reaction and may involve one or more molecules. Simple or monomeric lactones result from the elimination of water from one molecule of the hydroxy acid by a process of intraesterification. The ester, therefore, possesses a heterocyclic ring, and the relative stability of such rings is directly related to the Baeyer strain theory.[62, 63] Thus, the ease of lactone formation varies greatly with the position of the hydroxyl group in the hydrocarbon chain, the so-called γ- and δ-lactones being the most stable. Hydroxy acids which contain the hydroxyl group in the 4- or 5-position exhibit such a marked tendency towards lactone formation that the free acid is frequently extremely difficult to obtain. For example, 4-hydroxyvaleric acid forms γ-valerolactone as follows:

$$CH_3CH(OH)CH_2CH_2CO_2H \rightarrow CH_3CHCH_2CH_2CO$$
$$\underset{O}{\rule{0pt}{0pt}}$$

5-Hydroxyvaleric acid forms the monomeric δ-lactone, thus:

$$HOCH_2CH_2CH_2CH_2CO_2H \rightarrow CH_2CH_2CH_2CH_2CO$$
$$\underset{O}{\rule{0pt}{0pt}}$$

Lactonization is an equilibrium reaction, the equilibrium mixture generally containing large amounts of the lactone.[64, 65] Monomeric lactones containing a large number of atoms in the ring are frequently formed from higher hydroxy acids which possess a hydroxy group remote from the carboxyl group. Dimeric and trimeric lactones result from the cyclization of two or more molecules of hydroxy acids.

The lactones are neutral liquids which possess a faint aromatic odor and yield salts of the hydroxy acids when treated with alkalies. The higher lactones have a musklike odor, and an appreciable amount of work has been done in an attempt to correlate their odors with their chemical structures.[58, 66] The lactones can be distilled without decomposition. They yield brominated fatty acids when treated with hydrogen bromide. Stoll and Rouvé [67] have made an extensive study of the formation of monomeric and polymeric lactone rings from hydroxy acids of the type $HO(CH_2)_xCO_2H$. They observed that $HO(CH_2)_4CO_2H$ gives predominantly the monomeric lactone; $HO(CH_2)_{10}CO_2H$ gives 11% of the monomeric lactone, 69% of the dimeric lactone, and 20% of the trimeric lactone; while $HO(CH_2)_{22}CO_2H$ gives 61% of the monomer and 33% of the dimer. Lactonization was effected in benzene solution in the presence of benzenesulfonic acid, by a method which they had previously described.[68] A study of the kinetics of cyclization [69] has led to the conclusion that high temperatures favor the formation of the unimolecular cyclic product, owing to the higher heat of activation of the primary unimolecular reaction. The degree of cyclization and, consequently, the yield of monomeric lactone were found to vary inversely with the concentration of the hydroxy acid.

Cyclization or lactone formation should be distinguished from the so-called etholide formation, which is essentially a linear esterification and results in simple or polyetholides as follows:

$$HOCH_2(CH_2)_xCH_2CO \underline{[OH \quad H]} OCH_2(CH_2)_xCO_2H \longrightarrow HOCH_2(CH_2)_xCH_2COOCH_2(CH_2)_xCO_2H$$

Etholides combine the properties of alcohols, acids, and esters. They are present in the waxes of pines and similar plants, being first encountered during an investigation of conifer waxes.[70] Chuit and Hausser [71] have studied etholide formation with a number of hydroxy acids which contain the hydroxyl group in the terminal position.

In view of the many possible reactions which hydroxy acids undergo, it is quite apparent why their isolation from the naturally occurring sources is often accomplished only with considerable difficulty. The various reactions of hydroxy acids are discussed under the individual acids. A detailed treatment of cyclization and linear esterification, however, would go far beyond the interest and purpose of this present writing.

The following is a description of the naturally occurring and synthetic hydroxy acids which contain five or more carbon atoms. Only straight-chain hydroxy acids are discussed, since such acids are directly related to the fatty acids.

HYDROXYPENTANOIC ACIDS (HYDROXYVALERIC ACIDS)

All the four theoretically possible hydroxypentanoic acids have been described. They are extremely soluble in water, ethanol, and ether, and their chemical properties differ materially depending upon the position of the hydroxyl group in the alkyl chain.

2-Hydroxypentanoic acid, $CH_3CH_2CH_2CH(OH)CO_2H$, has been prepared by the action of sodium hydroxide on ethyl 2-bromovalerate [72] and also by the reduction of 2-ketovaleric acid with sodium amalgam.[73] The acid is hygroscopic and freezes at 34°. 3-Hydroxypentanoic acid, $CH_3CH_2CH(OH)CH_2CO_2H$, can be obtained from 3-bromovaleric acid by boiling with water for several hours,[74] or by the treatment of 3-pentenoic acid with sodium hydroxide.[75] The acid is a liquid which easily yields 3-pentenoic acid upon heating. 4-Hydroxypentanoic acid, $CH_3CH(OH)CH_2-CH_2CO_2H$, is generally encountered as the γ-lactone, from which the free acid can be obtained by treatment with alkalies followed by careful acidification. Fittig and coworkers [76, 77] have described the preparation of 4-hydroxypentanoic acid by the action of water or sodium hydroxide solution on 4-bromovaleric acid. Fittig and Hjelt [53] have also prepared the acid by heating (2-hydroxypropyl)-malonic acid or its lactone. The dry distillation of methylparaconic acid yields 4-hydroxypentanoic acid [77] together with other products. The reduction of 4-ketovaleric acid (levulinic acid) with sodium amalgam,[78] as well as its catalytic hydrogenation in the presence of nickel,[79] yields 4-hydroxypentanoic acid. This acid is quite unstable and easily forms the γ-lactone. 5-Hydroxypentanoic acid, $HOCH_2(CH_2)_3CO_2H$, has been prepared by the action of alcoholic sodium ethylate on 5-iodovaleric acid,[80] and by the reduction of glutaric anhydride by means of aluminum amalgam.[81] The heating of 5-chloropentanoic acid results in the elimination of hydrogen chloride with the formation of δ-valerolactone, from which the free acid can be obtained. 5-Hydroxyvaleric acid is an oil which easily forms a δ-lactone. All the hydroxyvaleric acids can be purified by the crystallization of their barium salts.

HYDROXYHEXANOIC ACIDS (HYDROXYCAPROIC ACIDS)

The action of nitrous acid on 2-aminohexanoic acid yields 2-hydroxyhexanoic acid, $CH_3(CH_2)_3CH(OH)CO_2H$, together with 2-hexenoic acid.[82] 2-Hydroxyhexanoic acid results from the debromination of 2-bromohexanoic acid by means of sodium hydroxide. Jelissafow [83] obtained the sodium salt of the acid in this manner, acidified its solution with hydrogen sulfide, extracted the free acid with ether, and purified it by crystallization as the sodium salt. 2-Hydroxyhexanoic acid freezes at 60–62°, and yields valeraldehyde and 2- and 3-hexenoic acids upon distillation. 3-Hydroxyhexanoic acid, $CH_3(CH_2)_2CH(OH)CH_2CO_2H$, results from the debromination of 3-bromohexanoic acid by means of steam or alkaline solutions. The acid is also formed by the treatment of 2-hexenoic acid with sodium hydroxide solution.[84] It has been described as a liquid which is easily soluble in water. 4-Hydroxyhexanoic acid, $CH_3CH_2CH(OH)(CH_2)_2CO_2H$, has been prepared by several methods. It easily forms a γ-lactone and consequently the free acid is isolated only with great difficulty. 4-Hydroxyhexanoic acid or its γ-lactone results from the action of sodium hydroxide solutions [85, 86] or of alcoholic or aqueous ammonium hydroxide [86] on 4-bromohexanoic acid. The action of concentrated sulfuric acid on hydrosorbic acid (3-hexenoic acid), followed by hydrolysis of the sulfuric addition product, yields 4-hydroxy-hexanoic acid.[87, 88] Fittig and Delisle [89] have observed that the distillation of ethylparaconic acid yields both 4-hydroxyhexanoic acid and hydrosorbic acid. Kiliani [90] has reported that 4-hydroxy-hexanoic acid results from the reduction, by means of phosphorus and hydrogen iodide, of various acids, such as mannonic and gluconic acids, which are obtained by the oxidation of hexoses. 5-Hydroxyhexanoic acid, $CH_3CH(OH)(CH_2)_3CO_2H$, like the preceding acid, is quite difficult to obtain in the free state owing to its tendency towards lactone formation. Salts of 5-hydroxyhexanoic acid may be prepared by treatment of the δ-lactone with solutions of barium hydroxide or alkali carbonates.[91] The δ-lactone is formed by the reduction of 5-ketohexanoic acid with sodium amalgam [91] or by boiling 5-bromohexanoic acid with water.[92] The free acid is easily soluble in water and ethanol. The terminal hydroxyhexanoic acid, $HO(CH_2)_5CO_2H$, was first described by Van Natta, Hill, and Carothers,[93] who obtained it in small amounts as a by-product during the reduction of dimethyl adipate. The free acid could not be purified by distillation or crystallization owing to its pronounced tendency towards lactone formation. The lactone is very soluble in water, ethanol, and benzene, and is insoluble in petroleum ether. The following physical constants have been reported for this lactone: b_2 98–99°, d_4^{24} 1.0698, and n_D^{24} 1.4608. The isolation of the pure acid has recently been reported by Stoll and Rouvé.[67]

HYDROXYHEPTANOIC ACIDS (HYDROXYENANTHIC ACIDS)

2-Hydroxyheptanoic acid, $CH_3(CH_2)_4CH(OH)CO_2H$, has been prepared by heating 2-bromoheptanoic acid with water under pressure [94] or with a solution of sodium hydroxide.[95] The acid freezes at 65° and is difficultly soluble in cold water. The oxidation of 2-hydroxyheptanoic acid with chromic acid yields caproic acid.[96] It gives hexanal together with other products when heated. 4-Hydroxyheptanoic acid, $CH_3(CH_2)_2CH(OH)(CH_2)_2CO_2H$, is extremely difficult to obtain in the free state owing to its tendency to form the γ-lactone. The acid has been described as a syrup which does not solidify at $-16°$. Fittig and Schmidt [97] have prepared this acid, together with its lactone, by heating 4-bromoheptanoic acid with water and also by the decomposition of γ-propylparaconic acid. 4-Hydroxyheptanoic acid has also been prepared from 3-heptenoic acid by treatment with sulfuric acid followed by hydrolysis of the resulting product.[98] 5-Hydroxy-heptanoic acid, $CH_3CH_2CH(OH)(CH_2)_3CO_2H$, also exhibits a marked tendency towards lactone formation. This acid has been prepared by Fichter and Gully [99] by the debromination of 5-bromo-heptanoic acid with water. The preparation of 7-hydroxyheptanoic acid, $HO(CH_2)_6CO_2H$, by the partial reduction of pimelic acid and its derivatives, has been described.[67, 100] The acid was reported to be a syrupy liquid.

HYDROXYOCTANOIC ACIDS (HYDROXYCAPRYLIC ACIDS)

Three of the hydroxyoctanoic acids have been prepared. The hydrolysis of 2-hydroxyoctanenitrile, $CH_3(CH_2)_5CH\Big\langle\begin{smallmatrix}OH\\CN\end{smallmatrix}$, in the presence of hydrochloric acid yields 2-hydroxyoctanoic acid, $CH_3(CH_2)_5CH(OH)CO_2H$.[101] The acid has also been prepared by the action of a solution of barium hydroxide on 2-bromoöctanoic acid, followed by acidification.[96, 102] 2-Hydroxyoctanoic acid freezes at 69.5°. It is difficultly soluble in cold water and is very soluble in ethanol and ether. 6-Hydroxyoctanoic acid, $CH_3CH_2CH(OH)(CH_2)_4CO_2H$, has been synthesized by the reduction of 6-ketoöctanoic acid with zinc and potassium hydroxide.[103] It has been described as a viscous liquid. Chuit and Hausser [71] have prepared 8-hydroxyoctanoic acid, $HO(CH_2)_7CO_2H$, by the partial reduction of potassium methyl suberate with sodium in ethanol. The pure acid melts at 58°. It yields a dimeric lactone (m.p. 92.5–93.5°, $b_{0.3}$ 150–152°, $d_4^{108.7}$ 0.9737, $n_D^{108.7}$ 1.4444) on heating with benzenesulfonic acid.[67]

HYDROXYNONANOIC ACIDS (HYDROXYPELARGONIC ACIDS)

Several of the hydroxynonanoic acids have been synthesized. 2-Hydroxynonanoic acid has been prepared by the action of potassium hydroxide on 2-bromononanoic acid.[104] The acid freezes at 70°, and yields octanal together with the lactide when heated. 3-Hydroxynonanoic acid, $CH_3(CH_2)_5CH(OH)CH_2CO_2H$, is formed along with enanthic acid and 1,2,4-decanetriol by the oxidation of hexyl allyl carbinol, $\begin{smallmatrix}C_6H_{13}\\CH_2:CHCH_2\end{smallmatrix}\Big\rangle CH(OH)$.[105]

The acid freezes at 48–51°.   7-Hydroxynonanoic acid, CH_3CH_2-$CH(OH)(CH_2)_5CO_2H$, has been obtained by the reduction of 7-ketononanoic acid with zinc and potassium hydroxide.[103]   The acid boils at 204° under 25 mm.   It has been reported to form 4-pentyl-butyrolactone by the action of sulfuric acid.   Chuit and Hausser [71] have prepared 9-hydroxynonanoic acid, $HO(CH_2)_8CO_2H$, by several methods.   The partial reduction of potassium methyl azelate by sodium in ethanol gives a 31.5% yield of 9-hydroxynonanoic acid, which can be purified through its acetyl derivative.   The reduction of dimethyl azelate results in an 8% yield of the hydroxy acid and a 73% yield of the corresponding glycol.   The oxidation of the bromohydrin $CH_2Br(CH_2)_7CH_2OH$ yields the corresponding carboxylic acid together with the brominated etholide.   Treatment of the bromohydrin with potassium ethylate, followed by hydrolysis of the resulting product, yields the free acid together with its etholide.   9-Hydroxynonanoic acid melts at 51–51.5°, and its lactone at 24–26.5°.

HYDROXYDECANOIC ACIDS (HYDROXYCAPRIC ACIDS)

Three of the hydroxydecanoic acids have been prepared and their properties described.   2-Hydroxydecanoic acid, $CH_3(CH_2)_7$-$CH(OH)CO_2H$, results from the treatment of 2-bromodecanoic acid with potassium hydroxide.[95]   It freezes at 70.5°, and decomposes upon distillation to give nonanal.   4-Hydroxydecanoic acid, $CH_3(CH_2)_5CH(OH)(CH_2)_2CO_2H$, easily forms a γ-lactone, 4-hexylbutyrolactone.   The acid together with its lactone results from the treatment of 4-bromodecanoic acid with sodium hydroxide.[106]   The lactone has also been prepared by the distillation of hexylparaconic acid.[106]   Goldsobel [107] has reported the formation of 4-hydroxydecanoic acid by the action of fuming hydrochloric acid on the oxime of 12-hydroxy-9-ketostearic acid.   10-Hydroxydecanoic acid, $HO(CH_2)_9CO_2H$, results from the partial reduction of sebacic acid derivatives.[71]   It easily forms a mono- and also a dietholide.   The lactone melts at 4–5° and boils at 67–75° at 0.3 mm.   10-Hydroxydecanoic acid forms a dimeric and a trimeric lactone.[67]

HYDROXYUNDECANOIC ACIDS

2-Hydroxyundecanoic acid, $CH_3(CH_2)_8CH(OH)CO_2H$, has been obtained by Bagard [95] by the treatment of 2-bromoundecanoic acid with potassium hydroxide.   It freezes at 69°, and yields decanal upon distillation. 4-Hydroxyundecanoic acid, $CH_3(CH_2)_6CH-(OH)(CH_2)_2CO_2H$, has been reported to be formed by the hydrolysis of the sulfuric acid addition product of 10-undecenoic acid.[108] The acid freezes at 34° and forms a γ-lactone upon standing at ordinary temperatures. 11-Hydroxyundecanoic acid, $HO(CH_2)_{10}-CO_2H$, has been synthesized by several methods. Walker and Lumsden [109] have reported its preparation from 11-bromoundecanoic acid by the action of silver oxide in alkaline solution. Chuit and Hausser [71] have obtained 11-hydroxyundecanoic acid by the hydrolysis of 11-hydroxyundecanenitrile, $HOCH_2(CH_2)_9CN$, and also by heating the condensation product of 9-bromo-1-nonanol and dimethyl sodiomalonate. The reactions involved in the latter instance are as follows:

$$HO(CH_2)_8CH_2Br + NaHC(CO_2CH_3)_2 \rightarrow$$
$$HO(CH_2)_8CH_2CH(CO_2CH_3)_2 + NaBr$$
$$HO(CH_2)_8CH_2CH(CO_2H)_2 \rightarrow HO(CH_2)_8CH_2CH_2CO_2H + CO_2$$

11-Hydroxyundecanoic acid freezes at 70° and is easily soluble in ethanol and ether. It is very slightly soluble in water (0.04 part in 100 parts at 20°). The following constants have been reported for the monomeric lactone: $b_{0.04}$ 58–60°, d_4^{16} 0.9928, and n_D^{16} 1.4727. The dimeric lactone melts at 71.5–72°.[67]

HYDROXYDODECANOIC ACIDS (HYDROXYLAURIC ACIDS)

2-Hydroxydodecanoic acid, $CH_3(CH_2)_9CH(OH)CO_2H$, has been prepared by the action of aqueous potassium hydroxide on 2-bromolauric acid.[110] The acid freezes at 73–74° and yields undecanal upon distillation. The preparation of 4-hydroxydodecanoic acid, $CH_3(CH_2)_7CH(OH)(CH_2)_2CO_2H$, by the saponification of its lactone has been described.[111] The acid melts at 62.5–63.5°. 12-Hydroxydodecanoic acid (sabinic acid), $HO(CH_2)_{11}CO_2H$, occurs as its etholide in the waxlike substances present in various species of conifers. Etholides were first described by Bougault and Bourdier,[70] who obtained them by the alcohol extraction of pine needles. Saponification of the etholides yields only salts of the hydroxy acids, thus showing them to be waxes in which the hydroxy acid functions as both the alcohol and the acid. Two hydroxy acids, sabinic acid and juniperic acid (16-hydroxypalmitic acid), have been separated from the conifer waxes, the former being reported to occur only in the wax obtained from *Juniperus sabina*, whereas the latter is present in all conifer waxes which have been examined. The structure of sabinic acid as 12-hydroxy-lauric acid was established by Bougault,[112] who observed that it gave dodecanedioic acid upon oxidation. The reduction of sabinic acid with zinc and acetic acid yields lauric acid. Sabinic acid gives 12-iodolauric acid when treated with iodine and phosphorus. The hydroxy acid melts at 84°, and is quite soluble in ethanol. Chuit and Hausser[71] have synthesized sabinic acid by the condensation of 10-bromo-1-decanol with dimethyl malonate in the presence of sodium and also by the oxidation of 12-tridecenyl acetate. The reaction involved in the latter procedure is as follows:

$$CH_3CO_2(CH_2)_{11}CH:CH_2 \xrightarrow{O_3} CH_3CO_2(CH_2)_{11}CO_2H \xrightarrow{\text{Hydrolysis}} HO(CH_2)_{11}CO_2H$$

Hydroxytridecanoic Acids

Le Sueur[113] has prepared 2-hydroxytridecanoic acid, $CH_3(CH_2)_{10}$-$CH(OH)CO_2H$, by the action of potassium hydroxide on 2-bromo-tridecanoic acid. It freezes at 78° and is easily soluble in ethanol and ether but insoluble in petroleum ether and benzene. 4-Hydroxytridecanoic acid has been obtained by the saponification of its γ-lactone[111] which has been prepared by the action of sulfuric acid on 12-tridecenoic acid. The free acid melts at 66–66.5°. The terminal hydroxy acid, 13-hydroxytridecanoic acid, $HO(CH_2)_{12}$-CO_2H, has been prepared by the partial reduction of the dimethyl ester of tridecanedioic acid, $(CH_2)_{11}(CO_2CH_3)_2$, with sodium and ethanol.[71] It was purified as the acylated acid, $CH_2(OAc)(CH_2)_{11}$-CO_2H (b_{760} 202–203°, m.p. 49–49.2°), the saponification of which yielded the free acid. 13-Hydroxytridecanoic acid melts at 79–79.5°, and its methyl ester at 44°. The lactone, prepared in benzene solution in the presence of benzenesulfonic acid,[67] has the following physical constants: m.p. 20–21°, b_{10} 139–142°, d_4^{33} 0.9614, and n_D^{33} 1.4707. The dimeric lactone melts at 80–81°.

Hydroxytetradecanoic Acids (Hydroxymyristic Acids)

Several naturally occurring hydroxytetradecanoic acids have been described, although the terminal hydroxy acid, corresponding to sabinic acid and juniperic acid, has not as yet been isolated. A dihydroxymyristic acid has been obtained from the seed fat of *Pharbitis nil* Chois, by hydrolysis of pharbitic acid with sulfuric acid.[114] Power and Rogerson[115] had previously isolated this acid, which they termed ipurolic acid, by hydrolysis of the seed fat of

Ipomea purpurea, and had determined it to be a dihydroxy-myristic acid. Asahina and Shimidzu [116] studied the oxidation products of ipurolic acid and showed it to be 3,11-dihydroxy-myristic acid, a structure which was later confirmed by Asahina and Nakanishi.[117] The removal of the 3-hydroxy group from ipurolic acid by partial dehydration yields 11-hydroxy-2-tetra-decenoic acid, the hydrogenation of which gives 11-hydroxy-tetradecanoic acid, melting at 51°. The question of the identity of this acid with a monohydroxymyristic acid, melting at 51°, obtained many years ago by Müller [118] from *Angelica archangelica* oil, has not been answered.

In addition to the above naturally occurring hydroxymyristic acids, at least two synthetic acids have been prepared. 2-Hydroxy-tetradecanoic acid, $CH_3(CH_2)_{11}CH(OH)CO_2H$, has been obtained by the action of alkali-metal hydroxides on 2-bromomyristic acid.[113, 119] The acid melts at 51–51.5° and is easily soluble in ethanol, acetone, and ether. It forms tridecanal together with the lactide when heated.[104, 120] 14-Hydroxytetradecanoic acid has been prepared by several methods.[71] The partial reduction of the methyl ester of tetradecanedioic acid results in a waxlike conden-sation product consisting of the hydroxy acid and the unreduced dicarboxylic acid. The hydroxy acid is obtained by saponification of this ester and is purified as the acylated acid, $CH_2(OAc)(CH_2)_{12}$-CO_2H, m.p. 54–54.5°. The condensation of dimethyl sodiomal-onate with 12-bromo-1-dodecanol has been used for the prepara-tion of 14-hydroxytetradecanoic acid. The acid has also been syn-thesized by the conversion of 13-bromo-1-tridecanol to 13-cyano-1-tridecanol, followed by the saponification of this nitrile to the corresponding acid. The monomeric lactone of 14-hydroxytetra-decanoic acid boils at 106–109° under 0.2 mm. pressure, and the dimeric lactone melts at 106–107°.[67]

Hydroxypentadecanoic Acids

2-Hydroxypentadecanoic acid, $CH_3(CH_2)_{12}CH(OH)CO_2H$, has been prepared by the action of sodium hydroxide on 2-bromo-pentadecanoic acid.[113] The acid melts at 84.5°. It is easily soluble in ethanol but difficultly soluble in cold benzene. A hydroxy-pentadecanoic acid, convolvulinolic acid, has been reported to be present in convolvulin resin, a substance obtained from the roots of plants of the *convolvulaceae* family.[121, 122] Convolvulinolic acid was initially considered to be 11-hydroxy-12-methyltetradecanoic acid, $CH_3CH_2CH(CH_3)CH(OH)(CH_2)_9CO_2H$, a structure which was accepted by Power and Rogerson.[123] The acid was reported to be optically active. Later, Asahina and Akasu [124] reported that convolvulinolic acid gives pentadecanoic acid upon reduction and a study of the rearrangement of the oxime of the corresponding keto acid led to the conclusion that this acid is 11-hydroxypentadecanoic acid. Davies and Adams [57] have synthesized 11-hydroxypentadecanoic acid by the use of methyl 11-aldoundecanoate and butylmagnesium bromide. The synthetic acid melted at 63.5–64° and was found to differ from the naturally occurring convolvulinolic acid. The structure of this latter acid is still, therefore, undetermined. A hydroxypentadecanoic acid was reported by Ciamician and Silber [125] to be present in angelica oil, and a number of years later Kerschbaum [66] observed this acid to yield pentadecanedioic acid, $(CH_2)_{13}(CO_2H)_2$, upon oxidation, thus indicating it to be 15-hydroxypentadecanoic acid, $HO(CH_2)_{14}CO_2H$. Chuit and Hausser [71] have prepared 15-hydroxypentadecanoic acid by the partial reduction of the dimethyl ester of pentadecanedioic acid and also by the malonic acid method from 13-bromo-1-tridecanol. The monomeric lactone melts at 34–35° and boils at 105–107° under 0.01 mm. pressure.[67]

Hydroxyhexadecanoic Acids (Hydroxypalmitic Acids)

At least two hydroxypalmitic acids have been identified in the naturally occurring fats and waxes. Jalapinolic acid (11-hydroxypalmitic acid) has been isolated from scammony root wax by Power and Rogerson,[123] and juniperic acid (16-hydroxypalmitic acid) has been obtained from the etholides of coniferous waxes by Bougault and Bourdier.[70] In addition to these naturally occurring acids, several of the members of this group have been synthesized and their properties described. 2-Hydroxyhexadecanoic acid, $CH_3(CH_2)_{13}CH(OH)CO_2H$, has been obtained by the action of potassium hydroxide on 2-bromopalmitic acid.[113, 126] Ponzio [127] prepared 2-hydroxypalmitic acid together with 2-hexadecenoic acid by the treatment of 2-iodopalmitic acid with alcoholic potassium hydroxide. The acid has been reported to freeze at 86.5–87°. 11-Hydroxyhexadecanoic acid, $CH_3(CH_2)_4CH(OH)(CH_2)_9CO_2H$, has been synthesized by Davies and Adams [57] by the action of n-amylmagnesium bromide on methyl 11-aldoundecanoate. A comparison of the synthetic acid with the naturally occurring jalapinolic acid showed that the latter is the d-form of 11-hydroxy-hexadecanoic acid. The synthetic acid melted at 68–69°. 16-Hydroxyhexadecanoic acid, juniperic acid, $HO(CH_2)_{15}CO_2H$, was first obtained by Bougault and Bourdier [70] by hydrolysis of the etholides of coniferous waxes. One of these authors [112] later showed juniperic acid to be 16-hydroxypalmitic acid. The naturally occurring acid was reported to melt at 95°, its melting point decreasing to 83° if heated above the melting point for a short time. A hydroxyhexadecanoic acid melting at 73.8–74.2° has been isolated from beeswax by Ikuta; [128] however, it has not been determined whether this is an impure form of juniperic acid or another hydroxypalmitic acid. Juniperic acid has been synthesized by the reduction of dimethyl thapsate $(CH_2)_{14}(CO_2CH_3)_2$, and also by the oxidation of the monoacetate of 1,16-hexadecanediol. [71] The dietholide, which melts at 87.5–88.0°, has been prepared by heating the free acid to 125°. Stoll and Rouvé [67] have reported the following physical constants for the lactone: m.p. 15°, d_4^{33} 0.9397, and $n_D^{21.5}$ 1.4699.

HYDROXYHEXADECENOIC ACIDS

Kerschbaum [66] has observed that the odoriferous constituent of musk seed oil is a lactone (ambrettolide) which boils at 185–190° at 13 mm. Hydrolysis of this lactone gives 16-hydroxy-7-hexadecenoic acid, $CH_2(OH)(CH_2)_7CH:CH(CH_2)_5CO_2H$, ambrettolic acid. Upon reduction the acid yields juniperic acid, the oxidation of which gives thapsic acid. Oxidation of ambrettolic acid results in azelaic and pimelic acids, which indicates that the double bond is between the seventh and eighth carbon atoms.

HYDROXYHEPTADECANOIC ACIDS

Two hydroxyheptadecanoic acids have been synthesized. 2-Hydroxyheptadecanoic acid, $CH_3(CH_2)_{14}CH(OH)CO_2H$, has been prepared [129] by the action of potassium hydroxide on 2-bromoheptadecanoic acid. It melts at 89°, and forms palmitaldehyde together with a lactide when heated. 17-Hydroxyheptadecanoic acid, $HO(CH_2)_{16}CO_2H$, has been obtained by the partial reduction of the dimethyl ester of heptadecanedioic acid, $(CH_2)_{15}(CO_2CH_3)_2$. [71] It melts at 87.5–88.0° and yields both a monomeric lactone, $b_{0.2}$ 135–138°, and a dimeric lactone, m.p. 96–97°, when heated in benzene in the presence of benzenesulfonic acid. [68]

HYDROXYOCTADECANOIC ACIDS (HYDROXYSTEARIC ACIDS)

Ten of the seventeen hydroxystearic acids have been prepared and characterized. The question as to whether the hydroxystearic acids are present in the natural fats and waxes has not been conclusively answered. Hydroxystearic acids have been reported to occur in wool fat [130] and floral waxes.[131] The fatty acids of wool fat are discussed separately, since their exact constitution is still open to question.

2-Hydroxyoctadecanoic acid, $CH_3(CH_2)_{15}CH(OH)CO_2H$, has been obtained by heating 2-bromostearic acid with aqueous [129] or alcoholic [132] potassium hydroxide. Ponzio [133] has obtained this acid together with 2-octadecenoic acid by treating 2-iodostearic acid with alcoholic potassium hydroxide. 2-Hydroxyoctadecanoic acid yields heptadecanal and a lactide when heated. 3-Hydroxyoctadecanoic acid, $CH_3(CH_2)_{14}CH(OH)CH_2CO_2H$, has been prepared in a manner similar to that used for its 2-isomer.[134] It melts at 89° and is soluble in hot ethanol. 7-Hydroxyoctadecanoic acid has been prepared by hydrolysis of the sulfuric acid addition product of petroselinic acid (6-octadecenoic acid). The hydroxy acid melts at 82°. Tomecko with Adams [56] synthesized 9-hydroxyoctadecanoic acid, $CH_3(CH_2)_8CH(OH)(CH_2)_7CO_2H$, melting at 74–75°, by the Grignard reaction, employing 9-aldononanoic acid and nonylmagnesium bromide, the reaction being as follows:

$$C_9H_{19}MgBr + OCH(CH_2)_7CO_2H \rightarrow MgBrOCH(C_9H_{19})(CH_2)_7CO_2H \xrightarrow{H_2O}$$

$$C_9H_{19}CH(OH)(CH_2)_7CO_2H + MgBrOH$$

These authors have obtained 10-, 11-, 12-, and 13-hydroxyoctadecanoic acids by similar procedures. Methyl 9-hydroxyoctadecanoate melts at 45–46° and boils at 212–216° under 4 mm. pressure. 10-Hydroxyoctadecanoic acid, $CH_3(CH_2)_7CH(OH)(CH_2)_8CO_2H$, has been synthesized by a number of methods. This acid has been named rosilic acid,[131] owing to its supposed occurrence in the wax of the Druschky rose. Hydrolysis of the sulfuric acid addition product of oleic acid [135,136] or elaidic acid [137] yields 10-hydroxyoctadecanoic acid. Owing to an erroneous belief that the double bond in oleic and elaidic acids is between the third and fourth carbon atoms, the acid obtained by the above procedure has been described in some of the earlier literature [138,139,140] as 4-hydroxyoctadecanoic acid. 10-Hydroxyoctadecanoic acid has been prepared by the action of silver oxide on 10-iodostearic acid.[141]

Tomecko with Adams [56] obtained 10-hydroxyoctadecanoic acid by the Grignard method. These latter authors reported a melting point of 81–82° for the acid, and of 53–54° for its methyl ester. It is soluble in ethanol and ether and undergoes considerable dehydration to ethylenic acids when distilled under 15 mm. pressure. 11-Hydroxyoctadecanoic acid, $CH_3(CH_2)_6CH(OH)(CH_2)_9CO_2H$, has been obtained from 10-octadecenoic acid by the hydrolysis of its sulfuric acid addition product,[135] and also by the treatment of 11-iodostearic acid with silver oxide.[135] The acid has also been obtained by the Grignard method.[56] It has been reported to melt at 76–77°, and its methyl ester at 49–50°. This acid is somewhat more soluble in ethanol than its 10-isomer. 12-Hydroxyoctadecanoic acid, $CH_3(CH_2)_5CH(OH)(CH_2)_{10}CO_2H$, can readily be prepared from ricinoleic acid by hydrogenation, and Walden [142] has reported that this hydrogenation results in an optically inactive hydroxystearic acid. The reduction of the hydrogen bromide addition product of ricinoleic acid with zinc and hydrochloric acid has been observed to result in the formation of 12-hydroxyoctadecanoic acid.[143] The acid has also been prepared by the hydrogenation of methyl ricinoleate in the presence of platinum.[144] Tomecko with Adams [56] synthesized 12-hydroxyoctadecanoic acid by the Grignard method and reported a melting point of 78–79° for the acid and of 50–51° for its methyl ester. The following physical constants have been observed for the lactone: [145] $b_{0.11}$ 140–145°; d_4^{28} 0.8902, and n_D^{20} 1.452. 13-Hydroxyoctadecanoic acid, $CH_3(CH_2)_4CH(OH)(CH_2)_{11}CO_2H$, melting at 77–77.5° has been prepared by Tomecko and Adams by the Grignard method. The methyl ester melts at 52.0–52.5°. The terminal hydroxy acid, 18-hydroxyoctadecanoic acid, $HO(CH_2)_{17}CO_2H$, has been obtained [71] by the partial reduction of the dimethyl ester of octadecanedioic acid, $(CH_2)_{16}(CO_2CH_3)_2$. The acid melts at 96.6–97.2°, and its lactone [67] at 36–37°.

HYDROXYOCTADECENOIC ACIDS

12-Hydroxy-9-octadecenoic Acid (Ricinoleic Acid).
$CH_3(CH_2)_5CH(OH)CH_2CH:CH(CH_2)_7CO_2H$

Ricinoleic acid is the most important hydroxy fatty acid known. Its position among the hydroxy acids may be said to parallel that of oleic acid in the ethylenic series or palmitic and stearic acids among the saturated acids. Ricinoleic acid is the only naturally occurring hydroxy fatty acid which is present in sufficient quanti-

ties in the oils and fats to be of economic importance. The occurrence of ricinoleic acid is confined essentially to the seed oils of
plants of the Ricinus species; however, it has also been reported
to be present in several other oils. The most common source of
ricinoleic acid, castor oil, contains between 80 and 85% of this
acid as the glyceride,[146,147] and the high viscosity and other distinctive properties of castor oil are due to the presence of such
glycerides. As early as 1827, Bussy and Lecanu [148] observed that
the products of the pyrogenic distillation of castor oil differed from
those obtained when other oils are similarly treated. Eighteen
years later, Bussy [149] recognized enanthaldehyde as one of the
decomposition products of castor oil. The pyrolytic decomposition
of ricinoleic acid and of its derivatives has been studied extensively
(see 9,11-octadecadienoic acid). The heating of ricinoleic acid,
even under a high vacuum, results in two types of decomposition
which may proceed simultaneously. Heptanal and 10-undecenoic
acid are formed by the following reaction: [150]

$$CH_3(CH_2)_5CH(OH)CH_2CH:CH(CH_2)_7CO_2H \rightarrow$$

$$CH_3(CH_2)_5CHO + CH_2:CH(CH_2)_8CO_2H$$

Dehydration may also result with the formation of a mixture of
9,12- and 9,11-octadecadienoic acids.[151,152,153] Pyrolysis of ricinoleic acid and its derivatives results in the formation of an appreciable residue which is composed largely of polyricinoleic acids
and their decomposition products.[154,155,156] Ricinoleic acid was
probably first isolated by Saalmüller [157] who gave it its present
name. The accepted formula of ricinoleic acid, 12-hydroxy-9-
octadecenoic acid, has been established by the investigations of
Goldsobel.[107] The acid was first converted to ricinstearolic acid,
$CH_3(CH_2)_5CH(OH)CH_2C:C(CH_2)_7CO_2H$, then to 12-hydroxy-9-
ketostearic acid, the ketoxime of which was subjected to a Beckmann rearrangement, the product of which was split by means of
concentrated hydrochloric acid. The isolation of the lactone of
4-hydroxydecanoic acid, 2-hexyltrimethylenimine, 8-aminoöctanoic
acid, and of azelaic acid proved the hydroxyl group to be on the
twelfth carbon atom and the ethylenic bond to be between the
ninth and tenth carbon atoms. The method is similar to that
employed by Baruch [4,42,158] for the determination of the positions
of the double bonds in oleic and erucic acids. The formula proposed by Goldsobel for ricinoleic acid was verified in the same year
by Walden [159] and has since been confirmed by a number of inves-

tigators.[143, 160, 161, 162] The proof of the structure of ricinoleic acid by Goldsobel was preceded by a very appreciable amount of work on this subject which, however, resulted in erroneous conclusions concerning the positions of the hydroxyl and ethylenic groups in this acid. Krafft,[163] for example, considered ricinoleic acid to be 12-hydroxy-10-octadecenoic acid.

A large number of methods have been proposed for the preparation of ricinoleic acid from castor oil. Krafft [163] removed the saturated fatty acids from castor oil fatty acids by cooling and pressing. Juillard [164] attempted to purify ricinoleic acid by crystallization of the barium salts, a procedure which was later employed by Kozlowski [165] and Halvorson.[166] Alcoholysis followed by ester fractionation was used by Haller; [167] others have employed solvent extraction with petroleum ether.[147, 168] Rider [169] has obtained ricinoleic acid, melting at 4–5°, by distillation of the acylated methyl esters of castor oil fatty acids. The saturated acids had been removed previously by precipitation in an equal volume of ethanol at −15°. Straus and others [170] have prepared ricinoleic acid by crystallization of the lead salts and the methyl esters of the benzoylated castor oil acids. In spite of the many procedures which have been suggested for the preparation of ricinoleic acid, the pure acid has not as yet been obtained from castor oil. Recently, Brown and Green [171] have attempted the preparation of the pure acid by the low-temperature solvent crystallization of methyl ricinoleate. It was found to be possible to prepare the methyl ester by this method; however, a pure acid was not obtained on saponification, since hot saponifications resulted in the formation of polyacids and of diethylenic acids as impurities, while cold saponifications were observed to be incomplete. Ricinoleic acid of 96.5% purity, however, was prepared by direct crystallization of the acid mixture from acetone at −70°.

The following physical constants have been reported for ricinoleic acid: m.p. 5.5°,[171] $d_4^{27.4}$ 0.940, n_D^{20} 1.4716, acetyl value 137.9 (theory 144.2).[171] The acid is optically active $[\alpha]_D^{7.5} + 6.25°$ (acetone), $[\alpha]_D^{26} + 7.15°$ (acetone). Haller and Brochet [161] have reported that the 3-hydroxynonanoic acid, m.p. 47–48°, formed together with azelaic acid by the decomposition of ricinoleic acid ozonide, is dextrorotatory $[\alpha]_D + 2.26$; however, Matthes and Kürschner [172] have reported it to be levo- and not dextrorotatory. The mild oxidation of ricinoleic acid with potassium permanganate yields two isomeric trihydroxystearic acids.[173] The chemical reactions and derivatives of ricinoleic acid are discussed in another chapter.

As previously stated, the chief source of ricinoleic acid is the seed fats of plants of the Ricinus species, the most common of which is castor oil. Eibner and Münzing [146] have reported that castor oil contains 80% ricinoleic acid, 9% oleic acid, 3% linoleic acid, and 3% stearic and hydroxystearic acids. The chief constituent is, therefore, triricinolein. A hydroxyoctadecenoic acid obtained from oil of ergot [174] has been shown to be ricinoleic acid.[172] Ricinoleic acid has been reported to be present in ivory-wood oil,[175] 47%, *Argemone* oil,[176] 9.84%, and *Agonandra* seed fat.[177] An isomer of ricinoleic acid, which possibly contains the hydroxyl group in a different position, has been obtained by Vidyarthi and Mallya [178] from the seed oil of *Veronica anthelmintica*. A hydroxy acid of unknown constitution has been separated from grape seed oil,[179] and a hydroxyoleic acid, isomeric with ricinoleic acid, has been observed in quince seed oil. [80]

Ricinelaidic Acid

The elaidinization reaction discovered by Poutet [181] in 1819 was later applied by Boudet [182] to a number of oils, one of which was castor oil. It was observed that castor oil yields a solid fat when treated with nitrogen oxides. The name "palmine" was given to this solidified fat, and the acid, m.p. 50°, obtained from this fat was termed "palmic acid," which name was later changed to ricinelaidic acid. This acid, which is the *trans* form of ricinoleic acid, can be prepared by the same procedures employed for the conversion of oleic acid into elaidic acid. Ricinelaidic acid, like elaidic acid, is not present in the naturally occurring fats and oils. It has been prepared by Playfair [183] by the action of nitrous acid on ricinoleic acid, and this method has been employed subsequently by others.[163,184] The acid may also be obtained by the elaidinization of the glycerides of ricinoleic acid followed by saponification and acidification.[185] The oxidation of ricinelaidic acid by potassium permanganate yields two isomeric trihydroxystearic acids which melt at 117–120° and 113–116°. Acetylricinelaidic acid has been reported to be an oil which is easily soluble in ethanol and ether. A dihydroxystearic acid, probably 10,12-dihydroxystearic acid, has been prepared from ricinelaidic acid.[186]

Ricinelaidic acid melts at 52–53° and is optically active, $[\alpha]_D^{20} + 6.67°$ (ethanol).

HYDROXYOCTADECYNOIC ACIDS

12-Hydroxy-9-octadecynoic acid (ricinstearolic acid), $CH_3-(CH_2)_5CH(OH)CH_2C\!:\!C(CH_2)_7CO_2H$, has been prepared by Ulrich [187] by the treatment of 12-hydroxy-9,10-dibromostearic acid with alcoholic potassium hydroxide solution. It was later found [144] to be necessary to reflux the reaction mixture for twenty hours instead of the eight hours originally proposed. Ricinstearolic acid melts without decomposition at 53° [176] and is optically active, $[\alpha]_D + 13.67°$ (acetone). It is converted by the action of concentrated sulfuric acid into 12-hydroxy-10-ketostearic acid, which melts at 84–85°.

An acid termed ricinic acid has been obtained by the pyrolysis of barium ricinoleate.[159, 163] The purified acid melts at 81° and is soluble in ethanol. Perrotte [188] has studied the pyrolysis of barium ricinoleate and has obtained methyl hexyl ketone and 12-ketostearic acid. The formation of 12-ketostearic acid indicated the displacement of the double bond from the 9- to the 11-position.

HYDROXYNONADECANOIC ACIDS

The terminal hydroxynonadecanoic acid, 19-hydroxynonadecanoic acid, $HO(CH_2)_{18}CO_2H$, is the only member of this series which has been described.[71] It is formed in small yields by the partial reduction of the dimethyl ester of nonadecanedioic acid, $(CH_2)_{17}(CO_2CH_3)_2$. The free acid melts at 91–91.5°, its acetyl derivative at 70.0–70.2°, and its methyl ester at 65.6–66.0°.

HYDROXYEICOSANOIC ACIDS (HYDROXYARACHIDIC ACIDS)

2-Hydroxyeicosanoic acid, $CH_3(CH_2)_{17}CH(OH)CO_2H$, has been obtained by heating 2-bromoarachidic acid with alcoholic sodium hydroxide.[189] It melts at 91–92°. 20-Hydroxyeicosanoic acid, $HO(CH_2)_{19}CO_2H$, is formed in small yields by the partial reduction of the dimethyl ester of eicosanedioic acid.[71] The free acid melts at 97.4–97.8°, its acetyl derivative at 77°, and its methyl ester at 68–68.5°.

HYDROXYHENEICOSANOIC ACIDS

21-Hydroxyheneicosanoic acid, $HO(CH_2)_{20}CO_2H$, has been obtained by the partial reduction of the dimethyl ester of heneicosanedioic acid, $(CH_2)_{19}(CO_2CH_3)_2$.[71] The acid melts at 92.5–93.0° and its acetyl derivative at 73.8–74.2°.

Hydroxydocosanoic Acids (Hydroxybehenic Acids)

2-Hydroxybehenic acid, $CH_3(CH_2)_{19}CH(OH)CO_2H$, results from the action of aqueous potassium hydroxide on 2-bromobehenic acid. An acid stated to be 2-hydroxybehenic acid has been reported to be present in cork and has been identified as one of the products formed by the hydrolysis of suberin.[47] This acid has been named phellonic acid. An acid, melting at 88–91°, and stated to be either 13- or 14-hydroxydocosanoic acid, has been obtained by the action of potassium hydroxide on 14-bromobehenic acid.[190]

High Molecular Weight Hydroxy Acids

2-Hydroxycerotic acid, $CH_3(CH_2)_{23}CH(OH)CO_2H$, has been synthesized by Marie [191] through the action of alcoholic potassium hydroxide on 2-bromocerotic acid and also by the saponification of ethyl 2-acetylcerotate, which is obtained by the action of lead acetate on 2-bromocerotic acid. 2-Hydroxycerotic acid melts at 86.5°. 2-Hydroxymelissic acid, $CH_3(CH_2)_{27}CH(OH)CO_2H$, m.p. 97.5°, has been prepared by similar procedures.

Other Hydroxy Acids of Natural Origin

In the above descriptions of the hydroxy fatty acids we have considered only those acids which have been synthesized by recognized procedures or the naturally occurring acids of proved structure. A number of fatty substances of both animal and vegetable origin are known to contain hydroxy acids; however, in several of these cases, the actual identities and structures of the individual acids are still undetermined. In such cases, it is probably advisable to consider such acids with reference to their source, since much research is still necessary upon these acid mixtures before their components are separated and positively identified. The principal fatty substances which have been reported to contain hydroxy fatty acids are as follows.

Wool Wax

It has long been recognized that wool fat differs materially from other animal fats. The work which has been done upon this substance has served to point out its distinctive characteristics but has given us only a superficial knowledge of many of its important components. This is particularly true of the fatty acids of wool fat, which are deserving of much more attention than they have received to date. Wool fat consists almost exclusively of the fatty acid esters of cholesterol, isocholesterol, and higher aliphatic alcohols, and since it does not contain glycerol it is properly classed as a wax rather than a fat. Early investigations [192, 193] indicated the waxy structure of wool fat, and somewhat later Lewkowitsch [194] announced that the fatty acids of wool wax contain hydroxy acids, since these acids form lactones upon heating and are reactive with acetic anhydride. The extensive investigations of Darmstaedter and Lifschütz [195] upon the fatty acids of wool wax confirmed the presence of hydroxy acids and resulted in the isolation of a di-hydroxy acid, $C_{30}H_{60}O_4$, melting at 104–105°, which they termed lanoceric acid. Lanopalmic acid, $C_{16}H_{32}O_3$, melting at 87–88°, and several other hydroxy acids of undetermined composition were also shown to be present. They also isolated a large amount of a saturated acid melting at 72–73° which was considered to be either $C_{26}H_{52}O_2$ or $C_{27}H_{54}O_2$. A number of years later, Röhmann [130] reported that wool fat contains stearic, cerotic, and hydroxy fatty acids, the last of which are optically active. The presence of saturated acids such as myristic, palmitic, stearic, and cerotic acids was confirmed by Drummond and Baker; [196] however, they failed to obtain the lanoceric or lanopalmic acids which had been previously described. In 1935, Abraham and Hilditch [197] reported the results of their investigation of wool wax fatty acids in which they separated the acids by fractionation of the methyl esters. This work confirmed the previous observation of Darmstaedter and Lifschütz [195] that the chief acid present is a hexacosanoic acid melting at 73–75°, isomeric but not identical with cerotic acid. Lanopalmic acid and lanoceric acid were identified, as were a series of acids whose compositions approximated the following formulas: $C_{15}H_{30}O_2$, $C_{20}H_{40}O_2$, $C_{20}H_{40}O_3$ (or $C_{20}H_{38}O_3$), and $C_{30}H_{60}O_3$ (or $C_{30}H_{58}O_3$). The hydroxy acids present are optically active and can be easily converted into lactones by boiling with dilute mineral acids. The saturated acids were observed to possess lower melting points than the corresponding normal acids, and it was therefore concluded that acids of the normal aliphatic series are not present in wool wax. These authors suggested that the acids of sterol waxes secreted in sebaceous and similar glands are probably derived from isoprene or terpenes. The saturated acids of wool wax were subsequently studied by Kuwata and Ishii,[198] who concluded that they are not identical with the normal acids. They reported the presence of lanomyristic acid, melting at 58.5–

59.5°, lanopalmitic acid, melting at 44.5–46.0°, lanostearic acid, melting at 54–56°, and lanoarachidic acid, melting at 56.8–58.4°. The hydroxy acids lanopalmic and lanoceric were also investigated by these authors, and in 1938 Kuwata [199] showed that lanopalmic acid is a stereoisomer of 2-hydroxypalmitic acid. Oxidation of the methyl ester gave 2-ketopalmitic acid, the further oxidation of which yielded pentadecanoic acid, which was also obtained by cleavage of the oxime. Lanopalmic acid melts at 86–87° and is optically active, $[\alpha]_D$ $-1.0°$ (ethanol); its methyl ester melts at 45–46° and shows $[\alpha]_D-1.5°$. Several derivatives of lanoceric acid have been described.[200] In 1945, Weitkamp [201] published the results of an extensive investigation of the fatty acids of wool fat, in which the acids were separated by the distillation of their methyl esters and identified. This author observed that the fatty acids of wool fat fall into four general groups, which are: (1) normal saturated acids; (2) 2-hydroxy acids; (3) iso-acids corresponding to the general formula, $CH_3CH(CH_3)(CH_2)_{2n}CO_2H$, in which n is 3 to 12 inclusive; and (4) iso-acids whose general structure is $CH_3CH_2CH(CH_3)(CH_2)_{2n}CO_2H$, in which n is 2 to 13 inclusive. The normal saturated acids which were isolated contained an even number of carbon atoms ranging from C_{10} to C_{26}. Of these acids only myristic and palmitic acids appeared to be major components. 2-Hydroxymyristic and 2-hydroxypalmitic acids were isolated, and it was assumed that higher homologs of these acids were originally present. These hydroxy acids were assumed to be levorotatory. Those iso-acids in which the methyl group is attached to the penultimate carbon atom were shown to possess an even number of carbon atoms. The C_{10} to C_{28} members of this series were isolated. The members of that series of iso-acids in which the methyl group is attached to the antepenultimate carbon atom were stated to contain an uneven number of carbon atoms and to be dextrorotatory. The members of this series from C_9 to C_{31} were isolated. It is quite apparent that considerably more work is required upon both the saturated and the hydroxy fatty acids of wool wax before their structures and configurations are definitely determined. It is further evident that the origin of these acids and their possible relationship to the sterols are matters of profound biological interest.

Brain Lipides

The brain is frequently referred to as the master tissue of the body since it controls and regulates all bodily functions. The relative size of the brain differs markedly in the various animal species, being much larger in the higher forms of animal life. It attains its greatest development in man, and because of this most of the work upon the structure and composition of the brain has been done on human brain substance. The brain is unusual among body tissues in that it undergoes progressive changes in composition with increasing age of the individual. One of the most significant features concerning the composition of the brain is the very large amount of lipid substance which it contains, the amount being greater than that found in any other bodily organ and second only to fatty tissue itself. It is thus apparent that the lipides play an extremely important role in this vital organ. The studies which have been made thus far upon the fatty substance of the brain have served to point out its very unusual structure and extreme complexity. The brain contains no neutral glycerides, the fatty substance being composed essentially of cholesteryl esters, phosphatides (lecithins), amino phosphatides such as brain cephalin, and cerebrosides (glycolipides). The cerebrosides are found chiefly in the white matter of the brain and contain nitrogen, a sugar which is mainly galactose, and fatty acids. They contain no phosphorus and are present only in traces in the embryonic brain. The most important of the cerebrosides are phrenosin and kerasin. The hydroxy acids present in brain substance are mainly confined to these cerebrosides. The cerebrosides have been observed to comprise roughly 7% of the white matter and 0.5% of the gray matter of the brain, while the cholesteryl esters, phosphatides, etc., comprise 11.5% of the white matter. The brain contains, in addition to the hydroxy acids, various unsaturated acids such as nervonic acid; however, it is the presence of large amounts of hydroxy acids which serves to distinguish the fatty acids of brain substance from those of other animal fats. The fatty acids of the brain show an interesting similarity to those contained in the waxes of sebaceous origin, such as wool wax. The significance of this correlation is not at present understood.

The principal hydroxy fatty acid which has been isolated from the brain has been termed cerebronic acid. The questions as to the actual structure of cerebronic acid and as to whether it represents an individual acid or a mixture of hydroxy acids have not been settled. The original work upon the chemical constitution of the brain was done by Thudichum,[202] and one of the results of this work was the isolation of a hydroxy acid termed "neurostearic acid," which he considered to be a C_{18} acid. The acid was later named cerebronic acid and was reported to be a hydroxypentacosanoic acid.[203] Subsequently, Levene and coworkers [204, 205, 206] supposedly proved it to be 2-hydroxypentacosanoic acid. However, Klenk [207, 208] has presented evidence showing that the hydroxy acid isolated from phrenosin is a hydroxytetradecanoic acid. Levene and coworkers [209, 210, 211] made a further study of the cerebronic acid fraction and concluded that this acid is actually a mixture of hydroxy acids, a finding which is in agreement with that of Grey [212] who reported the isolation of at least three hydroxy acids from the cerebrosides of the human brain. Cerebronic acid was again examined by Levene and Yang [213] who reported it to be a mixture of hydroxy fatty acids of both lower and higher molecular weights than hydroxytetradecanoic acid. Recent studies [214, 215, 216] of the hydroxy acids of brain cerebrosides (phrenosin and kerasin) have indicated that these cerebrosides contain 2-hydroxy acids of the C_{22}, C_{24}, and C_{26} series with the C_{24} acid greatly predominating. Müller [217] has recently synthesized 2-hydroxytetracosanoic acid by the action of potassium hydroxide on 2-bromotetracosanoic acid. The dextro acid, separated by means of its strychnine salt, was reported to be identical with naturally occurring cerebronic acid. Cerebronic acid melts at 99.5–100.5° and is optically active, $[\alpha]_D^{25} + 3.7°$ (pyridine).

The hydroxy acids of the brain occur principally in the cerebrosides; however, Levene [218] has reported the presence of hydroxy acids in sphingomyelin. The hydroxy acids of brain substance offer a problem of exceptional interest to both the chemist and the biologist and will undoubtedly be the subject of much future investigational work.

Bacterial Waxes

The fatty acids of tubercle bacteria wax contain small amounts of hydroxy acids, several of which have been isolated and tentatively identified. A high molecular weight hydroxy acid, possibly $C_{88}H_{176}O_4$, termed mycolic acid, has been obtained from the wax of human and bovine tubercle bacteria.[219, 220] Chargaff [45] has separated a hydroxy acid, $C_{52}H_{104}O_3$, melting at 63–65°, from the lipides of Calmette-Guérin bacillus, and a hydroxy acid named leprosinic acid has recently been isolated from leprosy bacteria wax.[44]

Miscellaneous Naturally Occurring Hydroxy Acids

Hydroxy fatty acids of high molecular weight have been reported to be present in *Swertia japonica* root fat,[221] cork,[47, 222] and "carnaubon," an alcoholic extract of kidney lipids.[223] The acid obtained from the last source has been named phrenosinic acid and has been assigned the formula $C_{25}H_{50}O_3$. The presence of hydroxy acids has been suggested in many of the naturally occurring fatty mixtures; however, in many of these instances the actual acids have not been isolated and identified.

PART 3   THE KETO FATTY ACIDS

The keto fatty acids comprise a group of straight-chain carboxylic acids which contain one or more carbonyl groups in the hydrocarbon portion of the molecule. The hydrocarbon chain may be either saturated or unsaturated. Such acids, therefore, show the characteristic reactions of the ketones in addition to the typical reactions of the carboxylic acids. They form derivatives with hydroxylamine, phenylhydrazine, semicarbazide, and other reagents which react with carbonyl groups; and, in general, they can be assumed to possess most of the typical properties of ketones. The number of theoretically possible isomeric keto acids increases with increase in the chain length of the acid. Thus, four isomeric monoketohexanoic acids are possible, the keto group including either the second, third, fourth, or fifth carbon atom as follows:

2-ketohexanoic acid, $CH_3CH_2CH_2CH_2COCO_2H$

3-ketohexanoic acid, $CH_3CH_2CH_2COCH_2CO_2H$

4-ketohexanoic acid, $CH_3CH_2COCH_2CH_2CO_2H$

5-ketohexanoic acid, $CH_3COCH_2CH_2CH_2CO_2H$

Sixteen monoketoöctadecanoic acids are possible, the keto group being in any one of the positions indicated below.

$$CH_3 \overset{17}{C} \overset{16}{C} \overset{15}{C} \overset{14}{C} \overset{13}{C} \overset{12}{C} \overset{11}{C} \overset{10}{C} \overset{9}{C} \overset{8}{C} \overset{7}{C} \overset{6}{C} \overset{5}{C} \overset{4}{C} \overset{3}{C} \overset{2}{C} CO_2H$$

The number of keto acids theoretically possible is one less than the number of hydroxy acids, the terminal keto acid functioning as an aldehydo rather than as a keto acid. Since the keto acids possess the group $—CH_2CO—$, they are capable of undergoing enolization

with the formation of the group —CH:CHOH—, and many of
the reactions of the keto acids are due to the presence of this enol
form.   The properties of specific keto acids depend, to a very
considerable extent, upon the position of the keto group with
reference to the carboxyl group.   This is particularly true with
those acids which contain the keto group in close proximity to the
carboxyl.   2-Keto acids, $RCOCO_2H$, have a tendency to lose
carbon dioxide when heated with aqueous sulfuric acid, thus
forming aldehydes containing one less carbon atom than the
original acids.[224]   Such acids also lose carbon monoxide upon
heating, with the formation of the next lower saturated acid.[225]
3-Keto acids are quite unstable, easily losing carbon dioxide to
form ketones.   The 4-keto acids, however, are more stable.   Those
high molecular weight keto acids which contain the carbonyl
group in a position remote from the carboxyl are qualitatively
similar to each other in their chemical and physical properties.
All the keto acids can be reduced to the corresponding hydroxy
acids, which can in turn be further reduced to the saturated acids.
The position of the carbonyl group in a keto acid is best determined by subjecting the oxime to a Beckmann rearrangement
followed by a cleavage of the resulting products.   This method,
which was first described by Baruch,[4] has been extensively employed for the determination of the configuration of keto acids and
also of various unsaturated acids from which keto acids can be
prepared.*

Keto acids are rarely found in the naturally occurring fats and
oils.   Oiticica oil has been shown to contain α-licanic acid (4-keto-
9,11,13-octadecatrienoic acid), and lactorinic acid (6-ketostearic
acid) has been stated to be present in the petroleum ether extract
of the fungus Lactarius.   Small amounts of keto acids are apparently formed by the action of microörganisms upon fats.   Since
keto acids are not common to the natural fats, practically our entire
knowledge of this group is confined to the preparation and properties of the synthetic acids.   Perhaps the most widely used procedure
for the preparation of the keto acids consists of the hydration of
the triple bond of acetylenic acids; however, this method is somewhat limited because of the difficulty of obtaining the acetylenic
acids.   The direct addition of water to a triple bond can be brought
about at high temperatures, or the hydration may be accomplished

* For the reactions involved see Oleic Acid, Stearolic Acid.

in the presence of sulfuric acid or other hydrating agents. The hydration of acetylenic hydrocarbons by means of concentrated sulfuric acid is a well-known reaction and has been frequently employed for the preparation of ketones.[226] Generally speaking, the conditions for the hydration of acetylenic hydrocarbons are applicable to the acetylenic acids. The use of alcoholic potassium hydroxide to effect this reaction has been extensively investigated.[227] The addition of water to the triple bond of an acetylenic acid results in the formation of two isomeric keto acids. The isomer formed in the larger amount will be the keto acid which results from the oxygen atom attaching itself to the more electropositive of the two carbon atoms forming the acetylenic group. The relative amounts of the isomeric keto acids depend, therefore, upon the particular acid hydrated and to some extent upon the reaction conditions employed. The hydration of acetylenic acids may also be brought about by hydrolysis of the addition products of acetylenic acids and mercuric salts in the presence of acids such as acetic acid.[228] Keto acids have been prepared by the action of Grignard reagents upon cyano acids according to the following equations:

(I) $\quad HO_2C(CH_2)_xCN + RMgX \rightarrow HO_2C(CH_2)_xRC:NMgX$

(II) $\quad HO_2C(CH_2)_xRC:NMgX + 2HX + H_2O \rightarrow$

$$HO_2C(CH_2)_xCOR + MgX_2 + NH_4X$$

The action of dialkylzincs or of alkylzinc halides on the acid chlorides of the mono esters of dicarboxylic acids offers an excellent method for the preparation of keto acids. It is known that alkylmagnesium halides generally yield tertiary alcohols with acid chlorides, the ketone being an intermediate product which can be isolated only in certain instances.[229, 230] Blaise and Koehler [231] have shown, however, that the acid chlorides of the mono esters of dibasic acids give high yields of keto acids when treated with alkylzinc halides. Acid chlorides of dibasic acids yield diketones by the same procedure. The reactions for the formation of keto acids by this method are as follows:

$$CH_3O_2C(CH_2)_xCOCl + RZnX \rightarrow CH_3O_2C(CH_2)_xC\underset{Cl}{\overset{OZnX}{\underset{|}{\overset{|}{C}}}}R \xrightarrow{HOH}$$

$$CH_3O_2C(CH_2)_xCOR + ZnX(OH) + HCl$$

The action with alkylzincs proceeds in a somewhat similar manner:

$$CH_3O_2C(CH_2)_xCOCl + ZnR_2 \rightarrow CH_3O_2C(CH_2)_xC\overset{OZnR}{\underset{Cl}{\diagup}}R \xrightarrow{HOH}$$

$$CH_3O_2C(CH_2)_xCOR + RZn(OH) + HCl$$

Tertiary alcohols may result if the addition products are not quickly hydrolyzed. The hydrolysis of acyl cyanides, RCOCN, yields 2-keto acids, and this method has been frequently employed for the preparation of the lower molecular weight 2-keto acids. Acyl cyanides may be prepared by the action of silver cyanide on acid chlorides, thus:

$$RCOCl + AgCN \rightarrow RCOCN + AgCl$$

The following is a description of the aliphatic keto acids containing five or more carbon atoms. Only the straight-chain keto acids have been considered and they have been grouped according to the number of carbon atoms in the molecules. Many of the keto acids, particularly those of high molecular weight, have not been synthesized, and consequently generalizations with reference to the effect of the position of the carbonyl group upon the physical and chemical properties of these acids should not be given too much consideration.

KETOPENTANOIC ACIDS (KETOVALERIC ACIDS)

All three possible ketovaleric acids have been synthesized and described. 2-Ketovaleric acid, $CH_3(CH_2)_2COCO_2H$, has been prepared by the hydrolysis of butyryl cyanide, $CH_3(CH_2)_2COCN$, which results from the treatment of butyryl chloride with silver cyanide.[232] The acid has also been obtained by the oxidation of propylfumaric acid with potassium permanganate.[73] It is a colorless liquid boiling at 179°, and is soluble in water and easily soluble in benzene, ether, ethanol, and other organic solvents. 3-Ketovaleric acid, $CH_3CH_2COCH_2CO_2H$, has been prepared by the action of ethylmagnesium iodide on ethyl cyanoacetate, as follows:[233]

(I) $C_2H_5O_2CCH_2CN + C_2H_5MgI \rightarrow C_2H_5O_2CCH_2C{:}NMgI \xrightarrow[HOH]{2HCl}$
                                                  $\underset{C_2H_5}{|}$

$$C_2H_5O_2CCH_2\underset{\underset{O}{\|}}{C}C_2H_5 + MgICl + NH_4Cl$$

(II) $C_2H_5O_2CCH_2CC_2H_5 \overset{HOH}{\longrightarrow} HO_2CCH_2COC_2H_5 + C_2H_5OH$
                      ‖
                      O

It has been described as a colorless liquid which boils at 191°.[13]
The 4-ketovaleric acid, levulinic acid, $CH_3CO(CH_2)_2CO_2H$, was
first prepared by the action of dimethylzinc on the acid chloride
of the monoethyl ester of succinic acid, the reaction being as
follows: [234]

$$C_2H_5O_2C(CH_2)_2COCl + Zn(CH_3)_2 \rightarrow C_2H_5O_2C(CH_2)_2C\overset{OZnCH_3}{\underset{Cl}{\diagup\!\diagdown}}CH_3 \overset{HOH}{\longrightarrow}$$

$$C_2H_5O_2C(CH_2)_2COCH_3 + ZnCH_3OH + HCl$$
$$\downarrow HOH$$
$$HO_2C(CH_2)_2COCH_3$$

Levulinic acid undergoes enolization and dehydration upon distillation or treatment with acetic anhydride, yielding a 3,4-un-
saturated lactone, angelica lactone, as follows:

$$CH_3COCH_2CH_2CO_2H \rightarrow CH_3C\!:\!CHCH_2CO$$
$$\underset{O}{|}\rule{2cm}{0.4pt}|$$

The keto acid may be obtained by the hydrolysis of this lactone
either with boiling water or by treatment with barium hydroxide
solution.[235] The hydrolysis of the 4-lactone of 3,4-dihydroxy-
valeric acid has been shown by Fittig[236] to yield levulinic acid,
and Harries[237] has described the preparation of 4-ketovaleric acid
by the oxidation of its corresponding aldehyde. Levulinic acid
is formed by the action of acids upon levulose, cane sugar, cellulose,
and other carbohydrates. It is a solid which melts at 31°.

KETOHEXANOIC ACIDS (KETOCAPROIC ACIDS)

2-Ketocaproic acid, $CH_3(CH_2)_3COCO_2H$, has been obtained by
the saponification of its ethyl ester.[238] The acid boils at 98° under
14 mm. pressure. 3-Ketocaproic acid, $CH_3(CH_2)_2COCH_2CO_2H$,
has been prepared by hydrolysis of the complex formed by the
action of propylmagnesium iodide on cyanoacetic acid.[233] It has
also been obtained by the action of alcoholic potassium hydroxide
on 2-hexynoic acid, $CH_3(CH_2)_2C\!:\!CCO_2H$.[227] Zanetti[239] has described the preparation of 4-ketocaproic acid, $CH_3CH_2CO(CH_2)_2$-
CO_2H, by the hydrolysis of the corresponding oxime. Fittig[85,240]
has reported the synthesis of this acid by the prolonged action of

water on 3,4-dibromocaproic acid. 4-Ketocaproic acid has been shown to be one of the products formed when 1-methyl-2-ethyl-1-cyclopenten-5-one is oxidized with potassium permanganate.[241] The acid freezes at 32°, and boils at 183° at 20 mm.[242] Its semicarbazone freezes at 176°. It is soluble in water and most organic solvents. 5-Ketocaproic acid, $CH_3CO(CH_2)_3CO_2H$, has been synthesized by a number of methods. Vorländer [243] and also Ruzicka [244] have reported its preparation by the hydrolytic cleavage of dihydroresorcinol, thus:

$$\underset{\substack{\\ H}}{\overset{\substack{H \\ C}}{\underset{H_2C\diagdown\diagup}{\overset{H_2C\diagup\diagdown}{}}}}\quad \longrightarrow \quad \cdots \quad \xrightarrow{HOH} \quad CH_3COCH_2CH_2CH_2CO_2H$$

The latter author has also prepared 5-ketocaproic acid by the action of methylenemalonic ester and acetoacetic ester as follows:

$$CH_3C\!:\!CHCO_2C_2H_5 + H_2C\!:\!C(CO_2C_2H_5)_2 \rightarrow H_2CCH(CO_2C_2H_5)_2$$

$$\underset{\substack{ONa \\ \text{Ethyl sodioaceto-} \\ \text{acetate}}}{|} \qquad \underset{\substack{\text{Diethyl methylene-} \\ \text{malonate}}}{} \qquad CH_3C\!:\!CCO_2C_2H_5 \rightarrow$$

$$\underset{\substack{ \\ }}{|ONa}$$

$$\underset{\substack{ \\ }}{H_2CCH(CO_2C_2H_5)_2} \qquad H_2CCH(CO_2C_2H_5)_2$$
$$\underset{\substack{ \\ }}{CH_3C\!:\!CCO_2C_2H_5} \rightarrow CH_3CCHCO_2C_2H_5 \xrightarrow{-2CO_2}$$
$$\underset{\substack{ \\ OH}}{|} \qquad\qquad \underset{\substack{ \\ O}}{|}$$

Triethyl 2-ketopentane-3,5,5-tricarboxylate

$$CH_3COCH_2CH_2CH_2CO_2H$$

Its preparation by the oxidation of 4-acetyl-1-butanol has been described by Lipp.[245] It has also been prepared by the oxidation of 1-methyl-1-cyclohexen-3-one,[246] 1-methylcyclopentan-2-one,[247] 1-methyl-5-cyclopentene-2-carboxylic acid,[248] 1-methyl-2-acetyl-1-cyclopentene,[249] 1,2-dimethyl-1-cyclohexen-3-one,[250] and 1-methyl-2-isopropyl-1-cyclohexen-3-one.[251] The partial decomposition of 2-acetylglutaric acid and also the heating of diethyl 2-acetylglutarate with hydrochloric acid has been observed to give good yields of 5-ketocaproic acid.[91, 252] The acid freezes at 13°, and boils with decomposition at 274–275°. It boils at 195–200° at 65 mm., and at 180° at 20 mm. 5-Ketocaproic acid is easily soluble in water, ethanol, ether, and other organic solvents.

KETOHEPTANOIC ACIDS (KETOENANTHIC ACIDS)

3-Ketoenanthic acid, $CH_3(CH_2)_3COCH_2CO_2H$, a homolog of acetoacetic acid, has been prepared by a reaction similar to that used for the synthesis of this latter compound. Wahl and Doll [253] have obtained 3-ketoenanthic acid by the condensation of ethyl valerate and ethyl acetate according to the following equations:

$$C_4H_9CO_2C_2H_5 + CH_3CO_2C_2H_5 \xrightarrow{Na} C_4H_9C{:}CHCO_2C_2H_5 + C_2H_5OH$$
$$\underset{\overset{|}{OH}}{}$$

$$C_4H_9COCH_2CO_2C_2H_5 \rightarrow C_4H_9COCH_2CO_2H$$

The reaction of ethyl acetoacetate with n-valeryl chloride followed by ammonolysis yields 3-ketoenanthic acid as follows: [254]

$$CH_3COCH_2CO_2C_2H_5 + C_4H_9COCl \rightarrow CH_3COCHCO_2C_2H_5 \xrightarrow{NH_3}$$
$$\underset{\overset{|}{C_4H_9CO}}{}$$

$$C_4H_9COCH_2CO_2C_2H_5 \xrightarrow{HOH} C_4H_9COCH_2CO_2H$$

3-Ketoenanthic acid is a colorless liquid which boils at 110–112° at 16 mm. 4-Ketoenanthic acid, $CH_3(CH_2)_2CO(CH_2)_2CO_2H$, results from the treatment of the dimethyl ester of butyrylsuccinic acid with hydrochloric acid, thus: [255]

$$CH_3O_2CCH(COC_3H_7)CH_2CO_2CH_3 \xrightarrow{HCl} CH_3(CH_2)_2CO(CH_2)_2CO_2H$$

The acid freezes at 46.7° and is easily soluble in organic solvents. 5-Ketoenanthic acid, $CH_3CH_2CO(CH_2)_3CO_2H$, has been isolated as one of the oxidation products of ethylcyclopentane [256] and also has been obtained by the oxidation of 1-ethyl-2-propionyl-1-cyclopentene.[249] The acid has been prepared by the hydrolysis of 1-methyl-6-ethyl-6-hydroxy-2-piperidone, as follows: [257]

$$\xrightarrow{HOH} CH_3CH_2CO(CH_2)_3CO_2H + CH_3NH_2$$

The acid obtained by the latter procedure melted at 55° and was soluble in water and organic solvents. 6-Ketoenanthic acid, $CH_3CO(CH_2)_4CO_2H$, has been synthesized by several methods, one of which is the action of methylzinc iodide on the acid chloride of monomethyl adipate.[231] It has been reported to be formed by the oxidation of 1-methylcyclohexene with potassium permanganate[258] or of 1-methyl-2-cyclohexanone with chromic acid.[259] Fichter and Gully[99] have prepared 6-ketoenanthic acid from diethyl 2-acetyladipate, and Perkin[260] has reported its formation by the saponification of 2,5-diacetylvaleric acid with alcoholic potassium hydroxide. The acid has been obtained by the treatment of ethyl 2-acetyl-5-cyanovalerate with hydrochloric acid, the reaction being as follows:

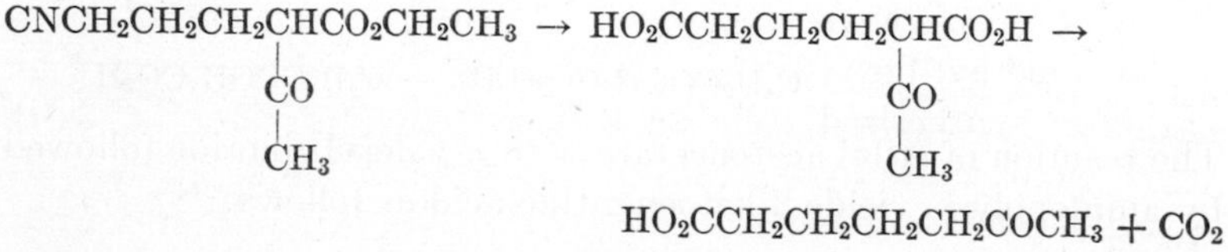
CNCH2CH2CH2CHCO2CH2CH3 → HO2CCH2CH2CH2CHCO2H →
CO
CH3
CO
CH3
HO2CCH2CH2CH2CH2COCH3 + CO2

6-Ketoenanthic acid freezes at 31–32° and was reported to be soluble in water and organic solvents.

KETOÖCTANOIC ACIDS (KETOCAPRYLIC ACIDS)

3-Ketocaprylic acid, $CH_3(CH_2)_4COCH_2CO_2H$, has been obtained by the treatment of 3-octynoic acid with alcoholic potassium hydroxide.[227] The acid freezes at 73–74° and its semicarbazone at 153°. Blaise and Koehler[231] have prepared 4-ketocaprylic acid, $CH_3(CH_2)_3CO(CH_2)_2CO_2H$, by the action of butylzinc iodide on the acid chloride of monoethyl succinate. The acid freezes at 53°. 5-Ketocaprylic acid, $CH_3(CH_2)_2CO(CH_2)_3$-CO_2H, was first obtained by Wolffenstein[261] by ring cleavage of the hemlock alkaloid coniine, $C_8H_{17}N$, the reaction being as follows:

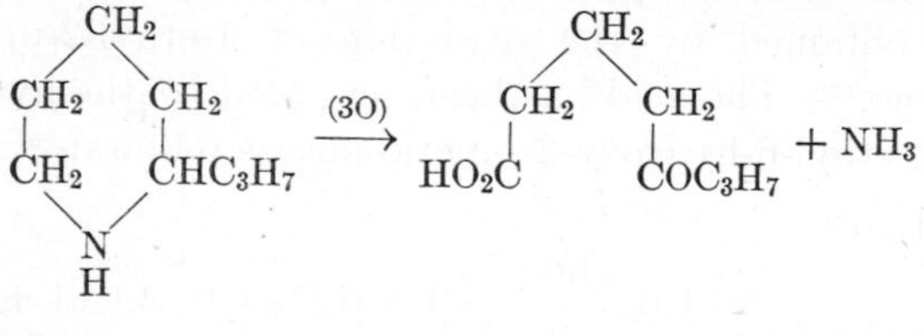
CH2
CH2
CH2
CH2
CHC3H7
N
H
(3O)
CH2
CH2
CH2
HO2C
COC3H7
+ NH3

The acid freezes at 34° and boils at 280–285°. 6-Ketocaprylic acid, $CH_3CH_2CO(CH_2)_4CO_2H$, has been prepared by the action of ethylzinc iodide on the acid chloride of monoethyl adipate.[231] The acid melts at 52°, and boils at 160–161° at 9 mm. pressure. Its semicarbazone freezes at 190°. 7-Ketocaprylic acid, $CH_3CO(CH_2)_5CO_2H$, has been obtained by the oxidation of 1-methylcycloheptene.[262] The acid has also been prepared by the action of potassium hydroxide on ethyl 2,6-diacetylcaproate, $CH_2(COCH_3)(CH_2)_3CH(COCH_3)CO_2C_2H_5$.[263] Its freezing point has been reported to be 29–30°, which is the lowest among the ketocaprylic acids. It boils at 184–185° under 15 mm. pressure.

KETONONANOIC ACIDS (KETOPELARGONIC ACIDS)

3-Ketopelargonic acid, $CH_3(CH_2)_5COCH_2CO_2H$, has been obtained by the action of alcoholic potassium hydroxide on 2-nonynoic acid.[227,264] The free acid is reported to be unstable, decomposing into methyl hexyl ketone and carbon dioxide. Its ethyl ester has been synthesized by the reaction of ethyl enanthate with ethyl acetoacetate in the presence of sodium. Lukeš [265] has obtained 4-ketopelargonic acid, $CH_3(CH_2)_4CO(CH_2)_2CO_2H$, by the action of pentylmagnesium bromide on N-methylsuccinimide, the reaction being as follows:

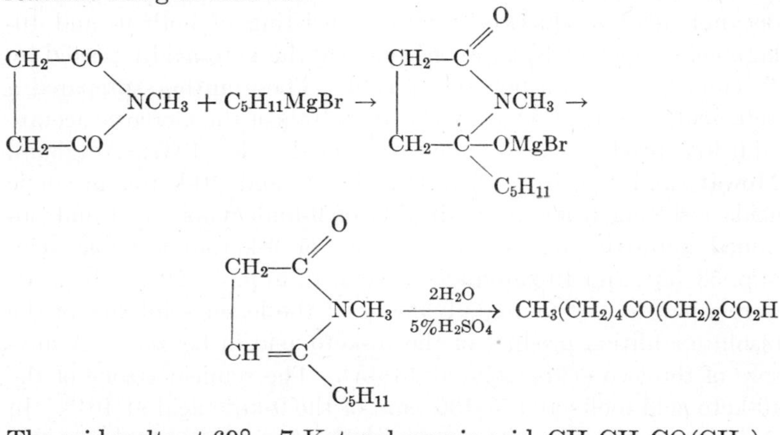

The acid melts at 69°. 7-Ketopelargonic acid, $CH_3CH_2CO(CH_2)_5CO_2H$, has been prepared by Blaise and Koehler [231] by the action of ethylzinc iodide on the acid chloride of monoethyl pimelate. The acid was reported to freeze at 42°.

KETODECANOIC ACIDS (KETOCAPRIC ACIDS)

Only two ketocapric acids have been described. 4-Ketocapric acid, $CH_3(CH_2)_5CO(CH_2)_2CO_2H$, has been prepared by Lukeš [265] by the reaction of hexylmagnesium bromide with N-methylsuccinimide, the reaction being similar to that shown for the preparation of 4-ketopelargonic acid. 4-Ketocapric acid melts at 70–71°. Blaise and Koehler [231] have described the preparation of

8-ketocapric acid, $CH_3CH_2CO(CH_2)_6CO_2H$, melting at 64°, by the action of ethylzinc iodide on the acid chloride of monoethyl suberate.

KETOUNDECANOIC ACIDS

Ethyl 3-ketoundecanoate, $CH_3(CH_2)_7COCH_2CO_2C_2H_5$, has been prepared by Asahina and Nakayama,[266] who reported that its saponification with 0.5% sodium hydroxide solution results in the formation of methyl octyl ketone and pelargonic acid. The oxidation of undecane-1,10-diol has been shown to yield 10-keto-undecanoic acid, $CH_3CO(CH_2)_8CO_2H$, melting at 58.5–59.5°, together with the ketone alcohol $CH_3CO(CH_2)_8CH_2OH$.[267] Welander [268] first reported the preparation of this acid by the hydration of 9-undecynoic acid. The acid melted at 49°. Myddleton and Barrett [228] have pointed out that the hydration of 9-undecynoic acid produces a mixture consisting of both 9- and 10-ketoundecanoic acids, and consequently the keto acid reported by Welander was not a pure compound. These authors prepared a keto acid melting at 59.5° by the hydrolysis of the mercuric acetate addition product of 9-undecynoic acid. In 1937, Abraham, Mowat, and Smith [269] separated the 9- and 10-ketoundecanoic acids resulting from the hydration of 9-undecynoic acid and obtained approximately equal amounts of 9-ketoundecanoic acid, m.p. 53–55°, and 10-ketoundecanoic acid, m.p. 58–59°. The acids were separated by taking advantage of the lesser solubility of the bisulfite addition product of the 10-keto acid in benzene. A mixture of the two acids melts at 43–45°. The semicarbazone of the 10-keto acid melts at 135–136° and of the 9-keto acid at 161°. In the same year, Sherrill and Smith [270] studied the hydration of 9-undecynoic acid and reported a yield of 59% of 9-ketoundecanoic acid and 41% of 10-ketoundecanoic acid, the oxygen atom attaching itself preferentially to the more electro-positive carbon atom. The preparation of the keto acids by the hydrolysis of the product obtained by the action of mercuric acetate in acetic acid upon 9-undecynoic acid resulted in 46% of the 9-keto acid and 54% of the 10-keto acid, indicating that an electrometric rearrangement was induced by the presence of the mercuric salts.

KETODODECANOIC ACIDS (KETOLAURIC ACIDS)

Only a few of the ketolauric acids have been described. 4-Ketolauric acid, $CH_3(CH_2)_7CO(CH_2)_2CO_2H$, has been prepared by the action of alcoholic potassium hydroxide upon 3-dodecynoic acid.[227, 264] Asano [271] has described the synthesis of 9-ketolauric acid, $CH_3(CH_2)_2CO(CH_2)_7CO_2H$, melting at 50°, by the action of propylzinc iodide on the acid chloride of monoethyl azelate. The preparation of 10-ketolauric acid, $CH_3CH_2CO(CH_2)_8CO_2H$, melting at 72°, by the action of ethylmagnesium bromide on sebacic bis(diethylamide), $(C_2H_5)_2NCO(CH_2)_8CON(C_2H_5)_2$, has been described.[272]

KETOTRIDECANOIC ACIDS

Robinson [273] has obtained 10-ketotridecanoic acid, $CH_3(CH_2)_2$-$CO(CH_2)_8CO_2H$, melting at 63°, by the reaction of ethyl sodio-2-acetylbutyrate with 9-carbethoxynonanoyl chloride. 12-Ketotridecanoic acid, $CH_3CO(CH_2)_{10}CO_2H$, has been prepared by the oxidation of tridecane-1,12-diol. It melts at 70–71°, and boils at 185–186° at 1 mm. pressure.

KETOTETRADECANOIC ACIDS (KETOMYRISTIC ACIDS)

Several of the ketomyristic acids have been prepared and their properties described. Asahina and Nakayama [266] have reported that the saponification of ethyl 3-ketomyristate with sodium hydroxide solution yields methyl undecyl ketone together with lauric acid. 4-Ketomyristic acid, $CH_3(CH_2)_9CO(CH_2)_2CO_2H$, has been synthesized by the hydrolysis of the condensation product of undecanoyl chloride and the sodium derivative of ethyl acetylsuccinate, the reaction being as follows:

$$CH_3OCCHCO_2C_2H_5 \; + \; C_{10}H_{21}COCl \; \xrightarrow{\;Na\;} \; CH_3OCCCO_2C_2H_5 \; \xrightarrow{\;3HOH\;}$$

(with $CH_2CO_2C_2H_5$ groups and CO / $C_{10}H_{21}$ substituent)

$$CH_3(CH_2)_9CO(CH_2)_2CO_2H \; + \; 2C_2H_5OH \; + \; CH_3CO_2H \; + \; CO_2$$

A 72% yield of 4-ketomyristic acid melting at 87° was obtained.[273] A 26% yield of 4-ketomyristic acid had been previously reported by the action of the sodium derivative of ethyl 2-acetylundecanoate on the acid chloride of monomethyl succinate.[274] 13-Ketomyristic acid has been obtained by Robinson [275] by the hydrolysis of ethyl 2-acetylbrassylate, which was prepared by the action of ethyl sodioacetoacetate on ethyl 11-chloroundecanoate, the reactions involved being as follows:

$CH_3CONa:CHCO_2C_2H_5 + Cl(CH_2)_{10}CO_2C_2H_5 \rightarrow$

$$C_2H_5O_2CCH(CH_2)_{10}CO_2C_2H_5 \xrightarrow{HOH} CH_3CO(CH_2)_{11}CO_2H$$

$$\underset{\underset{CH_3}{|}}{\overset{|}{CO}}$$

Ethyl 2-acetylbrassylate   13-Ketomyristic acid

KETOPENTADECANOIC ACIDS

4-Ketopentadecanoic acid, $CH_3(CH_2)_{10}CO(CH_2)_2CO_2H$, has been obtained by the oxidation of either 4-hydroxy-3,5-dicarboxy-pentadecanoic acid or its lactone with potassium permanganate.[276] 4-Ketopentadecanoic acid melts at 92.6°. Davies and Adams [57] have prepared 11-ketopentadecanoic acid, $CH_3(CH_2)_3CO(CH_2)_9$-CO_2H, melting at 70–71°, by the oxidation of 11-hydroxypenta-decanoic acid with chromic acid. 14-Ketopentadecanoic acid, $CH_3CO(CH_2)_{12}CO_2H$, has been obtained by the oxidation of 1,14-pentadecanediol by means of chromic acid.[111] The acid melts at 78.4–79.4°.

KETOHEXADECANOIC ACIDS (KETOPALMITIC ACIDS)

Several of the fourteen theoretically possible ketopalmitic acids have been prepared. 4-Ketopalmitic acid, $CH_3(CH_2)_{11}CO(CH_2)_2$-$CO_2H$, has been obtained [277] by the action of the sodium derivative of ethyl 2-acetyltridecanoate on 3-carbomethoxypropionyl chloride. The acid melted at 91–92° and its oxime at 54°. Robinson [273] has synthesized 5-ketopalmitic acid, $CH_3(CH_2)_{10}CO(CH_2)_3CO_2H$, melting at 88°, by the action of lauroyl chloride with diethyl sodio-2-acetylglutarate, as follows:

$$C_2H_5O_2C(CH_2)_2CCO_2C_2H_5 + C_{11}H_{23}COCl \rightarrow$$

$$\underset{\underset{CH_3}{|}}{\overset{\overset{\|}{CONa}}{|}}$$

$$C_2H_5O_2C(CH_2)_2CCO_2C_2H_5 \xrightarrow{Hydrolysis} HO_2C(CH_2)_2CH_2CO(CH_2)_{10}CH_3$$

with the side groups:
$$\overset{C_{11}H_{23}}{\underset{CO}{|}} \quad \overset{CO}{\underset{CH_3}{|}}$$

The same investigator has also prepared the 7-keto acid, $CH_3(CH_2)_8CO(CH_2)_5CO_2H$, which melted at 78°, by the action of ethyl sodio-2-acetyldecanoate with 6-carbethoxyhexanoyl chlo-ride, thus:

$$ClOC(CH_2)_5CO_2C_2H_5 + CH_3(CH_2)_7CCO_2C_2H_5 \rightarrow$$

$$\underset{\underset{CH_3}{|}}{\overset{\parallel}{C}ONa}$$

$$\begin{array}{c} CO_2C_2H_5 \\ | \\ (CH_2)_5 \\ | \\ CO \\ | \\ CH_3(CH_2)_7CCO_2C_2H_5 \xrightarrow{\text{Hydrolysis}} CH_3(CH_2)_7CH_2\overset{\parallel}{\underset{O}{C}}(CH_2)_5CO_2H \\ | \\ CO \\ | \\ CH_3 \end{array}$$

8-Ketopalmitic acid, $CH_3(CH_2)_7CO(CH_2)_6CO_2H$, melting at 77–78°, has been prepared in a similar manner from 7-carbethoxy-heptanoyl chloride and ethyl sodio-2-acetylnonanoate. The preparation of 8-ketopalmitic acid by the hydration of palmitolic acid had been described previously by Bodenstein,[18] who reported a freezing point of 74°. The hydration of palmitolic acid actually yields a mixture of 7-keto- and 8-ketopalmitic acids. In 1926, Robinson and Robinson [274] studied the hydration of various acetylenic acids such as palmitolic, stearolic, and behenolic acids with the object of developing generalizations with reference to the relative proportions of isomeric keto acids formed during this reaction. Stearolic acid, $CH_3(CH_2)_7C\!:\!C(CH_2)_7CO_2H$, contains the acetylenic bond in the middle of the carbon chain and the orienting influence is due entirely to the terminal methyl and carboxyl groups. In considering the general formula $RC\!:\!CR'$, these authors pointed out that the formation of $RCOCH_2R'$ is favored by increasing the length of the hydrocarbon chain R; by branching of the R group; by introducing groups such as CO_2H, NO_2, or Cl into the group R'; or by bringing the carboxyl group in R' nearer to the acetylenic bond. The hydration of stearolic acid has been shown to yield more of the 10-keto acid than of the 9-keto acid, and this ratio is increased in the case of palmitolic acid since the carboxyl group is nearer to the triple bond. In the case of behenolic acid the ratio of 14-keto to 13-keto acid produced is lower than in the case of either palmitolic or stearolic acid, owing to the fact that the carboxyl group is more remote from the triple bond. Fordyce and Johnson [278] have prepared 10-ketopalmitic acid, $CH_3(CH_2)_5CO(CH_2)_8CO_2H$, which melted at 75.0–75.8°, by the action of hexylmagnesium bromide on the acid chloride of mono-methyl sebacate. 11-Ketopalmitic acid, $CH_3(CH_2)_4CO(CH_2)_9$-

CO_2H, melting at 74–75°, has been obtained by the oxidation of 11-hydroxypalmitic acid.[57] Robinson [273] has obtained 4,13-diketo-palmitic acid, $CH_3(CH_2)_2CO(CH_2)_8CO(CH_2)_2CO_2H$, melting at 101°, by the action of 10-ketotridecanoyl chloride on diethyl sodio-acetylsuccinate.

KETOHEPTADECANOIC ACIDS (KETOMARGARIC ACIDS)

Only one ketomargaric acid has been described. 9-Keto-margaric acid, $CH_3(CH_2)_7CO(CH_2)_7CO_2H$, which freezes at 78.5°, has been prepared [279] by the oxidation of 2-hydroxy-2-octylsebacic acid with potassium permanganate. The acid has also been obtained by the action of potassium hydroxide or sulfuric acid on the above compound.

KETOÖCTADECANOIC ACIDS (KETOSTEARIC ACIDS)

The ketostearic acids have received more attention than any other group of high molecular weight keto acids, and most of our knowledge of the higher keto acids has been derived from a study of this group. All the ketostearic acids are insoluble in water and easily soluble in hot ethanol, ether, and acetic acid. None of the ketostearic acids is found in the naturally occurring fats and oils, although they are apparently present in the decomposition products formed by the action of microörganisms on fats,[280] and they have been observed in some of the fatty material obtained by the alcoholic extraction of fungi. Zellner [281] has obtained a 1% yield of a ketostearic acid, melting at 86°, by the extraction of *Lactarius rufus*. The acid so obtained was designated lactarinic acid and has since been shown to be 6-ketostearic acid. Ketostearic acids frequently result from the oxidation of naturally occurring hydroxy acids; for example, a hydroxystearic acid which melted at 81–82°, obtained from chicken bile, has been oxidized to yield a ketostearic acid melting at 83–84°.[282]

Asahina and Nakayama [266] have reported that 3-ketostearic acid, $CH_3(CH_2)_{14}COCH_2CO_2H$, can be obtained by the saponi-fication of its ethyl ester. Since saponification of the lower 3-keto acid esters resulted in the decomposition of the acids with the formation of ketones and saturated acids, it is evident that the 3-keto acids become more stable with increase in the length of the carbon chain. 4-Ketostearic acid, $CH_3(CH_2)_{13}CO(CH_2)_2CO_2H$, has been prepared by the oxidation of the lactone of 4-hydroxystearic acid with chromic acid in acetic acid.[283] Brown and Farmer [284] have obtained 4-ketostearic acid by the hydrogenation of licanic acid in the presence of platinum. The free acid freezes at 95° and its semicarbazone melts at 126°. Robinson and Robinson [277] have synthesized 6-ketostearic acid, $CH_3(CH_2)_{11}CO(CH_2)_4CO_2H$, by the action of 5-carbethoxypentanoyl chloride on the sodium derivative of ethyl 2-acetyltridecanoate. The acid melted at 87° and its oxime at 59–61°, and it was apparently identical with lactarinic acid. Lactarinic acid, freezing at 87°, has been obtained by the extraction of dried fungi with hot ethanol, yields of 2 to 3% having been reported.[285] 7-Ketostearic acid, $CH_3(CH_2)_{10}CO(CH_2)_5CO_2H$, has been prepared by Arnaud [286] by the action of concentrated sulfuric acid on tariric acid (6-octadecynoic acid). The acid was reported to freeze at 75°. The preparation of a mixture of 8-ketostearic acid, $CH_3(CH_2)_9CO(CH_2)_6CO_2H$, and 9-ketostearic acid, $CH_3(CH_2)_8CO(CH_2)_7CO_2H$, by the treatment of 8-octadecynoic acid with concentrated sulfuric acid, has been reported.[34] The 9-ketostearic acid had been prepared previously by the reduction of 12-chloro-9-ketostearic acid with zinc and hydrochloric acid.[287] The acid freezes at 83°. Robinson and Robinson [274] have also synthesized this acid by the action of the acid chloride of monoethyl azelate on the sodium derivative of ethyl 2-acetyldecanoate. The hydration of the triple bond of stearolic acid (9-octadecynoic acid) has been studied by Baruch,[4] who considered that the reaction yields essentially 10-ketostearic acid, $CH_3(CH_2)_7CO(CH_2)_8CO_2H$. The hydration actually yields a mixture of 9-keto- and 10-ketostearic acids,* the latter, however, being present in the greater amount. The hydration of stearolic acid with sulfuric acid has been studied by Arnaud and Posternak.[34] 10-Ketostearic acid has been obtained by the oxidation of 10-hydroxystearic acid with a mixture of chromic and acetic acids [283] and also by the pyrolysis of the zinc salt of 9,10-dihydroxystearic acid.[288] The condensation of heptylsodiomalonic ester with 9-carbethoxynonanoyl chloride results in a small yield of 10-ketostearic acid.[284] Better yields of the keto acid are obtained by the reaction of 9-carbethoxynonanoyl chloride with ethyl 2-acetylnonanoate. Fordyce and Johnson [278] have prepared 10-ketostearic acid by the action of octylmagnesium bromide on sebacyl chloride. 10-Ketostearic acid melts at 83°. King [289] has recently described the preparation of 9-hydroxy-10-ketostearic acid, melting at 74°, and of 10-hydroxy-9-ketostearic acid, melting at 75.5°. The semicarbazones melt at 152° and

---

* For a discussion of the hydration of acetylenic acids see 8-ketopalmitic acid.

138.5°, respectively. 11-Ketostearic acid, $CH_3(CH_2)_6CO(CH_2)_9$-CO_2H, has been prepared by the oxidation of 11-hydroxystearic acid [283,290] and also by the action of sulfuric acid on 10-octadecynoic acid.[34] Perrotte [291] has obtained 12-ketostearic acid (ricinic acid), $CH_3(CH_2)_5CO(CH_2)_{10}CO_2H$, by the saponification of the corresponding nitrile. This acid had previously been obtained by Perrotte [292] by the pyrolysis of barium ricinoleate, the pyrolysis yielding a mixture of methyl hexyl ketone and 12-ketostearic acid. The keto acid melts at 81°. The formation of this acid assumes the displacement of the double bond from the 9- to the 11-position during the reaction. The same investigator has described the preparation of 12-ketostearic acid, melting at 79–80°, by the oxidation of ethyl 12-hydroxystearate. The latter compound can be prepared easily by the catalytic hydrogenation of the ethylenic bond of ethyl ricinoleate.

Licanic Acid

α-Licanic acid, originally supposed to be an isomer of eleostearic acid,[293] is found in substantial amounts in oiticica oil. The acid was first described by Wilborn,[294] who termed it couepic acid, owing to its supposed occurrence in the seed oil of *Couepia grandiflora*. Brown and Farmer [284] have investigated this acid and observed that it yields 4-ketostearic acid upon hydrogenation. A study of the products of oxidation established that α-licanic acid is 4-keto-9,11,13-octadecatrienoic acid, $CH_3(CH_2)_3(CH:CH)_3$-$(CH_2)_4CO(CH_2)_2CO_2H$. α-Licanic acid melts at 74–75° and is converted into its higher-melting isomer, m.p. 99.5°, by treatment with traces of iodine or sulfur, or by exposure to sunlight. α-Licanic acid is unusual in that it is the only example of a keto acid which appears in significant amounts in a seed oil. Since it possesses a conjugated system of three double bonds, it forms addition products with maleic anhydride [295] and also undergoes other reactions typical of conjugated unsaturated systems.

Keto Acids Containing More Than Eighteen Carbon Atoms

Only a comparatively few of the many theoretically possible high molecular weight keto fatty acids have been described. 10-Ketononadecanoic acid, $CH_3(CH_2)_8CO(CH_2)_8CO_2H$, which melts at 86–87°, has been synthesized [274] by the reaction of ethyl 2-acetyldecanoate with 9-carbethoxynonanoyl chloride. Le Sueur and Withers [279] have prepared 13-ketoheneicosanoic acid, $CH_3(CH_2)_7$-

$CO(CH_2)_{11}CO_2H$, by the oxidation of 13-hydroxy-13-carboxyheneicosanoic acid. The keto acid freezes at 89–90° and is easily soluble in chloroform but difficultly soluble in ethanol and ether. *Trans*-4-keto-12-heneicosenoic acid has been obtained by the action of diethyl sodioacetylsuccinate on elaidoyl chloride.[273]   4-Ketodocosanoic acid, $CH_3(CH_2)_{17}CO(CH_2)_2CO_2H$, has been prepared by the oxidation of the lactone of 4-hydroxybehenic acid with chromic acid in acetic acid solution.[108]   It was reported to freeze at 103°. The hydration of behenolic acid yields 14-ketobehenic acid, $CH_3(CH_2)_7CO(CH_2)_{12}CO_2H$.[158, 296]   This hydration also yields the isomeric acid, 13-ketobehenic acid.   14-Ketobehenic acid has also been obtained by the action of concentrated sulfuric acid on 14-chlorobrassidic acid [297] and on 14-chloroerucic acid.[298]   The condensation of the sodium derivative of ethyl 2-acetylbrassylate with stearoyl chloride followed by hydrolysis of the resulting product yields 13-ketotriacontanoic acid, $CH_3(CH_2)_{16}CO(CH_2)_{11}$-$CO_2H$, melting at 104°.[275]   This acid was previously described by Chibnall and coworkers.[299]

PART 4   THE CYCLIC ACIDS AND VARIOUS SYNTHETIC ACIDS POSSESSING BACTERICIDAL ACTIVITY

Three cyclic acids, chaulmoogric acid ($C_{18}H_{32}O_2$), hydnocarpic acid ($C_{16}H_{28}O_2$), and gorlic acid ($C_{18}H_{30}O_2$), have been separated from the natural oils and definitely identified.   The tropical plants from which these seed oils are obtained belong to the family *Flacourtiaceae*, comprising the various hydnocarpus species from which oils such as chaulmoogra oil, lukrabo oil, and gorli seed oil are procured.   Chaulmoogra oil is the best known and most important member of this group, having long been a subject of intensive medical and scientific interest.   The use of chaulmoogra oil as a specific for the treatment of leprosy originated many centuries ago with the Chinese.   Chaulmoogra and similar oils, together with the simple derivatives of the acids contained therein, have been, for generations, the only effective substances against this deadly disease.   Thus, it is not surprising that the acids occurring in these oils, the cyclic acids, have been the subject of many chemical and biological studies.   These investigations have not only been concerned with the isolation and structures of the naturally occurring cyclic acids, but have also included the synthesis of other closely related acids in an endeavor to correlate bactericidal activity with chemical structure. In any consideration of the cyclic acids it should, therefore, be borne in mind that their medical background transcends all other considerations.

The naturally occurring cyclic acids are characterized by the presence of a terminal cyclopentene group and possess the following general formula:

$$\begin{array}{c} CH_2 \\ CH_2 \qquad CHRCO_2H \\ CH\!=\!\!=\!CH \end{array}$$

It has been conclusively proved [300, 301, 302] that the cyclic acids present in chaulmoogra and allied oils are responsible for their curative properties. It has been shown by Dean and coworkers [303] that these curative properties are likewise possessed by the ethyl esters of chaulmoogra oil fatty acids. The sodium salts of these cyclic acids have also been extensively investigated. [304] Chaulmoogric acid and its derivatives are somewhat toxic and can be administered orally only in small amounts. [305] Although chaulmoogra oil has been known for many centuries, it was not until 1904 that a systematic study was made of the fatty acids contained in it. Between the years 1904 and 1907 Power and associates [306] reported the results of their investigations of chaulmoogric and hydnocarpic acids, and although these studies led to a somewhat erroneous conclusion regarding the actual structures, they can be said to have formed the basis of our present-day knowledge of these substances. Chaulmoogric acid, which is optically active ($[\alpha]_D$ + 62.1°), was found to have the formula $C_{18}H_{32}O_2$ and to yield an optically inactive dihydrochaulmoogric acid upon reduction. Oxidation with potassium permanganate yields two dihydroxy-dihydrochaulmoogric acids to which the following formulas were assigned:

$$\begin{array}{c} CHOH\!-\!CHOH \\ CH(CH_2)_{12}CO_2H \\ CH_2\!-\!CH_2 \\ [\alpha]_D + 11.6°, \text{ m.p. } 105° \end{array} \qquad \begin{array}{c} CHOH\!-\!CH_2 \\ COH(CH_2)_{12}CO_2H \\ CH_2\!-\!CH_2 \\ [\alpha]_D - 14.2°, \text{ m.p. } 93° \end{array}$$

Further oxidation yields a hydroxy keto acid:

$$\begin{array}{c} CHOH\!-\!CO \\ CH(CH_2)_{12}CO_2H \\ CH_2\!-\!\!-\!\!-\!CH_2 \end{array}$$

This latter acid was further oxidized to 4-carboxyheptadecanedioic acid, $HO_2CCH_2CH_2CH(CO_2H)(CH_2)_{12}CO_2H$, 4-ketoheptadecanedioic acid, $HO_2CCH_2CH_2CO(CH_2)_{12}CO_2H$, tetradecanedioic acid, $HO_2C(CH_2)_{12}CO_2H$, and tridecanedioic acid, $HO_2C(CH_2)_{11}CO_2H$. Chaulmoogric acid adds one molecule of hydrogen bromide, the removal of which by alcoholic potassium hydroxide yields an isochaulmoogric acid containing some chaulmoogric acid. Power has observed that the isochaulmoogric acid gives 3-methyl-4-ketoheptadecanedioic acid upon oxidation and postulated the following series of reactions:

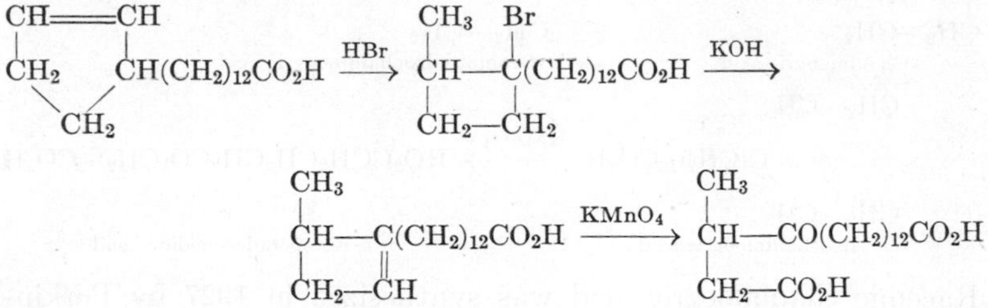

On the basis of these observations it was considered that chaulmoogric acid is a tautomeric substance which possesses the structure (I) and that its homolog, hydnocarpic acid, has a similar structure (II).

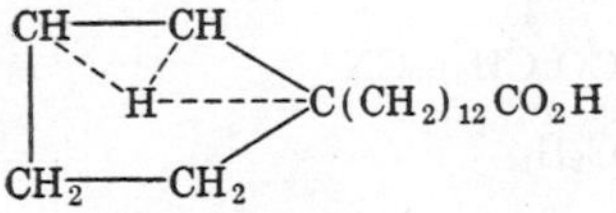

(I) 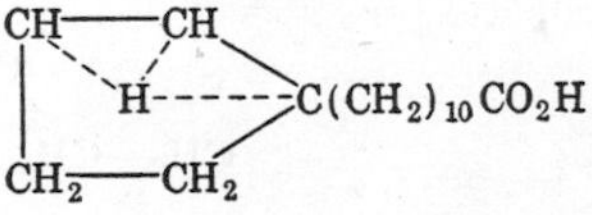   (II)

These structures were accepted for many years and have been used to interpret many of the reactions of these acids. It is quite interesting to note that chaulmoogric and hydnocarpic acids contain eighteen and sixteen carbon atoms respectively, which further emphasizes the preponderance of acids of these chain lengths in the natural oils. In 1925, Shriner and Adams [307] reported the results of an extensive investigation upon the structure of chaulmoogric acid and stated that the keto acid obtained by the oxidation of isochaulmoogric acid is 5-ketoöctadecanedioic acid, $HO_2C(CH_2)_3CO(CH_2)_{12}CO_2H$, and not 3-methyl-4-ketoheptadecanedioic acid as postulated by Power and associates. The tautomeric formula assumed by these latter authors was, therefore, no longer tenable, and chaulmoogric acid was assigned the structure (III). Its homolog, hydnocarpic acid, has the structure (IV).

$$\begin{array}{ll}
\underset{|}{CH}\!\!=\!\!\underset{|}{CH} & \underset{|}{CH}\!\!=\!\!\underset{|}{CH} \\
\quad\; CH(CH_2)_{12}CO_2H & \quad\; CH(CH_2)_{10}CO_2H \\
CH_2\!\!-\!\!CH_2 & CH_2\!\!-\!\!CH_2 \\
\quad\;\;\; (III) & \quad\;\;\; (IV)
\end{array}$$

Shriner and Adams assumed the keto dicarboxylic acid to result from the following series of reactions:

$$\underset{\substack{| \quad\quad\quad | \\ CH_2\!\!-\!\!CH_2 \\ \text{Chaulmoogric acid}}}{CH\!\!=\!\!CH} \!\quad CH(CH_2)_{12}CO_2H \xrightarrow{HBr} \underset{\substack{| \quad\quad\quad | \\ CH_2\!\!-\!\!CH_2 \\ \text{Bromohydrochaulmoogric acid}}}{CH_2\!\!-\!\!CHBr}\!\quad CH(CH_2)_{12}CO_2H \xrightarrow{KOH}$$

$$\underset{\substack{| \quad\quad\quad\;\; | \\ CH_2\!\!-\!\!CH_2 \\ \text{Isochaulmoogric acid}}}{CH_2\!\!-\!\!CH}\!\quad\; C(CH_2)_{12}CO_2H \xrightarrow{KMnO_4} \underset{\text{5-Keto\"octadecanedioic acid}}{HO_2CCH_2CH_2CH_2CO(CH_2)_{12}CO_2H}$$

Racemic chaulmoogric acid was synthesized in 1927 by Perkins and Cruz [308] by the condensation of acetoacetic ester with 11-cyanoundecanoic acid, $CN(CH_2)_{10}CO_2H$, followed by reaction of the resulting product with 3-chloro-1-cyclopentene. This resulted in a compound of the following structure:

$$\underset{\substack{| \quad\quad\quad\quad\quad\quad\quad\quad | \\ CH_2\!\!-\!\!CH_2 \quad\quad CO_2C_2H_5}}{CH\!\!=\!\!CH \quad\quad\quad COCH_3} \!\quad CH\!\!-\!\!C\!\!-\!\!CO(CH_2)_{10}CN$$

This compound gives the keto acid $C_5H_7CH_2CO(CH_2)_{10}CO_2H$ upon hydrolysis, the reduction of which yields dl-chaulmoogric acid. A number of attempts have been made to prepare racemic chaulmoogric acid from the naturally occurring d-chaulmoogric acid; however, this was not accomplished until 1933. In this year, Hinegardner [309] reported that an optically inactive chaulmoogronitrile is obtained when the d-amide, prepared from the natural acid, is distilled in the presence of phosphoric anhydride. The hydrolysis of this nitrile gave the optically inactive acid. The nitrile obtained from d-chaulmoogramide by treatment with thionyl chloride was found to be optically active ($[\alpha]_D^{25} + 55.2°$). However, when this nitrile was distilled in the presence of phosphoric anhydride the racemic nitrile resulted. The mechanism of this racemization is not known, although Hinegardner postulated the formation and subsequent breakdown of a weak addition product. It was also observed that the optically inactive chaulmoogric acid yields a crystalline derivative with brucine, which suggests the possibility that l-chaulmoogric acid could be obtained. The synthesis of chaulmoogric acid from hydnocarpic acid has been accomplished by Stanley and Adams.[310] The reduction of ethyl hydnocarpate (b_2 143–144°, d_4^{25} 0.9087, n_D^{25} 1.4502, $[\alpha]_D$ 70.5°) yielded hydnocarpyl alcohol (m.p. 23°, b_2 144–145°, d_4^{25} 0.8022, n_D^{25} 1.4709, $[\alpha]_D$ 75.2°), which was converted into the corresponding bromide and thence to diethyl hydnocarpylmalonate. The hydrolysis and partial decarboxylation of this latter compound gave hydnocarpylacetic acid, which is identical with the naturally occurring chaulmoogric acid.

Both chaulmoogric and hydnocarpic acids can easily be obtained from chaulmoogra oil by saponification, acidification, and separation of the acid mixture. Shriner and Adams [307] separated the saponification mixture into three fractions by vacuum distillation: the first, largely hydnocarpic acid; the second, a eutectic mixture which was refractionated; and the third, essentially chaulmoogric acid. Repeated crystallizations of the first fraction from petroleum ether gave pure hydnocarpic acid which melted at 59–60° and was optically active, $[\alpha]_D$ 68.3°. Crystallization of the third fraction from ethanol gave chaulmoogric acid, m.p. 68–68.5°, $[\alpha]_D$ 62.4°. The separation of chaulmoogric and hydnocarpic acids from chaulmoogra oil fatty acids by fractionation of the mixed acids under a high vacuum followed by crystallizations has also been described by Hashimoto.[311] Both chaulmoogric and hydnocarpic acids turn yellow upon prolonged exposure to light, the resulting change being attended by a diminution in specific rotation and a lowering of the melting point.

The hydrogenation of chaulmoogric and hydnocarpic acids proceeds smoothly in the presence of platinum and palladium to give the optically inactive dihydro derivatives.[312] Shriner and Adams [307] have recommended a platinum-platinum oxide catalyst for this hydrogenation. The dihydro acids may also be obtained by the reduction of the ethylenic acids with zinc and ethanol or by reduction with phosphorus and hydriodic acid, the latter of which methods also results in the formation of the hydrocarbon chaulmoogrene, $C_{18}H_{34}$, as a by-product. The reduction of chaulmoogric acid by means of sodium and ethanol yields chaulmoogryl alcohol together with chaulmoogryl chaulmoograte. Both dihydrochaulmoogric acid (13-cyclopentyltridecanoic acid) and dihydro-hydnocarpic acid (11-cyclopentylundecanoic acid) have been prepared synthetically by Noller and Adams [313] and have been found to be identical with the compounds obtained by the hydrogenation of the naturally occurring acids. Dihydrochaulmoogric acid melts at 70–71° and its homolog dihydrohydnocarpic acid melts at 63–63.5°. The treatment of chaulmoogric acid with hydrogen bromide in glacial acetic acid yields the optically inactive hydrogen bromide addition product, bromodihydrochaulmoogric acid, melting at 36–38°. The dehydrobromination of bromodihydrochaulmoogric acid forms isochaulmoogric acid together with some chaulmoogric acid, the latter being observed to be optically active.

Several acids other than chaulmoogric and hydnocarpic acids have been reported to occur in chaulmoogra and similar oils, and the identity of one of these, gorlic acid, has been definitely established. The presence in chaulmoogra oil of a liquid cyclic acid more unsaturated than chaulmoogric acid was first suggested by the work of Dean, Wrenshall, and Fujimoto.[312] The acid gave dihydrochaulmoogric acid upon hydrogenation, and it was considered to be similar to chaulmoogric acid with the exception that it contains a double bond in the side chain. André and Jouatte [314] separated an apparently similar acid, to which they gave the name gorlic acid, from *Oncoba echinata* oil (gorli seed oil), and Paget [315] later obtained this acid from *C. brasiliensis* and observed that it yielded adipic acid and 4-carboxyundecanedioic acid upon oxidation, thus establishing its structure as 13-(2-cyclopentenyl)-6-tridecenoic acid,

$$CH=CH$$
$$CH(CH_2)_6CH=CH(CH_2)_4CO_2H$$
$$CH_2-CH_2$$

Gorlic acid has recently been studied by Cole and Cardoso,[316] who succeeded in separating the pure acid from gorli seed oil fatty acids by the removal of the solid acids by low-temperature solvent crystallization followed by fractional distillation of the ethyl esters of the liquid fatty acids. The following physical constants were reported for this acid: m.p. 6°, b.p. 232.5°, d_{25}^{25} 0.9436, n_D^{25} 1.4782, and $[\alpha]_D^{25} + 60.7°$. The methyl and ethyl esters boil at 209° and 214° at 10 mm., respectively.

In view of the great interest which has centered around the bactericidal properties of the naturally occurring cyclic acids and their various derivatives, a large number of cyclic acids have been synthesized in an attempt to emulate the properties of the natural acids. This endeavor not only has resulted in the preparation and study of many cyclic acids but also has served to increase greatly our knowledge of the relationship which exists between the chemical structure and bactericidal activity of fatty acids, particularly towards *B. leprae*. Adams and coworkers have described the preparation and properties of an imposing number of cyclic acids and have investigated their bactericidal action *in vitro* upon *B. leprae*. No study of the cyclic acids would be complete without specific reference to these accomplishments. The *in vitro* results obtained by these investigators have indicated that many of the synthetic acids possess bactericidal activities comparable to those of the natural acids when tested against *B. leprae*. However, the actual value of these compounds as curative agents against the disease itself will require many years of clinical evaluation.

One of the obvious steps in the correlation of chemical constitution with bactericidal action against *B. leprae* was the investigation of the homologs of the natural cyclic acids, chaulmoogric and hydnocarpic acids. Sacks and Adams [317] have prepared homochaulmoogric acid,

$$CH\!\!=\!\!CH$$
$$CH(CH_2)_{13}CO_2H$$
$$CH_2\!\!-\!\!CH_2$$

and homohydnocarpic acid,

$$CH\!\!=\!\!CH$$
$$CH(CH_2)_{11}CO_2H$$
$$CH_2\!\!-\!\!CH_2$$

by the reduction of ethyl chaulmoograte and ethyl hydnocarpate to the corresponding alcohols, which were converted through the bromides to the nitriles, the hydrolysis of which yielded acids containing one more carbon atom than the original acids. Homochaulmoogric acid melts at 66–67° with $[\alpha]_D$ +54°, whereas homohydnocarpic acid melts at 56–57° with $[\alpha]_D$ +56.7°. It is rather surprising that neither of these acids was reported to be effective against *B. leprae*. In the same year, Van Dyke and Adams [318] synthesized chaulmoogrylacetic acid,

$$CH\!=\!\!CH$$
$$\Big| \quad \Big\rangle CH(CH_2)_{13}CH_2CO_2H$$
$$CH_2\!-\!CH_2$$

melting at 72–73°, by the condensation of chaulmoogryl bromide with diethyl malonate. A series of 2-cyclopentenyl-2-alkylacetic acids of the general formula

$$CH\!=\!\!CH$$
$$\Big| \quad \Big\rangle CHCH(CO_2H)R$$
$$CH_2\!-\!CH_2$$

in which the R group varied from pentyl to nonyl, has been synthesized by Arvin and Adams, [319] and the acids have been tested against *B. leprae*. The bactericidal activity of this series increased from pentyl to nonyl. The following physical constants were reported: (R, b°C., n_D^{20}, d_4^{20}) C_5H_{11}, 142–145 (5 mm.), 1.4659, 0.9629; C_6H_{13}, 150–155 (5 mm.), 1.4671, 0.9573; C_7H_{15}, 162–165 (4 mm.), 1.4683, 0.9499; C_8H_{17}, 170–173 (4 mm.), 1.4687, 0.9452; C_9H_{19}, 173–176 (3 mm.), 1.4690, 0.9436. The synthesis of 2-cyclopentenylacetic acid by the condensation of diethyl malonate with 2-cyclopentenyl chloride has been described by Noller and Adams. [320] The acid boils at 94–95° at 3 mm. and has n_D^{20} 1.4682 and d_4^{20} 1.0519.

Since Dean, Wrenshall, and Fujimoto [312] and also Schöbl [321] have shown that ethyl dihydrochaulmoograte is nearly as effective as ethyl chaulmoograte itself in the treatment of leprosy, it is evident that the presence of an ethylenic bond in the cyclopentene ring is not a prerequisite for curative action. As a consequence of this observation, Adams and associates synthesized several series of cyclic acids possessing cyclobutyl, cyclopentyl, and cyclohexyl groups, and evaluated their bactericidal activity against *B. leprae*. Hiers and Adams [322] prepared cyclohexyltridecanoic acid by the condensation of cyclohexylmagnesium bromide with methyl 13-aldotridecanoate followed by the reduction of the resulting 13-cyclohexyl-13-hydroxytridecanoic acid, the reactions being as follows:

$$\underset{\substack{CH_2-CH_2\\ \diagup \qquad \diagdown \\ CH_2 \qquad \qquad CHMgBr \\ \diagdown \qquad \diagup \\ CH_2-CH_2}}{} + CHO(CH_2)_{11}CO_2CH_3 \rightarrow$$

$$\underset{\substack{CH_2-CH_2\\ \diagup \qquad \diagdown \\ CH_2 \qquad \qquad CHCH(OH)(CH_2)_{11}CO_2H \\ \diagdown \qquad \diagup \\ CH_2-CH_2}}{} \rightarrow$$

$$\underset{\substack{CH_2-CH_2\\ \diagup \qquad \diagdown \\ CH_2 \qquad \qquad CH(CH_2)_{12}CO_2H \\ \diagdown \qquad \diagup \\ CH_2-CH_2}}{}$$

The lower homolog cyclohexylundecanoic acid was prepared in a similar manner. 13-Cyclohexyltridecanoic and 11-cyclohexylundecanoic acids melted at 63–64° and 58–59°, respectively, and were found to be effective against *B. leprae*. These authors subsequently reported [323] the preparation by the malonic acid method of a series of ω-cyclohexyl-substituted fatty acids of the general formula $R(CH_2)_nCO_2H$, where R represents a cyclohexyl group and *n* is one to twelve. The following physical constants were reported: $(n, m°C., b_4°C., n_D^{38}, d_4^{38})$ 1, 29–30, 116–117, 1.4537, 1.0020; 2, 15–16, 125–126, 1.4553, 0.9848; 3, 29–30, 132–134, 1.4562, 0.9693; 4, 6–8, 151–153, 1.4570, 0.9589; 5, 33–34, 157–158, 1.4580, 0.9506; 6, 25–26, 171–172, 1.4588, 0.9436; 7, 37–38, 182–183, 1.4598, 0.9359; 8, 45.5–46.5; 9, 52.5–53.5; 10, 58–59; 11, 61.5–62; 12, 63–64. Those containing from three to nine carbon atoms in the side chain were reported to possess bactericidal activity. The investigations of the synthetic acids have been extended to a number of cyclopropyl, cyclobutyl, cyclopentyl, and cyclohexyl alkylacetic acids. Yohe and Adams [324] have prepared a series of cyclopentyl alkylacetic acids of the general formula

$$\underset{\substack{CH_2-CH_2\\ \diagup \qquad \diagdown \\ \quad \qquad CHCH(CO_2H)R \\ \diagdown \qquad \diagup \\ CH_2-CH_2}}{}$$

and a series of cyclopentylethyl alkylacetic acids of the general formula

$$\underset{\substack{CH_2-CH_2\\ \diagup \qquad \diagdown \\ \quad \qquad CH(CH_2)_2CH(CO_2H)R \\ \diagdown \qquad \diagup \\ CH_2-CH_2}}{}$$

The following physical constants were reported for the cyclopentyl alkylacetic acids: (R,$b°$C.,$m°$C.,n_D^{20},d_4^{20}) C_7H_{15}, 155–160 (1.4 mm.), —, 1.4594, 0.9312; C_8H_{17}, 166–169 (2 mm.), —, 1.4609, 0.9279; C_9H_{19}, 177–178.5 (1.4 mm.), 37–37.5; $C_{10}H_{21}$, 189–190.5 (1.7 mm.), 34.5–36; $C_{11}H_{23}$, 193–197 (1.3 mm.), 43.5–45.5. The physical constants of the cyclopentylethyl alkylacetic acids were reported to be as follows: (R, $b°$C., n_D^{20}, d_4^{20}) H, 115–118 (2.4 mm.), 1.4575, 0.9849; C_2H_5, 122–124.5 (1.3 mm.), 1.4950, 0.9602; C_3H_7, 130–132 (1.9 mm.), 1.4595, 0.9533; C_4H_9, 136–137 (1 mm.), 1.4608, 0.9435; C_5H_{11}, 150–154 (1.9 mm.), 1.4610, 0.9360; C_6H_{13}, 157–161 (1.9 mm.), 1.4616, 0.9303; C_7H_{15}, 167–169 (2 mm.), 1.4621, 0.9252; C_8H_{17}, 173–176 (1.5 mm.), 1.4629, 0.9210. Cyclohexyl-n-valeric acid and cyclopentyl-n-valeric acid have been synthesized by Katsnel'son and associates.[325, 326] The cyclohexyl alkylacetic acids, $C_6H_{11}CH(CO_2H)R$, and cyclohexylmethyl alkylacetic acids, $C_6H_{11}CH_2CH(CO_2H)R$, have been described by Adams, Stanley, and Stearns.[327] The cyclohexyl alkylacetic acids were reported to have the following physical constants: (R, $b°$C., n_D^{25}, d_4^{25}) C_5H_{11}, 136–139 (3 mm.), 1.4640, 0.9544; C_6H_{13}, 145–149 (3 mm.), 1.4641, 0.9449; C_7H_{15}, 148–152 (2 mm.), 1.4641, 0.9350; C_8H_{17}, 158–161 (2 mm.), 1.4642, 0.9298; C_9H_{19}, 167–171 (3 mm.), 1.4645, 0.9245; $C_{10}H_{21}$, 165–169 (2 mm.), 1.4649, 0.9224; $C_{11}H_{23}$, 173–177 (2 mm.), 1.4650, 0.9166; $C_{12}H_{25}$, 187–191 (2 mm.), 1.4653, 0.9129. The following physical constants were observed for the cyclohexylmethyl alkylacetic acids: (R, $b°$C., n_D^{25}, d_4^{25}) C_2H_5, 131–132 (2 mm.), 1.4623, 0.9814; C_3H_7, 141–143 (4.5 mm.), 1.4628, 0.9720; C_4H_9, 133–136 (3 mm.), 1.4620, 0.9564; C_5H_{11}, 139–142 (2 mm.), 1.4630, 0.9516; C_6H_{13}, 174–175 (3 mm.), 1.4627, 0.9448; C_7H_{15}, 202–204 (3 mm.), 1.4632, 0.9393; C_8H_{17}, 186–190 (4 mm.), 1.4640, 0.9331. A study of the bactericidal activity of these cyclopentyl and cyclohexyl acids indicated that there was no essential difference between the two series when members of equal molecular weight were compared. The highest activity was exhibited by those acids containing sixteen and eighteen carbon atoms, the lower and higher homologs showing very markedly reduced, if any, bactericidal properties. The conclusion that the bactericidal action of these acids is independent of the number of carbon atoms in the cyclic group was further strengthened by a study of the cyclopropylmethyl alkylacetic acids, $C_3H_5CH_2CH(CO_2H)R$. In this series also, no activity was evidenced until at least sixteen carbon atoms were present in the molecule. The cyclopropylmethyl alkylacetic acids were prepared by Arvin and Adams [328] and were observed to have the following physical constants: (R, $b°C.$, n_D^{20}, d_4^{20}) C_5H_{11}, 112–115 (1.4 mm.), 1.4469, 0.9375; C_6H_{13}, 130–132 (1.8 mm.), 1.4498, 0.9253; C_7H_{15}, 136–139 (2 mm.), 1.4509, 0.9236; C_8H_{17}, 146–149 (2.1 mm.), 1.4529, 0.9142; C_9H_{19}, 162–164 (2.3 mm.), 1.4545, 0.0105; $C_{10}H_{21}$, 176–178 (2.7 mm.), 1.4553, 0.9064; (R, $m°C.$) $C_{11}H_{23}$, 27–28; $C_{12}H_{25}$, 29–30; $C_{14}H_{29}$, 35–37. The cyclobutylmethyl alkylacetic acids containing sixteen and eighteen carbon atoms were likewise found to be the most effective of their series against *B. leprae* and to be comparable to the other cyclic-substituted acetic acids of equal molecular weight. The physical constants of the cyclobutylmethyl alkylacetic acids as reported by Ford and Adams [329] are as follows: (R, $b°C.$, n_D^{25}, d_4^{25}) C_8H_{17}, 150–152 (2 mm.), 1.4615, 0.9154; C_9H_{19}, 177–181 (3.5 mm.), 1.4622, 0.9124; $C_{10}H_{21}$, 176–179 (2.7 mm.), 1.4628, 0.9095; $C_{11}H_{23}$, 188–192 (2.5 mm.), 1.4635, 0.9080; $C_{12}H_{25}$, 204–205 (2.5 mm.), 1.4642, 0.9046. It had been previously shown by Adams and others [330] that the position of the carboxyl group in the cyclic acids is of secondary importance as regards bactericidal activity toward *B. leprae*. This was shown by a comparison of the bactericidal properties of various ω-cyclohexylalkyl alkylacetic acids, the results indicating that the activity is a function of the molecular weight of the cyclic acid rather than of its structure. Three series of cyclohexylalkyl alkylacetic acids were prepared; namely, β-cyclohexylethyl, γ-cyclohexylpropyl, and δ-cyclohexylbutyl alkylacetic acids. The acids were obtained from ω-cyclohexylalkyl alkylmalonates prepared by the condensation of ω-cyclohexylalkyl bromides with the sodium derivatives of the diethyl alkylmalonates. The physical constants which were reported for these various acids are as follows: (R, $b°C.$, n_D^{25}, d_4^{25}) β-cyclohexylethyl alkylacetic acids [$C_6H_{11}(CH_2)_2CH(CO_2H)R$], C_2H_5, 121–124 (3 mm.), 1.4613, 0.9619; C_3H_7, 122–125 (2 mm.), 1.4623, 0.9486; C_4H_9, 139–142 (4 mm.), 1.4624, 0.9410; C_5H_{11}, 182–185 (5 mm.), 1.4626, 0.9350; C_6H_{13}, 174–177 (2 mm.), 1.4628, 0.9285; C_7H_{15}, 182–185 (2 mm.), 1.4631, 0.9222; C_8H_{17}, 193–196 (4 mm.), 1.4640, 0.9193; γ-cyclohexylpropyl alkylacetic acids [$C_6H_{11}(CH_2)_3CH(CO_2H)R$], C_2H_5, 146–147 (2 mm.), 1.4622, 0.9509; C_3H_7, 148–150 (2 mm.), 1.4627, 0.9419; C_4H_9, 153–154 (2 mm.), 1.4630, 0.9317; C_5H_{11}, 188–192 (5 mm.), 1.4634, 0.9266; C_6H_{13}, 208–211 (8 mm.), 1.4638, 0.9221; C_7H_{15}, 199–203 (2 mm.), 1.4642, 0.9137; δ-cyclohexylbutyl alkylacetic acids [$C_6H_{11}(CH_2)_4$-

CH(CO$_2$H)R], C$_2$H$_5$, 173–175 (3 mm.), 1.4622, 0.9447; C$_3$H$_7$, 156–158 (1 mm.), 1.4627, 0.9408; C$_4$H$_9$, 178–180 (4 mm.), 1.4631, 0.9300; C$_5$H$_{11}$, 207–209 (8 mm.), 1.4633, 0.9254; C$_6$H$_{13}$, 187–189 (1 mm.), 1.4638, 0.9191. Several di(cyclohexylalkyl)acetic acids have been synthesized by Davies and Adams [331] and have been investigated for bactericidal activity, *in vitro*, against *B. leprae*. The results obtained showed that the presence of a second ring in the acid molecule does not increase its effectiveness. The di(ω-cyclohexylalkyl)acetic acids have the following general formula:

$$\begin{array}{c} \text{CH}_2 \\ \text{CH}_2 \quad \text{CH}-(\text{CH}_2)_x-\text{CH}-(\text{CH}_2)_y-\text{CH} \quad \text{CH}_2 \\ \text{CH}_2 \quad \text{CH}_2 \qquad \text{CO}_2\text{H} \qquad \text{CH}_2 \quad \text{CH}_2 \\ \text{CH}_2 \qquad\qquad\qquad\qquad \text{CH}_2 \end{array}$$

The following physical constants were reported: (x, y, $b°$C., $m°$C., n_D^{25}, d_4^{20}) 0, 2, 182–186 (4 mm.), —, 1.4852, 0.9915; 1, 2, 207–208 (5 mm.), 50–51, —, —; 2, 2, 210–213 (1.5 mm.), 73–76, —, —; 2, 3, 213–214 (3 mm.), 46.5–47, —, —; 3, 3, 216–218 (3 mm.), 42.5–45, —, —; 2, 4, 221–223 (4 mm.), —, 1.4831, 0.9647.

Since the many observations which were made upon the bactericidal properties of the synthetic cyclic acids indicated that there was no essential difference between acids containing three-, four-, five-, or six-membered rings, the suppositions that a ring structure is a prerequisite for bactericidal activity against *B. leprae* became open to question. On the other hand, it has been conclusively shown that molecular weight is an important consideration and that only those acids containing sixteen or eighteen carbon atoms possess decided bactericidal activity. These conclusions led Stanley, Jay, and Adams [332] to synthesize and evaluate a series of octadecanoic and hexadecanoic acids in which the carboxyl group varied from a terminal to a center position. The results obtained indicated that a ring structure is unnecessary for bactericidal activity, but that the activity is dependent upon the particular configuration of the acid and, as had previously been shown, upon its molecular weight. Acids containing a terminal carboxyl group were not effective, *in vitro*, against *B. leprae*, and the greatest activity was obtained when the carboxyl group was attached either at or near the middle carbon atom of the chain. The hexadecanoic acids were shown to be somewhat more effective than the

TABLE I

Octadecanoic Acids

Acid	M.P.,°C.	B.P.,°C.	n_D^{25}	d_4^{25}
$CH_3CH(CO_2H)C_{15}H_{31}$	34–35	179–183 (5 mm.)	......	......
$C_2H_5CH(CO_2H)C_{14}H_{29}$	23–24	167–170 (2.5 mm.)	1.4531	0.8767
$C_3H_7CH(CO_2H)C_{13}H_{27}$	31–32	179–183 (5 mm.)	......	......
$C_4H_9CH(CO_2H)C_{12}H_{25}$	23–24	180–184 (4 mm.)	1.4528	0.8743
$C_5H_{11}CH(CO_2H)C_{11}H_{23}$	.....	180–185 (4 mm.)	1.4519	0.8829
$C_6H_{13}CH(CO_2H)C_{10}H_{21}$	.....	182–184 (5 mm.)	1.4527	0.8741
$C_7H_{15}CH(CO_2H)C_9H_{19}$	.....	180–183 (5 mm.)	1.4528	0.8747
$C_8H_{17}CH(CO_2H)C_8H_{17}$	35–36	183–185 (5 mm.)	......	......
$(CH_3)_2CHCH(CO_2H)C_{13}H_{27}$	58–59	178–182 (5 mm.)	......	......
$(CH_3)_2CHCH_2CH(CO_2H)C_{12}H_{25}$	26–27	175–180 (4 mm.)	......	......
$C_2H_5CH(CH_3)CH(CO_2H)C_{12}H_{25}$	38–39	178–183 (6 mm.)	......	......
$C_3H_7CH(CH_3)CH(CO_2H)C_{11}H_{23}$	37–38	175–178 (5 mm.)	......	......

TABLE II

Hexadecanoic Acids

Acid	M.P.,°C.	B.P.,°C.	n_D^{25}	d_4^{25}
$CH_3CH(CO_2H)C_{13}H_{27}$	24	172–173 (2.5 mm.)	1.4453	0.8765
$C_2H_5CH(CO_2H)C_{12}H_{25}$	23	178–179 (3 mm.)	1.4460	0.8808
$C_3H_7CH(CO_2H)C_{11}H_{23}$	16.5–17	178–179 (3 mm.)	1.4460	0.8808
$C_4H_9CH(CO_2H)C_{10}H_{21}$	13–14	175–176 (3 mm.)	1.4458	0.8789
$C_5H_{11}CH(CO_2H)C_9H_{19}$	9–10	178–179 (3 mm.)	1.4518	0.8887
$C_6H_{13}CH(CO_2H)C_8H_{17}$	....	165–168 (2 mm.)	1.4495	0.8768
$C_7H_{15}CH(CO_2H)C_7H_{15}$	26–27	187–189 (4 mm.)	1.4497	0.8771
$(CH_3)_2CHCH_2CH(CO_2H)C_{10}H_{21}$	17.5–18	187–188 (9 mm.)	1.4448	0.8763
$C_2H_5CH(CH_3)CH(CO_2H)C_{10}H_{21}$	38–39	185–186 (9 mm.)	......	......

octadecanoic acids. Table I shows the physical properties of the various octadecanoic acids and Table II of the hexadecanoic acids, as reported by Stanley, Jay, and Adams. The supposition that acids which contain sixteen or eighteen carbon atoms possess the highest bactericidal activity against *B. leprae* has been further substantiated by the work of Armendt and Adams [333] and also of Greer and Adams. [334] The former prepared and tested several dialkylacetic acids containing twelve, thirteen, and fourteen carbon atoms, and the latter prepared and tested a series of pentadecanoic, heptadecanoic, and nonadecanoic acids. The results showed that the dodecanoic acids possessed no bactericidal activity against *B. leprae* whereas the tri- and tetradecanoic acids were only very slightly effective. The pentadecanoic and heptadecanoic acids were not so effective as the previously studied hexadecanoic acids.

The nonadecanoic acids were less active than the octadecanoic acids. These results, therefore, were in complete agreement with previous conclusions. Tables III to VI list the physical constants of the dialkylacetic acids, the pentadecanoic acids, the heptadecanoic acids, and the nonadecanoic acids which were synthesized and investigated by these authors.

TABLE III
DIALKYLACETIC ACIDS

Acid	B.P., °C.	d_4^{20}	n_D^{20}
$C_5H_{11}CH(CO_2H)C_5H_{11}$	141–143 (4 mm.)	0.8900	1.4381
$C_4H_9CH(CO_2H)C_6H_{13}$	134–135 (4 mm.)	0.8945	1.4391
$C_4H_9CH(CO_2H)C_7H_{15}$	148–149 (3 mm.)	0.8911	1.4409
$C_5H_{11}CH(CO_2H)C_6H_{13}$	149–150 (4 mm.)	0.8850	1.4410
$C_4H_9CH(CO_2H)C_8H_{17}$	160–161 (4 mm.)	0.8873	1.4435
$C_5H_{11}CH(CO_2H)C_7H_{15}$	155.5–157 (4 mm.)	0.8900	1.4430
$C_6H_{13}CH(CO_2H)C_6H_{13}$	159–160 (4 mm.)	0.8895	1.4421

TABLE IV
PENTADECANOIC ACIDS

Acid	B.P., °C.	d_4^{20}	n_D^{20}
$CH_3CH(CO_2H)C_{12}H_{25}$	172–175 (2–3 mm.)	m.p. 34–36	
$C_2H_5CH(CO_2H)C_{11}H_{23}$	160–163 (2–3 mm.)	0.8821	1.4455
$C_3H_7CH(CO_2H)C_{10}H_{21}$	164–167 (2–3 mm.)	0.8819	1.4450
$C_4H_9CH(CO_2H)C_9H_{19}$	159–162 (2–3 mm.)	0.8824	1.4459
$C_5H_{11}CH(CO_2H)C_8H_{17}$	161–164 (2–3 mm.)	......	......
$C_6H_{13}CH(CO_2H)C_7H_{15}$	156–159 (1–2 mm.)	0.8806	1.4450

TABLE V
HEPTADECANOIC ACIDS

Acid	B.P., °C.	d_4^{20}	n_D^{20}
$CH_3CH(CO_2H)C_{14}H_{29}$	174–177 (1–2 mm.)	m.p. 45.5–47.5	
$C_2H_5CH(CO_2H)C_{13}H_{27}$	164–168 (1–2 mm.)	0.8810	1.4480
$C_3H_7CH(CO_2H)C_{12}H_{25}$	183–187 (2.5–3.5 mm.)	0.8827	1.4483
$C_4H_9CH(CO_2H)C_{11}H_{23}$	174–177 (2–3 mm.)	0.8783	1.4484
$C_5H_{11}CH(CO_2H)C_{10}H_{21}$	177–182 (2–3 mm.)	......	......
$C_6H_{13}CH(CO_2H)C_9H_{19}$	182–185 (2–3 mm.)	0.8821	1.4489
$C_7H_{15}CH(CO_2H)C_8H_{17}$	184–187 (2–3 mm.)	0.8780	1.4483

TABLE VI
NONADECANOIC ACIDS

Acid	B.P., °C.	d_4^{20}	n_D^{20}
$C_3H_7CH(CO_2H)C_{14}H_{29}$	182–185 (0.5–1.5 mm.)	m.p. 35–37	
$C_5H_{11}CH(CO_2H)C_{12}H_{25}$	184–188 (0.5–1.5 mm.)	0.8752	1.4508
$C_7H_{15}CH(CO_2H)C_{10}H_{21}$	180–184 (0.5–1.5 mm.)	m.p. 31.5–33.5	

The influence of an ethylenic linkage upon the bactericidal activity of the substituted acetic acids has been investigated by Browning, Woodrow, and Adams.[335] The activity of these acids was shown to be similar to that of the saturated acids of equal molecular weight, thus indicating that the presence of a double bond in the hydrocarbon chain has little effect on the action of such acids upon *B. leprae*. Three series of acids were prepared and investigated during this study; namely, undecenyl alkylacetic acids, α,β-unsaturated dialkylacetic acids, and allyl alkylacetic acids. The physical constants which were reported are shown in Tables VII, VIII, and IX.

TABLE VII

UNDECENYL ALKYLACETIC ACIDS

Acid	B.P.,°C.	d_{20}^{20}	n_D^{20}
$C_{11}H_{21}CH(CO_2H)C_4H_9$	175–180 (3 mm.)	0.8929	1.4566
$C_{11}H_{21}CH(CO_2H)C_5H_{11}$	186–190 (3 mm.)	0.8956	1.4575
$C_{11}H_{21}CH(CO_2H)C_6H_{13}$	200–204 (3 mm.)	0.8915	1.4564
$C_{11}H_{21}CH(CO_2H)C_7H_{15}$	205–209 (5 mm.)	0.8870	1.4572

TABLE VIII

α,β-UNSATURATED DIALKYLACETIC ACIDS

Acid	B.P.,°C.	d_{20}^{20}	n_D^{20}
$C_4H_9C(CO_2H)CHC_3H_7$	121–123 (2 mm.)	0.9456	1.4484
$C_7H_{15}C(CO_2H)CHC_6H_{13}$	180–182 (2 mm.)	0.8993	1.4566
$C_8H_{17}C(CO_2H)CHC_7H_{15}$	185–186 (1 mm.)	0.8983	1.4625

TABLE IX

ALLYL ALKYLACETIC ACIDS

Acid	B.P.,°C.	d_4^{20}	n_D^{20}
$C_3H_5CH(CO_2H)C_9H_{19}$	148–150 (3 mm.)	0.9015	1.4510
$C_3H_5CH(CO_2H)C_{10}H_{21}$	149–151 (1–1.5 mm.)	0.8989	1.4520
$C_3H_5CH(CO_2H)C_{11}H_{23}$	167–169 (4 mm.)	0.8953	1.4530
$C_3H_5CH(CO_2H)C_{12}H_{25}$	164–166 (1–2 mm.)	0.8933	1.4540
$C_3H_5CH(CO_2H)C_{13}H_{27}$	179–183 (2.5 mm.)	0.8879	1.4556
$C_3H_5CH(CO_2H)C_{14}H_{29}$	187–188 (2.5 mm.)	0.8865	1.4538

The large number of acids which have been prepared and evaluated for bactericidal activity against *B. leprae* have not only thrown some light upon the reasons for the particular effectiveness of the naturally occurring acids but have also done much to develop generalizations regarding the relationship which exists between bactericidal activity and chemical structure.

PART 5   THE SATURATED DICARBOXYLIC ACIDS

The saturated dicarboxylic acids conform to the general formula $(CH_2)_x(CO_2H)_2$. This series of acids is frequently referred to as the oxalic acid series. The acids are much more soluble in water than the corresponding monocarboxylic acids; however, the lower members possess quite limited solubilities in many organic solvents. Their solubility in water decreases rapidly with increase in molecular weight, and the higher members show many of the characteristics of the high molecular weight monocarboxylic acids. Owing to the presence of two carboxyl groups in the molecule, the dicarboxylic acids form two series of salts, esters, or other derivatives, depending upon whether one or both of the carboxyl groups is saponified, esterified, or otherwise modified. The dicarboxylic acids are, therefore, excellent synthetic agents and have been employed for the preparation of many types of fatty derivatives. It is quite unfortunate that no large natural source or satisfactory commercial synthesis has been developed for the higher members of this series. The dicarboxylic acids are of exceptional interest in the preparation of high molecular weight condensation products, linear polymers, and other materials having plastic properties. Much of the progress which has been made in recent years in the synthetic plastic and textile fields has revolved around these dicarboxylic acids and their simple derivatives. A number of the reaction products of the dicarboxylic acids are discussed in some detail in a later chapter, and this present writing is, therefore, confined to a description of these acids together with their occurrence, methods of preparation, and intramolecular reactions.

Like the members of most other acid series, the various dibasic acids are best known by their common names, and although such names reveal nothing concerning the structures of the various acids, their use will undoubtedly be continued. Several alternate methods of nomenclature have been employed in the chemical literature for these acids, and this situation has led to some confusion and uncertainty regarding the particular acid to which reference is made. In the present accepted method of nomenclature, the carbon atom of the carboxyl group is considered as part of the chain, and the acid is named according to the number of carbon atoms in this chain. Unfortunately, this system was not employed in the earlier chemical literature, the older method being to designate the number of methylene groups present. For example, suberic acid is the common name of the dicarboxylic acid having the formula $(CH_2)_6(CO_2H)_2$. The name suberic acid is derived from suberose, meaning corklike, and probably refers to the fact that suberic acid is one of the products formed by the action of nitric acid upon cork. The approved name for this acid is octanedioic acid, showing that it contains eight carbon atoms. The name which will frequently be encountered in the earlier chemical literature is hexamethylene-1,6-dicarboxylic acid, which indicates a chain of six methylene groups to which are attached two carboxyl groups in terminal positions. Table X shows the common names, formulas, and scientific names of some of the more important saturated dicarboxylic acids.

TABLE X

Common and Scientific Names of Dicarboxylic Acids

Common Name	Formula	Scientific Names	
Oxalic	$(CO_2H)_2$	Ethanedioic	
Malonic	$CH_2(CO_2H)_2$	Propanedioic	
Succinic	$(CH_2)_2(CO_2H)_2$	Butanedioic	
Glutaric	$(CH_2)_3(CO_2H)_2$	Pentanedioic	Trimethylene-1,3-dicarboxylic
Adipic	$(CH_2)_4(CO_2H)_2$	Hexanedioic	Tetramethylene-1,4-dicarboxylic
Pimelic	$(CH_2)_5(CO_2H)_2$	Heptanedioic	Pentamethylene-1,5-dicarboxylic
Suberic	$(CH_2)_6(CO_2H)_2$	Octanedioic	Hexamethylene-1,6-dicarboxylic
Azelaic	$(CH_2)_7(CO_2H)_2$	Nonanedioic	Heptamethylene-1,7-dicarboxylic
Sebacic	$(CH_2)_8(CO_2H)_2$	Decanedioic	Octamethylene-1,8-dicarboxylic
Brassylic	$(CH_2)_{11}(CO_2H)_2$	Tridecanedioic	Undecamethylene-1,11-dicarboxylic
Thapsic	$(CH_2)_{14}(CO_2H)_2$	Hexadecanedioic	Tetradecamethylene-1,14-dicarboxylic
Japanic	$(CH_2)_{19}(CO_2H)_2$	Heneicosanedioic	Nonadecamethylene-1,19-dicarboxylic

The saturated dicarboxylic acids are crystalline solids which can be distilled under a high vacuum without undergoing extensive decomposition. In common with the saturated monobasic acids, the dicarboxylic acids exhibit an alternation in melting points and other physical properties in their solid states. Fairweather [336] has reported that if the melting points are plotted as ordinates and the number of carbon atoms as abscissas, members containing an even number of carbon atoms lie on a curve with a downward slope and those containing an odd number of carbon atoms on a rising curve. Little difference in melting points is observed between members having twenty or more carbon atoms, the curves for the even and odd members being within a few degrees of each other at this point. Thus, in the even series butanedioic acid melts at 185°, hexanedioic acid at 153°, octanedioic acid at 145°, decanedioic acid at 133°, dodecanedioic acid at 129°, tetradecanedioic acid at 126.5°, hexadecanedioic acid at 125°, and octadecanedioic acid at 124°. In the odd series pentanedioic acid melts at 97.5°, heptanedioic acid at 105.7°, nonanedioic acid at 107°, undecanedioic acid and tridecanedioic acid at 113.5°, pentadecanedioic acid at 114.8°, heptadecanedioic acid at 118°, and nonadecanedioic acid at 119.2°. The first member of the odd group, propanedioic acid, is an exception to this generalization since it melts at 132°. The alternation is not observed with the diesters of these acids, Fairweather having observed that the melting points of the diethyl esters of acids containing from seven to thirty-two carbon atoms lie on an ascending curve. In a study of the relative stability of the dibasic acids, Challenor and Thorpe [337] have called attention to the tendency of the even acids to lose an even number of carbon atoms upon oxidation, whereas the odd acids lose an odd number of carbon atoms, the products in both cases being even acids. The saturated dicarboxylic acids exhibit polymorphism and are capable of existing in both stable and unstable forms. This dimorphism has been studied by la Tour,[338] Caspari,[339] and others, who have observed that in azelaic acid the transition $\beta \rightarrow \alpha$ occurs at 74–75° and that the difference in lattice energy is small. The differences in melting points were stated to be too small to be detected by ordinary procedures. Several x-ray investigations, which are discussed in a subsequent chapter, have been made upon the polymorphic forms of these acids. The boiling points of the dicarboxylic acids increase with increase in the number of carbon atoms. Krafft and Noerdlinger [340] have reported the boiling points at 10, 15, 50, and 100 mm. to be as follows: adipic acid, 205.5°, 216.5°, 244.5°, 265°; pimelic acid, 212°, 223°, 251.5°, 272°; suberic acid, 219.5°, 230°, 258.5°, 279°; azelaic acid, 225.5°, 237°, 265°, 286.5°; and sebacic acid, 232°, 243.5°, 273°, 294.5°.

The higher molecular weight dicarboxylic acids do not occur abundantly in nature. The lower molecular weight dibasic acids, however, are of somewhat more frequent occurrence, having been observed in a number of plant juices. Oxalic acid occurs as its potassium acid salt in wood sorrel, as its calcium salt in rhubarh root and several other plants; malonic acid is present in beet roots as the calcium salt, and succinic acid has been stated to occur in grapes, amber, and various plant resins. Lippmann [341] has reported the presence of adipic acid in beet juice and thapsic acid has been observed in the dried roots of *Thapsia garganica*. [342] Azelaic acid has been reported to occur in small amounts in linseed oil [343] and has been identified in the product obtained by the hydrolysis of the fatty material of mold spores. [344] Azelaic acid is one of the products resulting from the oxidation of keratin [345] and has been shown by Nicolet and Liddle [346] to be formed during the spontaneous oxidation of fats. Several investigators have reported the presence of azelaic acid in naturally occurring fatty mixtures. However, since it is one of the products formed during the oxidative cleavage of most of the naturally occurring fatty acids, these observations require confirmation. That atmospheric oxidation can result in the cleavage of unsaturated fatty acids with the formation of dibasic acids is illustrated by the observation of Banks and Hilditch [347] that specimens of ointments removed from Egyptian tombs after 5000 years contained large amounts of azelaic acid. High molecular weight dicarboxylic acids occur in various plant waxes, notably Japan wax. This wax, the principal component of which is palmitic acid, has been observed to contain from 5 to 7% of high molecular weight dibasic acids such as heneicosanedioic acid, docosanedioic acid, and tricosanedioic acid. [348, 349, 350, 351, 352, 353, 354] Since palmitic acid is the principal acid of Japan wax, Schaal [350] has postulated that the high molecular weight dicarboxylic acids are intermediates in its formation in the various plants from which Japan wax is obtained. Tsujimoto [355] has reported the presence of high molecular weight dibasic acids in sumach berry waxes, and it is highly probable that many other plant waxes contain small amounts of such acids.

The question as to whether the dicarboxylic acids are intermediates in the metabolism of certain fatty acids is a subject of considerable interest which has not, as yet, been conclusively settled. Many investigators believe that the dicarboxylic acids are involved in the metabolism of the unsaturated and the shorter-chain saturated acids while others hold a contrary opinion. It is known that the low molecular weight dicarboxylic acids, oxalic and malonic, are exceedingly toxic. The administration of oxalic acid produces hypocalcemia, and the acid also functions as a powerful local irritant.[356] The higher molecular weight dicarboxylic acids, however, are either oxidized in the body or excreted unchanged in the urine. Biological oxidation of the monocarboxylic acids is known to occur at the β carbon atom with the removal of successive pairs of carbon atoms. Flaschenträger and Bernhard [357] have studied the fate of numerous glycerides, salts, and methyl and ethyl esters of individual fatty acids and have stated that saturated acids containing from eight to eleven carbon atoms undergo, in addition to β-oxidation, a small amount of ω-oxidation with the formation of dicarboxylic acids. ω-Oxidation, however, is not observed with those higher molecular weight fatty acids which contain twelve or more carbon atoms. Since few edible fats contain significant amounts of short-chain saturated acids, dicarboxylic acids evidently do not play a major role in ordinary fat metabolism. The higher molecular weight dicarboxylic acids when administered in small amounts are excreted largely unchanged, only a small proportion undergoing β-oxidation. The presence of azelaic acid has been observed in the urine of humans following the administration of tripelargonin and tricaprin.[358] Verkade and coworkers [359] have made an extensive study of the biological oxidation of low molecular weight fatty acids and have expressed the opinion that such acids undergo some initial ω-oxidation with the formation of dicarboxylic acids and then undergo β-oxidation at one or both ends of the molecule. Only small amounts of dicarboxylic acids were found in the urine of dogs after the feeding of triglycerides of short-chain fatty acids. Significant amounts of the shorter-chain dicarboxylic acids were present in the urine after the injection of the disodium salts of dibasic acids. Succinic, adipic, suberic, azelaic, sebacic, and octadecanedioic acids have been observed to be oxidized oxybiotically by sections of liver and kidney; glutaric acid, however, was unaffected.[360] Fats such as elm seed oil, which contain large amounts of the shorter-chain saturated acids, are stated to be objectionable as foods since they cause acidosis owing to the formation of dicarboxylic acids by ω-oxidation.[361] It should be borne in mind, however, that the short-chain acids themselves may be responsible for this effect. Bernhard and Andreae [362] have fed C_4, C_6, C_8, and C_{10} dicarboxylic acids to both humans and dogs, reporting that whereas the C_4 acids were completely oxidized large amounts of the others appeared in the urine unchanged, thus indicating that the dicarboxylic acids are not intermediates in fat metabolism. The large amount of conflicting evidence concerning the role of the dibasic acids in the metabolism of the shorter-chain acids certainly does not warrant any specific generalizations, and much additional work is required before the function of the dibasic acids can be evaluated.

A number of general methods are available for the synthesis of the dicarboxylic acids. Several of these are adaptable to the synthesis of any member of the series although others are limited to the preparation of specific acids. The malonic acid synthesis has been frequently used for their preparation. For example, azelaic acid may be synthesized by the reaction of pentamethylene dibromide with diethyl sodiomalonate, followed by the partial decarboxylation of the resulting tetracarboxylic acid.[363] Dicarboxylic acids can be prepared by Holbe's electrolytic method, which involves the electrolysis between platinum electrodes of a concentrated aqueous solution of the half ester of a lower dicarboxylic acid. Thus ethyl succinate is obtained by the electrolysis of potassium ethyl malonate as follows:[364]

$$2(C_2H_5O_2CCH_2COO) \rightarrow C_2H_5O_2C(CH_2)_2CO_2C_2H_5 + 2CO_2$$

Adipic acid has been prepared from succinic acid, sebacic acid from adipic acid, and octadecanedioic acid from sebacic acid by this method. When acids of different chain lengths are electrolyzed, a mixture of dicarboxylic acids is obtained. For example, the electrolysis of a mixture of potassium ethyl malonate and potassium ethyl suberate yields diethyl azelate, diethyl succinate, and diethyl tetradecanedioate.[365] This electrolytic method, therefore, can be employed for the synthesis of any member of the dicarboxylic acid series above malonic acid. The hydrolysis of the corresponding dinitriles yields dicarboxylic acids, which provides a method for the preparation of dibasic acids from lower dibasic acids by the following series of reactions:

$$R(CO_2H)_2 \rightarrow R(CH_2OH)_2 \rightarrow R(CH_2Br)_2 \rightarrow R(CH_2CN)_2 \rightarrow R(CH_2CO_2H)_2$$

The dinitriles may be prepared by the action of potassium cyanide on α,ω-dihalohydrocarbons. Dibasic acids are frequently obtained by the hydrolysis of ω-cyano acids which can be prepared from ω-hydroxy acids. The ω-hydroxy acids are generally obtained by the partial reduction of dicarboxylic acids or their derivatives. Dibasic acids containing one more carbon atom than the starting acid may be synthesized by this procedure. Dibasic acids can also be prepared from terminally unsaturated acids by halohydrogenation to the ω-halo acid, followed by conversion to the nitrile and hydrolysis to the corresponding acid. Dodecanedioic acid has been prepared from 10-undecenoic acid by the application of this method.[366] Dibasic acids result from the oxidation of the corresponding glycols. The oxidative cleavage of unsaturated fatty acids results in the formation of both mono- and dicarboxylic acids. Thus, azelaic acid may be obtained by the decomposition of oleic acid ozonide,[367] or by the oxidation of oleic acid with chromic acid, potassium permanganate, nitric acid, or other oxidizing agents. Both suberic and azelaic acids result from the oxidation of ricinoleic acid with nitric acid [368, 369] or potassium permanganate.[370] The oxidation of ricinoleic acid with nitric acid has also been reported to yield substantial amounts of pimelic acid.[371] The particular dicarboxylic acid obtained by the oxidation of a specific ethylenic acid or hydroxy acid frequently depends upon the oxidizing agent used and the conditions employed. Variations may be occasioned by a shift in the position of the ethylenic bond during the reaction or by secondary oxidations. Frequently the oxidative cleavage of unsaturated acids yields two or more dicarboxylic acids in addition to several monocarboxylic acids.

The procedures for the synthesis of the dicarboxylic acids which have so far been discussed are applicable, with a few exceptions, to any member of the series. A number of methods for the preparation of specific dicarboxylic acids have been described in the literature, several of these procedures being of considerable academic interest and also of potential industrial importance. The synthesis of adipic acid by the oxidation of cyclohexanol, cyclohexanone, and related compounds falls in this latter category. The preparation of adipic acid has been extensively studied and large amounts of this acid have been prepared by these various methods. A convenient method for the preparation of pimelic acid is its synthesis from piperidine.[372] Treatment of the benzoyl derivative of piperidine with phosphorus pentachloride yields 1,5-dichloropentane, which is converted to the dinitrile and hydrolyzed to pimelic acid, as follows:

$$\underset{\text{CH}_2-\text{CH}_2}{\overset{\text{CH}_2-\text{CH}_2}{\diagdown}}\text{N}\underset{\text{O}}{\overset{\parallel}{\text{CC}_6\text{H}_5}} \xrightarrow{\text{PCl}_5} \underset{\text{CH}_2-\text{CH}_2-\text{N}=\overset{\mid}{\underset{\text{Cl}}{\text{C}}}-\text{C}_6\text{H}_5}{\overset{\text{CH}_2-\text{CH}_2-\text{Cl}}{\diagup}} \xrightarrow{\Delta}$$

$$\underset{\text{CH}_2-\text{CH}_2-\text{Cl}}{\overset{\text{CH}_2-\text{CH}_2-\text{Cl}}{\diagdown}}\text{CH}_2 \quad + \text{C}_6\text{H}_5\text{CN}$$

$$\underset{\text{CH}_2-\text{CH}_2-\text{Cl}}{\overset{\text{CH}_2-\text{CH}_2-\text{Cl}}{\diagdown}}\text{CH}_2 \xrightarrow{\text{KCN}} \underset{\text{CH}_2-\text{CH}_2-\text{CN}}{\overset{\text{CH}_2-\text{CH}_2-\text{CN}}{\diagdown}}\text{CH}_2 \xrightarrow{\text{HOH}} \underset{\text{CH}_2-\text{CH}_2-\text{CO}_2\text{H}}{\overset{\text{CH}_2-\text{CH}_2-\text{CO}_2\text{H}}{\diagdown}}\text{CH}_2$$

The oxidation of various natural products has been observed to yield dibasic acids. For example, oxalic acid is obtained by the oxidation of carbohydrates with nitric acid or by the fusion of cellulose with alkalies. Suberic acid is obtained by the action of nitric acid on cork. Such processes are frequently used for the commercial preparation of specific dibasic acids.

Anhydride and ketone formation with the dicarboxylic acids presents a more complicated problem than with the monocarboxylic acids. Anhydride formation in the monobasic acids simply involves the loss of a molecule of water from two acid molecules, which results in the formation of either simple or mixed acid anhydrides. Ketone formation with the monocarboxylic acids takes place with the loss of carbon dioxide and water from two molecules of acids. Owing to the polyfunctional nature of the dicarboxylic acids, anhydride formation may produce linear polymers, some of which have been shown to be of quite high molecular weight, or it may result in cyclic anhydrides which incorporate one or more of the acid molecules into the ring structure. The studies of Hill and Carothers upon anhydride formation with the dicarboxylic acids and upon the formation and stability of large rings, combined with the previous work of Ruzicka upon the formation of cyclic ketones from the dibasic acids, are classical examples of scientific investigations.

Ketones are formed from the dicarboxylic acids by heating the acids in the presence of catalytic materials such as iron filings; by decomposition of the calcium, thorium, or other alkaline earth or rare earth salts of the acids; by passing the acid vapors over metallic oxides; or by heating the acids themselves. The methods used for the preparation of ketones from the dibasic acids are, therefore, similar in principle to those employed for the formation of ketones from the monobasic acids. With the dibasic acids, however, ketone formation is attended by a very marked degree of cyclization. The amount of cyclic ketone obtained is dependent upon the specific dibasic acid and, to a very great extent, upon the reaction conditions. The cyclic ketones formed from the dicarboxylic acids are of two types: monoketones resulting from an intramolecular cyclization (I) and cyclic ketones formed by the condensation of two molecules of acid (II), as shown in the following equations:

$$
\begin{array}{ccccc}
CH_2 & & CH_2CO_2H & & CH_2COCH_2 \\
(CH_2)_x \quad CO & \leftarrow & (CH_2)_x & \rightarrow & (CH_2)_x \quad (CH_2)_x \\
CH_2 & & CH_2CO_2H & & CH_2COCH_2 \\
I & & & & II
\end{array}
$$

Ruzicka and coworkers [373] have stated that on the basis of their relative ease of formation carbon rings may be arranged in three classes: 5- and 6-membered rings, 4- and 7-membered rings, and 8- and higher-membered rings. The 5- and 6-membered rings are characterized by their ease of formation and stability. Cyclopentanone results from the dry distillation of the calcium salt [374, 375] or the barium salt [376, 377] of adipic acid. It is also formed by heating adipic acid in the presence of metallic oxides such as manganous oxide,[378] thorium oxide,[379] or barium oxide,[379] or in the presence of various salts [380] or other catalysts.[381] Aschan [382] has claimed the formation of cyclopentanone by heating adipic acid in the presence of carbon dioxide. Cyclohexanone results from the dry distillation of the calcium salt of pimelic acid,[383] cyclooctanone is prepared from azelaic acid,[383, 384, 385, 386] and the dry distillation of calcium suberate yields cyclononanone (suberone).[387, 388] Harries and Tank [389] have stated that the dry distillation of calcium azelate yields a mixture of cyclic ketones. The preparation of cyclic ketones by the heating of dibasic acids in the presence of metallic catalysts has been patented.[390] The catalytic process was observed to give high yields of cyclopentanone from adipic acid;[391] however, the results were not satisfactory for the preparation of cyclononanone.[392] Vogel,[393] on the other hand, has reported a 40% yield of suberone when suberic acid is heated with an equal weight of iron filings mixed with 5% of barium oxide. This latter author expressed the opinion that ketone formation takes place in two stages; namely, anhydride formation and the loss of carbon dioxide, thus:

$$\begin{array}{c} CH_2CH_2CH_2CO_2H \\ | \\ CH_2CH_2CH_2CO_2H \end{array} \xrightarrow{-H_2O} \begin{array}{c} CH_2CH_2CH_2CO \\ \diagdown O \\ CH_2CH_2CH_2CO \diagup \end{array} \xrightarrow{-CO_2} \begin{array}{c} CH_2CH_2CH_2 \\ | \diagdown CO \\ CH_2CH_2CH_2 \diagup \end{array}$$

An alternate mechanism is as follows:

$$\begin{array}{c} CH_2CH_2CH_2CO_2H \\ | \\ CH_2CH_2CH_2CO_2H \end{array} \xrightarrow{-H_2O} \begin{array}{c} CH_2CH_2CHCO_2H \\ | \diagdown CO \\ CH_2CH_2CH_2 \diagup \end{array} \xrightarrow{-CO_2} \begin{array}{c} CH_2CH_2CH_2 \\ | \diagdown CO \\ CH_2CH_2CH_2 \diagup \end{array}$$

The intermediate formation of iron soap affords another possible mechanism.

The preparation of cyclic ketones by the dry distillation of the thorium, cerium, yttrium, or other rare earth salts of the dibasic acids has been extensively investigated.[373, 393, 394] Ruzicka and coworkers have described the preparation and properties of cyclic ketones containing a large number of carbon atoms in the rings. The decomposition of the thorium salts gave cyclic ketones, the yields decreasing as the number of carbon atoms in the ring increases from nine to seventeen.[395] Higher yields were obtained, however, for ketones containing eighteen or more carbon atoms. The yield of cyclic ketones of nine or more carbon atoms is quite small, being about 1.5% for the 9-membered ketone, 0.1–0.2% for the 10-membered ketone, and so on. All the cyclic ketones which contain twelve or more carbon atoms are solids which resemble camphor in appearance; the odor of the 10- to 12-membered ketones is quite similar to that of camphor, the 13-membered ketone has a cedar wood odor, and those containing from 14 to 18 carbon atoms have a musklike odor. Cycloheptadecanone is identical with dihydrocivetone, the formula for civetone having been previously ascertained to be $CH_2(CH_2)_6CH:CH(CH_2)_7CO$.[396] The following physical constants have been reported for the cyclic ketones which contain from 10 to 18 carbon atoms: C_{10}, b_{12} 100–102°; C_{11}, b_{12} 110°; C_{12}, m.p. 59°, b_{12} 126–128°; C_{13}, m.p. 32°, b_{12} 137–139°; C_{14}, m.p. 52°, b_{12} 155–156°; C_{15}, m.p. 63°, $b_{0.3}$ 120°;

C_{16}, m.p. 56°, $b_{0.5}$ 138°; C_{17}, m.p. 63°, $b_{0.3}$ 140°; and C_{18}, m.p. 71°, $b_{0.3}$ 157–159°. The yield of cyclic ketone is dependent to a large extent upon the particular salt decomposed. Ruzicka and Brugger [386] have reported a 10% yield of cyclononanone by the distillation of calcium azelate, whereas the cerium, zirconium, and lead salts yielded 10, 2, and 2%, respectively. Much higher yields of cyclic ketones were obtained with the lower dibasic acids,[373] although the yields were largely dependent upon the particular salt pyrolyzed. The copper salt of adipic acid gave 43% of cyclopentanone, the lead salt 35%, and the thallium salt 15%. The thallium salt of pimelic acid gave 75–80% of cyclohexanone, and the thallium or cerium salt of suberic acid yielded 45% of cycloheptanone. The formation of a cyclic diketone has been observed by Ruzicka, Stoll, and Schinz [397] during the pyrolysis of the yttrium salt of dodecanedioic acid, the amount of diketone formed, however, being less than that of the monomeric cyclic ketone. Several other high molecular weight dibasic acids yield small amounts of diketones together with monomeric ketones upon the dry distillation of their salts. The pyrolysis of the cerium salt of tetracosanedioic acid, $(CH_2)_{22}(CO_2H)_2$, has been observed to yield 2% of cyclotricosanone, no C_{46} ketone being formed.[398] It must be borne in mind that the yields obtained during the formation of cyclic ketones from the high molecular weight dibasic acids are exceedingly low, which indicates that reactions other than cyclization must take place. A further study of these products should throw light upon the actual mechanism of these decompositions.

Anhydride formation involving the dicarboxylic acids results in the formation either of linear polymers of high molecular weight or of cyclic compounds containing one or more structural units. The possibility that the dicarboxylic acids can form cyclic monomeric anhydrides was probably first suggested by Anschütz [399] during his study of the action of acetyl chloride on dibasic acids. Anhydride formation results when the dibasic acids are treated with dehydrating agents such as acetyl chloride or acetic anhydride.

All the cyclic anhydrides of the dibasic acids containing from three to ten carbon atoms are known, and of these acids only succinic and glutaric form monomeric anhydrides.[400] These two acids form monomeric rings containing five and six atoms respectively. Adipic anhydride, which was prepared by Voerman [401] and later by Farmer and Kracovski,[402] was subsequently shown by

Hill [403] to be polymeric. The monomer melts at 22° and the dimer at 81–85°. Sebacic anhydride has been shown to be a linear polymer of high molecular weight.[404] Monomeric anhydrides can be distinguished from polymeric anhydrides by their behavior with aniline.[404] The monomer when treated with this reagent yields only the monoanilide; however, the polymer gives a mixture of the dianilide, the monoanilide, and the dibasic acid in the ratio 1, 2, 1. The preparation of pimelic anhydride by heating the acid with acetic anhydride has been described.[405] In a study of anhydride formation with those dibasic acids which contain from seven to eighteen carbon atoms, Hill and Carothers [406] have shown that the action of acetic anhydride or of acetyl chloride on these acids first forms linear polymers (α-anhydrides) whose structure is represented by —O—CO—R—CO—O—CO—R—CO—O—CO— R—CO—. These polymers have molecular weights from 3000 to 5000. Distillation under a high vacuum produces the so-called β-, γ-, and ω-anhydrides according to the following diagram:

α-Anhydride, linear polymer, $\rightarrow$ β-Anhydride (distillate),
mol. wt. *ca.* 5000 cyclic monomer or dimer
$\downarrow$ $\nearrow$ $\downarrow \uparrow$
ω-Anhydride, super polymer, γ-Anhydride, linear polymer
very high molecular weight (similar to α-anhydride)

These authors state that the α- and γ-anhydrides are practically identical in physical properties, the latter probably being composed of very large rings whereas the former possess a chain structure. Adipic acid yields a monomeric β-anhydride containing seven atoms in the ring. Monomeric β-anhydrides are also encountered with pimelic, azelaic, undecanedioic, brassylic, tetradecanedioic, and octadecanedioic acids. Adipic β-anhydride polymerizes completely after heating at 100° for seven hours. The 8-, 10-, and 12-membered rings are extremely unstable. The 14-membered ring is more stable than the 8-, 10-, or 12-membered ring, and the 15- and 19-membered rings are comparatively stable. Suberic, sebacic, and dodecanedioic acids, on the other hand, form only dimeric anhydrides which contain 18, 22, and 26 atoms in the rings, and these anhydrides are stable up to their melting points. The melting points reported for the α-anhydrides as given by these authors are as follows: pimelic, 53–55°; suberic, 65–66°; azelaic, 53–53.5°; undecanedioic, 69–70°; dodecanedioic, 86–87°; brassylic, 76–78°; tetradecanedioic, 89–91°; octadecanedioic, 94–95°. The physical constants of the cyclic anhydrides as reported by Hill and Carothers [406] are shown in Table XI.

TABLE XI

CYCLIC ANHYDRIDES

Acid	Structural Unit of Anhydride	Product of Depolymerization and Size of Ring		Stability	M.P.
Adipic	—OC(CH$_2$)$_4$CO—O—	Monomer	7	Unstable	20
Pimelic	—OC(CH$_2$)$_5$CO—O—	Monomer	8	Extremely unstable	Liq.
Suberic	—OC(CH$_2$)$_6$CO—O—	Dimer	18	Stable up to m.p.	56.7
Azelaic	—OC(CH$_2$)$_7$CO—O—	Monomer	10	Extremely unstable	Liq.
Sebacic	—OC(CH$_2$)$_8$CO—O—	Dimer	22	Stable up to m.p.	68
Undecanedioic	—OC(CH$_2$)$_9$CO—O—	Monomer	12	Extremely unstable	Liq.
Dodecanedioic	—OC(CH$_2$)$_{10}$CO—O—	Dimer	26	Stable up to m.p.	76–78
Brassylic	—OC(CH$_2$)$_{11}$CO—O—	Monomer	14	Unstable	Liq.
Tetradecanedioic	—OC(CH$_2$)$_{12}$CO—O—	Monomer	15	Unstable	Liq.
Octadecanedioic	—OC(CH$_2$)$_{16}$CO—O—	Monomer	19	Unstable	36–37

The cyclic anhydrides differ from the cyclic ketones in that the anhydrides form either monomers or dimers but not mixtures of the two. Those containing nine or more carbon atoms possess odors qualitatively similar to the cyclic ketones, the 15-membered anhydride having the odor of musk.[407] The fact that large rings may exist in a strainless form has been suggested by Mohr.[408] In their discussion of the mechanism of formation and the stability of large rings, Carothers and Hill [409] have stated that the formation of macrocyclic ketones involves the preliminary formation of a linear polyketone which is subsequently decomposed into cyclic ketones. The mechanism of cyclic ketone formation, therefore, is probably similar to that involved in anhydride formation. It had previously been assumed that cyclic ketone formation was entirely an intramolecular reaction.

The following contains a description of the preparation and properties of the saturated dicarboxylic acids containing six or more carbon atoms.

Hexanedioic Acid (Adipic Acid). $(CH_2)_4(CO_2H)_2$

Adipic acid has been prepared by the saponification of 1,4-dicyanobutane, which can be obtained by the action of potassium cyanide on 1,4-dibromo- or 1,4-diiodobutane.[410, 411] The acid has been obtained by the treatment of 3-iodopropionic acid with metallic silver [412] or metallic copper.[413] Brown and Walker [364] have described the preparation of adipic acid by the electrolysis of potassium ethyl succinate. Adipic acid is one of the products formed by the oxidation of castor oil with nitric acid.[414] The preparation of adipic acid by the oxidation of various cyclohexane and cyclohexene derivatives has been extensively investigated and offers a commercial source of this acid. Mannich [415] first announced the synthesis of adipic acid by the oxidation of cyclohexenyl acetate with potassium permanganate in alkaline solution, and two months later Rosenlew [416] described the preparation of adipic acid by the oxidation of cyclohexanone under similar conditions. The oxidation of either cyclohexanol or cyclohexanone with alkaline potassium permanganate has been studied by several investigators.[417, 418, 419] The oxidation of cyclohexanol or of cyclohexanone with nitric acid, which was first studied by Zélinsky,[420] has proved to be a satisfactory method for the synthesis of adipic acid and has frequently been employed.[377, 380, 421, 422] The various methods have been the subject of several patents.[423, 424, 425] Directions for the oxidation of cyclohexanol with nitric acid in the presence of ammonium vanadate have been published by Ellis.[426] More recently, Foster [427] has introduced certain modifications and has reported yields as high as 72% of the theoretical. The preparation of adipic acid by the oxidation of cyclohexene with solutions of potassium dichromate in the presence of sulfuric acid has been described,[428] and in 1940 Aronow [429] patented a continuous method for the preparation of adipic acid by the oxidation of cyclohexanol with nitric acid. The formation of adipic acid by the oxidation of 6-membered carbon rings simply involves a ring cleavage with the oxidation of two adjacent carbon atoms to carboxyl groups, the oxidation either being initiated at an ethylenic linkage or upon a substituted carbon atom. For example, the oxidation of cyclohexanol proceeds as follows:

$$\text{cyclohexanol} \xrightarrow{(40)} \text{adipic acid}$$

The oxidation of cyclohexanone may take place thus:

$$\text{cyclohexanone} \rightleftharpoons \text{enol} \xrightarrow{(30)} \text{adipic acid}$$

The intermediate products of these oxidations have not been isolated. Harries and coworkers [430, 431] have investigated the preparation of cyclohexene ozonide and its decomposition into adipic acid.

Adipic acid melts at $153.0-153.1°$ [432] and has the following boiling points: b_{10} $205.5°$, b_{15} $216.5°$, b_{50} $244.5°$, and b_{100} $265°$. [340] It is easily soluble in ethanol; 1.44 parts dissolve in 100 parts of water at $15°$, and 0.605 part dissolves in 100 parts of ether at $19°$.

Heptanedioic Acid (Pimelic Acid). $(CH_2)_5(CO_2H)_2$

Pimelic acid has been obtained by the saponification of the corresponding nitrile [433] and by the action of carbon dioxide on pentamethylene-1,5-dimagnesium dibromide. [434] Carpenter and Perkin [435] have prepared pimelic acid by the action of the sodium derivative of cyanoacetic ester and trimethylene dibromide followed by the saponification of the resulting product. The acid has also been prepared by the oxidation of 7-aminoenanthic acid [436] and by the malonic acid method. [437] Gantter and Hell [371] have observed that pimelic acid is one of the products formed during the oxidation of ricinoleic acid. A 60% yield of pimelic acid has been obtained by v. Braun [372] by the action of phosphorus pentachloride or pentabromide on the benzoyl derivative of piperidine, followed by conversion of the resulting 1,5-dihalopentane to the dinitrile and saponification of this latter compound.

Pimelic acid melts at $105.7-105.8°$ [432] and has the following boiling points: b_{10} $212°$, b_{15} $223°$, b_{50} $251.5°$, and b_{100} $272°$. [340] The acid is soluble in water to the extent of 2.52 parts in 100 parts at $13.5°$. It is easily soluble in ethanol and ether and almost insoluble in cold benzene.

Octanedioic Acid (Suberic Acid). $(CH_2)_6(CO_2H)_2$

Suberic acid derives its name from the fact that it is one of the products of the action of nitric acid on cork. It is also obtained, along with azelaic acid, in the oxidation of castor oil with nitric acid, [368, 438] and has been reported to be contained in the oxidation products of several other fats and oils. [439, 440] It has been separated from azelaic acid by virtue of the greater water solubility of its calcium or magnesium salt. [369, 384] Suberic acid has been prepared by the electrolysis of potassium ethyl glutarate. [441] The acid has been obtained by the oxidation of cyclooctane with nitric acid [442] or chromic acid. [443] Zelinsky and Gutt [444] have prepared suberic acid by the action of carbon dioxide on the residue obtained from the reaction of magnesium and trimethylene dibromide.

Suberic acid melts at $114°$ [418] and has the following boiling points: [340] b_{10} 219.5°, b_{15} 230°, b_{50} 258.5°, and b_{100} 279°. Partial anhydride formation results when the acid is distilled at ordinary temperatures. [445] The acid is soluble in ethanol and somewhat soluble in water (0.08 part in 100 cc. at 0°, 0.98 part at 50°, and 2.22 parts at 65°). It is soluble to the extent of 0.8 part in 100 parts of ether at 15°.

Nonanedioic Acid (Azelaic Acid). $(CH_2)_7(CO_2H)_2$

Azelaic acid is perhaps the best known of the high molecular weight dicarboxylic acids, since it is one of the products resulting from the oxidation of many of the naturally occurring fatty acids. The oxidative cleavage of oleic acid with potassium permanganate yields azelaic acid together with pelargonic acid. [446, 447] High yields of azelaic and pelargonic acids are obtained by the oxidation of oleic acid with potassium permanganate in acetone solution. [448] The oxidation of oleic acid or castor oil with nitric acid frequently yields a mixture of azelaic and suberic acids [369] and has been the subject of a recent patent. [449] The preparation of azelaic acid by the oxidation of ricinoleic acid with alkaline potassium permanganate has been described by Hill and McEwen. [450] The decomposition of oleic acid ozonide yields azelaic acid, pelargonic acid, azelaic acid semi-aldehyde, and nonanal. [367, 451] The oxidation of either di- or polyethylenic acids generally yields azelaic acid together with monocarboxylic and other dicarboxylic acids. [452, 453, 454] Acetylenic acids yield a mixture of azelaic and suberic acids together with monobasic acids upon oxidation. [30, 455, 456] Azelaic acid is one of the products of the spontaneous combustion of fats. [346, 457] The oxidation of 9,10-dihydroxystearic acid by potassium permanganate or other oxidizing agents yields both azelaic and pelargonic acids. [458, 459] Azelaic acid has been prepared by several methods in addition to the above described oxidative procedures. Among these may be mentioned Haworth and Perkin's [373] malonic ester synthesis using pentamethylene dibromide and diethyl sodiomalonate.

Azelaic acid melts at 107° [460] and has the following boiling points: b_{10} 225.5°, b_{15} 237°, b_{50} 265°, and b_{100} 286.5°. [340] The acid is dimorphic, the β-modification separating from a warm saturated solution and the α-modification being formed by the slow evaporation of its solution at ordinary temperatures.[339]   It is only slightly soluble in cold water (0.1 g. in 100 cc. at 0°; 0.212 g. at 22°) but is somewhat more soluble at elevated temperatures (1.648 g. at 55°; 2.2 g. at 65°).[461, 462] It is extremely soluble in ethanol and is soluble in ether (2.68 parts in 100 parts at 15°).

Decanedioic Acid (Sebacic Acid). $(CH_2)_8(CO_2H)_2$

Sebacic acid results from the dry distillation of castor oil or ricinoleic acid in the presence of sodium hydroxide.[463] Boedtker [464] has studied the preparation of sebacic acid by this method and has offered a possible reaction mechanism.   Verkade, Hartman, and Coops [465] have prepared the acid by this procedure and recently Bruson and Covert [466] have claimed that higher yields are obtained if the reaction is conducted under pressure.   Sebacic acid can easily be prepared by the oxidation of 10-undecenoic acid,[162, 465] one of the products resulting from the oxidation of castor oil.   The electrolysis of an aqueous solution of potassium ethyl adipate yields the diethyl ester of sebacic acid.[441]

Sebacic acid melts at 133° and has the following boiling points: b_{10} 232°, b_{15} 243.5°, b_{50} 273°, and b_{100} 294.5°.[340] It is very slightly soluble in cold water [461] (0.004 g. in 100 cc. at 0°) and slightly soluble in hot water (0.42 g. in 100 cc. at 65°; 2.0 g. in 100 cc. at 100°).   It is easily soluble in ethanol and ether.

The Higher Molecular Weight Dicarboxylic Acids

The dicarboxylic acids containing from eleven to twenty-four carbon atoms and also a few of the quite high molecular weight aliphatic dibasic acids have been prepared and described.   The higher molecular weight dibasic acids are essentially insoluble in water but soluble in ethanol and ether.   The melting points of those acids which contain twenty or more carbon atoms differ only slightly from each other irrespective of whether the acids contain an even or an odd number of carbon atoms.   The melting points of the even acids below twenty carbon atoms fall upon a descending curve, but those of the odd acids fall upon an ascending curve.   A variety of methods have been employed for the synthesis of these higher dicarboxylic acids, some of which methods are of general application whereas others pertain rather specifically to an individual acid.   Walker and Lumsden [467] have obtained un-decanedioic acid, $(CH_2)_9(CO_2H)_2$, by the oxidation of 11-hydroxy-undecanoic acid with chromic acid in acetic acid solution.   Dodecanedioic acid has also been prepared from 11-hydroxyundecanoic acid by conversion of the hydroxy acid to 11-bromoundecanoic acid and thence to the nitrile, which is saponified.[366, 467] The hydrolysis of the dinitrile prepared from 1,10-diiodododecane yields dodecanedioic acid.[468] Chuit,[469] using nonanedioic and decanedioic acids and employing either the nitrile or the malonic acid method, has synthesized the members of the dicarboxylic acid series containing from eleven to nineteen carbon atoms. The following melting points were reported by this author: C_{11}, 111°; C_{12}, 128°; C_{13}, 113–113.2°; C_{14}, 125.8°; C_{15}, 114.6–114.8°; C_{16}, 125–125.2°; C_{17}, 118°; C_{18}, 124.6–124.8°; and C_{19}, 119.2°. Several of these syntheses were later repeated by Chuit and Hausser.[470] The malonic acid method is frequently resorted to for the preparation of these acids because of its convenience.[471] Tridecanedioic acid, brassylic acid, results from the oxidative cleavage of the ethylenic bonds of erucic or brassidic acid.[465, 472, 473] The oxidation of behenolic acid by means of nitric acid yields brassylic acid.[474] It has also been obtained by the condensation of ethyl 11-bromoundecanoate and diethyl sodiomalonate, followed by saponification and partial decarboxylation of the resulting tricarboxylic acid.[467, 475] The electrolytic method has frequently been employed as a means of obtaining the higher molecular weight dibasic acids. Tetradecanedioic acid, $(CH_2)_{12}(CO_2H)_2$, results from the electrolysis of potassium ethyl suberate;[365, 441] hexadecanedioic acid, thapsic acid, is obtained by the electrolysis of potassium ethyl azelate;[365] while octadecanedioic acid results from the electrolysis of potassium ethyl sebacate.[441] Thapsic acid is said to be contained in the rosin-like extract obtained from the dried roots of *Thapsia garganica*.[342]

Only a few dicarboxylic acids containing twenty or more carbon atoms have been described. At least one, and perhaps several, high molecular weight dibasic acids are present in Japan wax. This wax has been reported to contain from 6 to 7% of higher dicarboxylic acids. The name Japanic acid is most frequently associated with heneicosanedioic acid, $(CH_2)_{19}(CO_2H)_2$, although it more properly refers to the mixture of dibasic acids obtained from this wax. Heneicosanedioic acid was first recognized as a component of Japan wax in 1888 by Eberhardt.[476] The wax consists chiefly of palmitin. Japanic acid was first reported to be docosanedioic acid,[348] but later Schaal [350] stated that the dibasic acids of Japan wax consist principally of heneicosanedioic acid, $(CH_2)_{19}(CO_2H)_2$ (Japanic acid), together with eicosanedioic acid and nonadecanedioic acid. Tsujimoto [354] observed in 1931 that the main constituent of the dibasic acids of Japan wax is tricosanedioic acid, $(CH_2)_{21}(CO_2H)_2$, melting at 123.5°, together with a smaller amount of docosanedioic acid, $(CH_2)_{20}(CO_2H)_2$, and several years later these conclusions were apparently verified. In 1940, Shiina [477] isolated docosanedioic acid melting at 125.7–126.3° from Japan wax. Flaschenträger and Halle [353] obtained from Japan wax tricosanedioic acid, which they reported to melt at 127.5°; however, they could not identify heneicosanedioic acid as a component of this wax. It has been observed [397] that the distillation of the thallium salts of the dibasic acids of Japan wax yields substantial quantities of cycloeicosanone, thus indicating the presence of heneicosanedioic acid. It is quite evident that, although the presence of high molecular weight dibasic acids in Japan wax has been established, the actual identity of these acids is not as yet definitely determined.

Our knowledge of the higher molecular weight dibasic acids is not confined to the naturally occurring acids since several such acids have been synthesized and described. Ruzicka, Stoll, and Schinz [397] have obtained heneicosanedioic acid by electrolyzing a mixture of sodium 7-octenoate and the sodium salt of the monomethyl ester of hexadecanedioic acid, followed by ozonolysis of the resulting 21-docosenoic acid. The reactions involved are as follows:

$$CH_2{:}CH(CH_2)_5CO_2H + CH_3O_2C(CH_2)_{14}CO_2H \rightarrow$$
$$CH_2{:}CH(CH_2)_{19}CO_2CH_3 \xrightarrow{O_3} (CH_2)_{19}(CO_2H)_2$$

Fairweather [336] has prepared docosanedioic acid, m.p. 123.8°, hexacosanedioic acid, m.p. 123.5°, triacontanedioic acid, m.p. 123.5°, and tetratriacontanedioic acid, m.p. 123°, by the electrolytic method. Recently, Shiina [478] has synthesized both docosanedioic acid and tetracosanedioic acid by the nitrile method, using eicosanedioic acid as the starting material.

References

1. Kuhn and Meyer, *Z. physiol. Chem.*, **185**, 193 (1929).
2. Böeseken and Slooff, *Rec. trav. chim.*, **49**, 95 (1930).
3. Overbeck, *Ann.*, **140**, 39 (1866).
4. Baruch, *Ber.*, **27**, 172 (1894).
5. Haussknecht, *Ann.*, **143**, 40 (1867).
6. Chablay, *Compt. rend.*, **142**, 93 (1906).

7. Wislicenus and Schmidt, *Ann.*, **313**, 210 (1900).

8. Bodroux, *Compt. rend.*, **208**, 1022 (1939).

9. Tishchenko, Shabashova, and Sysoeva, *J. Gen. Chem. (U.S.S.R.)*, **10**, 1042 (1940).

10. Perkin and Simonsen, *J. Chem. Soc.*, **91**, 816 (1907).

11. Gardner and Perkin, *ibid.*, **91**, 848 (1907).

12. Faworsky and Jocitsch, *J. Russ. Phys. Chem. Soc.*, **29**, 90 (1897).

13. Dupont, *Compt. rend.*, **148**, 1522 (1909).

14. Faworsky, *J. prakt. Chem.* [2], **37**, 417 (1888).

15. Moureu and Delange, *Compt. rend.*, **136**, 552 (1903); *Bull. soc. chim.* [3], **29**, 648 (1903).

16. Krafft, *Ber.*, **29**, 2232 (1896).

17. Welander, *ibid.*, **28**, 1448 (1895).

18. Bodenstein, *ibid.*, **27**, 3397 (1894).

19. Krafft and Heizmann, *ibid.*, **33**, 3586 (1900).

20. Arnaud, *Compt. rend.*, **114**, 79 (1892); *Bull. soc. chim.* [3], **7**, 233 (1892).

21. Grützner, *Chem.-Ztg.*, **17**, 1851 (1893).

22. Grimme, *Chem. Rev. Fett- u. Harz-Ind.*, **17**, 156 (1910).

23. Steger and van Loon, *Rec. trav. chim.*, **52**, 593 (1933).

24. Vongerichten and Köhler, *Ber.*, **42**, 1638 (1909).

25. Arnaud, *Compt. rend.*, **122**, 1000 (1896).

26. Behrend, *Ber.*, **28**, 2248 (1895).

27. Kino, *J. Soc. Chem. Ind., Japan*, **32**, S.b. 187 (1929).

28. Kimura, *ibid.*, **37**, S.b. 476 (1934).

29. Limpach, *Ann.*, **190**, 294 (1878).

30. Arnaud and Hasenfratz, *Compt. rend.*, **152**, 1603 (1911).

31. Hazura and Grüssner, *Monatsh.*, **9**, 947 (1888).

32. Beckmann, *Ber.*, **19**, 988 (1886).

33. Arnaud and Posternak, *Compt. rend.*, **150**, 1130 (1910).

34. Arnaud and Posternak, *ibid.*, **150**, 1245 (1910).

35. Posternak, *ibid.*, **162**, 944 (1916).

36. Steger and van Loon, *Fette u. Seifen*, **44**, 243 (1937).

37. Castille, *Ann.*, **543**, 104 (1940).

38. Steger and van Loon, *Rec. trav. chim.*, **59**, 1156 (1940).

39. Otto, *Ann.*, **135**, 226 (1865).

40. von Grossmann, *Ber.*, **26**, 639 (1893).

41. Holt, *ibid.*, **25**, 961 (1892).

42. Baruch, *ibid.*, **26**, 1867 (1893).

43. Spieckermann, *ibid.*, **28**, 276 (1895); **29**, 810 (1896).

44. Anderson, Crowder, Newman, and Stodola, *J. Biol. Chem.*, **113**, 637 (1936).

45. Chargaff, *Z. physiol. Chem.*, **217**, 115 (1933).

46. Rabak, *J. Ind. Eng. Chem.*, **12**, 46 (1920).

47. Zetzsche and Sonderegger, *Helv. Chim. Acta*, **14**, 632 (1931).

48. Schneider and Jantsch, *Ges. Abhandl. Kenntnis Kohle*, **4**, 118 (1919).

49. Shoruĭgin and Kreshkov, *J. Gen. Chem. (U.S.S.R.)*, **4**, 988 (1934).

50. Friedmann and Maase, *Biochem. Z.*, **27**, 474 (1910).

51. Chibnall and Piper, *Biochem. J.*, **28**, 2209 (1934).

52. Chernoyarova, *J. Gen. Chem. (U.S.S.R.)*, **10**, 146 (1940).

53. Fittig and Hjelt, *Ann.*, **216**, 52 (1883).
54. Noller with Adams, *J. Am. Chem. Soc.*, **48**, 1074 (1926).
55. Hiers with Adams, *ibid.*, **48**, 1089, 2385 (1926).
56. Tomecko with Adams, *ibid.*, **49**, 522 (1927).
57. Davies and Adams, *ibid.*, **50**, 1749 (1928).
58. v. Braun, *Ber.*, **70B**, 1250 (1937).
59. Hill, U. S. Patent 2,073,799 (1937).
60. Lewkowitsch, *J. Soc. Chem. Ind.*, **16**, 503 (1897).
61. Hinsberg, *Biochem. Z.*, **285**, 125 (1936).
62. Baeyer, *Ber.*, **18**, 2269 (1885).
63. Perkin, *ibid.*, **18**, 3246 (1885).
64. Johansson and Sebelius, *ibid.*, **51**, 480 (1918).
65. Kailan, *Z. physik. Chem.*, **94**, 111 (1920).
66. Kerschbaum, *Ber.*, **60**, 902 (1927).
67. Stoll and Rouvé, *Helv. Chim. Acta*, **18**, 1087 (1935).
68. Stoll and Rouvé, *ibid.*, **17**, 1283 (1934).
69. Stoll and Rouvé, *14me Congr. chim. ind.*, 9 pp. (October, 1934); *Helv. Chim. Acta*, **19**, 1079 (1936).
70. Bougault and Bourdier, *J. pharm. chim.* [6], **29**, 561; **30**, 10 (1909).
71. Chuit and Hausser, *Helv. Chim. Acta*, **12**, 463 (1929).
72. Juslin, *Ber.*, **17**, 2504 (1884).
73. Fittig and Dannenberg, *Ann.*, **331**, 123 (1904).
74. Fittig and MacKenzie, *ibid.*, **283**, 82 (1894).
75. Fittig and Spenzer, *ibid.*, **283**, 66, 80 (1894).
76. Fittig and Messerschmidt, *ibid.*, **208**, 92 (1881).
77. Fittig and Fränkel, *ibid.*, **255**, 18 (1889).
78. Fittig and Wolff, *ibid.*, **208**, 104 (1881).
79. Sabatier and Mailhe, *Ann. chim. phys.* [8], **16**, 70 (1909).
80. Cloves, *Ann.*, **319**, 357 (1901).
81. Fichter and Beisswenger, *Ber.*, **36**, 1200 (1903).
82. Schulze and Likiernik, *ibid.*, **24**, 669 (1891); *Z. physiol. Chem.*, **17**, 513 (1893).
83. Jelissafow, *J. Russ. Phys. Chem. Soc.*, **12**, 367 (1880).
84. Fittig and Baker, *Ann.*, **283**, 117 (1894).
85. Fittig, *ibid.*, **200**, 21 (1880).
86. Fittig and Hjelt, *ibid.*, **208**, 67 (1881).
87. Fittig, *Ber.*, **16**, 373 (1883).
88. Fittig and Dubois, *Ann.*, **256**, 134 (1890).
89. Fittig and Delisle, *ibid.*, **255**, 56 (1889).
90. Kiliani and Kleeman, *Ber.*, **17**, 1296 (1884); Kiliani, *ibid.*, **18**, 1555 (1885); **20**, 339 (1887).
91. Fittig and Wolff, *Ann.*, **216**, 127 (1883).
92. Fichter and Langguth, *Ber.*, **30**, 2050 (1897).
93. Van Natta, Hill, and Carothers, *J. Am. Chem. Soc.*, **56**, 455 (1934).
94. Helms, *Ber.*, **8**, 1167 (1875).
95. Bagard, *Bull. soc. chim.* [4], **1**, 307 (1907).
96. Ley, *J. Russ. Phys. Chem. Soc.*, **9**, 139 (1877).
97. Fittig and Schmidt, *Ann.*, **255**, 68 (1889).
98. Rupe, Ronus, and Lotz, *Ber.*, **35**, 4265 (1902).

99. Fichter and Gully, *ibid.*, **30**, 2047 (1897).
100. Baeyer and Villiger, *ibid.*, **33**, 858 (1900).
101. Erlenmeyer and Sigel, *Ann.*, **177**, 102 (1875).
102. Ley, *Ber.*, **10**, 230 (1877).
103. Blaise and Koehler, *Compt. rend.*, **148**, 1772 (1909).
104. Blaise, *Bull. soc. chim.* [3], **31**, 483 (1904).
105. Wagner, *Ber.*, **27**, 2434 (1894).
106. Fittig and Schneegans, *Ann.*, **227**, 79 (1885).
107. Goldsobel, *Ber.*, **27**, 3121 (1894).
108. Shukoff and Schestakoff, *J. Russ. Phys. Chem. Soc.*, **40**, 830 (1908).
109. Walker and Lumsden, *J. Chem. Soc.*, **79**, 1191 (1901).
110. Guérin, *Bull. soc. chim.* [3], **29**, 1124 (1903).
111. Chuit, Boelsing, Hausser, and Malet, *Helv. Chim. Acta*, **10**, 113 (1927).
112. Bougault, *Compt. rend.*, **150**, 874 (1910).
113. Le Sueur, *J. Chem. Soc.*, **87**, 1888 (1905).
114. Asahina and Terada, *J. Pharm. Soc. Japan*, No. **452**, 821 (1919).
115. Power and Rogerson, *Am. J. Pharm.*, **80**, 251 (1908).
116. Asahina and Shimidzu, *J. Pharm. Soc. Japan*, No. **479**, 1 (1922).
117. Asahina and Nakanishi, *ibid.*, No. **520**, 515 (1925).
118. Müller, *Ber.*, **14**, 2476 (1881).
119. Hell and Twerdomedoff, *ibid.*, **22**, 1745 (1889).
120. Blaise, *Compt. rend.*, **138**, 697 (1904).
121. Taverne, *Rec. trav. chim.*, **13**, 187 (1894).
122. Hoehnel, *Arch. Pharm.*, **234**, 647 (1896).
123. Power and Rogerson, *J. Am. Chem. Soc.*, **32**, 80 (1910); *J. Chem. Soc.*, **101**, 1 (1912).
124. Asahina and Akasu, *J. Pharm. Soc. Japan*, No. **523**, 779 (1925).
125. Ciamician and Silber, *Ber.*, **29**, 1811 (1896).
126. Hell and Jordanoff, *ibid.*, **24**, 936 (1891).
127. Ponzio, *Gazz. chim. ital.*, **35**, II, 132 (1905).
128. Ikuta, *J. Soc. Chem. Ind.*, *Japan*, **36**, S.b. 444 (1933).
129. Le Sueur, *J. Chem. Soc.*, **85**, 827 (1904).
130. Röhmann, *Biochem. Z.*, **77**, 298 (1916).
131. d'Ambrosio, *Ann. chim. applicata*, **16**, 443 (1926).
132. Hell and Sadomsky, *Ber.*, **24**, 2388 (1891).
133. Ponzio, *Gazz. chim. ital.*, **34**, II, 77 (1904).
134. Ponzio, *ibid.*, **35**, II, 569 (1905).
135. M. Saytzeff, C. Saytzeff, and A. Saytzeff, *J. prakt. Chem.* [2], **35**, 369 (1887).
136. Sabaneieff, *J. Russ. Phys. Chem. Soc.*, **18**, 35, 87 (1886).
137. Tscherbakoff and Saytzeff, *J. prakt. Chem.* [2], **57**, 27 (1898).
138. Geitel, *ibid.* [2], **37**, 53 (1888).
139. David, *Compt. rend.*, **124**, 466 (1897).
140. Shukoff, Ger. Patent 150,798 (1902).
141. Saytzeff, *J. Russ. Phys. Chem. Soc.*, **17**, 417 (1885); *J. prakt. Chem.* [2], **33**, 300 (1886).
142. Walden, *Chem. Umschau*, **32**, 275 (1925).
143. Kasansky, *J. Russ. Phys. Chem. Soc.*, **32**, 149 (1900); *J. prakt. Chem.* [2], **62**, 363 (1900).

144. Grün and Woldenberg, *J. Am. Chem. Soc.*, **31**, 490 (1909).
145. Stoll and Gardner, *Helv. Chim. Acta*, **17**, 1609 (1934).
146. Eibner and Münzing, *Chem. Umschau*, **32**, 153 (1925).
147. Panjutin and Rapoport, *ibid.*, **37**, 130 (1930).
148. Bussy and Lecanu, *J. pharm. chim.* [2], **13**, 57 (1827).
149. Bussy, *J. Pharm.* [3], **8**, 321 (1845).
150. Krafft, *Ber.*, **10**, 2034 (1877).
151. Fokin, *J. Russ. Phys. Chem. Soc.*, **46**, 224 (1914).
152. Scheiber, *Farbe u. Lack*, 153 (1929); 513 (1930).
153. Böeseken and Hoevers, *Rec. trav. chim.*, **49**, 1165 (1930).
154. Staněk, *J. prakt. Chem.* [1], **63**, 138 (1854).
155. Leeds, *Ber.*, **16**, 290 (1883).
156. Scheurer-Kestner, *Compt. rend.*, **113**, 201 (1891).
157. Saalmüller, *Ann.*, **64**, 108 (1848).
158. Holt and Baruch, *Ber.*, **26**, 838 (1893).
159. Walden, *ibid.*, **27**, 3471 (1894).
160. Chonowsky, *ibid.*, **42**, 3339 (1909).
161. Haller and Brochet, *Compt. rend.*, **150**, 496 (1910).
162. Noorduyn, *Rec. trav. chim.*, **38**, 317 (1919).
163. Krafft, *Ber.*, **21**, 2730 (1888).
164. Juillard, *Bull. soc. chim.* [3], **13**, 240 (1895).
165. Kozlowski, *J. Bact.*, **16**, 203 (1928).
166. Halvorson, *Proc. Soc. Exptl. Biol. Med.*, **22**, 553 (1925).
167. Haller, *Compt. rend.*, **144**, 462 (1907).
168. Fahrion, *Chem. Umschau*, **23**, 60, 71 (1916).
169. Rider, *J. Am. Chem. Soc.*, **53**, 4130 (1931).
170. Straus, Heinze, and Salzmann, *Ber.*, **66**, 631 (1933).
171. Brown and Green, *J. Am. Chem. Soc.*, **62**, 738 (1940).
172. Matthes and Kürschner, *Arch. Pharm.*, **269**, 101 (1939).
173. Hazura and Grüssner, *Monatsh.*, **9**, 475 (1888).
174. Matthes and Schütz, *Arch. Pharm.*, **265**, 541 (1927).
175. Gurgel and de Amorim, *Mem. Inst. Chim. Rio de Janeiro*, No. **2**, 31 (1929).
176. Iyer, Sudborough, and Ayyar, *J. Indian Inst. Sci.*, **8A**, 29 (1925).
177. Margaillan, *Compt. rend.*, **192**, 373 (1931).
178. Vidyarthi and Mallya, *J. Indian Chem. Soc.*, **16**, 479 (1939).
179. André, *Compt. rend.*, **176**, 843 (1923).
180. Herrmann, *Arch. Pharm.*, **237**, 358 (1899).
181. Poutet, *Ann. chim. phys.* [2], **12**, 58 (1819).
182. Boudet, *ibid.* [2], **50**, 391 (1832); *J. pharm. chim.* [2], **18**, 469 (1832).
183. Playfair, *Phil. Mag.*, **29**, 475 (1846).
184. Mangold, *Monatsh.*, **15**, 307 (1894).
185. Bouis, *Ann. chim. phys.* [3], **44**, 77 (1855).
186. Mühle, *Ber.*, **46**, 2091 (1913).
187. Ulrich, *Z. Chem.* [2], **3**, 545 (1867).
188. Perrotte, *Compt. rend.*, **199**, 358 (1934).
189. Baczewski, *Monatsh.*, **17**, 528 (1896).
190. Epifanov, *J. Russ. Phys. Chem. Soc.*, **40**, 133 (1908).
191. Marie, *Bull. soc. chim.* [3], **15**, 576 (1896).
192. Schulze, *Ber.*, **5**, 1075 (1872); **6**, 251 (1873); **7**, 570 (1874).

193. de-Sanctis, *Gazz. chim. ital.*, **24**, I, 14 (1894).
194. Lewkowitsch, *J. Soc. Chem. Ind.*, **11**, 134 (1892); **15**, 14 (1896).
195. Darmstaedter and Lifschütz, *Ber.*, **28**, 3133 (1895); **29**, 618, 1474, 2890 (1896); **31**, 97, 1122 (1898).
196. Drummond and Baker, *J. Soc. Chem. Ind.*, **48**, 232T (1929).
197. Abraham and Hilditch, *ibid.*, **54**, 398T (1935).
198. Kuwata and Ishii, *J. Soc. Chem. Ind., Japan*, **30**, B.L. 317 (1936).
199. Kuwata, *J. Am. Chem. Soc.*, **60**, 559 (1938).
200. Heiduschka and Nier, *J. prakt. Chem.* [2], **149**, 98 (1937).
201. Weitkamp, *J. Am. Chem. Soc.*, **67**, 447 (1945).
202. Thudichum, *Die Chemische Konstitution des Gehirns des Menschen und der Tiere*, Tübingen, Verlag von Franz Pietzcker (1901).
203. Thierfelder, *Z. physiol. Chem.*, **43**, 21 (1904).
204. Levene and Jacobs, *J. Biol. Chem.*, **12**, 381 (1912).
205. Levene and West, *ibid.*, **18**, 477 (1914); **26**, 115 (1916).
206. Levene and Taylor, *ibid.*, **52**, 227 (1922).
207. Klenk, *Z. physiol. Chem.*, **145**, 244 (1925); **153**, 74 (1926); **157**, 283, 291 (1926); **166**, 268, 287 (1927); **174**, 214 (1928).
208. Klenk and Diebold, *ibid.*, **215**, 79 (1933).
209. Taylor and Levene, *J. Biol. Chem.*, **84**, 23 (1929).
210. Levene and Heymann, *ibid.*, **102**, 1 (1933).
211. Taylor and Levene, *ibid.*, **102**, 535 (1933).
212. Grey, *Biochem. J.*, **7**, 148 (1913).
213. Levene and Yang, *J. Biol. Chem.*, **102**, 541 (1933).
214. Chibnall, Piper, and Williams, *Biochem. J.*, **30**, 100 (1936).
215. Robinson and Smith, *J. Chem. Soc.*, 283 (1936); Smith, *ibid.*, 625 (1936).
216. Crowfoot, *ibid.*, 716 (1936).
217. Müller, *Ber.*, **72B**, 615 (1939).
218. Levene, *J. Biol. Chem.*, **24**, 69 (1916).
219. Stodola, Lesuk, and Anderson, *ibid.*, **126**, 505 (1938).
220. Cason and Anderson, *ibid.*, **126**, 527 (1938).
221. Kuwada and Matsukawa, *J. Pharm. Soc. Japan*, **53**, 680 (1933).
222. Zetzsche and Bähler, *Helv. Chim. Acta*, **14**, 846 (1931).
223. Rosenheim and Maclean, *Biochem. J.*, **9**, 103 (1915).
224. Beilstein and Wiegand, *Ber.*, **17**, 840 (1884).
225. Claisen, *ibid.*, **12**, 626 (1879).
226. Béhal, *Bull. soc. chim.* [2], **47**, 33 (1887).
227. Moureu and Delange, *Compt. rend.*, **132**, 1121 (1901); **136**, 753 (1903).
228. Myddleton and Barrett, *J. Am. Chem. Soc.*, **49**, 2258 (1927).
229. Acree, *Ber.*, **37**, 625 (1904).
230. Oddo, *ibid.*, **43**, 1012 (1910).
231. Blaise and Koehler, *Compt. rend.*, **148**, 489 (1909).
232. Moritz, *J. Chem. Soc.*, **39**, 13 (1881).
233. Blaise, *Compt. rend.*, **132**, 978 (1901).
234. Blaise, *ibid.*, **128**, 183 (1899); *Bull. soc. chim.* [3], **21**, 647 (1899).
235. Wolff, *Ann.*, **229**, 249 (1885).
236. Fittig, *Ber.*, **29**, 2582 (1896).
237. Harries, *ibid.*, **31**, 37 (1898).
238. Kondo, *Biochem. Z.*, **38**, 407 (1912).

239. Zanetti, *Gazz. chim. ital.*, **21**, II, 166 (1891).
240. Fittig and Hillert, *Ann.*, **268**, 67 (1892).
241. Blaise, *Compt. rend.*, **158**, 708 (1914).
242. Campbell and Thorpe, *J. Chem. Soc.*, **97**, 1299 (1910).
243. Vorländer, *Ann.*, **294**, 253 (1897).
244. Ruzicka, *Helv. Chim. Acta*, **2**, 144 (1919).
245. Lipp, *Ber.*, **18**, 3275 (1885); *Ann.*, **289**, 173 (1896).
246. Hagemann, *Ber.*, **26**, 876 (1893).
247. Wallach and Collmann, *Ann.*, **331**, 318 (1904).
248. Haworth and Perkin, *J. Chem. Soc.*, **93**, 573 (1908).
249. Blaise and Koehler, *Compt. rend.*, **148**, 852 (1909).
250. Kötz, Blendermann, Mähnert, and Rosenbusch, *Ann.*, **400**, 72 (1913).
251. Dieckmann, *Ber.*, **45**, 2697 (1912).
252. Bentley and Perkin, *J. Chem. Soc.*, **69**, 1510 (1896).
253. Wahl and Doll, *Bull. soc. chim.* [4], **13**, 265 (1913).
254. Blaise and Luttringer, *ibid.* [3], **33**, 1095 (1905).
255. Bouveault and Bongert, *ibid.* [3], **27**, 1088 (1902).
256. Dupont and Chavanne, *Bull. soc. chim. Belg.*, **42**, 537 (1933).
257. Lukeš and Gorocholinskij, *Collection Czechoslov. Chem. Commun.*, **8**, 223 (1936).
258. Wallach, *Ann.*, **359**, 265 (1908).
259. Wallach with Franke, *ibid.*, **329**, 368 (1903).
260. Perkin, *J. Chem. Soc.*, **57**, 204 (1890).
261. Wolffenstein, *Ber.*, **28**, 1459 (1895).
262. Wallach, *Ann.*, **345**, 139 (1906).
263. Kipping and Perkin, *J. Chem. Soc.*, **55**, 330 (1889).
264. Moureu and Delange, *Bull. soc. chim.* [3], **29**, 666 (1903).
265. Lukeš, *Chem. Listy*, **24**, 197 (1930).
266. Asahina and Nakayama, *J. Pharm. Soc. Japan*, No. **526**, 1058 (1925).
267. Chuit, Boelsing, Hausser, and Malet, *Helv. Chim. Acta*, **9**, 1074 (1926).
268. Welander, *Ber.*, **28**, 1448 (1895).
269. Abraham, Mowat, and Smith, *J. Chem. Soc.*, 948 (1937).
270. Sherrill and Smith, *ibid.*, 1501 (1937).
271. Asano, *J. Pharm. Soc. Japan*, No. **504**, 75 (1924).
272. Paraskova, *Compt. rend.*, **198**, 1701 (1934).
273. Robinson, *J. Chem. Soc.*, 745 (1930).
274. Robinson and Robinson, *ibid.*, 2204 (1926).
275. Robinson, *ibid.*, 1543 (1934).
276. Clutterbuck, Raistrick, and Rintoul, *Trans. Roy. Soc. (London)*, **220B**, 301 (1931).
277. Robinson and Robinson, *J. Chem. Soc.*, **127**, 175 (1925).
278. Fordyce and Johnson, *J. Am. Chem. Soc.*, **55**, 3368 (1933).
279. Le Sueur and Withers, *J. Chem. Soc.*, **105**, 2800 (1914).
280. Pigulewski and Charik, *Biochem. Z.*, **200**, 201 (1928).
281. Zellner, *Monatsh.*, **41**, 443 (1920).
282. Windaus and van Schoor, *Z. physiol. Chem.*, **161**, 143 (1926).
283. Shukoff and Schestakoff, *J. Russ. Phys. Chem. Soc.*, **35**, 1 (1903).
284. Brown and Farmer, *Biochem. J.*, **29**, 631 (1935).
285. Bougault and Charaux, *Compt. rend.*, **153**, 572, 880 (1911).

286. Arnaud, *ibid.*, **134**, 547 (1902); *Bull. soc. chim.* [3], **27**, 489 (1902).

287. Behrend, *Ber.*, **29**, 806 (1896).

288. M. Saytzeff and A. Saytzeff, *J. Russ. Phys. Chem. Soc.*, **35**, 1193 (1903); *J. prakt. Chem.* [2], **71**, 422 (1905).

289. King, *J. Chem. Soc.*, 1788 (1936).

290. Shukoff and Schestakoff, *J. prakt. Chem.* [2], **67**, 414 (1903).

291. Perrotte, *Compt. rend.*, **200**, 746 (1935).

292. Perrotto, *ibid.*, **199**, 358 (1934).

293. van Loon and Steger, *Rec. trav. chim.*, **50**, 936 (1931).

294. Wilborn, *Chem.-Ztg.*, **55**, 434 (1931).

295. Morrell and Davis, *J. Chem. Soc.*, 1481 (1936).

296. Baruch, *Ber.*, **27**, 176 (1894).

297. Fileti, *J. prakt. Chem.* [2], **48**, 336 (1893).

298. Fileti and Baldracco, *Gazz. chim. ital.*, **24**, II, 289 (1844).

299. Chibnall, Latner, Williams, and Ayre, *Biochem. J.*, **28**, 313 (1934).

300. Muir, *Indian Med. Gaz.*, **54**, 130 (1919); *Indian J. Med. Research*, **11**, 543 (1923).

301. Walker and Sweeney, *J. Infectious Diseases*, **26**, 238 (1920).

302. Schöbl, *Philippine J. Sci.*, **23**, 533 (1923).

303. Hollman and Dean, *J. Cutan. Dis.*, **37**, 367 (1919); Dean and Wrenshall, *J. Am. Chem. Soc.*, **42**, 2626 (1920); McDonald and Dean, *J. Am. Med. Assoc.*, **76**, 1470 (1921).

304. Rogers, *Lancet*, **190**, 288 (1916); **200**, 1178 (1921); **206**, 1297 (1924).

305. Bernhard and Müller, *Z. physiol. Chem.*, **256**, 85 (1938).

306. Power and Gornall, *J. Chem. Soc.*, **85**, 838, 851 (1904); Power and Barrowcliff, *ibid.*, **87**, 884 (1905); **91**, 557 (1907); *Proc. Chem. Soc.*, **23**, 70 (1907).

307. Shriner and Adams, *J. Am. Chem. Soc.*, **47**, 2727 (1925).

308. Perkins and Cruz, *ibid.*, **49**, 1070 (1927).

309. Hinegardner, *ibid.*, **55**, 2831 (1933).

310. Stanley and Adams, *ibid.*, **51**, 1515 (1929).

311. Hashimoto, *ibid.*, **47**, 2325 (1925).

312. Dean, Wrenshall, and Fujimoto, *U. S. Pub. Health Service Bull. No. 141*, 24 (1924).

313. Noller with Adams, *J. Am. Chem. Soc.*, **48**, 1080 (1926).

314. André and Jouatte, *Bull. soc. chim.* [4], **43**, 347 (1928).

315. Paget, *J. Chem. Soc.*, 955 (1937).

316. Cole and Cardoso, *J. Am. Chem. Soc.*, **60**, 612 (1938).

317. Sacks with Adams, *ibid.*, **48**, 2395 (1926).

318. Van Dyke and Adams, *ibid.*, **48**, 2393 (1926).

319. Arvin with Adams, *ibid.*, **49**, 2940 (1927).

320. Noller with Adams, *ibid.*, **48**, 2444 (1926).

321. Schöbl, *Philippine J. Sci.*, **25**, 123, 135 (1924).

322. Hiers with Adams, *J. Am. Chem. Soc.*, **48**, 1089 (1926).

323. Hiers with Adams, *ibid.*, **48**, 2385 (1926).

324. Yohe and Adams, *ibid.*, **50**, 1503 (1928).

325. Katsnel'son and Dubinin, *Compt. rend. acad. sci. U. R. S. S.*, **4**, 405 (1936).

326. Katsnel'son and Kondakova, *ibid.*, **17**, 367 (1937).

327. Adams, Stanley, and Stearns, *J. Am. Chem. Soc.*, **50**, 1475 (1928).

328. Arvin and Adams, *ibid.*, **50**, 1983 (1928).
329. Ford and Adams, *ibid.*, **52**, 1259 (1930).
330. Adams, Stanley, Ford, and Peterson, *ibid.*, **49**, 2934 (1927).
331. Davies and Adams, *ibid.*, **50**, 2297 (1928).
332. Stanley, Jay, and Adams, *ibid.*, **51**, 1261 (1929).
333. Armendt and Adams, *ibid.*, **52**, 1289 (1930).
334. Greer and Adams, *ibid.*, **52**, 2540 (1930).
335. Browning, Woodrow, and Adams, *ibid.*, **52**, 1281 (1930).
336. Fairweather, *Proc. Roy. Soc. Edinburgh*, **45**, 283 (1925); **46**, 71 (1926); *Phil. Mag.* [7], **1**, 944 (1926).
337. Challenor and Thorpe, *J. Chem. Soc.*, **123**, 2480 (1923).
338. la Tour, *Compt. rend.*, **201**, 479 (1935).
339. Caspari, *J. Chem. Soc.*, 2709 (1929).
340. Krafft and Noerdlinger, *Ber.*, **22**, 816 (1889).
341. Lippmann, *ibid.*, **24**, 3299 (1891).
342. Canzoneri, *Gazz. chim. ital.*, **13**, 514 (1883).
343. Haller, *Compt. rend.*, **146**, 259 (1908).
344. Kiesel, *Z. physiol. Chem.*, **149**, 231 (1925).
345. Lissizin, *ibid.*, **62**, 226 (1909).
346. Nicolet and Liddle, *J. Ind. Eng. Chem.*, **8**, 416 (1916).
347. Banks and Hilditch, *Analyst*, **58**, 265 (1933).
348. Geitel and van der Want, *J. prakt. Chem.* [2], **61**, 153 (1900).
349. Majima and Cho, *Ber.*, **40**, 4390 (1907).
350. Schaal, *ibid.*, **40**, 4784 (1907).
351. Tassilly, *Bull. soc. chim.* [4], **9**, 608 (1911).
352. Fels, *Seifenfabr.*, **36**, 141 (1916).
353. Flaschenträger and Halle, *Z. physiol. Chem.*, **190**, 120 (1930).
354. Tsujimoto, *Bull. Chem. Soc. Japan*, **6**, 325 (1931); *J. Soc. Chem. Ind., Japan*, **42**, S.b. 22 (1939).
355. Tsujimoto, *Bull. Chem. Soc. Japan*, **6**, 337 (1931).
356. Goodman and Gilman, *The Pharmacological Basis of Therapeutics*, p. 624, The Macmillan Co., New York (1941).
357. Flaschenträger and Bernhard, *Z. physiol. Chem.*, **238**, 221 (1936).
358. Verkade and van der Lee, *Proc. Acad. Sci. Amsterdam*, **36**, 314 (1933).
359. Verkade and van der Lee, *Z. physiol. Chem.*, **227**, 213 (1934); Verkade, van der Lee, and van Alphen, *ibid.*, **247**, 111 (1937); **252**, 163 (1938); *Proc. Acad. Sci. Amsterdam*, **40**, 411 (1937).
360. Mazza, *Arch. sci. biol. Italy*, **22**, 307 (1936).
361. Verkade and van der Lee, *Proc. Acad. Sci. Amsterdam*, **36**, 876 (1933); *Z. physiol. Chem.*, **225**, 230 (1934).
362. Bernhard and Andreae, *ibid.*, **245**, 103 (1937).
363. Haworth and Perkin, *Ber.*, **26**, 2246 (1893).
364. Brown and Walker, *Chem. News*, **66**, 91 (1892).
365. Carmichael, *J. Chem. Soc.*, **121**, 2545 (1922).
366. Noerdlinger, *Ber.*, **23**, 2356 (1890).
367. Molinari and Soncini, *ibid.*, **39**, 2735 (1906); Harries and Türk, *ibid.*, **39**, 3732 (1906); Harries, *ibid.*, **42**, 446 (1909).
368. Gantter and Hell, *ibid.*, **14**, 1545 (1881).
369. Markownikow, *J. Russ. Phys. Chem. Soc.* [1], **25**, 378 (1893).

370. Stosius and Wiesler, *Biochem. Z.*, **111**, 1 (1920).
371. Gantter and Hell, *Ber.*, **17**, 2212 (1884).
372. v. Braun, *ibid.*, **37**, 3588 (1904).
373. Ruzicka, Brugger, Pfeiffer, Schinz, and Stoll, *Helv. Chim. Acta*, **9**, 499 (1926).
374. Hentzschel and Wislicenus, *Ann.*, **275**, 312 (1893).
375. Holleman, van der Laan, and Slijper, *Rec. trav. chim.*, **24**, 19 (1905).
376. Harries and Wagner, *Ann.*, **410**, 29 (1915).
377. Thorpe and Kon, *Organic Syntheses*, Coll. Vol. 1, Gilman, editor, p. 187, John Wiley & Sons, New York (1932).
378. Sabatier and Mailhe, *Compt. rend.*, **158**, 985 (1914).
379. Vavon and Apchié, *Bull. soc. chim.* [4], **43**, 667 (1928).
380. Chavanne and Simon, *Compt. rend.*, **168**, 1324 (1919).
381. Vogel, *J. Chem. Soc.*, 2010 (1928).
382. Aschan, *Ber.*, **45**, 1603 (1912).
383. Wislicenus and Mager, *Ann.*, **275**, 356 (1893).
384. Derlon, *Ber.*, **31**, 1957 (1898).
385. Markownikoff, *Ann.*, **307**, 367 (1899).
386. Ruzicka and Brugger, *Helv. Chim. Acta*, **9**, 339 (1926).
387. Zelinsky, *Ber.*, **40**, 3277 (1907).
388. Willstätter and Kametaka, *ibid.*, **40**, 3876 (1907).
389. Harries and Tank, *ibid.*, **40**, 4555 (1907).
390. Bayer and Co., Ger. Patent 256,622 (1911).
391. Kon and Thorpe, *J. Chem. Soc.*, **115**, 686 (1919).
392. Day, Kon, and Stevenson, *ibid.*, **117**, 639 (1920).
393. Vogel, *ibid.*, 2032 (1928).
394. Naef et Cie., Brit. Patent 251,188 (1925).
395. Ruzicka, Stoll, and Schinz, *Helv. Chim. Acta*, **9**, 249 (1926).
396. Ruzicka, *ibid.*, **9**, 230 (1926).
397. Ruzicka, Stoll, and Schinz, *ibid.*, **11**, 670 (1928).
398. Ruzicka and Stoll, *ibid.*, **16**, 493 (1933).
399. Anschütz, *Ber.*, **10**, 1881 (1877).
400. Carothers, *J. Am. Chem. Soc.*, **51**, 2548 (1929).
401. Voerman, *Rec. trav. chim.*, **23**, 265 (1904).
402. Farmer and Kracovski, *J. Chem. Soc.*, 680 (1927).
403. Hill, *J. Am. Chem. Soc.*, **52**, 4110 (1933).
404. Hill and Carothers, *ibid.*, **54**, 1569 (1932).
405. Blanc, *Compt. rend.*, **144**, 1356 (1907); *Bull. soc. chim.* [4], **3**, 778 (1908).
406. Hill and Carothers, *J. Am. Chem. Soc.*, **55**, 5023 (1933).
407. Hill and Carothers, *ibid.*, **55**, 5039 (1933).
408. Mohr, *J. prakt. Chem.* [2], **98**, 315 (1918).
409. Carothers and Hill, *J. Am. Chem. Soc.*, **55**, 5043 (1933).
410. Hamonet, *Compt. rend.*, **132**, 345 (1901).
411. Henry, *Rec. trav. chim.*, **21**, 1 (1902).
412. Wislicenus, *Ann.*, **149**, 215 (1869).
413. Ince, *J. Chem. Soc.*, **67**, 155 (1895).
414. Dieterle and Hell, *Ber.*, **17**, 2221 (1884).
415. Mannich, *ibid.*, **39**, 1594 (1906).
416. Rosenlew, *ibid.*, **39**, 2202 (1906).

417. Mannich and Hâncu, *ibid.*, **41**, 575 (1908).
418. Blaise and Koehler, *Bull. soc. chim.* [4], **5**, 681 (1909).
419. v. Braun and Lemke, *Ber.*, **55**, 3526 (1922).
420. Zélinsky, *J. Russ. Phys. Chem. Soc.*, **35**, 1280 (1903); *Bull. soc. chim.* [3], **34**, 208 (1905).
421. Bouveault, *ibid.* [4], **3**, 437 (1908).
422. Edwards and Reid, *J. Am. Chem. Soc.*, **52**, 3235 (1930).
423. Deutsche Hydrierwerke A.-G., Ger. Patent 473,960 (1926).
424. Claasen, Fr. Patent 32,991 (1927).
425. Schrauth, U. S. Patent 1,921,101 (1933).
426. Ellis, *Organic Syntheses*, Coll. Vol. 1, Gilman, editor, p. 18, John Wiley & Sons, New York (1932).
427. Foster, *Organic Syntheses*, **13**, 110 (1933).
428. Zal'kind and Markov, Russ. Patent 50,394 (1937).
429. Aronow, U. S. Patent 2,191,786 (1940).
430. Harries and Neresheimer, *Ber.*, **39**, 2846 (1906).
431. Harries and von Splawa-Neymann, *ibid.*, **41**, 3552 (1908).
432. Serwy, *Bull. soc. chim. Belg.*, **42**, 483 (1933).
433. Hamonet, *Compt. rend.*, **139**, 59 (1904); *Bull. soc. chim.* [3], **33**, 528 (1905).
434. Grignard and Vignon, *Compt. rend.*, **144**, 1358 (1907).
435. Carpenter and Perkin, *J. Chem. Soc.*, **75**, 921 (1899).
436. Wallach, *Ann.*, **343**, 40 (1905).
437. Perkin and Prentice, *J. Chem. Soc.*, **59**, 818 (1891).
438. Tilley, *Ann.*, **39**, 160 (1841).
439. Wirz, *ibid.*, **104**, 257 (1857).
440. Arppe, *ibid.*, **120**, 288 (1861).
441. Brown and Walker, *ibid.*, **261**, 107 (1891).
442. Willstätter and Veraguth, *Ber.*, **40**, 957 (1907).
443. Wallach, *Ann.*, **353**, 318 (1907).
444. Zelinsky and Gutt, *Ber.*, **40**, 3049 (1907).
445. Anderlini, *Gazz. chim. ital.*, **24**, I, 474 (1894).
446. Saytzeff, *J. Russ. Phys. Chem. Soc.*, **17**, 417 (1885); *J. prakt. Chem.* [2], **31**, 541 (1885); [2], **33**, 300 (1886).
447. Spiridonoff, *ibid.* [2], **40**, 243 (1889).
448. Armstrong and Hilditch, *J. Soc. Chem. Ind.*, **44**, 43T (1925).
449. Ellingboe, U. S. Patent 2,203,680 (1940).
450. Hill and McEwen, *Organic Syntheses*, **13**, 4 (1933).
451. Harries, *Ber.*, **36**, 1933 (1903); **39**, 3728 (1906); *Ann.*, **374**, 288 (1910); Harries and Türk, *Ber.*, **38**, 1630 (1905); Harries and Thieme, *Ann.*, **343**, 354 (1905); Molinari and Barosi, *Ber.*, **41**, 2794 (1908); Haller and Brochet, *Compt. rend.*, **150**, 496 (1910).
452. Majima, *Ber.*, **42**, 674 (1909).
453. Morrell, *Proc. Chem. Soc.*, **28**, 235 (1912); *J. Chem. Soc.*, **101**, 2082 (1912).
454. Smit, *Rec. trav. chim.*, **49**, 539 (1930).
455. Böeseken and Slooff, *ibid.*, **49**, 95 (1930).
456. Harries, *Ber.*, **40**, 4905 (1907).
457. Tschirch, *Chem. Umschau*, **32**, 29 (1925).
458. Edmed, *J. Chem. Soc.*, **73**, 627 (1898).
459. Asahina and Ishida, *J. Pharm. Soc. Japan*, **481**, 171 (1922).

460. Normand, Ross, and Henderson, *J. Chem. Soc.*, 2632 (1926).
461. Lamouroux, *Compt. rend.*, **128**, 998 (1899).
462. Molinari and Fenaroli, *Ber.*, **41**, 2789 (1908).
463. Bouis, *Ann.*, **80**, 303 (1851); **92**, 395 (1854); **97**, 34 (1856); *Ann. chim. phys.* [3], **44**, 77 (1855).
464. Boedtker, *J. pharm. chim.*, **29**, 313 (1924).
465. Verkade, Hartman, and Coops, *Rec. trav. chim.*, **45**, 373 (1926).
466. Bruson and Covert, U. S. Patent 2,182,056 (1939).
467. Walker and Lumsden, *J. Chem. Soc.*, **79**, 1191 (1901).
468. v. Braun, *Ber.*, **42**, 4541 (1909).
469. Chuit, *Helv. Chim. Acta*, **9**, 264 (1926).
470. Chuit and Hausser, *ibid.*, **12**, 850 (1929).
471. Franke and Hankam, *Monatsh.*, **31**, 177 (1910).
472. Fileti and Ponzio, *J. prakt. Chem.* [2], **48**, 323 (1893).
473. Ponzio, *Gazz. chim. ital.*, **34**, II, 50 (1904).
474. von Grossmann, *Ber.*, **26**, 639 (1893).
475. Krafft and Seldis, *ibid.*, **33**, 3571 (1900).
476. Eberhardt, *Dissertation Strassburg*, 1888.
477. Shiina, *J. Soc. Chem. Ind., Japan*, **43**, S.b. 173 (1940).
478. Shiina, *ibid.*, **42**, S.b. 147 (1939).

IV

THE PREPARATION OF THE FATTY ACIDS FROM THE NATURALLY OCCURRING FATS

The glycerides constitute by far the greatest source of the naturally occurring fatty acids. Although the various animal, vegetable, and insect waxes also offer substantial quantities of certain fatty acids, these waxes are a minor source of the fatty acids when compared to the enormous amounts which are available in the naturally occurring fats and oils. Therefore, the problem of obtaining fatty acids from natural products is essentially concerned with their liberation from the naturally occurring glycerides and with their separation into pure compounds, or into mixtures of acids the various components of which possess similar chemical properties. The ease of separation of the various fatty acid mixtures depends quite largely upon the composition and complexity of these mixtures. For example, the saturated acids can generally be separated from the unsaturated acids, and the former can in turn be easily separated one from the other. Extreme difficulty, however, is frequently encountered in the separation of the highly unsaturated acids. In separating the fatty acids from their mixtures recourse is taken to distillation, solvent crystallization of the acids or their simple derivatives, crystallization in the absence of solvents, pressing, centrifugation, and other procedures. Frequently, several of these processes are combined in order to obtain effective separations. This chapter discusses the various methods which have been employed for obtaining fatty acid mixtures from the glycerides or other naturally occurring fatty substances and considers the various means which have been proposed for the separation of such mixtures into their individual components. It should be realized that many of the proposed procedures are useful only for the preparation of fatty acids on a laboratory scale, whereas others lend themselves to large-scale commercial operations.

HYDROLYSIS OF FATS

The fatty acids are liberated from the glycerides by hydrolysis of the ester molecule into its component parts, glycerol and the fatty acids. If the glycerides are split by strong alkalies or metallic oxides the process is known as saponification, whereas if the hydrolysis is brought about catalytically or enzymatically, the process is generally designated as splitting. Although acid splitting was employed at an early date, the industrial preparation of the fatty acids undoubtedly found its beginning in the saponification process. The glycerides were converted to soap and glycerol, and the free acids were obtained by the acidification of the former. Since the saponification process has been known for hundreds of years, it is not surprising that the first large-scale preparation of the fatty acids was by this method. Although the saponification process is now infrequently employed for obtaining fatty acids from the fats, having been replaced by more modern methods such as catalytic splitting, its historical significance has been profound.

Soaps were known and used by the ancients.[1] There is considerable evidence to support the belief that the early Romans employed certain types of soaps as detergents. Pliny has described the preparation of soaps by the Gauls, who obtained them by heating goat tallow with wood ashes. Soap boiling was extensively practiced in Germany during the ninth century; however, since the composition of the fats was unknown until the beginning of the nineteenth century, it is apparent that these early processes must have been built upon a very empirical foundation. Scheele's discovery of glycerol in 1779 and his announcement several years later that it is a common component of all fats threw some light upon the saponification process; however, it was not until the work of Chevreul (1813–1823) that the true character of the saponification reaction was rendered understandable. When Chevreul showed that the fats are fatty acid esters of glycerol, it became apparent that the soaps are the metal salts of these acids. The process, therefore, consists of the hydrolysis of the fats by means of basic substances to yield metal salts and glycerol. The industrial preparation of fatty acids by the treatment of soap with hydrochloric acid was undertaken by Chevreul and also by Gay-Lussac. The solid acids so obtained were used for candle manufacture and the liquid acids for soap making. Considerable difficulty was experienced in removing the last traces of hydrochloric acid from the fatty acids, and the acid process was eventually replaced by lime saponification followed by acidification of the lime soaps with sulfuric acid.

When fats are saponified with caustic alkalies or other bases for the purpose of obtaining soaps and glycerol, it is necessary to employ somewhat more than the theoretical quantity of the base in order to convert the fatty acids completely into soaps. If, however, the primary object was to change the fats into fatty acids and glycerol, it was soon recognized that complete conversion into soaps is not necessary or desirable. This led to the so-called catalytic splitting process, in which the fats are autoclaved under pressure in the presence of small amounts of alkalies, the resulting product consisting of a mixture of glycerol, fatty acids, and soaps. Caustic alkalies, calcium, magnesium, or zinc oxides, and other bases were employed for preparing fatty acid mixtures from fats. Such methods have been largely replaced by the hydrolysis of fats with acids or acid catalysts and to a limited extent by enzymatic hydrolysis. The mechanism of the saponification process has long been a controversial question, and before we consider the various specific processes it would be interesting, and perhaps helpful, to discuss certain aspects of this subject.

Mechanism of Hydrolysis

When we consider the triglyceride molecule, it is apparent that its saponification may proceed by at least two possible mechanisms. Either all the fatty radicals may be removed simultaneously with the formation of soaps and glycerol, or the saponification may proceed stepwise with the formation of a diglyceride, then a monoglyceride, and finally glycerol, as follows:

(I) $\quad C_3H_5(OCOR)_3 + MOH \rightarrow C_3H_5OH(OCOR)_2 + MOCOR$
$\qquad\qquad$ Triglyceride $\qquad\qquad\qquad\qquad$ Diglyceride

(II) $\quad C_3H_5OH(OCOR)_2 + MOH \rightarrow C_3H_5(OH)_2OCOR + MOCOR$
$\qquad\qquad\qquad\qquad\qquad\qquad\qquad\qquad$ Monoglyceride

(III) $\quad C_3H_5(OH)_2OCOR + MOH \rightarrow C_3H_5(OH)_3 + MOCOR$

There can be little question but that the stepwise process is the correct mechanism. However, a heated controversy raged for years concerning this point, and it has only been within comparatively recent years that there has been substantial agreement that saponification is a stepwise procedure. All hydrolytic processes which involve triglycerides undoubtedly proceed by this stepwise mechanism. This does not mean, however, that all the triglycerides in a saponification mixture are first hydrolyzed to diglycerides, thence to monoglycerides, and so on, since the various reactions proceed at somewhat different rates, and the physical properties of the reaction mixture exert a profound influence. If the saponification or hydrolytic process is stopped at an intermediate stage, products representing all degrees of hydrolysis will be present. This point has been proved analytically, for example, in the hydrolysis of trilaurin by sulfuric acid;[2] however, in most cases the isolation of the intermediate products of hydrolysis is attended with great difficulty.

The mechanism of the saponification reaction was first intensively studied by Geitel [3] and by Lewkowitsch,[4] both of whom considered the reaction to proceed stepwise. Balbiano [5] and Kremann [6] studied the process and reported it to proceed stepwise, although the former stated that no intermediate products could be isolated. The kinetic studies made by Meyer [7] also indicated a stepwise mechanism. The failure to isolate the intermediate products led Marcusson [8] to question the stepwise mechanism and to suggest that the results based upon acetyl determinations were erroneous, an opinion which was also expressed by Kellner,[9] who believed that alkali saponifications proceed with the simultaneous removal of the three acyl groups. The saponification of rape seed oil was studied by Stritar and Fanto,[10] who concluded that it proceeds stepwise, but that no large amounts of intermediate products are present at any specific time. Wegscheider [11] has stated that under the conditions which seem most probable for saponification in a heterogeneous system one would not expect to find appreciable quantities of intermediate products, although the reaction was actually taking place through their formation. Intermediate products have been isolated in the hydrolysis of distearo-α-chlorohydrin with sulfuric acid [12] and in the hydrolysis of glyceryl trinitrate.[13]

With all due respect to the many technical advances and to the large amount of experimental work which has been done upon saponification and other hydrolytic reactions involving triglycerides, it must be admitted that the mechanisms by which these reactions proceed are not, as yet, clearly understood. It is quite probable that such reactions follow similar mechanisms irrespective of whether they are conducted in the presence of excess acids or bases or in the presence of catalytic amounts of these substances.

When neutral oils are boiled with aqueous alkali, the initially slow reaction rate becomes rapid, and then finally undergoes a marked retardation. This can be partially explained on the basis that saponification is a surface reaction and that the soap formed initially functions as an emulsifying agent to increase the area of contact between the reactants. Treub [14] has stated that saponification takes place at the surface of contact of the fat and aqueous phase, and therefore depends upon the adsorption of the glycerides on the contact surface. He also stated that saponification in the aqueous phase is negligible owing to the slow rate of diffusion. Norris and McBain [15] believe that the reaction takes place at the oil surface and consequently that the rate depends quite largely upon the degree of emulsification. Physical processes such as vigorous stirring increase the reaction rate perceptibly, whereas processes such as "salting out" materially reduce the reaction rate. Lederer [16] has concluded that the ionic combination of the alkali with the fatty acids of the glycerides is preceded by an adsorption phenomenon which follows Freundlich's adsorption law. Smith,[17] however, has stated that the reaction at the interface is of important magnitude only during the early stages of saponification, where no soap is present initially. Since saponification reactions appear to be bimolecular, especially after the reaction has passed through the initial stage, it appears that interfacial reactions do not afford a complete explanation of the entire process. Although the rate of saponification is high in the presence of excess caustic, it is well known that the reaction can easily be brought to completion at higher temperatures with only catalytic amounts of basic materials. The results of Rowe [18] upon saponification in the presence of varying amounts of caustic support the previous contention that basic materials play a catalytic role, which indicates that, in the case of saponification in an aqueous medium, the primary reactants are water and fat. Recently, Lascaray [19] has studied the influence of various factors upon the rate of saponification of tallow by sodium hydroxide and has observed that varying the amount of water from 20 to 200% substantially increases the extent of splitting at equilibrium, although the rate of splitting is only slightly influenced. The catalytic effect of the bases investigated increases in the following order: NH_3, KOH, NaOH, LiOH, CaO, MgO, and ZnO. It was concluded that the saponification of fats is a homogeneous reaction which occurs in the fat phase between fat and the water dissolved therein. Saponification in alcoholic caustic solutions proceeds more rapidly than that in an aqueous medium, owing, undoubtedly, to the greater solvent power of the alcohol. The solvent, however, does not fundamentally influence the reaction mechanism. The kinetic experiments of Strohecker [20] indicated that the initial reaction of fat saponification in alcoholic solution is neither uni- nor bimolecular, but that the reaction becomes bimolecular as the saponification proceeds. Kurz [21] has shown that the rate of glyceride splitting in alcoholic solution increases with increasing water content of the alcohol and also with increasing caustic concentration.

Splitting by means of acids and acid catalysts such as Twitchell's reagent probably proceeds by a physical mechanism similar to that of alkali saponification. Treub [22] has observed that the reaction velocity during acid splitting cannot be dependent upon emulsification alone. It was stated that acid catalysts not only increase the contact surface but also the concentration of hydrogen ion at the interface, and it has been postulated by v. Braun and Fischer [23] that saponification consists of the primary addition of OH or OR to the carbon of the C:O group. Since hydrocarbon radicals possess an electron-repelling effect, it follows that CH_3CO_2H should be saponified at a much slower rate than CCl_3CO_2H, a conclusion which has received experimental verification.

Among the interesting points which have been raised concerning the rate of hydrolytic reactions is the question as to whether all triglycerides are hydrolyzed at the same speed, or whether the rate of hydrolysis is influenced by the types of fatty acids in the glyceride molecule. A consideration of this point, together with the question as to the relative rates of hydrolysis of triglycerides as compared to di- and monoglycerides, is essential for any complete understanding of these hydrolytic processes. It appears logical to assume that the type of glyceride entering into this reaction, particularly as regards the nature of the fatty acids in the glyceride molecule, should rather materially affect the rate of hydrolysis. This has been partially borne out by the experimental work. However, several controversial opinions have been expressed, and it certainly cannot be said that this subject has been sufficiently explored. The difficulty which arises is that in most of the experimental work several variables have been considered simultaneously, precluding a definite evaluation of the influence of any one specific factor. Henriques [24] saponified a number of glycerides with insufficient caustic to bring about complete saponification and reported that there was no difference in the reaction rates. Thum [25] found no selectivity in the reaction of sodium hydroxide with a mixture of stearic and oleic acids. Experiments performed using castor oil lipase appeared to indicate that all glycerides are saponified at the same rate,[26] although Longenecker and Haley [27] have observed that the percentage of hydrolysis in the presence of plant lipase varies for different oils. Studies on the saponification of coconut oil have shown that the glycerides of the lower fatty acids are hydrolyzed more readily than those of their higher homologs.[28, 29] Several studies have been made upon the rate [15, 30, 31] of saponification of pure glycerides, and in 1926 McBain and others [32] reported that there is no correlation between the molecular weight of a triglyceride and its rate of saponification by aqueous alkali but that the time required for saponification increases with the degree of unsaturation. Verkade and de Willigen [33] have observed that triglycerides whose fatty acids contain from eight to thirteen carbon atoms are hydrolyzed at the same rate during homogeneous saponification with potassium hydroxide in 96% ethanol; on the other hand, Stohecker [20] has stated that the low molecular weight glycerides are saponified at a very accelerated rate, and he has developed a method for the detection of adulteration in oils based upon his kinetic studies. Recently, Ono [34] has stated that the saponification of solid fats is more rapid than that of oily fats; however, the highly unsaturated fish oils were observed to be more readily saponified than the more saturated vegetable oils. From the above discussion it is apparent that very little work has been done upon the saponification of pure triglycerides under carefully controlled conditions and that little agreement is evidenced in the work of the various investigators in this field.

The important point as to the relative rates of saponification of triglycerides as compared to di- and monoglycerides has been essentially disregarded. In 1940, Ono [35] stated that the hydrolysis of the glycerides of palmitic, stearic, and oleic acids increases in the order tri-, di-, and monoglycerides, and that the difference between the reaction coefficients for monostearin and tristearin is greater than that for monoölein and triolein. This author also attempted to correlate the rate of saponification with the position of the fatty acid radical in the glyceride molecule. Previously, Franck [36] had studied the saponification rates of the ethyl and glycol esters of linseed oil fatty acids and reported no significant differences. It has been stated that triglycerides are much more readily hydrolyzed by pancreatic lipase than are either di- or monoglycerides.

The rates of saponification in aqueous media are generally increased by the addition of small amounts of alcohol. Undoubtedly the solvents employed in saponification processes exert a rather significant influence upon the reaction rate, and Henriques [37] has reported that fats dissolved in a mixture of petroleum ether and alcoholic sodium hydroxide are completely saponified at room temperature in twelve hours. Anderson and Brown [38] have studied the rates of saponification of several fats in methanol, ethanol, and pentanol, and have reported that at 15.5° the velocity of saponification of the glycerides is about twice as great in pentanol as in ethanol and about ten times as great in ethanol as in methanol. The addition of small amounts of water to these alcohols materially increases the reaction rates.

Processes of Fat Hydrolysis

The various methods which have been proposed or used for the splitting of triglycerides or other fatty esters can be roughly divided into four general procedures: splitting by acids or in the presence of acid catalysts, hydrolysis by basic materials, direct splitting by steam at elevated temperatures, and enzymatic hydrolysis. In the following discussion of these various processes it should be borne in mind that they do not differ fundamentally, since the actual hydrolyzing agent is probably water in all cases.

Acid Hydrolysis

Acid hydrolysis is, at present, the most important industrial method for preparing fatty acids from fats. Its importance has largely been occasioned by the advent of the various acid catalytic agents. In spite of the antiquity of such processes, it was not until the latter part of the last century that they received serious study. The principal problem which had to be solved was to effect an intimate contact of the acid with the unhydrolyzed or partially hydrolyzed fat, since without intimate contact such reactions are incomplete. In 1903, Lewkowitsch [39] published the results of studies upon acid hydrolysis in which he pointed out that in order for this process to be satisfactory a suitable emulsifying agent must be found. For example, it was observed that dilute sulfuric acid is without material action upon the fats and that only slight hydrolysis is obtained with dilute hydrochloric acid. Hydrolysis by means of concentrated hydrochloric acid produces substantial, although not complete, hydrolysis, and the free fatty acids initially present in the oil appear to exert a catalytic effect. It has been shown [2] that fats are almost quantitatively hydrolyzed in the cold by treatment with concentrated sulfuric acid; however, the extent of hydrolysis decreases rapidly upon dilution of the acid. Thus, when one mole of trilaurin is treated with twenty-five moles of concentrated sulfuric acid at 1–2° for six hours, complete hydrolysis results, whereas if less acid is used the reaction is incomplete. Van Eldik Thieme showed that the hydrolysis of fats with sulfuric acid is a reversible reaction, esterification of the fatty acids and glycerol being catalyzed by dilute acid. The strong hydrolytic properties of concentrated sulfuric acid may be ascribed to its solvent power for fats and to its formation of addition compounds with glycerol and the glycerides.[40] It is well known that unsaturated fatty acids form addition compounds with concentrated sulfuric acid, and these may well exert a catalytic effect. The hydrolysis of fats with concentrated sulfuric acid has little commercial significance owing to the large amount of acid required and the obvious difficulties of obtaining and purifying the resulting products. The use of more dilute acids at elevated temperatures under pressure, on the other hand, was not successful because of the difficulty of obtaining an emulsion of the fat and water with the reactants. That the problem of the acid hydrolysis of fats is essentially one of emulsification has been shown by the observation that triacetin is completely hydrolyzed by treatment with either dilute or concentrated hydrochloric acid. It became strikingly evident, therefore, that emulsification is necessary for the satisfactory acid hydrolysis of fats and that such processes would be of only academic interest until catalysts possessing emulsifying properties were developed.

The status of acid saponification was changed, almost overnight, by the introduction of the so-called Twitchell reagent, modifications of which are widely employed today for obtaining fatty acids from fats. Such fat-splitting agents have been the subject of many chemical studies and of an extensive patent literature. The original Twitchell reagent consisted of the reaction product of benzene, oleic acid, and concentrated sulfuric acid, and was described by Twitchell [41] as benzenestearosulfonic acid, $C_6H_4(SO_3H)$-

$C_{18}H_{35}O_2$. Products possessing similar properties were also prepared from naphthalene and phenol, and the former has been extensively employed. Catalytic amounts of these reagents (1–2%) were observed to bring about essentially complete hydrolysis when heated with fat-water systems, an action which was ascribed to their high acidity combined with their emulsifying powers. Several patents covering the use of these reagents were issued to Twitchell.[42] Such agents are soluble in water and insoluble in dilute hydrochloric or sulfuric acids or in salt solutions. They are also insoluble in petroleum ether and can easily be purified by means of their solubility characteristics. Twitchell [43] explained their function as follows: "The special catalytic action of these sulphonic acids, or 'sulpho-fatty acids' can be explained as follows: They are soluble in water and their aqueous solutions dissolve fatty bodies, acting like soap solutions. At the same time they are acids which are electrolytically dissociated to a high degree. . . ." Twitchell [44] also showed that these reagents not only function as hydrolyzing agents but also are esterification catalysts for fatty acids and glycerol. Fat-splitting agents, termed "Pfeilring reagents," have been prepared by the action of concentrated sulfuric acid upon aromatic hydrocarbons and hydroxy acids, such as ricinoleic acid or the hydroxystearic acid obtained by the hydrogenation of ricinoleic acid.[45] A comparison [46] of such agents with those prepared by the use of oleic acid indicated that the former yield lighter-colored fatty acids and "glycerol waters" than the latter. Kita and Yamano [47] have compared the activities of hydrolyzing agents prepared from various aromatic and fatty acids. They have reported that reagents prepared from rape seed oil acids and also olive oil acids are more active than those prepared from the acids of soybean oil, castor oil, linseed oil, or herring oil. Of the reagents prepared from phenol, benzene, naphthalene, and anthracene, that from naphthalene is the most active and that from anthracene the least active. Grimlund [48] has stated that such agents consist of a hydrolyzing and an emulsifying component.

The sulfuric acid contained in the various Twitchell reagents is apparently the actual hydrolyzing catalyst, since, when such reagents are washed with salt solutions until the washings are no longer acidic, they lose their hydrolyzing powers. The reagent can be regenerated by the addition of sulfuric acid, thus indicating that these fat-splitting catalysts must possess both emulsifying and acidic properties. Hoyer [49] has observed that substances which unite with sulfonic acids reduce the hydrolytic properties of such reagents by decreasing their emulsifying powers. The initial splitting of fats in the presence of the Twitchell reagents is apparently accelerated by the presence of a small quantity of free fatty acids in the oil.[50] Twitchell reagents may be purified by conversion to their sodium salts, washing of these salts with naphtha, conversion to alkaline earth salts, and transformation of the latter into the free acids.[51]

Since the introduction of the aromatic sulfonic fatty acids as fat-splitting catalysts, a large number of substances possessing similar properties have been proposed. Several of these are now widely employed, among the most important of which are the water-soluble sulfonic acids which result from the acid refining of petroleum distillates. The use of such products as fat-splitting catalysts was probably first proposed by Petrov,[52] and they have since been extensively investigated particularly as regards the various means of extracting them from the acid sludges.[53] Their purification by the use of aluminum salts has been proposed by Divine.[54] The splitting of fats by the use of aromatic sulfonic acids has been patented by Riedel, A.-G.,[55] who investigated the action of cyclohexylnaphthalenesulfonic acid, octahydroanthracenesulfonic acid, and other aromatic sulfonic acids. A rather large number of aromatic sulfonic acids, among which may be mentioned cymenesulfonic acid [56] and octadecylbenzenesulfonic acid,[57] have been studied as fat-hydrolyzing catalysts. According to Sandelin,[58] all the aromatic sulfonic acids which possess fat-splitting properties are of high molecular weight, can be precipitated from solution by the addition of acids or salts, and function as both emulsifying and acidic agents. The use of the sulfonic acids obtained by the sulfonation of fatty acid distillation residues has been proposed.[59] Moore and Wallace [60] have suggested the use of a common solvent for the fat and water, such as acetone, in order to bring about a more rapid hydrolysis.

One of the principal objections to acid hydrolysis is that frequently the fatty acids and glycerol which result are quite dark in color. This is particularly true when highly unsaturated fats are split or when the fats contain substantial amounts of unsaponifiable matter. One of the methods which have been proposed for improving the quality of the acids is to conduct the acid-splitting reaction in the presence of decolorizing agents such as fuller's earth, animal charcoal, or wood charcoal, and it has been claimed [61] that lighter-colored products are obtained in the presence of such substances.

It has been stated that the acid-splitting process is more efficient if it is divided into two steps, the first being a partial hydrolysis after which a portion of the "glycerol water" is removed, and the final step being the completion of hydrolysis.[62, 63] The advantages claimed for this procedure are rather hard to visualize, since the intermediate reaction products are generally quite difficult to separate. The use of an alternating current to facilitate the splitting of fats by acids or acid catalysts has been proposed.[64] It has frequently been observed that the acid hydrolysis of castor oil results in low yields of fatty acids. In his study of this hydrolysis, Jones [65] reported that the splitting is essentially complete, as shown by the glycerol yield, and that the low recovery of fatty acids is due to the formation of polyricinoleic acids during the splitting process.

Twitchell reagents have occupied a dominant place in the field of fat hydrolysis for a number of years; however, other acid catalysts such as aluminum chloride, recently investigated by Ott,[66] and sulfur dioxide, proposed by Budde,[67] have been suggested from time to time. The particular advantages of the Twitchell process are that it does not require pressure, although the rate of splitting is materially increased if pressure is used, and that the fats are split directly into fatty acids and glycerol.

BASIC HYDROLYSIS

The complete saponification of fats by means of excess caustic alkali is one of the oldest chemical reactions known. When the primary object, however, is to obtain the free fatty acids, it is apparent that the complete conversion of the acids into soaps is unnecessary. Although it is known that saponification by aqueous caustic solutions cannot be brought to completion at atmospheric pressure, unless an excess of alkali is employed, it is also known that the amount of alkali required may be considerably reduced if the reaction is conducted at higher temperatures under pressure. Under these conditions, fats may be completely split into fatty acids and glycerol by the use of catalytic amounts of basic materials. In such processes the small amount of soap initially formed evidently serves as an emulsifying agent, since any basic material which yields a soluble soap under the reaction conditions has been shown to be a satisfactory catalyst. The substances most frequently employed as basic catalysts, in addition to the alkali metal hydroxides, are calcium oxide or hydroxide, magnesium oxide, barium oxide, zinc oxide, and similar materials. The preparation of fatty acids by the hydrolysis of fats in the presence of basic catalysts has received increased attention in recent years. The production of soaps from fatty acids rather than from fats offers several advantages, and as a consequence the splitting of fats to fatty acids and glycerol assumes an additional industrial significance.

The saponification of fats by the use of aqueous lime under pressure is known as the Krebitz [68, 69] process. The older processes have been replaced by those using catalytic amounts of lime under high steam pressure. The use of magnesium oxide as a substitute for lime was first proposed by Freestone.[70] Hefter [71] has compared the catalytic effects of calcium, magnesium, and zinc oxides in the autoclave process, reporting complete splitting in the presence of 0.5–1% of magnesium oxide in 7–8 hours at 8–10 atmospheres, whereas 0.33–0.5% of zinc oxide produces a similar result under 6 atmospheres. Large amounts of lead oxide are required to produce splitting. Nakae and Nakamura [72] have studied the hydrolysis of soybean oil with 30% of water in the presence of 1% of lime, zinc oxide, or magnesium oxide at 8 atmospheres, and reported the fatty acids obtained from the use of zinc oxide to be paler in color than those obtained from the use of calcium or magnesium oxide. The use of lead oxide was also stated to yield pale fatty acids. The cleavage of fats by means of catalytic amounts of zinc oxide has also been reported by Krause [73] to yield quite light-colored fatty acids. The use of a mixture of zinc oxide and metallic zinc was observed to give quite satisfactory results, although it has been stated that zinc dust alone presents certain difficulties, owing to its tendency to settle out.[71] The importance of the fat-water ratio in the catalytic hydrolysis of fats has been pointed out by Kaufmann and Keller,[74] who reported that maximum splitting is obtained when a 2:1 ratio is employed. The use of magnesium oxide for the autoclaving of low-grade fats has been recommended.[75] Fish oils have been reported to require more catalyst and higher pressures than animal fats.

The speed of saponification by bases has been stated [76] to be influenced by the addition of small amounts of aromatic hydrocarbons. Phenol and eugenol accelerate emulsification, whereas the cresols and naphthols evidently promote saponification since their presence has been reported to raise the reaction temperature. It has been proposed [77, 78] to conduct the splitting in the presence of a chemically inert solvent in order to insure more efficient contact between the reactants. De Grousseau [79] has recommended dissolving the fat in a hydrocarbon prior to its saponification.

It has been observed that higher quality fatty acids result from basic hydrolysis if the process is conducted in two stages. Welter [80] has suggested an initial hydrolysis by heating the aqueous fat system under 6–7 atmospheres pressure followed by removal of the "glycerol water," and completion of the splitting under pressure in the presence of alkaline catalysts. A somewhat similar procedure has been disclosed by Reuter [81] and also by Bergell. [82] Bolis [83] has suggested an initial saponification with sodium carbonate followed by a final treatment with caustic alkali.

The use of aqueous ammonia as a hydrolyzing catalyst has been known for some time. Barbe, Garelli, and de Paoli [84] suggested 0.5% ammonia with steam under 3–6 atmospheres pressure, and Barbe [85] proposed to decompose the residual ammonium soaps by steam. The advantages which have been claimed for the ammonia saponification process have been severely questioned by Keutgen. [86] The use of alcoholic solutions of ammonia for hydrolyzing fats has been suggested. [87] The hydrolysis of fats by liquid ammonia produces glycerol and fatty acid amides, and it has recently been stated [88] that this reaction is catalyzed by the presence of ammonium salts. Fats are converted into glycerol and anilides when heated to 230° in the presence of aniline; [89] aniline derivatives such as m-xylidine, p-anisidine, and p-phenetidine exert similar actions, although the hydrolysis does not proceed to completion. [90] Fatty hydrazides are produced when fats are hydrolyzed by hydroxylamine in absolute methanol solution. [91, 92]

The use of sodium carbonate both as a saponifying agent and as a hydrolyzing catalyst has been proposed; [93, 94] however, Welter [95] has claimed that satisfactory results cannot be obtained by the use of this reagent. It has been observed that the efficiency of sodium carbonate as a hydrolyzing agent is materially increased by the presence of lipolytic substances such as sulfonated castor oil. [96]

Although the hydrolysis of fats under high pressure in the presence of catalytic amounts of basic substances is frequently employed for the industrial preparation of fatty acids, it is apparent that this process is not adaptable to obtaining fatty acids from fats on a laboratory scale. Complete saponification by means of alkali metal hydroxides, however, offers a very convenient means of splitting fats, and this process is frequently employed in the laboratory. The most satisfactory procedure is to saponify the fats in alcoholic alkali, the reaction being conducted under a reflux condenser in the presence of a small excess of the alkali. The alcohol is then evaporated, and the fatty acids are liberated from the soap by acidification, washed free of mineral acid, and dried. Anderson and Brown [38] have observed that the velocity of saponification is twice as great in pentanol as in ethanol and about ten times as great in ethanol as in methanol. It is generally preferable to employ potassium hydroxide rather than sodium hydroxide, because of the greater solubility of the potassium soaps. A small amount of water markedly increases the rate of saponification. Henriques [97] has proposed dissolving the fat in petroleum ether, adding alcoholic sodium hydroxide, and allowing the mixture to stand for twelve hours. This method is somewhat time-consuming, and also has the disadvantage that anhydrous alcohol must be employed. Alkali metal hydroxides exert a catalytic effect upon fat splitting in alcoholic solutions, the reaction, however, being essentially one of alcoholysis. The mechanism of this reaction apparently does not differ fundamentally from that of catalytic splitting in aqueous solutions, since the actual hydrolyzing agent is undoubtedly water in both cases.[18] It has been known for some time [98, 99] that reactions of alcoholysis are catalyzed by the presence of caustic alkalies. For example, tristearin is largely converted into ethyl stearate and glycerol by heating with a small amount of sodium ethylate in ethanol. Larger amounts of alkali reduce the amount of alcoholysis, and theoretically equivalent amounts result in complete saponification.

HYDROLYSIS BY WATER

Fats are appreciably hydrolyzed by prolonged contact with water at ordinary temperatures. An increase of temperature greatly increases the velocity of splitting by water, and when fats are treated with superheated steam in an autoclave substantial splitting results. In 1901, Klimont [100] subjected a number of fats to the action of superheated steam, under pressures varying from 3 to 15 atmospheres, and obtained a high degree of hydrolysis of the glycerides, especially at the higher pressures. The results obtained when olive oil was heated with steam for six hours at varying pressures are shown in Table I. The data shown in this table indicate that at elevated temperatures and pressures steam alone is an effective hydrolyzing catalyst.

TABLE I

ACTION OF STEAM UPON OLIVE OIL

Pressure in Atmospheres	Acid Value [101]
3	6.4
5	35.3
6	41.7
7	53.0
10	62.3
13	108.3
15	159.5

Early workers, such as Bertholet and Menschutkin, have shown that hydrolytic reactions are reversible, and that either hydrolysis or esterification is encountered depending upon the reaction conditions. Sabatier and Mailhe [102] obtained esterification of aliphatic acids and primary alcohols by passing their vapors over TiO_2 at 280–300° and showed that complete hydrolysis results if the ester vapors and steam are passed over the catalyst at higher temperatures. Mailhe [103] completely hydrolyzed esters by passing their vapors mixed with excess steam over lithium oxide at 280–300°.

The direct splitting of fats by means of high-pressure steam or superheated water has been the subject of an appreciable patent literature. Böhm [104] has claimed a process whereby fat and water are heated in an autoclave at 200° with mechanical stirring, under such a pressure that steam cannot be generated. The splitting can be accomplished by the reaction of countercurrent streams of fats and water at high temperatures and pressures,[105] and Henkel et Cie.[106] have disclosed a countercurrent splitting process with water under high temperature and pressure, wherein the fatty acids are removed at one end of the apparatus and the "glycerol water" at the other. Mills [107] heats fats and water separately and passes them countercurrently through an apparatus at 185–300° under 1600 lb. per sq. in. pressure. Water at high pressure and temperature can be percolated downward through an upwardly flowing column of fat in order to effect hydrolysis,[108] and Eisenohr [109] has disclosed a process whereby water and fat are passed through a high-pressure coil, the temperature being maintained between 260 and 320°. It has been observed that if the splitting is carried out in the presence of a small amount of split oil and "glycerol water" the time required for hydrolysis is shortened.[110] The presence of colloidal clay has been stated to have a catalytic effect.[111]

The direct hydrolysis of fats by water alone offers the advantage that the resulting products are not contaminated with soap, acidic substances, or other catalytic materials. Owing to the high pressures involved, such processes are of interest only for the commercial splitting of fats. It is possible that with the many improvements which have been made in pressure techniques and equipment, such processes may be widely used industrially in the future.

HYDROLYSIS BY ENZYMES

The metabolism of fats in both plant and animal systems is inherently associated with the presence in these organisms of enzymes which possess the property of hydrolyzing fatty esters and, to a certain extent, of esterifying fatty acids and alcohols. Such substances are known as lipases, and the fact that they can be separated from the plant or animal organisms in an active state has made them of industrial significance. The lipases apparently function as true catalysts in hydrolytic or esterification reactions and owe their activity to both their emulsifying and hydrolyzing powers. They are qualitatively divided into the plant and animal lipases, and although these two groups have much in common, they possess several characteristic and distinguishing differences. The true lipases of both animal and vegetable origin possess very marked hydrolyzing powers towards the glycerides and other esters of the higher fatty esters; however, they exhibit little if any activity towards the more water-soluble esters of the lower molecular weight acids. Certain animal organs, mainly the liver and the blood—and to a much more limited extent certain plant tissues—contain enzymes which show no hydrolytic activity towards the higher molecular weight esters but possess the property of rapidly hydrolyzing the simple water-soluble esters. These substances are known as esterases and are frequently found associated with true lipases in many plant and animal juices and tissues. The conditions for their maximum activity differ from those for the true lipases, and their presence in certain lipase mixtures can be easily demonstrated.

Because of their ease of preparation and ready availability, the plant lipases are of greater industrial interest as fat-hydrolyzing catalysts than those of animal origin. Plant lipases are present in the seeds of all plants,[112] their biological function being to render the fat of the seeds available during the germination process. Lipase activity increases with germination and is said to reach a maximum in three days, at 30°, after which time it decreases materially.[113] The most widely investigated plant lipase is that found in the castor bean. In 1890, Green[114] and Sigmund,[115] working independently, established the presence of a fat-splitting enzyme in castor beans. The hydrolyzing activity of this lipase was later extensively investigated by Connstein, Hoyer, and Wartenberg,[116] who studied its fat-splitting activity towards a number of fatty esters. Ricinus lipase is insoluble in water, and its activity is materially reduced by contact with water. The enzyme is stabilized by the presence of fats. It is very sensitive to ethanol; however, it is resistant to benzene, ether, or carbon disulfide. It is rapidly inactivated by alkalies and functions only in a neutral or slightly acidic medium. Haley and Lyman[117] have stated that its greatest activity in the presence of oil is at pH 4.7–4.8. The enzyme is apparently activated by the presence of acids, weak acids exerting the greatest accelerating effect. The enzymatic activity of seeds is confined to the cytoplasm, and Nicloux[118] attributes lipase activity in plant seeds to the presence of carbon dioxide. However, he also stated that it functions in neutral solutions, especially in the presence of salts such as magnesium sulfate. Pottevin[119] had previously observed the activating influence of metallic salts. Tanaka[120] showed that the function of the acid is to liberate the enzyme, and observed that an active lipase can be prepared by treating the castor oil cake with the optimum amount of acid and then washing out all the water-soluble substances. Crude oils are hydrolyzed when stirred with crushed castor beans and water, although no action takes place when refined oils are similarly treated.[121] Kita and Osumi,[122] on the other hand, have observed that while activated lipase can act without the addition of any acid, the addition of a small amount of acid accelerates the action. They also pointed out that the sensitivity of lipase to acid depends upon the amount of oil present. Lipase functions most efficiently in a water-in-oil emulsion. The retarding action of sodium or calcium chloride solutions is counteracted by the addition of acetic acid. Tantzov[123] has stated that the optimum concentration of activator and substrate is that which gives the most rapid formation and decomposition of intermediate products, and that with very low concentrations of acids the hydrolysis is reversible, while irreversible changes occur with higher concentrations. The optimum temperature for the action of ricinus lipase is around 35°. It can be heated as high as 165° in the presence of fat, although it is rapidly inactivated even at 60° in the absence of fat.

The activity of castor bean lipase is apparently confined to the hydrolysis of the higher molecular weight fatty esters. Armstrong and Ormerod [124] have stated that the activity of lipase on an ester is inversely proportional to the affinity of the ester for water, on account of the necessity which exists for a direct association of the enzyme with the carboxyl group. It has been stated,[113] on the other hand, that a highly purified lipase splits simple esters as well as those of high molecular weight. Attention has been called [26, 125] to the observations that substantial amounts of lower fatty acids inhibit the lipase activity. Since it has been observed that triacetin is hydrolyzed by castor bean enzymes, it is apparent that castor beans contain not only a lipase but probably an esterase. Falk and Sugiura [126] have claimed the separation of the castor bean enzymes into a lipase and an esterase fraction, and Kelsey [127] has prepared separate fractions, one capable of splitting fats and the other of splitting cholesteryl esters.

A number of methods for obtaining an active lipase from castor beans have been proposed.[128] Most of them endeavor to isolate the enzyme in a pure state relatively free from extraneous matter. Generally the hulled seeds are ground in water, the solids filtered, and the lipase obtained in the form of an emulsion by centrifugation. Jalander [129] ground the dry seeds in cottonseed oil and centrifuged the mixture. Longenecker and Haley [27] have prepared a dry, stable lipase by extracting the macerated beans with petroleum ether, drying, pulverizing, and sifting the product. A sample so prepared was reported to have retained a considerable portion of its original activity after a period of ten years. The hydrolysis of fats with castor bean lipase simply involves mixing from 3 to 8% of the lipase preparation with the fat, containing from 40 to 50% of water, adding a small amount of an acid such as acetic acid, or of an activating salt such as manganese sulfate, and permitting the mixture to stand at about 35° for twenty-four to forty-eight hours, with frequent stirring. The hydrolysis is stopped by heating the mixture with steam or by the addition of strong acids. When the hydrolysis is completed and the mass allowed to settle, the reaction mixture separates into three layers, the upper layer consisting of fatty acids and any unhydrolyzed fat, the lower layer the glycerol and water, and the middle layer an emulsion of fat and albuminous materials. The formation of this middle layer has always presented a great obstacle to enzyme splitting, since it represents an appreciable loss in fatty material and no satisfactory method has been developed to treat it effectively. Altenburg [130] has suggested working this layer up into soap directly. According to Sachs,[131] the advantage of enzyme splitting is that light-colored acids are obtained, essentially unaltered in composition by the process. The disadvantages are the loss of fatty materials occasioned by the formation of a middle layer, the long time required for the reaction, and the fact that the splitting is never complete. The hydrolytic reaction is reversible.[132, 133]

Enzymes possessing fat-hydrolyzing properties have been reported as present in a large number of seeds, and it is reasonable to assume that all seeds contain such substances. It is interesting to note, however, that the various seed enzymes appear to differ greatly in their fat-hydrolyzing powers and in their optimum conditions of operation. Fernández and Pizarroso [134] have investigated the hydrolyzing enzymes present in almonds, hazelnuts, peanuts, walnuts, poppy and hemp seeds, corn, pine kernels, and castor beans, and have found that many of these are more active towards lower esters than towards the fats, indicating a high degree of esterase activity. Mastbaum [135] has reported the presence of a fat-hydrolyzing enzyme in cola nuts. This enzyme differs from other plant lipases in that its hydrolyzing properties are destroyed by water or dilute acids. He reported a similar enzyme to be present in chestnuts, nutmegs, oats, and black pepper. Plant lipases have been observed in papaw seeds,[136] sunflower seeds,[137] sweet almonds,[138] and fungi.[139, 140, 141] The latter were found to be most active in slightly alkaline solutions.

The animal lipases and esterases have been the subject of a large amount of investigational work, a detailed discussion of which would be beyond the scope or intention of this book. The true lipases appear to be essentially confined to the pancreas and the intestinal tract, while the esterases are found widely distributed throughout the animal system. The ability of pancreatic extracts to hydrolyze fats has been known for many years, and it has also been recognized that the reaction is reversible.[119, 142] Balls and Matlack [143] have observed that pancreatic lipase (steapsin) is as effective with the ethyl esters of the fatty acids as with the fats themselves and that only primary ester groups are attacked, indicating that the hydrolysis of a β-group in a fat molecule is preceded by a migration of this group to the α-position. Weber and King [144] have reported that the α- and β-monoglycerides of lauric, myristic, palmitic, and stearic acids are hydrolyzed equally well by pancreatic lipase. The extent of hydrolysis is increased by increasing the amount of lipase, and Bradley [145] has stated that the complete hydrolysis of triolein is possible, since a definite amount of enzyme is able to hydrolyze a definite amount of fat irrespective of the mass of the latter. Reversion is not encountered if more than 50% of water is employed. The enzyme functions at as low as 0° and is inactivated at 54° or higher temperatures.[146] The addition of bile salts has an accelerating effect upon the lipase activity, which Terroine [147] attributed to a direct action on the enzyme itself, although others have considered that it simply furthers emulsification and thus accelerates the hydrolysis without displacing the final limit.[148, 149]

Pancreatic lipase is prepared by drying the pancreatic glands with dehydrating agents such as acetone, extracting with water or ethanol mixtures, centrifuging, and drying. The enzyme can be purified by adsorption on aluminum hydroxide followed by removal with ammonium phosphate.[150] A separate lipase appears to exist in the stomach, since von Pesthy [151] has stated that fat digestion in the stomach is due to the presence of a specific enzyme secreted by that organ. There is little question but that a separate gastric lipase exists, but although many experiments have been performed to show its presence, it has not been separated in an active form. Izar [152] has demonstrated the presence of lipases in many of the animal organs such as the kidneys, liver, intestines, testes, and adrenal glands. The lungs have frequently been reported to contain fat-splitting enzymes.[153, 154]

In addition to lipases, the various animal organs also contain enzymes capable of splitting the lower esters but possessing little if any activity on the higher molecular weight esters. The best known of such enzymes is liver esterase. A study of the kinetics of hydrolysis by liver esterase has shown that the speed of hydrolysis of ethyl butyrate is proportional to the concentration of the enzyme and inversely proportional to that of the ester.[155] Nogaki [156] found that the course of the reaction is not the same for all esters, and that after an initial steep drop or slight rise the reaction velocity decreases to the end of the reaction. He attributed these results to a binding of the enzyme by the various cleavage products.

The fat-splitting activity of bacteria has been clearly demonstrated, the enzymes appearing to have a marked hydrolytic action on the lower molecular weight esters such as tributyrin.[157] Collins [158] has observed that the hydrolysis of simple triglycerides by bacteria becomes more difficult with increase in the molecular weight of the glycerides. A close relationship between the lipolytic and proteolytic abilities was noted.

METHODS OF SEPARATION OF THE FATTY ACIDS

Our present-day knowledge of the fatty acids represents the culmination of many years of study and research. No single factor has contributed more towards this knowledge than the many investigations which have been made upon the separation of the fatty acids, and it is safe to conclude that future advancement in this field will be intimately associated with the development of more effective methods for the separation of these acids from one another. The many processes which have been investigated for fatty acid separation, such as crystallization of the acids or their derivatives, distillation of the acids or their esters, and other methods, can be roughly divided into two groups. The first of these comprises those processes which are useful for analytical or identification purposes only and which, because they are time-consuming or costly, have either no or very limited commercial application. The second group consists of those processes which are adaptable to the large-scale preparation of the acids. A rigid classification of the methods for fatty acid separation is not possible, since many of the commercial processes are also excellent laboratory procedures and future research may convert some of the now strictly academic methods into commercially feasible processes. Among the procedures which have been suggested for the separation of the fatty acids we find distillation, crystallization, pressing, graining, and centrifugation, together with combinations of one or more of these methods. All these unit processes have been widely employed, and each has its special advantages together with its limitations. Probably the most satisfactory means for obtaining pure fatty acids is not confined to a single method of separation but combines two or more procedures. This is particularly true in the laboratory-scale separation of fatty acid mixtures, where a number of crystallizations are often combined with several fractional distillations. Generally the methyl esters of the acids are employed in the distillation procedures. The choice of the method of separation depends quite largely upon the starting material available and upon the object to be attained. In the following discussion of fatty acid separations it appears logical to consider the various unit processes separately, although we should realize that they can frequently be advantageously combined and that the various methods differ greatly with regard to their practical importance.

Non-Solvent Crystallization (Graining and Pressing)

The non-solvent separation of the fatty acids depends upon the fact that they are completely miscible in the liquid state. However, if such solutions are cooled, the higher-melting acids crystallize and can then be separated from the liquid acids by suitable mechanical means such as pressing. This process has long been employed for the preparation of commercial stearic acids, and the so-called double- and triple-pressed stearic acids are familiar articles of commerce. The fatty acids of animal oils are usually employed as the starting material in this process. Since such oils generally contain more palmitic than stearic acid, the so-called stearic acids obtained are actually mixtures of acids, palmitic being present in somewhat the greater amount. The composition of the solid and the liquid (red oil) acids obtained is dependent upon the time and temperature of the crystallization, and upon the temperature and efficiency of the subsequent pressing operations. The crystallization process is generally performed in a refrigerated room, the fatty acids being contained in trays. The temperature of the room is so adjusted that the fatty acid mixtures are cooled slowly, in order to insure the formation of large, well-defined crystals. Rapid cooling must be avoided, since this results in a crystal meal or an amorphous mass from which it is extremely difficult to separate the liquid acids. When the crystallization has proceeded to the desired extent the entire mass is transferred to a filter press and the liquid acids separated from the solid cake. This initial pressing is conducted at a low temperature in a cold press and the resulting solid acids still contain an appreciable amount of liquid unsaturated acids. The solid acids are then transferred to a hot press and pressed at a higher temperature, thereby removing more of the liquid acids. A repetition of this process results in solid acids which contain only a very small amount of unsaturated acids. Since the liquid acids from the hot pressing operations have a composition approaching that of the original mixture, they are returned to the crystallization trays. The crystallization and pressing operations have been described by Lewkowitsch [159] and also by Dubovitz.[160] The solid acids are generally white and somewhat crystalline in appearance and, as before stated, consist of a mixture of palmitic and stearic acids. The process is of general application for the separation of solid from liquid fatty acids.

Solvent Crystallization

Solubility differences among the fatty acids or their derivatives are frequently employed in analytical procedures and also as a means of obtaining individual acids from fatty acid mixtures and of purifying specific acids. The fractional crystallization of the acids themselves or of their simple alkyl esters, in the presence of solvents, is found among our earliest analytical procedures. Such methods have recently attracted considerable attention in the low-temperature solvent separation of unsaturated acids. A number of the earlier analytical methods are primarily concerned with the solubility characteristics of metallic soaps, and some of these procedures are still extensively used today, particularly for the laboratory separation of saturated from unsaturated acids. In the solvent separation of any system containing two or more substances we must appreciate that at least two factors are involved. First we have the solubility of the individual substances in the particular solvent, and second we have the mutual solubility influences of the substances upon one another. The first of these can be determined by actual solubility measurements; however, the second is somewhat more complex and involves factors such as solid-solution or mixed-crystal formation and also association either between the components themselves or between the components and the solvent.

One of the earliest and most effective procedures for the separation of solid saturated from liquid unsaturated fatty acids is known as the Varrentrapp [161] method, which is based upon the insolubility of the lead salts of the solid saturated acids in ether. This method was first proposed by Gusserow [162] as early as 1828. The lead salts of myristic, palmitic, stearic, and higher saturated acids are practically insoluble in ether, whereas those of oleic, linoleic, and linolenic acids are appreciably soluble. By converting an acid mixture into its lead salts and treating these salts with ether, a separation of saturated from unsaturated acids can, therefore, be effected. This separation is at best rather qualitative, since solid unsaturated acids, such as elaidic or erucic acid, yield lead salts which have a limited solubility in ether, and it has also been observed that mutual solubility influences are encountered. The method does, however, afford a reasonably accurate analytical means for determining the composition of many naturally occurring fatty acid mixtures. After the soluble and insoluble lead soaps are separated, the free acids are obtained from them and the composition of the solid and liquid acids can be determined by the appropriate analytical procedures. A number of modifications of the original method have been proposed.[163, 164, 165, 166, 167] Twitchell [168] has suggested the use of 95% ethanol instead of ether as the solvent, and Farnsteiner [169] has recommended the use of benzene. The Twitchell method has been investigated by Steger and Scheffers,[170] who reported it to be accurate only to within a few per cent but to be preferable to the other lead salt methods previously proposed. The use of three solvents, ethanol, chloroform, and ether, has been suggested by Seidenberg.[171] The last two solvents are then volatilized from the solvent mixture and the insoluble lead soaps of the saturated acids separated. It has been observed that the lead salts of the saturated acids are more soluble in ether than in petroleum ether,[172, 173] which indicates that the latter is a better solvent in which to effect the separation. Several workers [174, 175, 176] have called attention to the observation that the solubilities of lead salts of saturated acids are much greater if substantial quantities of the unsaturated lead salts are present in the solution. It has been suggested that lead salts may exert an isomerizing influence upon oleic acid.[177] Keffler and McLean [178] have reported that the lead salt-ether method failed to remove the final 3 to 4% of the saturated acids from oleic acid and that the addition of an excess of lead acetate did not render the separation more effective. Meigen and Neuberger [179] have reported the lead salt-ether method to extract four-fifths of the total oleic acid and 5 to 10% of the palmitic acid from a fatty acid mixture. The lead salt-benzene method yielded liquid acids of iodine number 81.4 and solid acids of iodine number 4.5, from a mixture of saturated and unsaturated acids. Although the various lead salt methods offer analytical procedures for the investigation of fatty acid mixtures, they are adaptable only to the separation of the solid saturated acids from the liquid acids. Such methods are, therefore, of limited value as a means for obtaining pure acids even upon a laboratory scale, and can be considered only as methods for final purification.

The solubility characteristics of a large number of fatty acid salts have been investigated, and many methods of separation of fatty acids have been proposed, based upon the solubility behavior of these various salts. Such procedures are, in general, confined to the separation of liquid unsaturated acids such as oleic, linoleic, and linolenic acids from solid saturated acids such as palmitic and stearic acids. Although such methods have frequently been investigated for the separation of one saturated acid from another, they are of limited use because of the small solubility differences of the soaps of closely allied saturated acids. They are, therefore, satisfactory for the purification of acids only when the fatty acid mixture contains a major percentage of one compound, and are not adaptable *per se* to the separation of mixtures containing three or more components. They are, however, of potential interest in certain instances as a means of obtaining pure acids from mixtures resulting from fractional distillation.

The solubilities of the lithium salts of the higher acids have been intensively investigated, and several methods based upon these solubilities have been suggested as a means of fatty acid separation. Partheil and Ferié [180] have proposed the fractionation of the lithium salts of the fatty acids in ethanol as a separation procedure. Although this method has been criticized by Fahrion [176] and also by Farnsteiner,[181] it appears to have been employed successfully by André [182] for the separation of palmitic from stearic acid, and Holde and Godbole [183] have claimed the separation of tetracosanoic acid from hexacosanoic acid through their lithium salts. In the latter instance a mixture of chloroform and ethanol was employed as the solvent. Lauric acid has been separated from myristic acid by Jacobson and Holmes,[184] by reason of the greater solubility of lithium laurate in water. The higher acids present in the mixture were separated by fractional crystallization of their magnesium salts in 50% aqueous ethanol. These authors [185] have determined the solubilities of the lithium salts of lauric, myristic, palmitic, and stearic acids in a number of solvents. The solubility of lithium laurate was found to be appreciably greater than that of lithium myristate in most of the solvents investigated. Although lithium palmitate is more soluble than the stearate, the difference is not so great as that exhibited by the two lower acids. For example, the solubility in grams per 100 g. of these various salts in water at 25° was reported to be: laurate, 0.187; myristate, 0.036; palmitate, 0.015; and stearate, 0.010. The solubilities of the lithium salts of these four acids in various organic solvents were observed to be as follows: methanol (25°) 3.773, 1.680, 0.771, 0.439; ethanol (25.4°) 0.447, 0.224, 0.118, 0.089; pentanol (25.7°) 0.111, 0.046, 0.032, 0.028; amyl acetate (25°) 0.064, 0.034, 0.024, 0.029; acetone (25°) 0.376, 0.447, 0.508, 0.706; ether (15.8°) 0.011, 0.013, 0.007, and 0.011. Caprylic and capric acids have been separated from coconut oil fatty acids by fractional crystallization of their lithium salts followed by fractional crystallization of their barium salts.[186] The lithium salt-acetone method has been applied to the separation of the highly unsaturated acids of cod liver oil,[187] of sardine oil,[188] and of whale oil.[189] Tsujimoto[190] has observed that the lithium salts of the highly unsaturated fatty acids of fish oils are quite soluble in acetone containing 5% of water, whereas those of the saturated or less unsaturated are not. Keffler and McLean[178] have studied the lithium salt-alcohol method and have reported that highly unsaturated acids can be removed from saturated acids, although at least twelve crystallizations are required.

The solubilities of the ammonium soaps in absolute ethanol have been proposed for use in separating oleic acid from palmitic and stearic acids.[191] The ammonium soaps are first formed by passing ammonia into an ether solution of the mixed acids, the ether is then removed by evaporation, and the soap is treated with a small quantity of cold ethanol. The acids are obtained from the ammonium soaps by treatment with hydrochloric acid. The use of acetone as a solvent for the separation of the ammonium soaps has been proposed by Bull and Fjellanger,[192] and David[193] has claimed the separation of solid from liquid acids by the preferential solubilities of the ammonium soaps in aqueous ammonia. It has been reported[194] that ammonium laurate and myristate are appreciably soluble in aqueous ammonia, so that the value of this latter method is questionable. Meigen and Neuberger[179] have observed that the method of Bull and Fjellanger[192] gives results varying with the kind and amount of the acids present, while David's [193] method extracted 0.953 g. of oleic acid out of a total of 1.003 g., and the iodine number was 82 instead of 90. A method has been suggested [195] for the separation of oleic and stearic acids by the gradual and successive decomposition of their ammonium salts in cold water.

The separation of oleic acid from stearic acid by virtue of the different solubilities of their thallium salts in 95% ethanol has been reported by Meigen and Neuberger.[179] Improvements in this method were announced two years later by Holde, Selim, and Bleyberg,[196] who reported the solubility of thallium oleate in 96% ethanol to be 2.254 g. per 100 g. of solvent at 15°. The solubility in 50% ethanol at 15° is only 0.924 g. per 100 g. of solvent and the solubility in water at 80° is 0.3034 g. per 100 g. of solvent. Holde and Takehara [197] have stated that the solubilities of thallium laurate and thallium myristate in 50% ethanol are too great to permit of their separation from the thallium salts of unsaturated acids such as thallium oleate. The use of ether as a solvent for the separation of the thallium salts of the fatty acids has been suggested,[198] thallium oleate being approximately forty times more soluble in this solvent at 30° than the stearate, and approximately one hundred times more soluble than the laurate.

The solubilities of the potassium salts of the fatty acids in acetone have been proposed by Fachini and Dorta [199] as a means of separating liquid from solid acids. The fatty acids are dissolved in acetone and neutralized by the addition of potassium hydroxide solution, the solution is then cooled to 15°, and the crystals are separated by filtration. Modifications of this method have been suggested by Rideal and Acland [200] and by de Waele.[201] However, Meigen and Neuberger [179] have reported the method to give unreliable results. The use of ethanol as a solvent for the potassium salts has been proposed, Scheringa [202] having claimed the separation of palmitic from stearic acid by treatment of their potassium salts with ethanol. The solubility of potassium stearate in aqueous ethanol of 96, 79.5, 66, and 49% was reported to be 0.62, 1.8, 2.6, and 4.4% respectively, whereas potassium palmitate in the same solvents was soluble to the extent of 1.4, 6.5, 19, and 45%, at 18°. The solubility of the sodium salts in acetone has been used as a method for the separation of the highly unsaturated acids of fish oils from the more saturated acids.[203, 204]

The solubility behaviors of a number of other metallic soaps have been investigated and proposed for use in separating the fatty acids. Gascard and Damoy [205] have separated the fatty acids of beeswax by the fractional crystallization of their calcium soaps from ethanol, and a method for the separation of acids based on the fractional crystallization of their calcium soaps has been patented.[206] The solubilities of the barium salts in methanol [207] and of the zinc salts in ethanol [208] have been used to effect fatty acid separations. According to Agde,[209] the zinc salts do not afford a satisfactory means of separation. Jacobson and Holmes [185] have reported the solubilities of the barium salts of lauric, myristic, palmitic, and stearic acids in a number of solvents. The separation of the highly unsaturated from the less unsaturated acids of fish oils by reason of the differing solubilities of their barium salts in benzene has been investigated.[210] The magnesium salts have been rather intensively studied,[211] and these salts have proved to be of exceptional usefulness for the separation of certain dibasic acids.[212] Gsell [213] has stated that caproic and caprylic acids can be separated by means of their strontium salts.

The fractional crystallization of the acids themselves from their solutions in organic solvents offers a method which shows considerable promise not only for the separation of saturated from unsaturated acids but also for the separation of an unsaturated acid from one more highly unsaturated. Although the fractional crystallization of acids from solvents such as ethanol or acetone is broadly old, the earlier workers generally attempted separations at only moderately reduced temperatures in somewhat concentrated solutions, and in most cases incomplete separations were encountered. The recent investigations which have been made in this field employ dilute solutions at greatly reduced temperatures, and they are of exceptional interest since they show promise of affording a practical method for the large-scale separation of acids, particularly when such processes are employed subsequently to distillation or other means of separation. Low-temperature solvent crystallization permits not only of the removal of saturated from unsaturated acids but also of the separation of the unsaturated acids themselves. It has been shown by several investigators [214, 215] that high molecular weight saturated acids form solid solutions with one another, while this phenomenon is either greatly reduced or absent when the system involves a saturated acid and an unsaturated acid possessing a *cis* configuration. The *trans* modification of an unsaturated acid, on the other hand, forms a solid-solution system with a saturated acid. Since, however, naturally occurring unsaturated acids are of the *cis* form, solid-solution formation would not be evidenced between naturally occurring saturated and unsaturated acids. The unsaturated acids themselves apparently do not exhibit a marked tendency toward solid-solution formation or toward association, since a study [216] of mixtures of stearic, oleic, and linoleic acids has indicated that an increase in unsaturation is accompanied by a decreased tendency toward association. It has been observed that the saturated acids exert profound mutual solubility influences; [217, 218, 219, 220] for example, the solubility of palmitic acid in carbon tetrachloride has been reported to be materially increased by the presence of lauric acid. Recently, Ralston and Hoerr [221] have shown that the mutual solubility effect is due to the lowering of the melting point and is not so great as previously supposed. Association may take place between the acids themselves or between the acids and the solvent. The tendency toward mixed-crystal formation has been observed by many investigators [222, 223, 224, 225, 226, 227, 228] and has been attributed to association of the acids at the carboxyl group.

Solvent crystallization as a means of final purification is an old procedure; however, only within comparatively recent years has it been considered as a process for separating complex fatty acid mixtures. It should be borne in mind that unsaturation in the hydrocarbon chain is generally accompanied by an increased solubility in organic solvents, and that the liquid saturated acids are generally more soluble than their higher homologs. The mutual solubility influence of one acid upon another can be largely explained on the basis of a lowered melting point for the higher-melting component. Factors such as association or solid-solution formation, therefore, are generally antagonistic to well-defined solvent separations. However, where these exert a minimum influence, such as in the separation of a saturated from an unsaturated acid of the same chain length, well-defined separations are possible.

In 1910, Fachini and Dorta [229] investigated the solubilities of the fatty acids in petroleum ether at low temperatures and suggested this procedure as a means of separating saturated from unsaturated acids. The use of acetone for the crystallization of oleic acid has been investigated by Bertram, [230] who purified this acid by crystallization from acetone at $-15°$. Two years later, Raymond [231] reported the use of ethanol as a solvent for the same procedure. The solvent separation of fatty esters and acids derived from waxes has been proposed,[232] the list of solvents employed including phenol, nitrobenzene, furfural, acetone, carbon tetrachloride, and cyclohexanone. Wolff[233] has studied the fractional crystallization of the fatty acids of lard, employing ethanol as the solvent. In 1937, Brown and Stoner[234] published their results upon the low-temperature solvent preparation of linoleic acid. These authors subjected the fatty acids of cottonseed oil and also of corn oil to preliminary crystallizations from several solvents at $-20°$, which effectively removed the saturated acids. A number of solvents were then investigated for the further separation of the unsaturated acids. The fractionation of 10% solutions of the acid mixture from toluene at $-70°$ and from ether and acetone at $-50°$ yielded filtrates high in linoleic acid. Successive crystallizations at very low temperatures gave precipitates high in linoleic acid; for example, crystallization from methanol at $-85°$ yielded a precipitate containing 86% of linoleic acid, crystallization from acetone at $-60°$ a precipitate containing 85%, and crystallization from ethanol at $-70°$ one containing 79%. The precipitate from 76% aqueous acetone contained 77% of linoleic acid and the filtrate 81%. The fractional crystallization of the methyl esters from acetone yielded a final precipitate at $-75°$ which contained 82% of methyl linoleate. The crystallization of the lithium soaps from butanol and of the potassium soaps from absolute ethanol was also investigated as a means of obtaining linoleic acid concentrates. It was concluded that the crystallization of unsaturated fatty acids from appropriate solvents at low temperatures is a useful procedure for their separation. In 1938, Brown and Frankel[235] obtained a precipitate containing 93% of linoleic acid by low-temperature solvent crystallization, and later these authors[236] succeeded in obtaining essentially pure linoleic acid by a preliminary separation of the fatty acids of corn oil from acetone at $-20°$ to $-50°$, followed by crystallization of the linoleic acid fraction from acetone at $-70°$. The acid was further purified by crystallizations from petroleum ether at $-48°$, $-60°$, and finally $-62°$. Previous to this work the only source of pure linoleic acid had been the debromination of linoleic acid tetrabromides, a procedure which is open to question because of the possibility of isomerization. However, a comparison of the naturally occurring linoleic acid with that prepared by the debromination procedure has indicated that the two are essentially

identical.[237]   The preparation of oleic acid of high purity by the
fractional solvent crystallization of olive oil fatty acids from
acetone at low temperature has been described by Brown and
Shinowara.[238]   The method depends upon the great difference in
the solubilities of oleic and linoleic acids, the latter being found
in the various filtrates, the separation of which permits of a final
precipitation of the oleic acid.   Pure samples of oleic acid have
subsequently been prepared by Hartsuch [239] and by Smith [240] by a
similar procedure.   Wheeler and Riemenschneider [241] have reported the preparation of pure methyl oleate by a fractional distillation of the methyl esters of olive oil followed by low temperature crystallizations from acetone.   Linolenic acid has been prepared by Shinowara and Brown [242] by the fractional crystallization
of the fatty acids of linseed and perilla oils from acetone at −65°,
the linolenic acid which remained in the filtrate being subsequently
crystallized from petroleum ether.   Later, Brown and Green [243]
prepared methyl ricinoleate and ricinoleic acid from castor oil
acids by low-temperature solvent crystallization, and Shinowara
and Brown [244] obtained methyl arachidonate by the fractional
crystallization from acetone of the methyl esters of suprarenal
phosphatides.   The separation of eleostearic acid by the solvent
crystallization of the fatty acids of tung oil has been reported by
several investigators.[245, 246, 247]   Pure erucic [248] and brassidic [249] acids
have been obtained by crystallization methods.

A process of separation of the saturated fatty acids through their
anhydrides has been suggested,[213] the method being based upon
the assumption that if a mixture of saturated acids is treated with
acetyl chloride, lauric, myristic, palmitic, and stearic acids form
the corresponding simple anhydrides while caproic, caprylic, and
capric acids form mixed anhydrides.   When the mixture is dissolved
in pyridine and poured into water, the simple anhydrides will
precipitate while the mixed anhydrides remain in solution.   The
use of diffusion methods for the separation of high molecular weight
saturated acids has been investigated by Heiduschka and Ripper.[250]

Distillation

The fractional distillation of fatty acid esters, particularly the
methyl esters, has been extensively employed as a means of analysis
of fatty acid mixtures, and the fractionation of the methyl esters is
frequently used for the laboratory preparation of individual acids.
Although the distillation of the fatty acid esters offers a convenient

method for the laboratory separation of the acids, large-scale fractionation of the acids themselves offers a much more practical process for their commercial preparation. Distillation methods can be effectively employed for the separation of mixtures of fatty acids of differing chain lengths, and such methods are now used for the preparation of commercially pure fatty acids. Although acids of different chain lengths can be easily separated by distillation methods, the boiling points of saturated and unsaturated acids which possess the same number of carbon atoms do not differ sufficiently to permit of their separation. Distillation of the glycerides themselves is not adaptable to the preparation of pure acids because of the heterogeneous nature of the glyceride molecules. The most important earlier studies concerned with the fractional distillation of fatty acids and their esters were those reported by Krafft and coworkers,[251] who investigated the boiling points of the acids and their esters under high vacuum. Caldwell and Hurtley [252] have determined the boiling points of lauric, myristic, palmitic, stearic, and oleic acids in the cathode vacuum, using a Gaede pump with a Crookes tube between the receiver and pump, and obtained values materially lower than those previously reported. These authors stated that at a very high vacuum a liquid has no boi ing point, but that it sublimes or evaporates, just as water does in air, at a rate and at a temperature depending on the nature of the substance and on the temperature to which it is heated. The fatty acids of butter and of coconut oil were fractionated by Caldwell and Hurtley using the very-low-pressure apparatus described by them. Brown [253] has also described an apparatus for the distillation of the fatty acids under very high vacuum. The separation of palmitic and stearic acids by vacuum distillation was reported simultaneously by Krafft [254] and by Kreis and Hafner.[255] The separation of the fatty acids of coconut oil [256] and of cod liver oil [257] by the distillation of their methyl esters was announced several years later. The fatty acids of butter fat have also been separated by the fractional distillation of their methyl esters,[258, 259, 260, 261, 262, 263] and Elsdon [264] has separated the fatty acids of both coconut and palm kernel oils by a similar method. The fractional distillation of methyl esters has also been applied to the separation of the fatty acids of cottonseed oil,[265] hydrogenated herring oil,[266] human milk,[267] chaulmoogra oil,[268] and peanut oil.[269] Stokoe [270] has also described the fractional distillation of the methyl esters of coconut oil fatty acids, and Armstrong, Allan, and Moore [271] have reported the separation of the fatty acids of coconut oil and palm kernel oil by the fractional distillation of their ethyl esters. In 1923, Brown and Beal [210] separated the methyl esters of the fatty acids of menhaden oil by vacuum distillation and concluded that it is possible to make a rough separation of the acids according to their molecular weights by this method. Later, Brown [272] reported the separation of the methyl esters of the fatty acids of brain lipids by fractional distillation at pressures varying from 4 to 7 mm. The separation of the highly unsaturated fatty acids of beef brains was attempted by the fractional distillation of their methyl esters. Previously, Brown and Ault [273] had reported the fractional distillation of the methyl esters of the debrominated acids of beef, hog, and sheep brains.

Although the laboratory separation of fatty acid mixtures by the fractional distillation of either the acids or their esters has been studied for a number of years, the separations obtained have been quite crude. Channon, Drummond, and Golding,[262] for example, have indicated that the method is of little quantitative value. It, therefore, became quite evident that material improvements in distillation procedures were necessary before the full possibilities of this method of separation could be even partially realized. It is very fortunate that during the past fifteen years this subject has been intensively studied and that these studies have resulted in the development of apparatuses capable of effecting separations with a much greater degree of accuracy than was formerly possible. In the simple type of laboratory equipment such as flasks, unpacked columns, and similar equipment, equilibrium between the vapor and liquid phases is not obtained, and such factors as reflux ratio and rate of distillation are essentially uncontrolled. Separations performed in such equipment are consequently highly unsatisfactory. Improvements in laboratory distillation apparatus have been described by a number of investigators,[274, 275, 276, 277, 278] and in 1930 Jantzen and Tiedcke [279] developed an electrically heated, packed column which contained an evacuated jacket to protect it against temperature fluctuation. The working of this apparatus was illustrated by the separation of the methyl esters of palmitic and stearic acids, and the device was also employed by these authors for the fractionation of the high-melting acids of peanut oil. The apparatus was subsequently modified by later investigators,[280, 281] and an improved apparatus was later employed by Lepkovsky, Feskov, and Evans [282] for the separation of caprylic, capric, lauric, myristic, palmitic, and erucic acids. Indications of association were observed in the separation of the higher acids, but their complete separation could be effected by the fractionation of their methyl esters. The separation of the methyl esters of saturated and unsaturated acids has been described by Keffler

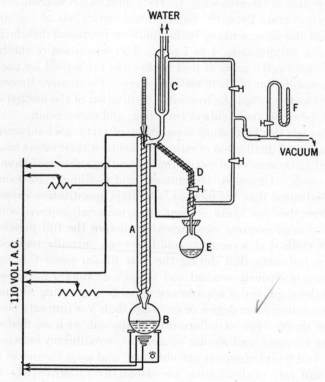

FIG. 1. Laboratory distillation apparatus.

and McLean,[178] and distillation of the methyl esters has been proposed as a method for the separation of certain dicarboxylic acids.[283]

Modern laboratory distillation apparatus consists of an electrically heated, packed column, permitting a high reflux ratio and adjustable distillate collection, the column being packed in a highly thermally insulated outer shell to minimize thermal fluctuations. A diagram of a typical laboratory apparatus for the fractionation of the fatty acids or their derivatives is shown in Fig. 1.

The apparatus consists of a thermally insulated, packed column (A) attached to a distilling flask (B), receiver (E), and condenser

(*C*). Standard taper, ground-glass joints are generally employed. The temperature at the top of the column is measured by a thermometer and the pressure is measured on the manometer (*F*). The distilling flask and the column are electrically heated, the temperature being controlled by means of rheostats. The side arm (*D*) is also electrically heated in order to prevent the distillate from solidifying. The vacuum is obtained by a standard vacuum pump attached to a large, evacuated steel drum in order to insure against rapid pressure changes during the distillation. The laboratory columns are generally three to four feet in length and are permanently mounted. Their efficiency depends largely upon the type of packing material employed.

Industrial columns are usually of the bubble-cap type, the various plates exerting a scrubbing action and thus giving the effect of multiple distillations. This type of apparatus has too high a hold-up for ordinary laboratory distillations and is only adaptable to large-scale continuous work. The various packed columns which have been developed give materially less hold-up and are quite adaptable to the distillation of small amounts of materials. A large amount of investigational work has been done upon the development of various types of packing materials. In 1932, Whitmore and Lux [284] described a column in which the packing consists of Lessing rings (5 × 5 mm.) made of 50-mesh copper screen, and in the next year Wilson, Parker, and Laughlin [285] described a column in which the packing consists of a glass modification of the single- and double-turn wire helices previously used. Weston [286] developed a fractionating column which is a modification of that previously described by Cooper and Fasce.[278] The extensive investigations of Podbielniak have contributed materially to the development of efficient small-scale distillation equipment, and many of his results are summarized in his excellent article published in 1933.[287] In this article he describes fractionating columns having separate, sleevelike, metal reflector type vacuum jackets for thermal insulation. The distilling tubes were packed with spiral, continuous, wire coil packings, and such columns were shown to be more effective than others of similar size which had been previously developed. The advantage of a continuous packing was pointed out, and it was shown that such packings are superior to a chance-arrangement, non-continuous packing. Klem [288] has reported the separation of the methyl esters of palmitic, stearic, oleic, and elaidic acids by the use of the Podbielniak apparatus. Fenske, Tongberg, and Quiggle [289] have compared the efficiency of a number of types of packing material, the materials investigated including one-, two-, and six-turn helices, glass helices, crimped wire, straight carding teeth, bent carding teeth, double-cross wire forms, various types of rings, glass tubes, BB shot, bird shot, and various types of rivets and jack chains. These authors stated that of this group the better packings are the wire or glass helices, the carding teeth, and the jack chains. The shape and distribution of the packing material are, undoubtedly, determinative factors in the efficiency of fractionating columns, and the importance of such factors as the contact surface and the proper drain-back of the liquid cannot be over-emphasized. An efficient fractionating column packed with one-turn glass helices has been described by these authors.[290] Packing material composed of wire helices has been claimed to be extremely efficient,[291, 292, 293] and a column packed with a close-fitting wire helix was used by Schoenheimer and Rittenberg[294] for the fractionation of methyl palmitate from methyl stearate. A simple method for preparing glass helices suitable for packing laboratory fractionating columns has been described.[295] The use of a fractionating column packed with single-turn glass helices has been investigated by Longenecker[296] for the separation of the solid acids of beef tallow, the acids of peanut oil, and the liquid esters of butter fat, and by Hilditch and Longenecker[297] for the separation of the methyl esters of butter fat fatty acids. The use of fatty acid ester distillation methods of fat analysis has recently been reviewed by Longenecker.[298] The conical type of packing developed by Stedman,[299] the use of which has been described by him,[300] has proved to be one of the most effective packing materials now known. A detailed description of this type of packing, together with a number of efficiency tests, has been reported by Bragg.[301] He describes this packing as follows:

The conical type of packing is made of wire cloth which has been embossed and trimmed into flat, truncated, conical disks. A semicircular hole is cut out of one side of the cone and extends about two thirds of the distance from the edge of the cone to the flat in the center. The disks are welded together alternately back to back and edge to edge, so as to form a regular series of cells, with the holes which serve as vapor passageways located alternately on opposite sides of the section of packing.

The construction of this packing is shown in Fig. 2. These packings are generally fitted into Pyrex tubes, the tube being then placed in a highly thermally insulated metal container. Such columns have been found to be highly efficient for the separation of many fatty derivatives, including the acids themselves and their simple alkyl esters. The importance of the improvements which have been made in laboratory fractionating equipment cannot be over-emphasized, and many separations which were formerly impossible can now be performed easily and effectively.

The use of molecular distillation, although essentially confined to fractionation of the glycerides or other very high-boiling substances, is of interest for the separation of the high molecular weight acids, particularly where such acids are highly unsaturated and sensitive to high temperatures. Molecular distillation of the highly unsaturated acids of fish oils has been studied by Farmer and Van den Heuvel.[302]

The large-scale separation of the fatty acids by fractional distillation is a comparatively recent development. Although the commercial distillation of the alkyl esters of the acids has been suggested [303] as a method of separating acids, and this method is frequently employed as a laboratory procedure, it is evident that the direct fractionation of the acids themselves is a much more practical process. All

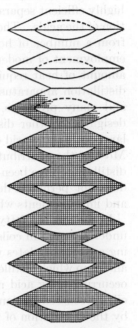

Fig. 2. Diagram of Stedman type of packing.

fractionating stills for fatty acids operate under a high vacuum, which is necessitated by the fact that the higher fatty acids undergo material changes at high temperatures, and, consequently, distillation at ordinary pressures is attended by a large amount of decomposition. The older type of still consisted of a direct-fired still pot attached to an evacuated column and condenser and operated in batch processes, the charges sometimes being as much as 10,000 lb. and the distillation rate being maintained at approximately 1000 lb. per hour. The prolonged heating, together with the unequal heat distribution due to the direct firing, resulted in appreciable decarboxylation and polymerization of the acid mixture and, consequently, in the conversion of a substantial portion of the fatty acids to an undesired pitch. This residue is termed "stearin pitch" and is of a complex and variable composition [304] which depends upon the material from which it results and its conditions of formation. The older types of fatty acid fractionating apparatus have given way to the modern, indirectly heated, flash distillation processes which yield highly efficient separations with a minimum amount of decomposition of the acids. The time of heating of the acids has been reduced from a number of hours to a period of several minutes, and the employment of modern heat exchangers has greatly decreased the amount of heat required. The transition from the older type of distillation apparatus to those now employed has not been easy, and many problems, such as excessive corrosion, improper still design, and other disturbing factors had to be overcome before large-scale fatty acid distillation became commercially practicable. Most of the contributions which have been made upon fatty acid distillation have been described in the patent literature, and space does not permit a detailed treatment of all the many processes and improvements which have been suggested.

In the modern fatty acid distillation still the feed stock is heated under pressure in coils and flashed into a vacuum column containing a series of plates which give the effect of multiple distillations and from which distilled fractions can be removed. Either naturally occurring fatty acid mixtures, such as the fatty acids of soybean oil, cottonseed oil, and fish oils, or fatty acid mixtures obtained by the acidulation of foots are employed as the starting material. Generally, steam is used to lower the partial pressures of the acids and permit of a more effective separation. Multiple-stage distillation processes employing hot furnace gases have been suggested.[305] The use of steam or other gaseous carriers to facilitate the distillation of high-boiling materials, such as fatty acids, has been described by a number of investigators, among whom may be mentioned Bodman,[306] Pickering,[307] Leimdörfer,[308] Franzen,[309] and Schönberger.[310] The use of organic solvents has also been frequently suggested. Distillation processes employing steam have been the subject of several patents [311, 312, 313] and the behavior of fatty acids during steam distillation has been investigated.[314] The passage of the steam through a compressor in order to raise its temperature has been suggested.[315] A large number of processes have been proposed and employed for the distillation of high molecular weight substances, and the fractionating stills suggested differ radically in principle and design. As previously stated, the older type of still consisted of a still pot connected with a fractionating column, condenser, and receiver and was generally operated on a non-continuous principle. It has been claimed that high-grade fatty acids can be obtained by the use of such stills,[316, 317, 318] although it is quite apparent that a sizable amount of feed stock is converted to a refractory residue because of the long period of heating and the direct firing.

In 1934, a process for distilling acids was described [319] in which the acid mixture was brought to a vaporizing temperature in a confined passage and then discharged into a chamber at reduced pressure. A process of separating the vapors from the entrained matter was also disclosed,[320] and the compression of the vapors before being withdrawn has been suggested as a means of producing a higher vacuum during the distillation process. [321] Goranflo [322] has described a process of distillation in which the feed stock is heated to a volatilizing temperature while passing in a restricted stream through a heating zone, and the vapors are discharged upon an intermediate upper plate of a bubble tower. The stock then descends in the bubble tower countercurrently to a stream of superheated steam, and the uncondensed vapors from each plate are passed through the bodies of liquid in the plates above. The final vapors are then removed from the upper plate and condensed. The operating results obtained by this process have been reported by Tolman and Goranflo.[323] Processes in which the heated stock is introduced into the fractionating column countercurrently with steam have also been described by Tolman.[324] A fractionating apparatus involving an injector, flash chamber, and surface condenser has been described by Sieck,[325] and Bergell [326] has disclosed a process in which the liquids flow in films over an upright surface, the films being heated by radiation from a heated surface a short distance from and surrounding the surface of the film. In 1936, Potts and McKee [327] described a distillation process by which fatty acid mixtures may be simultaneously and continuously separated into a series of components of different boiling points. The process consists of heating the stock in a heating coil to a temperature sufficient to insure vaporization at a reduced pressure and flashing the materials into a zone of reduced pressure. The heated vapors pass through a series of heat-exchanging pools of condensed fatty acids having successively lower boiling points, and the vapors from the last pool are condensed, a portion being returned as reflux liquid. There may be withdrawn from any of the pools a liquid of lower boiling point than that contained in the next lower pool. Steam may be employed to create a partial pressure and assist in the vaporization by lowering the distillation temperature. A process involving serially arranged vaporization stages has been disclosed by Brücke,[328] and McCulloch[329] has proposed an arrangement in which fractions of intermediate boiling range are subjected to a stripping medium and a portion of each fraction is recirculated. Lee [330] has suggested atomizing the feed stock with an inert gas, heating the atomized mist to a temperature sufficient to insure vaporization at sub-atmospheric pressure, and expanding the atomized mist into an evacuated column. A process of fatty acid distillation which includes countercurrent contact of the hot vapors from the bottom of the still with the feed stock has been described.[331]

Light-colored distillates are generally obtained during fatty acid distillations in spite of the fact that many of the feed stocks employed contain substantial amounts of colored material. Dubovitz [323] has shown that the coloring material is higher boiling than the fatty acids and is susceptible to polymerization. The prior heat treatment of the fatty acids in the presence of hydrogen but without substantial hydrogenation, in order to obtain color-stable fatty acids, has been recently proposed,[333] and preliminary oxidation of the stock has also been suggested.[334]

The separation of fatty acids by converting them into mixtures of nitriles corresponding to the acids, separating the nitriles by fractional distillation, and finally reconverting the nitriles to fatty acids has been studied.[335]

Although crystallization and distillation procedures are the most important methods for the separation of the fatty acids, other processes have been proposed for the separation of specific acid mixtures. For example, Kurtz and Schaffer [336] have described the separation of hydroxy from non-hydroxy acids by heating mixtures of their esters with dibasic acid anhydrides. The reaction mixture is then dissolved in petroleum ether, and the derivative formed with the hydroxy esters is extracted with alkali.

THE IDENTIFICATION OF THE FATTY ACIDS

The methods used for the identification of pure organic compounds and for ascertaining the components of mixtures are generally familiar to all chemists. Physical constants such as the melting points, refractive indices, and specific gravities are universally recognized as contributing to the identification of organic compounds. The preparation of a characterizing derivative frequently offers further proof of the identity and purity of the compound in question. Unfortunately, very few acceptable derivatives of the unsaturated fatty acids have been described; however, a number of investigators have developed derivatives of the saturated acids which have proved to be very useful in the identification of these compounds. The close structural similarity of the various series of fatty acids has made possible the use of a number of analytical procedures which have proved to be of great value, and several of these are recognized as standard constants in the fatty acid field. Such constants as the neutralization equivalent, the iodine number, the acetyl value, and the more recent thiocyanate number are well-known terms and have been applied to the fats and fatty acids for many years. Without attempting to detract from the usefulness of such analytical constants it should be pointed out that they are not, *per se*, proof of the identity or purity of an individual acid. For instance, an equimolecular mixture of palmitic and stearic acids will possess the neutralization equivalent of margaric acid, and a mixture of unsaturated acids may possess the theoretical iodine number of oleic acid.

Physical Constants

The physical constants of the fatty acids are determined by procedures similar to those generally employed with other types of organic compounds, and a detailed discussion of such methods is probably not necessary. A very satisfactory procedure for the determination of the melting point, where a sufficient amount of sample is available, is to obtain a heating curve. The sample is placed in a test tube which is then immersed in a heating bath, and the temperature of the sample is raised slowly, the temperature being measured either by an accurate thermometer or by a potentiometer. A plot of the sample temperature against time shows a thermal halt at the transition point, the value and length of the halt indicating not only the melting point of the sample but also its purity. The determination of the freezing point by obtaining a cooling curve has been observed by the author to be a very satisfactory procedure, the purity of a sample being easily ascertained by this method. The values obtained are easily reproducible, and very small amounts of impurities can be detected by this procedure. Mixed melting points are often of questionable value for the higher acids and their derivatives, since significant melting point depressions are not always observed.

The boiling point of an organic compound is, in most cases, a recognized and characteristic constant and is frequently used as an aid to its identification. The accurate determination of the boiling point is, however, a somewhat difficult process, and its value as a physical constant, particularly for the identification of the higher molecular weight acids, is somewhat questionable. This is due to the fact that the boiling points of acids containing the same number of carbon atoms, but differing in the degree of unsaturation, are so similar that a distinction between such acids or their simple derivatives by this method is extremely difficult. Since fractional distillation is a recognized method for separating acids, the boiling points of the acids or of their esters are frequently obtained incidental to their separation and purification. An apparatus for the determination of the boiling points of high molecular weight compounds has been described,[337] and Pool and Ralston [338] have reported the boiling points of the saturated fatty acids containing from six to eighteen carbon atoms inclusive at pressures varying from 1 to 760 mm. (see Chapter V, Table XXXVIII).

The refractive index is one of the most accurately and easily obtained physical constants, and, where an acceptable orienting value is available, the refractive index is of great value as an aid to the identification of a fatty acid or its derivative. Since the refractive index is materially influenced by the presence of impurities, the purification of many of the fatty acids or their derivatives can easily be followed by the determination of this constant. The refractive indices, n_D^t, of the normal saturated fatty acids, together with their molar refractivities and densities at 80°, have recently been reported.[339] A discussion of these values is contained in Chapter V.

Analytical Methods *

The various chemical constants which are employed for the study of the fatty acids or their mixtures are of great technical and practical importance, and, although they fall short of a positive

---

* For a more complete description of the methods employed for the determination of the various analytical constants of the fatty acids, the reader is referred to Lewkowitsch, *Chemical Technology and Analysis of Oils, Fats and*

identification, their value as auxiliary constants is unquestioned. Such constants as the neutralization value, the iodine number, or the acetyl value are universally employed in fatty acid work. They are of particular usefulness where one is dealing with fatty acid mixtures, the determination of whose actual composition would be essentially impossible or would involve time-consuming and difficult analytical procedures. Chemical constants such as the iodine number, therefore, have a definite place in the investigation of the fatty acids, and their usefulness as analytical tools will probably continue indefinitely.

The neutralization value of a fatty acid is defined as the number of milligrams of potassium hydroxide required to neutralize 1 g. of the fatty acid. The value is determined by weighing the acid sample into an Erlenmeyer flask, adding neutral ethanol, and heating gently until the acid is completely dissolved. The sample is then titrated with a standardized potassium hydroxide solution using phenolphthalein as the indicator. The mean molecular weight can be calculated from the neutralization value.

The iodine number is, perhaps, the most widely employed constant in all analytical work involving the fats or fatty acids. This constant is based upon the ability of an unsaturated carbon-to-carbon bond to add halogen and is, therefore, a measure of the degree of unsaturation of a fat or fatty acid. By definition, the iodine number is the number of grams of iodine absorbed by 100 g. of a fat or fatty acid. A large number of procedures have been suggested for determining this value, and that proposed by Wijs [340] is most generally employed. The forerunner of the iodine number was the bromine number originally suggested by Mills and Snodgrass;[341] however, the tendency of bromine to be introduced by substitution renders the results obtained by this method of somewhat doubtful value. In 1884, Hübl [342] proposed a method for determining the amount of unsaturation based upon the absorption of iodine in alcoholic solution in the presence of mercuric chloride, the actual halogenating agent probably being iodine monochloride, which is formed by the following reaction:

$$HgCl_2 + 2I_2 \rightarrow HgI_2 + 2ICl$$

The Wijs method can be considered as a modification of the

Waxes, 6th ed., Vol. 1, Macmillan and Co., London (1921); Jamieson, *Vegetable Fats and Oils*, 2nd ed., A.C.S. Monograph No. 58, Reinhold Publishing Corp., New York (1943); *Official and Tentative Methods of the American Oil Chemists' Society* (1941).

original Hübl procedure, since Wijs' solution consists essentially of a solution of iodine monochloride in glacial acetic acid. It is prepared by dissolving 13 g. of resublimed iodine in 1 l. of glacial acetic acid, titrating an aliquot portion, and then passing in dry chlorine until the original titration value is almost doubled. It is advisable to withhold a small portion of the solution and add this at the completion of the chlorination, since it is desirable to have a slight excess of iodine present in the finished reagent. The determination of the iodine number is performed by adding a small sample (0.2 g.) of the material under investigation to 15 cc. of chloroform and then adding 25 cc. of the standardized Wijs reagent. The solution is then allowed to remain in the dark for thirty minutes after which 15 cc. of potassium iodide solution (15%) and 75 cc. of water are added and the liberated iodine titrated with a standardized thiosulfate solution, using starch as the indicator. The method proposed by Hanuš [343] employs iodine monobromide rather than the monochloride as the addition agent. Hanuš' solution is prepared by adding bromine to a glacial acetic acid solution of iodine, the amount of bromine added being sufficient to double the original titration value. This reagent is often preferred because of its keeping qualities; however, the values obtained by its use are generally somewhat lower than those resulting from the use of Wijs' solution. It should be remembered that acids containing acetylenic bonds or conjugated unsaturation add the theoretical amount of iodine with great difficulty.

The thiocyanogen value originally proposed by Kaufmann [344] is frequently employed in conjunction with the iodine number for the determination of the composition of mixtures of unsaturated acids. The method is based upon the finding that thiocyanogen adds to the ethylenic bond of oleic acid but that only one of the double bonds of linoleic and two of linolenic acid are reactive. Since iodine adds to all the double bonds, a determination of both the iodine and the thiocyanogen values permits of the calculation of the percentages of oleic, linoleic, and linolenic acids in a mixture containing these acids. It has been found that, although the experimental value agrees closely with the theoretical value for oleic acid, the thiocyanogen numbers of linoleic and linolenic acids present in a mixture containing these acids differ from the theoretical values and are quite sensitive to the experimental conditions employed. [345, 346, 347, 348] Riemenschneider, Swift, and Sando [349] have investigated the thiocyanogen values of the methyl esters of oleic, linoleic, and linolenic acids and have suggested the values of 89.4 for oleic acid, 93.9 for linoleic acid, and 162.0 for linolenic acid if $0.1N$ thiocyanate solutions are used, and 89.4, 96.8, and 167.5, respectively, when $0.2N$ solutions are employed. The method of preparation of the lead thiocyanate solution and the procedure employed in the determination of the thiocyanogen value, together with the methods used for calculating the results, have been discussed in detail elsewhere.[350, 351, 352]

In addition to the analytical procedures of rather general application, a number of methods have been developed which are useful in determining the amount of specific types of acids present in an acid mixture. The addition of maleic anhydride to a conjugated system is employed as a measure of the percentage of conjugated unsaturated acids in an acid mixture. The application of the Diels-Alder reaction to the analysis of fatty acids and fats was first suggested by Kaufmann and coworkers,[353] and a simplified and quite satisfactory procedure for the determination of diene values has been reported by Ellis and Jones.[354]

The determination of the acetyl value is the commonly accepted procedure for the estimation of hydroxy acids. The method is based upon the esterification of the hydroxyl group of a hydroxy acid by acetic anhydride, followed by saponification of the acylated acid with a known amount of potassium hydroxide and determination of the excess alkali by titration with standardized hydrochloric acid solution, using phenolphthalein as the indicator. When determining the acetyl value of a fatty acid or of a mixture of fatty acids, it is, of course, necessary to subtract the acid value. The acetyl value is defined as the number of milligrams of potassium hydroxide required for the neutralization of the acetic acid obtained on saponifying one gram of an acylated fat. The method has been studied in detail by a number of investigators,[355, 356, 357, 358, 359] and an official method for the determination of this constant has been adopted.[360]

Characterizing Derivatives

The preparation of a previously described derivative is one of the recognized methods for establishing the identity and purity of an organic compound. A satisfactory derivative should be a well-defined and easily prepared crystalline solid. In addition, its melting point should differ sufficiently from the melting points of closely allied compounds to be useful as a basis for distinguishing between them, and its mixed melting points should be decidedly lower than that of the pure derivative. The problem of finding satisfactory derivatives for the lower members of the saturated fatty acid series has not been extremely difficult, and a number of excellent derivatives have been described. Since, however, the differences between the individual members of the series become relatively less with increase in molecular weight, few satisfactory derivatives for the higher acids are known. These acids are so similar that, in spite of the fact that quite a number of derivatives have been proposed, few, if any, are entirely satisfactory. The search for qualifying derivatives for the higher fatty acids should be continued. It should be borne in mind that any crystalline compound which can be prepared from a fatty acid is a potential derivative; however, in many instances, the compounds are so difficult and time-consuming to prepare that they are of little value for this purpose. The derivatives described below include those compounds which have been proposed as characterizing derivatives for distinguishing one fatty acid from another and which have been prepared from a sufficient number of fatty acids to indicate their value in characterizing the individual members of a homologous series.

The amides and related compounds such as the anilides have been frequently suggested as characterizing derivatives for the saturated fatty acids. The amides can be prepared by passing ammonia into the acids at 190–210° for ten to fourteen hours. Although this is best done under pressure, it can be accomplished in an open flask if a continuous stream of ammonia is present. When only small amounts of material are available, it is advisable first to prepare the acid chloride and treat this with ammonia in the presence of a non-hydrolyzing solvent. The anilides, p-toluidides, and similar derivatives are also best prepared through the fatty acid chlorides. Robertson [361] has prepared the amides, anilides, p-toluidides, o-toluidides, o-bromo-p-toluidides, p-bromoanilides, 2,4,6-tribromoanilides, β-naphthylamides, and the α-bromo-β-naphthylamides of the saturated acids. The melting points reported are shown in Table II.

The solubilities of several aliphatic amides in a number of organic solvents have been recently reported by Ralston, Hoerr, and Pool.[362] These authors observed the freezing points of the amides containing an even number of carbon atoms to be as follows: caprylamide, 105.9°; capramide, 98.5°; lauramide, 102.4°; myrist-

TABLE II

MELTING POINTS OF FATTY ACID DERIVATIVES, °C.

No. of C Atoms	Amides	Anilides	p-Toluidides	o-Toluidides	o-Bromo-p-toluidides	p-Bromo-anilides	2,4,6-Tribromo-anilides	β-Naphthyl-amides	α-Bromo-β-naphthyl-amides
2	82	112	153	110	118	167	232	132	138
3	77	106	126	87	111	149	203	...	139
4	115	96	75	79	90	115	179	125	139
5	106	63	74	70	100	108	...	112	136
6	101	92	73	71	84	105	136	107	120
7	96	65	80	68	90	98	134	101	111
8	105	55	70	69	78	103	131	103	104
9	99	57	84	73	86	100	131	103	103
10	99	70	78	76	82	102	129	104	102
11	99	71	80	78	91	102	129	...	...
12	100	78	87	83	85	104	126	106	99
13	100	80	88	85	95	...	...	107	...
14	103	84	93	88	89	107	124	108	100
16	106	89	98	...	...	110	124	...	...
18	109	94	102	97	97	114	126	112	106

amide, 105.1°; palmitamide, 107.0°; and stearamide, 109.7°. The aliphatic amides are peculiar in that there is little relationship between the molecular weight of an amide and its melting point, and also in that the melting point range of the entire series covers only a few degrees. They are, therefore, of little value as derivatives for establishing the identity of any particular acid. The data shown in Table II indicate that the same comments apply to the anilides, p-toluidides, and other similar derivatives. Hann and Jamieson [363] have proposed the 2-methyl-5-isopropylanilides as derivatives for the fatty acids. These are prepared by treating the fatty acid chlorides dissolved in ether with an excess of cymidine (2-methyl-5-isopropylaniline). The melting points reported are as follows: lauric, 82–83°; myristic, 88–89°; palmitic, 90–91°; stearic, 93–94°; arachidic, 81–82°; and lignoceric, 84–85°. The fact that the 2-methyl-5-isopropylanilides of arachidic and lignoceric acids have lower melting points than those of myristic and palmitic acids renders their value as derivatives quite questionable. Bryant and Mitchell [364] have made some crystallographic studies of the p-bromoanilides of a number of acids; however, the only fatty acid investigated was n-valeric acid.

The p-nitrobenzyl esters of several fatty acids have been prepared by Lyons and Reid [365] by methods previously described.[366] The p-nitrobenzyl ester of palmitic acid melts at 42–42.5°, whereas oleic, erucic, and linoleic acids give oily esters. These authors were unable to prepare a satisfactory derivative from margaric or stearic acid by this method. The p-nitrobenzyl esters of several dibasic acids have been prepared by Kelly and Segura,[367] who reported the following melting points: glutarate, 69°; adipate, 105.6°; suberate, 85°; and azelate, 43.8°. The phenacyl esters originally proposed by Rather and Reid [368] have been extensively investigated and have proved to be valuable derivatives for the identification of the lower fatty acids. A number of p-halophenacyl esters were later described,[369] and Rather and Reid [370] have suggested their use for the separation of the fatty acids. The phenacyl esters are easily prepared by the action of the phenacyl bromide upon the sodium salt of an acid in aqueous ethanol, the reaction being as follows:

$$p\text{-}XC_6H_4COCH_2Br + NaOCOR \rightarrow p\text{-}XC_6H_4COCH_2OCOR + NaBr$$

The preparation of the phenacyl, p-chlorophenacyl, and p-bromophenacyl esters of lauric, myristic, palmitic, stearic, arachidic, and lignoceric acids has been reported.[371] Drake and Bronitsky,[372] who prepared the phenacyl and p-halophenacyl esters of a number of fatty acids, have commented that the melting points of the esters for any given acid increase as the *para* substituent is varied from hydrogen to chlorine, to bromine, to iodine. The iodophenacyl esters possess the highest melting point, but these authors considered that for the higher acids they are still not sufficiently high to be easily purified by crystallization. They have, therefore, suggested the p-phenylphenacyl esters as derivatives, since they were shown to possess somewhat higher melting points than other phenacyl esters previously reported. Lundquist [373] has reported the phenacyl ester of heptanoic acid to be a liquid. An extensive investigation of the p-halophenacyl esters was made by Moses and Reid [374] in 1932. The melting points of the phenacyl and substituted phenacyl esters which have been reported are listed in Table III.

TABLE III

MELTING POINTS OF PHENACYL, p-HALOPHENACYL, AND p-PHENYLPHENACYL
ESTERS OF NORMAL SATURATED ALIPHATIC ACIDS, °C.

Acid	Phenacyl Ester	p-Chloro-phenacyl Ester	p-Bromo-phenacyl Ester	p-Iodo-phenacyl Ester	p-Phenyl-phenacyl Ester
Acetic	40	72.4	86.0	117.0	111.0
Propionic		98.2	63.4	98.0	102.0
Butyric	Oil	55.0	63.0	81.5	97.0
Valeric	Oil	97.8	75.0	81.0	63.5
Caproic		62.0	72.0	84.0	65.0
Enanthic	Oil	65.0	72.0	78.8	62.0
Caprylic		63.0	67.4	79.2	67.0
Pelargonic		59.0	68.5	77.0	
Capric		61.6	67.0	82.0	
Undecanoic		60.2	68.2	81.8	
Lauric	48.9	70.0	76.0	85.8	84
Tridecanoic		67.0	75.0	88.5	
Myristic	56	76.0	81.0	89.8	90
Pentadecanoic		74.0	77.2	93.0	
Palmitic	63.0	82.0	86.0	94.2	94
Margaric		78.8	82.6	92.0	91
Stearic	69.0	86.0	90.0	97.2	97
Arachidic	85–86	86.0	89		
Lignoceric	87–88	99–100	90–91		

A study of the melting points of the esters included in Table III shows that the substituted phenacyl esters are reasonably satisfactory derivatives for the higher fatty acids. Both the p-bromo- and p-iodophenacyl esters of palmitic and stearic acids differ by about four degrees in melting points, which is probably sufficient for purposes of characterization. Unfortunately, no mixed melting point data have been reported for these esters, and their value as derivatives depends quite largely upon the extent of the melting point depression. The substituted phenacyl esters of the acids of the oleic series have been described by Kimura,[375] who reported the following melting points: p-phenylphenacyl esters, oleate, 61°; erucate, 76°; cetoleate, 72.5°; p-chlorophenacyl esters, oleate, 40°; erucate, 56°; cetoleate, 54.5°; p-bromophenacyl esters, oleate, 46°; erucate, 62.5°; cetoleate, 60.5°. From these values it is evident that any of these derivatives would be suitable for the identification of oleic and erucic acids. The phenacyl and p-bromophenacyl esters of a number of dibasic acids have been reported by Kelly and Kleff,[376] and the p-phenylphenacyl esters by Drake and Sweeney.[377] The melting points reported by these investigators are shown in Table IV.

TABLE IV

MELTING POINTS OF PHENACYL, p-BROMOPHENACYL, AND p-PHENYLPHENACYL
ESTERS OF DIBASIC ACIDS, °C.

Acid	Phenacyl Ester	p-Bromo-phenacyl Ester	p-Phenylphenacyl Ester
Malonic			175
Glutaric		136.8	152
Adipic	87.6	154.5	148
Pimelic	72.4	136.6	145–148 (decomp.)
Suberic	102.4	144.2	151
Azelaic	69.7	130.6	141
Sebacic	80.4		140

It will be noted that the melting points of the phenacyl and p-bromophenacyl esters of dibasic acids which contain an uneven number of carbon atoms are materially lower than those of the adjacent even acids. The p-phenylphenacyl esters cannot be considered as satisfactory derivatives for the dibasic acids because of the close agreement in melting points between the adipate and suberate, and also between the azelate and sebacate. Although the phenacyl esters of dibasic acids possess much lower melting points than the substituted esters, the difference between individual members is sufficiently great to permit an identification. The various substituted phenacyl esters merit further investigation as derivatives, not only for the saturated mono- and dibasic acids but also for the unsaturated acids.

The arylhydrazides of a number of higher fatty acids have been studied by Veselý and Haas.[378] These investigations were undertaken with the view of utilizing the hydrazides not only for the identification of the fatty acids but also for effecting their separation. In general, however, the solubilities of the hydrazides were found to be too similar to accomplish this latter purpose. The hydrazides were prepared by a method proposed by Strache and Iritzer,[379] which consists of refluxing the acids with a 50% excess of the hydrazine for about one hour at 130–140°. The reaction is as follows:

$$RNHNH_2 + RCO_2H \rightarrow RNHNHCOR + H_2O$$

The melting points of the hydrazides prepared by these authors are given in Table V.

TABLE V

MELTING POINTS OF HYDRAZIDES OF SOME FATTY ACIDS, °C.

	Hydrazide					
Acid	Phenyl-	β-Naphthyl-	α,α-Methyl-phenyl-	Diphenyl-	Phenyl-ditolyl-	2,4-Xylyl-phenyl-
Lauric	105–106	136	56			
Myristic	108	139	63			
Palmitic	109	135	74	124		
Stearic	110	132–133	78.5	122.5	115–116	119–120
Oleic	91–93			83–86	78–79	92–93
Erucic	82–83	107	74	88		
Brassidic	98	121–122	69	106		

Pollard, Adelson, and Bain [380] have investigated the piperazine salts of several dibasic acids and of the lower molecular weight fatty acids. These salts are prepared by adding 0.05 mole of piperazine hexahydrate to 0.1 mole of the acid, washing the product with ether, and crystallizing from the appropriate solvent. The reaction involved is as follows:

$$
\begin{array}{ccc}
& \text{H} & \\
& \text{N} & \\
\text{H}_2\text{C} & \quad & \text{CH}_2 \\
\text{H}_2\text{C} & \quad & \text{CH}_2 \\
& \text{N} & \\
& \text{H} &
\end{array}
+ 2RCO_2H \rightarrow
\begin{array}{ccc}
& \text{CO}_2\text{R} & \\
& \text{NH}_2 & \\
\text{H}_2\text{C} & \quad & \text{CH}_2 \\
\text{H}_2\text{C} & \quad & \text{CH}_2 \\
& \text{NH}_2 & \\
& \text{CO}_2\text{R} &
\end{array}
$$

The following melting points were reported for the piperazine salts of several monobasic acids: 1,4-dibutyrate, 121–122°; 1,4-divalerate, 112.5–113°; 1,4-dicaproate, 111–111.5°; and 1,4-diheptanoate, 95–96°. Since no salts of the higher acids were prepared the evaluation of this derivative is difficult. The use of S-benzyl-thiuronium chloride, $C_6H_5CH_2S$⟨$\begin{smallmatrix}NH\cdot HCl\\ NH_2\end{smallmatrix}$, for the identification of aliphatic acids has been suggested,[381] and the salts of lauric, myristic, palmitic, and stearic acids were reported to melt at 141°, 139°, 141°, and 143°, respectively. It is apparent that these melting points do not differ sufficiently to be useful for the identification of the higher acids. The salts of benzylamine have been proposed as acid derivatives; however, only the caproate has been prepared in the fatty acid series.

The 2-alkylbenzimidazoles, prepared by the reaction of the fatty acids with o-phenylenediamine, have recently been suggested [382] as derivatives for the identification of aliphatic acids. The reaction involved in their preparation is as follows:

$$\bigcirc\begin{smallmatrix}NH_2\\ NH_2\end{smallmatrix} + RCO_2H \rightarrow \bigcirc\begin{smallmatrix}NH\\ N\end{smallmatrix}\!\!>\!\!CR + 2H_2O$$

It was observed that with the lower members of the series the melting point interval between adjacent members was large and there

TABLE VI

Constants for 2-Alkylbenzimidazoles

Acid	M.P., °C.	Mixed M.P. with Next Higher Homolog
Formic	172.0–173.0	130–132
Acetic	177.0–177.5	157–158
Propionic	174.5	155–156
Butyric	157.0–157.5	141–143
Valeric	155.0–155.5	152–153
Caproic	163.0–163.5	138–143
Enanthic	137.5–138.0	132–135
Caprylic	144.5–145.0	136–137
Pelargonic	139.5–140.5	128–131
Capric	127.0–127.5	117–120
Undecanoic	114.0–114.5	106–107
Lauric	107.5	107–108
Tridecanoic	109.0–109.5	105–106
Myristic	105.0–105.5	100–102
Pentadecanoic	98.5–99.5	97–98
Palmitic	96.5–97.0	94–96
Heptadecanoic	93.5–94.5	93–94
Stearic	93.5–94.5	

was considerable depression in the melting point of mixtures of adjacent members. The 2-alkylbenzimidazoles of the acids above lauric acid, however, do not offer a very satisfactory means of distinguishing these acids from one another because of the small differences in melting points of the higher members. The melting points and mixed melting points of the 2-alkylbenzimidazoles are shown in Table VI.

In 1939, Ralston and McCorkle [383] proposed the use of 4,4'-diaminodiphenylmethane as a reagent for the identification of monobasic saturated aliphatic acids. The diamides are prepared by heating one part of 4,4'-diaminodiphenylmethane with slightly more than two parts of the acids. Although the lower acids require refluxing, a few minutes heating is sufficient to prepare the diamides of the higher acids. The products are crystallized from a mixture of benzene and methanol or from benzene and 1-butanol. These diamides are easily prepared and purified and have proved to be reasonably satisfactory derivatives. The melting points and mixed melting points of the diamides are shown in Table VII.

TABLE VII

CONSTANTS FOR DIAMIDES OF 4,4'-DIAMINODIPHENYLMETHANE

Acid	M.P., °C.	Mixed M.P. with Next Higher Homolog
Acetic	227–228	205–210
Propionic	212–213	188–193
Butyric	197–198	185–188
Valeric	188–189	179–181
Caproic	185–186	179–181
Enanthic	183–184	176–178
Caprylic	182–183	176–179
Pelargonic	176–177	175–177
Capric	178–179	173–175
Undecanoic	175–176	172–174
Lauric	174–175	171–173
Tridecanoic	172–173	170–172
Myristic	170–171	167–169
Pentadecanoic	167–168	166–168
Palmitic	167–168	164–166
Heptadecanoic	164–165	163–165
Stearic	164–165	

Recently, Gilman and Ford [384] have prepared an imposing number of derivatives of lauric, myristic, palmitic, and stearic acids with the purpose of studying their suitability for characterization of the high molecular weight fatty acids. The derivatives investigated by these authors are as follows: N-acylcarbazoles, N-acylphenothiazines, N-acyl-p-toluenesulfonamides, p-phenyl-phenacyl esters, p-nitroanilides, N-acylsaccharines, 2,4-dinitro-phenylhydrazides, N-acyl-2-nitro-p-toluidides, p-tolylmercuric salts, phenylmercuric salts, triphenyllead salts, monoureides, p-xenylamides, p-acylbiphenyls, 2,8-diacylcarbazoles, p-acylamino-benzoic acids, acylated aminodibenzofuranes, and sym-diacylbenzi-dines. Of this large number of derivatives the N-acylcarbazoles and the N-acyl-p-toluenesulfonamides were considered to be the most satisfactory, since they are easily prepared and show a difference of three to five degrees in the melting points between adjacent members and a mixed melting point depression of from four to eight degrees. The former are prepared by heating 0.01 mole of carbazole with 0.01 mole of the acid chloride at 100–150° until hydrogen chloride ceases to be evolved, and the latter are obtained by heating equivalent quantities of the acid chloride and p-toluenesulfonamide for two hours at 100–125°. The melting points of the N-acylcarbazoles are shown in Table VIII and of the N-acyl-p-toluenesulfonamides in Table IX.

TABLE VIII

N-ACYLCARBAZOLES

Compound	M.P., °C.	Mixed M.P. with Next Higher Derivative
N-Lauroylcarbazole	78–79	68–72
N-Myristoylcarbazole	81–82	73–78
N-Palmitoylcarbazole	85–86	75–78
N-Stearoylcarbazole	91–92	

TABLE IX

N-ACYL-p-TOLUENESULFONAMIDES

Acid	M.P., °C.	Mixed M.P. with Next Higher Derivative
Lauric	83–84	70–73
Myristic	89–90	75–78
Palmitic	93–94	83–85
Stearic	98–99	

Data similar to that contained in Tables VIII and IX were presented by these authors for all the derivatives investigated, and the reader is referred to the original article for the physical constants and the various details of preparation.

References

1. Feldhaus, *Chem.-Ztg.*, **32**, 837 (1908).
2. van Eldik Thieme, *Proc. Acad. Sci. Amsterdam*, **10**, 855 (1908).
3. Geitel, *J. prakt. Chem.* [2], **55**, 429 (1897).
4. Lewkowitsch, *J. Soc. Chem. Ind.*, **17**, 1107 (1898); *Ber.*, **33**, 89 (1900); **39**, 4095 (1906).
5. Balbiano, *Gazz. chim. ital.*, **32**, I, 265 (1902); *Ber.*, **36**, 1571 (1903).
6. Kremann, *Monatsh.*, **27**, 607 (1906).
7. Meyer, *Seifensieder Ztg.*, **38**, 794 (1911).
8. Marcusson, *Ber.*, **39**, 3466 (1906); **40**, 2905 (1907).
9. Kellner, *Chem.-Ztg.*, **33**, 453, 661 (1909).
10. Stritar and Fanto, *Monatsh.*, **28**, 383 (1907).
11. Wegscheider, *ibid.*, **29**, 83 (1908).
12. Grün and Theimer, *Ber.*, **40**, 1792 (1907).
13. Will, *ibid.*, **41**, 1107 (1908).
14. Treub, *J. chim. phys.*, **16**, 107 (1918).
15. Norris and McBain, *J. Chem. Soc.*, **121**, 1362 (1922).
16. Lederer, *Z. deut. Oel-Fett-Ind.*, **45**, 749 (1925).
17. Smith, *J. Soc. Chem. Ind.*, **51**, 337T (1932).
18. Rowe, *ibid.*, **52**, 49T (1933).
19. Lascaray, *Fette u. Seifen*, **46**, 628 (1939).
20. Strohecker, *Z. Untersuch. Lebensm.*, **69**, 521 (1935).
21. Kurz, *Fette u. Seifen*, **44**, 144 (1937).
22. Treub, *Rec. trav. chim.*, **42**, 556 (1923).
23. v. Braun and Fischer, *Ber.*, **66B**, 101 (1933).
24. Henriques, *Z. angew. Chem.*, **11**, 338 (1898).
25. Thum, *ibid.*, **3**, 482 (1890).
26. Urbain, Saugon, and Feige, *Bull. soc. chim.* [3], **31**, 1194 (1904).
27. Longenecker and Haley, *J. Am. Chem. Soc.*, **57**, 2019 (1935).
28. Haller, *Compt. rend.*, **143**, 657 (1906).
29. Vandevelde and Vanderstricht, *Ann. fals.*, **5**, 417 (1912).
30. Finch and Karim, *J. Soc. Chem. Ind.*, **45**, 35T, 469T (1926).
31. McBain, Howes, and Thorburn, *J. Phys. Chem.*, **31**, 131 (1927).
32. McBain, Humphreys, and Kawakami, *J. Chem. Soc.*, 2185 (1929).
33. Verkade and de Willigen, *Rec. trav. chim.*, **54**, 353 (1935).
34. Ono, *J. Agr. Chem. Soc. Japan*, **15**, 843 (1939); *Bull. Agr. Chem. Soc. Japan*, **15**, 131 (1939).
35. Ono, *J. Agr. Chem. Soc. Japan*, **16**, 197 (1940); *Bull. Agr. Chem. Soc. Japan*, **16**, 41 (1940).
36. Franck, *Seifenfabr.*, **40**, 293 (1920).
37. Henriques, *Z. angew. Chem.*, **8**, 721 (1895); **9**, 221 (1896).
38. Anderson and Brown, *J. Phys. Chem.*, **20**, 195 (1916).
39. Lewkowitsch, *J. Soc. Chem. Ind.*, **22**, 67 (1903).
40. Geitel, *J. prakt. Chem.* [2], **37**, 53 (1888).
41. Twitchell, *J. Am. Chem. Soc.*, **22**, 22 (1900).
42. Twitchell, Brit. Patent 4,741 (1898); Ger. Patent 114,491 (1898); U. S. Patents 601,603 (1898); 628,503 (1899).
43. Twitchell, *J. Am. Chem. Soc.*, **28**, 196 (1906).

44. Twitchell, *ibid.*, **29**, 566 (1907).

45. Vereinigte Chem. Werke Akt.-Ges., Brit. Patent 749 (1912); Fr. Patent 439,209 (1912); von Schönthan, U. S. Patent 1,058,633 (1913).

46. Ubbelohde and Roederer, *Seifenfabr.*, **38**, 425 (1918).

47. Kita and Yamano, *Bull. Inst. Phys. Chem. Research Tokyo*, **2**, 169 (1923).

48. Grimlund, *Z. angew. Chem.*, **25**, 1326 (1912).

49. Hoyer, *Z. deut. Oel-Fett-Ind.*, **41**, 113 (1921).

50. Chang, *Trans. Sci. Soc. China*, **1**, 46 (1922).

51. Twitchell, Holl. Patent 1,360 (1916); Brit. Patent 9,160 (1916); Swed. Patent 43,923 (1918); U. S. Patent 1,170,468 (1916).

52. Petrov, Russ. Patents 500 (1911); 1,521 (1914).

53. Twitchell Process Co., Brit. Patent 143,682 (1919); Mellersh-Jackson, Brit. Patent 149,748 (1919).

54. Divine, U. S. Patents 1,438,101 (1922); 1,495,891 (1924).

55. Riedel, A.-G., Brit. Patent 224,869 (1923).

56. McKee and Lewis, *Chem. & Met. Eng.*, **24**, 969 (1921).

57. Nishizawa and Tokuriki, *J. Soc. Chem. Ind., Japan*, **39**, S.b. 488 (1936).

58. Sandelin, *Ann. acad. sci. Fennicae* [A], **19**, 13 pp. (1922).

59. Rayner and Price's Patent Candle Co., Ltd., Brit. Patent 194,804 (1921).

60. Moore and Wallace, *Am. Perfumer*, **33**, 47 (August, 1936); U. S. Patent 1,967,319 (1934).

61. Riedel, A.-G., Brit. Patent 227,089 (1924); Petrov, Brit. Patent 252,211 (1925); Rabinovich, *Masloboĭno Zhirovoe Delo*, **9**, No. 5, 26 (1934); *Chimie & industrie*, **32**, 1406 (1934).

62. Reuter, Aust. Patent 71,425 (1916).

63. Schulz, *Chem. Umschau*, **32**, 186 (1925).

64. Spellmeyer, U. S. Patent 1,976,376 (1934).

65. Jones, *J. Soc. Chem. Ind.*, **36**, 359 (1917).

66. Ott, *Ber.*, **70B**, 2362 (1937).

67. Budde, Brit. Patent 5,715 (1909).

68. Krebitz, Ger. Patent 155,108 (1904); U. S. Patent 858,295 (1907).

69. Barrett, U. S. Patent 898,547 (1908).

70. Freestone, Brit. Patent 7,573 (1884).

71. Hefter, *Chem. Rev. Fett- u. Harz-Ind.*, **17**, 134 (1910).

72. Nakae and Nakamura, *J. Soc. Chem. Ind., Japan*, **37**, S.b. 583 (1934).

73. Krause, *Z. deut. Oel-Fett-Ind.*, **45**, 527 (1925).

74. Kaufmann and Keller, *Fette u. Seifen*, **44**, 42 (1937).

75. Knorr, *Seifensieder-Ztg.*, **47**, 105 (1920).

76. Roshdestvenskii, *ibid.*, **55**, 127 (1928).

77. Vidal, Brit. Patent 223,601 (1923).

78. Kokatnur, Can. Patent 270,652 (1927).

79. De Grousseau, Fr. Patent 376,122 (1907).

80. Welter, Brit. Patent 223,898 (1923); U. S. Patent 1,612,682 (1926).

81. Reuter, Norw. Patent 29,281 (1918).

82. Bergell, U. S. Patent 1,799,496 (1931).

83. Bolis, *L'ind. sapon.*, **2**, 10 (1902).

84. Barbe, Garelli, and de Paoli, Brit. Patent 9,758 (1908).

85. Barbe, Brit. Patent 12,210 (1907).

86. Keutgen, *Seifensieder-Ztg.*, **57**, 697 (1930).

87. Wilhelm, U. S. Patent 1,616,292 (1927).
88. Balaty, Fellinger, and Audrieth, *Ind. Eng. Chem.*, **31**, 280 (1939).
89. de'Conno and Biazzo, *Rend. accad. sci. Napoli*, **54**, 322 (1915).
90. de'Conno and Tarsitano, *Ann. chim. applicata*, **22**, 433 (1932).
91. van Alphen, *Rec. trav. chim.*, **44**, 1064 (1925).
92. Morelli, *Atti accad. Lincei* [5], **17**, II, 74 (1908).
93. Jourdan, Fr. Patent 339,154 (1903).
94. Bacon, Brit. Patent 27,280 (1906).
95. Welter, *Z. deut. Oel-Fett-Ind.*, **45**, 685 (1925).
96. Deutsche Gold- und Silber-Scheideanstalt, Vorm. Roessler, Brit. Patent 308,603 (1928).
97. Henriques, *Z. angew. Chem.*, **8**, 721 (1895); **9**, 221 (1896).
98. Kossel and Krüger, *Z. physiol. Chem.*, **15**, 321 (1891).
99. Henriques, *Z. angew. Chem.*, **11**, 338 (1898).
100. Klimont, *ibid.*, **14**, 1269 (1901).
101. The percentage of hydrolysis is approximately one-half the acid value.
102. Sabatier and Mailhe, *Compt. rend.*, **152**, 494 (1911).
103. Mailhe, *Chem.-Ztg.*, **35**, 485 (1911).
104. Böhm, Ger. Patent 292,496 (1913).
105. Colgate-Palmolive-Peet Co., Fr. Patent 822,503 (1937).
106. Henkel et Cie. G.m.b.H., Fr. Patent 808,069 (1937).
107. Mills, Can. Patent 365,544 (1937).
108. Mills, U. S. Patent 2,156,863 (1939).
109. Eisenlohr, U. S. Patent 2,154,835 (1939).
110. Metallgesellschaft, A.-G., Fr. Patent 799,274 (1936).
111. Fryer, Can. Patent 223,833 (1922); U. S. Patent 1,657,440 (1928).
112. Pelouze, *Compt. rend.*, **40**, 605 (1855).
113. Willstätter and Waldschmidt-Leitz, *Z. physiol. Chem.*, **134**, 161 (1924).
114. Green, *Proc. Roy. Soc. (London)*, **48**, 370 (1890).
115. Sigmund, *Monatsh.*, **11**, 272 (1890).
116. Connstein, Hoyer, and Wartenberg, *Ber.*, **35**, 3988 (1902).
117. Haley and Lyman, *J. Am. Chem. Soc.*, **43**, 2664 (1921).
118. Nicloux, *Lab. Faculté Méd. Paris* (1906).
119. Pottevin, *Compt. rend.*, **136**, 767 (1903).
120. Tanaka, *J. Coll. Eng. Tokyo Imp. Univ.*, **5**, 25 (1910).
121. Sudborough and Watson, *J. Indian Inst. Sci.*, **5**, 119 (1922).
122. Kita and Osumi, *J. Tokyo Chem. Soc.*, **39**, 387 (1918).
123. Tantzov, *J. Russ. Phys. Chem. Soc.*, **46**, 333 (1914).
124. Armstrong and Ormerod, *Proc. Roy. Soc. (London)*, **78B**, 376 (1906).
125. Hoyer, *Z. physiol. Chem.*, **50**, 414 (1907).
126. Falk and Sugiura, *J. Am. Chem. Soc.*, **37**, 217 (1915).
127. Kelsey, *J. Biol. Chem.*, **130**, 187 (1939).
128. Nicloux, Fr. Patent 335,902 (1903); Ger. Patents 188,511 (1903); 197,444 (1904); Brit. Patents 8,233, 8,304 (1904).
129. Jalander, *Biochem. Z.*, **36**, 435 (1911).
130. Altenburg, *Seifensieder-Ztg.*, **54**, 449 (1927).
131. Sachs, *J. Oil & Fat Ind.*, **3**, 237 (1926).
132. Armstrong and Gosney, *Proc. Roy. Soc. (London)*, **88B**, 176 (1914).
133. Velluz, *Bull. soc. chim. biol.*, **16**, 909 (1934).

134. Fernández and Pizarroso, *Anales soc. españ. fís. quim.*, **15**, 138 (1917).
135. Mastbaum, *Chem. Rev. Fett- u. Harz-Ind.*, **14**, 44 (1907).
136. Sandberg and Brand, *J. Biol. Chem.*, **64**, 59 (1925).
137. Traetta-Mosca and Milletti, *Ann. chim. applicata*, **13**, 270 (1923).
138. Tonegutti, *Staz. sper. agrar. ital.*, **43**, 723 (1910).
139. Zellner, *Monatsh.*, **27**, 295 (1906).
140. Mallinckrodt-Haupt, *Centr. Bakt. Parasitenk.*, **103**, Abt. 1, 73 (1927).
141. Iuracec, *Bull. sect. sci. acad. roumaine*, **13**, 103, 169 (1930).
142. Artom and Reále, *Bull. soc. chim. biol.*, **18**, 959 (1936).
143. Balls and Matlack, *J. Biol. Chem.*, **123**, 679 (1938).
144. Weber and King, *ibid.*, **108**, 131 (1935).
145. Bradley, *ibid.*, **8**, 251 (1910).
146. Terroine, *Biochem. Z.*, **23**, 404 (1910).
147. Terroine, *ibid.*, **23**, 429 (1910).
148. Frouin, *Compt. rend. soc. biol.*, **61**, 665 (1906).
149. Visco, *Atti accad. Lincei* [5], **20**, I, 780 (1911).
150. Willstätter and Memmen, *Z. physiol. Chem.*, **138**, 216 (1924).
151. von Pesthy, *Biochem. Z.*, **34**, 147 (1911).
152. Izar, *ibid.*, **40**, 390 (1912).
153. Sieber, *Z. physiol. Chem.*, **55**, 177 (1908).
154. Rordorf, *Arch. sci. biol. Italy*, **20**, 267 (1934); *Boll. soc. ital. biol. sper.*, **9**, 169 (1934).
155. Knafffl-Lenz, *Medd. Vetenskapsakad. Nobelinst.*, **6**, No. 3, 1 (1922).
156. Nogaki, *Z. physiol. Chem.*, **152**, 101 (1926).
157. Michaelis and Nakahara, *Z. Immunitäts.*, **36**, 449 (1923).
158. Collins, *Iowa State College J. Sci.*, **8**, 187 (1933).
159. Lewkowitsch, *Chemical Technology and Analysis of Oils, Fats and Waxes*, 6th ed., Vol. III, p. 228; Macmillan and Co., London (1923).
160. Dubovitz, *Seifensieder-Ztg.*, **37**, 1063 (1910).
161. Varrentrapp, *Ann.*, **35**, 197 (1840).
162. Gusserow, *Arch. Pharm.*, **27**, 153 (1828).
163. Kremel, *Pharm. Zentralhalle*, **5**, 337 (1864).
164. Oudemans, *J. prakt. Chem.* [1], **99**, 407 (1866).
165. Röse, *Repert. anal. Chem.*, **6**, 685 (1886).
166. Muter and de Koningh, *Analyst*, **14**, 61 (1889).
167. Lane, *J. Am. Chem. Soc.*, **15**, 110 (1893).
168. Twitchell, *J. Ind. Eng. Chem.*, **13**, 806 (1921).
169. Farnsteiner, *Z. Untersuch. Nahr.- u. Genussm.*, **1**, 390 (1898).
170. Steger and Scheffers, *Rec. trav. chim.*, **46**, 402 (1927).
171. Seidenberg, *J. Am. Chem. Soc.*, **43**, 1323 (1921).
172. Twitchell, *ibid.*, **17**, 289 (1895).
173. Neave, *Analyst*, **37**, 399 (1912).
174. Mulder, *Die Chemie der austrocknenden Oele ihre Bereitung und ihre technische Anwendung in Künsten und Gewerben*, p. 44, Julius Springer, Berlin (1867).
175. Lewkowitsch, *J. Soc. Chem. Ind.*, **9**, 842 (1890).
176. Fahrion, *Z. angew. Chem.*, **17**, 1482 (1904).
177. Christopoulos, *Praktika (Akad. Athenon)*, **9**, 220 (1934).
178. Keffler and McLean, *J. Soc. Chem. Ind.*, **54**, 362T (1935).

179. Meigen and Neuberger, *Chem. Umschau*, **29**, 337 (1922).

180. Partheil and Ferié, *Arch. Pharm.*, **241**, 545 (1903).

181. Farnsteiner, *Z. Untersuch. Nahr.- u. Genussm.*, **8**, 129 (1904).

182. André, *Compt. rend.*, **175**, 107 (1922).

183. Holde and Godbole, *Ber.*, **59B**, 36 (1926); *Z. deut. Oel-Fett-Ind.*, **46**, 129, 145, 163, 179 (1926).

184. Jacobson and Holmes, *J. Biol. Chem.*, **25**, 55 (1916).

185. Jacobson and Holmes, *ibid.*, **25**, 29 (1916).

186. Walker, *J. Chem. Soc.*, **123**, 2837 (1923).

187. Tsujimoto and Kimura, *J. Soc. Chem. Ind., Japan*, **26**, 1162 (1923).

188. Tsujimoto, *Bull. Chem. Soc. Japan*, **3**, 299 (1928).

189. Armstrong and Hilditch, *J. Soc. Chem. Ind.*, **44**, 180T (1925).

190. Tsujimoto, *J. Soc. Chem. Ind., Japan*, **23**, 1007 (1920).

191. Falciola, *Gazz. chim. ital.*, **40**, II, 217 (1910).

192. Bull and Fjellanger, *Tids. Kemi, Farm. Terapi*, **12**, 366 (1915).

193. David, *Compt. rend.*, **151**, 756 (1910).

194. Jungkunz, *Chem. Umschau*, **39**, 171 (1932).

195. Barbe, Garelli, and de Paoli, Brit. Patent 24,836 (1908).

196. Holde, Selim, and Bleyberg, *Z. deut. Oel-Fett-Ind.*, **44**, 277 (1924).

197. Holde and Takehara, *Ber.*, **58B**, 1788 (1925).

198. Canneri and Bigalli, *Ann. chim. applicata*, **26**, 430 (1936).

199. Fachini and Dorta, *Seifenfabr.*, **32**, 3, 105 (1912); *Rendi. soc. chim. ital.* [2], **4**, 51 (1912); *Chem.-Ztg.*, **38**, 18 (1914).

200. Rideal and Acland, *Analyst*, **38**, 259 (1913).

201. de Waele, *ibid.*, **39**, 389 (1914).

202. Scheringa, *Chem. Weekblad*, **29**, 605 (1932).

203. Takano, *J. Soc. Chem. Ind., Japan*, **36**, S.b. 549 (1933).

204. Kino, *ibid.*, **37**, S.b. 439 (1934).

205. Gascard and Damoy, *Compt. rend.*, **177**, 1222 (1923).

206. Chemisches Laboratorium C. Stiepel, Ger. Patent 625,577 (1936).

207. Escher, *Helv. Chim. Acta*, **12**, 103 (1929).

208. Erdmann, *Z. physiol. Chem.*, **74**, 179 (1911).

209. Agde, *J. prakt. Chem.* [2], **112**, 37 (1926).

210. Brown and Beal, *J. Am. Chem. Soc.*, **45**, 1289 (1923).

211. Heintz, *J. prakt. Chem.* [1], **66**, 1 (1855).

212. Verkade, Hartman, and Coops, *Rec. trav. chim.*, **45**, 373 (1926).

213. Gsell, *Chem.-Ztg.*, **31**, 100 (1907).

214. Bruni and Gorni, *Atti accad. Lincei* [5], **8**, I, 454 (1899); *Gazz. chim. ital.*, **30**, I, 55 (1900).

215. Mascarelli, *Atti accad. Lincei* [5], **23**, II, 583 (1914); *Gazz. chim. ital.*, **45**, I, 213 (1915); Mascarelli and Toschi, *Atti accad. Lincei* [5], **23**, II, 586 (1914); Mascarelli and Sanna, *ibid.* [5], **24**, II, 91 (1915).

216. Brocklesby, *Can. J. Research*, **14B**, 222 (1936).

217. Waentig and Pescheck, *Z. physik. Chem.*, **93**, 529 (1919).

218. François, *Compt. rend.*, **193**, 1008 (1931).

219. Boutaric and Roy, *J. pharm. chim.* [8], **15**, 161 (1932).

220. Broughton, *Trans. Faraday Soc.*, **30**, 367 (1934).

221. Ralston and Hoerr, *J. Org. Chem.*, **7**, 546 (1942).

222. Morrow, *Phys. Rev.* [2], **31**, 10 (1928).

223. Trillat, *Compt. rend.*, **187,** 168 (1928).
224. Hendricks, *Chem. Rev.*, **7,** 431 (1930).
225. Francis, Piper, and Malkin, *Proc. Roy. Soc.* (*London*), **128A,** 214 (1930); Piper, *Trans. Faraday Soc.*, **25,** 348 (1929); Francis and Piper, *J. Am. Chem. Soc.*, **61,** 577 (1939).
226. Smith, *J. Chem. Soc.*, 625 (1936).
227. Hrynakowski and Zochowski, *Ber.*, **70B,** 1739 (1937).
228. Kulka and Sandin, *J. Am. Chem. Soc.*, **59,** 1347 (1937).
229. Fachini and Dorta, *Boll. chim.-farm.*, **49,** 237 (1910).
230. Bertram, *Rec. trav. chim.*, **46,** 397 (1927).
231. Raymond, *Chimie & industrie*, Special No., 523 (February, 1929).
232. Edeleanu G.m.b.H., Fr. Patent 775,700 (1935).
233. Wolff, *Chimie & industrie*, Special No., 885 (April, 1934).
234. Brown and Stoner, *J. Am. Chem. Soc.*, **59,** 3 (1937).
235. Brown and Frankel, *ibid.*, **60,** 54 (1938).
236. Brown and Frankel, *ibid.*, **63,** 1483 (1941).
237. Matthews, Brode, and Brown, *ibid.*, **63,** 1064 (1941).
238. Brown and Shinowara, *ibid.*, **59,** 6 (1937).
239. Hartsuch, *ibid.*, **61,** 1142 (1939).
240. Smith, *J. Chem. Soc.*, 974 (1939).
241. Wheeler and Riemenschneider, *Oil & Soap*, **16,** 207 (1939).
242. Shinowara and Brown, *J. Am. Chem. Soc.*, **60,** 2734 (1938).
243. Brown and Green, *ibid.*, **62,** 738 (1940).
244. Shinowara and Brown, *J. Biol. Chem.*, **134,** 331 (1940).
245. Schumann, *J. Ind. Eng. Chem.*, **8,** 5 (1916).
246. Thomas and Thomson, *J. Am. Chem. Soc.*, **56,** 898 (1934).
247. Ku, *Ind. Eng. Chem., Anal. Ed.*, **9,** 103 (1937).
248. Holde and Wilke, *Z. angew. Chem.*, **35,** 289 (1922).
249. Keffler, *J. Soc. Chem. Ind.*, **55,** 331T (1936).
250. Heiduschka and Ripper, *Z. Elektrochem.*, **29,** 552 (1923).
251. Krafft, *Ber.*, **13,** 1413 (1880); Krafft and Noerdlinger, *ibid.*, **22,** 816 (1889); Krafft and Dÿes, *ibid.*, **28,** 2583 (1895); Krafft and Weilandt, *ibid.*, **29,** 1316 (1896).
252. Caldwell and Hurtley, *J. Chem. Soc.*, **95,** 853 (1909).
253. Brown, *Proc. Chem. Soc.*, **26,** 149 (1910).
254. Krafft, *Ber.*, **36,** 4339 (1903).
255. Kreis and Hafner, *ibid.*, **36,** 2766 (1903).
256. Haller and Youssoufian, *Compt. rend.*, **143,** 803 (1906).
257. Bull, *Ber.*, **39,** 3570 (1906).
258. Holland, *J. Ind. Eng. Chem.*, **3,** 171 (1911).
259. Smedley, *Biochem. J.*, **6,** 451 (1912).
260. Holland, Reed, and Buckley, *J. Agr. Research*, **6,** 101 (1916); Holland and Buckley, *ibid.*, **12,** 719 (1918); Holland, Garvey, Pierce, Messer, Archibald, and Dunbar, *ibid.*, **24,** 365 (1923).
261. Crowther and Hynd, *Biochem. J.*, **11,** 139 (1917).
262. Channon, Drummond, and Golding, *Analyst*, **49,** 311 (1924).
263. Bosworth and Brown, *J. Biol. Chem.*, **103,** 115 (1933).
264. Elsdon, *Analyst*, **38,** 8 (1913); **39,** 78 (1914).
265. Meyer, *Chem.-Ztg.*, **31,** 793 (1907).

266. Grün, *Chem. Umschau*, **26**, 101 (1919).
267. Bosworth, *J. Biol. Chem.*, **106**, 235 (1934).
268. Hashimoto, *J. Am. Chem. Soc.*, **47**, 2325 (1925).
269. Cohen, *Verslag Akad. Wetenschappen Amsterdam*, **34**, 462 (1925).
270. Stokoe, *Analyst*, **49**, 577 (1924).
271. Armstrong, Allan, and Moore, *J. Soc. Chem. Ind.*, **44**, 63T, 143T (1925).
272. Brown, *J. Biol. Chem.*, **83**, 769 (1929).
273. Brown and Ault, *ibid.*, **89**, 167 (1930).
274. Dufton, *J. Soc. Chem. Ind.*, **38**, 45T (1919).
275. Clarke and Rahrs, *Ind. Eng. Chem.*, **15**, 349 (1923).
276. Widmer, *Helv. Chim. Acta*, **7**, 59 (1924).
277. Peters and Baker, *Ind. Eng. Chem.*, **18**, 69 (1926).
278. Cooper and Fasce, *ibid.*, **20**, 420 (1928).
279. Jantzen and Tiedcke, *J. prakt. Chem.* [2], **127**, 277 (1930).
280. Evans, Cornish, Lepkovsky, Archibald, and Feskov, *Ind. Eng. Chem.*, *Anal. Ed.*, **2**, 339 (1930).
281. Bush and Schwartz, *ibid.*, **4**, 142 (1932).
282. Lepkovsky, Feskov, and Evans, *J. Am. Chem. Soc.*, **58**, 978 (1936).
283. Rennkamp, *Z. physiol. Chem.*, **260**, 276 (1939).
284. Whitmore and Lux, *J. Am. Chem. Soc.*, **54**, 3448 (1932).
285. Wilson, Parker, and Laughlin, *ibid.*, **55**, 2795 (1933).
286. Weston, *Ind. Eng. Chem.*, *Anal. Ed.*, **5**, 179 (1933).
287. Podbielniak, *ibid.*, **5**, 119 (1933).
288. Klem, *Nature*, **142**, 616 (1938).
289. Fenske, Tongberg, and Quiggle, *Ind. Eng. Chem.*, **26**, 1169 (1934).
290. Tongberg, Quiggle, and Fenske, *ibid.*, **26**, 1213 (1934).
291. Fenske, U. S. Patent 2,037,317 (1936).
292. Tongberg, Lawroski, and Fenske, *Ind. Eng. Chem.*, **29**, 957 (1937).
293. Fenske, Lawroski, and Tongberg, *ibid.*, **30**, 297 (1938).
294. Schoenheimer and Rittenberg, *J. Biol. Chem.*, **120**, 155 (1937).
295. Price and McDermott, *Ind. Eng. Chem.*, *Anal. Ed.*, **11**, 289 (1939).
296. Longenecker, *J. Soc. Chem. Ind.*, **56**, 199T (1937).
297. Hilditch and Longenecker, *J. Biol. Chem.*, **122**, 497 (1937).
298. Longenecker, *Oil & Soap*, **17**, 53 (1940).
299. Stedman, U. S. Patent 2,047,444 (1936); Can. Patent 361,043 (1936).
300. Stedman, *Can. J. Research*, **15B**, 383 (1937).
301. Bragg, *Ind. Eng. Chem.*, *Anal. Ed.*, **11**, 283 (1939).
302. Farmer and Van den Heuvel, *J. Soc. Chem. Ind.*, **57**, 24T (1938).
303. Le Kétol, Fr. Patent 663,425 (1928).
304. Würth, *Farben-Ztg.*, **30**, 1806 (1925).
305. Apostel, Brit. Patent 500,375 (1939).
306. Bodman, U. S. Patent 1,372,477 (1921).
307. Pickering, *J. Soc. Chem. Ind.*, **44**, 424T (1925).
308. Leimdörfer, *Seifensieder-Ztg.*, **56**, 321 (1929).
309. Franzen, U. S. Patent 1,871,051 (1932).
310. Schönberger, *Fette u. Seifen*, **43**, 109 (1936).
311. van Reesema, Brit. Patent 396,095 (1933).
312. Riley and George Scott and Son, Brit. Patent 412,080 (1934).
313. New Process Fat Refining Corp., Ger. Patent 665,874 (1938).

314. Heiduschka and Pfizenmaier, *Pharm. Zentralhalle*, **50**, 85 (1909).
315. Metallbank und Metallurgische Ges., A.-G., Brit. Patent 291,093 (1927).
316. Paris and Picard, Fr. Patent 465,418 (1918).
317. Oel- und Fett-Chemie G.m.b.H., Brit. Patent 296,079 (1927).
318. Krebs, *Teer u. Bitumen*, **29**, 71 (1931).
319. New Process Fat Refining Corp., Fr. Patent 773,635 (1934).
320. New Process Fat Refining Corp., Brit. Patent 421,733 (1934); Tolman, U. S. Patent 2,006,491 (1935).
321. Metallbank und Metallurgische Ges. and Gensecke, Brit. Patent 225,552 (1923).
322. Goranflo, U. S. Patent 1,951,241 (1934).
323. Tolman and Goranflo, *Oil & Soap*, **12**, 26 (1935).
324. Tolman, U. S. Patents 1,998,997, 1,998,998 (1935).
325. Sieck, U. S. Patent 1,982,598 (1934).
326. Bergell, Brit. Patent 419,566 (1934).
327. Potts and McKee, U. S. Patent 2,054,096 (1936).
328. Brücke, U. S. Patent 2,184,579 (1939).
329. McCulloch, U. S. Patent 2,147,306 (1939).
330. Lee, U. S. Patent 2,177,664 (1939).
331. Ittner, U. S. Patent 2,202,007 (1940).
332. Dubovitz, *Mat. grasses*, **8**, 4326 (1915).
333. Sheely, U. S. Patent 2,062,837 (1936).
334. N. V. Maatschappij tot Exploitatie der Vereenigde Oliefabrieken "Zwijndrecht," Brit. Patent 391,825 (1933).
335. Ralston, Pool, and Harwood, U. S. Patent 2,042,729 (1936).
336. Kurtz and Schaffer, *J. Am. Chem. Soc.*, **62**, 1304 (1940).
337. Ralston, Selby, Pool, and Potts, *Ind. Eng. Chem.*, **32**, 1093 (1940).
338. Pool and Ralston, *ibid.*, **34**, 1104 (1942).
339. Dorinson, McCorkle, and Ralston, *J. Am. Chem. Soc.*, **64**, 2739 (1942).
340. Wijs, *Z. angew. Chem.*, **11**, 291 (1898); *J. Soc. Chem. Ind.*, **17**, 698 (1898).
341. Mills and Snodgrass, *ibid.*, **2**, 435 (1883).
342. Hübl, *Dingl. Polyt. Journ.*, **253**, 281 (1884); *J. Soc. Chem. Ind.*, **3**, 641 (1884).
343. Hanuš, *Z. Untersuch. Nahr.- u. Genussm.*, **4**, 913 (1901).
344. Kaufmann, *Z. Untersuch. Lebensm.*, **51**, 15 (1926); *Analyst*, **51**, 264 (1926).
345. van Loon, *Chem. Umschau*, **38**, 279 (1931).
346. van der Veen and van Loon, *ibid.*, **39**, 56 (1932).
347. Gay, *J. Soc. Chem. Ind.*, **51**, 126T (1932).
348. Kass, Lundberg, and Burr, *Oil & Soap*, **17**, 50 (1940).
349. Riemenschneider, Swift, and Sando, *ibid.*, **18**, 203 (1941).
350. Irwin *et al.*, *Ind. Eng. Chem., Anal. Ed.*, **8**, 233 (1936).
351. Anon., *J. Assoc. Official Agr. Chem.*, **21**, 87 (1938).
352. Jamieson, *Vegetable Fats and Oils*, 2nd ed., A.C.S. Monograph No. 58, pp. 395, 474, Reinhold Publishing Corp., New York (1943).
353. Kaufmann and Baltes, *Fette u. Seifen*, **43**, 93 (1936); Kaufmann, Baltes, and Büter, *Ber.*, **70B**, 903 (1937).
354. Ellis and Jones, *Analyst*, **61**, 812 (1936).
355. Lewkowitsch, *J. Soc. Chem. Ind.*, **16**, 503 (1897).
356. André, *Compt. rend.*, **172**, 984 (1921); *Bull. soc. chim.* [4], **29**, 745 (1921).

357. Cook, *J. Am. Chem. Soc.*, **44**, 392 (1922).

358. Andrews and Reed, *Oil & Soap*, **9**, 215 (1932).

359. Roberts and Schuette, *Ind. Eng. Chem., Anal. Ed.*, **4**, 257 (1932).

360. *Official and Tentative Methods of the American Oil Chemists' Society*, p. 41 (1941).

361. Robertson, *J. Chem. Soc.*, **115**, 1210 (1919).

362. Ralston, Hoerr, and Pool, *J. Org. Chem.*, **8**, 473 (1943).

363. Hann and Jamieson, *J. Am. Chem. Soc.*, **50**, 1442 (1928).

364. Bryant and Mitchell, *ibid.*, **60**, 2748 (1938).

365. Lyons and Reid, *ibid.*, **39**, 1727 (1917).

366. Reid, *ibid.*, **39**, 124 (1917); Lyman and Reid, *ibid.*, **39**, 701 (1917).

367. Kelly and Segura, *ibid.*, **56**, 2497 (1934).

368. Rather and Reid, *ibid.*, **41**, 75 (1919).

369. Judefind and Reid, *ibid.*, **42**, 1043 (1920).

370. Rather and Reid, *ibid.*, **43**, 629 (1921).

371. Hann, Reid, and Jamieson, *ibid.*, **52**, 818 (1930)

372. Drake and Bronitsky, *ibid.*, **52**, 3715 (1930).

373. Lundquist, *ibid.*, **60**, 2000 (1938).

374. Moses and Reid, *ibid.*, **54**, 2101 (1932).

375. Kimura, *J. Soc. Chem. Ind., Japan*, **35**, S.b. 221 (1932).

376. Kelly and Kleff, *J. Am. Chem. Soc.*, **54**, 4444 (1932).

377. Drake and Sweeney, *ibid.*, **54**, 2059 (1932).

378. Veselý and Haas, *Chem. Listy*, **21**, 351 (1927); *Chimie & industrie*, Special No., 507 (April, 1928).

379. Strache and Iritzer, *Monatsh.*, **14**, 33 (1893).

380. Pollard, Adelson, and Bain, *J. Am. Chem. Soc.*, **56**, 1759 (1934).

381. Donleavy, *ibid.*, **58**, 1004 (1936).

382. Pool, Harwood, and Ralston, *ibid.*, **59**, 178 (1937).

383. Ralston and McCorkle, *ibid.*, **61**, 1604 (1939).

384. Gilman and Ford, *Iowa State Coll. J. Sci.*, **13**, 135 (1939).

V

THE STRUCTURE AND PHYSICAL PROPERTIES OF THE FATTY ACIDS

When Baeyer [1] in 1877 stated that the melting points of the fatty acids do not increase uniformly with progressive increase in chain lengths but apparently form two series, one for those acids which contain an even number of carbon atoms and another for those which contain an odd number, he initiated a fundamental study of fatty acid molecular structure and turned the attention of both chemists and physicists to the many correlations which exist between the physico-chemical properties of these acids and their molecular configurations. Studies of the relationships between the chain lengths of fatty acid molecules and their physico-chemical properties in the solid state, such as melting points, heats of crystallization, and molecular volumes, have provided many clues to their physical structure. The many x-ray investigations which have been made both upon crystals and upon films of fatty acids have permitted calculations of their atomic and molecular distances and of the constitution of their unit cells. Such data have afforded an insight into the actual arrangement of the carbon atoms in the acid molecules and the positions of the various molecules in the unit cells. Information obtained from x-ray and other studies has served to explain the phenomenon of polymorphism and to interpret this phenomenon in terms of the atomic configuration of the fatty acid molecule. We are, therefore, indebted both to the chemist and to the physicist for our present knowledge of the molecular structure of fatty acids. Although much is already known concerning this interesting subject, much still remains to be learned, and most of the questions which still exist can only be answered by the combined efforts of physicists and chemists. In the following discussion the author has endeavored not only to present the most important and useful data pertaining to the physico-chemical properties of the various series of acids but also to point out the relationship between the physical constants and molecular structures of the acids and some of their derivatives. The reader should bear in mind that the physico-chemical properties of the fatty acids, particularly those properties which relate to the solid state, are manifestations of the molecular configurations of the acids themselves. A mere tabulation of these properties, therefore, without reference to their usefulness in the interpretation of molecular structures, would disregard much of their actual meaning and importance.

THE PHYSICAL PROPERTIES OF FATTY ACIDS IN THE SOLID STATE

Our present knowledge of the structure of fatty acids has largely been derived from the numerous studies of their physico-chemical properties in the solid state. Most of these studies have been concerned with the saturated acids, since these offer a perfect example of a homologous series whose individual members can be

TABLE I *

FREEZING POINTS OF SATURATED MONOCARBOXYLIC ACIDS

No. of C Atoms	F.P., °C.	No. of C Atoms	F.P., °C.
6	−3.24	21	75.2 (m.p.)
7	−6.26	22	79.70
8	16.30	23	78.7
9	12.25	24	83.90
10	31.24	25	82.91
11	28.13	26	87.4
12	43.92	27	87.0
13	41.76	28	90.5
14	54.10	29	90.3
15	52.54	30	93.6
16	62.74	31	92.6
17	60.94	32	95.5
18	69.60	34	98.0
19	69.5	35	98.0
20	74.2	36	99.7

* The values recorded in this table have been reported by Francis, Piper, and Malkin, *Proc. Roy. Soc.* (*London*), **128A**, 214 (1930); Deffet, *Bull. soc. chim. Belg.*, **40**, 385 (1931); Piper, Chibnall, and Williams, *Biochem. J.*, **28**, 2175 (1934); Francis and Piper, *J. Am. Chem. Soc.*, **61**, 577 (1939); Pool and Ralston, *Ind. Eng. Chem.*, **34**, 1104 (1942); Ralston and Hoerr, *J. Org. Chem.*, **7**, 546 (1942).

obtained in a state of high purity. Those saturated fatty acids which contain six or more carbon atoms are either solids at ordinary temperatures or are relatively high-boiling liquids which can easily be crystallized.

Alternation in the Properties of Long-Chain Compounds

The freezing points of the monocarboxylic saturated acids containing from six to thirty-six carbon atoms are shown in Table I.

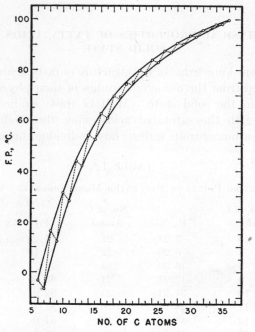

FIG. 1.   Freezing points of saturated monocarboxylic acids.

The plot of these freezing points against the number of carbon atoms in the acids (Fig. 1) shows that these values do not increase uniformly with successive additions of carbon atoms, but that they alternate from odd to even acids in such a manner that the freezing points of the even acids fall upon one curve and those of the odd acids upon another. It will be noted that the curve formed by the even acids is above that formed by the odd acids, and that the alternation becomes less as the series is ascended. This alternation appears in many of the properties of the fatty acids in the solid state. For example, the heats of crystallization of the saturated acids as reported by Garner and coworkers [2, 3, 4] (Table II) show a decided alternation.

When these values are plotted against the carbon content of the acids (Fig. 2), they fall upon two curves which differ from

TABLE II

HEATS OF CRYSTALLIZATION OF SATURATED MONOCARBOXYLIC ACIDS

No. of C Atoms	Heat of Crystallization Cal./Mole
1	2.52
2	2.77
3	2.26
4	2.64
5	....
6	3.60
7	3.58
8	5.11
9	4.85
10	6.69
11	5.99
12	8.75
13	8.02
14	10.74
15	10.30
16	12.98
17	12.22
18	13.49 *
19	.....
20	16.95
21	.....
22	18.75
23	17.60
24	21.10
25	20.00

* Bruner, Ber., 27, 2102 (1894). Since the melting point of the acid was reported to be 64°, this value is probably low.

those formed by the freezing points in that they do not converge at the higher members but form two nearly parallel curves for the acids containing ten or more carbon atoms, the increments approaching a constant value.

The heats of crystallization of the even members can be expressed by the equation $Q = 1.030n - 3.61$, and of the odd members by the equation $Q = 0.9651n - 4.49$, where n equals the number of carbon atoms. Q/T is essentially linear in both cases, being expressed by $Q/T = 0.002652n - 0.0043$ for the even acids and $Q/T = 0.002505n - 0.0071$ for the odd acids. The values of the setting points T, calculated from the above expressions, are in reasonable agreement with the observed values. The convergence temperatures have been calculated to be 115.5° for the even and 112.2° for the odd acids.

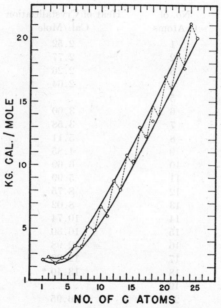

FIG. 2.   Heats of crystallization of saturated monocarboxylic acids.

Alternation in the properties of the solid state is a phenomenon which is apparently characteristic of most series of straight-chain aliphatic compounds. Thus, Fairweather [5] has shown that the melting points of the dicarboxylic acids show a marked alternation, those containing an even number of carbon atoms falling upon a curve with a downward slope whereas the odd members fall upon a rising curve. The alternation becomes quite small, however, for those dicarboxylic acids containing twenty or more carbon atoms. The reported melting points for the dicarboxylic acids containing from four to nineteen carbon atoms inclusive are shown in Table III and are plotted in Fig. 3. It does not necessarily follow that the odd members of an alternating series possess lower melting points than the adjacent even members. For example,

TABLE III *

MELTING POINTS OF DICARBOXYLIC ACIDS

No. of C Atoms	M.P., °C.
4	185
5	97.5
6	153
7	105.7
8	140
9	107
10	133
11	111
12	129
13	113.5
14	126.5
15	114.8
16	125
17	118
18	124
19	119.2

* The values in this table have been reported by Fairweather, *Phil. Mag.* [7], **1,** 944 (1926); Normand, Ross, and Henderson, *J. Chem. Soc.*, 2632 (1926); Chuit, *Helv. Chim. Acta,* **9,** 264 (1926); Erwy, *Bull. soc. chim. Belg.*, **42,** 483 (1933).

Meyer and Reid [6] have shown that the melting points of the 1-bromoalkanes containing an odd number of carbon atoms lie on a curve above that formed by the even members. The values reported by these authors are shown in Table IV.

Some series of aliphatic compounds appear to exhibit little if any alternation, especially for the higher members. Thus, Fairweather [5] observed that the melting points of the diethyl esters of dicarboxylic acids containing from seven to thirty-two carbon atoms lie on an ascending curve. This has been confirmed by Normand, Ross, and Henderson [7] and is especially significant in view of the marked alternation shown by the acids themselves. Meyer and Reid [6] have stated that while the melting points of the even alcohols from 1-butanol to 1-decanol fall on a slightly higher curve than that formed by the odd members, alternation in the melting points of the alcohols which contain ten or more carbon atoms either is not present or is too small to be measured. Piper, Chibnall, and Williams [8] have also confirmed the apparent lack of alternation in the melting points of the higher alcohols. Although the paraffins do not form an alternating series in the sense that the odd members possess lower freezing points than the neighboring even members, they do exhibit weak alternation in that the freezing points of the odd members containing twenty or less carbon atoms fall upon a curve which is below that formed by the

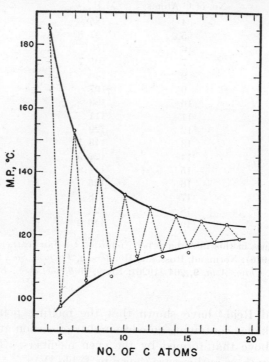

FIG. 3.   Melting points of dicarboxylic acids.

TABLE IV

MELTING POINTS OF 1-BROMOALKANES

No. of C Atoms	M.P., °C.
10	−29.62
11	−13.15
12	−9.60
13	5.94
14	5.67
15	18.63
16	17.54
17	28.40
18	27.35

even members.   The freezing points of the paraffins containing from four to eighteen carbon atoms are shown in Table V, and these values are plotted in Fig. 4.

TABLE V *

FREEZING POINTS OF PARAFFINS

No. of C Atoms	F.P., °C.	No. of C Atoms	F.P., °C.
4	−138.29	12	−9.61
5	−129.73	13	−6.0
6	−95.34	14	5.5
7	−90.62	15	10.0
8	−56.82	16	18.145 ± 0.003
9	−53.70	17	22.0
10	−29.68	18	28.0
11	−25.61		

* The values in this table have been reported by Shepard, Henne, and Midgley, Jr., *J. Am. Chem. Soc.*, **53**, 1948 (1931); Mair, *Bur. Standards J. Res.*, **9**, 457 (1932); Francis, *Ind. Eng. Chem.*, **33**, 554 (1941); Deanesly and Carleton, *J. Phys. Chem.*, **45**, 1104 (1941).

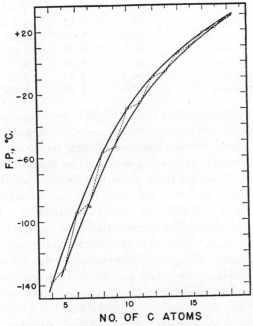

FIG. 4. Freezing points of paraffins.

Structure of Long-Chain Compounds

Although alternation in physical properties such as heats of crystallization, molecular volumes, and freezing points is generally encountered within the various aliphatic series, it is apparent that the extent of alternation differs materially among the various series. Mono- and dibasic acids, methyl esters, haloalkanes, and nitriles show marked alternation in the solid state, whereas alcohols, methyl ketones, and hydrocarbons are weakly alternating and ethyl esters are apparently non-alternating. It is evident, therefore, that although alternation is actually a function of the lengths of the hydrocarbon chains, the extent and kind of alternation is in some way influenced by the nature of the polar group attached

TABLE VI

CRYSTAL SPACINGS OF MONOBASIC SATURATED ACIDS

Spacings in Ångströms

Acid	d_1	d_2	d_3
Capric	23.2	....	....
Undecanoic	25.8	....	....
Lauric	27.0	4.11	3.68
Myristic	32.2	4.12	3.72
Pentadecanoic	36.2	4.00	3.76
Palmitic	34.7	4.08	3.65
Margaric	39.2	4.05	3.77
Stearic	38.7	4.05	3.62
Behenic	47.8	4.10	3.66

to the chain. Compounds which are highly polar and consequently possess a strong tendency towards association apparently form alternating series, whereas those possessing feeble powers of association yield weakly alternating series. The study of Morgan and Holmes [9] upon 2-methyl fatty acids has shown that the length of the longest chain, and not the total number of carbon atoms in the chain, is determinative as regards alternation. The general phenomenon of alternation largely finds its interpretation in the many studies made upon the structural configuration of long-chain compounds. X-ray measurements of the crystal spacings of aliphatic acids, esters, and simple derivatives show them to possess three characteristic spacings, two of which are essentially constant for any given series while the third is a function of the length of the hydrocarbon chain. These spacings have been designated as d_1, d_2, and d_3 and correspond to the c, a, and b axes of the crystal cell. The measurements of the d_1, d_2, and d_3 spacings of some saturated monobasic acids as reported by Müller [10] and Müller and Shearer [11] are shown in Table VI.

It will be noted that the spacings d_2 and d_3 are nearly constant for these acids, but that the spacing d_1 is a function of the chain length. This indicates that the unit cell is a long prism and that the short spacings, d_2 and d_3, are related to the cross section and are independent of the length of the cell. The observations of Shearer [12] on the crystal spacings of several esters of palmitic and stearic acids are shown in Table VII. It is apparent that the spacings d_2 and d_3 are essentially independent of the number of carbon atoms in these esters, and it is significant that measure-

TABLE VII

CRYSTAL SPACINGS OF FATTY ACID ESTERS

Spacings in Ångströms

Ester		d_1	d_2	d_3
Methyl palmitate		22.0	4.07	3.72
Ethyl	"	23.2	4.07	3.67
Octyl	"	30.4	4.16	3.72
Cetyl	"	40.4	4.05	3.69
Methyl stearate		24.0	4.07	3.74
Ethyl	"	25.2	4.14	3.69

ments of a number of series of long-chain compounds show the characteristic spacings of 4.1 and 3.7 Å which relate to the cross-sectional areas of the unit cells. In 1925, Garner and Ryder [13] showed that the molecular volumes of the solid acids alternate from odd to even member. Calculations of the areas of the unit cells, employing the equation $S = MV/6.06d \times 10^{-15}$ sq. Å, where d is the length of one molecule in the crystal cell and MV is the molecular volume, gave identical values for both odd and even members. Since the value of the cross section of the unit cell is a non-alternating property, alternation in the physical properties between the various members of a homologous series must be due to differences in the chain lengths. Thus, alternation is associated with the long spacings of the crystal cells, and it follows that the explanation of this phenomenon is to be found not only in the arrangement of the carbon atoms along the hydrocarbon chain but also in the relative positions of these chains in the crystal cells. The realization that the differences in the longitudinal spacings of straight-chain compounds offered a clue to the phenomenon of alternation within the various homologous series has led to intensive studies of this property, and the information resulting from such studies has given us our present conception of the structure of the fatty acids and related compounds.

Polymorphism

Before we further consider the significance of alternation and its relation to the actual structure of the fatty acid molecules, as disclosed by x-ray and film studies, it is necessary to mention another characteristic property of long-chain compounds. It has been realized for some time that glycerides exist in several polymorphic forms, but it was not at first assumed that polymorphism is a general property of long-chain compounds. It is now known that many straight-chain compounds are capable of existing in more than one form, the particular modification assumed being dependent not only upon the substance itself but upon its previous treatment and to a large extent upon its present environment. Polymorphism is a common phenomenon with the fatty acids and many of their derivatives, and the various enantiotropic forms and their transitions can now be given logical interpretations based upon the molecular structure of the long-chain compounds. It is customary to designate one form as the stable modification and to regard the other form or forms as metastable. Since the modifications generally appear to be enantiotropic, it is necessary to define the conditions before it can be stated that one form is stable with reference to another. The stable form, however, generally refers to that modification which is stable under ordinary conditions of temperature and pressure. The transition from one form to another takes place at a definite transition temperature and is generally accompanied by a measurable heat effect. In many cases it is possible to isolate the metastable form, whereas in other instances its existence is manifested only by a thermal effect. The type of polymorphism exhibited by long-chain compounds is somewhat peculiar in that the transition from a form stable at one temperature to one stable at a different temperature frequently appears to be unilateral, since the first form does not reappear when the original conditions are again established. Failure to consider the possibility of polymorphism has led to some confusion in the earlier literature upon the physical properties of the members of homologous series. Where the physical properties of the individual members of any series are compared it is essential that these properties refer to the same modification throughout, in order to avoid erroneous and misleading conclusions. It should be realized that both alternation and polymorphism are phenomena related to the actual structures of these compounds and that they can only be explained by fundamental studies of molecular configuration.*

With all due regard to the excellent work which has been done in correlating polymorphism with molecular structure, it is necessary to point out that many unanswered questions still challenge any conclusion. For example, there is no present explanation for the influence of impurities on the relative stabilities of polymorphic forms. Small amounts of octadecane cause the formation of two crystalline forms in hexadecane.[14] The presence of a homolog stabilizes the metastable form of higher alcohols [14] and nitriles.[15]

Recent work upon the dimorphism of long-chain secondary amines [16] has shown that the relative stabilities of the polymorphic forms are influenced by *extremely small* amounts of impurities. The curves formed by the melting points of the two forms of the symmetrical secondary amines cross at ditetradecylamine. A small amount of impurity is apparently necessary for the realization of the higher-melting forms of dihexylamine, dioctylamine, and didecylamine. It thus appears that the effect of an impurity is not necessarily confined to a retardation of the rate of transition of a metastable form, as previously assumed.[17, 18] The profound influence of small traces of impurities on the polymorphic behavior of long-chain compounds raises the question as to whether some of the observations upon the polymorphic behavior of pure compounds may actually relate to the behavior of mixtures.

The fatty acids exhibit at least three polymorphic forms. These modifications are generally designated as α, β, and γ, and although they apparently possess similar melting points they are distinguished by differences in a number of physical properties. X-ray measurements show that these crystal modifications possess different spacings along the d_1 or long crystal axis, thus indicating a fundamental difference in their crystal cells.† The α-modification is generally obtained when the melted acid solidifies or when a

---

* For a discussion of the polymorphic behavior of long-chain compounds the reader is referred to Smith, "Fatty Acids and Other Long-Chain Compounds," in *Annual Reports on the Progress of Chemistry for 1938*, Vol. XXXV, The Chemical Society, London (1939).

† A uniform nomenclature has not been followed by all authors for the crystal modifications and for designating the long crystal spacings. This should be borne in mind when the original literature upon this subject is consulted.

solution of the acid is rapidly evaporated. This modification is transformed into the more stable β-form at a definite temperature for the particular acid in question. This temperature is termed the transition temperature, and Dupré la Tour [19] has reported the $\alpha \rightarrow \beta$ transition to occur in films of lauric, myristic, palmitic, stearic, and cerotic acids at 6.5°, 24.5°, 40°, 53°, and 80°, respectively. In the case of the acids which contain an odd number of carbon atoms, the α-modification which forms upon solidification

TABLE VIII

CRYSTAL SPACINGS OF EVEN SATURATED ACIDS

Spacings in Ångströms

No. of C Atoms	B	C
16	39.1	35.6
18	43.75	39.75
22	52.95	48.3
24	57.75	52.6
26	62.2	56.25
28	67.15	61.05
30	71.4	65.2
32	76.3	69.25
34	80.5	73.3
36	85.25	78.1
38	90.0	82.1
46	108.2	99.05

of the melted acids goes over very rapidly into the β-form upon further cooling, a property which distinguishes the odd from the even acids. The β- or stable modification is generally obtained when the acids crystallize slowly, although crystallization of the even acids from highly polar solvents yields the α-form. The α-form shows upon x-ray examination a C spacing along the long crystal axis, while the β- or stable modification shows a B spacing. The latter spacing is longer than the former, as shown by the observations of Francis, Collins, and Piper [20] upon the B and C spacings of even saturated acids, Table VIII.

In 1926, Piper, Malkin, and Austin [21] described a third modification which exhibits a still longer crystal spacing than the B spacing. This γ-modification shows an A crystal spacing and was obtained by these authors when either stearic or palmitic acid was carefully pressed upon a glass plate. This spacing can coexist with the C spacing, and B and C spacings can also occur simultaneously, but

A and B spacings do not exist together. There is no detectable difference in the melting points of these three forms, and recent studies [22] have indicated that there is no abrupt change in the temperature-density curves of the pure acids in the solid state. The failure to find differences in the physical properties of the various polymorphic forms of the long-chain, saturated acids has not yet been satisfactorily explained. The A spacing is frequently shown by paraffins, esters, and odd-carbon alcohols in the vicinity of their melting points; however, Piper, Chibnall, and Williams [8] have stated that no odd or even acids containing more than eighteen carbon atoms have been found to occur in this modification.

The α- and β-forms, which show C and B spacings respectively, are the types most frequently encountered among both even and odd acids, and as a consequence they have received the greater amount of attention from investigators. Acids containing an **even** number of carbon atoms show a short or C spacing when solidification of the melted acids takes place, or when rapid crystallization from solvents occurs. Ordinary crystallization of **even** acids from non-polar solvents yields directly the β-acid, which shows a B spacing. On the other hand, crystallization of **even** acids from highly polar solvents, such as acetic acid, results in the α-acid, which possesses a C spacing. When the **even** acids are crystallized in the presence of impurities, there is a decided tendency to assume the C spacing, which may coexist with crystals having a B spacing. It is evident, therefore, that when **even** acids are crystallized from solvents, the form assumed is dependent upon the particular solvent employed and, to a certain extent, upon the conditions of crystallization. Some conflicting statements have appeared in the literature owing to the failure of authors to state the conditions employed in crystallizing these acids. As stated before, the **even** acids show well-defined transition temperatures below which the α-form and above which the β-form is stable. According to Thibaud and Dupré la Tour,[23] the reverse transition upon cooling is not observed. The **odd**-carbon acids show a relationship among the various forms somewhat different from that exhibited by the even acids. When the melted **odd** acid solidifies, it first deposits crystals showing a C spacing (α-form), which are rapidly transformed into crystals having a B spacing (β-form). The work of de Boer [24] shows that the α-acid can only be retained in a metastable condition by very rapid cooling. The form actually realized upon cooling an **odd** acid at a normal rate is, therefore, the β-form of the acid and not the α-form as in the case of the **even** acids. The transition $\alpha \rightarrow \beta$ for the **odd** acids is unilateral for acids which contain thirteen or more carbon atoms, but it has been found to be reversible for undecanoic, nonanoic, and lower acids.[4,25] A further distinction between odd and even acids is that a solution of the **odd** acids always deposits crystals having a B spacing, independent of the nature of the solvent, whereas with the **even** acids the particu-

TABLE IX

CRYSTAL SPACINGS OF SATURATED ACIDS

Spacings in Ångströms

No. of C Atoms	B	C	A	D
13	31.65	30.00	35.3	25.8
14	34.9	31.60	....	....
15	35.8	34.2	40.0	29.9
16	39.1	35.60	41.0	....
17	40.45	38.6	....	33.9
18	43.75	39.75	46.6	
19	44.50	43.15		
20	48.45	44.15		
21	49.25	47.8		
22	52.95	48.3		
23	53.40	51.8		
24	57.75	52.6		
25	57.65	56.2		
26	62.2	56.25		
27	62.0	60.5		
28	67.15	61.05		
29	66.35	64.8		
30	71.4	65.2		

lar form obtained is dependent upon the polarity of the solvent employed.

In the above discussion it has been shown that the fatty acids exist in at least three polymorphic modifications and that these forms possess different long crystal spacings, thus indicating a fundamental difference in the crystal cells. The most important of these modifications are designated as α- and β-, the former showing a C crystal spacing and the latter a somewhat longer B spacing. Crystals showing the latter spacing are more stable than those possessing the former. It has also been shown that with the fatty acids and many of their derivatives there is an alternation in physical properties between the odd and even members of a series and that this alternation is related fundamentally to the molecular configuration of these long-chain compounds. This alternation is accompanied by apparent differences in the long crystal spacings of the polymorphic forms, so that if one plots either the B or the C spacings against the number of carbon atoms, the values fall upon two curves, one for the odd and one for the even acids. This is

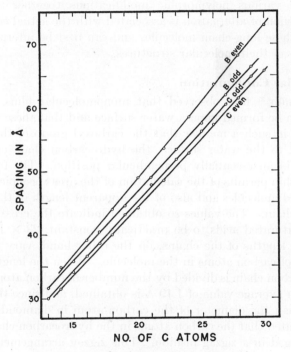

ᵢFɪɢ. 5.   Crystal spacings of saturated acids.

illustrated by the values for the spacings of the monocarboxylic acids containing from thirteen to thirty carbon atoms, reported by Francis and coworkers [26, 27] and shown in Table IX. Values in close agreement with these have been observed by Slagle and Ott.[28]

When the values of the B and C spacings are plotted against the number of carbon atoms in the acids (Fig. 5), they fall upon four curves, namely, B- odd, B- even, C- odd, and C- even.

The x-ray studies of Thibaud [29] have shown that the increase in chain length per carbon atom is 1.327 and 1.146 Å for the B and C forms of the odd acids, and 1.21 and 1.10 Å for the B and C forms of the even acids. The values of the still longer A spacings, which characterize the γ-modifications and are exhibited by acids carefully pressed on glass plates, fall on straight lines for both even and odd members of the series. Piper [30] has designated the various spacings as A, B, and C for the even acids and A', B', and C' for the odd acids. A fourth spacing, D, for the odd acids has also been described by this author. As has been stated, the significance of these various polymorphic modifications together with the phenomenon of alternation is associated with the actual configuration of these long-chain molecules and can best be interpreted on the basis of their molecular structures.

Molecular Configuration

Langmuir [31] first observed that monomolecular films of fatty acids can be formed upon a water surface and that these films are oriented in such a manner that the carboxyl group of the acid is attached to the water surface, the hydrocarbon chain extending upward in an essentially perpendicular position. The force-area relationship permits of the calculation of the areas occupied by the fatty acid molecules and also of the apparent length of the hydrocarbon chain. The values so obtained indicate the cross sections of the saturated acids to be practically constant, 23×10^{-16} sq. cm.; the lengths of the chains, on the other hand, vary with the number of carbon atoms in the molecule. When the length of the hydrocarbon chain is divided by the number of carbon atoms in the chain, an average value of 1.19 Å is obtained, and since this value is less than the diameter of the carbon atom in diamond, 1.54 Å, it was stated that the carbon atoms in the hydrocarbon chain must be arranged in a zigzag fashion. This zigzag arrangement of the carbon atoms is not confined to the acids alone, since measurements have shown this to be the configuration of the paraffins, alcohols, esters, soaps, and, in fact, all the high molecular weight straight-chain compounds so far examined. If we assume a straight hydrocarbon chain in which the carbon atoms are arranged in a zigzag manner, the tetrahedral angle being 109° 28', it follows that the distance between alternate carbon atoms is 2.52 Å or 1.26 Å per carbon atom. This is illustrated in Fig. 6, and values in close agreement with this spacing have been observed for the primary alcohols, paraffins, and several other aliphatic series.

The large amount of confirmatory data which have been obtained have served to establish beyond a reasonable doubt that the carbon atoms in the hydrocarbon chains actually occupy a zigzag position. It must be recognized, however, that other structures can account, at least in part, for the observed carbon-to-carbon distances in these chains. For example, Lee and van Rysselberge [32] have proposed a helicoidal configuration for long-chain compounds and have stated that such a structure, in addition to accounting for many of the physical and chemical properties of these compounds, explains an apparent 5, 10, 15 periodicity, in that the physical properties tend towards a maximum or a minimum at C_5, C_{10}, and C_{15}. Calculations of the molecular

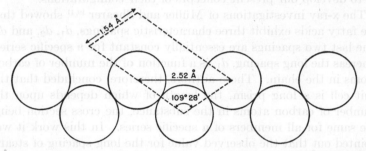

FIG. 6. Arrangement of carbon atoms in hydrocarbon chain. (Courtesy Glasstone, *Textbook of Physical Chemistry*, 2nd ed., D. Van Nostrand Co., New York, 1946.)

diameters based upon these helicoidal structures were stated to be in fair agreement with the observed values. This theory has been challenged by Broughton [33] on the basis that the break in physical properties at decanoic and pentadecanoic acids is not so marked as that observed between other adjacent members of the series. Nietz,[34] for example, in his studies on the work of adhesion of fatty acids to water, observed a minimum between the C_{12} and C_{14} members.

It is apparent that, although the concept of a zigzag arrangement of carbon atoms within the chain is an important observation as regards the structure of long-chain compounds, it cannot, of itself, account either for polymorphism or for alternation within a given series. Tammann [35] sought to explain alternation within an acid series by assuming that the even acids exist in two modifications whereas the odd exist only in one. Since it is now known that the odd acids also exhibit several modifications, this explanation is of little value and, as pointed out by Cuy,[36] it simply shifts the question as to why enantiotropism actually exists. Alternation of the physical properties is a property common to the crystalline state of long-chain compounds, the statement of Biach [37] that alternation is also encountered in the liquid state having been disproved. If we assume the chain to be perpendicular to the carboxyl plane, *cis* and *trans* arrangements of the carboxyl and terminal methyl groups are possible, but this would not bring about an alternation in physical properties within a specific series. X-ray studies have, however, been able to supply additional data concerning the structures of long-chain molecules, and have helped us to develop our present concepts of their configurations.

The x-ray investigations of Müller and Shearer [10,11] showed that the fatty acids exhibit three characteristic spacings, d_1, d_2, and d_3. The last two spacings are essentially constant for a specific series, whereas the long spacing, d_1, is a function of the number of carbon atoms in the chain. These authors, therefore, concluded that the unit cell is a long prism, the length of which depends upon the number of carbon atoms in the substance, the cross section being the same for all members of a specific series. In this work it was pointed out that the observed value for the long spacing of stearic acid, 38.7 Å, is greater than the value 30 Å which would be obtained by piling all the carbon and oxygen atoms on top of one another. It was, therefore, concluded that in the case of the acids the long spacings can only be accounted for by two molecules placed end to end and joined at their carboxyl groups. Verification of this is also found in the fact that the values of the chain lengths as determined by Langmuir are approximately half those obtained by x-ray measurements of the long spacings. Müller and Shearer [11] postulated several arrangements of the carbon atoms within the chain in an attempt to explain the observed values of these long spacings. The saturated acids crystallize in the monoclinic system with the symmetry plane perpendicular to the long face. In his calculation of the volume of the unit cell of stearic acid, Müller [38] determined that this cell contains four molecules so arranged that their carboxyl groups are in contact. The distance between two successive carbon atoms in the chain is considerably smaller than the distance between the chains themselves, showing that the mass density along the chain axis is higher than along any other line of the crystal. The following values for stearic acid were reported: Γ lattice, space group C_2^h, $a = 5.546$ Å, $b = 7.381$ Å, $c = 48.84$ Å, $\beta = 63° 38'$, c sine $\beta = 43.76$ Å. The average cross section of the unit cell of the saturated acids is 18.3 sq. Å. The addition of a

CH_2 group to a fatty acid molecule will thus produce twice the difference in distance between 001 planes as a similar addition produces in compounds such as the paraffins and ethyl esters, where bimolecular association is not encountered. This is illustrated in Fig. 7.

The importance of the observation that fatty acids are bimolecular in the solid state cannot be over-emphasized, since it forms the

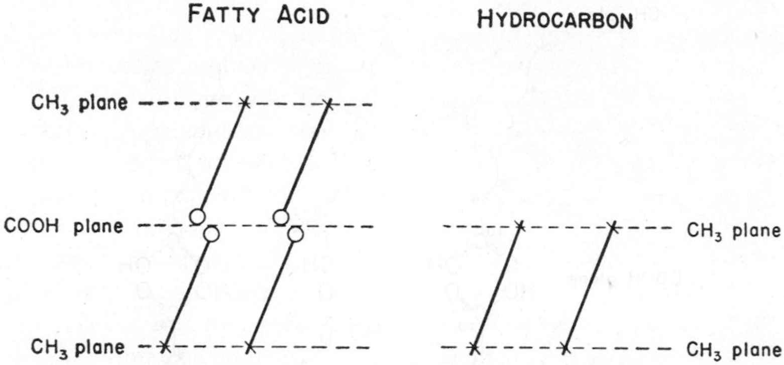

FIG. 7. Unit cells of fatty acids and hydrocarbons.

basis of our present-day belief concerning their crystal structure. In 1924, Garner and Randall,[2] in their studies of the heats of crystallization of the fatty acids, called attention to the important role played by the carboxyl group and suggested that it is oriented in two different manners in the crystal forms of the α- odd and α- even acids. The structural arrangements suggested by these authors are shown in Fig. 8.

Several structural configurations of the carboxyl groups and also of the terminal methyl groups of the even and α- and β- odd acids were subsequently proposed by Garner and Ryder.[13] In the postulated structures the hydrogen atom of the carboxyl group is assumed not to add to the chain length; however, in the modification showing the longest spacing, the γ-form, this possibility must be considered. While the different arrangements of the carboxyl groups as suggested by various authors offer an explanation for the existence of polymorphic forms of the fatty acids and similar compounds, they do not account for the fact that certain series are alternating and others are non-alternating. In 1931, Malkin [39] suggested that the essential difference between alternating and non-alternating series is that in the former the zigzag chain is tilted with respect to the terminal plane. Those series in which the chain is vertical with reference to the terminal plane do not exhibit alternation, whereas alternation is encountered if the chain is tilted. The various polymorphic forms result, therefore, from differences in the angles of tilt of the hydrocarbon chains. The successive additions of methylene groups to these tilted chains result in an alternation in the long crystal spacings and conse-

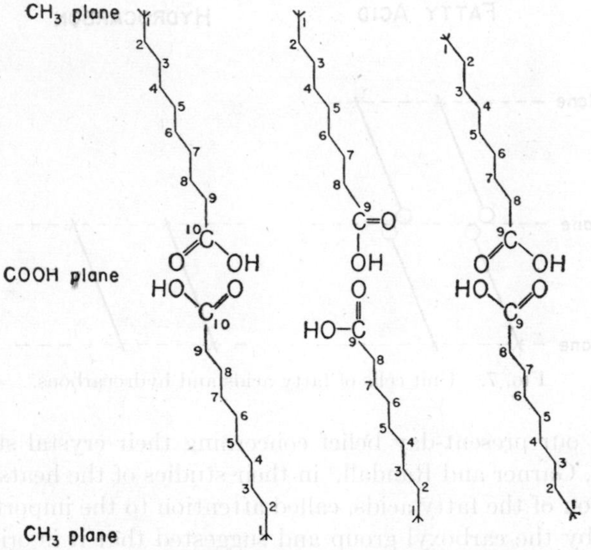

FIG. 8. Orientation of carboxyl groups in polymorphic forms of fatty acids.

quently in the physical properties of such compounds in the solid state. The characteristic crystal spacings exhibited by a zigzag chain of carbon atoms are, therefore, functions not only of the total number of carbon atoms but also of the angle of tilt of the chain. Vertical chains possess the longest crystal spacings and yield non-alternating series, whereas tilted chains show apparently shorter carbon-to-carbon distances and exhibit alternation in their physical properties. When several polymorphic modifications are capable of existence within a given series, such as the fatty acids, that form which possesses the longest crystal spacing generally corresponds to a vertical chain and shows non-alternating properties among the individual members. The crystal spacings, molecular volumes, and other physical properties of this modification will, therefore, fall upon essentially smooth curves comprising both odd and even members of the series. Those forms which show smaller crystal spacings along the long crystal axis possess tilted chains which give rise to alternating series. Examples of vertical and tilted hydrocarbon chains are shown in Fig. 9.

An examination of Fig. 9 shows that in the vertical chains d_1 increases uniformly with the number of carbon atoms, whereas in

VERTICAL **TILTED**

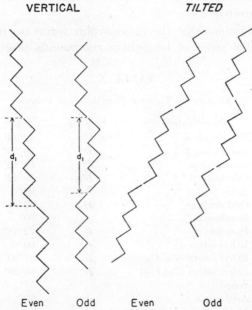

Even   Odd   Even   Odd

FIG. 9. Hydrocarbon chains. (Courtesy Glasstone, *Textbook of Physical Chemistry*, 2nd ed., D. Van Nostrand Co., New York, 1946.)

the tilted chains the density of the packing differs for the odd and even members, thus giving rise to an alternation in the d_1 spacings. The tilt of the hydrocarbon chain is largely dependent upon the orientation of the polar groups and is therefore quite dependent upon the nature of these groups. Where the groups are strongly associated, as in the acids or their methyl esters, the tilted forms are generally stable, whereas in the weakly associated compounds such as the higher esters, the vertical forms are stable, especially in the neighborhood of the melting points. The spacings vary directly with the sine of the angle of tilt of the hydrocarbon chain. King and Garner [40] have suggested discontinuance of the terms α, β, and γ in distinguishing the various polymorphic forms, and substitution of the classification of such forms into those which possess vertical and those which possess tilted chains. The influence of polymorphism upon the physical properties of the solid acids should be borne in mind in the following discussion of their properties.

Atomic Spacings, Angles of Tilt, Molecular Volumes, and Dipole Moments

The observations that the polymorphic forms occurring within any particular series of long-chain compounds possess different

TABLE X

ANGLES OF TILT OF POLYMORPHIC FORMS

Modification	Spacing	Angle
Even acids α	C	59°12′
Even acids β	B	70°36′
Odd acids α	C'	59°12′
Odd acids β	B'	59°12′
Acids	A	90°
Odd acids γ	D	52°59′
Paraffins α	A	90°
Paraffins β	B	72°48′
Ethyl esters α	A	90°
Ethyl esters (C_{16}–C_{26})	B	67°30′
Ethyl esters (C_{20}–C_{26})	B	64°26′
Soaps		57°
Acid soaps	A	90°
Alcohols	A	90°
Alcohols	B	55°40′
1-Monoglycerides α	A	90°
1-Monoglycerides β	B	59°

apparent carbon-to-carbon spacings along the long crystal axis, and that these spacings are a function of the angle of tilt of the hydrocarbon chain, are of fundamental significance. The tilt of the chain with reference to the terminal plane is largely dependent upon the nature of the terminal group. The various series of long-chain compounds would be expected to exhibit different angles of tilt, the value of the angle being characteristic not only of the particular series but also of the polymorphic form which is assumed by the individual members. The angles of tilt of various polymorphic forms of the fatty acids and several of their derivatives have been determined and are of importance in explaining the crystal structures of these compounds. For example, Piper [30] has observed that the lines formed by plotting the long crystal spacings against the number of carbon atoms (Fig. 5) are parallel for the even and odd acids having a C spacing and for the odd acids showing a B spacing, and that the carbon-to-carbon distance is 1.084 Å, thus indicating that the chain axis is inclined at an angle of 59° 12′. The values which have been reported in the literature for the angles of tilt of the polymorphic forms of the acids and several of their derivatives are shown in Table X.

Those series in which the chain is vertical (90° angle) do not show alternation in their physical properties, whereas those which possess tilted chains exhibit this phenomenon.

TABLE XI

LONG CRYSTAL SPACINGS OF THE ETHYL ESTERS, POTASSIUM SOAPS, AND ACID POTASSIUM SOAPS

No. of C Atoms in Acid	Spacings in Ångströms		
	Ethyl Esters	K Soaps	Acid K Soaps
12	.....	30.2	35.52
13	.....	31.85	.....
14	.....	33.95	40.45
15	.....	35.8	42.9
16	22.9	37.9	45.3
17	24.6	39.8	48.1
18	25.8	41.97	50.5
19	26.8	43.8	53.03
20	27.6	46.45	55.65
21	29.2	47.85	58.35
22	30.1	50.7	60.8
23	31.36	51.8	63.25
24	32.1	54.45	65.94

The long crystal spacings of the acids and a number of their derivatives have been reported in the literature. Those for the α- and β-forms of the acids as determined by Francis, Piper, and Malkin [26] have been recorded previously in this chapter in Table IX and Fig. 5. The long crystal spacings of the ethyl esters, the potassium soaps, and the acid potassium soaps have also been published by these authors and are shown in Table XI.

Francis, Collins, and Piper [20] have measured the long spacings of a number of high molecular weight acids, ethyl esters, alcohols, and 1-iodoalkanes containing an even number of carbon atoms.

Their values for the alcohols and 1-iodoalkanes are shown in Table XII.

TABLE XII

LONG CRYSTAL SPACINGS OF ALCOHOLS AND 1-IODOALKANES

Spacings in Ångströms

No. of C	Alcohols		Iodoalkanes
Atoms	A	B	B
18	.....	41.35	47.2
22	.....	50.0	56.10
24	.....	54.25	60.7
26	70.7	58.0	65.85
28	75.95	62.3	70.2
30	.....	66.4	74.15
32	.....	71.0	79.15
34	90.8	74.65	83.85
36	.....	.....	88.4

The long crystal spacings of several 1-monoglycerides as reported by Malkin and el Shurbagy [41] are shown in Table XIII.

TABLE XIII

LONG CRYSTAL SPACINGS OF 1-MONOGLYCERIDES

Spacings in Ångströms

No. of C Atoms in Acid	α	β and β'
10	37.2	32.9
11	40.2	35.2
12	43.2	37.3
13	46.2	39.6
14	....	41.5
15	51.3	43.8
16	....	45.8
17	....	48.2
18	58.3	50.0

The dicarboxylic acids offer an interesting and unusual case of dimorphism. The observations of Fairweather and others [5,7] on the melting points of the various members of this series have previously been presented in Table III and Fig. 3. These indicate a high degree of alternation, so that the curves of the odd and even members are practically mirror images of each other and show a convergence in the neighborhood of the thirty-carbon member. In 1925, Trillat [42] measured the long crystal spacings of several of the lower members of this series and reported the following rela-

TABLE XIV

SPACINGS OF DICARBOXYLIC ACIDS

No. of C Atoms	M.P., °C.	Spacings in Ångströms				
		d_1	d_2	d_3	d_4	d_5
9	107	9.56	4.67	3.87	3.28	....
12	129	13.25	4.17	3.77	2.98	4.63
13	113.5	13.3	4.70	3.93	3.21	....
14	126.5	15.4	4.13	3.71	2.97	....
16	125	17.4	4.14	3.67	....	4.60
18	124	19.55	4.12	3.69	2.95	4.63
22	123.8	23.6	4.13	3.75	....	....
26	123.5	27.8	4.16	3.74	2.97	4.62
34	123	35.9	4.11	3.67	2.98	4.51

tionship between the number of carbon atoms and the spacings in Å: C_4, 4.5; C_6, 7.0; C_7, 7.6; C_8, 9.3; C_9, 9.6; and C_{10}, 11.4. Normand, Ross, and Henderson [7] have made an extensive x-ray investigation of the spacings of a number of dicarboxylic acids and also of their ethyl esters, the results of which are shown in Tables XIV

TABLE XV

SPACINGS OF ETHYL ESTERS OF DICARBOXYLIC ACIDS

No. of C Atoms in Acid	M.P., °C.	Spacings in Ångströms				
		d_1	d_2	d_3	d_4	d_5
13	20	22.7	....	....	....	4.63
14	27	23.7	4.09	3.64	....	....
18	43	28.5	4.08	3.56	....	....
22	56	33.6	4.14	3.70	....	4.63
30	74	43.7	4.10	3.69	....	4.53
34	80	49.0	4.17	3.71	....	4.63
Monoethyl Esters						
14	55	42.1	4.14	3.66	....	....
18	71	50.5	4.12	3.66	....	....

and XV. In these tables the d_1 spacing refers to the length along the long crystal axis, while the spacings d_2, d_3, d_4, and d_5 relate to the cross section.

These authors have pointed out that the increment in the long spacing, d_1, in passing from an even to an odd acid (0.6–0.05 Å) is much different from that in passing from an odd to an even acid (1.7–2.1 Å). The spacings d_2, d_3, and d_4 also differ for the odd and even acids. These differences in both linear and cross-sectional values indicate a fundamental difference in the structures of the even and odd dicarboxylic acids. The increment in the long crystal spacing brought about by the addition of a methylene group to the diethyl esters is constant (1.2–1.3 Å); however, the increment in the d_1 spacing for a similar addition to a monoethyl ester

TABLE XVI

CELL DIMENSIONS OF DICARBOXYLIC ACIDS

No. of C Atoms	Dimensions in Ångströms			
	a	b	c	Angle β
6	10.27	5.16	10.02	137°5′
7	9.93	4.82	22.12	130°40′
8	10.12	5.06	12.58	135°0′
9	9.72	4.83	27.14	129°30′
10	10.05	4.96	15.02	133°50′
13	9.63	4.82	37.95	128°20′
18	9.76	4.92	25.10	131°10′

is 2.1 Å, which indicates that the monoethyl esters contain two molecules and the diethyl esters only one molecule between successive reflecting planes. In 1928, Caspari [43] investigated the crystal structure of single crystals of adipic (C_6), pimelic (C_7), suberic (C_8), azelaic (C_9), sebacic (C_{10}), brassylic (C_{13}), and octadecanedioic (C_{18}) acids. The cell dimensions and values of the β angles of these acids as reported by Caspari are shown in Table XVI.

It was observed that while the c dimensions of the unit cells of the even dicarboxylic acids are proportional to the number of carbon atoms, the values for the odd acids are proportional to twice this number. The odd and even dicarboxylic acids, therefore, fall into two series, the former of which contains four molecules to the unit cell and has an effective length equal to twice the length of the dicarboxylic acid molecule, whereas the latter contains only two molecules to the unit cell and is one molecule in length. Thus, for those acids whose cell dimensions are shown in Table XVI, the C_7, C_9, and C_{13} acids contain four molecules to their unit cells and the remainder contain two molecules. It was postulated that the molecules of the odd-carbon dicarboxylic acids are asymmetrical, as are the molecules of the monocarboxylic acids, whereas the molecules of the even-carbon dicarboxylic acids are symmetrical. The example shown in Fig. 10 was cited by Caspari.

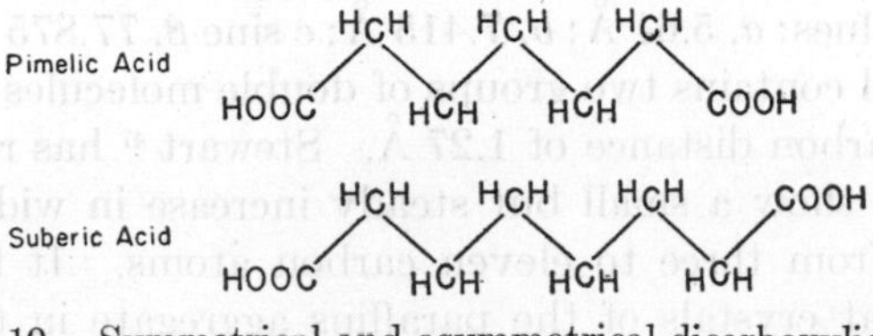

FIG. 10. Symmetrical and asymmetrical dicarboxylic acids.

The dicarboxylic acids are unique in that they contain a carboxyl group at each end of the molecule and thus show a repetition of the carboxyl plane. This is not the case with the monoesters of these acids, as illustrated in Fig. 11.

The above values for the dicarboxylic acids refer to the so-called α-modification. In 1929, Caspari [44] obtained a β-modification of azelaic acid by rapid crystallization of a saturated aqueous solu-

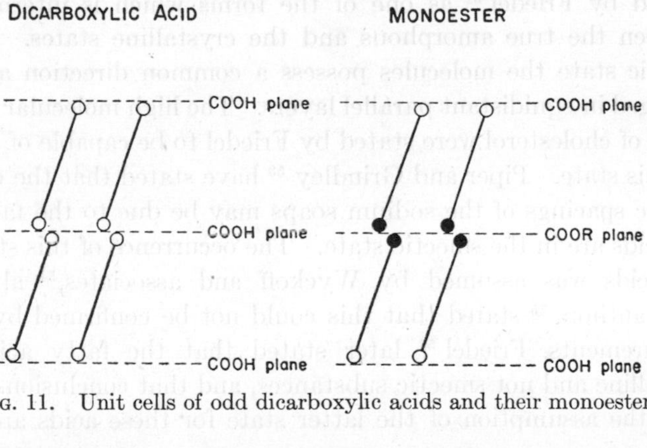

FIG. 11. Unit cells of odd dicarboxylic acids and their monoesters.

tion. The dimensions of the unit cell of this β-form are: a, 5.61 Å; b, 9.58 Å; c, 27.20 Å; and β, 136°30′. The cell length corresponds to two molecules. The difference in lattice energy between the α- and β-modifications of azelaic acid is small, since the two forms could not be distinguished by melting points. α- and β-Forms of pimelic acid have been described by Dupré la Tour,[45] the irreversible change $\beta \rightarrow \alpha$ occurring at 74–75°. The same author [19] had previously shown that malonic, succinic, and glutaric acids exist in α- and β-forms, with transition points of 80°, 137°, and 74°, respectively.

Kohlhaas [46] has measured the dimensions of the unit cell of cetyl palmitate crystallized from amyl butyrate, and has reported the following values: a, 5.61 Å; b, 7.415 Å; c sine β, 77.875 Å; β, 61°31'. The unit cell contains two groups of double molecules and shows a carbon-to-carbon distance of 1.27 Å. Stewart [47] has reported that the alcohols show a small but steady increase in width of chains containing from three to eleven carbon atoms. It has been reported [48] that crystals of the paraffins aggregate in the direction of their angles, whereas the fatty acids aggregate in the direction of their sides. X-ray analysis * of the liquid paraffins has shown that the tendency of the chains to assume a parallel arrangement is evidenced even in the liquid state.[49, 50]

Trillat [51] has made x-ray examinations of palmitic acid films on mica and also on water, and has observed sharp reflections which he considered to be characteristic of a smectic or soaplike substance. This work indicated that the molecules lie in parallel planes, the spacing being 36 Å. The smectic state was first described by Friedel [52] as one of the forms which is intermediate between the true amorphous and the crystalline states. In the smectic state the molecules possess a common direction and are arranged in equidistant parallel layers. The high molecular weight esters of cholesterol were stated by Friedel to be capable of assuming this state. Piper and Grindley [53] have stated that the characteristic spacings of the sodium soaps may be due to the fact that the acids are in the smectic state. The occurrence of this state for the acids was assumed by Wyckoff and associates,[54] although these authors [55] stated that this could not be confirmed by x-ray measurements. Friedel [56] later stated that the fatty acids are crystalline and not smectic substances, and that conclusions based upon the assumption of the latter state for these acids are erroneous.

* For a general treatment of the application of x-ray analysis to the determination of crystal structure, the reader is referred to Wyckoff, *The Structure of Crystals*, A.C.S. Monograph Series No. 19, 2nd ed., The Chemical Catalog Co., New York (1931); Randall, *The Diffraction of X-Rays and Electrons by Amorphous Solids, Liquids, and Gases*, Chapman and Hall, London (1934); Clark, *Applied X-Rays*, 3rd ed., McGraw-Hill Book Co., New York (1940).

The molecular volumes of the liquid acids undergo a constant increase of 16.8 cc. per gram-molecule for each addition of a methylene group. Garner and Ryder [13] have observed that for the even-carbon acids in the solid state the increment in molecular volume due to the addition of two methylene groups is 27.5 cc per gram molecule, but that the molecular volume of an odd-carbon acid in the solid state is greater than the mean of the two adjacent even acids. The molecular volumes of the acids in the solid state, therefore, alternate from odd to even acids, as does also the volume change due to fusion. The values of the molecular volumes for

TABLE XVII

MOLECULAR VOLUMES OF LIQUID AND SOLID ACIDS

Acid	Mol. Vol. (liq.) cc./g.-mol. at 50°	Δcc.	Mol. Vol. (sol.) cc./g.-mol. at 15°	Δcc.
Octanoic	162.61		140.2	
Nonanoic (α)	179.43	16.82	160.1	19.9
Decanoic	196.20	16.77	167.8	7.7
Undecanoic (α)	212.95	16.75	186.5	18.7
Lauric	229.84	16.89	195.2	8.7
Undecanoic (β)	......		180.0	

several acids as reported by Garner and Ryder [13] are shown in Table XVII.

In 1922, Pauly [57] called attention to the fact that the relatively smaller molecular volumes correspond to lower melting points and heats of crystallization. Gómez Aranda [58] has proposed the equation $V = aM + b$ for the molecular volumes, in which a is a homology constant and b a functional constant characteristic for each series. The equation for the density, $D = 1/[a + (b/M)]$, indicates that if b is greater than zero the density increases with molecular weight, whereas if it is less than zero the reverse is true.

Since the dipole moment is a function of the polar group, it should not materially vary among the members of any specific homologous series. Wolf and Gross [59] have stated that the dipole moment alternately rises and falls as a homologous series is ascended, molecules with an even number of carbon atoms possessing the higher moments. The alternation, however, if present at all, is exceedingly small, and most of the data so far recorded indicate that the dipole moment is essentially a constant and non-alternating value, especially for the higher members of any specific homologous series. The dipole moments of some of the aliphatic alcohols are recorded in Table XVIII.

TABLE XVIII

DIPOLE MOMENTS OF ALIPHATIC ALCOHOLS *

No. of C Atoms	Dipole Moment $\times 10^{18}$
1	1.68
2	1.70
3	1.66
4	1.65
5	1.7
6	1.6
7	1.71
8	1.68
9	1.6
10	1.6
11	1.66
12	1.62
16	1.66

* The values contained in this table have been reported by Williams, *Physik. Z.*, **29**, 174 (1928); Stranathan, *Phys. Rev.* [2], **31**, 653 (1928); Miles, *ibid.* [2], **34**, 964 (1929); Mahanti and Dasgupta, *Indian J. Phys.*, **3**, 467 (1929); Müller and Sack, *Physik. Z.*, **31**, 815 (1930).

Few values for the dipole moments of high molecular weight compounds other than the alcohols have been reported in the literature, and it is rather difficult to draw generalizations. Zahn [60] has reported a value of 1.51×10^{-18} for formic acid and 1.4×10^{-18} for acetic acid, and Briegleb [61] has observed values of 1.45, 1.04, 0.93, and 0.88×10^{-18} for formic, acetic, propionic, and butyric acids, respectively, whereas Pohl, Hobbs, and Gross [62] have reported 1.77, 1.63, 1.68, and 1.9×10^{-18} for these acids. Values of 0.75, 0.77, and 0.77×10^{-18} have been reported [63] for lauric, myristic, and palmitic acids, and Volarovich and Stepanenko [64] have obtained values of 1.506, 1.452, and 1.512×10^{-18} for stearic, oleic, and linoleic acids, respectively. It is evident that the values which have been reported are not in agreement, and some of them appear to be materially lower than would be expected. Those observed for the lower molecular weight amines [65, 66, 67] are in fair agreement, being in the neighborhood of 1.3×10^{-18}. The values for the nitriles indicate them to be highly polar, Werner [68] having reported 3.2, 3.34, and 3.46×10^{-18} for acetonitrile, propionitrile, and butyronitrile, respectively, and Williams [69] having observed values in close agreement with those found by Werner for acetonitrile and propionitrile. In 1933, Smith [70] determined the dipole moments of several homologous series of aliphatic compounds. The results reported by this author are shown in Table XIX.

TABLE XIX

DIPOLE MOMENTS ($\times 10^{18}$) OF HOMOLOGOUS SERIES OF STRAIGHT-CHAIN ALIPHATIC COMPOUNDS

	Cl	Br	I	OH	NH$_2$	CHO	CN
H	1.03	0.79	0.38	1.85	1.5	....	2.65
CH$_3$	1.85	1.5	1.3	1.68	1.23	2.7	3.11
C$_2$H$_5$	1.99	1.83	1.66	1.70	1.3	....	3.34
C$_3$H$_7$	2.0	1.8	1.6	1.66	1.4	2.46	3.46
C$_4$H$_9$	1.97	1.97	1.88	1.65	1.3	....	....
C$_5$H$_{11}$	....	....	....	....	1.3	....	....
C$_6$H$_{13}$	....	....	....	1.6		2.56	....
C$_7$H$_{15}$	1.85	1.84	1.84	1.71	....	....	....

The dielectric constants of the fatty acids decrease with increase in molecular weight of the acids. The following values have been reported [71] for several of the fatty acids: formic, 19.0 at 2°; acetic, 6.29 at 19°; propionic, 3.15 at 17°; butyric, 2.70 at 17°; valeric, 2.67 at 20°; and caproic, enanthic, caprylic, palmitic, and stearic acids at 71°, 2.632, 2.587, 2.544, 2.34, and 2.318, respectively. Baker and Smyth [72] have determined the dielectric constants of ethyl undecanoate, ethyl palmitate, ethyl stearate, and cetyl alcohol in both the liquid and the solid states over a wide range of temperature and frequency.

Melting Points of Long-Chain Compounds

In an earlier portion of this chapter it was pointed out that the melting points of the individual members of certain series of long-chain compounds alternate as the series is ascended, but that in other series the melting points show an essentially linear increase with successive additions of carbon atoms. It was also observed that alternation is a characteristic of those compounds which possess chains which are tilted with reference to the terminal groups, whereas those forms which possess vertical chains are non-alternating. It follows, therefore, that in those series where the chains are vertical with reference to the terminal planes, or where a vertical form is assumed in the vicinity of the melting point, the values for this constant will be non-alternating. It has also been shown that the alternation in melting points for any particular series becomes less with increase in molecular weight of the individual members, the curves for the even and odd compounds tending to converge as the series is ascended. For any particular series, this convergence occurs at a definite temperature, which is generally designated as the convergence temperature. According to Timmermans,[73] organic compounds obey a law of convergence in that the melting points of the higher members tend toward a common limit of 117°. Convergence has only been experimentally demonstrated in the dicarboxylic·acid series, in which it occurs at 123°, which is the approximate melting point of the thirty-carbon acid.

In a theoretical discussion of the convergence temperature, King and Garner [40] have pointed out that since both the terminal and the methylene groups occupy the same cross-sectional areas, they are both subject to some distortion. The melting point is dependent upon both the nature of the terminal group and the length of the hydrocarbon chain, and since terminal groups generally possess negative heats and entropies of crystallization, they easily enter the liquid state. Thus the lower members of a homologous series generally possess low melting points, which frequently tend toward a minimum in the vicinity of the five-carbon member. Beyond this point successive additions of methylene groups are generally attended by melting point increases, and the convergence temperature is that point where the hydrocarbon chain is sufficiently long to minimize the effect of the terminal group, the compound thus resembling a hydrocarbon in physical properties. Since at the convergence temperature the long hydrocarbon chain is determinative with respect to the thermal properties, it would be expected that convergence temperatures would not differ greatly between respective series, being differentiated only by differences in the manner of packing as determined by the angle of tilt of the chain. Calculations of convergence temperatures from available thermal data have given the following values: 112.2° and 115.5° for the odd and even acids, 135° for the even hydrocarbons, 121.2° for the α even ethyl esters, and 108.5° for the even methyl esters.

When a compound is capable of existing in two or more polymorphic modifications, the melting point reported in the literature generally refers to the stable or higher-melting form, which may possess either a vertical or a tilted chain, depending upon the particular compound in question. In certain instances, as in the cases of ethyl esters of monobasic acids containing less than twenty carbon atoms, and ethyl esters of dibasic acids, the melting points are non-alternating, although measurements of the atomic spacings indicate the chain to be tilted. Malkin [39] has suggested that in such instances the vertical position is assumed just below the melting point. Polymorphism of acids and many derivatives is frequently evidenced by unilateral conversion of one solid form to another. This transition occurs within a definite temperature interval and

TABLE XX

MELTING POINTS OF α- AND β-FORMS OF 1-IODOALKANES, °C.

No. of C Atoms	α	β
22	41.5	48.2
24	48.1	54.2
26	54.4	59.1
28	59.6	63.15
30	64.0	67.0
32	68.2	.....
34	71.6	.....
36	74.9	.....

is accompanied by a significant heat effect. Garner and King [4] have determined the heats of the transition $\alpha \longrightarrow \beta$ of the saturated monocarboxylic acids containing 9, 11, 13, 15, 17, 23, and 25 carbon atoms to be 1.37, 1.84, 0.94, 1.20, 1.55, 1.62, and 1.47 kg. cal./mole, respectively. In the case of many fatty acid derivatives, the metastable or lower-melting form can actually be isolated. For example, Phillips and Mumford [74] have isolated α- and β-forms of ethyl myristate melting at 11.7° and 12.3°, respectively, and Smith [75] obtained two forms of ethyl stearate, one melting at 32.5° and the other at 34°. Polymorphic modifications of the individual members of several series of long-chain compounds have since been isolated, among which may be mentioned, in addition to the ethyl esters,[76, 77] the 1-iodoalkanes,[20] the alkyl acetates,[78] and the alkylammonium acetates.[79] The melting points of the α- and β-modifications of several 1-iodoalkanes are shown in Table XX, and of the α- and β-forms of the ethyl esters of a number of even-carbon, saturated, monocarboxylic acids in Table XXI.

Calculations of the melting points from the heats and entropies of crystallization have been shown by several authors to yield

values which agree rather closely with those determined experimentally. For example, Garner, Van Bibber, and King [80] found the relationship between the heat of crystallization, the temperature, and the number of carbon atoms for the α-forms of the hydrocarbons to be expressed by the equations (1) $Q = 0.6085n - 1.75$ and (2) $Q/T = 0.001491n + 0.00404$. When equation (1) is divided by equation (2), the resulting equation, $T = (0.6085n - 1.75) \div (0.001491n + 0.00404)$, yields the calculated values for the

TABLE XXI

MELTING POINTS OF α- AND β-FORMS OF EVEN ETHYL ESTERS, °C.

No. of C Atoms in Acid	α	β
16	24.4	. . . . .
18	31.4	33.9
20	40.54	41.65
22	48.7 *	48.25 †
24	54.8 *	54.35 †
26	60.2 *	59.95 †
28	64.6	
30	68.45	
32	72.5	
34	75.4	
36	78.6	
38	80.55	
46	90.5 §	

* Listed under "γ" by Francis and Piper, *J. Am. Chem. Soc.*, **61**, 577 (1939).
† Listed under "α" by Francis and Piper, *loc. cit.*
§ Listed under "β" by Francis, Collins, and Piper, *Proc. Roy. Soc. (London)*, **158A**, 691 (1937).

setting points. These authors have calculated the setting points of a number of hydrocarbons between C_5 and C_{70}, and the agreement between the calculated and observed values is shown in Table XXII. It will be noted that while the calculated and observed setting points of the lower members differ materially, the values for the higher members are in fair agreement.

King and Garner [81] have expressed the melting points of the ethyl esters of even ac ds containing twenty or less carbon atoms by the equation $T_m = (0.7630n + 0.63)/(0.00179n + 0.01475)$, and of those of even acids containing more than twenty carbon atoms by the equation $T_m = (0.7081n - 3.28)/(0.001796n - 0.0012)$.

The β-form is stable at the melting point for esters of acids which contain less than twenty carbon atoms, and the α-form is stable for the higher esters. The agreement between the observed and .

TABLE XXII

CALCULATED AND OBSERVED SETTING POINTS OF HYDROCARBONS, DEGREES ABSOLUTE

No. of C Atoms	Observed	Calculated
5	143.4	112.4
6	178.6	146.3
7	182.2	173.4
8	215.6	195.2
9	222.0	213.4
10	241	228.8
11	246.5	241.9
12	261	253.2
13	266.8	263.1
14	278.5	271.7
15	283	279.4
16	293	286.3
17	295	292.7
18	301	298.0
19	304	303.1
20	309.7	307.7
22	316.8	316.0
26	329.1	328.6
30	338.5	338.6
34	345.4	346.0
35	347.0	347.7
36	349	349.2
40	353.8	354.6
50	365.1	365.0
54	368	367.9
60	371.9	371.8
62	373.5	372.9
64	375	374.0
70	378.3	377.2

experimental values for the setting points of the even ethyl esters as reported by these authors is shown in Table XXIII.

Later these authors [82] developed the equation $T = (1.083n - 4.15)/(0.002839n - 0.00185)$ for the even methyl esters and the equation $T = (0.8389n - 5.58)/(0.00224n - 0.00904)$ for the odd ethyl esters. The agreement between the observed and calculated values is shown in Table XXIV.

Assuming that the increments in the heats of crystallization are the same for all homologous series, Garner and Rushbrooke [83] have developed the following equation for the melting points of

TABLE XXIII

CALCULATED AND OBSERVED SETTING POINTS OF EVEN ETHYL ESTERS, DEGREES ABSOLUTE

No. of C Atoms in Acid	Calculated	Observed
6	204.4	205.5 *
8	231.6	229 *
10	253	253.1 *
12	270.1	271.3
14	284.1	284.0
16	295.9(β)	296.2(β)
	292.3(α)	292.3(α)
18	305.9(β)	306.4(β) *
	304.2(α)	304.1(α)
20	313.4	313.4
22	321.0	320.8
24	327.1	327.2
26	332.4	332.6
30	341.0	341.3

* Denotes melting point.

the even members of a homologous series: $T = (x + 1.030n) \div (y + 0.0002652n)$, where x and y are constants depending upon the nature of the terminal group. The values of x and y for myristic

TABLE XXIV

OBSERVED AND CALCULATED SETTING POINTS OF ESTERS, DEGREES ABSOLUTE

No. of C Atoms in Acid	Methyl Esters		Ethyl Esters	
	Calcd.	Observed	Calcd.	Observed
10	251.7	255	.....	.....
12	274.4	278	.....	.....
14	290.5	291.4	.....	.....
15	.....	.....	285.1	285
16	302.5	302.1	.....	.....
17	.....	.....	299.0	298.2
18	311.4	310.8	.....	.....
19	.....	.....	309.1	309.1
20	318.7	318.4	.....	.....
21	.....	.....	317.0	318
22	324.5	324.8	.....	.....

acid and several of its derivatives were determined by these authors. These values were then employed in the calculation of the melting points of the various members of the respective series. The values of x and y were reported to be as follows: myristic acid, -3.68, -0.00426; myristamide, -1.50, -0.00277; methyl myristate, -3.79, -0.00066; ethyl myristate, -3.25, $+0.00220$; and myristyl alcohol, -2.66, $+0.00072$. It is of interest to note that although the melting points of the higher members of most homologous series increase with an increase in molecular weight, those of the anilides and p-toluidides [84] exhibit a distinct minimum, and no correlation exists between the melting points of the amides and the number of carbon atoms. The various melting points reported in this chapter have been given for the purpose of illustrating correlations which exist between these values and the structures and other thermal properties of long-chain compounds. Readers interested in the melting points of individual members of aliphatic series should consult those chapters where such compounds are discussed in detail.

The Heats of Crystallization, Specific Heats, and Heats of Transition of Long-Chain Compounds

The heats of crystallization of the monobasic acids are recorded in Table II. Figure 2 shows that these values when plotted against the number of carbon atoms form two parallel lines which do not converge with increase in molecular weight. If we consider the odd and even acids as separate series, it will be noted that, for acids containing ten or more carbon atoms, the increment in the heat of crystallization brought about by the addition of a methylene group is constant for each series, being 1.03 kg. cal. for the even and 0.97 kg. cal. for the odd acids. The heats of crystallization reported in the literature for long-chain compounds generally refer to the forms stable at the melting points. Since the heats of crystallization of the various polymorphic forms differ by the heats of transition, generalizations regarding increments in the heats of crystallization with increase in carbon content within any particular series should refer to identical forms. For example, Garner and Randall [2] reported the heats of crystallization of the α-forms of nonanoic and undecanoic acids to be 4.85 and 6.00 kg. cal./mole respectively, the heats of the transition $\alpha \rightarrow \beta$ being 1.33 and 1.84 kg. cal./mole, and the heats of crystallization of the β-forms, 6.17 and 7.84 kg. cal./mole. The heats of crystallization of the different series vary, and it is evident that the nature of the terminal group exerts a decided influence. The heat of crystallization of a long-chain compound is a function of the heats of crystallization of both the terminal group and the hydrocarbon chain. The former of these is constant for any particular series, such as similar forms of the odd acids, the even acids, the odd or even esters, and so on, but the latter is a function of the chain length. The effect of the terminal group is more pronounced in the shorter-chain compounds, and this fact probably accounts for the various abnormalities, such as the maxima or minima in physical properties, which are frequently encountered at the five-carbon member.

King and Garner [40] stated that long-chain compounds can be divided sharply into two classes, namely, tilted and vertical forms. In the tilted forms the increments in the heats and the entropies of crystallization are approximately the same for the different series. Variations in the angle of tilt, therefore, do not profoundly influence these values. In this group the specific heats for the solid state are lower than those for the liquid state, and the values obtained for the cross-sectional areas, 18.3 to 18.5×10^{-16} sq. cm., indicate that the chains are closely packed. Malkin [85] has postulated that those forms of even-carbon compounds which contain tilted chains are separated by similar, closely packed planes, while the odd-carbon members containing tilted chains are separated by alternate loosely and closely packed planes. The latter structure accounts for the lower melting points of the odd members of a homologous series. Those forms which possess chains which are vertical with respect to the plane containing the terminal groups possess distinctly lower heats and entropies of crystallization, the values varying among the different series. Members of this group possess smaller specific heats and larger cross-sectional areas, 19.6 to 19.9×10^{-16} sq. cm., indicating a less-dense packing. It has been stated [86] that these vertical chains are free to oscillate about the chain axis, and that the energy of oscillation increases rapidly with increase in temperature. Consequently, because of the oscillation energy, less thermal energy is required for the conversion from the solid to the liquid state. The thermal behavior of the odd-carbon saturated hydrocarbons has been explained on the basis of the possession of rotating and non-rotating vertical chains. The odd paraffins above undecane crystallize in the vertical, rotating form, which changes reversibly into a non-rotating form upon further cooling.[87, 88, 89] King and Garner [40] assembled the data upon the thermal properties of several series of long-chain compounds, and the summary is shown in Table XXV.

TABLE XXV

THERMAL PROPERTIES OF SEVERAL SERIES OF LONG-CHAIN COMPOUNDS

Series	Heat of Crystn. per CH_2, kg. cal.	Entropy per CH_2 Group $\times 10^6$	Av. Sp. Heat of Solid Forms, cal./g.	Av. Sp. Heat of Liq. for Range 30° above M.P., cal./g.	Convergence Temp. (calc.), °Abs.	Heat of Crystn. of Terminal Groups, kg. cal.
Even Acids	1.03	2562	0.48	0.53	388.5	−1.55
Odd Acids	0.97	2505	0.44	0.54	385.2	−2.56
Even Me Esters	1.08	2839	0.43	0.52	381.5	−1.98
(T) Hydrocarbons	1.0	....	0.44	0.57	.....	......
(T) Ethyl Esters	1.04	....	0.43	0.52	.....	......
(V) Odd Et Esters	0.84	2240	0.63	0.50	.....	−3.90
(V) Even Et Esters	0.71	1796	0.71	0.52	394.2	−1.86
(V) Even Hydrocarbons	0.61	1491	1.05	0.57	408.0	−0.53

(Tilted Forms: Even Acids, Odd Acids, Even Me Esters, (T) Hydrocarbons, (T) Ethyl Esters; Vertical Forms: (V) Odd Et Esters, (V) Even Et Esters, (V) Even Hydrocarbons)

The heats of crystallization of several series of aliphatic compounds have been investigated, and the data so obtained have been of value in correlating the thermal properties of these substances. An appreciable amount of work, for example, has been done by King and Garner [40, 81] and by van Bellinghen [78] on the methyl and ethyl esters of the saturated acids. The x-ray studies of Malkin [90] indicate that the methyl esters exist as double molecules, whereas the ethyl esters form single molecules. The latter exhibit at least two modifications, a vertical or transparent α-form and a tilted or opaque β-form, the angle of tilt being 67°35′. The transformation is reversible for the odd esters but is irreversible for the even esters. The relative stability of the vertical form becomes greater with increasing molecular weight, the β-form being stable for even esters of acids containing twenty or less carbon atoms. Since the vertical forms are stable for the ethyl esters of the C_{17} and C_{19} acids, the shift in relative stability occurs at a lower chain length for the odd esters.

The methyl esters of acids which contain an even number of carbon atoms are apparently obtained only in the tilted form, the angle of tilt being 63°, whereas the methyl esters of the odd acids exist in at least two modifications, the angles of tilt having been reported to be 67.5° and 75°. The latter form was assumed by Malkin [90] to consist of single molecules, but the investigation of King and Garner [82] did not reveal any unusual thermal effects which should accompany a dissociation from double to single molecules, and these authors were of the opinion that this form possesses a vertical chain. The heats of crystallization, specific heats, and heats of transition of the ethyl esters of the saturated acids as reported by King and Garner [82] and by van Bellinghen [78] are shown in Table XXVI.

TABLE XXVI

THERMAL PROPERTIES OF ETHYL ESTERS OF SATURATED ACIDS

No. of C Atoms in Acid	Heats of Crystn. (kg. cal./g.-mol.)		Heat of the Transition $\alpha \rightarrow \beta$ (kg. cal./g.-mol.)	Specific Heats (cal./g.)		
	α	β		Liquid	Solid α	β
1	......	2.2	.....	....	....	....
2	......	2.25	.....	....	....	....
3	......	3.0	.....	....	....	....
8	......	5.75	.....	....	....	....
9	......	7.10	.....	....	....	....
10	......	7.56	.....	....	....	....
11	......	7.62	.....	....	....	....
12	......	9.475	.....	0.48	....	0.34
13	......	10.20	.....	....	....	....
14	......	11.17	.....	0.50	....	....
16	......	12.68	.....	0.50	....	0.39
17	8.66	12.62	3.96	0.50	0.76	0.44
18	9.436	14.31	4.874	0.50	....	0.45
19	10.32	14.74	4.42	0.50	0.64	0.46
20	10.93	16.39	5.46	0.53	0.72	0.44
22	12.42	18.63	6.21	0.55	0.65	0.44
24	13.82	20.57	6.75	0.53	0.72	0.42
26	15.22	22.66	7.44	0.53	0.73	0.43
30	17.93	25.98	8.05	0.55	0.79	0.45

Similar data for several of the methyl esters as reported by King and Garner [82] are shown in Table XXVII.

TABLE XXVII

THERMAL PROPERTIES OF METHYL ESTERS OF SATURATED ACIDS

No. of C Atoms in Acid	Heat of Crystn. (kg. cal./g.-mol.) (Tilted Form)	Specific Heats (cal./g.)	
		Liquid	Solid (Tilted Form)
14	10.63	0.53	0.48
16	13.23	0.52	0.44
18	15.40	0.51	0.43
20	17.62	0.52	0.42
22	19.68	0.54	0.42

The only methyl ester of an odd-carbon acid examined by these authors was methyl nonadecanoate. The observed heats of crystallization were 14.87 and 10.24 kg. cal./g.-mol. for the tilted and vertical forms respectively, the heat of transition was 4.63 kg. cal./g.-mol., and the specific heats were 0.45 and 0.62 cal./g. for the tilted and vertical forms respectively.

The heats of crystallization of several higher hydrocarbons have been determined by Garner, Van Bibber, and King,[80] and their results are shown in Table XXVIII.

TABLE XXVIII

THERMAL PROPERTIES OF HYDROCARBONS

No. of C Atoms	Heats of Crystallization (kg. cal./g.-mol.)		Heat of Transition (kg. cal./g.-mol.)
	α-Form	β-Form	
22	11.70	18.60	6.90
26	14.04	22.41	8.37
30	16.45	25.17	8.72
34	19.11	30.59	11.48

The α-form possesses a glasslike appearance and is stable at the melting point. This form is transformed into the opaque β-modification at a temperature several degrees below the melting point, the transition being reversible.

Physical Properties of Mixtures of Long-Chain Compounds

The physical properties of binary mixtures of fatty acids have been extensively investigated, particularly as regards the melting or setting points of such mixtures and also their atomic spacings. The actual structure of binary or polycomponent mixtures of fatty acids is still not clearly understood, in spite of the rather large amount of experimental data which have been accumulated. The pioneer investigations of de Visser [91] upon mixtures of stearic and palmitic acids led to the conclusion that compounds are encountered in the vicinity of the 50-50 mixture. Heintz,[92] in a study of mixtures of lauric, myristic, palmitic, and stearic acids, had observed equal lowering of the freezing points for the addition of equimolecular proportions of a lower-melting to a higher-melting acid; however, since he considered the molecular weights of these four acids to be equal these data are of questionable significance. In 1914, Twitchell [93] investigated binary systems of fatty acids with the object of using the freezing point method as an analytical procedure. Most of this preliminary work, however, was done upon acids of such doubtful purity that the results were extremely qualitative in nature and frequently led to erroneous conclusions.

The melting points and long crystal spacings of a number of equimolecular mixtures of both even and odd acids have been determined by Francis, Piper, and Malkin,[26] and their results have been of value in helping to evolve the structures of such mixtures. The melting points of the equimolar binary fatty acid mixtures investigated by these authors are shown in Table XXIX.

TABLE XXIX

MELTING POINTS OF EQUIMOLAR MIXTURES OF ACIDS

C Content of Acids	M.P., °C.	Δ M.P. of Lower Acid in Mixture	C Content of Acids	M.P., °C.	Δ M.P. of Lower Acid in Mixture
14 + 15	47.7	−6.3	14 + 16	48.3	−5.7
15 + 16	54.6	+2.5	15 + 17	51.4	−0.7
16 + 17	58.0	−5.1	16 + 18	57.0	−6.1
17 + 18	62.8	+0.8	17 + 19	59.2	−2.8
18 + 19	65.0	−5.1	18 + 20	64.6	−5.5
19 + 20	69.8	+0.4	19 + 21	67.0	−2.4
20 + 21	70.8	−4.4	20 + 22	70.8	−4.4
21 + 22	74.9	−0.3	21 + 23	72.7	−2.5
22 + 23	75.8	−4.2	22 + 24	75.7	−4.3
23 + 24	79.8	+0.2	23 + 25	77.1	−2.5
24 + 25	80.6	−3.4	24 + 26	79.8	−4.2
25 + 26	83.1	−0.1			

The crystal spacings of a number of equimolar mixtures of odd and even acids have also been determined by these authors, and some of their results are shown in Table XXX.

TABLE XXX

CRYSTAL SPACINGS OF BINARY FATTY ACID MIXTURES

C Content of Acids	Observed Spacings (C) in Å
14 + 15	32.9
15 + 16	35.8
16 + 17	37.2
17 + 18	39.8
18 + 19	41.6
19 + 20	43.7
20 + 21	45.6
21 + 22	47.9
22 + 23	50.0
23 + 24	52.1

The following comments were made by these authors upon the observed crystal spacings:

> . . . A fused equimolar mixture of acids with chains of n and $n + 1$ carbon atoms appears to crystallize with the molecule of n atoms joined carboxyl to carboxyl with that containing the $n + 1$ atoms. The spacing of such crystals falls on one of the C lines (spacings plotted against carbon content) exactly halfway between those of the acids containing the n and $n + 1$ carbon atoms. It is interesting that these mixed crystals tend to have alternately the habit of the odd and even acids, the form assumed being that of the *shorter* molecule. For instance, the combined molecules of the acids with $16 + 17$ carbon atoms give a spacing which falls on the *even* C line at a point midway between the pure acids 16 and 17. But the mixture of acids with carbon contents of $17 + 18$ gives a spacing on the *odd* C line also midway between those of the pure acids.

The unit cells of pure acids and of binary acid mixtures as depicted by Francis, Piper, and Malkin are shown in Fig. 12.

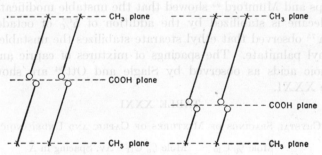

FIG. 12. Unit cells of fatty acids and their binary mixtures.

The assumption that double molecules are formed between acids having different carbon contents appears to be a logical explanation of the observations resulting from the study of equimolar acid mixtures. It is evident, however, that mixtures of equimolar composition represent only a specific case, and that it is necessary to obtain data upon mixtures which vary over a wide range of composition before generalizations relative to the physical state of fatty acid mixtures can safely be presented. The extensive x-ray investigations of Slagle and Ott [94] have shown that each mixture gives a single spacing and that the sharpness of the lines is comparable to those observed for the pure acids. Thus, for any composition a definite spacing is obtained which is characteristic of that particular mixture. The data of Slagle and Ott indicate that complete solid-solution formation is encountered in binary mixtures even when the components vary by as many as four carbon atoms, that is, C_n and C_{n+4}, and that at least partial solid solutions exist for mixtures whose components differ by five, six, or eight carbon atoms. Single spacings are also observed in mixtures containing more than two components, thus indicating that solid solutions are also formed in these polycomponent mixtures.

Fatty acid mixtures apparently occur in several polymorphic modifications, and according to Slagle and Ott these mixtures can exhibit more modifications than those observed for the pure acids. For instance, a sample containing 43.8% capric acid and 56.2% lauric acid, when observed immediately after preparation, gave two spacings, 25.12 Å and 25.90 Å; after two days the sample showed the spacings 25.08 Å and 26.92 Å; and after two weeks, only one spacing, 26.92 Å. The former spacings, therefore, represent unstable modifications. Four modifications were observed in a sample containing 24.8% capric acid and 75.2% tridecanoic acid. Phillips and Mumford [95] showed that the unstable modification of hexadecane is stabilized by the addition of 5% of octadecane. Smith [75] observed that ethyl stearate stabilizes the unstable form of ethyl palmitate. The spacings of mixtures of capric and undecanoic acids as observed by Slagle and Ott [94] are shown in Table XXXI.

TABLE XXXI

LONG CRYSTAL SPACINGS OF MIXTURES OF CAPRIC AND UNDECANOIC ACIDS

Mole % C_{10}	Mole % C_{11}	Av. Spacing in Å
0.0	100.0	25.32
10.7	89.3	25.03
20.8	79.2	24.69
30.2	69.8	24.55
41.8	58.2	24.38
51.8	48.2	24.20
61.9	38.1	23.71
71.4	28.6	23.58
81.2	18.8	23.33
90.7	9.3	23.19
100.0	0.0	23.02

Table XXXII shows the spacings observed by these authors for mixtures of palmitic and stearic acids. The values are in agreement with those reported previously by Piper, Malkin, and Austin.[21]

TABLE XXXII

LONG CRYSTAL SPACINGS OF MIXTURES OF PALMITIC AND STEARIC ACIDS

Mole % C_{16}	Mole % C_{18}	Av. Spacing in Å
0.0	100.0	39.83
10.7	89.3	39.72
27.2	72.8	39.49
52.5	47.5	38.50
76.7	23.3	38.14
90.7	9.3	35.88
100.0	0.0	35.52

A plot of the spacings of mixtures of capric and undecanoic acids from Table XXXI shows that the values fall approximately upon a line connecting the spacings of the pure acids. When the spacings of the mixtures of palmitic and stearic acids are plotted against percentage composition of the mixture, however, it becomes apparent that these mixtures exist in more than one modification. The fact that definite single spacings are obtained for binary as well as for polycomponent mixtures of acids can be taken as indicative that such mixtures form complete solid solutions, but further confirmation is necessary before this statement can be considered as conclusively proved.

Studies of the freezing points and other thermal effects in binary mixtures of fatty acids have supplied an extensive amount of data upon the physical state of such mixtures. Although these studies have somewhat correlated the investigation of the spacings as shown by x-ray measurements, it cannot be stated that the two are in complete agreement. It must be realized, therefore, that conclusions developed as a result of either type of analysis of fatty acid mixtures are only tentatively acceptable until they can unqualifiedly be correlated to those of the other types or until other methods of study are applied.

The binary system eicosanoic acid-stearic acid has been investigated by Morgan and Bowen,[96] who concluded that the type of curve obtained by plotting the melting points of the mixtures against their composition indicates the formation of a bimolecular complex containing one molecule of eicosanoic acid and one of stearic acid. Compound formation between adjacent pairs of even acids has also been suggested by the studies of Bhatt, Watson, and Patel [97] and of Meyer and associates,[98, 99] the latter of whom investigated the binary systems of lignoceric acid with palmitic and stearic acids. The studies of Efremov and coworkers [100, 101] on binary systems of palmitic acid with lauric acid, myristic acid, elaidic acid, and oleic acid indicate that palmitic acid forms solid solutions with myristic, lauric, and elaidic acids, but not with oleic acid. Although this latter observation is surprising, it has received partial confirmation from Brocklesby,[102] who has shown that unsaturation decreases the extent to which acids of the same carbon content associate. Bruni and Gorni [103] and also Mascarelli and coworkers [104] had previously stated that *cis* ethylenic acids do not form solid solutions with saturated acids, and the more recent investigations of Smith [105] indicate the absence of compound formation between oleic and stearic acids. Whatever the explanation, it must be admitted that binary systems which involve unsaturation in one or both of the components show liquidus curves which are quite different from those shown by systems involving only saturated acids. Since it has been shown that compound formation occurs between saturated acids,[102, 106, 107, 108] it has been postulated [105] that lack of symmetry may retard the crystallization of a compound formed between a saturated and an unsaturated acid.

The binary systems palmitic acid-stearic acid, palmitic acid-margaric acid, and margaric acid-stearic acid, as well as the ternary system palmitic acid-margaric acid-stearic acid, have been investigated by Shriner, Fulton, and Burks.[109] The freezing points of the mixtures of palmitic and stearic acids as determined by these authors are shown in Table XXXIII. The plot of these freezing

TABLE XXXIII

FREEZING POINTS OF BINARY MIXTURES OF STEARIC AND PALMITIC ACIDS

Mole Palmitic Acid	Mole Stearic Acid	F.P., °C.
0.0	1.0	68.40
0.1	0.9	66.25
0.2	0.8	63.65
0.3	0.7	61.20
0.4	0.6	58.15
0.47	0.53	56.10
0.5	0.5	55.90
0.6	0.4	55.40
0.7	0.3	54.00
0.725	0.275	53.60
0.75	0.25	53.95
0.8	0.2	54.85
0.9	0.1	57.50
1.0	0.0	60.70

points against molecular composition (Fig. 13) shows a change of direction in the vicinity of the equimolecular mixture, and a "eutectic" or minimum melting point at 53.6°, corresponding to the sample having the composition 0.725 mole of palmitic acid and 0.275 mole of stearic acid.   This indicates the formation of an equimolar compound possessing a non-congruent melting point, although Slagle and Ott[94] have contended that the change of direction shows a change in modification only, and Shriner, Fulton,

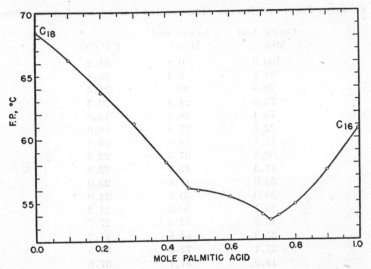

FIG. 13.   Freezing points of binary mixtures of stearic and palmitic acids.

and Burks[109] observed no evidence of compound formation in the systems palmitic acid-margaric acid and stearic acid-margaric acid. Later, Ashton, Robinson, and Smith[110] stated that mixtures of tricosanoic and tetracosanoic acids form simple Type III[111] solid solutions with no evidence of compound formation. In the same year, however, Smith[112] observed changes in direction in the neighborhood of equimolar mixtures for the systems formed by margaric and palmitic acids and margaric and stearic acids and stated that compound formation between odd and even acids is clearly indicated. According to Smith, the shapes of the liquidus curves show that in such mixtures the double molecules of palmitic acid (P_1-P_1), margaric acid (M_1-M_1), and stearic acid (S_1-S_1) are replaced by double molecules of the type (P_1-M_1) or (M_1-S_1).   The suggestion was advanced that compounds of the type (M_3-P_1), (M_3-S_1), or (M_1-S_3) are also present.

In a study of the systems ethyl stearate-ethyl palmitate and 1-hexadecanol–1-octadecanol, Smith[75] reported that such systems form solid solutions, complicated by the presence of polymorphism in the former. Both liquidus and solidus curves were determined for these two systems. Smith[14] likewise studied the system 1-iodo-

TABLE XXXIV

FREEZING POINTS OF BINARY MIXTURES OF CAPRIC AND LAURIC ACIDS

Capric Acid Mole %	Lauric Acid Mole %	F.P., °C.
100.0	0.0	31.2
91.7	8.3	26.8
79.9	20.1	21.3
75.6	24.4	20.3
73.4	26.6	19.8
72.5	27.5	19.6
71.1	28.9	20.4
62.5	37.5	22.3
57.3	42.7	22.9
52.6	47.4	23.0
50.0	50.0	24.0
49.7	50.3	24.2
43.0	57.0	27.7
35.2	64.8	31.2
27.1	72.9	34.5
18.9	81.1	37.6
9.6	90.4	40.9
0.0	100.0	43.9

hexadecane–1-iodoöctadecane, which apparently forms an equimolar compound possessing a non-congruent melting point. The system shows a minimum melting point at 20.1° corresponding to approximately 22% of the higher-melting component. No eutectic halt was observed for the system, its absence being attributed to polymorphism of the 1-iodohexadecane. Both liquidus and solidus curves were obtained by Smith for the system hexadecane-octadecane, the system apparently forming a series of solid solutions. The presence of octadecane stabilizes the metastable, transparent modification of hexadecane, large transparent crystals first appearing and then transforming into the stable form. The metastable modification can be retained for a period of several hours if the mixture is not stirred. This presents an example of the greater stability of metastable phases in mixtures as compared to those of the pure components. The amides and anilides were observed by Guy and Smith [113] to form solid solutions exhibiting minimum melting points and indicating the formation of equimolar compounds possessing non-congruent melting points. The data ob-

TABLE XXXV

FREEZING POINTS OF BINARY MIXTURES OF UNDECANOIC AND LAURIC ACIDS

Undecanoic Acid Mole %	Lauric Acid Mole %	F.P., °C.
100.0	0.0	28.2
92.4	7.6	27.6
85.4	14.6	27.4
80.0	20.0	27.3
77.6	22.4	27.4
74.6	25.4	27.6
71.3	28.7	28.0
67.6	32.4	28.6
64.6	36.4	29.2
59.3	40.7	29.9
53.8	46.2	30.7
50.9	49.1	31.1
48.7	51.3	31.5
47.5	52.5	31.6
46.3	53.7	31.9
44.0	56.0	32.4
42.6	57.4	32.8
41.2	58.8	33.1
36.1	63.9	34.4
33.0	67.0	35.1
25.0	75.0	37.4
22.6	77.4	38.0
10.3	89.7	41.2
9.8	90.2	41.4
0.0	100.0	43.9

tained by these authors for the system methyl palmitate-methyl stearate are inconclusive, owing to variation in the relative stabilities of the polymorphic forms with change in composition of the mixture.

In their study of binary mixtures of fatty acids, Kulka and Sandin [114] called attention to the fact that whatever conclusions are accepted as a result of the previous work upon binary fatty acid systems, all the melting point curves of systems involving even acids which differ by two carbon atoms are quite similar, showing an inflection in the vicinity of the equimolar mixture and a minimum at approximately 72.5 mole per cent of the lower-melting acid. Although systems involving odd and even acids show much less abrupt changes, they do exhibit significant inflections. This is shown by the data presented by Kulka and Sandin on the binary systems capric acid-lauric acid (Table XXXIV) and undecanoic acid-lauric acid (Table XXXV).

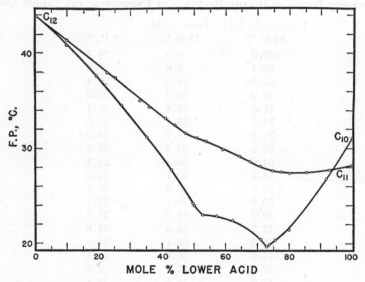

FIG. 14.   Systems: capric acid-lauric acid; undecanoic acid-lauric acid.

A plot of the values contained in Tables XXXIV and XXXV (Fig. 14) shows a minimum melting point for the capric acid-lauric acid system at 19.6°, the composition being 0.725 mole of capric acid and 0.275 mole of lauric acid. The curve of the undecanoic acid-lauric acid system shows a change of direction in the vicinity of the equimolar mixture. The eutectic temperature for the system myristic acid-palmitic acid was shown to be 45.2° at a composition containing 0.75 mole of myristic acid.

Schuette and associates [115] have investigated the binary systems formed by adjacent pairs of the even acids from capric to triacontanoic acid, and have observed two distinct points of inflection in the freezing point-composition curves for all binary systems of the lower molecular weight acids studied. The values for the higher molecular weight acids approach a smooth curve which these authors interpreted as evidence of a decreased tendency toward compound formation. This conclusion, however, is only tentatively acceptable, since the absence of decided points of inflection in these curves would be logically expected when compounds possessing very long chains are involved. The transition from a discontinuous to an approximately smooth curve with increase in the chain lengths of the acids is shown in Fig. 15, in which the values reported by these authors for the freezing points of the systems capric acid-lauric acid, stearic acid-arachidic acid, and octacosanoic acid-triacontanoic acid are plotted against the molecular compositions of the mixtures. One of the confusing points in the study of the binary fatty acid systems is the difficulty in locating the solidus curve, although Jantzen [116] has reported that its position can be determined by employing extremely slow rates of cooling. Schuette and associates are of the opinion that the solid-solutions area between the liquidus and solidus curves is quite small, so that the two curves

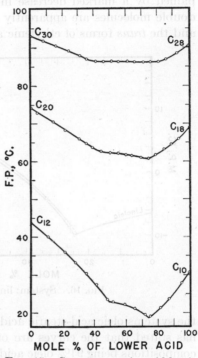

FIG. 15. Systems: capric acid-lauric acid; stearic acid-arachidic acid; octacosanoic acid-triacontanoic acid.

are nearly superimposable. The difficulty in obtaining eutectic halts in mixtures of saturated acids is significant and may be considered as evidence of solid-solution formation. A major difficulty in the study of binary mixtures of long-chain compounds is that of obtaining equilibrium conditions. The transition of a metastable to a stable form is often very rapid, and determinations of the cooling and heating curves frequently give inconclusive results. Dilatometric studies are very valuable in locating transition points and can be employed advantageously in conjunction with other thermal studies.

Binary systems involving unsaturated components have not been extensively investigated. The work which has so far been reported indicates that these systems differ rather materially from systems involving only saturated components. The comment has previously been made in this chapter that unsaturation is accompanied by a marked decrease in association tendency; however, double molecules are apparently formed between saturated acids and the *trans* forms of ethylenic acids. Smith[105] has investigated

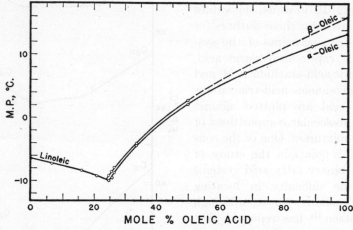

Fig. 16.   System: linoleic acid-oleic acid.

the systems oleic acid-stearic acid and oleic acid-palmitic acid and has stated that the curves are of the eutectic type, the eutectic compositions being 94% oleic acid-6% palmitic acid and 98% oleic acid-2% stearic acid, the eutectic temperatures being 12.10° and 13.1°, respectively. Smith attributes the lack of compound formation to the presence of the "bent" methylene chain. The ternary system stearic acid-palmitic acid-oleic acid has been reported to form a continuous solid solution.[117] Stewart and Wheeler[118] have investigated the binary systems formed by oleic, linoleic, and linolenic acids. Linoleic acid appears to form a eutectic with α-oleic acid at 75.2 mole per cent linoleic acid and with β-oleic acid at 76.3 mole per cent linoleic acid, the eutectic temperatures being −10.0° and −9.8°, respectively. Figure 16 shows the melting point-composition diagram of oleic acid-linoleic acid as obtained by these authors. Since the reported melting points were obtained by the capillary method, no thermal effects in the solid phase were investigated. The curves for the oleic acid-linolenic acid system are similar in form to those of the oleic acid-linoleic acid system. No compound formation is evidenced, the eutectic for the α-form of oleic acid appearing at 82.7 and for the β-form at 85.5 mole per cent linolenic acid, the temperatures being $-15.7°$ and $-15.1°$, respectively. The linoleic acid-linolenic acid mixtures exhibit no eutectic or compound formation, the curve indicating the formation of a continuous series of solid solutions.

From the above consideration of mixtures of fatty acids or their simple derivatives, it is evident that our knowledge of such mixtures is by no means complete. Compound formation in binary mixtures of saturated acids or some of their derivatives is certainly one of the logical conclusions which can be drawn from the existing data. Solid-solution formation between either the saturated compounds or their complexes is likewise clearly indicated, although the failure in many instances to locate a solidus curve is somewhat confusing. Polymorphism appears to play a more prominent role in mixtures than in the pure compounds themselves, particularly with reference to the stabilization of metastable forms. No logical explanation of this effect has been advanced, as yet. Systems containing unsaturated components have not been studied sufficiently to warrant many generalizations regarding their structures. Although they appear to differ from mixtures which contain only saturated components, the question as to whether this difference is real or only apparent has not been answered conclusively. It should be realized that it has been only within comparatively recent years that fatty acid mixtures have received much attention, and that many of the questions which now exist concerning their structures can only be answered by further research in this field.

THE SOLUBILITIES OF LONG-CHAIN COMPOUNDS

Studies of the solubilities of the fatty acids and their derivatives not only afford a large amount of useful data *per se* but also provide valuable information relative to molecular association and the molecular structures of long-chain compounds. Owing to the rather appreciable effect of one compound upon the solubility of another, it is of extreme importance that solubility measurements be made upon highly purified compounds. Unfortunately, some of the reported solubilities of long-chain compounds have been obtained upon substances of somewhat questionable purity, and considerable disagreement among the recorded values has resulted. Solubility data for some of the saturated acids have been compiled by Seidell,[119] Lewkowitsch,[120] and Brown,[121] and, in addition, the literature contains many references to the solubilities of certain acids in specific solvents.*

A number of cryoscopic and ebullioscopic measurements have been made upon solutions of fatty acids in organic solvents, most of the studies indicating that the fatty acids are appreciably associated, especially in non-polar solvents. François[122] has determined the degree of association of the fatty acids in benzene and nitrobenzene, and has reported that association in the former solvent decreases regularly up to myristic acid, after which essentially constant values are obtained. Association of the fatty acids in benzene has since been reported by several authors.[71, 102, 123, 124] Broughton[33] has shown that molecular association of the fatty acids in cyclohexane decreases regularly until lauric acid is reached, after which it commences to increase. Matavulj[125] has reported that fatty acids are associated in quinoline and pyridine solutions. A number of investigators[126, 127, 128, 129, 130, 131] have reported that the amides, and to a lesser extent the anilides, associate in various non-polar solvents.

The solubilities of long-chain compounds in organic solvents have been the subject of a number of theoretical studies, and the complexity of this problem has been pointed out by Hildebrand in a paper presented before the Faraday Society,[132] in which the fundamental principles involved were ably outlined. Solubility behavior is generally defined in relation to Raoult's law. Deviations from ideal behavior result from dissociation, solvation, or association of either component by the interaction of permanent or induced dipoles, or by chemical interaction such as the formation of hydrogen bonds. Many of these effects are predictable from thermodynamic considerations. Although deviations from ideal behavior are generally attributable to the operation of such factors, the influence of the so-called van der Waals' forces is often determinative as regards solubility behavior. The application of statistics has afforded considerable insight into the solubility characteristics of long-chain molecules. Raoult's law follows from simple

* For a complete treatment of the solubility of non-electrolytes, the reader is referred to Hildebrand, *Solubility of Non-Electrolytes*, A.C.S. Monograph No. 17, 2nd ed., Reinhold Publishing Corporation, New York (1936).

statistical considerations only when the molecules are of equal size and field. Mathematical treatments of the solubility behavior of long-chain molecules in organic solvents are, therefore, quite involved, owing to the differences in molecular size and shape of the components of such solutions. The question of the application of Raoult's law to molecules of different size was raised by Guggenheim,[133] and the validity of this law for paraffin molecules has been discussed by Hildebrand,[134] who determined the solubilities of dotriacontane in propane, butane, and heptane. More recently, Huggins [135] has shown that the large deviations from ideal behavior of solutions of long-chain molecules result from a non-ideal entropy of mixing rather than from thermal effects. An equation for the solubility of a solid, long-chain compound in an organic solvent has been developed by this author and has been shown to be in partial agreement with measurements of the solubilities of tetratriacontane and hexacontane in decalin. The entropy of mixing of long-chain molecules had previously been the subject of several theoretical papers.[136, 137, 138]

The reader can easily surmise that the various theoretical studies of the solubility behavior of long-chain compounds comprise a subject which will occupy the attention of scientists for some time to come. Such studies will have to include many more solubility determinations upon compounds of established purity than have so far been presented. It is beyond the intent or purpose of this present writing to attempt more than a mention of the major aspects of this interesting problem.

Until quite recently, only random solubility measurements of pure fatty acids and their derivatives had been recorded in the literature, and no comprehensive studies involving complete series had been made. Within the past several years, Ralston and associates have made an extended study of the solubilities of a number of series of high molecular weight aliphatic compounds in a wide variety of solvents and have developed several interesting correlations between molecular structure and solubility. These investigations have included not only the solubilities of fatty acids [139, 140, 141] in water and organic solvents, but also the solubilities in organic solvents of aliphatic ketones,[142] amines, anilides, and N,N-diphenylamides,[143] nitriles,[144] primary amines[145] and their salts,[79, 146] secondary [147] and tertiary [148] amines, alcohols,[149] and hydrocarbons.[150] The solubilities of the fatty acids in water as determined by Ralston and Hoerr are tabulated in Table XXXVI. Isolated data upon the solubilities of the fatty acids in water have previously been reported by several investigators.[151,152,153,154,155,156]

TABLE XXXVI

SOLUBILITIES OF THE FATTY ACIDS IN WATER

Grams Acid per 100 g. H_2O

No. of C Atoms	0.0°	20.0°	30.0°	45.0°	60.0°
6	0.864	0.968	1.019	1.095	1.171
7	.190	.244	0.271	0.311	0.353
8	.044	.068	.079	.095	.113
9	.014	.026	.032	.041	.051
10	.0095	.015	.018	.023	.027
11	.0063	.0093	.011	.013	.015
12	.0037	.0055	.0063	.0075	.0087
13	.0021	.0033	.0038	.0044	.0054
14	.0013	.0020	.0024	.0029	.0034
15	.00076	.0012	.0014	.0017	.0020
16	.00046	.00072	.00083	.0010	.0012
17	.00028	.00042	.00055	.00069	.00081
18	.00018	.00029	.00034	.00042	00050

It will be noted from Table XXXVI that the solubilities of the acids in water decrease tremendously with increasing molecular weight. Water is miscible with the first four members of the normal saturated series of acids and is appreciably soluble in the higher members, although the solubility diminishes with increase in molecular weight. The effect of water upon the solidification points of the fatty acids from caproic to stearic acid has been reported by Hoerr, Pool, and Ralston.[140] The solubility of water in the fatty acids as reported by these authors is shown in Table XXXVII.

Measurements of dissociation constants of monocarboxylic acids [157,158,159,160,161,162,163] indicate a small decrease in dissociation with increase in molecular weight; however, direct comparisons are rather difficult because of the limited solubilities of the higher members of the series in water. Conant [164] has made the following statement concerning the dissociation constants of the members of the fatty acid series: " . . . In the case of the whole group of fatty acids I feel that probably the only conservative statement is that they all have the same acid strength within the significance of the experimental results (± 0.5 pK unit)." Stable hydrosols of both palmitic and stearic acids have been described by Mukherjee and Datta,[156, 165] and these authors have calculated the dissociation constants of stearic acid to be 1.7×10^{-6} at $35°$ and 2.6×10^{-6} at $50°$, from the solubility and conductivity values of its hydrosol.

TABLE XXXVII

SOLUBILITY OF WATER IN FATTY ACIDS

Acid	% H$_2$O	Solution Temp., °C.
Caproic	2.21	−5.4
	4.73	12.3
	7.57	31.7
	9.70	46.3
Heptanoic	2.98	−8.3
	9.98 *	42.5
Caprylic	3.88	14.4
Nonanoic	3.45	10.5
Capric	3.12	29.4
Undecanoic	2.72	26.8
	4.21	57.5
Lauric	2.35	42.7
	2.70	75.0
	2.85	90.5
Tridecanoic	2.00	40.8
Myristic	1.70	53.2
Pentadecanoic	1.46	51.8
	1.62	90.0
Palmitic	1.25	61.8
Heptadecanoic	1.06	60.4
Stearic	0.92	68.7
	1.02	92.4

* This value is erroneously reported as 8.98 in the original article, and the author is indebted to Dr. E. Solomon for calling this error to his attention.

The solubilities of the fatty acids in organic solvents as determined by Ralston and Hoerr [139, 141] show the liquid acids to be miscible with all the solvents studied. The solubility of an odd-carbon acid is generally greater than that of its next-lower, even homolog, so that the solubility curves appear in pairs each containing an odd and an even acid. This is illustrated in Fig. 17, which shows the solubilities of the fatty acids in 95% ethanol * as determined by these authors.

Alternation in the solubilities of the even and odd acids is not surprising in view of the alternation in melting points. It is generally recognized that a solid having a higher melting point is less soluble at any given temperature than one having a lower melting

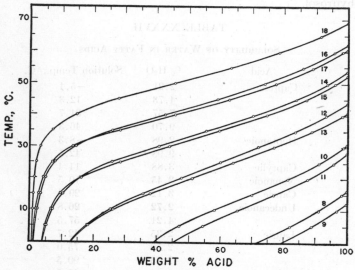

FIG. 17. Solubilities of fatty acids in 95% ethanol.

point, provided the heats of fusion are not materially different. The solubility of an individual member of a homologous series in a specific solvent can, therefore, be predicted by its melting point, and increase in the solubility brought about by the addition of

* The solubilities of the even acids from lauric to stearic in 99.4% ethanol by weight, of both even and odd acids from caprylic to stearic acid in 95% ethanol, of palmitic and stearic acids in 91.1% ethanol, and of stearic acid in 80.8% ethanol, at temperatures from 0° to 60° in increments of 10°, have been reported by Ralston and Hoerr. Solubility measurements of several members of this series in ethanol have also been reported by the following: Timofejew, *Dissertation* (*Kharkow*) (1894); Hehner and Mitchell, *Analyst*, **21**, 316 (1896); Kreis and Hafner, *Z. Untersuch. Nahr.- u. Genussm.*, **6**, 22 (1903); *Ber.*, **36**, 2766 (1903); Emerson, *J. Am. Chem. Soc.*, **29**, 1750 (1907); Falciola, *Gazz. chim. ital.*, **40**, II, 217 (1910); Ruttan, *Orig. Com. 8th Intern. Congr. Appl. Chem.* (Appendix), **25**, 431 (1912); Kröber, *Z. physik. Chem.*, **93**, 641 (1919); Thomas and Mattikow, *J. Am. Chem. Soc.*, **48**, 968 (1926); Ekwall and Mylius, *J. prakt. Chem.*, **136**, 133 (1933); Ku, *Ind. Eng. Chem., Anal. Ed.*, **9**, 103 (1937).

another member of the series is in proportion to the melting point lowering. The solubilities of binary mixtures of the fatty acids illustrate the close correlation which exists between melting point and solubility. A study of the solubilities of mixtures of palmitic and stearic acids [166] shows that maximum solubility occurs at 70% palmitic acid and 30% stearic acid, which is the minimum-melting mixture of the system palmitic acid-stearic acid. The solubilities

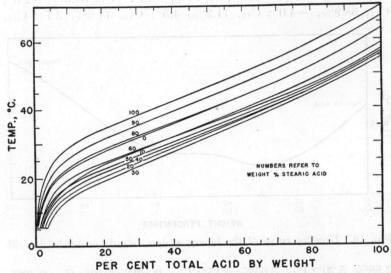

FIG. 18.   Solubilities of stearic-palmitic acid mixtures in benzene.

of all mixtures of these two components are in relation to the melting points of the mixtures. This is illustrated by a comparison of the solubility curves for mixtures of palmitic and stearic acids in benzene, Fig. 18, with the liquidus curve for the system palmitic acid-stearic acid, Fig. 19, as published by Schuette and Vogel.[167] The same relationship was observed in the other solvents investigated. Binary mixtures of palmitic acid and heptadecane show solubilities in 2-butanone which lie between those of the pure components, the solubilities showing a direct relationship to the melting points of the mixtures. Waentig and Pescheck [168] have reported several-fold increases in the solubility of a fatty acid in a non-polar solvent by the addition of a small amount of a lower homolog. Increases in the solubilities of the acids of the magnitudes reported by these authors could not be duplicated by the writer. Solubility measurements of the fatty acids in acetone and 2-butanone show pairing of the even and odd members.

The fatty acids form eutectics with benzene, the eutectic mixture containing less of the acid component with increase in molecular weight of the acid. Pairing of adjacent odd and even members is observed. The eutectics of the acids with benzene occur at the following concentrations of acid and melt at the following temperatures:[139] C_8, 50.4%, $-10.5°$; C_9, 54%, $-13.1°$; C_{10}, 34.5%, $-2.0°$; C_{11}, 38.9%, $-4.0°$; C_{12}, 11.2%, 4.5°; C_{13}, 14.6%, 3.7°; C_{14},

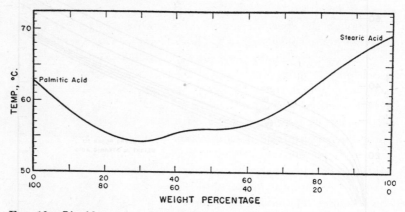

FIG. 19. Liquidus curve of the binary system: stearic acid-palmitic acid.

2.88%, 5.20°; C_{15}, 3.65%, 5.15°; C_{16}, 0.19%, 5.40°; C_{17}, 0.42%, 5.35°; C_{18}, 0.015%, 5.50°. The acids also form eutectic systems with glacial acetic acid, the eutectics having the following compositions and melting points: C_6, 97.7%, $-5.4°$; C_7, 98.8%, $-6.5°$; C_8, 80.0%, 3.1°; C_9, 83.6%, 1.6°; C_{10}, 55.1%, 8.6°; C_{11}, 57.5%, 8.0°; C_{12}, 17.3%, 12.8°; C_{13}, 15.9%, 13.1°; C_{14}, 5.3%, 15.18°; C_{15}, 4.3%, 15.40°; C_{16}, 1.23%, 16.17°; C_{17}, 0.58%, 16.34°; C_{18}, 0.03%, 16.48°.

Brown and Foreman [169] have recently determined the solubilities of a number of both saturated and unsaturated fatty acids in organic solvents at low temperatures (10° to $-70°$). The solubilities in acetone of some of the acids investigated are as follows: stearic acid, 46.9 g. per 1000 g. solution at 10°, 2.19 g. at 0°, and 0.38 g. at $-10°$; oleic acid, 14.2 g. at $-30°$, 5.16 g. at $-40°$, 1.89 g. at $-50°$, 0.61 g. at $-60°$, and 0.40 g. at $-70°$; linoleic acid, 48.2 g. at $-50°$, 14.2 g. at $-60°$, and 5.19 g. at $-70°$.

The solubility behavior of the amides [143] is unusual in that there is little correlation with molecular weight, particularly in non-polar solvents. There is also no correlation between their solubilities and the polarities of the solvents. The solubility curves indicate the amides to be highly associated, since they exhibit a decided deviation from lineality. The solubility curves of the anilides and N,N-diphenylamides differ from those of the amides in that they fall in homologous order, although the solubilities of the latter are linear with temperature only in benzene and the former show a decided deviation from lineality even in this solvent.

Although the specific solubility data for the various fatty acid derivatives are considered in the later chapters where these derivatives are discussed in detail, there are some interesting correlations which may be presented at this time. Immiscibility of the fatty acid derivatives in the liquid state is encountered only with solvents of high polarity, such as acrylonitrile, and then only for the higher members of the series. The solubility curves generally show an abrupt departure from lineality, supposedly indicative of association, and this departure from a linear relationship is apparently more marked the longer the alkyl chain. The solubility character- istics of the aliphatic ketones, RCOR, resemble those of straight- chain compounds having an equivalent number of carbon atoms, and it is interesting to note that the secondary amines, RNHR, show a similar relationship. An especially significant observation is that the shapes of all the solubility curves of the various deriva- tives in any specific solvent are qualitatively similar, irrespective of the nature of the polar group. Thus, the solubility curves for the nitriles, amines, alcohols, acids, and ketones containing the same number of carbon atoms show a striking resemblance to each other, indicating that the length of the alkyl chain is an important factor in the solubility characteristics of long-chain compounds. Although the solubilizing influence of polar groups is evidenced by the fact that the hydrocarbons show very limited solubilities in the highly polar solvents, it is noteworthy that the slopes of the solu- bility curves of the hydrocarbons in a specific solvent are quite similar to those of compounds which contain polar groups. This is illustrated by the benzene-solubility curves of several compounds containing sixteen carbon atoms, Fig. 20, and by the curves of the same compounds in 2-propanol, Fig. 21.

It is improbable that the hydrocarbons form associated molecules in solution, and it is therefore apparent that the length of the alkyl

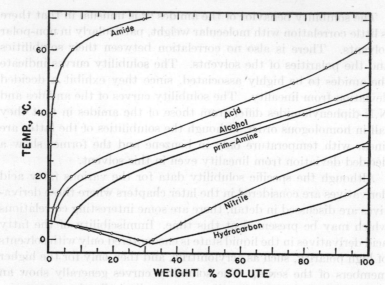

FIG. 20. Solubilities of palmitic acid and its derivatives in benzene.

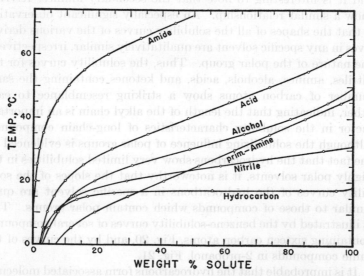

FIG. 21. Solubilities of palmitic acid and its derivatives in 2-propanol.

chain is a factor as regards the shape of the solubility curves. The mutual attraction of hydrocarbon chains due to van der Waals' forces should not be overlooked, and the decreased solubilities of the higher molecular weight compounds, including the hydrocarbons themselves, in the polar solvents may be due to the difficulty of such solvents to overcome this attraction. Since association increases the apparent chain length, the correlation of these results with previous findings concerning molecular association in solution should contribute information of fundamental importance regarding the physical state of solutions of long-chain aliphatic compounds.

PHYSICAL PROPERTIES OF FATTY ACIDS IN THE LIQUID STATE

Structure

The general properties of the liquid state are characterized by high internal pressures, evidencing a balance between repulsive and attractive forces. Since molecules in the body of a liquid are uniformly subjected to such forces, whereas those in the surface are unequally influenced owing to the smaller number of molecules per unit volume in the vapor phase as compared to the liquid phase, the properties of the liquid state comprise not only those which relate to the body of the liquid but also those which are concerned with the surface. Temperature increases are accompanied by increases in the kinetic energy of the molecules which militate against their orderly arrangement, the effect becoming quite pronounced at the higher temperatures. It is not surprising, however, that the physical properties of long-chain compounds, determined by x-ray or other means at temperatures only slightly above their melting points, show some resemblance to the properties of the solid state, and this has led some investigators to postulate that such compounds imitate a crystalline structure for this state. The investigations of Stewart and Morrow [170] upon the liquid primary alcohols and of Morrow [171] upon the liquid acids indicate that the molecules are arranged longitudinally. The latter author observed two characteristic spacings, one corresponding to the lateral separation of the molecules and the other containing the diffraction centers of the molecules and passing transversely through the chains. The longitudinal spacing varies with the number of carbon atoms in the molecule, whereas the transverse spacing was observed to be 4.55 Å for the acids. Warren [172] has stated that long-chain molecules are straight in liquids and that neighboring molecules are roughly parallel, and Stewart [173] has concluded that there is a high probability that the polar groups in long-chain alcohols have a three-dimensional space relation in the liquid state. The assumption of any crystalline structure in liquid alcohols has been questioned,[174] since the length of the carbon chain for liquid 1-undecanol is less than that observed for the solid. Orientation of the molecules in the surface of the liquid has long been accepted and has been verified by the work of Trillat [175] upon the liquid fatty acids and the liquid alcohols. In generalizing upon the structure of the liquid state of long-chain molecules, one must realize that increasing motion of the particles attending increases in the temperature of the liquid brings about a departure from an orderly arrangement. Measurements made in the vicinity of the melting points, therefore, are probably not representative of the structural characteristics at higher temperatures.

Molecular association of the fatty acids and many of their derivatives is clearly indicated. Generalizations with reference to the influences which affect association in the crystalline state, such as the nature of the polar group or the degree of unsaturation, undoubtedly apply also to the liquid state and are helpful in explaining many of the observed properties.

Boiling Points

The boiling points of the saturated fatty acids increase with the number of carbon atoms, the increase per carbon atom becoming less as the series is ascended. The higher members undergo appreciable decomposition at boiling temperatures under atmospheric pressure. Association in the vapor phase is evidenced, Fenton and Garner [176] having determined the heat of association of heptanoic acid in the vapor phase to be 7050 cal. per gram-mole between 185° and 230°, the value varying somewhat with temperature. The heat of association decreases with increase in the length of the carbon chain.

Pool and Ralston [177] have determined the boiling points of the saturated acids from caproic to stearic acid inclusive at a number of pressures, and the values reported are shown in Table XXXVIII. The reader is referred to this article for previously reported boiling points of these acids. The boiling points of the nitriles, amines, and some of the esters are somewhat lower than those of the acids

TABLE XXXVIII

BOILING POINTS OF n-ALKYL ACIDS

Boiling Points in °C. at Following Pressures in Millimeters

No. of C Atoms	1	2	4	8	16	32	64	128	256	512	760
6	61.7	71.0	82.8	94.6	107.3	120.8	136.0	152.5	171.5	192.5	205.8
7	74.9	85.3	96.3	108.3	121.1	135.2	150.8	168.2	187.5	209.3	223.0
8	87.5	97.9	109.1	121.3	134.6	149.2	165.3	183.3	203.0	225.6	239.7
9	98.9	109.6	121.2	134.0	147.5	162.4	178.8	196.9	217.4	240.9	255.6
10	110.3	121.1	132.7	145.5	159.4	174.6	191.3	209.8	230.6	254.9	270.0
11	119.8	131.1	143.3	156.5	170.8	186.1	203.1	222.2	243.8	268.7	284.0
12	130.2	141.8	154.1	167.4	181.8	197.4	214.6	234.3	256.6	282.5	298.9
13	139.9	151.5	164.2	177.8	192.2	207.9	225.8	245.9	268.6	295.4	312.4
14	149.2	161.1	173.9	187.6	202.4	218.3	236.3	257.3	281.5	309.0	326.2 *
15	157.8	169.7	182.8	196.8	212.0	228.1	246.4	268.0	292.7	321.2	339.1 *
16	167.4	179.0	192.2	206.1	221.5	238.4	257.1	278.7	303.6	332.6 *	351.5 *
17	175.1	187.6	200.8	214.9	230.7	247.9	266.6	288.4	314.3	343.8 *	363.8 *
18	183.6	195.9	209.2	224.1	240.0	257.1	276.8	299.7	324.8	355.2 *	376.1 *

* Values obtained by extrapolation.

and are discussed in the later chapters where these specific derivatives are considered.

Refractive Indices, Densities, and Molecular Refractivities of the Fatty Acids in the Liquid State

Both the refractive indices and the densities of the liquid fatty acids are easily determined constants, and the refractive index is frequently employed as a criterion of purity. The importance of these values is enhanced by the fact that by their use other fundamental constants such as the molecular volumes or molecular refractivities can easily be calculated. The molecular refractivity, which has been shown to be partly constitutive and partly additive, is obtained by the application of the Lorentz-Lorenz equation,

$$R = \frac{n^2 - 1}{n^2 + 1} \cdot \frac{M}{d}$$, in which R is the molecular refractivity, n is the refractive index, M is the molecular weight, and d is the density.

The investigations of Eijkman [178] and Scheij [179] upon the refractive indices of the naturally occurring acids, and of Falk [180] upon those of butyric acid, were noteworthy contributions to this field. The value of much of this earlier work is, however, limited by the fact that the determinations were made at arbitrary and scattered temperatures and with a limited number of compounds, thus rendering it difficult to make comparisons among the recorded values. Generalizations based upon these early values are, therefore, of somewhat questionable significance. In 1927, Waterman and Bertram [181] determined the refractive indices at 70° of the saturated acids from acetic to stearic acid inclusive. Eisenlohr and Wöhlisch [182] had previously shown that, except for small constitutional differences, the product of the refractive index and the molecular weight is additive. Waterman and Bertram [181] stated that the increments of this value show two distinct series which change signs between the C_{11} and C_{12} acids. This, however, has been criticized by Verkade and Coops [183] on the basis that alternation does not occur in the liquid state and that the fluctuations actually reported fall within the limits of experimental error. Undecanoic, lauric, and myristic acids have been examined by Taylor and King [184] by the total reflection method. Within a temperature range from one to five degrees above the solidification points, the surface layers of these acids showed birefringence, indicating that within this temperature range an orientation is encountered similar to that observed in liquid crystals. From a study of thin films of the saturated acids, Thibaud and Dupré la Tour [185] have stated that the polymorphic forms of these acids show important differences in their indices of refraction. Dorinson, McCorkle, and Ralston [186] have determined the refractive indices, n_D^t, of the saturated fatty acids from caproic to stearic acid inclusive, at a number of temperatures. When the values of the refractive indices are plotted against temperature, those between 40° and 80° fall upon straight lines; however, a change of direction is observed below 40°. A similar change of slope has recently been reported [187] for the refractive indices of the aliphatic nitriles. The electron polarization of such compounds depends upon the statistical orientation of the individual molecules within the body of the liquid, but increasing temperatures, by causing an increase in the thermal motion of the molecules, tend to produce random distribution and overcome the restraints imposed by dipole interaction. These authors suggest that the change of direction represents the overbalancing of the former effect by the latter. The values of the refractive indices of the saturated acids as reported by Dorinson, McCorkle, and Ralston are shown in Table XXXIX.

The densities of the liquid state are essentially a linear function of temperature. The values for the liquid saturated acids, d_4^t, as reported by several investigators [186,188,189,190] are shown in Table XL. An examination of the values recorded in this table shows that the densities of the liquid acids at any given temperature decrease with increase in molecular weight.

Garner and Ryder [13] determined the absolute densities together with the temperature coefficients of caprylic, pelargonic, capric, undecanoic, and lauric acids. These authors have also determined the specific volumes of the solid and liquid acids at their melting

TABLE XXXIX

REFRACTIVE INDICES (n_D^t) OF SATURATED FATTY ACIDS

Acid	20.0°	25.0°	30.0°	40.0°	45.0°	50.0°	55.0°	60.0°	65.0°	70.0°	80.0°
Caproic	1.4170	1.4150	1.4132	1.4095	......	1.4054	......	1.4012	......	1.3972	1.3931
Enanthic	1.4230	1.4209	1.4192	1.4155	......	1.4114	......	1.4073	......	1.4037	1.3993
Caprylic	1.4280	1.4260	1.4243	1.4205	......	1.4167	......	1.4125	......	1.4089	1.4049
Pelargonic	1.4322	1.4301	1.4287	1.4250	......	1.4210	......	1.4171	......	1.4132	1.4092
Capric	......	......	......	1.4288	......	1.4248	......	1.4210	.....:	1.4169	1.4130
Undecanoic	......	......	......	1.4319	......	1.4279	......	1.4240	......	1.4202	1.4164
Lauric	......	......	......	......	1.4323	1.4304	1.4288	1.4267	1.4250	1.4230	1.4191
Tridecanoic	......	......	......	......	......	1.4328	1.4310	1.4290	1.4272	1.4252	1.4215
Myristic	......	......	......	......	......	1.4329	1.4310	1.4291	1.4273	1.4236
Pentadecanoic	......	......	......	......	......	1.4348	1.4329	1.4310	1.4292	1.4254
Palmitic	......	......	......	......	......	......	......	1.4328	1.4309	1.4272
Heptadecanoic	......	......	......	......	......	......	......	1.4340	1.4324	1.4287
Stearic	......	......	......	......	......	......	......	......	1.4337	1.4299

points, the values for the solid acids being as follows: C_8, 0.9737; C_9, 1.0104; C_{10}, 0.9870; C_{11}, 1.0121; and C_{12}, 0.9971; and for the liquid acids: 1.0925, 1.0966, 1.1169, 1.1206, and 1.1403, respectively. The changes in molecular volume, Δ cc. per gram mole, at the melting points were calculated to be: C_8, 17.51; C_9, 13.95;

TABLE XL

DENSITIES (d_4^t) OF LIQUID SATURATED ACIDS

Acid	15°	20°	25°	30°	40°	50°	70°	80°	90°
Valeric	......	0.9387	......	......	0.9205	0.9104	0.8924	......	
Caproic	......	......	0.9234	0.9276	0.9108	......	......	0.8751	0.873
Enanthic	0.92099	0.9172	......	0.90863	0.9011	0.8909	0.876	0.8670	......
Caprylic	......	0.90884	......	0.90087	......	......	......	0.8615	......
Pelargonic	0.90932	0.90552	0.9022	0.89782	0.8901	0.883	......	0.8570	......
Capric	......	......	......	......	......	......	......	0.8531	......
Undecanoic	......	......	......	......	......	......	......	0.8505	......
Lauric	......	......	......	......	......	0.8690	0.8544	0.8477	0.8386
Tridecanoic	......	......	......	......	......	......	......	0.8458	......
Myristic	......	......	......	......	......	......	0.8528	0.8439	0.8394
Pentadecanoic	......	......	......	......	......	......	......	0.8423	......
Palmitic	......	......	......	......	......	......	0.8487	0.8414	0.8347
Heptadecanoic	......	......	......	......	......	......	......	0.8396	......
Stearic	......	......	......	......	......	......	0.849	0.8390	0.835

C_{10}, 23.24; C_{11}, 20.68; and C_{12}, 29.07. The mean temperature coefficient for the solid acids is 0.00077 per 1°, and for the liquid acids 0.00103 per 1°. Dorinson, McCorkle, and Ralston [186] have reported the experimental and calculated values for the molecular volumes at 20° of the acids from formic to pelargonic and at 80° of the acids from acetic to stearic. Values for the former series were calculated by use of the equation $V_m = 16.89n + 23.62$ and for the latter by the equation $V_m = 17.25n + 28.88$.

The molecular refractivities at 80° of the liquid saturated acids from caproic to stearic inclusive can be calculated from the equation $R_m = 4.654n + 3.83$. A comparison of the molecular refractivities obtained by the use of the Lorentz-Lorenz equation and those calculated from the above equation is shown in Table XLI.

TABLE XLI

MOLECULAR REFRACTIVITIES OF SATURATED FATTY ACIDS AT 80°

Acid	R_m (L–L)	R_m (calcd.)
Caproic	31.70	31.75
Enanthic	36.34	36.40
Caprylic	41.08	41.06
Pelargonic	45.66	45.71
Capric	50.36	50.37
Undecanoic	55.02	55.02
Lauric	59.73	59.68
Tridecanoic	64.35	64.33
Myristic	69.00	68.99
Pentadecanoic	73.65	73.64
Palmitic	78.30	78.30
Heptadecanoic	80.01	82.95
Stearic	87.59	87.61

The refractive indices of the unsaturated acids increase with the degree of unsaturation. The refractive indices, n_D^{20}, of oleic, linoleic, and linolenic acids have been reported to be as follows:[191, 192, 193] oleic acid, 1.4585; linoleic acid, 1.4699; and linolenic acid, 1.4800. Conjugation is accompanied by a marked increase in the refractive index, α-eleostearic acid showing 1.5112 at 50°, and β-eleostearic acid, 1.5022 at 75°.[194] The molecular refractivities show a decided exaltation over the calculated values, the exaltation being ascribed to the presence of conjugated unsaturation.[194, 195] Owing to the extreme difficulty of obtaining unsaturated acids in a state of purity comparable to that of the saturated acids, the values recorded for the former are probably subject to some revision.

Surface Tension and Parachor Values

The surface tensions of the liquid acids are related to their densities and molecular weights by the equation $P = M\gamma^{1/4}/(D - d)$, where M is the molecular weight, γ is the surface tension, and D and d are the densities in the liquid and vapor states, respectively, at the same temperature. The value P is known as the parachor and relates the surface tension to the molecular volume. The above equation may be considered as defining the molecular volume of a substance of unit surface tension, and permits a comparison of molecular volumes at points where the surface tensions are identical. Since the parachor does not vary with temperature, its use is very satisfactory for comparing molecular volumes. The parachor values for lauric, palmitic, and stearic acids have been calculated [196] to be 522.5, 668, and 735 respectively. Semeria and Ribotti-Lissone [197] have reported the following values for the surface tensions and parachors of acids at 90° and 95°: oleic acid, 27.94, 27.52, 765.07, 766.93; elaidic acid, 26.56, 26.31, 760.44, 764.93; stearic acid, 26.99, 26.42, 777.79, 778.87; erucic acid, 28.56, 27.77, 932.40, 938.91; brassidic acid, 27.40, 27.28, 929.20, 934.36; and behenic acid, 37.77, 37.61, 950.07, 951.36. The reader is referred to a complete treatment of this subject by Sugden [198] for information concerning the theoretical aspects and use of the parachor.

Specific Conductances

The specific conductances of capric, myristic, palmitic, stearic, and oleic acids have been determined between 100° and 200° by Lederer and Hartleb,[199] who have extrapolated these values to the melting and boiling point temperatures. The values for the specific conductances of the acids at these two points did not vary from member to member and were stated to be 0.1×10^{-11} mhos at the melting points and 2×10^{-9} mhos at the boiling points.

Specific Heats

The specific heats of the liquid acids or their derivatives are materially lower than those of the solid acids and are distinguished from the latter in that the values do not alternate from even to odd member. In addition, it is noteworthy that the rather wide deviation among the specific heats in the different solid series is not encountered in the liquid series. Garner and Randall [2] reported the specific heats in the liquid state for the saturated acids from acetic to lauric acid inclusive, and more recently King and Garner [40] compiled the specific heats, C_p, of several series of long-chain compounds. The values reported by these latter authors

for a temperature range thirty degrees above the melting points
are as follows: acids, 0.53–0.54 cal./g.; ethyl esters, 0.50–0.52
cal./g.; methyl esters, 0.52 cal./g.; and hydrocarbons, 0.57 cal./g.
The specific heats of the liquid acids vary considerably with temperature, Lederer [200] having reported the specific heats of lauric
acid to vary between 0.513 and 0.674 cal./g. between 50° and 200°;
of stearic acid, 0.560 and 0.660 between 125° and 200°; and of
oleic acid, 0.489 and 0.638 between 50° and 150°. Huggins [201] has
developed equations for the entropy of long-chain compounds in
the gaseous state.

Viscosity

In contrast to compounds which possess ring or compact structures, long-chain molecules are characterized by low mobilities in
the liquid state.[202] Dunstan [188] determined the viscosities of the
liquid fatty acids from propionic to stearic acid inclusive at a
number of temperatures, and a plot of $\eta \times 10^5$ against temperature
shows that the values for each acid fall on a smooth curve, the
viscosity decreasing rapidly with an increase in temperature. The
value $\eta \times 10^5$ increases appreciably with increase in the chain
length of the acid. Although the values for the first two members
of the saturated series, formic and acetic acids, are abnormally
high, the logarithms of the viscosities when plotted against molecular weight show a linear relationship at each temperature for the
acids between propionic and pelargonic acids inclusive. The higher
acids show a constant decrease in the homologous increment. Some
of the representative values reported by Dunstan [188] for the viscosities of the acids are as follows: (poises $\times 10^5$) propionic, 956
at 30°; butyric, 1301 at 30°; valeric, 230 at 20°; caproic, 2840 at
25°; enanthic, 3800 at 25°; pelargonic, 7000 at 25°; lauric, 7300 at
50°; myristic, 7430 at 60°; palmitic, 7835 at 70°; and stearic,
9870 at 70°. Deffet [189] has reported the following values: enanthic,
4766 at 15°, 3300 at 30°; caprylic, 5828 at 20°, 4690 at 30°; pelargonic, 9661 at 15°, 6110 at 30°. Lederer [203] has proposed the equation $\log \eta = (q°/4.571T) - 2.75 \log T + ET + C$ for the calculation of the viscosity, where η is the viscosity in poises, $q°$ is the
heat of association at 0° in calories per mole, and E and C are
constants. The following values for $q°$, E, and C were reported:
butyric acid, 1960, 0.001770, 2.9952; valeric acid, 2330, 0.001663,
2.9050; caproic acid, 2740, 0.001401, 2.8200; enanthic acid, 3210,
0.001470, 2.5791; caprylic acid, 3475, 0.001576, 2.4883; pelargonic

acid, 3655, 0.001696, 2.4160; capric acid, 3700, 0.001992, 2.3865; myristic acid, 5030, 0.001670, 2.0221; and stearic acid, 5490, 0.001907, 1.7920. The viscosity of dilute solutions of long-chain compounds has been the subject of several theoretical papers.[204] Theis and Bull [205] have made a viscosimetric study of stearic acid in carbon tetrachloride solution, reporting a length:diameter ratio of 6 for this acid. Later, Hollihan and Briggs [206] confirmed this value at high rates of flow. The values obtained at a low rate of flow show a distinctly higher length:diameter ratio. A calculated partial specific volume of 1.41 for stearic acid in carbon tetrachloride solution is about 30% higher than the specific volume in the solid state. It was concluded that the particles of stearic acid are spherical in carbon tetrachloride over the range of flow rates investigated.

Absorption Spectra

Owing to the presence of the double bond in the carbonyl group, the saturated fatty acids show a typical absorption spectrum. The ethylenic acids, on the other hand, exhibit not only an absorption due to the carbonyl group, but also show characteristic absorption values dependent upon the number and relative positions of the double bonds.

Since the ultraviolet absorption properties of the saturated fatty acids are essentially dependent upon the presence of the chromophoric carbonyl group, it is evident that the absorption characteristics of the saturated acids should be qualitatively similar. Ramart-Lucas and associates [207] have investigated the ultraviolet absorption properties of formic, acetic, butyric, caproic, caprylic, lauric, myristic, palmitic, and stearic acids between wavelengths of 2000 and 2555 Å and have stated that the absorption coefficients of the higher members are essentially similar. They concluded, therefore, that since the length of the chain does not materially affect the absorption coefficient, methyl and methylene groups cannot be considered as chromophores in this region of the spectrum. Bielecki and Henri [208] had previously studied a number of saturated acids in the range $\lambda = 2144$ to 2600 Å, and had contended that an increase in the length of the hydrocarbon chain was attended by a shift in the absorption band toward the red, and also by an increase in the magnitude of the total absorption; however, Ley and Arends [209] stated that this generalization does not apply to the higher saturated acids. Burr and Miller [210] have compared the values of λ for acetic and palmitic acids for various values of the molecular extinction coefficient ϵ. The relationship between $\log \epsilon$, $\lambda_{\text{acetic acid}}$, and $\lambda_{\text{palmitic acid}}$ as tabulated by these authors is shown in Table XLII.

TABLE XLII

COMPARISON OF MOLECULAR EXTINCTION COEFFICIENTS AND WAVELENGTHS OF ACETIC AND PALMITIC ACIDS IN ETHANOL

Log ϵ	$\lambda_{\text{Acetic Acid}}$	$\lambda_{\text{Palmitic Acid}}$
0.35	2411	2428
0.60	2390	2400
0.90	2350	2360
1.10	2315	2325
1.30	2269	2295

Studies of the absorption coefficients of the saturated acids have led to the postulate that the acids exist in a dissociated and a non-dissociated form in the liquid state.[211, 212] Ester formation does not materially affect the character of the absorption curve, since it has been shown that the values for the various esters differ only slightly from those of the parent acids.[208] The absorption is radically changed by salt formation.[209]

Unsaturation in the hydrocarbon chain produces a change in both the intensity and the position of the absorption bands, the absorption being due not only to the carbonyl group but also to the ethylenic bonds. Conjugation is attended by a marked shift in the absorption bands. This phenomenon has recently been extensively studied and has been proposed for use in distinguishing conjugated from unconjugated acids or their esters.[213, 214, 215] Van der Hulst [216] has made a study of the absorption spectra of unsaturated acids and has reported characteristic maxima depending upon the number and relative positions of the ethylenic bonds. Conjugation shifts the absorption band toward the red, Dingwall and Thomson [217] having reported the presence of a maximum at 2700 Å for α-eleostearic acid. An isolated double bond between carbon atoms produces an absorption maximum at 1800 Å. Mitchell and Kraybill [214] have stated from theoretical considerations that absorption bands in the spectral region of wavelength longer than 2200 Å are not characteristic of non-conjugated linoleic or linolenic acid. Burr and Miller [210] have recently extended the absorption studies of the unsaturated acids to 2100 Å and have noted that the unsaturated acids superimpose on the saturated absorption curves a band due to the ethylenic group. The new band for oleic acid occurs at a longer wavelength than that observed for 3-heptene, and a comparison of the absorption spectra of oleic, linoleic, and linolenic acids shows that the addition of ethylenic bonds produces a further shift of this characteristic band toward the longer wavelengths.

Determinations of the Raman and infrared spectra are frequently useful in establishing the structures of isomeric unsaturated compounds.[218, 219, 220] Characteristic Raman frequencies are observed for ethylenic compounds at approximately 1.650 cm.$^{-1}$ and 3.010 cm.$^{-1}$ frequency units, the former value being somewhat lower for the *cis* than for the *trans* form and the latter more intense for the *cis* form. *Cis* acids show a strong infrared absorption corresponding to a wavelength of about 6.0 μ in the neighborhood of the characteristic ethylenic bond frequency of 1.670 cm.$^{-1}$, but this absorption is absent in the *trans* form. The characteristic Raman frequencies and infrared transmissions of the ethyl esters of oleic, linoleic, and linolenic acids and their *trans* isomers have recently been determined,[221] and a correlation has been developed between these data and the ester structures. The Raman spectra of several of the saturated acids and their derivatives have been reported by Kohlrausch and associates.[222, 223]

MONOMOLECULAR AND POLYMOLECULAR FILMS OF LONG-CHAIN COMPOUNDS

It is well known that although pure high molecular weight paraffins do not spread upon a water surface, high molecular weight compounds which contain polar groups spread with great rapidity. The pioneer work of Langmuir,[31] Harkins,[224] and Adam[225] has shown that in such films the molecules are oriented with their polar groups attached to the surface of the water. A study of the force-area relationships and other physical properties of these films not only has contributed materially to our general knowledge of surface chemistry but also has developed information of great value relative to the physical structure of long-chain molecules. Such films can be considered as two dimensional and show positive film pressures, the resistance to compression becoming greater with reduction in the molecular area. According to Schofield and Rideal,[226] the pressure exerted by such films is essentially kinetic;

however, this is not necessarily true if the film is closely packed, since under such conditions pressure may be a manifestation of molecular repulsion. Our discussion of this subject must necessarily be confined to generalizations concerning the surface properties of high molecular weight aliphatic compounds. The experimental methods and the theoretical developments pertaining to them are a complete study in themselves, and the reader is referred to books [227, 228, 229] in which the subject is treated in detail.

In his discussion of surface films, Harkins [230] called attention to two types of films; namely, duplex or polymolecular films, which are generally unstable, and monomolecular films. The monomolecular films are capable of existing in three phases which correspond to those encountered in three-dimensional systems; that is, gaseous, liquid, and solid. Such a designation relates in general to the fact that the properties of a film conform to those customarily associated with a particular state, and not to the fact that the individual molecules are actually gaseous, liquid, or solid. Thus, a gaseous film conforms to the law $\pi\sigma = kT$, in which π is the film pressure, σ the molecular area, and k the Boltzmann constant. Gaseous films are encountered only at very large molecular areas. In the case of gaseous films of pentadecanoic acid, it has been found that the molecular area may be as large as 50,000 sq. Å. The transition of a gaseous monolayer to a liquid monolayer is accompanied by a heat of phase transition, the properties of the film in the latter state corresponding closely to those of a three-dimensional liquid. During the course of the many investigations upon monomolecular films, it has been noted that phases exist whose properties are intermediate between those of a gas and a liquid or a liquid and a solid, so that it was found necessary to enlarge somewhat upon this rigid classification. Unfortunately, a uniform classification for these various phases has not been employed. Adam designated the various phases as gaseous or vapor films, vapor expanded films, liquid expanded films, and condensed films. Harkins [230] has employed the following classification: (I) gaseous; (II) liquid, L_1, corresponding to the "liquid expanded" of Adam and representing a liquid of high compressibility ($-\kappa = 2$ to 7×10^{-2}); (III) intermediate or transition films whose properties resemble those of a liquid of extremely high compressibility ($-\kappa = 2$ to 5×10^{-1}); (IV) liquid, L_2, corresponding to the "liquid condensed" of Adam ($-\kappa = 5$ to 10×10^{-3}); and (V) solid of extremely low compressibility ($-\kappa = 7$ to 9×10^{-4}).

The films formed by any insoluble substance as portrayed by its pressure-area relationship are functions of the structure of the substance itself, the temperature, the subphase, and to a more limited extent, the rate of compression of the film. The type of film obtained is determined not only by the nature of the polar groups but also by the length of the hydrocarbon chain. High temperatures favor the formation of expanded films, the change from a condensed to an expanded film taking place at a definite temperature which is a characteristic of any particular substance. Increase in the length of the hydrocarbon chain within a homologous series raises the temperature of transition although it does not change the nature of the transition. Unsaturation within the hydrocarbon chain materially lowers the transition temperature. Stable films of long-chain compounds are encountered where a strongly hydrophilic group is attached to a chain of sufficient length to render the molecule insoluble. Adam [231] proposed the following classifications: (1) non-film-forming substances possessing very weak attraction: hydrocarbons, $-CH_2I$, $-CH_2Br$, $-CH_2Cl$; (2) unstable films (in order of increasing attraction for water): $-CH_2OCH_3$, $-C_6H_4OCH_3$, $-CO_2CH_3$; (3) stable films (substances possessing limited solubilities if the chain contains at least sixteen carbon atoms): $-CH_2OH$, $-CO_2H$, $-CN$, $-CONH_2$, $-CH:NOH$, $-C_6H_4OH$, $-CH_2COCH_3$. Owing to the strong solubilizing action of highly hydrophilic groups such as $-SO_3H$ or $-OSO_3H$, only very high molecular weight substances containing these groups form stable films. Unstable films are characterized by their inability to withstand compression, such films collapsing under moderate pressures. In solid films the molecules are very closely packed and there is a strong lateral attraction between the long chains, so that they assume a vertical or nearly vertical position. Influences which tend to increase the molecular area, such as an increase in temperature or a release of pressure, reduce this attraction, so that either liquid or vapor films are formed, depending upon whether there is a strong or a weak lateral attraction between the terminal groups. In such expanded films the alkyl chains are probably no longer normal to the surface, and in many instances are probably lying flat.

It is a well-known fact that water in contact with air possesses a definite and measurable surface potential. The work of Guyot [232] and others [233, 234, 235, 236] has shown that this surface potential is materially changed by the presence of a film upon the aqueous subphase, and their observations have afforded a very powerful tool for the study of such films. The surface potential of a film is defined as the difference in the potential of a film-covered surface and that of a clean liquid surface. This potential may be either positive or negative, the latter being encountered with films of fatty acid salts [237] and the former with films of the fatty acids themselves or many other long-chain compounds, such as the alcohols, esters, and ketones. The surface potential is a function of the number of molecules per unit area in the film, and it is, therefore, generally possible to tell whether a film is heterogeneous or homogeneous by measurements of this property. Homogeneous films show a uniform surface potential, while films which are partly gaseous and partly liquid show a higher potential for the liquid areas. Harkins and Fischer [238] showed a wide fluctuation in surface potential for myristic acid films at a molecular area of 56.4 sq. Å, the values increasing and becoming constant at higher compressions. McBain and Foster [239] determined the surface conductivities of closely packed films of stearic, palmitic, and oleic acids, reporting 3.8, 4.0, and 8.4×10^{-8} mhos respectively.

The presence of dissolved substances in the subphase, particularly acids and bases, exerts a profound influence upon the adsorbed films.[240, 241] Acidic ions in the subphase weaken the lateral attraction between the adsorbed molecules and thus lower the temperature of expansion. Condensed films of fatty acids on pure water show a very steep slope for the pressure-area curve, an extrapolation of which cuts the abscissa at approximately 20.5 sq. Å, whereas films on dilute hydrochloric acid show a decidedly less steep slope below 17 dynes per cm., the extrapolated curve cutting the abscissa at about 25 sq. Å. Divalent ions favor the formation of closely packed films.[242] Alkaline solutions materially lower the lateral attraction between the molecules in fatty acid films, Adam and Miller [243] having shown much lower expansion temperatures for fatty acid films at pH 12 than at pH 4. Ionization of the end group, therefore, undoubtedly decreases the lateral attraction between the polar groups of the adsorbed film, as evidenced by the lower expansion temperatures observed. Similarly, Adam [244] observed much lower expansion temperatures for amine films over acid subphases than over alkaline. Since the nature of the packing is affected by the presence of acids, bases, or salts in the subphase, it is evident that their presence also influences the surface potentials.

The viscosities of monomolecular films comprise a subject which has been rather extensively investigated,[245, 246, 247, 248, 249, 250, 251] and Fourt and Harkins,[252] in a study of the monolayers of aliphatic alcohols, made a detailed investigation of the methods of evaluating this property. The viscosity of a liquid film is proportional to the closeness of packing of the molecules in the film. Boyd and Harkins [253] expressed the relationship between the logarithm of the surface viscosity (η) of a liquid film and the film pressure (π) by the equation $\log \eta = \log \eta_0 + k\pi$ and stated that the viscosity of a liquid film increases with the number of carbon atoms in the hydrocarbon chains. Such films show Newtonian viscosities, as evidenced by the fact that the viscosities are independent of the rate of shear. At the transition point the viscosity increases rapidly, pentadecanoic acid showing an increase from 0.005 to 0.107 surface poises between film pressures of 19.8 and 21.4 dynes per cm., the film being liquid below these pressures and plastic above them. Condensed films generally exhibit a non-Newtonian viscosity which decreases with the length of the hydrocarbon chain and varies with the rate of shear. Since the molecular areas occupied by the alcohols are less than those of the acids, the films are less dense and thus exhibit lower viscosities. The viscosities of films of several alcohols and acids as determined by Boyd and Harkins [253] are shown in Table XLIII. These authors have ob-

TABLE XLIII

SURFACE VISCOSITIES OF ACIDS AND ALCOHOLS

($\pi = 4$ dynes per cm.)

Viscosity in Surface Poises

No. of C Atoms	Acid	Alcohol
14	......	0.0005
15	......	.0031
16	0.0002	.0066
17	.0003	.0100
18	.0014	.0230
19	.0040	......
20	.0115	......

served that the viscosity of films of arachidic acid decreases with increase in the temperature.

Since many of the original concepts and many of the data upon surface chemistry have been derived from a study of films of fatty acids, it is not surprising that the literature contains a number of references to monolayers of these acids. The work of Adam and Jessop [254] and the more recent investigations of Nutting and Harkins [255] are outstanding in that these authors have made a comprehensive study of films of a number of members of the fatty

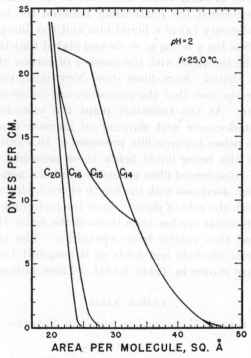

FIG. 22.   Pressure-area relations of films of fatty acids.

acid series under various conditions of temperature and pressure. Pressure-area diagrams were obtained by the former authors for monolayers of the fatty acids from lauric to palmitic, and Nutting and Harkins have studied monolayers of the acids containing from fourteen to twenty carbon atoms.   The pressure-area relationship of films of myristic, pentadecanoic, palmitic, and arachidic acids at pH 2 and 25.0°, as reported by Nutting and Harkins, are shown in Fig. 22.   An examination of the curves of myristic and pentadecanoic acids shows that they form an expanded type of film at this temperature, and that they exhibit sharp breaks at the kink point.   These authors have pointed out the great and rapidly changing compressibility of the films of these two acids above and below the kink point, and also the similarity of the two curves below the kink point of the pentadecanoic acid film. It will be noted that both palmitic and arachidic acids form much more condensed films than the two lower acids at this temperature, although the films are still rather highly compressible. Harkins [230] has stated that the molecular area occupied by the long-chain acids in the liquid condensed state decreases by about 0.3 sq. Å for every additional carbon atom.

TABLE XLIV

LIMITING AREAS, SLOPE OF PRESSURE-AREA CURVES, AND COMPRESSIBILITIES OF FATTY ACID MONOLAYERS

Acid	Limiting Area, sq. Å per Molecule	Slope, sq. Å per Dyne	Compressibility	
			$\pi = 0$	$\pi = 20$
Myristic	46.4	....	....	....
Pentadecanoic	45.6	....	....	....
Palmitic	26.75	....	....	....
Heptadecanoic	24.59	−0.180	−0.0073	−0.0086
Stearic	24.41	−0.177	−0.0072	−0.0085
Nonadecanoic	24.0	−0.163	−0.0065	−0.0075
Arachidic	23.64	−0.159	−0.0067	−0.0078

The limiting areas and compressibilities of liquid condensed monolayers on $0.01N$ H_2SO_4 at 25° as determined by Nutting and Harkins [255] are shown in Table XLIV.

The limiting areas are obtained by extrapolation of the pressure-area curves to zero pressure. At 25° the films of myristic and pentadecanoic acids are expanded, which accounts for their larger molecular areas. The pressure-area and pressure-temperature relationships of expanded monolayers of myristic and pentadecanoic acids have been investigated by Nutting and Harkins,[256] and the value of the slope $(\delta f/\delta T)_a$ for these monolayers was reported to be 0.8 to 1.2 for the intermediate, and 0.15 to 0.2 for the expanded films. The pressure-area curves of monolayers of pentadecanoic acid at various temperatures as reported by Harkins [230] are shown in Fig. 23. The effect of temperature upon the displacement of the kink point is clearly shown.

A large number of investigations have been made upon films formed by the high molecular weight esters, alcohols, nitriles, and other long-chain compounds, and the results obtained have led to many interesting correlations between the surface properties and structures of such compounds. It has already been pointed out that the attraction of the end group for water exerts a profound influence upon the film-forming properties. The lateral attraction

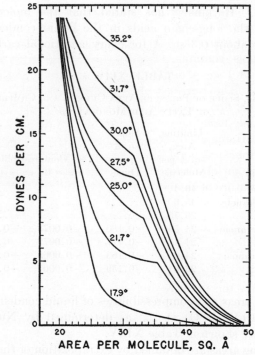

FIG. 23. Pressure-area relations of films of pentadecanoic acid.

between the end groups often determines the type of transition encountered in going from a condensed to an expanded type of film. It has been observed that the condensed films of many of the long-chain compounds approach a limiting area of 20.5 sq. Å at zero compression, but that other series, such as the esters, alcohols, and nitriles, show substantially larger molecular areas. Since in the condensed films it is assumed that the hydrocarbon chains are closely packed, it is evident that if the area occupied by the end group is smaller than that of the chain, the characteristics of the condensed film are essentially determined by the closeness of packing of the chains themselves. If, however, the reverse is true, as in the esters, nitriles, and alcohols, the molecular areas at high compression will be largely determined by the size and configuration of the polar group. The investigations of Adam [242, 257] and of Harkins and Boyd [258] upon esters of the fatty acids showed that the lateral attraction of the ester group is much less than that observed for the acids, condensed films going directly to gaseous monolayers. The area at zero compression, 22 sq. Å, is greater than that recorded for the acids on pure water, but less than that observed for the acids on acid subphases. Nutting and Harkins [255] have found the limiting molecular areas at zero pressure of the alcohols containing from fourteen to eighteen carbon atoms to be 21.9 sq. Å and to be essentially independent of the chain length. The transition pressure from a liquid to a condensed type of film increases with the chain length. Films of 2-nonadecanone have been investigated by Adam and associates,[259, 260] and Hoffman, Ralston, and Ziegler [261] have reported that films of stearone are much more compressible than those of 2-nonadecanone, an observation which they attributed to the unsymmetrical nature of the latter ketone. Films of phenoxyphenyl heptadecyl ketone, ⬡—O—⬡—$COC_{17}H_{35}$, were found to occupy larger molecular areas than films of diphenyl heptadecyl ketone, ⬡—⬡—$COC_{17}H_{35}$, at low pressures, owing to the hydrophilic properties of the ether oxygen. At higher pressures, however, the pressure-area curves are identical. The acetates of long-chain amines have been stated [244] to approach a gaseous type of film at high dilutions. A recent investigation [262] has shown that films of long-chain alkylammonium acetates below docosylammonium acetate are too soluble to obtain satisfactory pressure readings; however, octadecylammonium chloride has been shown [263] to give insoluble monolayers. Films of docosylammonium acetate [262] were observed to be vapor expanded at large molecular areas, the films becoming condensed with increased pressure. The extrapolated molecular area at zero pressure at 14.8° is 27.9 sq. Å; at 19.9°, 29.4 sq. Å; and at 24.9°, 30.4 sq. Å. Investigations of films of high molecular weight nitriles [242, 257, 264] show a value of 27.7 sq. Å for the limiting area of the condensed films, indicating that the nitrile group, $—C \colon N$, occupies a comparatively large area, a fact which is attributed to the presence of the triple bond.

Both mono- and polymolecular films of the fatty acids or other high molecular weight aliphatic compounds upon solid surfaces have been investigated and described.[51, 265, 266, 267, 268, 269, 270]   Blodgett [271] disclosed a method whereby successive monolayers may be deposited upon a glass or metallic surface, the method being generally referred to as the Langmuir-Blodgett method. Films previously formed upon a water surface are transferred to a solid surface, the films being composed either of alternating layers (Y-films) or of non-alternating layers (X-films). The orientation of the layers deposited upon a solid surface is determined by the direction in which the surface is passed through the monolayer, the pH of the subphase, and the temperature. Films of the fatty acid salts of calcium, barium, lead, zinc, and other metals have been studied. The structures of these films as shown by their x-ray, optical, and electrical properties have been the subject of numerous investigations.[272, 273, 274, 275, 276, 277, 278]

References

1. Baeyer, *Ber.*, **10**, 1286 (1877).
2. Garner and Randall, *J. Chem. Soc.*, **125**, 881 (1924).
3. Garner, Madden, and Rushbrooke, *ibid.*, 2491 (1926).
4. Garner and King, *ibid.*, 1849 (1929).
5. Fairweather, *Proc. Roy. Soc. Edinburgh*, **45**, 283 (1925); **46**, 71 (1926); *Phil. Mag.* [7], **1**, 944 (1926).
6. Meyer and Reid, *J. Am. Chem. Soc.*, **55**, 1574 (1933).
7. Normand, Ross, and Henderson, *J. Chem. Soc.*, 2632 (1926).
8. Piper, Chibnall, and Williams, *Biochem. J.*, **28**, 2175 (1934).
9. Morgan and Holmes, *J. Soc. Chem. Ind.*, **46**, 152T (1927).
10. Müller, *J. Chem. Soc.*, **123**, 2043 (1923).
11. Müller and Shearer, *ibid.*, **123**, 3156 (1923).
12. Shearer, *ibid.*, **123**, 3152 (1923).
13. Garner and Ryder, *ibid.*, **127**, 720 (1925).
14. Smith, *ibid.*, **737** (1932).
15. Hoffman, Hoerr, and Ralston, *J. Am. Chem. Soc.*, **67**, 1542 (1945).
16. Hoerr, Harwood, and Ralston, *J. Org. Chem.*, **11**, 199 (1946).
17. Bloom and Buerger, *Z. Krist.*, **96**, 365 (1937).
18. Ferguson and Lutton, *Chem. Rev.*, **29**, 355 (1941).
19. Dupré la Tour, *Ann. phys.* [10], **18**, 199 (1932).
20. Francis, Collins, and Piper, *Proc. Roy. Soc.* (*London*), **158A**, 691 (1937).
21. Piper, Malkin, and Austin, *J. Chem. Soc.*, 2310 (1926).
22. Unpublished observations.
23. Thibaud and Dupré la Tour, *J. chim. phys.*, **29**, 153 (1932).
24. de Boer, *Nature*, **119**, 634 (1927).
25. Baur, *Z. physik. Chem.*, **137**, 63 (1928).
26. Francis, Piper, and Malkin, *Proc. Roy. Soc.* (*London*), **128A**, 214 (1930).
27. Francis and Piper, *J. Am. Chem. Soc.*, **61**, 577 (1939).
28. Slagle and Ott, *ibid.*, **55**, 4396 (1933).
29. Thibaud, *Nature*, **119**, 852 (1927).

30. Piper, *Trans. Faraday Soc.*, **25**, 348 (1929).
31. Langmuir, *Proc. Natl. Acad. Sci. U. S.*, **3**, 251 (1917); *J. Am. Chem. Soc.*, **39**, 1848 (1917).
32. Lee and van Rysselberge, *J. Phys. Chem.*, **33**, 1543 (1929).
33. Broughton, *Trans. Faraday Soc.*, **30**, 367 (1934).
34. Nietz, *J. Phys. Chem.*, **32**, 255, 620 (1928).
35. Tammann, *Z. anorg. allgem. Chem.*, **109**, 221 (1920).
36. Cuy, *ibid.*, **115**, 273 (1921).
37. Biach, *Z. physik. Chem.*, **50**, 43 (1904).
38. Müller, *Proc. Roy. Soc.* (*London*), **114A**, 542 (1927).
39. Malkin, *Nature*, **127**, 126 (1931).
40. King and Garner, *J. Chem. Soc.*, 1368 (1936).
41. Malkin and el Shurbagy, *ibid.*, 1628 (1936).
42. Trillat, *Compt. rend.*, **180**, 1329 (1925).
43. Caspari, *J. Chem. Soc.*, 3235 (1928).
44. Caspari, *ibid.*, 2709 (1929).
45. Dupré la Tour, *Compt. rend.*, **201**, 479 (1935).
46. Kohlhaas, *Z. Krist.*, **98**, 418 (1938).
47. Stewart, *Proc. Iowa Acad. Sci.*, **35**, 251 (1928).
48. Tanaka, Kobayashi, and Shimizu, *J. Soc. Chem. Ind., Japan*, **33**, S.b. 364 (1930).
49. Stewart, *Proc. Natl. Acad. Sci. U. S.*, **13**, 787 (1927); *Phys. Rev.*, **31**, 174 (1928).
50. Warren, *Phys. Rev.*, **44**, 969 (1933).
51. Trillat, *Compt. rend.*, **180**, 280 (1925).
52. Friedel, *Ann. phys.* [9], **18**, 273 (1922).
53. Piper and Grindley, *Proc. Phys. Soc.* (*London*), **36**, 31 (1923).
54. Wyckoff, Hunt, and Merwin, *Z. Krist.*, **62**, 553 (1925).
55. Wyckoff, Hunt, and Merwin, *Science*, **61**, 613 (1925).
56. Friedel, *Compt. rend.*, **180**, 409 (1925).
57. Pauly, *Z. anorg. allgem. Chem.*, **119**, 271 (1922).
58. Gómez Aranda, *Anales soc. españ. fis. quím.* [5], **35**, 45 (1940).
59. Wolf and Gross, *Z. physik. Chem.*, **14B**, 305 (1931).
60. Zahn, *Phys. Rev.* [2], **37**, 1516 (1931).
61. Briegleb, *Z. physik. Chem.*, **10B**, 205 (1930).
62. Pohl, Hobbs, and Gross, *Ann. N. Y. Acad. Sci.*, **40**, 389 (1940).
63. Paranjpe and Deshpande, *J. Univ. Bombay*, **9**, Pt. 3, 24 (1940).
64. Volarovich and Stepanenko, *J. Exptl. Theoret. Phys. U.S.S.R.*, **10**, 817 (1940).
65. Smyth, *J. Am. Chem. Soc.*, **46**, 2151 (1924).
66. Höjendahl, *Physik. Z.*, **30**, 391 (1929).
67. Steiger, *Helv. Phys. Acta*, **3**, 161 (1930).
68. Werner, *Z. physik. Chem.*, **4B**, 371 (1929).
69. Williams, *ibid.*, **138A**, 75 (1928).
70. Smith, *J. Chem. Soc.*, 1567 (1933).
71. Hrynakowski and Zochowski, *Ber.*, **70B**, 1739 (1937).
72. Baker and Smyth, *J. Am. Chem. Soc.*, **60**, 1229 (1938).
73. Timmermans, *Bull. soc. chim. Belg.*, **28**, 392 (1914).
74. Phillips and Mumford, *J. Chem. Soc.*, 898 (1932).

75. Smith, *ibid.*, 802 (1931).
76. Carey and Smith, *ibid.*, 635, 1348 (1933).
77. Phillips and Mumford, *ibid.*, 1657 (1934).
78. van Bellinghen, *Bull. soc. chim. Belg.*, **47**, 640 (1938).
79. Harwood, Ralston, and Selby, *J. Am. Chem. Soc.*, **63**, 1916 (1941).
80. Garner, Van Bibber, and King, *J. Chem. Soc.*, 1533 (1931).
81. King and Garner, *ibid.*, 1449 (1934).
82. King and Garner, *ibid.*, 1372 (1936).
83. Garner and Rushbrooke, *ibid.*, 1351 (1927).
84. Robertson, *ibid.*, **93**, 1033 (1908).
85. Malkin, *ibid.*, 2796 (1931); *Trans. Faraday Soc.*, **29**, 977 (1933).
86. Pauling, *Phys. Rev.*, **36**, 430 (1930).
87. Müller and Saville, *J. Chem. Soc.*, **127**, 599 (1925).
88. Müller, *Proc. Roy. Soc. (London)*, **120A**, 437 (1928); **127A**, 417 (1930); **138A**, 514 (1932).
89. Carey and Smith, *J. Chem. Soc.*, 1348 (1933).
90. Malkin, *ibid.*, 2796 (1931).
91. de Visser, *Rec. trav. chim.*, **17**, 182 (1898).
92. Heintz, *Ann. Physik* [2], **92**, 588 (1854).
93. Twitchell, *J. Ind. Eng. Chem.*, **6**, 564 (1914).
94. Slagle and Ott, *J. Phys. Chem.*, **37**, 257 (1933); *J. Am. Chem. Soc.*, **55**, 4404 (1933).
95. Phillips and Mumford, *J. Chem. Soc.*, 1732 (1931).
96. Morgan and Bowen, *J. Soc. Chem. Ind.*, **43**, 346T (1924).
97. Bhatt, Watson, and Patel, *J. Indian Inst. Sci.*, **13A**, Pt. 11, 141 (1930).
98. Meyer and Beer, *Monatsh.*, **33**, 311 (1912).
99. Meyer, Brod, and Soyka, *ibid.*, **34**, 1113 (1913).
100. Efremov, *Ann. inst. polytech. Oural*, **6**, 155 (1927).
101. Efremov, Vinogradova, and Tikhomirova, *ibid.*, **9**, 117 (1929); *Bull. acad. sci. (U.R.S.S.), Classe sci. math. nat. Sér. chim.*, 443 (1937) [*C.A.*, **31**, 7731 (1937)].
102. Brocklesby, *Can. J. Research*, **14B**, 222 (1936).
103. Bruni and Gorni, *Atti accad. Lincei* [5], **8**, I, 454, 570 (1899); *Gazz. chim. ital.*, **30**, I, 55 (1900).
104. Mascarelli, *Atti accad. Lincei* [5], **23**, II, 583 (1914); *Gazz. chim. ital.*, **45**, I, 213 (1915); Mascarelli and Toschi, *Atti accad. Lincei* [5], **23**, II, 586 (1914); Mascarelli and Sanna, *ibid.* [5], **24**, II, 91 (1915).
105. Smith, *J. Chem. Soc.*, 974 (1939).
106. Robertson, *ibid.*, **83**, 1425 (1903).
107. Trautz and Moschel, *Z. anorg. allgem. Chem.*, **155**, 13 (1926).
108. Bury and Jenkins, *J. Chem. Soc.*, 688 (1934).
109. Shriner, Fulton, and Burks, *J. Am. Chem. Soc.*, **55**, 1494 (1933).
110. Ashton, Robinson, and Smith, *J. Chem. Soc.*, 283 (1936).
111. Roozeboom, *Z. physik. Chem.*, **30**, 385 (1899).
112. Smith, *J. Chem. Soc.*, 625 (1936).
113. Guy and Smith, *ibid.*, 615 (1939).
114. Kulka and Sandin, *J. Am. Chem. Soc.*, **59**, 1347 (1937).
115. Schuette and Vogel, *Oil & Soap*, **16**, 209 (1939); **17**, 155 (1940); **18**, 246 (1941); Schuette, Christenson, and Vogel, *ibid.*, **20**, 263 (1943).

116. Jantzen, Z. angew. Chem., **44**, 482 (1931).
117. Carlinfanti and Levi-Malvano, Gazz. chim. ital., **39**, II, 353 (1909).
118. Stewart and Wheeler, Oil & Soap, **18**, 69 (1941).
119. Seidell, Solubilities of Organic Compounds, 3rd ed., Vol. II, D. Van Nostrand Co., New York (1941).
120. Lewkowitsch, Chemical Technology and Analysis of Oils, Fats and Waxes, 6th ed., Vol. I, Macmillan and Co., London (1921).
121. Brown, Chem. Rev., **29**, 333 (1941).
122. François, Compt. rend., **193**, 1008 (1931).
123. Meisenheimer and Dorner, Ann., **523**, 299 (1936).
124. Dunken, Z. physik. Chem., **45B**, 201 (1938).
125. Matavulj, Bull. soc. chim. roy. Yougoslav, **10**, 33 (1939); Matavulj and Khojman, ibid., **10**, 49 (1939).
126. Mascarelli and Benati, Gazz. chim. ital., **39**, II, 642 (1909).
127. Meldrum and Turner, J. Chem. Soc., **93**, 876 (1908); **97**, 1605, 1805 (1910).
128. Howells, ibid., 910 (1929).
129. Lassettre, Chem. Rev., **20**, 259 (1937).
130. Chaplin and Hunter, J. Chem. Soc., 1114 (1937).
131. Auwers, Z. physik. Chem., **23**, 449 (1897); **42**, 513 (1903); Ber., **70B**, 964 (1937).
132. Hildebrand, Trans. Faraday Soc., **33**, 144 (1937).
133. Guggenheim, ibid., **33**, 151 (1937).
134. Hildebrand, J. Am. Chem. Soc., **59**, 794 (1937).
135. Huggins, ibid., **64**, 1712 (1942).
136. Meyer, Z. physik. Chem., **44B**, 383 (1939); Helv. Chim. Acta, **23**, 1063 (1940).
137. Flory, J. Chem. Phys., **9**, 660 (1941); **10**, 51 (1942).
138. Huggins, ibid., **9**, 440 (1941); J. Phys. Chem., **46**, 151 (1942).
139. Ralston and Hoerr, J. Org. Chem., **7**, 546 (1942).
140. Hoerr, Pool, and Ralston, Oil & Soap, **19**, 126 (1942).
141. Hoerr and Ralston, J. Org. Chem., **9**, 329 (1944); Hoerr, Sedgwick, and Ralston, ibid., **11**, 603 (1946).
142. Garland, Hoerr, Pool, and Ralston, ibid., **8**, 344 (1943).
143. Ralston, Hoerr, and Pool, ibid., **8**, 473 (1943).
144. Hoerr, Binkerd, Pool, and Ralston, ibid., **9**, 68 (1944).
145. Ralston, Hoerr, Pool, and Harwood, ibid., **9**, 102 (1944).
146. Sedgwick, Hoerr, and Ralston, ibid., **10**, 498 (1945).
147. Hoerr, Harwood, and Ralston, ibid., **9**, 201 (1944).
148. Ralston, Hoerr, and Du Brow, ibid., **9**, 259 (1944).
149. Hoerr, Harwood, and Ralston, ibid., **9**, 267 (1944).
150. Ralston, Hoerr, and Crews, ibid., **9**, 319 (1944).
151. Lumsden, J. Chem. Soc., **87**, 90 (1905).
152. Moore, Wilson, and Hutchinson, Biochem. J., **4**, 346 (1909).
153. Seidell, U. S. Pub. Health Service, Hyg. Lab. Bull. No. 67 (1910).
154. Faucon, Ann. chim. phys. [8], **19**, 70 (1910).
155. Lipetz and Rimskaya, Tsvetnye Metal., 594 (1931) [C.A., **26**, 5519 (1932)].
156. Mukherjee and Datta, J. Indian Chem. Soc., **16**, 563 (1939); Datta, ibid., **16**, 573 (1939).
157. Kortright, Am. Chem. J., **18**, 365 (1896).

158. Pomeranz, *Monatsh.*, **18**, 575 (1897).
159. White and Jones, *Am. Chem. J.*, **44**, 159 (1910).
160. Wightman and Jones, *ibid.*, **46**, 56 (1911).
161. Wilsdon and Sidgwick, *J. Chem. Soc.*, **103**, 1959 (1913).
162. Harned and Ehlers, *J. Am. Chem. Soc.*, **55**, 652, 2379 (1933).
163. Dippy, *J. Chem. Soc.*, 1222 (1938).
164. Conant, *Ind. Eng. Chem.*, **24**, 466 (1932).
165. Mukherjee, *J. Indian Chem. Soc.*, **14**, 17 (1937).
166. Ralston and Hoerr, *J. Org. Chem.*, **10**, 170 (1945).
167. Schuette and Vogel, *Oil & Soap*, **17**, 155 (1940).
168. Waentig and Pescheck, *Z. physik. Chem.*, **93**, 529 (1919).
169. Brown and Foreman, *Oil & Soap*, **21**, 183 (1944).
170. Stewart and Morrow, *Phys. Rev.* [2], **30**, 232 (1927).
171. Morrow, *ibid.* [2], **31**, 10 (1928).
172. Warren, *ibid.* [2], **44**, 969 (1933).
173. Stewart, *Proc. Iowa Acad. Sci.*, **43**, 268 (1930).
174. Stewart and Mannheimer, *Z. anorg. allgem. Chem.*, **171**, 61 (1928).
175. Trillat, *Z. Physik*, **64**, 191 (1930).
176. Fenton and Garner, *J. Chem. Soc.*, 694 (1930).
177. Pool and Ralston, *Ind. Eng. Chem.*, **34**, 1104 (1942).
178. Eijkman, *Rec. trav. chim.*, **12**, 157 (1893).
179. Scheij, *ibid.*, **18**, 169 (1899).
180. Falk, *J. Am. Chem. Soc.*, **31**, 86 (1909).
181. Waterman and Bertram, *Rec. trav. chim.*, **46**, 699 (1927).
182. Eisenlohr and Wöhlisch, *Ber.*, **53**, 1746 (1920).
183. Verkade and Coops, *Rec. trav. chim.*, **47**, 45 (1928).
184. Taylor and King, *J. Optical Soc. Am.*, **23**, 308 (1933).
185. Thibaud and Dupré la Tour, *Compt. rend.*, **190**, 945 (1930).
186. Dorinson, McCorkle, and Ralston, *J. Am. Chem. Soc.*, **64**, 2739 (1942).
187. Dorinson and Ralston, *ibid.*, **66**, 361 (1944).
188. Dunstan, *J. Chem. Soc.*, **107**, 667 (1915).
189. Deffet, *Bull. soc. chim. Belg.*, **40**, 385 (1931).
190. Bilterys and Gisseleire, *ibid.*, **44**, 567 (1935).
191. Brown and Shinowara, *J. Am. Chem. Soc.*, **59**, 6 (1937).
192. Matthews, Brode, and Brown, *ibid.*, **63**, 1064 (1941).
193. Frankel and Brown, *ibid.*, **63**, 1483 (1941).
194. Wan and Chen, *ibid.*, **61**, 2283 (1939).
195. Smit, *Rec. trav. chim.*, **49**, 539 (1930).
196. Lederer, *Seifensieder-Ztg.*, **57**, 575 (1930).
197. Semeria and Ribotti-Lissone, *Gazz. chim. ital.*, **60**, II, 862 (1930).
198. Sugden, *The Parachor and Valency*, George Routledge & Sons, London (1930).
199. Lederer and Hartleb, *Seifensieder-Ztg.*, **56**, 345 (1929).
200. Lederer, *ibid.*, **57**, 329 (1930).
201. Huggins, *J. Chem. Phys.*, **8**, 181 (1940).
202. Backer, *Chem. Weekblad*, **31**, 71 (1934).
203. Lederer, *Allgem. Oel- u. Fett-Ztg.*, **27**, 237 (1930).
204. Huggins, *J. Phys. Chem.*, **42**, 911 (1938); **43**, 439 (1939); *J. Applied Phys.*, **10**, 700 (1939).

205. Theis and Bull, *J. Phys. Chem.*, **40**, 125 (1936).

206. Hollihan and Briggs, *ibid.*, **46**, 685 (1942).

207. Ramart-Lucas, Biquard, and Grunfeldt, *Compt. rend.*, **190**, 1196 (1930).

208. Bielecki and Henri, *Ber.*, **46**, 1304 (1913).

209. Ley and Arends, *Z. physik. Chem.*, **17B**, 177 (1932).

210. Burr and Miller, *Chem. Rev.*, **29**, 419 (1941).

211. Hantzsch, *Z. Elektrochem.*, **29**, 221 (1923).

212. Hartleb, *Strahlentherapie*, **39**, 442 (1931).

213. Bradley and Richardson, *Ind. Eng. Chem.*, **32**, 963 (1940).

214. Mitchell and Kraybill, *Ind. Eng. Chem., Anal. Ed.*, **13**, 765 (1941); *J. Am. Chem. Soc.*, **64**, 988 (1942).

215. Mitchell, Kraybill, and Zscheile, *Ind. Eng. Chem., Anal. Ed.*, **15**, 1 (1943).

216. van der Hulst, *Rec. trav. chim.*, **54**, 639, 644 (1935).

217. Dingwall and Thomson, *J. Am. Chem. Soc.*, **56**, 899 (1934).

218. Bourguel, Gredy, and Piaux, *Compt. rend.*, **195**, 129 (1932).

219. Gredy, *Bull. soc. chim.* [5], **2**, 1029, 1951 (1935); [5], **3**, 1101 (1936); [5], **4**, 415 (1937).

220. Delaby, Piaux, and Guillemonat, *Compt. rend.*, **205**, 609 (1937).

221. McCutcheon, Crawford, and Welsh, *Oil & Soap*, **18**, 9 (1941).

222. Kohlrausch, Köppl, and Pongratz, *Z. physik. Chem.*, **21B**, 242 (1933).

223. Kohlrausch, Pongratz, and Seka, *Ber.*, **66B**, 1 (1933).

224. Harkins, Brown, and Davies, *J. Am. Chem. Soc.*, **39**, 354 (1917); Harkins, Davies, and Clark, *ibid.*, **39**, 541 (1917).

225. Adam, *Proc. Roy. Soc. (London)*, **99A**, 336 (1921).

226. Schofield and Rideal, *ibid.*, **110A**, 167 (1926).

227. Rideal, *Introduction to Surface Chemistry*, 2nd ed., University Press, Cambridge, England (1930).

228. Adam, *Physics and Chemistry of Surfaces*, 2nd ed., Clarendon Press, Oxford, England (1938).

229. Moulton, editor, *Surface Chemistry*, Pub. No. 21, American Association for the Advancement of Science, Washington, D. C. (1943).

230. Harkins, *Chem. Rev.*, **29**, 385 (1941).

231. Adam, *Trans. Faraday Soc.*, **24**, 149 (1928).

232. Guyot, *Ann. phys.* [10], **2**, 506 (1924).

233. Frumkin, *Z. physik. Chem.*, **116**, 485 (1925).

234. Schulman and Rideal, *Proc. Roy. Soc. (London)*, **130A**, 259 (1931).

235. Adam and Harding, *ibid.*, **138A**, 411 (1932).

236. Yamaguchi and Mizuno, *J. Electrochem. Assoc. Japan*, **3**, 2 (1935).

237. Frumkin, *Z. physik. Chem.*, **109**, 34 (1924); **111**, 190 (1924); Frumkin, Donde, and Kulvarskaya, *ibid.*, **123**, 321 (1926).

238. Harkins and Fischer, *J. Chem. Phys.*, **1**, 852 (1933).

239. McBain and Foster, *J. Phys. Chem.*, **39**, 331 (1935).

240. Myers and Harkins, *Nature*, **139**, 367 (1937).

241. Mitchell, Rideal, and Schulman, *ibid.*, **139**, 625 (1937).

242. Adam, *Proc. Roy. Soc. (London)*, **101A**, 452 (1922).

243. Adam and Miller, *ibid.*, **142A**, 401 (1933).

244. Adam, *ibid.*, **126A**, 526 (1930).

245. Plateau, *Phil. Mag.* [4], **38**, 445 (1869).

246. Stables and Wilson, *ibid.* [5], **15**, 406 (1883).

247. Schütt, *Ann. Physik* [4], **13**, 712 (1904).
248. Langmuir and Schaefer, *J. Am. Chem. Soc.*, **59**, 2400 (1937).
249. Myers and Harkins, *J. Chem. Phys.*, **5**, 601 (1937).
250. Harkins and Myers, *Nature*, **140**, 465 (1937).
251. Dervichian and Joly, *Compt. rend.*, **204**, 1318 (1937).
252. Fourt and Harkins, *J. Phys. Chem.*, **42**, 897 (1938).
253. Boyd and Harkins, *J. Am. Chem. Soc.*, **61**, 1188 (1939); Harkins and Boyd, *J. Chem. Phys.*, **7**, 203 (1939).
254. Adam and Jessop, *Proc. Roy. Soc. (London)*, **110A**, 423 (1926).
255. Nutting and Harkins, *J. Am. Chem. Soc.*, **61**, 1180 (1939).
256. Nutting and Harkins, *ibid.*, **61**, 2040 (1939).
257. Adam, *Proc. Roy. Soc. (London)*, **101A**, 516 (1922); **103A**, 687 (1923); Adam and Dyer, *ibid.*, **106A**, 694 (1924).
258. Harkins and Boyd, *J. Phys. Chem.*, **45**, 20 (1941).
259. Adam and Jessop, *Proc. Roy. Soc. (London)*, **112A**, 362 (1926).
260. Adam, Danielli, and Harding, *ibid.*, **147A**, 491 (1934).
261. Hoffman, Ralston, and Ziegler, *J. Phys. Chem.*, **43**, 301 (1939).
262. Hoffman, Boyd, and Ralston, *J. Am. Chem. Soc.*, **64**, 2067 (1942).
263. Hoffman, Boyd, and Ralston, *ibid.*, **64**, 498 (1942).
264. Adam and Harding, *Proc. Roy. Soc. (London)*, **143A**, 104 (1933).
265. Adam and Jessop, *J. Chem. Soc.*, **127**, 1863 (1925).
266. Joffé and Lukirsky, *J. phys. radium* [7], **1**, 405 (1930).
267. Feachem and Tronstad, *Proc. Roy. Soc. (London)*, **145A**, 127 (1934).
268. Clark, Sterrett, and Leppla, *J. Am. Chem. Soc.*, **57**, 330 (1935).
269. Trillat and Motz, *Compt. rend.*, **200**, 1299 (1935).
270. Akamatu and Sameshima, *Bull. Chem. Soc. Japan*, **11**, 791 (1936).
271. Blodgett, *J. Am. Chem. Soc.*, **57**, 1007 (1935).
272. Havinga and de Wael, *Rec. trav. chim.*, **56**, 375 (1937); *Chem. Weekblad*, **34**, 694 (1937).
273. Holley and Bernstein, *Phys. Rev.* [2], **52**, 525 (1937); Holley, *ibid.* [2], **53**, 534 (1938).
274. Goranson and Zisman, *ibid.* [2], **53**, 668 (1938); [2], **54**, 544 (1938).
275. Germer and Storks, *Proc. Natl. Acad. Sci. U. S.*, **23**, 390 (1937); *J. Chem. Phys.*, **6**, 280 (1938); Germer, *Bell Labs. Record*, **17**, 12 (1938).
276. Porter and Wyman, *J. Am. Chem. Soc.*, **60**, 1083 (1938).
277. Stenhagen, *Trans. Faraday Soc.*, **34**, 1328 (1938).
278. Bernstein, *J. Am. Chem. Soc.*, **62**, 374 (1940).

VI

REACTIONS OF FATTY ACIDS NOT
INVOLVING THE CARBOXYL GROUP

The term "fatty acid derivative" is quite broad and can be assumed to include any chemical which is preparable from a fatty acid and which includes a fatty acid radical as an integral part of its structure. Fatty acid derivatives can be logically divided into two general groups. One of these comprises those prepared by modifying, chemically or otherwise, the hydrocarbon chain, and the other group those which result from a reaction of the carboxyl group. Examples of the former are the numerous products which result from oxidative reactions, halogenations, hydrohalogenations, and other reactions concerned primarily with the hydrocarbon portion of the fatty acid molecule. Compounds such as nitriles, amines, amides, ketones, esters, acid chlorides, and alcohols characterize the latter type of derivatives.

This chapter is concerned with those derivatives of the fatty acids which result from a reaction of the hydrocarbon chain. In the subsequent chapters, the various derivatives the preparation of which involves a change of the carboxyl group are discussed in detail. In the present instance it is convenient to consider the derivatives under the specific type of reaction by which they are obtained, rather than to attempt to distinguish them by chemical or structural characteristics. The most important reactions of the fatty acids in which the hydrocarbon chain is a primary reactant are thus discussed under the headings of oxidations, halogenations, hydrogenations, and other type reactions.

OXIDATIVE REACTIONS

As would be expected, the saturated fatty acids are quite resistant to chemical oxidation. The action of strong oxidizing agents on the saturated acids is a subject which has not been extensively investigated. Sufficient work has been done, however, to indicate that a rather wide variety of products result from such oxidations, the nature and composition of which are apparently quite dependent upon the oxidizing agents and the reaction conditions employed. In many instances the initial oxidation products are so transitory that their formation is only a matter of speculation. The major oxidative reaction of the saturated acids is undoubtedly an oxidative degradation, the oxidation taking place initially at the *alpha* carbon atom. This is evidenced by the large amounts of shorter-chain acids which have been observed among the oxidation products.

The saturated acids are not oxidized by air at ordinary temperatures; however, they are attacked by oxygen at elevated temperatures, especially in the presence of catalysts. In some of the earlier work upon the oxidation of hydrocarbons to fatty acids, Kharichkov and others [1, 2, 3, 4, 5, 6] showed that the products are quite heterogeneous. Solway and Williams [7] assumed that this is occasioned by the fact that the acids first formed are further oxidized. These authors showed that the oxidation of stearic acid in the presence of manganese stearate leads to the formation of a complex mixture which consists of shorter-chain carboxylic acids, dicarboxylic acids, lactones, lactonic acids, and carbon dioxide. This indicates that the stearic acid molecule is attacked at several points and that hydroxy acids appear among the primary oxidation products. The presence of substantial amounts of hydroxy acids in the products of oxidation of stearic acid was later confirmed by Zerner.[8] The saturated acids are apparently resistant to the action of hydrogen peroxide in the absence of catalysts. The original studies of Dakin [9] upon the oxidation of the ammonium salts of shorter-chain saturated acids by hydrogen peroxide showed that substantial amounts of ketones appear in the oxidation products. Smedley-Maclean and Pearce [10] reported the presence of hydroxy acids in the products of the oxidation of palmitic acid by hydrogen peroxide in the presence of cupric salts. More recently, Allen and Witzemann [11] studied the oxidation of acetic, butyric, valeric, caproic, caprylic, and capric acids by hydrogen peroxide in the presence of various catalysts. The major product consists of carbon dioxide (50–80%). Acetic acid appears to be a resistant intermediate product and acetone is present in those cases where acids higher than acetic are oxidized. Ammonia, glycine, ammonium salts,[12] alkali phosphates, and glucose [13, 14] have been reported to catalyze such oxidations.

The saturated acids are vigorously oxidized by concentrated nitric acid, the main product being a mixture of dicarboxylic acids together with carbon dioxide. Noerdlinger [15] obtained succinic, adipic, and glutaric acids mixed with smaller amounts of pimelic, suberic, and oxalic acids by the oxidation of myristic acid with concentrated nitric acid. Dietterle [16] had previously reported the presence of large amounts of sebacic and suberic acids in the oxidation products of stearic acid; however, Carrette [17] obtained only succinic and glutaric acids. Since sebacic and higher dicarboxylic acids are oxidized to lower acids by nitric acid,[18] it is evident that lower dicarboxylic acids will predominate in the products formed by prolonged oxidation with this reagent.

Potassium permanganate has been observed to oxidize acids such as caproic and enanthic [19] to lower-chain mono- and dicarboxylic acids. Small amounts of keto acids are also formed during this process. The saturated monocarboxylic acids are considerably degraded by the oxidative action of potassium permanganate in acetone. A phenyl-substituted fatty acid is oxidized by alkaline permanganate solutions preferably at the carbon atom next to the phenyl group, forming first a hydroxy acid, which is then further oxidized.[20, 21] Although the saturated dicarboxylic acids are resistant to oxidation by alkaline permanganate,[22] the hydroxy-substituted dicarboxylic acids are readily attacked. Ellis [23] has shown that α,α'-dihydroxyazelaic acid is degraded to adipic acid rather than pimelic acid, indicating that those dicarboxylic acids which contain an even number of carbon atoms are more resistant to oxidation than those containing an odd number. Thus, the major oxidation product of α-hydroxyazelaic acid is suberic acid. Potassium permanganate in acetone easily oxidizes 2-hydroxy monocarboxylic acids to their next lower homologs, 2-hydroxystearic acid yielding margaric acid and 2-hydroxypalmitic acid, pentadecanoic acid.[24] Monocarboxylic acids are oxidized upon heating with potassium persulfate or potassium percarbonate.[25]

Biological oxidative degradations apparently involve the β-carbon atom,[26, 27] and Jowett and Quastel [28] have explained the apparent absence of intermediate products by postulating a simultaneous oxidation of alternate carbon atoms. Verkade and others [29] have stated that biological oxidations frequently occur at the terminal methyl group and may occur simultaneously with β-oxidations. Biological oxidations are of interest with reference to the so-called ketonic rancidity frequently encountered with saturated fats. Such oxidations have been attributed to a peroxidase present in molds, the main products of their action being apparently methyl alkyl ketones.[30, 31] It has been stated that exposure to ultraviolet light is in itself sufficient to cause ketonic rancidity of lauric acid,[32] which indicates that the development of ketonic rancidity is not purely a biological reaction.

The ethylenic acids are reactive toward a large number of oxidizing agents, the action taking place preferentially at the unsaturated linkages. Oxidation of the monoethylenic acids first yields dihydroxy acids or allied products, and a continuation of the oxidation generally results in a scission of the double bonds with the formation of both mono- and dicarboxylic acids. Continued oxidation of a di- or polyethylenic acid results in the cleavage of each of the unsaturated bonds, the product being a mixture of mono- and dicarboxylic acids. The oxidation of the ethylenic fatty acids is a subject which has been extensively studied, not only with regard to the resulting products but also with reference to the various reaction mechanisms. The identification of the products of oxidative cleavage is a recognized method for establishing the position of the double bonds in unsaturated acids. The reliability of such methods is, however, often open to question, since it is well known that the products obtained by the oxidation of specific acids are frequently dependent upon the oxidizing agent employed. Although in many instances this may be ascribed to secondary oxidative reactions, there is little question that it is frequently due to a shift in the position of the unsaturated linkage prior to or during the actual cleavage.

Since the most common oxidizing agent is air, the atmospheric oxidation of unsaturated fatty acids and fats is a subject of extreme interest. The importance of atmospheric oxidation, however, does not lie in the fact that air is a satisfactory agent for the preparation of oxidation products from the unsaturated fatty acids, but rather in the fact that oxidative changes, particularly in the edible fats, are extremely undesirable. The susceptibility of fatty acids to oxidative reactions increases with their degree of unsaturaation, linolenic acid being more readily oxidized than linoleic, and linoleic more readily than oleic.[33, 34, 35, 36] The relative positions of the double bonds influence the rate of oxidation, conjugated acids being more readily oxidized than their unconjugated counterparts.[34, 37, 38] The large amount of literature which has been built up on the autoxidation of the unsaturated fats has been concerned primarily with the reaction mechanism and with a study of the various negative catalysts which retard such oxidative changes. The literature upon this subject is so voluminous that only brief mention can be made in this writing of our present theories regarding the reaction mechanism and the nature of the so-called antioxidants. The reader is referred to a monograph by Lea [39] for a more detailed discussion of this subject.

The autoxidation of fats, oils, and fatty acids has long been recognized to occur in two rather well-defined stages. The first stage constitutes a so-called inductive period during which peroxides are formed, which probably act as both catalysts and reactants in the later stage of the oxidation. The fact that these peroxides can liberate iodine from hydrogen iodide has been made the basis of several proposed tests for the determination of incipient rancidity.[40, 41] Organoleptic rancidity is generally first detectable at the end of this induction period. Because of the quite transitory nature of the peroxides their actual structure has not been definitely established. Oxidation inhibitors appear to function mainly in greatly prolonging the inductive period, by retarding or preventing the formation of the fatty acid peroxides. The later stage of autoxidation is accompanied by oxidative changes leading to the formation of hydroxy acids, hydroxy-keto acids, unsaturated hydroxy acids, lactones, and various condensation products, and finally by cleavage to aldehydes, aldehydo acids, and mono- and dicarboxylic acids. A possible mechanism of the oxidation of oleic acid to an aldehyde and an aldehydo acid is as follows:

$$CH_3(CH_2)_7CH:CH(CH_2)_7CO_2H \rightarrow CH_3(CH_2)_7CH———CH(CH_2)_7CO_2H \rightarrow$$
$$\diagdown\diagup$$
$$O_2$$

$$CH_3(CH_2)_7CH(OH)CO(CH_2)_7CO_2H \rightarrow CH_3(CH_2)_7CHO + OHC(CH_2)_7CO_2H$$

Many of the tests for indicating rancidity, such as the Kreis test [42] employing phloroglucinol in the presence of hydrochloric acid, are specific for the presence of aldehydes. It has been claimed that the color developed by this reagent is due to the presence of an epihydrinaldehyde.[43]

The amount of oxygen absorbed increases perceptibly, and the peroxides disappear during the period of active oxidation. A number of reactions apparently proceed simultaneously, and the autoxidation of ethylenic acids generally results in a heterogeneous mixture of oxidized products and polymerized materials. Probably no single reaction mechanism will suffice to explain the variety of products formed, and all investigators who have studied the products of autoxidation of unsaturated fatty acids have attested to the complexity of the reaction mixture. In 1936, Ellis [44] studied the oxidation of elaidic and oleic acids in the presence of cobalt soaps. The latter acid was reported to yield carbon dioxide, oxidoelaidic acid, and oxidoöleic acid, together with cleavage products consisting of equal amounts of azelaic and suberic acids and smaller amounts of oxalic, caprylic, and pelargonic acids. Several years ago, Olcott and others [45] studied the autoxidation of highly purified oleic acid, methyl oleate, oleyl alcohol, and cis-9-octadecene and reported that all the fundamental processes were similar. Oleyl alcohol absorbed the most oxygen and oleic acid the least. All these substances with the exception of oleyl alcohol showed an increase in the number of hydroxyl groups upon oxidation, and all except oleic acid showed an increase in the number of carboxyl groups. Aldehydes were present only in small amounts, indicating that they were rapidly oxidized under the conditions employed. These authors postulated that ethylene oxides are prominent oxidation products and that the oxide compounds are not formed by the action of peracids with the ethylenic linkage as was formerly considered.[46] Mattill [47] has suggested the following series of reactions to account for the water formed during the oxidation:

$$-CH_2CH_2CH-CH- + (O) \rightarrow -CH=CH-CH-CH- + H_2O \xrightarrow{O_2}$$

with the O—O groups shown below the second and third carbons on the left, and below the third and fourth carbons on the right.

$$-CH-CH-CH-CH- \rightarrow -CH-CH-CHO + -CHO$$

with O—O groups shown below the carbon pairs.

Skellon [48] obtained 9,10-dihydroxystearic acids melting at 95° and 132°, azelaic acid, 10-hydroxystearic acid melting at 84°, and crude hydroxy acids together with short-chain mono- and dicarboxylic acids, when oleic acid was oxidized in the presence of blown whale oil. Large amounts of polymerized products are obtained by the oxidation of β-eleostearic acid,[49] and it has been stated that polymerization during the oxidation of linolenic acid takes place only through oxygen bonds.[50] Bolam and Sim [51] have studied the oxidation of methyl linoleate in the presence of solvents and observed that a peroxide group is initially formed at one double bond and a keto group at the other. The rate of enolization of the keto group and the activity of the peroxide group are influenced by the solvent present. Le Gousse [52] observed the formation of large quantities of lactones and lactides during the autoxidation of oleic acid, and the tendency of monoölefinic acids to form hydroxy acids during their autoxidation was noted by Fahrion.[53] Farmer and associates [54] more recently studied the mechanism of the autoxidation of ethylenic compounds and stated that the primary reaction is the formation of a hydroperoxide (—OOH) on the methylene group *alpha* to the double bond, the unsaturation remaining unaffected. The action of the hydroperoxide group with the double bond is a secondary reaction, occurring spontaneously or under the influence of heat. This latter action yields the scission products. It must suffice to say that, in spite of the fact that the autoxidation of the unsaturated fatty acids and their derivatives is a subject which has interested scientists for years, many unsolved problems still remain in this field.

The rate of oxidation of unsaturated fatty acids and fats is materially influenced by the presence of catalysts, some materials exerting a pro-oxidative effect while others materially reduce the reaction rate. Materials of the latter type have been extensively studied and are of great practical interest. Many substances, particularly metallic salts and soaps, exert a powerful pro-oxidative effect, salts of cobalt, manganese, and iron being especially effective. Autoxidation is promoted by exposure to light, the amount of peroxides formed increasing with decreasing wavelength, particularly below 5400 Å.[55] Organic bases such as pyridine,[56] aniline, dimethylaniline, pyrrole, and piperidine [57] also increase the rate of autoxidation.

The important work of Moureu and Dufraisse [58] showed that phenolic substances materially inhibit the autoxidation of unsaturated materials, and since this discovery thousands of compounds, both natural and synthetic, have been investigated for their antioxidative properties. Phenolic compounds such as pyrogallol, phloroglucinol, catechol, and naphthols are strong negative catalysts for oxidative reactions; in fact, most effective antioxidants so far disclosed are characterized by the presence of a phenolic group. However, salicylic and benzoic acids have been stated to exert a pro-oxidative effect.[59, 60] It is well known that crude vegetable oils are quite resistant to oxidative changes and that this resistance is either materially reduced or destroyed by refining processes. The isolation and study of the naturally occurring inhibitols has been a major contribution to our knowledge of this subject. Inhibitols are apparently present in the unsaponifiable portion of all the vegetable oils. Their presence was first demonstrated in wheat germ oil [61, 62] and has since been established in a number of other vegetable oils. The tocopherols, particularly β- and γ-tocopherol,[63] are important naturally occurring inhibitols. These compounds are closely related structurally to vitamin E (α-tocopherol),[64, 65] α-tocopherol being 5,7,8-trimethyltocol;[66] β-tocopherol, 5,8-dimethyl-; and γ-tocopherol, 7,8-dimethyltocol. The tocopherols contain a phenolic group, an aromatic and a heterocyclic ring, and a long alkyl chain, as shown by the accepted formula for β-tocopherol:

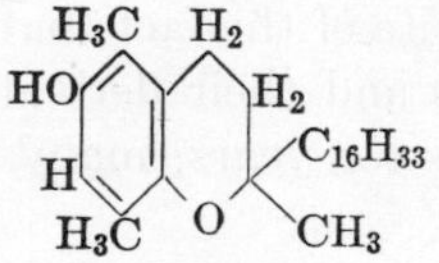

β-Tocopherol

Their separation and concentration has been the subject of several studies,[67, 68, 69, 70] as has their synergistic action with ascorbic acid and other substances.[67, 71, 72]

Crude cottonseed oil owes its resistance to oxidation to the presence of gossypol,[73, 74] the structure of which has been determined by Adams and coworkers [75] to be as follows:

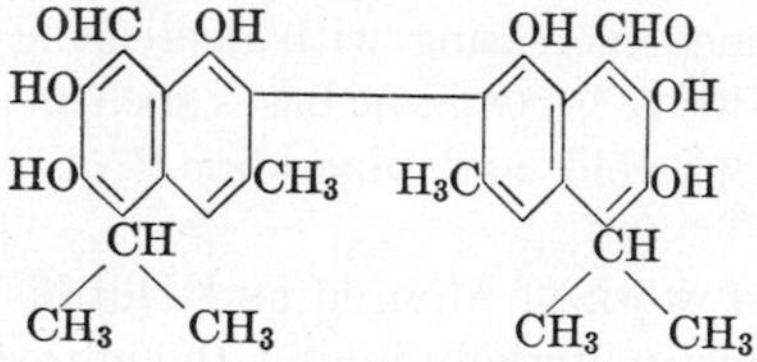

Crude sesame oil has been stated to contain the inhibitol sesamol.[76] Various phospholipides such as lecithin,[77, 78, 79] as well as the carotenoids [80] such as xanthophyll,[81] exhibit antioxidative properties. Naturally occurring antioxidants are not confined to the vegetable oils, for Newton and Grettie [82] have called attention to the inhibiting action of gum guaiac, and nordihydroguaiaretic acid, obtained from the creosote bush, has been shown [83] to be highly effective as an antioxidant for lard.

The ethylenic acids react with ozone, adding one molecule of ozone to each double bond to form the normal ozonide. This ozonide is capable of undergoing further oxidation with the formation of a perozonide and finally a super perozonide. The perozonides are reduced to the normal ozonide by washing with dilute sodium carbonate solution. The ozonides are viscous yellow liquids, soluble in most organic solvents and rapidly decomposed in hot water with the formation of cleavage products. The action of ozone on oleic acid was first investigated by Molinari,[84] who obtained the normal ozonide by treating oleic acid with ozonized air. Shortly thereafter, Harries and others [85] obtained the perozonide by the action of ozone on a chloroform solution of oleic acid. This led to a series of controversial papers between Molinari [86] and Harries [87] relative to the formation, structure, and decomposition products of the various ozonides, many of which papers are of historical interest only. Harries maintained that the decomposition of both the normal ozonide and the perozonides produces aldehydes and aldehyde peroxides. The aldehyde peroxides are converted into aldehydes by the loss of oxygen. The structure of the perozonide of oleic acid and the reaction for its decomposition were assumed to be as follows:

$$CH_3(CH_2)_7CH \underset{\underset{O-O-O}{|\qquad\qquad|}}{\quad\quad} CH(CH_2)_7CO_3H \xrightarrow{2H_2O}$$

$$CH_3(CH_2)_7CHO + CHO(CH_2)_7CO_2H + 2H_2O_2$$

The subsequent formation of acids was attributed to the oxidation of the aldehydes by the liberated hydrogen peroxide. Molinari, on the other hand, believed acids to be the principal cleavage products, oleic acid yielding hydroxystearic acid and an aldolazelaic acid, together with substantial amounts of azelaic and pelargonic acids. The aldolazelaic acid was assumed to result from an aldol condensation. When the ozonides were decomposed in the presence of potassium bisulfate solutions, acids were obtained with conditions under which the aldehydes had previously been shown to be resistant to oxidation. It is now known that the decomposition of oleic acid ozonides yields both nonanal and pelargonic acid, together with azelaic acid and its semialdehyde. If, however, the decomposition is effected in strongly alkaline solutions, according to the conditions employed by Molinari, the resulting aldehydes are further oxidized by the alkaline peroxides formed. The cleavage of ethylenic acid ozonides is frequently employed as a method for the determination of the position of double bonds, since this reaction is apparently not accompanied by a migration of the unsaturated linkage. However, considerable amounts of polymerization products are generally encountered.

The ozonide peroxide of linolenic acid has been described [88] as a viscous oil which explodes on heating. When heated with water it yields azelaic acid together with substantial amounts of azelaic acid semialdehyde and other products. The ozonide of ethyl linolenate, when decomposed in boiling water, yields a variety of products among which are azelaic acid, azelaic acid semialdehyde, propionic acid, malonic acid, and the ethyl esters of these acids. The cleavage products of methyl ricinoleate perozonide have been investigated by Haller and Brochet,[89] who obtained 3-hydroxy-pelargonic acid and azelaic acid together with other products. Studies of the rate of ozonization [90] of unsaturated compounds have shown that isolated double bonds are extremely reactive towards ozone; however, with conjugated compounds one double bond adds ozone rapidly while the others react quite slowly.* The *trans* forms have been stated to add ozone more rapidly than their *cis* isomers. Molinari [91] has claimed that acetylenic acids are not reactive towards ozone, thus distinguishing them from their isomeric ethylenic acids; however, this opinion has been questioned by Harries.[92]

The action of oxidizing agents upon the unsaturated fatty acids presents an extremely interesting subject. The better-known oxidizing agents such as chromic acid, nitric acid, peracetic acid, perbenzoic acid, benzoyl peroxide, potassium permanganate, and others are all reactive with the ethylenic acids. Although the oxidative mechanisms with these various chemical agents have many aspects in common, studies of the intermediate, and frequently the final, products indicate characteristic differences in their behavior. The course of the reaction is frequently influenced by the presence of solvents and by the reaction conditions employed. The extended oxidation of the unsaturated fatty acids is generally attended by a cleavage of the unsaturated linkages to form mono- and dibasic acids, aldehydes, and other scission products. The cleavage generally takes place at the position originally occupied by the double bond, although in many instances a shift in the double bond occurs either prior to or during the cleavage. Until this fact was fully appreciated, oxidation reactions frequently resulted in erroneous conclusions regarding the structure of certain unsaturated acids. In studies of the intermediate products of an

---

* For a general discussion of the relative reactivities of unsaturated linkages see Allen and Blatt, *Organic Chemistry*, 2nd ed., Gilman, editor, Chap. 7, John Wiley & Sons, New York (1943).

oxidation, the possibility of a geometrical isomerization during the reaction must be considered. For example, in the preparation of dihydroxystearic acids by the oxidation of oleic acid, the low-melting dihydroxystearic acid is obtained when peracids are employed as the oxidizing agents, whereas the use of dilute alkaline permanganate solutions yields the higher-melting isomer. Elaidic acid, on the other hand, yields the lower-melting acid with permanganate and the higher-melting form with the peracids. The causes of this inversion are not clearly understood. In the following paragraphs the actions of several representative oxidizing agents upon the unsaturated fatty acids are discussed as regards both the intermediate and final products and also the reaction mechanisms.

The ethylenic acids are vigorously oxidized by nitric acid with the formation of mixtures of mono- and dibasic acids.[93, 94] Lewkowitsch[95] obtained adipic, pimelic, and suberic acids together with the monobasic acids from formic acid to caproic acid by the action of nitric acid on oleic acid. The intermediate products formed by this oxidation contain appreciable amounts of nitrated materials. The oxidation of ricinoleic acid by nitric acid results in a mixture of suberic and azelaic acids together with short-chain monobasic acids. Pimelic acid has also been reported[96] to be formed under these conditions. The relative amounts of suberic and azelaic acids obtained by the nitric acid oxidation of ricinoleic acid vary according to the oxidizing conditions. Verkade[97] has reported that higher temperatures favor the formation of suberic acid, although a lower total yield of the mixed acids is obtained. Lower temperatures and the use of less-concentrated nitric acid result in higher yields of azelaic acid. The formation of suberic acid has been stated to be a secondary reaction. The action of dilute nitric acid on ricinoleic acid results in the formation of a nitric ester,[98] although the attending drop in the iodine value indicates that the double bond is also involved. The addition product of nitrogen dioxide and oleic acid has been observed to decompose in boiling water to yield nitrononane, pelargonic acid, and azelaic acid,[99] whereas the addition product of ricinoleic acid yields heptanoic and azelaic acids. The production of dibasic acids by the oxidation of oleic acid with nitric acid in the presence of ammonium vanadate has been patented.[100] Fuming nitric acid oxidizes acetylenic acids to a mixture of di- and monobasic acids with the intermediate formation of diketo acids, stearolic and behenolic acids having been shown to yield first stearoxylic and behenoxylic acids, respectively.[101, 102]

The oxidation of ethylenic acids and their derivatives by per-acids, such as persulfuric, peracetic, and perbenzoic acids, yields hydroxy acids which are stereoisomeric with those obtained by the oxidation of these same substances with alkaline permanganate. If the latter oxidation is not accompanied by a change in configuration (a view which has been frequently held [103, 104]), then inversion must be encountered where peracids are employed. If inversion is encountered it most likely takes place during the hydrolysis of the intermediate epoxide. Hilditch and Lea,[105] on the other hand, have contended that inversion is the result of the highly alkaline conditions employed in the permanganate oxidation. Whatever viewpoint is assumed, it is a well-recognized fact that two isomeric dihydroxy acids are obtained by the oxidation of a monoethylenic acid, and that the particular isomer which results is largely dependent upon whether the oxidation is conducted in an acid or an alkaline medium.

When ethylenic acids are treated with perbenzoic acid, oxido acids are first formed, and these can subsequently be hydrolyzed to yield hydroxy acids.[106] The reaction proceeds as follows:

$$CH_3(CH_2)_xCH:CH(CH_2)_yCO_2H \rightarrow CH_3(CH_2)_xCH\underset{\displaystyle O}{\underline{\quad\diagdown\diagup\quad}}CH(CH_2)_yCO_2H$$

$$\xrightarrow{H_2O} CH_3(CH_2)_xCH\underset{\displaystyle OH}{\overset{\displaystyle |}{}}{-}CH(CH_2)_yCO_2H \atop OH$$

The action of perbenzoic acid on linoleic acid has been studied by Bauer and Kutscher,[107] who observed that the products closely resemble those obtained by air oxidation. The later studies of Bauer and Bähr [108] indicated that polyethylenic acids apparently do not form simple oxy acids, but yield oily products of undetermined composition. Smit,[109] however, has since obtained a 9,12-dioxidostearate, m.p. 31°, by the oxidation of methyl linoleate with perbenzoic acid, the saponification of which yielded a dioxido-stearic acid, m.p. 79°. Hydration of this latter product with boiling 0.1N H_2SO_4 gives a tetrahydroxystearic acid melting at 95°, whereas hydration with 80% H_2SO_4 at 0° gives an isomeric tetrahydroxy acid, m.p. 148°. An oxy acid melting at 52° has been obtained [108] by the action of perbenzoic acid on oleic acid, and an isomeric acid melting at 57.5–58.5° by a similar treatment of elaidic acid. Hydrolysis of the former yields a dihydroxystearic acid, m.p. 96°, and of the latter a dihydroxystearic acid melting at 132°. Erucic acid gives, upon oxidation with perbenzoic acid, an oxy acid melting at 67.5° which yields a dihydroxybehenic acid, m.p. 133°. Hydrolysis of the oxy acids produced by the action of perbenzoic acid,[104] and also of benzoyl peroxide,[110] on oleic acid and elaidic acid yields dihydroxystearic acids. The hydration of the oxy acids obtained from methyl ricinoleate and methyl ricinelaidate yields isomeric trihydroxystearic acids.

The oxidation of ethylenic acids by means of peracetic acid probably follows a mechanism quite similar to that observed for perbenzoic acid. Oleic and elaidic acids when treated with hydrogen peroxide in glacial acetic acid (peracetic acid) yield hydroxy acids which melt at 95° and 132°, respectively, the reaction proceeding quite smoothly and, according to Hilditch,[111] without the formation of an intermediate oxy acid. However, when sodium oleate is oxidized with hydrogen peroxide in aqueous sodium hydroxide, the higher-melting dihydroxystearic acid is obtained, the formation of which Hilditch believes to be due to a change similar to a Walden inversion. The oxidation of methyl oleate and methyl elaidate by peracetic acid yields esters of dihydroxystearic acids, an increase in the temperature of the reaction bringing about an appreciable acylation of the hydroxyl groups.[105] Products similar to those produced by air oxidation are encountered if the reaction is conducted at low temperatures, and Bauer and Kutscher [107] have observed that the products obtained by the oxidation of linoleic acid with hydrogen peroxide resemble those resulting from autoxidation. The oxidative properties of hydrogen peroxide have been reported [112] to be greatly increased by the presence of copper salts. The unsaturated bonds of non-conjugated acids are oxidized by peracetic acid at about the same velocity;[113] however, acids with conjugated unsaturation show an appreciable decrease in the rate of oxidation after the reaction is half completed. Conjugated unsaturated compounds, on the other hand, absorb more than the theoretical quantity of oxygen, thus indicating an oxidation of the hydroxy compounds initially formed. King [114] has recently reported that the oxidation of oleic acid by hydrogen peroxide in acetic acid yields a mixture of monoacetates of the dihydroxystearic acid which melts at 95°. Elaidic acid yields the monoacetates of the isomeric dihydroxystearic acid melting at 132°, in addition to an appreciable amount of an oxido-stearic acid, m.p. 55.5°. The epoxide of oleic acid when treated with acetic acid yields a monoacetate similar to that obtained during the oxidation; however, the epoxide from elaidic acid is only partly converted to a monoacetate. If inversion accompanies the production of hydroxy acids from ethylenic acids by oxidation of the ethylenic acids with peracids or similar compounds, the inversion probably takes place during the opening of the oxido ring. This is still a very controversial question as will be shown later in our discussion of the subject. King has proposed the following mechanism for the oxidation of oleic and elaidic acids by hydrogen peroxide in acetic acid:

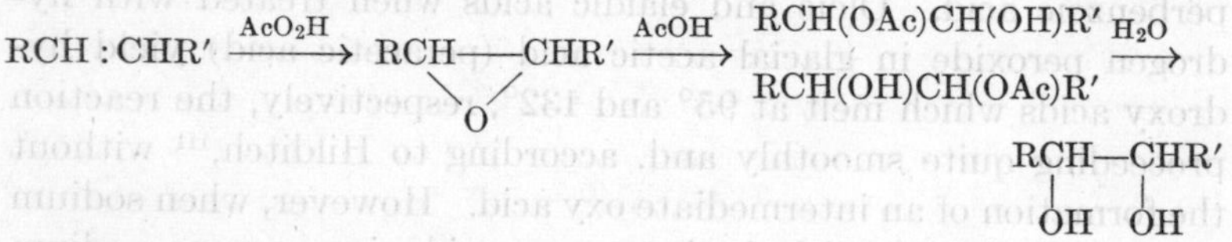

$$RCH:CHR' \xrightarrow{AcO_2H} RCH\underset{O}{\overset{}{\smile}}CHR' \xrightarrow{AcOH} \begin{array}{c} RCH(OAc)CH(OH)R' \\ RCH(OH)CH(OAc)R' \end{array} \xrightarrow{H_2O}$$

$$\begin{array}{cc} RCH-CHR' \\ | \quad | \\ OH \quad OH \end{array}$$

The action of persulfuric acid (Caro's acid) on ethylenic acids produces dihydroxy acids similar in configuration to those obtained by the use of peracetic and perbenzoic acids. Albitskiĭ [115] obtained the lower-melting hydroxy acids by the action of persulfuric acid on oleic and erucic acids, and the higher-melting acids by the oxidation of elaidic and brassidic acids. Similar findings have been reported for 6-oleic and 6-elaidic acids,[116] the following reaction mechanism having been proposed: [117]

$$RCH:CHR' \xrightarrow{H_2SO_5} RCH(OH)CH(OSO_3H)R' \xrightarrow{H_2O}$$

$$RCH(OH)CH(OH)R' + H_2SO_4$$

Chromic acid has long been employed for the oxidative cleavage of unsaturated acids, the reaction apparently taking place without a migration of the double bond. Grün and Wittka [118] obtained azelaic and pelargonic acids by the oxidation of stearolic acid with chromic acid and stated that a higher yield of pelargonic acid is recoverable by this method than when alkaline permanganate is employed. Chromic acid readily oxidizes dihydroxystearic acids,[119] the cleavage being between the two carbon atoms to which the hydroxyl groups are attached. Diketo acids result from the chromic acid oxidation of ketohydroxy acids.[120] 12-Ketostearic acid is formed when 12-hydroxystearic acid is treated with this reagent.[121] The oxidative cleavage of unsaturated bonds by means of chromic acid is considered to be reliable for the determination of their position, although potassium permanganate is more frequently employed. The oxidation of unsaturated acids by periodic acid has been the subject of several investigations.[122, 123]

Alkaline potassium permanganate is the reagent most frequently employed for the oxidation of the unsaturated acids, since reactions involving its use proceed smoothly and are susceptible to a high degree of control. This reagent is often used for determining the position of unsaturated linkages, the oxidation first yielding hydroxy acids and then cleavage products. Under ordinary conditions, cleavage occurs concurrently with the formation of hydroxy acids, although conditions have now been established whereby high yields of the intermediate hydroxy acids may be obtained. The oxidation of oleic acid with potassium permanganate in alkaline solution first forms a dihydroxystearic acid, m.p. 132°, isomeric with that obtained by the use of peracids. Saytzeff [124] has stated that this acid is similar to the dihydroxystearic acid prepared by Overbeck [125] by the treatment of dibromostearic acid with silver oxide. The oxidation of elaidic acid by alkaline permanganate yields a dihydroxystearic acid, melting at 95°, which is isomeric with that obtained from oleic acid and identical with that which results when oleic acid is oxidized by peracids or when halogenated oleic acid is treated with aqueous or alcoholic alkali.[115] The configuration of the dihydroxy acids formed by oxidation with alkaline permanganate is characteristic for oxidations conducted in highly alkaline media and, according to Hilditch,[111] their formation is accompanied by an inversion. This is still an open question,[126] since hydrolysis of the methylene oxide rings may be attended by a change in configuration.

The stereochemical relationships of the two dihydroxystearic acids obtained from oleic acid have recently been discussed by Atherton and Hilditch,[127] who arrived at the conclusion that inversion is encountered in the alkaline permanganate oxidation of oleic and elaidic acids and that this inversion is probably caused by the excess of alkali employed during the oxidation. It has been shown by King [128] that if the dihydroxystearic acid which melts at 132° is converted to a chlorohydrin and thence to an oxido acid, the hydration of this oxido acid yields a dihydroxystearic acid which melts at 95°. If the latter acid is so treated it is converted into the higher-melting acid, thus showing that this series of reactions is attended by a stereochemical change. It was pointed out that the oxido acid obtained from the chlorohydrin resulting from the action of hypochlorous acid on oleic acid is similar to that produced from the chlorohydrin obtained from the dihydroxystearic acid melting at 132°, owing to the fact that both yield the lower-melting acid upon hydration. Since such reactions are accompanied by inversion, it follows that the formation of a dihydroxystearic acid melting at 132° by the alkaline permanganate oxidation of oleic acid is likewise accompanied by a stereochemical change. The fact that the oxidation of sodium oleate by hydrogen peroxide in sodium hydroxide solution yields a dihydroxystearic acid melting at 132° is further evidence that highly alkaline conditions are conducive to such configurational changes. The action of alkaline potassium permanganate on erucic and brassidic acids [129, 130] yields high- and low-melting dihydroxybehenic acids, respectively. The action of potassium chlorate in the presence of osmium tetroxide on oleic and elaidic acids yields similar isomeric acids; [131] however, the reaction could not be brought to completion.

In 1898, Edmed [132] obtained a 60% yield of dihydroxystearic acid by the oxidation of oleic acid with alkaline potassium permanganate at 60°. Almost complete conversion of oleic acid to dihydroxystearic acid has since been realized by Lapworth and Mottram, [103] who recommend a temperature of 0° to 10°, a concentration of sodium or potassium oleate not exceeding 0.1%, and not over 1% of potassium permanganate, together with a short period of oxidation (5 minutes) and a slight excess of alkali at the beginning of the oxidation. It has been reported [133, 134] that in addition to dihydroxy acids small amounts of ketohydroxy acids are formed if the oxidation is conducted in weakly alkaline solution. The conditions for the formation of ketohydroxystearic acids have been extensively studied by King. [135]

The continued oxidation of ethylenic acids by alkaline permanganate solutions results in a cleavage of the double bonds with the formation of both mono- and dicarboxylic acids. [132] A highly satisfactory method for the oxidative cleavage of ethylenic acids has been proposed by Armstrong and Hilditch, [136] who employed powdered potassium permanganate in acetone or acetic acid solution. The oxidation of methyl oleate, for example, yields nonanoic acid and methyl hydrogen azelate according to the reaction

$$CH_3(CH_2)_7CH:CH(CH_2)_7CO_2CH_3 \rightarrow$$

$$CH_3(CH_2)_7CO_2H + HO_2C(CH_2)_7CO_2CH_3$$

The products obtained by the oxidative cleavage of ethylenic acids with alkaline permanganate are somewhat determined by the reaction conditions, as shown by the fact that Lapworth and Mottram[137] have reported high yields of caprylic, suberic, and oxalic acids by the oxidation of a dihydroxystearic acid prepared from oleic acid. The yield of azelaic acid obtained by the oxidation of 9-hydroxy-10-ketostearic acid in alcoholic solution has been shown to be materially increased by an increase in the amount of alkali.[138]

The oxidation of acetylenic acids by potassium permanganate results in a cleavage at the unsaturated bond. Stearolic acid, for example, when subjected to oxidative cleavage, has been reported[139] to yield pelargonic and suberic acids together with smaller amounts of caproic and azelaic acids. Careful oxidation of stearolic acid yields stearoxylic acid. The oxidation of ricinoleic acid by alkaline permanganate gives azelaic acid,[140] with the intermediate formation of two isomeric trihydroxy acids melting at 110–111° and 140–142°.[123, 128] The use of excess permanganate results in a degradation with the formation of caproic, enanthic, caprylic, azelaic, suberic, and 3-hydroxypelargonic acids. The conditions for the maximum yield of azelaic acid from ricinoleic acid have been reported.[141]

Hazura[142] obtained two tetrahydroxystearic acids, one melting at 157–159° and the other at 171–173°, by the action of alkaline permanganate on linoleic acid. The former has been claimed to be a eutectic mixture of an acid melting at 163.5° and the higher-melting isomer.[143] Two hexahydroxystearic acids (m.p. 203° and 173–175°) are obtained by the oxidation of linolenic acid.[142, 144] See Chapter II for a discussion of the configurational relationships which exist between these several polyhydroxy acids. The continued oxidation of these intermediate hydroxy acids yields cleavage products. It has been stated[145] that the cleavage of hydroxy acids takes place more readily at the 12,13- than at the 9,10-position. Lactone formation is apparently involved in the subsequent oxidation of polyhydroxy acids.[146] Oxidative cleavage by means of alkaline potassium permanganate is often employed to establish the structures of isomeric polyethylenic acids.[38, 147]

Unsaturated acids may be oxidized to dibasic and monobasic acids with the intermediate formation of hydroxy acids, by the action of sodium hypochlorite in the presence of nickel salts, the actual oxidizing agent probably being a peroxide of nickel.[148]

HYDROGENATION *

The addition of hydrogen to the unsaturated acids and their derivatives is a reaction which presents many elements of both scientific and technical interest. Although hydrogenation of the glycerides is of far greater commercial significance than hydrogenation of the acids themselves or their simple alkyl esters, much of our knowledge of the reaction mechanism has been derived from studies upon the latter compounds. Our discussion of this subject does not purport to cover the many technical advances which have been made by the fat and oil industry relative to the preparation of the many hydrogenated products which are now important articles of commerce. The following treatment of this subject is, therefore, necessarily confined to those studies which have been made upon the mechanism of hydrogenation and the influence of molecular structure upon the relative rates of hydrogen addition and to certain comments on the more important catalysts which have been proposed for this purpose. Since it is reasonable to assume that the hydrogenation characteristics of a fat are largely functions of the component acids contained therein, much of the following information can be considered as directly related to the many problems involved in the hydrogenation of oils and fats.

The pioneer researches of Sabatier and Senderens [149] upon catalytic hydrogenation are well known to students of chemistry. This classical work not only provided the stimulus for many subsequent investigations but also laid the foundation of a large modern-day industry. Prior to this work the hydrogenation of unsaturated acids could be accomplished only by difficult procedures, such as that of Goldschmiedt [150] which involved the conversion of oleic acid into stearic acid by the action of phosphorus and fuming hydriodic acid. All such chemical processes have been superseded commercially by the method of catalytic hydrogenation, which depends essentially upon the activation of molecular hydrogen by adsorption upon a metallic surface. This adsorption is of such a nature that the activated hydrogen can be used to bring about the addition of hydrogen to unsaturated linkages, the reaction taking place at the catalytic surface. The function of the

---

* For a complete treatment of catalytic hydrogenation of organic compounds, see Adkins and Shriner in *Organic Chemistry*, 2nd ed., Gilman, editor, Chap. 9, John Wiley & Sons, New York (1943).

metal is purely catalytic since it simply increases the rate at which equilibrium is attained. This is evidenced by the fact that all hydrogenating catalysts are also potential dehydrogenating catalysts at elevated temperatures. A large number of metals and metallic mixtures and also metallic compounds have been proposed and used as hydrogenating catalysts. By far the most important of these is metallic nickel, which is almost universally used in commercial hydrogenations. Certain noble metals, especially platinum and palladium, are also highly catalytic and are frequently employed as hydrogenating catalysts. It is also well known that small amounts of certain substances function as catalytic promoters, either increasing the hydrogenating activity or otherwise modifying the catalytic action. On the other hand, a number of substances, particularly sulfur compounds, act as catalytic poisons and either greatly reduce or destroy the catalytic activity. Since catalytic hydrogenations are fundamentally surface reactions, many efforts have been made to increase the catalytic surface. One of the most common of such methods consists of the use of catalyst supports such as kieselguhr and other inert materials. The subject of hydrogenating catalysts is discussed in greater detail later in this chapter.

The mechanism of hydrogenation is somewhat more complicated than is generally assumed. Even in the simplest case, that of the addition of hydrogen to the double bond of a monoethylenic acid, a study of the intermediate products of the reaction indicates that hydrogenation is accompanied by other reactions which may involve isomeric changes in the molecular structure of the ethylenic compound. Since the final product is, in all cases, the completely saturated acid, it is only by a study of the intermediate products produced by partial hydrogenation that we obtain a true picture of the accompanying changes. A number of studies have been made upon the hydrogenation of oleic acid and its esters which have conclusively shown that hydrogenation is accompanied by a shift in the position of the double bond. The intermediate products therefore contain, in addition to oleic and stearic acids, substantial quantities of so-called isoöleic acids. These isoöleic acids are generally formed by a shift of the ethylenic bond to positions adjacent to that originally occupied, the new products appearing as a mixture of both *cis* and *trans* forms. Hilditch and Vidyarthi [151] observed the formation of both 8- and 10-octadecenoates during the hydrogenation of methyl oleate at 217–220° in the presence of nickel, an observation which was later confirmed by a study of the oxidation products of partially hydrogenated methyl oleate.[152] Somewhat contrary results obtained by Bauer and Ermann [153] were ascribed to different reaction conditions. The presence of 8- and 10-octadecenoic acids in the products of the partial hydrogenation of linoleic acid has been explained by a shift in position of the double bond of the resulting oleic acid.[154] The studies of Moore [155] upon the hydrogenation of oleic acid led to the conclusion that the formation of isoöleic acids is coincident with hydrogenation, in that it takes place only during the actual hydrogenation. This investigation indicated that under uniform conditions of hydrogenation a definite ratio is established between the amounts of oleic and isoöleic acids. Normal oleic acid is also formed during the hydrogenation of isoöleic acids, although the ratio of isoöleic acids to oleic acid is much greater than in the hydrogenation of oleic acid. This shows that the formation of isoöleic acids is probably an equilibrium reaction and that isoöleic acids are a mixture of constituents at least one of which can revert to oleic acid. The amounts of isoöleic acids formed are highly dependent upon the reaction conditions and upon the particular catalyst employed. In general, high temperatures favor the formation of iso acids as does also an increase in the amount of catalyst. The latter factor, however, has been reported to exert only a slight effect. The use of metals of the platinum group as catalysts favors the formation of iso acids to a much greater extent than the use of nickel and allied catalysts. The formation of iso acids occurs largely during the initial period of hydrogenation, the amount decreasing as hydrogenation proceeds.[156] According to Steger and Scheffers,[157] ethyl esters form more iso acids than the corresponding glycerides when hydrogenated under similar conditions. The esters of elaidic acid yield substantial amounts of oleic acid esters, the amount of oleic ester formed being greater with the ethyl esters than with the glycerides. Bauer and Krallis [158] have maintained that the formation of 8- and 10-octadecenoic acids from oleic acid is brought about by heat alone, as evidenced by the observation that such acids are formed when oleic acid is heated at 250° in the presence of nickel in an atmosphere of nitrogen. It was further claimed that solid acids result when oleic acid is heated both in the absence and in the presence of catalysts; however, the presence of occluded hydrogen on the reduced nickel could account for this latter observation. It has further been shown that a shift of hydrogen from a saturated to an unsaturated compound takes place when such mixtures are heated in the presence of nickel, an example being the simultaneous hydrogenation and dehydrogenation of a mixture of stearic acid and ethylene.[159]

Unsaturated hydroxy acids, such as ricinoleic acid, can be hydrogenated to saturated hydroxy acids at temperatures below 200° in the presence of metallic nickel. At higher temperatures the hydroxyl group is also reduced.[160] The hydrogenation of ricinoleic acid produces an optically inactive hydroxystearic acid,[161] showing that the reaction is accompanied by a racemization.

The polyethylenic acids and their derivatives add hydrogen in the presence of catalytic materials with great rapidity, the rate of addition being, in general, proportional to the degree of unsaturation. When mixtures of unsaturated acids are catalytically hydrogenated, the more highly unsaturated acids are first reduced to a lesser degree of unsaturation before substantial reduction of the monoethylenic acids is encountered. In such reactions, therefore, we are confronted not only by the various isomeric changes which may involve a shift in the position or a change in the configuration of an ethylenic bond, but also by the differences in rates of reduction of the several unsaturated bonds. It is well known that if an acid contains two or more unsaturated linkages these bonds are reduced at different rates, depending upon their relative positions within the fatty acid molecule. Studies of the intermediate products of hydrogenation of the polyethylenic acids and their derivatives, however, have not led to clear-cut conclusions. This is occasioned by the fact that although the rates of hydrogenation of the several bonds do differ materially the reactions proceed simultaneously, so that products representing all degrees of unsaturation are present. Selective hydrogenation is a subject of considerable interest, and much work has been done upon the effects of various catalysts and hydrogenating conditions upon selectivity. Since the relative rates of hydrogenation are quite responsive to factors such as the amount and kind of catalyst, the temperature and time of reaction, and other variables, it is not surprising that investigators are in some disagreement as regards the reduction mechanism of polyethylenic acids. In their study of the hydrogenation of ethyl linolenate, Hilditch and Vidyarthi [162] concluded that with the more unsaturated acids the rate of reduction of an ethylenic bond is greater the farther it is removed from the carboxyl group. On the other hand, van der Veen [154] has

stated that the 12-ethylenic bond of linolenic acid is first reduced
to yield 9,15-linoleic acid, some of the double bonds of which shift
to the 10- and 14-positions. Continued hydrogenation results in
a saturation of the 14- and 15-positions, yielding 10- and 9-octa-
decenoic acids. These latter acids are partially converted to
isomeric acids by a shift of their ethylenic bonds to positions adjacent to those originally occupied. In contrast to the above, Bauer
and Ermann [153] have claimed that linolenic acid is first reduced at
the 9-bond and then at the 15-bond. In an appraisal of all this
work it is quite evident that the relative rate of hydrogenation of
an ethylenic bond is influenced by its position, and the writer is
inclined towards the view of Hilditch that those bonds closest to
the carboxyl are the most resistant to reduction. The tendency of
the ethylenic bonds to migrate during hydrogenation reactions,
however, renders any conclusions somewhat speculative. Conjugated acids are readily hydrogenated, Böeseken and Krimpen [163]
having shown that the addition of one mole of hydrogen to α-eleostearic acid produces 10,12-octadecadienoic acid, the intermediate
product thus retaining a conjugated system. Pelly [164] has stated
that acids are less readily hydrogenated than glycerides, but that
the rate of hydrogenation of the acids is increased if glycerides are
present.

We owe much of our present-day knowledge of hydrogenation
to the many studies made upon the mechanism of catalytic action
and upon the effect of the composition and physical state of the
catalyst on its activity. Catalytic hydrogenations are essentially
surface reactions and it is generally recognized that such reactions
are brought about by the adsorption of one or more of the reactants
upon the catalytic surface.* The fact that certain metals possess
the peculiar ability to absorb large amounts of hydrogen was recognized long before the advent of catalytic hydrogenation. Graham [165] observed that palladium absorbs 930 times its own volume
of hydrogen, and it was later stated that platinum black [166] can
absorb 110 times its volume.

Since catalytic hydrogenation is a surface reaction, it is natural
that many investigations have been made upon the nature of the

* The reader is referred to the following books upon catalysis: Sabatier and
Reid, *Catalysis in Organic Chemistry*, D. Van Nostrand Co., New York (1923);
Griffith, *The Mechanism of Contact Catalysis*, Oxford University Press, London
(1936); Ipatieff, *Catalytic Reactions at High Pressures and Temperatures*,
Macmillan Co., New York (1936); Berkman, Morrell, and Egloff, *Catalysis*,
Reinhold Publishing Corp., New York (1940).

catalytic surface. The metallic atoms in the surface are held by varying degrees of constraint, whereas those in the body of the metal are part of the normal crystal lattice. Taylor [167] has emphasized that the surface may be regarded as composed of atoms in varied degrees of contact with neighboring atoms. It has been postulated [168, 169] that this would result in the presence upon the surface of certain highly active points capable of adsorbing reactants in a highly activated state. Whether one or both of the reactants are adsorbed is probably largely dependent upon the type of reaction catalyzed. In hydrogenation reactions, however, it is possible that the reaction takes place entirely at the catalytic surface and that both the hydrogen and the unsaturated compound should be regarded as having an affinity for the catalyst. [170] Armstrong and Hilditch [171] have adhered to the theory that unstable intermediate compounds are actually formed between the reactants and the catalytic metal. Whatever the actual mechanism, it is apparent that the catalytic surface is not uniformly active but that the presence of points of activity brings about an activated adsorption in such a manner that the rate of a chemical reaction is enormously increased, and that the products formed have a decreased affinity for the catalytic surface.

The catalytic hydrogenation of fatty substances may be conducted in either the vapor or the liquid phase, and in the initial disclosure [172] of the process both types of reaction were considered. The process of mixing the catalyst with the oil and heating under hydrogen pressure with stirring was first announced by Kayser. [173] The use of stationary catalysts [174] and the spraying of a mixture of the oil and catalyst into a hydrogen atmosphere [175, 176] were among the early suggestions. Since the disclosures of these fundamental processes, a large number of improvements have been proposed and adopted relative to both the technical process and the apparatus employed in hydrogenating fatty materials.

Although many catalysts have been suggested for the hydrogenation of unsaturated fatty acids or their derivatives, metals of the platinum and nickel groups are the only ones which are generally employed, and of these, metallic nickel is by far the most frequently used. Related metals such as cobalt, copper, or iron [177] are less active and are infrequently employed in spite of the fact that they are more resistant to certain poisons.

Nickel catalysts are generally prepared by the reduction of nickel compounds by hydrogen or other means, the activity being largely dependent upon the method of preparation. This activity is known to be modified by the addition of so-called promoters. On the other hand, it is well known that very small amounts of halogens or sulfur compounds, and also some nitrogenous materials, greatly reduce or completely destroy the activity of nickel catalysts. The higher the initial activity the less the resistance to such poisons, and it is supposed that such substances are irreversibly adsorbed on the surface of the catalyst. The temperature at which the nickel compound is reduced has a quite decided effect upon the activity of the resulting catalyst. Nickel oxides begin to reduce below 200°; however, Ellis [178] has stated that the reduction is not complete at 270°, and that temperatures between 300° and 325° give the most satisfactory results. Nickel catalysts prepared at this temperature are black and possess a maximum surface. Higher temperatures (500°) produce a gray, sintered product which is devoid of activity. The use of inert supports, originally patented in 1910,[179] is now almost universally accepted.

A convenient method for the preparation of a nickel catalyst consists of absorbing a solution of a nickel salt upon an inert support, treating with sodium carbonate, heating, and reducing. The preparation of a nickel catalyst by absorption of a solution of nickel nitrate upon washed pumice or other support, followed by decomposition of the nitrate and reduction of the resulting oxide, is the subject of an early patent.[180] The supports generally employed include kieselguhr, clay, various diatomaceous earths, and silicates. Supports such as charcoal [181] and glass [182] have been suggested.

Many nickel compounds have been investigated as starting materials for the preparation of nickel catalysts. The use of reduced nickel borate has been claimed to yield a catalyst which is not easily poisoned.[183, 184, 185] Normann [186] has claimed that nickel borate decomposes into metallic nickel and boric acid when heated, and it has subsequently been claimed [187] that a mixture of nickel and boron trioxide is an active catalyst. It has further been observed [188] that a considerable increase in hydrogen adsorption is brought about by moistening a nickel catalyst with a $0.01N$ solution of sodium borate; higher concentrations, however, bring about an appreciable decrease in adsorption. The use of nickel silicates [189] or of mixtures of nickel and aluminum silicates [190, 191] has been disclosed. Myddleton [192] has proposed the use of mixtures of nickel oxide with silicate esters. Kahlenberg and Pi [193] have compared the activity of a number of nickel salts, such as the tungstate, borate, silicate, chromate, and molybdate, and have reported that the catalyst prepared from nickel silicate is the most active. Metallic aluminates, such as nickel aluminate, have been stated [194] to yield quite satisfactory hydrogenating catalysts.

As previously stated, it is known that the activity of nickel catalysts and also their resistance to poisoning can be increased by the addition of promoters. For example, the addition of copper salts has been claimed [195] to yield catalysts which will hydrogenate at lower temperatures and are more resistant to poisons than those obtained from the nickel compounds themselves. Nickel catalysts containing 0.3% copper give large amounts of iso acids; however, those containing 4% form only small amounts of such acids.[196] Salts of rare earth metals, beryllium, manganese, uranium, and vanadium, and the chromates, phosphates, molybdates, and tungstates have been stated [197] to exert a promoting action on nickel catalysts.

Many substances, particularly halogens, sulfur compounds, and nitrogenous compounds, reduce the activity of nickel catalysts. The addition of sodium sulfate, nickel sulfate, sodium carbonate, or sodium silicate to a reduced nickel catalyst partially destroys its activity.[198] Ueno [199] has listed a number of substances which reduce the activity of nickel catalysts, among which may be mentioned metallic soaps, arsenic trioxide, oxalic and similar acids, proteins, glucose, and certain hydroxy acids. The effect of metallic soaps upon a nickel-copper catalyst has been investigated recently.[200] It was noted that sodium and potassium soaps exert a strong poisoning effect, magnesium, calcium, barium, lead, iron, manganese, zinc, and cadmium soaps a lesser effect, whereas copper and silver soaps have a promoting action.

Active catalysts can be prepared by the reduction of nickel salts of organic acids, such as nickel oleate,[201, 202] nickel salts of fatty, resin, or naphthenic acids,[203] nickel oxalate,[204] nickel formate,[205, 206] or mixed nickel and copper formates.[207] Nickel carbonyl was among the first of the organic nickel compounds proposed for this purpose.[208] In the preparation of a catalyst from nickel formate the reduction of the catalyst is accomplished simply by heating the salt in oil in the presence of an inert atmosphere. Active nickel catalysts have been prepared [209] by heating a mixture of nickel nitrate and sucrose. One of the most widely used and successful hydrogenating catalysts is that proposed by Raney,[210] which is prepared by dissolving the aluminum from a nickel-aluminum alloy by use of sodium hydroxide solutions. Such catalysts are commonly known as "Raney catalysts," and details of the method employed for their preparation have been published.[211, 212] Colloidal catalysts can be prepared by producing metallic dispersions by the action of an electric arc between electrodes of catalytic metal immersed either in water[213] or in oil.[214]

The catalytic activity of the suboxides of nickel has been a controversial subject. Bedford and Erdmann[215] have contended that the lower oxides of nickel (Ni_3O or Ni_2O) are highly catalytic and are more resistant to poisons than metallic nickel catalysts, and several patents have been issued pertaining to the use of such catalysts.[216] Meigen,[217] on the other hand, has claimed that nickel oxides owe their activity to the presence of metallic nickel, a view which has been strongly contested by Erdmann.[218] It has been stated that nickel oxide catalysts reduce the hydroxyl group of ricinoleic acid more readily than the double bond.[160]

Catalysts prepared from metals of the platinum group are often used in laboratory hydrogenations although they are not generally employed in large-scale commercial operations. According to Richardson and Snoddy,[219] platinum catalysts are not so selective as nickel, and the hydrogenated products contain large amounts of iso acids. The reduction of unsaturated fats and fatty acids by hydrogenation in the presence of metals of the platinum group has been the subject of several patents.[220, 221] Higgins[222] has proposed a mixed catalyst prepared from nickel formate and palladium chloride, and Paal[223] has suggested the use of nickel catalysts which contain precipitated palladium or platinum on their surfaces. Mixed platinum or palladium and nickel catalysts which contain promoters have been described.[224] Platinum catalysts have been stated to be poisoned by phosphine, hydrogen sulfide, mineral acids, liquid hydrocarbons, carbon disulfide, and chloroform.[225]

Platinum or palladium black can be prepared by a variety of procedures, several of which were proposed over a century ago. Among these older methods may be mentioned the reduction of platinum chloride with alcohol and alkalies,[226] with sodium formate,[227] with glycerol and potash,[228] or with zinc or magnesium.[229] Among the most satisfactory methods for the preparation of a colloidal platinum catalyst is that proposed by Loew,[230] which consists of adding formalin to an aqueous solution of platinum chloride and then adding aqueous sodium hydroxide solution. The preparation of colloidal platinum has been accomplished by passing an electric arc between platinum electrodes immersed in water.[231] Such suspensions are quite unstable, although they can be stabilized by the addition of protective colloids such as egg albumen or gum arabic.[232] Palladium catalysts have been obtained by similar procedures. The preparation of colloidal platinum or palladium has been the subject of several investigations,[233, 234, 235] a satisfactory method for their preparation being as follows:

Dissolve 2 g. platinum chloride in a little water containing 1 g. dialyzed egg albumen, and make the solution slightly alkaline. Add a slight excess of hydrazine hydrate, dialyze, and dry the solution. The resulting black powder disperses readily.

Although metals of the nickel and platinum groups are the most common hydrogenating catalysts, other materials have been investigated. Examples of these latter substances are osmium dioxide [236] and metallic selenium.[237]

Although catalytic hydrogenation is the most important method for reducing unsaturated fatty substances, mention should be made of several other processes which have been investigated. Among the straight chemical methods proposed, the reduction of ethylenic compounds by the use of hydrazine hydrate is of interest, particularly as a laboratory procedure. Oleic acid has been observed to be easily reduced to stearic acid and ricinoleic acid to 12-hydroxystearic acid by its use at room temperature.[238, 239]

The possibility of the electrolytic reduction of unsaturated oils, probably first suggested by Weineck,[240] has been investigated by Magnier, Brangier, and Tissier.[241] An alcoholic solution of oleic acid has been reported [242] to yield approximately 15 to 20% of stearic acid when electrolyzed between nickel electrodes. The reduction of either a suspension or an alcoholic solution of unsaturated acids between platinized platinum or palladium electrodes at low current density has been described.[243] Pomilio [244] showed that the speed of reduction depends both upon the solvent and upon the nature of the acid.

Atomic hydrogen produced by the action of a silent electric discharge in a hydrogen atmosphere brings about appreciable hydrogenation of unsaturated fatty materials; however, the reduction is attended by a large amount of polymerization, especially when highly unsaturated acids are involved. Kroepelin and others [245] subjected thin films of oleic acid to the action of atomic hydrogen resulting from the glow discharge and reported 54% saturation of the double bonds with little apparent reduction of the carboxyl groups. A substantial amount of a viscous, sticky oil was also obtained, the formation of which was not ascribed to reactions at the double bonds since the unsaturation of this polymer was the same as that of the distillable fraction. The observations of Iwamoto [246] support the view that a saturated fatty acid, such as palmitic or stearic acid, when treated in the silent electric discharge, yields a liquid polymerization product having appreciable unsaturation. Eichwald, [247] in his studies of the action of the glow discharge upon pure oleic acid, accounted for the low yield of stearic acid by assuming that hydrogen is split off from the acid molecule to give highly unsaturated acids which readily polymerize. Only a portion of this hydrogen is reactive with the ethylenic linkage of the oleic acid. Substantial yields of stearic acid have been obtained from oleic and elaidic acids by passing these acids through a discharge tube containing tungsten filaments and operating under 6–7 mm. hydrogen pressure. [248] Waterman and Bertram [249] have emphasized the major role of polymerization reactions when oleic acid is treated with activated hydrogen, and it was observed [250] that when hexadecene is exposed to activated hydrogen for several hours the main reaction encountered is polymerization.

The catalytic effect of a number of substances upon hydrogenation by activated hydrogen has been investigated, [251] and platinum and palladium have been stated to exert a powerful hydrogenating effect whereas bismuth trioxide and ferric chloride accelerate polymerization. The addition of metallic catalysts to facilitate hydrogenation by activated hydrogen was patented in 1912 by Utescher. [252] The effects of various gases, temperature, voltage, polar distance, and gas pressure have been investigated. [253]

HALOGENATION

Halogenation takes place either by substitution or by addition, and reactions of both types are frequently employed for analytical or synthetic purposes with the fatty acids or their derivatives. The reactivity of the halogens for both substitution and addition reactions is in inverse relationship to their molecular weight, which is the opposite of that encountered with the hydrogen halides. Fluorine reacts violently with both saturated and unsaturated aliphatic compounds, the reactions frequently becoming uncontrollable. Chlorine and bromine are capable of both substitution and addition reactions, whereas iodine is added slowly and does not generally yield substitution products.

Saturated aliphatic compounds when subjected to the action of fluorine burn with incandescence, yielding hydrogen fluoride and carbon fluorides. Such reactions often take place with explosive violence.[254] Moissan [255] observed that even lamp black and charcoal react readily with fluorine to form carbon fluorides. Acetone reacts violently with fluorine but if the fluorine is diluted with an equal volume of carbon dioxide a smooth reaction ensues. On the other hand, distillation of the product which results under the latter conditions yields only a charred residue. Bockemüller [256] obtained a mixture of fluorine derivatives melting at 7° by the action of an equal mixture of fluorine and carbon dioxide on hexadecane dissolved in carbon tetrachloride. Butyric acid, when treated in a similar manner at a low temperature, gives a mixture of products including 3- and 4-fluorobutyric acids. Fluorination of hexadecene results in a small yield of a difluoro compound, and oleic acid gives a mixture of two difluorostearic acids which melt at 81° and 95°. Elaidic acid, under the same conditions, gives a difluorostearic acid which melts at 84–85°. Substantial yields of fluorinated compounds have been obtained [257] by the use of lead tetrafluoride as the fluorinating agent. Fluorinated aliphatic compounds can be obtained by the action of fluorine on halogenated compounds other than fluorides in the presence of catalysts such as antimony halides,[258, 259, 260] the reactions proceeding smoothly and resulting in high yields. It has been claimed that the formation of large amounts of resinous products can be avoided by the use of this procedure. An apparatus for the direct fluorination of organic compounds has been described.[261]

The substitution of chlorine or bromine for hydrogen in the alkyl chain of the fatty acids, with the formation of either mono- or polyhalo acids, can easily be accomplished. It is generally assumed that a hydrogen upon the α-carbon atom is first replaced so that monohalogenation yields essentially an α-halo acid. This preference for α-halogenation has been ascribed to enolization.[262] If the halogenation is continued, any of the hydrogens attached to methylene groups may be involved. The action of free bromine on stearic, palmitic, myristic, and lauric acids has been studied by Krafft and Beddies.[263] The reaction of monobrominated palmitic acid with potassium cyanide, followed by hydrolysis of the resulting cyanopalmitic acid, yields tetradecylmalonic acid,[264] thus showing that monobromination tends to form α-bromo acids. Halogen substitution in the saturated acids is catalyzed by the presence of phosphorus,[265] and this reaction is generally termed the "Hell-Volhard-Zelinsky reaction" because of their pioneer work in this field.[266, 267, 268] The bromination of a number of mono- and dicarboxylic acids in the presence of phosphorus has been described by Auwers and Bernhardi.[269] Palmitic acid when brominated in the presence of red phosphorus yields 2-bromopalmitoyl bromide, from which 2-bromopalmitic acid is readily obtained by treatment with water. This reaction is characteristic of the saturated acids and is generally employed for the preparation of their α-bromo derivatives.[270] Shorter-chain acids add bromine smoothly in the presence of hydrogen chloride dissolved in acetone.[271] Phosphorus chlorides are often used as halogenating catalysts; for example, the bromination of caproic acid in the presence of phosphorus trichloride has been reported [272] to yield 90% of 2-bromocaproic acid, and the bromination of 5-bromopentanoic acid in the presence of phosphorus tribromide gives 2,5-dibromopentanoic acid.[273] The action of hydrogen bromide or hydrogen iodide on saturated acids [274] in the presence of nitrosulfonic acid yields α-bromo or α-iodo acids, respectively. The chlorination of aliphatic esters of the saturated acids has been studied quite recently by Guest and Goddard.[275] It was observed that when methyl caprylate, laurate, myristate, and stearate are chlorinated in the presence of catalysts such as sulfur, phosphorus chlorides, or chloroacetyl chloride, a large proportion of polychloro esters is formed even in the presence of substantial amounts of unaltered esters. The amounts of the former ranged from 8% to 40% and of the latter from 13% to 54%. This indicated that, under the conditions investigated, the chlorination of aliphatic esters to produce α-chloro esters is a more complex reaction than formerly supposed, and that a variety of chlorinated products in addition to α-chloro esters are formed. In a recent study of the chlorination of saturated hydrocarbons such as dodecane or hexadecane, Asinger [276] observed that substitution takes place uniformly on all the methylene groups, thus yielding a mixture of all the theoretically possible isomeric mono-chloro derivatives. Substitution upon the methyl group is much less than upon any of the methylene groups. Chlorination of the paraffins results in an increase in molecular volume, a lowering of the melting point, and an increase in viscosity.[277]

The addition of halogens to the unsaturated fatty acids or their derivatives is one of the most important and frequently employed reactions in fatty acid chemistry. Such reactions not only offer many interesting synthetic possibilities but also form the basis of several analytical procedures. Halogenations involve the addition not only of the halogens themselves but also of halogen compounds such as ICl, IBr, or BrCl. The studies of White and Robertson [278] upon the kinetics of halogenation have indicated that chlorine reacts with olefins in acetic acid solution according to a bimolecular mechanism, whereas reactions involving bromine and iodine or their chlorides are trimolecular. The addition of these latter halogens is preceded by the formation of a complex which then reacts with a second mole of halogen, a reaction which is precluded for chlorine because of its inability to expand its outer ring of electrons. The rate of addition of halogens in acetic acid varies over a wide range, the following general ratios of reaction having been determined: I_2, 1; IBr, 3×10^3; Br_2, 10^4; ICl, 10^5; and BrCl, 4×10^6. In a more detailed study of the mechanism of bromination, Walker and Robertson [279] have considered the reaction rate to be a composite between a bi- and a trimolecular rate, the latter predominating at the higher concentrations. The bimolecular order is favored by dilution, high temperatures, and the presence of ionizing solvents. The addition of an unsymmetrical halogen halide such as ICl, IBr, or BrCl is subject to the same considerations regarding orientation as additions involving hydrogen halides, in that the more positive atom goes to the more negative carbon atom.[280] The contention that halogen additions to ethylenes constitute chain reactions involving radicals has received substantial support.[281] Burton and Ingold [282] have postulated a transition state for halogen additions, one of the halogen atoms accepting a pair of electrons from the ethylene, the other atom thus assuming a negative charge. The negative halogen then migrates to the positive carbon atom of the ethylene, thereby completing the addition. The action of bromine on an ethylenic bond may be represented as follows:

$$CH_2::CH_2 + Br:Br \rightarrow \overset{+}{CH_2}:CH_2:Br\overset{-}{:Br} \rightarrow Br:CH_2:CH_2:Br$$

The ethylenic bond thus functions as a pseudo base, the intermediate assuming a linear configuration the resonating forms of which are $CH_2::CH_2Br:Br$ and $CH_2:CH_2:Br:Br$. The effect of alkyl substitution upon orientation, the marked catalytic effect of water upon halogenation, and other considerations lend considerable support to this mechanism.

The halogenation of a monoethylenic acid presents the simplest case of halogenation of unsaturated fatty acids. The addition of chlorine, bromine, or iodine to a monoölefinic acid yields the corresponding dihalo saturated acids; for example, bromine adds to oleic acid to form a 9,10-dibromostearic acid which melts at 28.5–29° and is isomeric with the 9,10-dibromostearic acid melting at 29–30° obtained from elaidic acid. Removal of the bromine by zinc and hydrochloric acid regenerates the original acids.[283, 284] These findings confirm the view previously expressed by Nicolet [285] in his studies of the dibromides of oleic and elaidic anilides, that no isomerization is encountered in the addition and removal of halogen at an ethylenic bond; however, they do not preclude a double inversion. Iodination has been stated to be an equilibrium reaction, the equilibrium constant, in the case of the ethylenic acids, being independent of the concentration.[286] The rate of addition of iodine to ethylenic acids [287] varies according to the position of the double bond with reference to the carboxyl group. The activation energies for the bromination of 3- and 2-unsaturated acids have been calculated [288] to be 24.4 and 31.5 kg. cal./mole, indicating that the former should be more readily brominated. Margosches and associates [289] have studied the influence of a number of factors upon the rate of addition of halogens to monounsaturated acids. The acetylenic acids add either one or two moles of halogen to form the corresponding di- or tetrahalo derivatives.[290]

All the polyethylenic acids add halogens with the ultimate formation of the corresponding saturated halo acids. It is well known, however, that the rate of addition of halogens varies widely, depending upon the relative position of the double bonds; conjugated acids, for instance, have a markedly different rate of addition than those containing unconjugated systems. According to the data of Knauss and Smull,[291] the rate of addition of bromine to oleic, linoleic, and linolenic acids increases with increasing unsaturation; however, a longer time is required for the complete bromination of the more highly unsaturated acids.

The addition of bromine to linoleic acid produces approximately equal amounts of two tetrabromostearic acids, the one a solid melting at 114–115° and the other a liquid;[292] debromination of these bromides yields the so-called α- and β-linoleic acids, respectively.[293] Bromination of the regenerated α-linoleic acid again yields both a solid and a liquid tetrabromide. The bromination of linolenic acid likewise yields a mixture of isomeric hexabromostearic acids. The acid obtained by debromination of the solid hexabromide is known as α-linolenic acid and that from the liquid as β-linolenic acid. By virtue of the comparative insolubilities of the solid bromides in petroleum ether and other solvents, a pure solid tetrabromide or hexabromide can be obtained, the debromination of which offers a source of linoleic or linolenic acid. For a consideration of the configurational relationships of these brominated acids, refer to the previous discussion of linoleic and linolenic acids. The preparation and properties of the linoleic and linolenic acids obtained by bromination and debromination procedures have recently been described,[294] as has the bromination of elaidinized linolenic acid.[295] Toyama and Tsuchiya [296] have studied the chloroiodo derivatives of linoleic and linolenic acids. The formation of polyhalo acids has been described in several patents.[297, 298]

When two moles of halogen add to a conjugated unsaturated system the initial addition occurs in the 1,4-positions and is attended by a shift in the position of the double bond, thus:

$$-CH=CH-CH=CH- + Br_2 \rightarrow -CHBr-CH=CH-CHBr-$$

The addition of the first mole of halogen occurs at a rapid rate, the second mole of halogen being added with difficulty. Thus α-eleostearic acid, which contains three conjugated double bonds, readily adds two moles of bromine to form a tetrabromide, m.p. 115°, which is quite resistant to further bromination.[299] The bromination proceeds in accordance with the theory of 1,4-addition, the tetrabromide containing the group —CHBrCHBrCH:CHCHBr-CHBr—. By subjecting this tetrabromide to a large excess of bromine over a long period of time van Loon [300] obtained a hexabromide. Bauer and Rohrbach [301] had previously obtained a solid hexabromide, m.p. 139–141°, by the action of bromine on α-eleostearic acid in the presence of ultraviolet light, and the debromination of this hexabromide gave β-eleostearic acid, melting at 69–71°. These findings confirmed the previous work of Böeseken and associates [302] upon the bromination of α-eleostearic acid. Previously, Nicolet [303] had pointed out the non-identity of the tetrabromide obtained by the partial bromination of eleostearic acid with that resulting from the bromination of linoleic acid. The bromination of eleostearic acid has been reviewed by Merz,[304] although this author's treatment of the subject is weakened by his belief that only four bromine atoms are added.

HYDROHALOGENATION

By hydrohalogenation is meant the addition of a hydrogen halide, HX, to an unsaturated carbon-to-carbon linkage. The halogen may be chlorine, bromine, iodine, or fluorine. The order of activity of the hydrogen halides is the reverse of that encountered in halogenation. Thus, hydrogen iodide is more readily added than hydrogen bromide, which in turn is more active than hydrogen chloride. The last of these, hydrogen chloride, adds with great difficulty to the unsaturated acids, the reaction, if it proceeds at all, requiring several days for completion.[305, 306] Hydrogen halides may be added to unsaturated acids in either the presence or the absence of solvents.

When a hydrogen halide is added to an ethylenic bond of a fatty acid or other compound, two isomeric monohalogen derivatives result, thus:

$$R(CH_2)_x CH{=}CH(CH_2)_y CO_2H + HX \underset{(II)}{\overset{(I)}{\rightleftarrows}} \begin{matrix} R(CH_2)_x CH_2 CHX(CH_2)_y CO_2H \\ \\ R(CH_2)_x CHXCH_2(CH_2)_y CO_2H \end{matrix}$$

The relative rates at which these reactions take place depend upon several factors, such as the position of the double bond with reference to the carboxyl group, the nature of the groups attached to the double bond and, to a very appreciable extent, the environmental conditions under which the reaction is conducted. The earlier work upon this subject comprised many valuable observations and resulted in helpful generalizations; however, a recognition of the importance of the above factors and their interpretation in the light of the electronic forces involved is a comparatively recent accomplishment. The most important of the earlier generalizations regarding the relative rates of addition reactions is that proposed in 1870 by Markownikoff,[307] who postulated that when a hydrogen halide adds to an ethylenic bond the halogen adds to the carbon atom which holds the fewer number of hydrogen atoms. Thus, in the addition of hydrogen bromide to an ethylene of the structure $RCH{=}CH_2$, the compound $RCHBrCH_3$ is formed in preference to its isomer RCH_2CH_2Br. This rule applies to additions other than HX, such as the addition of $HHSO_4$, $HOCl$, and ICl. Attempts to explain the direction of addition on the purely inductive effect of the R group, i.e., that $RCH^+{=}CH_2^-$ is more stable than $RCH^-{=}CH_2^+$, frequently ran into difficulties. The uncertainties were largely occasioned by the fact that earlier workers attempted to explain the relative rates of addition strictly on the basis of the structure of the ethylenic acid without regard to the external conditions of the reaction. The earlier studies upon the hydrohalogenation of acids [308, 309, 310] were limited to the addition of hydrogen halide to the shorter-chain ethylenic acids. In the case of the α- or β-unsaturated acids the halogen was considered to add to the carbon atom farther from the carboxyl, whereas with the γ-unsaturated acids the reverse was encountered. With the higher molecular weight ethylenic acids it was generally considered that the halogen adds to the carbon atom farther from the carboxyl group. Thus, Brunner [311] and also Noerdlinger [312] considered that the addition of hydrogen bromide to 10-undecenoic acid or its esters yields the 11-bromo derivative. The important work of Walker and Lumsden,[313] however, showed that the direction of addition is largely dependent upon the solvent employed, 11-bromoundecanoic acid, m.p. 51°, being obtained when toluene is used as the solvent and the isomeric 10-bromo acid, m.p. 35°, being formed in ether solution. Hydrobromination of 10-undecenoic acid in the absence of a solvent results in a mixture of 10- and 11-bromoundecanoic acids. This discovery, therefore, suggested that the solvent affects the relative rates of addition and offered a partial explanation for the many controversial opinions which had been expressed regarding addition reactions involving the hydrogen halides.

Before we discuss further the influence of molecular structure, alkyl substitution, and solvents upon the hydrohalogenation of unsaturated acids and their derivatives, it is necessary to consider the electronic structure of these compounds, particularly as regards the influence of molecular structure upon the apparent polarity of the ethylenic linkage. In 1916, Lewis [314] showed that electronic displacement can satisfactorily explain the effect of substitution upon the relative strengths of organic acids. Lucas and Jameson [315] have compared the electron-repelling ability of certain groups with that of hydrogen and have pointed out that alkyl groups are more positive than hydrogen whereas halogens and carboxyl groups are more negative. Thus, in acrylic acid the carboxyl group exerts a strong pull upon the electron pair as follows:

$$\text{H}\ddot{:}\text{C} \vdots \text{C} :CO_2H \quad \text{or} \quad CH_2{}^+_-\!\!=\!\!CH^{+-}CO_2H$$

The addition of hydrogen iodide should lead, therefore, to the formation of $CH_2ICH_2CO_2H$. Cuy [316] has expressed the opinion that the carbon atoms of an open chain exhibit alternate positive and negative polarities and that the direction of addition of hydrogen halides to ethylenic bonds can be explained on this basis. The observation,[317] however, that the principal product of the addition of HBr to 2-pentene is 3-bromopentane substantiates the theory of the influence of electron displacement rather than that of alternate polarities. The work of Ingold and collaborators [318] lends further support to the electron-displacement theory.

The great attraction of hydrogen for electrons has been stated to account for enolization [319] and for polarization of the carboxyl group.[320] In the latter group the following displacements occur:

$$O \!=\!\!=\!\! C \text{---} OH$$

$$(b) \qquad (a)$$

Allan and collaborators [320] have contrasted $R \rightarrow CO_2H$ with $R' \leftarrow CO_2H$, R being an electron-repelling group and R' an electron-attracting group. The R group in repelling electrons competes with the OH group and thus inhibits process (a), whereas the opposite is true of R' which attracts electrons. Thus $R'CO_2H$ is a stronger acid than RCO_2H. In their study of the dissociation constants of aliphatic acids in water, Ives, Linstead, and Riley [321] have represented the reaction as follows:

$$RC \overset{O}{\underset{O\text{---}H}{\diagup}} + H_2O \longrightarrow RC \overset{O}{\underset{O^{\ominus}}{\diagup}} + H_3O^{\oplus}$$

It was pointed out that the olefins have almost negative polar moments, since they contain no permanent dipole. If, however, the ethylenic group is polarizable, there will be a latent source of adjustment present in the molecule and the double bond will polarize so as to present a positive face to the carboxyl group, dissociation thus being increased as follows:

$$\overset{a}{C}\!=\!\!C\overset{\delta^+}{\sim\!\sim\!\sim\!\sim}\overset{\delta^-}{CO.O}\overset{b}{\text{---}H}$$

It was observed that the polar effect of the double bond is eliminated when the bond is removed from the carboxyl by two or more methylene groups, since the dissociation constants of the unsaturated acids approach those of the corresponding saturated acids as the double bond recedes from the carboxyl group. We thus have a distinction between a permanent and a latent dipole as originally pointed out by Lapworth.[322] The dissociation constant increases tenfold when the double bond goes from the β- to the α-position. In studying the capacity of unsaturated acids for adjustment, Linstead, Noble, and Boorman [323] pointed out that it is possible to anticipate the direction of addition of hydrogen bromide to olefinic acids by the determination of their ionization constants. In a comprehensive article appearing simultaneously,[324] such reactions were investigated and the results interpreted on the basis of the above principles. It was stated that the addition of hydrogen bromide to an olefinic acid depends upon the external conditions and also upon the alkyl substitution about the double bond but is independent of the position of the double bond except in the case of the α-unsaturated acids. The effect of solvents is quite profound. When hydrocarbon solvents are employed, the bromine of the hydrogen bromide adds to the more distant carbon atom irrespective of the alkyl substitution, the orientation being directed by the carboxyl group. This addition is similar to that observed when hydrogen bromide is added to esters in the absence of solvents. The double bond behaves independently of the carboxyl group when the addition is performed without a solvent or in ether, acetic acid, or water, under which conditions substitution influences orientation in accordance with Markownikoff's rule. Thus, vinylacetic acid yields 3-bromobutyric acid when treated with hydrogen bromide either in the absence of a solvent or in water, ether, or acetic acid, thus:

$$CH_2:CHCH_2CO_2H + HBr \rightarrow CH_2CHBrCH_2CO_2H$$

In toluene the reverse addition takes place, 4-bromobutyric acid resulting as follows:

$$CH_2:CHCH_2CO_2H + HBr \rightarrow CH_2BrCH_2CH_2CO_2H$$

Esters of vinylacetic acid add hydrogen bromide according to the latter reaction. It was emphasized that the addition of hydrogen bromide is irreversible and not an equilibrium reaction, since the elimination of the hydrogen bromide yields a lactone rather than the original acid. In inert solvents the carboxyl group of an unsaturated acid polarizes like an ester, thus:

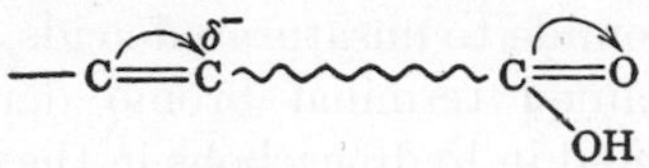

The bromine thus adds to the more positive or the distant carbon atom. Orientation is influenced by a "field effect" surrounding the molecule rather than by the effect of the carboxyl group transmitted along the chain. This field effect is rendered negligible if the acid is dissolved in polar solvents such as water or acetic acid. Such views are in harmony with many of the physical measurements which have been made upon solutions of the acids; however, attempts to correlate them with the various dielectric effects and internal pressures of the solvents have not been completely satisfactory.

In 1933, Kharasch and Mayo,[325] in studying the addition of hydrogen bromide to allyl bromide, observed that in the absence of oxygen or peroxides the reaction proceeds slowly with the formation of 1,2-dibromopropane, whereas in the presence of oxygen or peroxides 1,3-dibromopropane is rapidly formed. This effect can be eliminated by the addition of antioxidants. A subsequent study [326] of this effect led to the conclusion that Markownikoff's rule does not apply in the presence of peroxides, the speed of the reaction $RCH{=}CH_2 + HX \rightarrow RCH_2CH_2X$ being much greater than that of $RCH{=}CH_2 + HX \rightarrow RCHXCH_3$ if peroxides are present. If, therefore, solvents have no effect upon the direction of addition of hydrogen halides, except in so far as they contribute to the peroxide effect, much of the earlier work upon orientation is invalidated, particularly in those cases where peroxides are liable to be present. For example, Smith [327] observed that the addition of hydrogen bromide to 10-undecenoic acid in ligroin yields almost pure 11-bromoundecanoic acid; however, if oxygen is removed by hydrogen or by the addition of diphenylamine the 10-bromo acid is formed in predominant amounts, an observation which is in agreement with the peroxide effect. Later, Ashton and Smith [328] reported that the addition of hydrogen bromide to 10-undecenoic acid in any solvent in the absence of air yields 10-bromoundecanoic acid in accordance with Markownikoff's rule. However, in the presence of air the product varies with the solvent. Additions without solvent or in hexane, ligroin, ether, or acetic acid yield 10-bromoundecanoic acid, whereas additions in benzene or toluene yield the isomeric 11-bromo acid, showing that those conditions which favor the peroxide effect lead to the formation of the last-mentioned acid. In their study of the addition of hydrogen bromide to unsaturated acids, Gaubert, Linstead, and Rydon [329] obtained terminal bromo derivatives when the reaction was conducted in hydrocarbons in the presence of air, and non-terminal derivatives when antioxidants or no solvent was employed. However, it was observed that terminal bromo derivatives result when hexane or petroleum ether is used as the solvent even in the presence of hydrogen or antioxidants. It has been reported [330] that reduced nickel has an effect similar to that of oxygen in directing the addition of hydrogen bromide to 10-undecenoic acid. Diphenylamine only partially reduces the peroxide effect of reduced nickel, whereas both hydroquinone and catechol completely destroy the effects of both reduced nickel and oxygen.[331] Ashton and Smith [332] have reported that peroxides influence the hydrohalogenation of terminally unsaturated esters, both ethyl undecenoate and undecenyl acetate yielding the 11-bromo derivatives when treated with hydrogen bromide in the presence of air in ligroin or benzene, and the 10-bromo derivatives in the presence of hydrogen or antioxidants in the same solvents. It has been reported,[333] however, that the direction of addition of hydrogen bromide to 9-undecenoic acid, $CH_3CH:CH(CH_2)_7CO_2H$, is independent of the presence of peroxides, indicating that only the terminal bonds of ethylenic acids are susceptible to the peroxide effect. It has been claimed [334] that the addition of dry hydrogen bromide to 1-pentene in an organic solvent gives the 1-bromo derivative whereas the action of aqueous hydrogen bromide yields the 2-bromo derivative exclusively, an effect which is attributed to the difference in solvents rather than to the presence of peroxides. Linstead and Rydon [335] obtained 5-bromovaleric acid by the addition of hydrogen bromide to allylacetic acid in the presence of benzene and diphenylamine, an observation not in conformity with the peroxide effect.

Since hydrogen bromide has been more extensively studied than any of the other hydrogen halides, most of the above discussion has been concerned with this reagent, upon the reasonable assumption that it characterizes hydrogen halides. The action of hydrogen fluoride with several of the ethylenic acids, such as undecenoic acid, and with oleyl alcohol has been studied.[336] The heating of oleic acid with dry hydrogen chloride for several hours under pressure has been reported to yield a monochlorostearic acid [337] which melts at 39–41°. The action of hydrogen iodide on the higher unsaturated acids has been studied by Erdmann.[338] Aqueous hydrogen iodide has been reported [339] to yield 3-iodostearic acid, m.p. 60–61°, by addition to 2-oleic acid, and ricinoleic acid yields a diiodostearic acid when treated with hydrogen iodide.[340] Abraham and Smith [341] obtained 11-chloroundecanoic acid by the action of hydrogen chloride on 10-undecenoic acid in the presence of both reducing and oxidizing agents. Undecenoic acid and hydrogen iodide yield 10-iodoundecanoic acid even in the presence of strong peroxide catalysts. From these observations it was considered that the direction of addition of hydrogen chloride or iodide to terminally unsaturated acids differs from similar reactions with hydrogen bromide in that it is apparently not influenced by the presence of peroxides. This conclusion should be further investigated.

Acetylenic acids add first one and then a second mole of hydrogen halide to yield the monohalo and dihalo acids respectively. Stearolic acid was observed [342] to yield two isomeric acids, m.p. 39° and 23–24°, upon the addition of one mole of hydrogen iodide. It was assumed that the hydrogen iodide added *trans* and that the products are 9- and 10-iodo-*trans*-9-octadecenoic acids. The addition of two moles of hydrogen iodide gives two isomeric diiodostearic acids.[343] The same acids were obtained by the addition of a second mole of hydrogen iodide to the monoiodo acids described above. Harris and Smith [344] reported that the addition of hydrogen bromide to 10-undecynoic acid yields mainly 11-bromoundecenoic acid when the reaction is carried out in benzene and that the rate of addition is influenced by the presence of catalysts. Hydrogen fluoride adds to stearolic acid in the presence of inert solvents to give 9,10-difluorostearic acid melting at 70–74°.[345]

ADDITIONS INVOLVING HYPOHALOUS ACIDS

Hypochlorous acid and its bromine and iodine counterparts add directly to the ethylenic bonds of the unsaturated acids to form the corresponding halohydrins, thus:

$$-CH{=}CH- + HOX \rightarrow \underset{\underset{\displaystyle OH \quad X}{|\qquad|}}{-CH{-}CH-}$$

Such reactions resemble hydrohalogenations in that the hypohalous acid apparently functions as $HO^+ X^-$, and the direction of addition to an ethylenic bond is therefore subject to the same considerations as additions involving hydrogen halides. When treated with aqueous or alcoholic alkalies the halohydrin is converted to an epoxide, the hydrolysis of which yields a dihydroxy acid, thus:

$$\underset{\underset{\displaystyle OH \quad X}{|\qquad|}}{-CH{-}CH-} \xrightarrow{NaOH} \underset{\underset{\displaystyle O}{\diagdown\diagup}}{-CH{-}\!-CH-} \xrightarrow{H_2O} \underset{\underset{\displaystyle OH \quad OH}{|\qquad|}}{-CH{-}CH-}$$

The mechanism of the addition of hypophalous acids to, and their removal from, ethylenic bonds provides a somewhat controversial subject, and the stereochemical relationships which exist between these products have long been of interest.

In the initial work of Albitzkiĭ [115, 346] upon this subject it was reported that the chlorohydrin from oleic acid is an oil, and that from elaidic acid is a solid which melts at 44–45°. Treatment of these chlorohydrins with alkali and subsequent hydration of the epoxide yield a low-melting dihydroxystearic acid from oleic acid and a higher-melting dihydroxystearic acid from elaidic acid. The action of silver oxide on the oleic acid epoxide, however, yields the high-melting dihydroxy acid. Nicolet and Poulter [347] confirmed this previous work and obtained epoxides from both oleic and elaidic acids, each of which melted at 53.8° (mixed m.p. 45–47°). The acid hydrolysis of these epoxides was stated to yield chlorohydrins from which the original epoxides could be obtained by treatment with alkali. Differences in the physical properties, however, led to the assumption that the chlorohydrins obtained in this manner are the 9-hydroxy-10-chloro acids, whereas those resulting from the direct addition are the 10-hydroxy-9-chloro compounds. It has recently been observed [127] that the melting points of the epoxides obtained from the chlorohydrins prepared by the direct addition of hypochlorous acid to oleic and elaidic acids are practically the same, being 55–56° and 56–57°, respectively, although mixtures show a melting point depression of 8° to 10°. Hydrolysis of oleic epoxide yields a dihydroxystearic acid which melts at 95°, but hydrolysis of elaidic epoxide yields an isomeric acid melting at 132°. Erucic and brassidic acids when treated similarly [348, 349] also give a low- and a high-melting dihydroxybehenic acid. Hashi [350] has stated that the addition of hypochlorous acid to oleic acid, or of hydrogen chloride to its epoxide, yields a chlorohydrin melting at 38–38.3°, whereas the addition of hydrogen chloride to oxidoelaidic acid gives two chlorohydrins (m.p. 49.5–51.0° and 68–69.5°). The opinion has frequently been expressed [104, 351] that inversion occurs during the opening of an oxido ring. The recent work of King [128] in support of this viewpoint and the contrary opinion of Atherton and Hilditch [127] have been discussed previously.

The action of hypobromous acid on oleic and elaidic acids, followed by the removal of hydrogen bromide and subsequent hydration of the resulting product, has been reported [352] to yield low- and high-melting dihydroxystearic acids, respectively. The yield of bromohydrin from oleic acid is increased when the temperature is raised to 90°. Esafov [351] has studied the reaction of hypoiodous acid on oleic and elaidic acids and has advanced certain views relative to the isomeric changes which accompany the reaction. The reactions involved in the addition of aqueous hydrogen iodide to unsaturated acids have been investigated.[353, 354] It is of interest to note that the formation of hydroxy acids by the treatment of unsaturated acids with hypochlorous acid in the presence of alkalies is the subject of early patents.[355]

Nicolet and Poulter [347] have prepared several of the alkyl esters of oleic and elaidic acid epoxides and have also investigated the pyrolytic decomposition of oleic and elaidic acid chlorohydrins. This decomposition was reported to involve three main reactions, as follows: (1) hydroxy ester formation, (2) unsaturated hydroxy acid formation, and (3) rearrangement into ketostearic acids.

The addition of nitrosyl chloride and nitrosyl bromide to ethylenic acids to yield acids containing the group —CHX—CHNO— was originally investigated by Tilden and Forster [356] and has recently been studied [357] with the view of using this addition as a means of differentiating between unsaturated acids. The method, however, was considered to be unsatisfactory for this purpose.

DEHALOGENATION AND DEHYDROHALOGENATION

In the preceding discussion the addition and substitution of halogens and the addition of hydrogen halides have been considered in some detail. The removal of halogen from halo derivatives may be accomplished either by reduction, by removal as hydrogen halide, or by substitution, such as the replacement of the halogen by a hydroxyl or an amino group. Reductions and dehydrohalogenations yield unsaturated products, whereas substitution reactions can result in the preparation of a large number of fatty acid derivatives. It is quite apparent that, by the introduction of halogen and its subsequent substitution, many fatty acid derivatives can be prepared which would be quite difficult to synthesize by a direct procedure. Thus, halogenation may be considered as a means of attack upon the alkyl or alkylene chains, the products of which can serve as intermediates for the preparation of a wide variety of compounds. Certain comments regarding the reactions involved during halogen removal should be made before this subject is further considered. Although it is true that such reactions may be broadly considered as constituting reactions of reduction, dehydrohalogenation, or substitution, clear-cut demarkations between these various reactions actually do not exist. This is occasioned by the fact that substitution reactions are frequently accompanied by hydrogen halide removal, and the latter reaction generally involves or is attended by substitution. The type of product, therefore, which is obtained by dehydrohalogenation is frequently dependent upon the structure of the halo acid. Thus, when monohalo acids are subjected to the action of aqueous or alcoholic alkaline hydroxides, the reaction may essentially result in the formation of hydroxy acids or lactones, or hydrogen halide may be removed with the formation of unsaturated acids. These two reactions may proceed simultaneously, so that the reaction product is frequently a mixture of hydroxy acids and unsaturated acids. The position of the halogen atom with reference to the carboxyl group is quite important in determining which product will be obtained. With the α-halo acids substitution reactions predominate, whereas the β-halo acids generally yield unsaturated acids and the γ-halo acids yield lactones. When the halogen is remote from the carboxyl group, unsaturated acids generally form the major portion of the product. Irrespective of the position of the halogen atom, the product obtained either by dehydrohalogenation or by substitution is generally a mixture in which one product predominates. In the following discussion of halogen removal, the reader should, therefore, bear in mind that reactions of substitution and dehydrohalogenation can occur simultaneously and that low yields of a desired product often result because of this fact.

Nascent hydrogen reduces the monohalo acids to saturated acids; for example, monobromostearic acid is reduced to stearic acid by the action of zinc and water at high temperatures.[358] Fokin [359] has confirmed this reaction for the monobromo acids; however, when monochloro acids are similarly treated some ethylenic acids are formed together with the saturated acids. Monohalo ethylenic acids in which the halogen is attached to one of the double-bonded carbon atoms are reduced by zinc and acetic acid to ethylenic acids. For example, the reduction of either 9- or 10-iodo-9-octadecenoic acid with zinc and acetic acid yields 9-octadecenoic acid. When polyhalo acids or their derivatives are reduced, the resulting products are dependent not only upon the position of the halogens with reference to the carboxyl group but also upon their position in relation to each other. Products generally obtained from dihalo acids which contain the halogens upon adjacent carbon atoms are quite different from those in which the carbon atoms are separated by intervening methylene groups. Thus the reduction of 9,10-dibromostearic acid with zinc and acetic acid will yield oleic acid as the major product, whereas a similar treatment of 9,12-dibromostearic acid results in stearic acid. Rollet [293] observed that the reduction of the α-hexabromide obtained by the bromination of linolenic acid yields the original linolenic acid. This method has since been employed for the separation and purification of unsaturated acids, since the intermediate polybromides possess widely different solubilities in certain organic solvents.[285, 286, 295, 360, 361, 362, 363] A very pertinent observation with reference to this reduction is that the addition and removal of halogen by active hydrogen apparently leaves the double bond in its original position. The halogenation and dehalogenation of unsaturated acids may be accompanied by various stereochemical changes which have previously been discussed.

Alcoholic solutions of potassium hydroxide or of other alkali metal hydroxides remove hydrogen halide from both mono- and polyhalo acids with the attending formation of unsaturated acids. It was previously pointed out that the products resulting from the action of active hydrogen on the halo acids are determined by the relative positions of the halogens in the alkyl chain, and the same comment applies to dehydrohalogenations with alkalies. The simplest case of dehydrohalogenation involves the removal of hydrogen halide from a monohalo acid. α-Halo acids react with alcoholic potassium hydroxide to yield 2-ethylenic acids; thus, 2-bromostearic acid yields essentially 2-octadecenoic acid when treated with this reagent.[364] In a similar manner, the removal of hydrogen halide from ω-halo acids results primarily in the formation of ω-unsaturated acids. If the halogen is attached to an intermediate carbon atom, however, it is evident that the hydrogen may be obtained from either of the adjacent carbon atoms, so that two isomeric monoethylenic acids are theoretically possible. In generalizing upon the removal of halogen from monohalo compounds, Olivier [365] has stated that the elimination takes place so that the hydrogen atom attached to the carbon atom holding the more negative groups reacts preferentially. The addition and removal of a hydrogen halide has frequently been employed for the preparation of isomeric octadecenoic acids. It has been reported [337] that the addition of hydrogen chloride to oleic acid followed by its removal with nickel carbonate yields 10-octadecenoic acid, whereas 6-octadecenoic acid under similar conditions yields 7-octadecenoic acid, the double bond being shifted towards the methyl group in both cases. The removal of hydrogen iodide from 3-iodostearic acid forms 3-octadecenoic acid. [339]   Arnaud and Posternak [366] have reported that the addition of hydrogen iodide to oleic acid and its removal by alcoholic potassium hydroxide yield a mixture of acids containing oleic acid, *trans*-9- and -8-octadecenoic acids, and some hydroxystearic acid. The action of alcoholic potassium hydroxide on 12-bromostearic acid gives a mixture of 11- and 12-octadecenoic acids melting at 6–8° and 34–36°, respectively. [367]   The diiodostearic acid prepared from ricinoleic acid yields 9,11-octadecadienoic acid upon treatment with alkali, [340] thus illustrating the tendency to form conjugated systems under these conditions.

Hydrogen halide is removed from polyhalo acids by treatment with either alcoholic or strong aqueous alkaline solutions, with the formation of either polyethylenic acids or acetylenic acids depending upon the relative positions of the halogen atoms. When the halogens are on adjacent carbon atoms dehydrohalogenation with alkalies yields acetylenic acids. Overbeck [368] obtained stearolic acid from 9,10-dibromostearic acid by reaction with alcoholic potassium hydroxide, the reaction being confirmed many years later by Quensell. [369]   Behenolic acid is obtained from erucic acid dibromide by a similar procedure. [370, 371]   The preparation of 10-undecynoic acid by the removal of hydrogen bromide from 10,11-dibromoundecanoic acid has been studied by Krafft. [372]   The bromination of an ethylenic acid followed by dehydrobromination with alkalies to form an acetylenic acid is not accompanied by a shift in position of the unsaturated linkage. [373]   Ricinstearolic acid, which melts at 51°, has been prepared by the action of alkalies on the 9,10-dibromide of ricinoleic acid. [374, 375, 376]   The addition of hydrogen iodide to stearolic acid yields, among other products, two isomeric diiodostearic acids; namely, 9,9-diiodo- and 10,10-diiodostearic acids. [343]   The dehydroiodination of these acids by alcoholic alkali has been reported to yield 8-stearolic acid, m.p. 47.5°, and 10-stearolic acid, m.p. 47°. Treatment of the diiodo acids prepared from 6- and 8-stearolic acids by a similar procedure has been stated [377] to give 5- and 7-stearolic acids. The dehydrobromination of mono- and dibromohydrocarbons has been extensively studied by Bachman,[378] as has also the dehydrobromination of 2,3-dibromo- and 2,2,3-tribromoaliphatic acids. Inoue and Suzuki [379] have claimed that the action of alcoholic potassium hydroxide on 9,10-dibromostearic acids yields a mixture of acids in which stearolic acid is one of the components. The production of acetylenic acids by halogenation followed by dehydrohalogenation has been patented.[380, 381]

The removal of hydrogen halides from polyhalo acids in which the halogens are not upon adjacent carbon atoms yields polyethylenic acids. Thus, the dehydrohalogenation of 9,12-dibromostearic acid yields a mixture of isomeric dienoic acids. The halogenation of both saturated and unsaturated acids followed by removal of the halogen as hydrogen halide is often proposed as a method for the preparation of unsaturated acids. It has been claimed [382] that the dehydrobromination of the tetrabromide from linoleic acid gives a mixture of octadecatetraenoic acids.

It has previously been pointed out that the substitution of halogen by other groups is a quite common reaction for the preparation of fatty acid derivatives. Substitution reactions involving α-halo acids are frequently encountered, the halogen being easily replaceable by other groups. For example, the use of moist silver oxide for the preparation of α-hydroxy acids from α-halo acids is a well-known reaction,[383] the replacement of halogen being more difficult with the α-chloro than with the α-bromo or α-iodo acids. α-Hydroxy acids result from the action of aqueous potassium hydroxide on α-halo acids,[364, 384] and this reaction has been stated [385] to be adaptable to the preparation of other hydroxy acids. The substitution of hydroxyl for halogen probably proceeds with the initial formation of a lactone if the carbon atom to which the halogen is attached is removed by at least one methylene group from the carboxyl. The lactone is generally hydrolyzed under the reaction conditions to yield the hydroxy acid, although in some instances the lactone can be isolated. The lactone can frequently be isolated when ω-halo acids are subjected to this treatment.[386] Since such substitution reactions take place in a highly alkaline medium in which the reactants are quite soluble, the yield of hydroxy acids is often quite low owing to the tendency to remove hydrogen halide and form ethylenic acids. For example, low yields of hydroxy acids were obtained by Robinet [387] in his studies of the action of potassium hydroxide on the halogenated derivatives of palmitic acid. The action of alcoholic potassium hydroxide on

α-halo acids generally results in a mixture of α-unsaturated acids and α-hydroxy acids, whereas aqueous alkaline hydroxides favor the formation of α-hydroxy acids. Thus, the 2-hydroxystearic acid which was prepared by Hell and Sadomsky [265] by the action of alcoholic potassium hydroxide on 2-bromostearic acid was probably contaminated with 2-octadecenoic acid. Le Sueur [388] has prepared a number of α-hydroxy acids from α-bromo acids by the action of aqueous potassium hydroxide, the melting points of the α-bromo acids used and of the α-hydroxy acids obtained being as follows: tridecanoic, 30.5°, 78°; myristic, 41.5–42.5°, 81.5–82°; pentadecanoic, 42.5°, 84.5°; palmitic, 51.5–52°, 86.5–87°; margaric, 52.5°, 89°; and stearic, 60–61°, 91–92°. 2-Bromolauric acid, m.p. 30–31.5°,[389] yields 2-hydroxylauric acid melting at 73–74° when similarly treated.[390] Several of the higher molecular weight α-hydroxy acids have been prepared by this procedure, an example being 2-hydroxylignoceric acid obtained from 2-iodolignoceric acid.[391] Marie [384] has obtained 2-hydroxycerotic acid by the action of lead acetate on 2-bromocerotic acid followed by saponification of the resulting 2-acetylcerotic acid. 2-Bromosuberic acid and 2-bromosebacic acid yield the corresponding 2-hydroxy acids when boiled with alkali hydroxide solutions.[392] Dihydroxy acids have been prepared by the action of moist silver oxide on α,α'-dihalo dicarboxylic acids; thus, 2,9-dibromosebacic acid yields 2,9-dihydroxysebacic acid, m.p. 125–127°.[393, 394] The substitution of hydroxyl for halogen has frequently been suggested as a means of preparing hydroxy acids other than α-hydroxy acids, and the synthesis of polyhydroxy acids by the action of alkalies on polyhalo acids has been proposed.[395] In view of the foregoing considerations it is believed that such products must contain large amounts of unsaturated acids.

The removal of halogen from α-halo acids by the use of metallic silver yields *sym*-dialkylsuccinic acids, the reaction proceeding as follows:

$$\begin{array}{ccc} CO_2H & & CO_2H \\ | & & | \\ HC-X & 2Ag & X-CH \\ | & & | \\ R & & R \end{array}$$

Jones [396] obtained two isomeric ditetradecylsuccinic acids by the action of silver upon 2-bromo- and 2-iodopalmitic acids, one of which, m.p. 135–136°, was considered to be the *meso* form and the other, m.p. 95–96°, the racemic modification. The treatment of alkyl chlorides with silver salts of the higher fatty acids yields fatty acid esters of alcohols corresponding to the alkyl halides, thus:

$$RX \quad Ag OOCR'$$

Dodecyl stearate has been prepared [397] from dodecyl bromide and silver stearate by this method. The pyrolysis of the dodecyl stearate gives 1-dodecene and stearic acid, thus forming an ethylene corresponding to the alkyl halide. Asinger [398] concluded from his study of this reaction that if two methylene groups are adjacent to the carbon atom carrying the halogen, two isomeric olefins are obtained in equivalent amounts; however, if the carbon atom is adjacent to a methyl and a methylene group, the greater reactivity of the methylenic hydrogen leads to the predominant formation of one isomer over the other.

The reaction of α-halo acids with alcoholic solutions of ammonia or amines results in the formation of the corresponding amino acids. Hell and coworkers [265, 399] have prepared several α-amino acids by this procedure, examples being 2-aminostearic acid, m.p. 221–222°, 2-aminopalmitic acid, and 2-aminomyristic acid, m.p. 253°. The preparation of 2-aminocaproic acid [400] and 2-aminocerotic acid [384] has also been described. High yields of 2-aminocaproic acid have been obtained from 2-bromocaproic acid.[401] This reaction, however, has not been entirely satisfactory for the preparation of higher amino fatty acids other than the α-amino acids. The reaction of α-halo acids with amines such as dimethylamine has been patented,[402] and it has been claimed [403] that wetting agents are obtained by the action of ammonia on polychlorinated fatty acids such as hexachlorostearic acid. The α-halo acids react with aniline to yield the corresponding α-anilino acids, 2-anilinomyristic, -palmitic, and -stearic acids having been prepared in this manner.[265, 399] The action of monopotassium anilide on diiodoricinoleic acid and 9,10-diiodostearic acid has been investigated,[404] and it was observed that one mole of the anilide replaced both the iodine atoms with the formation of an anilido derivative containing

the group $\begin{array}{c} -CH-CH- \\ \diagdown \diagup \\ NC_6H_5 \end{array}$. The action of ethylolamines with α-halo acids has recently been studied.[275, 405]

The halo acids react with phenol in the presence of potassium chloride,[404] the primary reaction product being a phenoxy derivative, as follows:

$$CH_3(CH_2)_7CHBrCHBr(CH_2)_7CO_2K + 2C_6H_5OK \rightarrow$$

$$CH_3(CH_2)_7CH(C_6H_5O)CH(C_6H_5O)(CH_2)_7CO_2K + 2KBr$$

Subsequent reactions led to the formation of several condensation and degradation products, one of which is

$$C_6H_5OCH(CH_2)_7CO_2K$$
$$\overset{|}{C_6H_5OCH(CH_2)_7CO_2K}$$

The replacement of halogen by a cyano group may be accomplished by the action of alkali cyanides on the halo acids. Thus, 2-bromopalmitic acid yields 2-cyanopalmitic acid when treated with potassium cyanide. The hydrolysis of 2-cyanopalmitic acid yields tetradecylmalonic acid.[264] Tetracarboxylic acids can be prepared from the α,α'-dihalo dicarboxylic acids by conversion to the corresponding dicyano derivatives followed by hydrolysis. Diethyl malonate is reactive with the halo acids; for example, 2-methylundecanedioic acid has been prepared from 9-bromopelargonic acid by the use of diethyl methylmalonate.[406]

Various sulfur derivatives of the higher fatty acids have been prepared from the halo acids; for example, 2-bromostearic acid and sodium hydrosulfide in alcohol yield 2-mercaptostearic acid. Oxidation of these mercapto acids yields the corresponding sulfonic acids, and the removal of hydrogen sulfide from two molecules of the mercapto acids gives sulfodicarboxylic acids. The action of water-soluble sulfites on the halo acids has been claimed [407] to yield high molecular weight sulfo derivatives.

ADDITIONS INVOLVING SULFUR COMPOUNDS

The action of sulfur, sulfuric acid, chlorosulfonic acid, sulfur monochloride, and other sulfur-containing compounds with the fatty acids and their derivatives has been the subject of many investigations. The action of concentrated sulfuric acid on the ethylenic acids or the hydroxy acids is one of the most important and generally used reactions involving sulfur compounds and the fatty acids. In the former case there are obtained sulfuric addition compounds which can be easily hydrolyzed to yield saturated hydroxy acids, and this reaction is frequently employed for the preparation of such acids. The unsaturated hydroxy acids, such as ricinoleic acid, yield both esterification and addition products upon treatment with sulfuric acid. The reaction of sulfuric acid with castor oil yields "Turkey-red oil," a substance which is widely employed as an emulsifying agent.

The saturated acids, such as palmitic acid, dissolve in concentrated sulfuric acid without change, the original acid being obtained upon diluting the solution with water. The formation of addition products between the saturated acids and sulfuric acid, however, has been postulated.[408, 409]

The ethylenic bonds of unsaturated acids readily add sulfuric acid with the formation of the corresponding hydrogen sulfates. In such reactions the acid may be assumed to add as $\overset{+}{H}\ \overset{-}{HSO_4}$, the direction of addition being subject to Markownikoff's rule and various other considerations previously discussed. Hydrolysis of the resulting sulfuric addition products results in the formation of hydroxy acids and lactones together with secondary products. Sulfuric additions are best accomplished at low temperatures (0–15°), the reaction mixture then being diluted by the addition of ice and the product purified by conversion to the sodium or potassium salt. The sulfuric esters are then obtained by the acidification of these salts. Hydrolysis to hydroxy acids is accomplished by boiling with water or with alkaline solutions.

In one of the earlier studies concerning the action of sulfuric acid on oleic acid, Geitel [410] obtained an addition product the hydrolysis of which yielded a hydroxystearic acid, together with a lactone which gave a hydroxystearic acid upon treatment with alkaline hydroxides followed by acidification. Since he considered oleic acid to be 2-octadecenoic acid, however, his conclusions with reference to the resulting products were erroneous. The formation of both hydroxystearic acid and its lactone by this treatment was also observed by Sabainev,[411] and more recent studies [412] have been made upon the formation of stearolactone from the addition product of oleic and sulfuric acids. In reactions involving the addition of sulfuric acid to ethylenic acids followed by hydrolysis of the product with the ultimate formation of saturated hydroxy acids, it has rather generally been assumed that the hydroxyl group attaches itself to that carbon atom of the double bond which is farther removed from the carboxyl group. For example, Tschernovorowa [413] considered the hydroxystearic acid formed from 6-octadecenoic acid (petroselinic acid) to be 7-hydroxystearic acid. However, Grün and Janko [414] considered the acid obtained from erucic acid to be either 13- or 14-hydroxybehenic acid, and more recently it has been shown [415] that the dehydration of the hydroxystearic acid, m.p. 76°, obtained by the hydrolysis of the sulfuric addition product of oleic acid yields 8-, 9-, and 10-octadecenoic acids, thus indicating that both 9- and 10-hydroxystearic acids are present.

Chlorosulfonic acid can function either as an acid chloride or as an acid. In the former case its reaction with an ethylenic bond results in the addition of a chlorine atom and a sulfonic acid group to adjacent carbon atoms, whereas in the latter case a chlorosulfate is formed. Hydrolysis of the chlorosulfonic acid yields a hydroxysulfonic acid, and hydrolysis of the chlorosulfate yields a hydroxy compound. The latter type of reaction is apparently the one more commonly encountered with the ethylenic acids, although the action of chlorosulfonic acid on unsaturated acids presents a somewhat controversial subject. Bauer and Stockhausen [416] have stated that, when 10-undecenoic acid is treated with chlorosulfonic acid and the product is hydrolyzed, there is obtained a mixture of 10-hydroxy-11-sulfo- and 11-hydroxy-10-sulfoundecanoic acids, which melt at 208–209° and 186–187°, respectively. In a subsequent investigation of the action of chlorosulfonic acid on oleic acid, Pomeranz [417] denies the formation of chlorosulfonic derivatives with the unsaturated acids, claiming that the addition of chlorosulfonic acid proceeds in a manner similar to that of concentrated sulfuric acid.

The saturated hydroxy acids yield sulfuric esters when treated with either sulfuric acid or chlorosulfonic acid; 10-hydroxystearic acid [418] and 12-hydroxystearic acid,[419] for example, yielding the respective sulfates when treated with chlorosulfonic acid. Ether is usually employed as the solvent in this reaction.

There are several chemical reactions of the fats whose products, because of their wide utility and use over a period of years, merit special consideration. The action of sulfuric acid on castor oil, which yields the so-called Turkey-red oils widely used in dyeing and emulsification, is an example of such a reaction. Although the original Turkey-red oils were prepared from oleic acid,[420] these have largely been superseded by those obtained from castor oil. Because of this fact the action of sulfur acids on ricinoleic acid assumes a somewhat unusual significance. Concentrated sulfuric acid reacts energetically with ricinoleic acid, the primary reaction being a sulfation of the hydroxyl group.[419, 421] Simultaneous or subsequent reactions involve not only the sulfation of the ethylenic bond but also the formation of lactones and lactides, and possibly dehydrations and various esterifications, these last yielding poly-ricinoleic acids. The final reaction product is consequently complex and its composition is quite dependent upon the conditions employed for its preparation. In 1894, Juillard [422] claimed the isolation of the following substances from the product of the action of sulfuric acid on ricinoleic acid: the sulfuric ester, $HOSO_2OC_{17}H_{32}CO_2H$; the hydroxysulfuric ester, $(HOSO_2O)(OH)C_{17}H_{33}CO_2H$; a dibasic acid, $O(C_{17}H_{32}CO_2H)_2$; a diricinoleic acid, $HOC_{17}H_{32}CO_2C_{17}H_{32}CO_2H$; a dihydroxystearic acid; isoricinoleic acid, $C_{18}H_{34}O_3$; and an acid having the formula $C_{36}H_{70}O_7$. Woldenberg [423] observed that the free ricinoleic acid decreases gradually when treated with an equal amount of sulfuric acid. Chonowsky [424] has postulated that the main product of the reaction comprises two isomeric glycidic acids, the formulas of which were considered to be

$$CH_3(CH_2)_5\underset{\underset{O}{|\_\_\_\_|}}{CHCH_2CHCH_2}(CH_2)_7CO_2H \quad \text{and}$$

$$CH_3(CH_2)_5\underset{\underset{O}{|\_\_\_\_|}}{CHCH_2CH_2CH}(CH_2)_7CO_2H$$

It was assumed that the primary products from which these acids are derived are the corresponding sulfates containing the groups

Although such acids are probably formed, Grün [425] has stated that many other substances are also present in the reaction mixture. The products which have been reported to be formed by the action of concentrated sulfuric acid on ricinoleic acid have been compiled by Rassow,[426] the list including saturated and unsaturated lactones and lactides, glycidic acids, polyricinoleic acids, and other products. Grün [427] has reported that concentrated sulfuric acid and ricinoleic acid yield a mixture of sulfuric esters, the hydrolysis of which yields 12.6% ricinoleic acid, 6.4% of a dihydroxystearic acid melting at 67–69°, and 81% of a dihydroxystearic acid ester, $C_{17}H_{33}(OH)_2CO_2C_{17}H_{33}(OH)CO_2H$. Alcoholic potassium hydroxide converts the latter compound into the above-mentioned dihydroxy acid. Fractional crystallization of the dihydroxy acids gave dl-9,12-dihydroxystearic acid, m.p. 69.5°; d-9,12-dihydroxystearic acid, m.p. 90°; a dihydroxystearic acid, m.p. 108°; and an acid which melted at 120°. The acid which melted at 69.5° is probably a racemic mixture. Ricinoleic acid is dehydrated to a mixture of octadecenoic acids when heated in the presence of small amounts of sulfuric acid.[428, 429, 430, 431] Etherification is the predominant reaction when ricinoleic acid is treated with formaldehyde and sulfuric acid [432]

Ricinoleic acid when treated with chlorosulfonic acid first yields a sulfuric ester with the liberation of hydrogen chloride. Hydrolysis of this product gives substantial quantities of the ricinoleic ester of ricinoleic acid,[433] the further heating of which yields the lactide

$$
\begin{array}{ccc}
 & \text{O}\cdot\text{CO} & \\
 & \diagup \qquad \diagdown & \\
\text{C}_{17}\text{H}_{32} & & \text{C}_{17}\text{H}_{32} \\
 & \diagdown \qquad \diagup & \\
 & \text{CO}\cdot\text{O} &
\end{array}
$$

It has been suggested by Pomeranz [434] that chlorosulfonic acid functions towards ricinoleic acid as a sulfonating agent and that hydrolysis of the reaction product yields a hydroxy sulfonic acid containing the group $(\text{HO})\overset{|}{\text{C}}\text{H}\overset{|}{\text{C}}\text{H}(\text{SO}_3\text{H})$.

When acetylenic acids are treated with concentrated sulfuric acid and the product is hydrolyzed, saturated keto acids are obtained. The reaction can be represented as a sulfonation of the triple bond to form the ethylenic sulfate, the hydrolysis of which yields the ethylenic hydroxy acid which rearranges to the saturated keto acid, as follows:

$$-\text{C}:\text{C}-\xrightarrow{\text{H}_2\text{SO}_4} -\text{C}(\text{OSO}_3\text{H}):\text{CH}-\xrightarrow{\text{H}_2\text{O}} -\text{COH}:\text{CH}- \rightarrow -\text{COCH}_2-$$

It is generally assumed that the keto group involves the carbon atom of the original ethylenic bond which is remote from the carboxyl. Baruch [373] obtained 10-ketostearic and 14-ketobehenic acids from stearolic and behenolic acids, respectively, by this procedure. Treatment of the resulting keto acids with hydroxylamine hydrochloride yields two stereoisomeric oximes in each case, the products of hydrolysis of which are employed for the determination of the original position of the unsaturated linkage.

A very voluminous patent literature has been built around the sulfonation and sulfation of hydroxy and ethylenic fats and fatty acids or their derivatives. Many of the advances in the science and technology of sulfonation and sulfation have been recorded in this literature, and its importance demands at least a brief consideration. These patents pertain not only to the agents employed for sulfonation and to the conditions of their use, such as solvent, temperature, and pressure, but also to the various means of purifying the reaction products obtained. The action of sulfonating agents, such as sulfur trioxide, on hydroxy acids and unsaturated acids in the presence of pyridine and other organic bases has been disclosed,[435, 436, 437] and it has been claimed that the presence of organic bases minimizes side reactions. Sulfonation can be accomplished by the use of organic derivatives of sulfuric acid such as $BuHSO_4$ or Me_2SO_4 in the presence of various condensing agents such as $POCl_3$ or $AlCl_3$.[438] A large number of anhydrous organic solvents have been proposed as modifying agents for the sulfonation process. This list includes low molecular weight acids, their anhydrides or chlorides,[439, 440, 441, 442] halogenated unsaturated hydrocarbons such as trichloroethylene,[443] mineral oils and ketones,[444] and inert diluents.[445] The use of liquid sulfur dioxide;[446] of chlorides such as silicon chlorides, $COCl_2$, $SOCl_2$, SO_2Cl_2, and BCl_3;[447] and of phosphorus compounds such as PCl_3 and H_3PO_3[448] has also been disclosed. Sulfonation has been effected by agents such as SO_3 or fuming sulfuric acid at elevated temperatures (100°) in the presence of diluents such as nitrobenzene or carbon tetrachloride and of catalysts such as P_2O_5.[449] Hydroxy acids have been sulfonated by treatment with gaseous sulfur trioxide in the presence of inert chlorinated solvents,[450] and sulfonation of fatty substances with a fine mist of fuming sulfuric acid has been accomplished.[451] Randel[452] has proposed a process whereby fatty substances are sulfonated under reduced pressure, a volatile hydrocarbon solvent being added to exert a cooling effect. Frequently, sulfonation and condensation reactions are conducted simultaneously, an example being the preparation of the so-called Twitchell reagents,[453] obtained by sulfonating mixtures of unsaturated acids and aromatic hydrocarbons. Similar products are obtained by the sulfonation of the condensation products of oleic acid or its glycerides and benzyl chloride,[454] or of the condensation product of hydroxy fatty acids and sulfonated fatty acids.[455] The sulfonation of polymerized hydroxy acids,[456] of chlorinated fatty acids,[457] and of halogenated hydroxy acids such as hydroxydiiodostearic acid[458] has been described. Sulfonic acids can be prepared by treating α-halo acids with alkyl sulfites,[459] or by simultaneously causing these acids or their derivatives to react with a sulfite and an oxidizing agent.[460] The preparation of esters of sulfonated fatty acids has been disclosed.[461]

The various methods which have been proposed for purifying sulfonated fatty materials include their solution in an organic solvent followed by precipitation as inorganic salts,[462] washing with water and centrifugation,[463] neutralization with inorganic bases or alkaline salts,[464] purification through their calcium salts,[465] separation by means of aqueous alcohol,[466] and salting out.[467]

The unsaturated fatty acids react vigorously with sulfur monochloride, the reaction product containing both sulfur and chlorine and evidently being formed by a simple addition to the unsaturated linkage.[468] In a study of this reaction, Harvey and Schuette [469] have observed that both addition and substitution reactions occur simultaneously.

The saturated acids are resistant to the action of sulfur even at moderately elevated temperatures (130°).[470] Unsaturated acids, on the other hand, are quite reactive towards sulfur at these temperatures, the sulfur adding to the unsaturated bonds without a marked evolution of hydrogen sulfide. The sulfurized acids are stable at ordinary and slightly elevated temperatures, although hydrogen sulfide is eliminated at higher temperatures (150–200°). Mixtures of the sulfur or sulfur monochloride addition products of the unsaturated fats with mineral oils have been extensively used in high-pressure lubricating compositions.

The polyhalogenated acids are reactive towards solutions of alkali metal sulfides or polysulfides, the halogens being replaced by mercapto and hydroxyl groups and the reaction being attended by an increase in unsaturation.[471] The oxidation of these products has been claimed to yield disulfides and finally sulfonic acids.[472] The preparation of substances useful as protective colloids, by the action of aqueous alkaline sulfate solutions on halogenated fatty acids, has been described.[407]

Thiocyanic acid adds directly to the double bonds of ethylenic acids to form thiocyanate derivatives. The fact that only one double bond in linoleic acid and two in linolenic acid are reactive with this reagent [473] has been made the basis of an analytical procedure which has been discussed previously. It has recently been observed [474] that this generalization regarding the reactivity of unsaturated acids towards cyanogen is not strictly correct. Kaufmann [475] has succeeded in isolating the thiocyanogen derivatives of several ethylenic acids, and has reported that the 9,10-dithiocyanostearic acid from elaidic acid is a solid, whereas those obtained from oleic and erucic acids are liquids. These acids can be converted into mercaptans, disulfides, and sulfonates by various reactions. The preparation of the thiocyanogen derivatives of oleic, linoleic, and linolenic acids has been described,[476] as has also that of the cyano derivatives of hydnocarpic and chaulmoogric acids.[477] Toyama and Tsuchiya [478] have stated that the thiocyanate derivative of linoleic acid has the formula $CH_3(CH_2)_4$-$CH:CHCH_2CH(SCN)CH(SCN)(CH_2)_7CO_2H$, and the tetrathiocyanate of linolenic acid the formula $CH_3CH_2CH:CHCH_2$-$CH(SCN)CH(SCN)CH_2CH(SCN)CH(SCN)(CH_2)_7CO_2H$. The halogenation of these thiocyanates has been studied.[479]

OTHER ADDITIONS AND SUBSTITUTIONS

Many of the addition and replacement reactions which involve the unsaturated acids or the substituted acids have only been superficially studied and merit more attention. Acetylenic fatty acids are reactive with arsenic trichloride, forming addition products which probably contain the group $—C(AsCl_2):CCl—$. This reaction was first studied by Fischer,[480] who refluxed behenolic acid with $AsCl_3$ for six hours at 140°, the addition product being a thick, dark-colored liquid. The hydrolysis of this liquid yields a chloroarsenobehenolic acid to which he ascribed the formula $C_{22}H_{40}O_3AsCl$ and which was considered to contain the group $—C(AsO):CCl—$. Phosphorus trichloride adds to acetylenic acids in a similar manner. The preparation of addition products of acetylenic acids and the trihalides of arsenic and phosphorus has been patented by Heinemann,[481] who also studied the preparation of a number of derivatives of these products. The compounds were originally synthesized to study their value as therapeutic agents. The arsenic derivatives of chaulmoogric acid, such as 4-chaulmoogrylaminobenzenearsonic acid, however, have been found to be unsatisfactory for this purpose.[482] Organic phosphorus compounds, prepared by treating unsaturated fats with phosphorus pentoxide or acetylphosphoric acid, have been claimed [483] to be useful in the textile industry. High molecular weight phosphorus compounds have been prepared by the action of phosphorus acids on saturated keto acids obtained by the hydration of acetylenic acids. The reaction products of both phosphorous and phosphoric acids on the keto acids have been described,[484] and the esterification of the resulting hydroxyphosphoric acids has been studied.[485] It has been found that purer products can be obtained by the use of phosphorus trichloride followed by hydrolysis rather than by the direct action of phosphorous acid.[486] Backer and Mulder [487] have studied the preparation of α-arseno carboxylic acids by the treatment of potassium arsenate with the potassium salts of α-bromo acids, the reaction proceeding as follows:

$$RCHBrCO_2K + K_3AsO_3 \rightarrow RCH(AsO_3K_2)CO_2K + KBr$$

Hydrolysis yields the corresponding α-arseno acids, the melting points of which were reported to be as follows: propionic, 134°; butyric, 127°; valeric, 116–117°; caproic, 96°; enanthic, 82–83°; caprylic, 69°; and pelargonic, 115°.

Ethylenic acids, when heated with phosphorus and water in the presence of oxygen, form addition products the structure of which has not been conclusively determined. The following reaction has been postulated: [488]

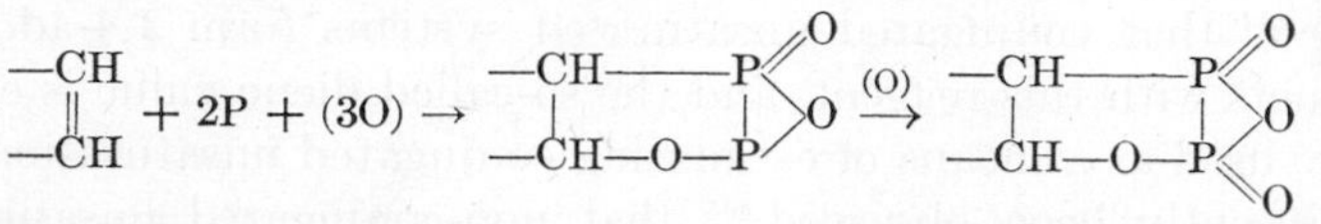

The ethylenic bonds of unsaturated acids are reactive with certain mercuric salts, such as mercuric acetate, with the formation of addition compounds in which the mercury atom is directly attached to a carbon atom. Leys [489] has reported that the action of mercuric acetate on olein in acetic acid solution does not yield products of definite composition. The preparation of a number of mercuric salt addition products has recently been studied.[490] For example, methyl 9-acetoxymercuri-10-methoxystearate results from the following reaction:

$$CH_3O_2C(CH_2)_7CH{=}CH(CH_2)_7CH_3 + Hg(OCOCH_3)_2 + CH_3OH \rightarrow$$

$$CH_3O_2C(CH_2)_7CH(HgOCOCH_3)CH(OCH_3)(CH_2)_7CH_3 + HO_2CCH_3$$

Compounds such as ethyl 9-acetoxymercuri-10-ethoxystearate, methyl 9-chloromercuri-10-methoxystearate, and ethyl 9-chloromercuri-10-ethoxystearate can be similarly prepared. These compounds are viscous oils. The ethylenic bonds contained in fatty derivatives such as unsaturated ketones, alcohols, and amines react in a similar manner.[491]

Mercuric acetate forms addition products with acetylenic acids, the hydrolysis of which yields saturated keto acids. The reaction product of methyl 2-nonynoate and mercuric acetate has been shown [492] to have the structure $CH_3(CH_2)_5C(OHgOAc){:}C(HgOAc){-}$

CO_2CH_3, and it has been stated that its hydrolysis with concentrated hydrochloric acid yields 3-ketononanoic acid. The mercuric derivative of stearolic acid yields, with chlorine or bromine in chloroform, chloro- or bromoketostearic acid, respectively, the reduction of which gives 10-ketostearic acid. The mercuric derivative of behenolic acid reacts similarly. Sherrill and Smith [493] have reported that the hydration of 9-undecynoic acid by means of sulfuric acid yields 59% of 9-keto- and 41% of 10-ketoundecanoic acids, whereas hydrolysis of the mercuric addition product yields 46% of 9-keto- and 54% of 10-ketoundecanoic acids. These authors have suggested that an electrostatic rearrangement is induced by the presence of the mercuric salt.

The addition of maleic anhydride to conjugated, unsaturated acids and their derivatives has been discussed previously (Chapter II). The reaction is based upon the original findings of Diels and Alder [494] that conjugated unsaturated systems form 1,4-addition products with this reagent, and the so-called diene value is extensively used as a means of estimating conjugated unsaturation. It has recently been observed [495] that non-conjugated unsaturated acids react with maleic anhydride at an elevated temperature (200°), methyl oleate reacting with one mole, methyl linoleate with two, and methyl linolenate with two and one-half moles of this reagent. Methyl stearate is unreactive under these conditions.

The treatment of high molecular weight unsaturated acids with formaldehyde or other aldehydes or ketones in the presence of acid condensing agents has been claimed to yield addition products.[496]

The preparation of silicyl derivatives of the hydroxy acids has been studied by Kaufmann.[497] Such compounds are obtained by the action of hydroxy carboxylic acids with the alkyl esters of silicic acid, or with silicon halides in the presence of organic bases such as pyridine. It has been stated that these silicyl derivatives are resistant to the action of water and of mild alkalies.

The acylation of hydroxy acids may be accomplished by the use of organic acids, their anhydrides, or chlorides. The use of a small quantity of chlorosulfonic acid has been suggested as a catalyst.[498] Benzene and other aromatic hydrocarbons add to the ethylenic bonds of unsaturated acids in the presence of an excess of sulfuric acid to yield aromatic sulfonic acid derivatives.[499] Aromatic hydrocarbons also add to unsaturated acids in the presence of Friedel-Crafts catalysts to give the corresponding aryl substituted acids. Nicolet and de Milt [500] have prepared phenylstearic acid by the action of oleic acid and benzene in the presence of aluminum chloride and have stated that the tolyl and naphthyl derivatives can be similarly obtained. Phenylstearic acid was observed to be resistant to oxidation by hot alkaline potassium permanganate. Nitration yields a dinitro derivative. Later, de Milt [501] characterized the reaction product of oleic acid and benzene as 10-phenylstearic acid, a viscous, pale yellow liquid. Schmidt [502] has observed that the phenylation of oleic acid proceeds rapidly in the presence of an equimolar quantity of aluminum chloride and an excess of benzene; however, prolonged heating leads to secondary reactions, one of which is probably ketone formation. Xylylstearic acid was prepared by a similar reaction. The triglyceride of phenylstearic acid has been reported to be a viscous, reddish yellow liquid, d_4^{21} 0.9746.[503] Phenylstearic acid has been characterized by the preparation of phenylstearyl-p-aminoazobenzene,[504] m.p. 82–82.5°; several other derivatives have subsequently been prepared for purposes of its identification.[505] The preparations of p-xylylstearic acid, ethyl tolylstearate, methyl phenoxyphenylstearate, and the p-methyl, p-chloro, p-bromo, p-methoxy, and p-phenoxy derivatives of phenylstearic acid have been described.[506] The introduction of alkylaryl groups into oleic or undecenoic acid, followed by sulfonation and neutralization of the resulting products, has been reported to give compounds which function as wetting agents.[507] Harmon and Marvel [508] have prepared a number of phenyl-substituted fatty acids by the reaction of phenyl-substituted alkyl chlorides with malonic anhydride, followed by hydrolysis and decarboxylation of the resulting esters. 10-Phenyloctadecanoic acid was observed to melt at 40–41.5°, and a comparison of this product with the phenylstearic acid obtained from oleic acid indicated the latter to be an equimolar mixture of 9- and 10-phenylstearic acids. Oleic acid yields 10-m-cresoxy-stearic acid when treated with m-cresol in the presence of H_2SO_4—AcOH; a subsequent rearrangement of the product yields 10-(2-hydroxy-4-methylphenyl)stearic acid, which melts at 37°.[509] The acylation of fats has been extensively studied by Kimura and Tsurugi.[510] The preparation of aralkylated fatty derivatives, by the action of oleic acid with benzyl chloride or other aralkyl halides in the presence of Friedel-Crafts catalysts, has been described.[511]

Alkylation of fatty acids may be accomplished by treating halo derivatives of the acids with the appropriate Grignard reagents.

For example, Morgan and Holmes [512] have obtained 2-methyl-stearic acid, m.p. 58°, by the action of MeMgI on 2-bromostearic acid. 2-Methylpalmitic acid, m.p. 54°, 2-methylpentadecanoic acid, m.p. 48°, and 2-methylmargaric acid, m.p. 51–51.5°, were prepared in a similar manner. Direct methylation is not generally employed for the preparation of branched-chain acids for obvious reasons; however, a number of processes have been employed for the synthesis of such acids.[406, 513, 514, 515, 516, 517] An example is that proposed by Cason,[516] who prepared 17-methyloctadecanoic acid by reduction of the keto acid obtained by the condensation of diisononylcadmium and 9-carbethoxynonanoyl chloride.

POLYMERIZATION

Partial polymerization of drying oils for the preparation of the so-called boiled oils has been known to the paint and varnish industry for many years. The effect of heat upon the drying and semi-drying oils and upon mixtures of such oils has, therefore, been the subject of a large amount of scientific study, which has resulted in many contributions to this field. In view of the complexity of this subject its detailed discussion would be out of place in this present writing. It is a significant fact, however, that the polymerization of the unsaturated acids and that of their glycerides are closely allied phenomena, inasmuch as the latter undoubtedly involves the former. It is also true that the many comparatively recent studies upon the polymerization of the unsaturated acids have, at least, afforded a partial explanation of the effect of heat upon the glycerides.

Polymerization reactions may be considered as addition reactions, and it is interesting to note that many of the principles which were discussed in connection with the various addition reactions apply with equal force to polymerization reactions. It is quite apparent that a close parallelism should exist between the mechanism of the polymerization of unsaturated hydrocarbons and that of unsaturated fatty acids. Few fields have received, in such a comparatively short period of time, the concentrated attention accorded that of hydrocarbon polymerization, and much of the information which has been obtained has a direct bearing upon the polymerization phenomena encountered with the unsaturated fatty acids.

Many of the earlier investigations upon the polymerization of fatty substances were concerned with thermal treatment of the glycerides rather than of their respective acids. However, in 1926 Bauer [518] studied the polymerization of α- and β-eleostearic acids by heating these acids in an atmosphere of carbon dioxide at 200°, and observed that the products possess materially lower iodine numbers than the starting acids. Hydrogenation of the polymerized product results in stearic acid, which shows that the carbon-to-carbon bonds formed during the polymerization are ruptured by hydrogen in the presence of catalysts. The studies of Kino [519] upon the polymerization of methyl linoleate and methyl linolenate led to the conclusion that rings containing four carbon atoms are formed. An investigation of the products of ozonization of polymerized methyl linoleate indicates that the polymerized ester possesses the following structure:

$$CH_3(CH_2)_4CHCHCH_2CH:CH(CH_2)_7CO_2CH_3$$
$$CH_3(CH_2)_4CHCHCH_2CH:CH(CH_2)_7CO_2CH_3$$

According to Kino,[520] methyl stearolate polymerizes to yield a dimer which probably contains double bonds. The methyl esters of highly unsaturated acids, such as methyl clupanodonate, were considered [521] to yield polymers which contain 4-carbon rings, increased unsaturation being conducive to more rapid polymerization. Polymers higher than dimers predominate if the original ester contains more than three ethylenic bonds. Recent work upon this subject has shown that polymerization reactions are much more complex than originally supposed.

It is well known that polymerizations proceed quite rapidly when conjugated unsaturated systems are involved. The important observation of Scheiber [522] that the rise in the refractive index of linseed oil during thermal treatment may be partially ascribed to a rearrangement into a conjugated system forms the basis of our present theories of the polymerization of unsaturated acids. Kappelmeier [523] has agreed that the Diels-Alder diene synthesis is one of the principal reactions which occur during the polymerization of both conjugated and unconjugated acids, and that the latter are transformed into the former prior to polymerization. In the same year, a conjugated acid containing two double bonds was isolated as an intermediate product in the thermal polymerization of linseed oil.[524] Kino,[525] however, has contended that the polymerization of methyl linolenate takes place without a shift in the positions of the double bonds and that the formation of a conjugated system is not always necessary for intramolecular polymerization. The work of Bradley and coworkers [526] has served to answer many of the questions pertaining to the polymerization of the unsaturated acids. Ultraviolet absorption studies indicate a progressive loss of conjugation during the polymerizations of tung oil and of methyl eleostearate. The formation and subsequent loss of conjugated unsaturation during the polymerization of unconjugated fatty acids and their esters support the isomerization theory. Molecular distillation shows the product of the thermal treatment of methyl linoleate to consist predominantly of a dimer with no indication that polymerization proceeds beyond the trimeric stage. It was suggested that such polymerizations are analogous to the 1,2-1,4-additions established for butadiene, the following parallelism being pointed out:

THERMAL POLYMERIZATION OF BUTADIENE

THERMAL POLYMERIZATION OF METHYL 9,11-OCTADECADIENOATE

The studies of Brod, France, and Evans [527] upon the polymerization of mixtures of ethyl 9,11- and 9,12-linoleates support the contention that substituted cyclohexenes resulting from a modified Diels-Alder reaction are formed during the polymerization of polyethenoic acids, and that their formation involves an isomerization of unconjugated to conjugated systems. Bradley suggests a bicyclic structure for the dimers derived from octadecatrienoates and a monocyclic structure for those resulting from octadecadienoates. Thus methyl octadecatrienoates polymerize by bimolecular addition followed by ring closure, yielding compounds having structures similar to the following:

$$
\begin{array}{c}
\text{O} \\
\| \\
\text{H} \quad (CH_2)_7COCH_3 \\
/ \\
C \\
/\quad\backslash \\
CH \quad HC\text{---}(CH_2)_7COCH_3 \\
\| \quad\quad \| \\
H \; H \quad C \quad\quad CH_2 \quad O \\
CH_3(CH_2)_3C{=}C\text{---}CH \quad CH \\
CH_3(CH_2)_3\text{---}CH \quad CH \\
\quad\quad\quad C \\
\quad\quad\quad | \\
\quad\quad\quad H
\end{array}
$$

Methyl oleate has been stated to undergo some polymerization at 300°, and it has been observed that geometrically isomeric forms have approximately the same rate of thermal polymerization.[528] The polymerization of β-eleostearic acid at various temperatures has recently been investigated by Bauer and Liao.[529] High pressures favor rapid polymerization rates, Starkweather [530] having shown that the rate of polymerization of conjugated compounds is doubled on increasing the pressure from 6000 to 7000 atmospheres. The polymerization of soluble salts of the unsaturated acids under pressure has been suggested [531] as a method of obtaining polymerized acids. The preparation of dimerized acids by the polymerization of their alkyl esters shows promise of considerable commercial interest.

ISOMERIZATION

The ethylenic acids exhibit both position and geometrical isomerism and the number of possible isomers of a specific unsaturated acid is sometimes quite large. The simplest case of isomerism involves the position of the double bond of an ethylenic acid with reference to the carboxyl group. Several chemical reactions have already been discussed whereby this position may be changed; for example, it has been shown that the addition and removal of hydrogen halide is frequently accompanied by a shift in the position of an ethylenic bond.[366] The migration of ethylenic bonds under hydrogenating conditions [151,152,153,154,155,156,157] and in the presence of various metals [158] has been considered, and comments have been made upon the possibility of a shift in the position of an ethylenic bond prior to oxidative cleavage. It is thus apparent that the probability of position isomerization must be considered in many of the reactions in which the unsaturated acids constitute a reacting component.

The observation of Varrentrapp [532] that palmitic acid results when oleic acid is fused with potassium hydroxide has been explained by assuming that under such conditions the ethylenic bond is shifted to the position adjacent to the carboxyl group. The significance of Varrentrapp's reaction was not at first recognized, since it was erroneously concluded that oleic acid is 2-octadecenoic acid. Later studies [533] upon this reaction also did not correctly interpret its meaning because of confusion regarding the structure of oleic acid. Subsequent work, however, has established the general tendency of double bonds to migrate under highly alkaline conditions and the importance of this isomerization is now fully recognized. The fusion with potassium hydroxide of ethylenic acids containing a double bond in the 2- or 3-position has been shown by Egorov [534] to yield similar saturated acids, requiring a shift in the double bond in the latter instance. Since oleic acid, which Egorov considered to be 8-octadecenoic acid, yields 5-octadecenoic acid together with palmitic acid when fused with potassium hydroxide, it became apparent that such a treatment results in a shift in the position of an ethylenic bond towards the carboxyl group irrespective of the original position of the bond. This conclusion was apparently confirmed by the preparation of 9-undecenoic acid from 10-undecenoic acid by such treatment. The presence of small amounts of hydroxystearic acid in the reaction product of the alkali fusion of oleic acid led to the belief, in support of a theory previously advanced by Wagner,[535] that hydroxy acids are intermediates in such isomerizations. It has, however, been claimed [536] that the effect of alkalies must be considered as a direct shifting of the double bond, and that mono- or dihydroxy acids are not intermediates in the isomerization, since the fusion of dihydroxy acids with potassium hydroxide results in a cleavage at the original position. Le Sueur [537] had previously shown that the potassium hydroxide fusion of the dihydroxystearic acid obtained from oleic acid yields a monohydroxy dicarboxylic acid as the principal product, and that azelaic and pelargonic acids constitute only a minor portion of the product. A subsequent study [538] showed the product to be 2-hydroxy-2-octylsebacic acid, the formation of which was postulated to involve the migration of an octyl group followed by an oxidation, thus:

$$
\begin{array}{ccc}
\text{CH}_3 & & \\
| & & \\
(\text{CH}_2)_7 & & \\
| & \text{CH}_2\text{OH} & \text{CO}_2\text{H} \\
\text{CHOH} & | & | \\
| & \text{C(OH)(CH}_2)_7\text{CH}_3 & \text{C(OH)(CH}_2)_7\text{CH}_3 \\
\text{CHOH} \rightarrow & | & \xrightarrow{\text{Oxidation}} \quad | \\
| & (\text{CH}_2)_7 & (\text{CH}_2)_7 \\
(\text{CH}_2)_7 & | & | \\
| & \text{CO}_2\text{H} & \text{CO}_2\text{H} \\
\text{CO}_2\text{H} & &
\end{array}
$$

The oxidation evidently occurs during the fusion, since the same product is obtained when dihydroxystearic acid is fused with potassium hydroxide in the presence of nitrogen. Dihydroxybehenic acid was shown to yield 2-hydroxy-2-octyltetradecanedioic acid by a similar procedure. In a further study of this reaction, Nicolet and Jurist [539] stated that diketo acids are intermediates and that their hydration yields the observed products, as follows:

$$
\text{CH}_3(\text{CH}_2)_7\text{CHOHCHOH(CH}_2)_7\text{CO}_2\text{H} \xrightarrow{-2\text{H}_2} \text{CH}_3(\text{CH}_2)_7\text{COCO(CH}_2)_7\text{CO}_2\text{H}
$$

$$
\xrightarrow{\text{H}_2\text{O}} \begin{array}{c} \text{CH}_3(\text{CH}_2)_7\text{COH(CH}_2)_7\text{CO}_2\text{H} \\ | \\ \text{CO}_2\text{H} \end{array}
$$

The migration of the double bonds of unsaturated acids at high temperatures was first studied by Fittig [309] and has recently been investigated by Linstead and others.[540, 541] These authors have made a detailed study of the tautomerism of 2- and 3-hexenoic, pentenoic, and butenoic acids both in the pure state and when dissolved in various solvents. Tautomerism occurred in the pure acids at their boiling points in the absence of catalytic materials. The reaction is of the first order, the percentage change being independent of the total concentration and of the presence of solvents. The rate at which equilibrium is attained is greatly increased by the presence of alkalies and is a function of the concentration rather than of the mole proportion of alkali employed.

Isomerization reactions involving the polyethenoic acids appear
to favor the formation of conjugated systems. That such migrations can take place at high temperatures in the absence of catalysts
has been pointed out in our discussion of fatty acid polymerization.
The treatment of acids or fats with excess of aqueous alkali at
elevated temperatures results in a comparatively rapid shift in the
relative positions of the double bonds with the apparent formation
of conjugated systems. In 1933, Scheiber [542] recognized that the
treatment of linoleic acid with an excess of aqueous alkali results
in a partial conversion of the unconjugated to a conjugated system.
The treatment of polyethenoic acids with excess aqueous alkali
had been studied previously by Stiepel; [543] however, he failed to
realize that the reaction involved ethylenic-bond migration. In
1937, Moore [544] observed that the prolonged refluxing of linseed oil
acids with aqueous potassium hydroxide causes an increase in the
ultraviolet absorption with the development of a maximum absorption at 270 mμ. A product melting at 77° and resembling eleostearic acid was separated from the reaction mixture. Later,
Kass and Burr [38] reported that the time required for isomerization
could be materially reduced if ethylene glycol rather than water is
employed as the solvent. The refluxing of 625 g. of linseed oil
fatty acids with an equal weight of potassium hydroxide in 2.5
liters of anhydrous ethylene glycol yielded an acid, m.p. 70°, which
appeared to be 10,12,14-octadecatrienoic acid and which these
authors termed pseudoeleostearic acid. It had previously been
shown [545] by molecular refraction comparisons that the reduction of
linoleic acid to linoleyl alcohol by sodium in butanol is accompanied by appreciable isomerization, the product being a mixture
of 9,12- and 10,12-octadecadienols, thus accounting for a former
observation by Turpeinen [546] that this reduction is accompanied
by secondary changes. A patent issued to Burr [547] in 1941 disclosed the alkali isomerization of several acids and acid mixtures
in the presence of anhydrous organic solvents. Mitchell and Kraybill [548] have observed that some conjugation is produced during
the bleaching of vegetable oils. Quite recently, Turk and Boone [549]
have stated that the rate of isomerization by heat is increased by
the presence of metallic oxides such as aluminum oxide.

The reader is referred to Chapter II for a discussion of geometrical isomerism as exemplified by oleic acid-elaidic acid, erucic acid-
brassidic acid, and also some of the more highly unsaturated acids.
The stereochemical relationships of some of the addition and oxida-

tion products have already been discussed in this present chapter. Optical isomerism will be considered only as it relates to investigations upon specific compounds.

PYROLYSIS *

Most of the work which has been reported upon the thermal decomposition of fatty substances has been of a somewhat empirical nature, and our knowledge of this subject is consequently not very profound. The pyrolysis of the fatty acids, their glycerides, and simple derivatives yields a mixture of liquid hydrocarbons, ketones, water, and gases, the components of which have not been definitely identified. Since the carboxyl group is relatively unstable at high temperatures, decarboxylation is a predominant reaction in the high-temperature behavior of the acids. Ketone formation, especially in the presence of catalysts, is generally encountered. The ketones may be present as their decomposition products, especially if quite high temperatures are employed. Soaps yield a mixture of hydrocarbons when heated to high temperatures. Mailhe [550] has shown that the thermal decomposition of the vegetable oils in the presence of Cu-Mg or Cu-Al catalysts gives liquid products which can be hydrogenated to saturated aliphatic, cycloaliphatic, and aromatic hydrocarbons. Carbon dioxide, gaseous hydrocarbons, water, and acrolein are also formed. Oleic acid when passed over a Cu-Al catalyst [551] at 600–650° yields liquid hydrocarbons, gases, and water. The resulting hydrocarbons are preponderantly aliphatic, and it is very doubtful if any substantial amounts of cyclic hydrocarbons are formed by this process. The lower acids have been stated by Mailhe [552] to yield ketones, olefins, and cyclic hydrocarbons when similarly treated. The pyrolysis of pelargonic acid [553] at 600–620° yields a considerable amount of liquid compounds, distilling below 150°, containing pelargonone and liquid hydrocarbons together with some unchanged pelargonic acid. The gases formed analyzed as follows: CO_2, 20%; CO, 11.5%; C_nH_{2n}, 8.5%; C_nH_{2n+2}, 25.5%; CH_4, 11%; and H_2, 23%. Unsaturated acids, such as oleic and linoleic acids, form ketones together with liquid and gaseous hydrocarbons, carbon dioxide, carbon monoxide, and water when subjected to thermal decomposition. The pyrolysis of palmitic

* For a complete treatment of the pyrolysis of organic compounds, the reader is referred to Hurd, *The Pyrolysis of Organic Compounds*, A.C.S. Monograph No. 50, Chemical Catalog Co., New York (1929).

acid has been studied by Araki,[554] who claimed that volatile acids constitute the main product. In view of the relative instability of the carboxyl group it is believed that these observations are in error. The presence of catalytic materials greatly lowers the temperature at which fatty acids undergo thermal decomposition. Oleic acid, for example, is converted into a mixture of liquid hydrocarbons and gases when heated for 2–3 hours at 150° in the presence of 30% aluminum chloride.[555] The thermal decomposition of hydroxy acids as exemplified by the dehydration and scission of ricinoleic acid has been discussed previously.

The question as to whether petroleum hydrocarbons owe their origin to the pyrolysis of fatty substances has long been a subject of interest. Engler and Lehmann [556] obtained chiefly straight-chain hydrocarbons by the cracking of fats or fatty acids at 350–400° under pressure. A study by Stadnikov and Ivanovskii [557] of the pyrolysis of unsaturated acids led to the conclusion that although it is likely that petroleum hydrocarbons of the aliphatic series were formed by the decomposition of animal fats, naphthenic petroleum must have had a different origin. The occurrence of small amounts of fatty acids in natural petroleums [558] has led many to believe that the fats of aquatic origin may be considered as a possible source of petroleum hydrocarbons. It has been stated [559] that the formation of optically active petroleum hydrocarbons cannot be ascribed alone to the pyrolysis of fatty materials but possibly to a decomposition of mixtures of such materials with proteins. The decomposition of fats by bacteria and fungi,[560, 561] in which decarboxylation is a predominant reaction, is of interest as regards its possible relationship to the formation of petroleum from such sources.

The effect of alpha particles upon organic materials has a possible bearing upon the origin of petroleum. This was first suggested by Lind and Bardwell [562] who stated that the radiations from the radioactive constituents in sedimentary rocks may be involved in petroleum formation. Subsequent studies [563, 564] lend considerable support to the belief that the action of radiations upon organic material offers a possible explanation for the formation of certain types of petroleum. The quite recent work of Sheppard and Burton [565] upon the products which result from the alpha particle bombardment of fatty acids is of exceptional interest. The major reactions were observed to be dehydrogenation and decarboxylation, the reactions taking place at much lower temperatures than those required for pyrolysis.

References

1. Kharichkov, *J. Russ. Phys. Chem. Soc.*, **40**, 1757 (1908); **41**, 345 (1909); Orlov, *ibid.*, **40**, 652 (1908).
2. Bergmann, *Z. angew. Chem.*, **31**, 69 (1918).
3. Fischer and Schneider, *Ber.*, **53**, 922 (1920).
4. Gruu, *ibid.*, **53**, 987 (1920).
5. Kelber, *ibid.*, **53**, 1567 (1920).
6. Löffl, *Seifensieder-Ztg.*, **47**, 622 (1920); *Chem.-Ztg.*, **44**, 561 (1920).
7. Solway and Williams, *J. Chem. Soc.*, **121**, 1343 (1922).
8. Zerner, *Naturprodukte*, 83 (1923).
9. Dakin, *J. Biol. Chem.*, **4**, 227 (1908).
10. Smedley-Maclean and Pearce, *Biochem. J.*, **28**, 486 (1934).
11. Allen and Witzemann, *J. Am. Chem. Soc.*, **63**, 1922 (1941).
12. Witzemann, *J. Biol. Chem.*, **35**, 83 (1918); **49**, 123 (1921); *J. Am. Chem. Soc.*, **49**, 987 (1927).
13. Witzemann, *J. Biol. Chem.*, **45**, 1 (1920).
14. Spoehr, *J. Am. Chem. Soc.*, **46**, 1494 (1924).
15. Noerdlinger, *Ber.*, **19**, 1893 (1886).
16. Dietterle, *Bern Dissertation, Commstadt* (1883).
17. Carrette, *Compt. rend.*, **102**, 692 (1886).
18. Carrette, *ibid.*, **101**, 1498 (1885).
19. Przheval'skii, *J. Russ. Phys. Chem. Soc.*, **43**, 1000 (1911).
20. Przheval'skii, *ibid.*, **49**, 567 (1917).
21. Skraup and Schwamberger, *Ann.*, **462**, 135 (1928).
22. Challenor and Thorpe, *J. Chem. Soc.*, **123**, 2480 (1923).
23. Ellis, *Biochem. J.*, **26**, 791 (1932).
24. Levene and West, *J. Biol. Chem.*, **16**, 475 (1914).
25. Fichter and Lapin, *Helv. Chim. Acta*, **12**, 993 (1929).
26. Knoop, *Beitr. chem. physiol. Path.*, **6**, 150 (1905).
27. Dakin, *J. Biol. Chem.*, **4**, 419 (1908); **5**, 173 (1908); **6**, 203, 221 (1909); **9**, 123 (1911).
28. Jowett and Quastel, *Biochem. J.*, **29**, 2143, 2159 (1935).
29. Verkade and van der Lee, *ibid.*, **28**, 31 (1934); Verkade, van der Lee, and van Alphen, *Z. physiol. Chem.*, **237**, 186 (1935); **247**, 111 (1937).
30. Stokoe, *J. Soc. Chem. Ind.*, **40**, 75T (1921).
31. Acklin and Schneider, *Biochem. Z.*, **202**, 246 (1928).
32. Schmalfuss and Werner, *Ber.*, **58**, 71 (1925); Schmalfuss, Werner, and Gehrke, *Fettchem. Umschau*, **40**, 102 (1933); *Fette u. Seifen*, **43**, 211, 243 (1936).
33. Holm, Greenbank, and Deysher, *Ind. Eng. Chem.*, **19**, 156 (1927).
34. Kuhn and Meyer, *Z. physiol. Chem.*, **185**, 193 (1929).
35. Barnicoat, *J. Soc. Chem. Ind.*, **50**, 361T (1931).
36. Vibrans, *Oil & Soap*, **18**, 109 (1941).
37. Miller, Brown, and Burr, *ibid.*, **15**, 62 (1938).
38. Kass and Burr, *J. Am. Chem. Soc.*, **61**, 3292 (1939).
39. Lea, *Rancidity in Edible Fats, Dept. Sci. Ind. Research, Food Invest. Special Rept. No. 46* (1938).
40. Taffel and Revis, *J. Soc. Chem. Ind.*, **50**, 87T (1931).
41. Lea, *Proc. Roy. Soc. (London)*, **108B**, 175 (1931).

42. Kreis, Z. Untersuch. Nahr.- u. Genussm., 9, 90 (1905).
43. Powick, J. Agr. Research, 26, 323 (1923).
44. Ellis, Biochem. J., 30, 753 (1936).
45. French, Olcott, and Mattill, Ind. Eng. Chem., 27, 724 (1935); Hamilton and Olcott, ibid., 29, 217 (1937).
46. Hyman and Wagner, J. Am. Chem. Soc., 62, 4345 (1930).
47. Mattill, Oil & Soap, 18, 73 (1941).
48. Skellon, J. Soc. Chem. Ind., 50, 382T (1931).
49. Miller and Claxton, Ind. Eng. Chem., 20, 43 (1928).
50. Goldschmidt and Freudenberg, Ber., 67, 1589 (1934).
51. Bolam and Sim, J. Soc. Chem. Ind., 60, 50 (1941).
52. Le Gousse, Arch. méd. pharm. navales, 128, 746 (1938).
53. Fahrion, Chem. Umschau, 27, 158, 201 (1920); 28, 5, 20 (1921).
54. Farmer and Sutton, J. Chem. Soc., 139 (1942); 119, 122 (1943); Farmer, Bloomfield, Sundralingam, and Sutton, Trans. Faraday Soc., 38, 348 (1942); Farmer and Sundralingam, J. Chem. Soc., 121 (1942); Farmer and Mitchell, ibid., 513 (1942); Farmer, Koch, and Sutton, ibid., 541 (1943).
55. Greenbank and Holm, Ind. Eng. Chem., 33, 1058 (1941).
56. Rona, Asmus, and Steineck, Biochem. Z., 250, 149 (1932).
57. Franke, Ann., 498, 129 (1932).
58. Moureu and Dufraisse, Compt. rend., 174, 258 (1922); Brit. Patent 181,365 (1922).
59. Täufel and Müller, Z. angew. Chem., 43, 1108 (1930).
60. Sabalitschka, Z. Untersuch. Lebensm., 79, 143 (1940).
61. Anderegg and Nelson, Ind. Eng. Chem., 18, 620 (1926).
62. Mattill, J. Am. Med. Assoc., 89, 1505 (1927).
63. Olcott and Emerson, J. Am. Chem. Soc., 59, 1008 (1937).
64. Evans, Emerson, and Emerson, J. Biol. Chem., 113, 319 (1936).
65. Emerson and Smith, J. Am. Chem. Soc., 62, 1869 (1940).
66. Karrer and Fritzsche, Helv. Chim. Acta, 21, 1234 (1938).
67. Olcott and Mattill, J. Am. Chem. Soc., 58, 2204 (1936).
68. Fawcett, J. Soc. Chem. Ind., 58, 43T (1939).
69. Eastman Kodak Co., Brit. Patent 507,471 (1939).
70. Riemenschneider, Swift, and Sando, Oil & Soap, 17, 145 (1940).
71. Isler, Helv. Chim. Acta, 21, 1756 (1938).
72. Golumbic and Mattill, J. Am. Chem. Soc., 63, 1279 (1941).
73. Mattill, J. Biol. Chem., 90, 141 (1931).
74. Royce, Oil & Soap, 10, 123 (1933); Royce and Lindsey, Ind. Eng. Chem., 25, 1047 (1933).
75. Adams, Morris, Geissman, Butterbaugh, and Kirkpatrick, J. Am. Chem. Soc., 60, 2193 (1938).
76. Böeseken, Cohen, and Kip, Rec. trav. chim., 55, 815 (1936).
77. Bollmann, U. S. Patent 1,575,529 (1926).
78. Evans, Ind. Eng. Chem., 27, 329 (1935).
79. Holmes, Corbet, and Hartzler, ibid., 28, 133 (1936).
80. Newton, Oil & Soap, 9, 247 (1932).
81. Täufel and Müller, Biochem. Z., 304, 137 (1940).
82. Newton and Grettie, U. S. Patent 1,903,126 (1933).

83. Lundberg, Halvorson, and Burr, *Oil & Soap*, **21**, 33 (1944).
84. Molinari, *Annuar. soc. chim. Milano*, **9**, 145 (1903).
85. Harries and Thieme, *Ann.*, **343**, 354 (1905); Harries and Türk, *Ber.*, **38**, 1630 (1905).
86. Molinari and Soncini, *ibid.*, **39**, 2735 (1906); Molinari, *ibid.*, **40**, 4154 (1907); **41**, 585, 2782 (1908); Molinari and Fenaroli, *ibid.*, **41**, 2789 (1908); Molinari and Barosi, *ibid.*, **41**, 2794 (1908).
87. Harries and Thieme, *ibid.*, **39**, 2844, 3667 (1906); Harries and Türk, *ibid.*, **39**, 3732 (1906); Harries, *ibid.*, **39**, 3728 (1906); **40**, 4905 (1907); **42**, 446 (1909); **45**, 936 (1912); *Ann.*, **374**, 288 (1910).
88. Erdmann, Bedford, and Raspe, *Ber.*, **42**, 1334 (1909).
89. Haller and Brochet, *Compt. rend.*, **150**, 496 (1910).
90. Noller, Carson, Martin, and Hawkins, *J. Am. Chem. Soc.*, **58**, 24 (1936).
91. Molinari, *Ber.*, **41**, 585, 2782 (1908).
92. Harries, *ibid.*, **40**, 4905 (1907).
93. Laurent, *Ann. chim. phys.* [2], **66**, 154 (1837).
94. Bromeis, *Ann.*, **35**, 86 (1840).
95. Lewkowitsch, *J. prakt. Chem.* [2], **20**, 159 (1879).
96. Gantter and Hell, *Ber.*, **17**, 2212 (1884).
97. Verkade, *Rec. trav. chim.*, **46**, 137, 200 (1927).
98. Brightman, *J. Soc. Chem. Ind.*, **36**, 984 (1917).
99. Jegorow, *J. prakt. Chem.* [2], **86**, 521 (1912).
100. Ellingboe, U. S. Patent 2,203,680 (1940).
101. Grossmann, *Ber.*, **26**, 639 (1893).
102. Spieckermann, *ibid.*, **28**, 276 (1895); **29**, 810 (1896).
103. Lapworth and Mottram, *J. Chem. Soc.*, **127**, 1628 (1925); *Mem. Proc. Manchester Lit. & Phil. Soc.*, **71**, 63 (1927).
104. Böeseken and Belinfante, *Rec. trav. chim.*, **45**, 914 (1926).
105. Hilditch and Lea, *J. Chem. Soc.*, 1576 (1928).
106. Böeseken, *Rec. trav. chim.*, **45**, 838 (1926); **46**, 619 (1927).
107. Bauer and Kutscher, *Chem. Umschau*, **32**, 57 (1925).
108. Bauer and Bähr, *J. prakt. Chem.* [2], **122**, 201 (1929).
109. Smit, *Rec. trav. chim.*, **49**, 675 (1930).
110. Pigulevskiĭ and Petrov, *J. Russ. Phys. Chem. Soc.*, **58**, 1062 (1926).
111. Hilditch, *J. Chem. Soc.*, 1828 (1926).
112. Smedley-Maclean and Pearce, *Biochem. J.*, **25**, 1252 (1931).
113. Smit, *Rec. trav. chim.*, **49**, 686 (1930).
114. King, *J. Chem. Soc.*, 37 (1943).
115. Albitskiĭ, *J. Russ. Phys. Chem. Soc.*, **31**, 76 (1899); **34**, 788 (1902); *Ber.*, **33**, 2909 (1900).
116. Athanas'evskii, *J. Russ. Phys. Chem. Soc.*, **47**, 2124 (1915).
117. Isii, *J. Soc. Chem. Ind., Japan*, **43**, S.b. 255 (1940).
118. Grün and Wittka, *Chem. Umschau*, **32**, 257 (1925).
119. Asahina and Ishida, *J. Pharm. Soc. Japan*, No. **481**, 171 (1922).
120. Goldsobel, Ger. Patent 180,926 (1904).
121. Asahina and Takimoto, *J. Pharm. Soc. Japan*, **49**, 1017 (1929).
122. King, *J. Chem. Soc.*, 1826 (1938).
123. Brady, *J. Am. Chem. Soc.*, **61**, 3464 (1939).

124. Saytzeff, *J. Russ. Phys. Chem. Soc.*, **17**, 417 (1885); *J. prakt. Chem.* [2], **33**, 300 (1886).
125. Overbeck, *Ann.*, **140**, 72 (1866).
126. Lapworth, *Chemistry & Industry*, **50**, 848 (1931).
127. Atherton and Hilditch, *J. Chem. Soc.*, 204 (1942).
128. King, *ibid.*, 387 (1942).
129. Hazura and Grüssner, *Monatsh.*, **9**, 947 (1888).
130. Joukowsky, *J. prakt. Chem.* [2], **50**, 68 (1894).
131. Medvedev and Alekseeva, *Papers Karpov Chem. Inst. Bach Memorial Vol.*, 128 (1927).
132. Edmed, *J. Chem. Soc.*, **73**, 627 (1898).
133. Holde and Marcusson, *Ber.*, **36**, 2657 (1903).
134. Saytzeff and Saytzeff, *J. prakt. Chem.* [2], **71**, 422 (1905).
135. King, *J. Chem. Soc.*, 1788 (1936).
136. Armstrong and Hilditch, *J. Soc. Chem. Ind.*, **44**, 43T (1925).
137. Lapworth and Mottram, *J. Chem. Soc.*, **127**, 1987 (1925).
138. Hilditch and Plimmer, *ibid.*, 204 (1942).
139. Arnaud and Hasenfratz, *Compt. rend.*, **152**, 1603 (1903).
140. Maquenne, *Bull. soc. chim.* [3], **21**, 1061 (1899).
141. Hill and McEwen, *Organic Syntheses*, Coll. Vol. II, Blatt, editor, p. 53, John Wiley & Sons, New York (1943).
142. Hazura, *Monatsh.*, **8**, 147 (1887).
143. Riemenschneider, Wheeler, and Sando, *J. Biol. Chem.*, **127**, 391 (1939).
144. Hazura, *Monatsh.*, **7**, 637 (1886); **8**, 260 (1887); **9**, 180 (1888); Hazura and Friedreich, *ibid.*, **8**, 156 (1887).
145. Nunn and Smedley-Maclean, *Biochem. J.*, **32**, 1974 (1938).
146. Nunn and Smedley-Maclean, *ibid.*, **29**, 2742 (1935).
147. von Mikusch, *J. Am. Chem. Soc.*, **64**, 1580 (1942).
148. Ralston and Bauer, *Oil & Soap*, **13**, 170 (1936); U. S. Patents 2,033,538 (1936); 2,133,008 (1939).
149. Sabatier and Senderens, *Compt. rend.*, **128**, 1173 (1899); **130**, 1761 (1900); **132**, 210, 566, 1254 (1902); **134**, 1127 (1902); **135**, 87 (1902).
150. Goldschmiedt, *Sitzber. kgl. preuss. Akad. Wiss.*, **72**, *Abt. II*, 366 (1875).
151. Hilditch and Vidyarthi, *Proc. Roy. Soc. (London)*, **122A**, 552 (1929).
152. Hilditch, *Chem. Umschau*, **37**, 354 (1930).
153. Bauer and Ermann, *ibid.*, **37**, 241 (1930).
154. van der Veen, *ibid.*, **38**, 89 (1931).
155. Moore, *J. Soc. Chem. Ind.*, **38**, 320T (1919).
156. Mazume, *J. Soc. Chem. Ind., Japan*, **31**, 470, S.b. 112 (1928).
157. Steger and Scheffers, *Chem. Umschau*, **38**, 45 (1931).
158. Bauer and Krallis, *ibid.*, **38**, 201 (1931); **41**, 194 (1934).
159. Armstrong and Hilditch, *Proc. Roy. Soc. (London)*, **96A**, 322 (1919).
160. Jurgens and Meigen, *Chem. Umschau*, **23**, 99, 116 (1916).
161. Walden, *ibid.*, **32**, 275 (1925).
162. Hilditch and Vidyarthi, *Proc. Roy. Soc. (London)*, **122A**, 563 (1929).
163. Böeseken and Krimpen, *Verslag Akad. Wetenschappen Amsterdam*, **37**, 66 (1928); *Proc. Acad. Sci. Amsterdam*, **31**, 238 (1928).
164. Pelly, *J. Soc. Chem. Ind.*, **46**, 449T (1927).
165. Graham, *Phil. Mag.* [4], **32**, 401, 503 (1866); *Proc. Roy. Soc. (London)*, **15**, 223, 502 (1867); **16**, 422 (1868); **17**, 500 (1869).

166. Mond, Ramsay, and Shields, *Trans. Roy. Soc. (London)*, **186A**, 675 (1896).
167. Taylor, *Proc. Roy. Soc. (London)*, **108A**, 105 (1925).
168. Armstrong and Hilditch, *ibid.*, **99A**, 490 (1921).
169. Taylor, *J. Phys. Chem.*, **30**, 145 (1926).
170. Armstrong and Hilditch, *Proc. Roy. Soc. (London)*, **96A**, 137 (1919).
171. Armstrong and Hilditch, *ibid.*, **98A**, 27 (1920).
172. Normann, Brit. Patent 1,515 (1903).
173. Kayser, U. S. Patent 1,004,035 (1911).
174. Ellis, U. S. Patent 1,026,156 (1912).
175. Testrup, Brit. Patent 7,726 (1910); U. S. Patent 1,114,067 (1914).
176. Wilbuschewitsch, U. S. Patent 1,024,758 (1912).
177. Mailhe, *Chem.-Ztg.*, **31**, 1083 (1907).
178. Ellis, *J. Ind. Eng. Chem.*, **5**, 95 (1913).
179. Wilbuschewitsch, Brit. Patent 15,439 (1910).
180. Crosfield and Sons, Brit. Patent 30,282 (1910).
181. Ellis, U. S. Patents 1,060,673 (1913); 1,320,039 (1919).
182. Wells, U. S. Patent 1,179,484 (1916).
183. Schönfeld, *Seifensieder-Ztg.*, **41**, 945 (1914).
184. Müller Speisefettfabrik A.-G., Brit. Patent 7,670 (1914).
185. Ellis, U. S. Patent 1,255,590 (1918).
186. Normann, *Seifensieder-Ztg.*, **42**, 46 (1915).
187. Bosch, Mittsch, and Schneider, U. S. Patent 1,215,334 (1917).
188. Kita, Mazume, and Kino, *Chem. Umschau*, **32**, 262 (1925).
189. Sulzberger, U. S. Patent 1,223,123 (1917).
190. Ittner, U. S. Patent, 1,238,774 (1917).
191. Grote, *Seifensieder-Ztg.*, **47**, 713 (1920).
192. Myddleton, Brit. Patent 397,295 (1933).
193. Kahlenberg and Pi, *J. Phys. Chem.*, **28**, 29 (1924).
194. Nordiske Fabriker de-no-fa Aktieselskap, Brit. Patent 140,371 (1920).
195. Dewar and Liebmann, U. S. Patent 1,275,405 (1918).
196. Mazume, *J. Soc. Chem. Ind., Japan*, **31**, 467, S.b. 111 (1928).
197. Badische, Brit. Patent 2,306 (1914).
198. Normann, *Chem. Umschau*, **32**, 262 (1925).
199. Ueno, *J. Chem. Ind. Japan*, **21**, 898 (1918).
200. Ueno, Miyake, and Anzai, *J. Soc. Chem. Ind., Japan*, **43**, S.b. 434 (1940).
201. Hausamann, Can. Patent 157,396 (1914).
202. Ellis, U. S. Patent 1,217,118 (1917).
203. Deutsche Hydrierwerke A.-G., Brit. Patent 396,311 (1933).
204. Kayser, U. S. Patent 1,236,446 (1917).
205. Higgins, Brit. Patent 23,873 (1913).
206. Wittka, Swiss Patent 151,955 (1930).
207. Ellis, U. S. Patent 1,645,377 (1927).
208. Shukoff, Ger. Patent 241,823 (1910).
209. Schuck, Brit. Patent 122,192 (1919); Can. Patent 200,591 (1920).
210. Raney, U. S. Patents 1,628,190 (1927); 1,915,473 (1933).
211. Paul and Hilly, *Bull. soc. chim.* [5], **3**, 2330 (1936).
212. Mozingo, *Organic Syntheses*, **21**, 15 (1941).
213. Ellis, U. S. Patent 1,092,206 (1914).
214. Richardson, U. S. Patents 1,177,896 (1916); 1,257,396, 1,257,397 (1918).
215. Bedford and Erdmann, *J. Russ. Phys. Chem. Soc.*, **45**, 616 (1913).

216. Bedford and Williams, Brit. Patent 29,612 (1910); Swiss Patent 61,925 (1911); Bedford, Williams, Erdmann and Hydroll, Ltd., Brit. Patent 28,981 (1912); Bedford and Erdmann, U. S. Patent 1,200,696 (1916).
217. Meigen, J. prakt. Chem. [2], 92, 390 (1915).
218. Erdmann, Seifensieder-Ztg., 40, 605 (1913).
219. Richardson and Snoddy, Ind. Eng. Chem., 18, 570 (1926).
220. Vereinigte Chemische Werke A.-G., Fr. Patent 425,729 (1911); Brit. Patent 20,329 (1911).
221. Paal, Brit. Patent 5,188 (1911).
222. Higgins, U. S. Patent 1,170,814 (1916).
223. Paal, U. S. Patent 1,222,660 (1917).
224. Sulzberger, U. S. Patent 1,338,709 (1920).
225. Goldschmidt, Seifenfabr., 32, 713 (1912).
226. Zeise, Ann. Physik [2], 9, 632 (1827).
227. Doebereiner, ibid. [2], 28, 180 (1833).
228. Zdrawkowitch, Bull. soc. chim. [2], 25, 198 (1876).
229. Boettger, J. prakt. Chem. [2], 2, 130 (1870).
230. Loew, Ber., 23, 289 (1890).
231. Bredig and Müller von Berneck, Z. physik. Chem., 31, 258 (1899).
232. Paal, Ber., 35, 2195 (1902); Paal and Gerum, ibid., 41, 2273 (1908); 42, 1553 (1909); Paal and Roth, ibid., 41, 2282 (1908); 42, 1541 (1909); Paal and Hartmann, ibid., 42, 2239, 3930 (1909); 43, 243 (1910).
233. Paal and Amberger, ibid., 37, 124 (1904); 38, 1398 (1905).
234. Kelber and Schwarz, ibid., 45, 1946 (1912).
235. Skita and Meyer, ibid., 45, 3579 (1912).
236. Lehmann, Arch. Pharm., 251, 152 (1913).
237. Yokoyama and Kotake, J. Chem. Soc. Japan, 57, 183 (1936).
238. Hanuš and Voříšek, Collection Czechoslov. Chem. Commun., 1, 223 (1929).
239. Voříšek, Chem. Listy, 28, 57 (1934).
240. Weineck, Austrian Patent 10,400 (1886).
241. Magnier, Brangier, and Tissier, Ger. Patent 126,446 (1899); Brit. Patent 3,363 (1900).
242. Petersen, Z. Elektrochem., 11, 549 (1905).
243. Boehringer & Söhne, Ger. Patents 187,788, 189,332 (1906).
244. Pomilio, Z. Elektrochem., 21, 444 (1915).
245. Kroepelin, Vogel, and Pfeiffer, Ber., 68B, 684 (1935).
246. Iwamoto, J. Soc. Chem. Ind., Japan, 33, S.b. 25 (1930).
247. Eichwald, Z. angew. Chem., 35, 505 (1922).
248. Zappi and Degiorgi, Anales asoc. quím. argentina, 26, 33 (1938).
249. Waterman and Bertram, Chem. Umschau, 34, 32, 255 (1927).
250. Waterman and Perquin, Ann. scuola ing. Padova, 3, 383 (1927).
251. Iwamoto, J. Soc. Chem. Ind., Japan, 33, S.b. 247 (1930).
252. Utescher, Brit. Patent 20,061 (1912).
253. Iwamoto, J. Soc. Chem. Ind., Japan, 32, S.b. 359 (1929); J. Chem. Soc. Japan, 52, 433 (1931).
254. Humiston, J. Phys. Chem., 23, 572 (1919).
255. Moissan, Compt. rend., 110, 276 (1890).
256. Bockemüller, Ann., 506, 20 (1933).
257. Dimroth and Bockemüller, Ber., 64, 516 (1931).

258. Kinetic Chemicals Inc., Fr. Patent 720,474 (1931).
259. Frigidaire Corp., Ger. Patent 594,751 (1934).
260. Henne, U. S. Patents 1,973,069 (1934); 1,990,692 (1935).
261. Fredenhagen and Cadenbach, *Ber.*, **67**, 928 (1934).
262. Aschan, *ibid.*, **45**, 1913 (1912); **46**, 2162 (1913).
263. Krafft and Beddies, *ibid.*, **25**, 481 (1892).
264. Hell and Jordanoff, *ibid.*, **24**, 987 (1891).
265. Hell and Twerdomedoff, *ibid.*, **22**, 1745 (1889); Hell and Sadomsky, *ibid.*, **24**, 2388 (1891).
266. Hell, *ibid.*, **14**, 891 (1881).
267. Volhard, *Ann.*, **242**, 141 (1887).
268. Zelinsky, *Ber.*, **20**, 2026 (1887).
269. Auwers and Bernhardi, *ibid.*, **24**, 2209 (1891).
270. Gantter and Hell, *ibid.*, **15**, 142 (1882).
271. Lapworth, *J. Chem. Soc.*, **85**, 30 (1904).
272. Clarke and Taylor, *Organic Syntheses*, Coll. Vol. I, Gilman, editor, p. 108, John Wiley & Sons, New York (1932).
273. Merchant, Wickert, and Marvel, *J. Am. Chem. Soc.*, **49**, 1828 (1927).
274. Varma and Menon, *J. Indian Chem. Soc.*, **10**, 591 (1933).
275. Guest and Goddard, *J. Am. Chem. Soc.*, **66**, 2074 (1944).
276. Asinger, *Ber.*, **75B**, 668 (1942).
277. Tanaka, Kobayashi, and Nishi, *J. Soc. Chem. Ind., Japan*, **37**, S.b. 208 (1934).
278. White and Robertson, *J. Chem. Soc.*, 1509 (1939).
279. Walker and Robertson, *ibid.*, 1515 (1939).
280. Ingold and Smith, *ibid.*, 2742 (1931).
281. Stewart and Smith, *J. Am. Chem. Soc.*, **51**, 3082 (1929); **52**, 2869 (1930).
282. Burton and Ingold, *J. Chem. Soc.*, 904 (1928).
283. Holde and Gorgas, *Z. angew. Chem.*, **39**, 1443 (1926).
284. Hilditch and Jasperson, *J. Soc. Chem. Ind.*, **58**, 233 (1939).
285. Nicolet, *J. Am. Chem. Soc.*, **43**, 2122 (1921).
286. van der Steur, *Rec. trav. chim.*, **46**, 278 (1927).
287. Ponzio and Gastaldi, *Gazz. chim. ital.*, **42**, II, 92 (1912).
288. Sun, *J. Chinese Chem. Soc.*, **4**, 1 (1936).
289. Margosches, Hinner, and Friedmann, *Z. deut. Oel-Fett-Ind.*, **44**, 205 (1924); Margosches, Friedmann, and Tschörner, *Ber.*, **58B**, 794 (1925).
290. Arnaud and Posternak, *Compt. rend.*, **149**, 220 (1909).
291. Knauss and Smull, *J. Am. Chem. Soc.*, **49**, 2808 (1927).
292. Reformatzky, *J. prakt. Chem.* [2], **41**, 529 (1890).
293. Rollett, *Z. physiol. Chem.*, **62**, 410 (1909).
294. Matthews, Brode, and Brown, *J. Am. Chem. Soc.*, **63**, 1064 (1941).
295. Kass, Nichols, and Burr, *ibid.*, **63**, 1060 (1941).
296. Toyama and Tsuchiya, *J. Soc. Chem. Ind., Japan*, **39**, S.b. 219 (1936).
297. I. G. Farbenind. A.-G., Brit. Patent 336,623 (1929); Fr. Patent 678,856 (1929).
298. Keller and Munz, U. S. Patent 1,862,596 (1932).
299. Kametaka, *J. Chem. Soc.*, **83**, 1042 (1903).
300. van Loon, *Rec. trav. chim.*, **50**, 32 (1931).
301. Bauer and Rohrbach, *Chem. Umschau*, **35**, 53 (1928).

302. Böeseken, Hoogl, Broek, and Smit, *Rec. trav. chim.*, **46**, 619 (1927).
303. Nicolet, *J. Am. Chem. Soc.*, **43**, 938 (1921).
304. Merz, *Farben-Ztg.*, **33**, 2423 (1928).
305. Piotrowski, *Ber.*, **23**, 2531 (1890).
306. Albitskiĭ, *J. Russ. Phys. Chem. Soc.*, **31**, 100 (1899).
307. Markownikoff, *Ann.*, **153**, 256 (1870).
308. Erlenmeyer, *Ber.*, **13**, 305 (1880).
309. Fittig, *ibid.*, **13**, 955 (1880); *Ann.*, **200**, 21 (1880); **208**, 71 (1881); **255**, 18 (1889); **283**, 73 (1894).
310. Fichter and Langguth, *ibid.*, **313**, 371 (1900).
311. Brunner, *Ber.*, **19**, 2224 (1886).
312. Noerdlinger, *ibid.*, **23**, 2356 (1890).
313. Walker and Lumsden, *J. Chem. Soc.*, **79**, 1191 (1901).
314. Lewis, *J. Am. Chem. Soc.*, **38**, 762 (1916).
315. Lucas and Jameson, *ibid.*, **46**, 2475 (1924).
316. Cuy, *ibid.*, **42**, 503 (1920).
317. Lucas and Moyse, *ibid.*, **47**, 1459 (1925).
318. Ingold and Ingold, *J. Chem. Soc.*, 2354 (1931); Ingold and Ramsden, *ibid.*, 2746 (1931).
319. Malkin and Robinson, *ibid.*, **127**, 369 (1925).
320. Allan, Oxford, Robinson, and Smith, *ibid.*, 401 (1926).
321. Ives, Linstead, and Riley, *ibid.*, 561 (1933).
322. Lapworth, *Nature*, **115**, 625 (1925).
323. Linstead, Noble, and Boorman, *J. Chem. Soc.*, 557 (1933).
324. Boorman, Linstead, and Rydon, *ibid.*, 568 (1933).
325. Kharasch and Mayo, *J. Am. Chem. Soc.*, **55**, 2468 (1933).
326. Kharasch, McNab, and Mayo, *ibid.*, **55**, 2521, 2531 (1933).
327. Smith, *Nature*, **132**, 447 (1933).
328. Ashton and Smith, *J. Chem. Soc.*, 435 (1934).
329. Gaubert, Linstead, and Rydon, *ibid.*, 1974 (1937).
330. Urushibara and Takebayashi, *Bull. Chem. Soc. Japan*, **13**, 331 (1938).
331. Urushibara and Takebayashi, *ibid.*, **13**, 404 (1938).
332. Ashton and Smith, *J. Chem. Soc.*, 1308 (1934).
333. Smith and Harris, *Nature*, **135**, 187 (1935).
334. Sherrill, Mayer, and Walter, *J. Am. Chem. Soc.*, **56**, 926 (1934).
335. Linstead and Rydon, *J. Chem. Soc.*, 2001 (1934); *Chemistry & Industry*, **54**, 1009 (1935).
336. I. G. Farbenind. A.-G., Fr. Patent 799,432 (1936).
337. Wanin and Tschernojarowa, *J. Gen. Chem. (U.S.S.R.)*, **5**, 1537 (1935).
338. Erdmann, Ger. Patent 233,893 (1910).
339. Eckert and Halla, *Monatsh.*, **34**, 1815 (1913).
340. Khonovskii, *J. Russ. Phys. Chem. Soc.*, **43**, 1457 (1911).
341. Abraham and Smith, *J. Chem. Soc.*, 1605 (1936).
342. Arnaud and Posternak, *Compt. rend.*, **150**, 1130 (1910).
343. Arnaud and Posternak, *ibid.*, **150**, 1245 (1910).
344. Harris and Smith, *J. Chem. Soc.*, 1572 (1935).
345. I. G. Farbenind. A.-G., Ger. Patent 621,977 (1935); Fr. Patent 786,112 (1935).
346. Albitzky, *J. prakt. Chem.* [2], **61**, 65 (1900).

347. Nicolet and Poulter, *J. Am. Chem. Soc.*, **52**, 1186 (1930).
348. Warmbunn and Stutzer, *Ber.*, **36**, 3604 (1902).
349. Hashi, *J. Soc. Chem. Ind.*, *Japan*, **39**, S.b. 469 (1936).
350. Hashi, *ibid.*, **39**, S.b. 18 (1936).
351. Esafov, *J. Gen. Chem. (U.S.S.R.)*, **7**, 1403 (1937).
352. Read and Reid, *J. Chem. Soc.*, 745 (1929).
353. Margosches, Friedmann, and Tschörner, *Ber.*, **58B**, 794 (1925).
354. Holde and Gorgas, *ibid.*, **58B**, 1071 (1925).
355. Imbert, Fr. Patent 368,543 (1906); U. S. Patent 901,905 (1908).
356. Tilden and Forster, *J. Chem. Soc.*, **65**, 324 (1894).
357. Kaufmann and Röver, *Fette u. Seifen*, **47**, 103 (1940).
358. Frankland, *Ann.*, **71**, 203 (1849); **74**, 41 (1850).
359. Fokin, *J. Russ. Phys. Chem. Soc.*, **44**, 155 (1912).
360. Erdmann and Bedford, *Ber.*, **42**, 1324 (1909).
361. Takahashi, *J. Tokyo Chem. Soc.*, **40**, 233 (1919).
362. Smith and West, *Philippine J. Sci.*, **32**, 297 (1927).
363. Kimura, *Chem. Umschau*, **36**, 125 (1929).
364. Le Sueur, *J. Chem. Soc.*, **85**, 1708 (1904).
365. Olivier, *Rec. trav. chim.*, **53**, 1093 (1934).
366. Arnaud and Posternak, *Compt. rend.*, **150**, 1525 (1910).
367. Fokin, *J. Russ. Phys. Chem. Soc.*, **44**, 653 (1912).
368. Overbeck, *Ann.*, **140**, 40 (1866).
369. Quensell, *Ber.*, **42**, 2440 (1909).
370. Otto, *Ann.*, **135**, 226 (1865).
371. Haussknecht, *ibid.*, **143**, 41 (1867).
372. Krafft, *Ber.*, **29**, 2232 (1896).
373. Baruch, *ibid.*, **27**, 172 (1894).
374. Ulrich, *Z. Chem.* [2], **3**, 545 (1867).
375. Mangold, *Monatsh.*, **15**, 314 (1894).
376. Mühle, *Ber.*, **46**, 2091 (1913).
377. Posternak, *Compt. rend.*, **162**, 944 (1916).
378. Bachman, *J. Am. Chem. Soc.*, **55**, 4279 (1933); **57**, 1088 (1935).
379. Inoue and Suzuki, *Proc. Imp. Acad. Tokyo*, **7**, 261 (1931).
380. Arnaud and Posternak, Brit. Patent 24,721 (1909).
381. Hoffmann-LaRoche and Co., Ger. Patent 243,582 (1909).
382. Maruyama and Suzuki, *Proc. Imp. Acad. Tokyo*, **8**, 186 (1932).
383. M. Saytzeff, K. Saytzeff, and A. Saytzeff, *J. Russ. Phys. Chem. Soc.*, **18**, 328 (1886).
384. Marie, *Bull. soc. chim.* [3], **15**, 576 (1896).
385. Epifanov, *J. Russ. Phys. Chem. Soc.*, **40**, 133 (1908).
386. Firmenich & Cie., Swiss Patent 175,340 (1935).
387. Robinet, *Bull. soc. chim. Belg.*, **40**, 710 (1931).
388. Le Sueur, *J. Chem. Soc.*, **85**, 827 (1904); **87**, 1888 (1905).
389. Auwers and Bernhardi, *Ber.*, **24**, 2209 (1891).
390. Guérin, *Bull. soc. chim.* [3], **29**, 1124 (1903).
391. Meyer, Brod, and Soyka, *Monatsh.*, **34**, 1113 (1913).
392. Hell and Rempel, *Ber.*, **18**, 812 (1885); Weger, *ibid.*, **27**, 1210 (1894).
393. Claus and Steinkauler, *ibid.*, **20**, 2882 (1887).
394. Le Sueur, *J. Chem. Soc.*, **91**, 1365 (1907).

395. Keller, U. S. Patent 1,959,478 (1934).
396. Jones, *J. Am. Chem. Soc.*, **37**, 586 (1915).
397. Asinger, *Ber.*, **75B**, 660 (1942).
398. Asinger, *ibid.*, **75B**, 664 (1942).
399. Hell and Jordanoff, *ibid.*, **24**, 936 (1891).
400. Kudielka, *Monatsh.*, **29**, 351 (1908).
401. Marvel and du Vigneaud, *Organic Syntheses*, Coll. Vol. I, Gilman, editor, p. 40, John Wiley & Sons, New York (1932).
402. Henke and Schofield, U. S. Patent 2,279,138 (1942).
403. Keller, U. S. Patent 1,947,650 (1934).
404. Honovski, *J. Am. Chem. Soc.*, **36**, 1028 (1914).
405. Guest, U. S. Patents 2,277,015–6 (1942).
406. Chuit, Boelsing, Hausser, and Malet, *Helv. Chim. Acta*, **10**, 167 (1927).
407. Kalischer and Keller, U. S. Patents 1,851,102 (1932); 1,949,837 (1934).
408. van Eldik Thieme, *J. prakt. Chem.* [2], **85**, 284 (1912).
409. Grün and Corelli, *Z. angew. Chem.*, **25**, 665 (1912).
410. Geitel, *J. prakt. Chem.* [2], **37**, 53 (1888).
411. Sabainev, *J. Russ. Phys. Chem. Soc.*, **18**, 35, 87 (1886).
412. Blumenstock, *Monatsh.*, **46**, 334 (1925).
413. Tschernovorowa, *J. Gen. Chem. (U.S.S.R.)*, **10**, 146 (1940).
414. Grün and Janko, *Chem. Umschau*, **23**, 15 (1916).
415. Steger, van Loon, Jellenga, and Pennekamp, *Rec. trav. chim.*, **57**, 25 (1938).
416. Bauer and Stockhausen, *J. prakt. Chem.* [2], **130**, 35 (1931).
417. Pomeranz, *Seifensieder-Ztg.*, **59**, 3, 79 (1932).
418. Seck and Dittmar, *Fettchem. Umschau*, **40**, 146 (1933).
419. Grün and Woldenberg, *J. Am. Chem. Soc.*, **31**, 490 (1909).
420. Runge, *Farbenchemie*, Part 1, p. 213, Mittler, Berlin (1834).
421. Nishizawa and Winokuti, *Chem. Umschau*, **36**, 79 (1929); Nishizawa and Sinozaki, *J. Soc. Chem. Ind.*, Japan, **32**, 779 (1929).
422. Juillard, *Bull. soc. chim.* [3], **11**, 280 (1894).
423. Woldenberg, *Dissertation*, Zurich (1908).
424. Chonowsky, *Ber.*, **42**, 3339 (1909).
425. Grün, *ibid.*, **42**, 3759 (1909).
426. Rassow, *Z. angew. Chem.*, **26**, 316 (1913).
427. Grün, *Ber.*, **39**, 4400 (1906).
428. Rassow, *Orig. Com. 8th Intern. Congr. Appl. Chem. (Appendix)*, **25**, 421 (1912).
429. Kulikov, *Byull. Obmena Opyt. Lakokrasoch. Prom.*, No. **3**, 49 (1939).
430. Ivanova, Bogoslovskii, and Buman, *ibid.*, No. **4**, 9 (1940).
431. Osnos and Golovistikov, *Masloboĭno-Zhirovaya Prom.*, **16**, No. 5/6, 33 (1940).
432. Chilikin, *J. Russ. Phys. Chem. Soc.*, **44**, 515 (1912).
433. Grün and Wetterkamp, *Z. Farben-Ind.*, **7**, 375 (1909).
434. Pomeranz, *Seifensieder-Ztg.*, **54**, 272 (1927).
435. Siebenbürger, U. S. Patent 1,942,577 (1934).
436. Soc. pour l'ind. chim. à Bâle, Ger. Patent 645,608 (1937).
437. Crowder, U. S. Patent 2,268,443 (1941).
438. Chemische and Seifenfabrik R. Baumheier A.-G., Fr. Patent 721,041 (1931); Ger. Patent 636,136 (1936).

439. H. Th. Böhme A.-G., Brit. Patents 261,385, 263,117 (1925); Fr. Patent 637,338 (1927).
440. Farb.- und Gerbstoffwerke C. Flesch, Brit. Patents 282,626 (1926); 284,206 (1927).
441. I. G. Farbenind. A.-G., Brit. Patent 288,127 (1927).
442. Bertsch, U. S. Patent 1,801,189 (1931).
443. I. G. Farbenind. A.-G., Brit. Patent 296,999 (1927); Ger. Patent 501,086 (1928).
444. Chemische Fabrik Milch A.-G., Brit. Patent 288,126 (1927).
445. Böhme Fettchemie-Ges. m. b. H., Ger. Patent 664,387 (1938).
446. Moyer, U. S. Patents 2,195,186-8 (1940).
447. H. Th. Böhme A.-G., Fr. Patent 694,692 (1930).
448. N. V. Chemische Fabrieken "Servo" and M. D. Rozenbroek, Dutch Patents 26,131, 26,710 (1932).
449. I. G. Farbenind. A.-G., Brit. Patent 272,967 (1926).
450. I. G. Farbenind. A.-G., Brit. Patent 330,904 (1929).
451. Dreyfus, Fr. Patent 636,488 (1927).
452. Randel, U. S. Patent 1,374,607 (1921).
453. Twitchell, Dutch Patent 1,360 (1916); U. S. Patent 1,170,468 (1916).
454. Thauss, Mauthe, and Günther, U. S. Patents 1,667,225-6 (1928).
455. Soc. anon. pour l'ind. chim. à Bâle, Ger. Patent 548,799 (1930).
456. H. Th. Böhme A.-G. and Heinrich Bertsch, Ger. Patent 552,327 (1926).
457. Oranienburger Chemische Fabrik A.-G., Ger. Patent 625,637 (1936).
458. Bertsch, U. S. Patent 1,910,459 (1933).
459. H. Th. Böhme A.-G., Fr. Patent 694,692 (1930).
460. I. G. Farbenind. A.-G., Ger. Patent 551,424 (1930).
461. Böhme Fettchemie-Ges. m. b. H., Ger. Patent 633,082 (1936).
462. National Oil Products Co., Brit. Patent 526,960 (1940).
463. Russ, U. S. Patent 1,081,775 (1913); Brit. Patent 21,853 (1913).
464. H. Th. Böhme A.-G., Fr. Patent 701,187 (1930).
465. Chemische Fabrik Milch A.-G., Brit. Patent 275,267 (1926).
466. Petroff and Shestakoff, U. S. Patent 1,642,595 (1927).
467. Maruyama, Jap. Patent 132,621 (1939).
468. Ditmar, Z. angew. Chem., 27, 537 (1914).
469. Harvey and Schuette, Trans. Wisconsin Acad. Sci., 26, 225 (1931).
470. Altschul, Z. angew. Chem., 8, 535 (1895).
471. I. G. Farbenind. A.-G., Brit. Patent 340,012 (1929); Ger. Patent 539,449 (1929).
472. I. G. Farbenind. A.-G., Brit. Patent 353,736 (1930).
473. Kaufmann, Z. Untersuch. Lebensm., 51, 15 (1926); Analyst, 51, 264 (1926).
474. Riemenschneider, Swift, and Sando, Oil & Soap, 18, 203 (1941).
475. Kaufmann, Chem. Umschau, 37, 113 (1930).
476. Matthews, Brode, and Brown, Oil & Soap, 18, 182 (1941).
477. Arnold, Arch. Pharm., 277, 206 (1939).
478. Toyama and Tsuchiya, J. Soc. Chem. Ind., Japan, 38, S.b. 35 (1935).
479. Kimura, Ber., 69, 786 (1936).
480. Fischer, Ann., 403, 106 (1914).
481. Heinemann, Ger. Patents 257,641 (1911); 273,219 (1913); Brit. Patent 10,379 (1913).
482. Dewar, U. S. Pub. Health Service, Pub. Health Bull., No. 168, 31 (1927).

483. H. Th. Böhme A.-G., Brit. Patent 281,232 (1926).
484. Hoffmann-LaRoche and Co., Ger. Patents 280,411, 281,801 (1913).
485. Hoffmann-LaRoche and Co., Ger. Patent 285,991 (1914).
486. Hoffmann-LaRoche and Co., Ger. Patent 284,736 (1914).
487. Backer and Mulder, Rec. trav. chim., 55, 357 (1936).
488. Willstätter and Sonnenfeld, Ber., 47, 2801 (1914).
489. Leys, Bull. soc. chim. [4], 1, 543 (1907).
490. Ralston, Christensen, and Josh, Oil & Soap, 14, 5 (1937).
491. Ralston and McCorkle, U. S. Patents 2,262,430 (1941); 2,284,067 (1942); 2,356,884 (1944).
492. Myddleton, Barrett, and Seager, J. Am. Chem. Soc., 52, 4405 (1930).
493. Sherrill and Smith, J. Chem. Soc., 1501 (1937).
494. Diels and Alder, Ann., 460, 98 (1928).
495. Bickford, Krauczunas, and Wheeler, Oil & Soap, 19, 23 (1942).
496. Farbwerke vorm. Meister Lucius und Brüning, Ger. Patent 226,222 (1908).
497. Kaufmann, Brit. Patent 343,165 (1928); Fr. Patent 684,814 (1929); U. S. Patent 1,918,338 (1933).
498. Oranienburger Chemische Fabrik A.-G., Ger. Patent 515,679 (1928).
499. Twitchell, J. Am. Chem. Soc., 22, 22 (1900).
500. Nicolet and de Milt, ibid., 49, 1103 (1927).
501. de Milt, Abstracts of Theses, Univ. Chicago Sci. Series, 4, 123 (1925) (publ. May, 1928).
502. Schmidt, J. Am. Chem. Soc., 52, 1172 (1930).
503. Roberti, Piutti, and Dinelli, Ricerca sci., 7, II, 10 (1936).
504. Mazume and Kino, J. Soc. Chem. Ind., Japan, 32, S.b. 338 (1929).
505. Kimura and Taniguchi, ibid., 42, S.b. 234 (1939).
506. Stirton and Peterson, Ind. Eng. Chem., 31, 856 (1939).
507. Stirton, Peterson, and Groggins, ibid., 32, 1136 (1940).
508. Harmon and Marvel, J. Am. Chem. Soc., 54, 2515 (1932).
509. Niederl and Liotta, ibid., 55, 3025 (1933).
510. Kimura and Tsurugi, J. Soc. Chem. Ind., Japan, 42, S.b. 390 (1939).
511. I. G. Farbenind. A.-G., Brit. Patent 286,796 (1926).
512. Morgan and Holmes, J. Soc. Chem. Ind., 46, 152T (1927).
513. Fordyce and Johnson, J. Am. Chem. Soc., 55, 3368 (1933).
514. Spielman, J. Biol. Chem., 106, 87 (1934).
515. Fieser, Gates, and Kilmer, J. Am. Chem. Soc., 62, 2966 (1940).
516. Cason, ibid., 64, 1106 (1942).
517. Schneider and Spielman, J. Biol. Chem., 142, 345 (1942).
518. Bauer, Chem. Umschau, 33, 198 (1926).
519. Kino, Sci. Papers Inst. Phys. Chem. Research Tokyo, 16, 127, 133 (1931); 20, 103 (1933).
520. Kino, ibid., 28, 140 (1935).
521. Kino, ibid., 24, 218 (1934); J. Soc. Chem. Ind., Japan, 33, S.b. 305 (1930).
522. Scheiber, Farbe u. Lack, 585 (1929); 315 (1936); Fette u. Seifen, 43, 103 (1936).
523. Kappelmeier, Farben-Ztg., 38, 1018 (1933).
524. Wolff and Rabinovicz, Fettchem. Umschau, 40, 115 (1933).
525. Kino, Sci. Papers Inst. Phys. Chem. Research Tokyo, 26, 91 (1935).

526. Bradley, *Ind. Eng. Chem.*, **29**, 440, 579 (1937); **30**, 689, 1087 (1938); Bradley, Kropa, and Johnston, *ibid.*, **29**, 1270 (1937); Bradley and Pfann, *ibid.*, **32**, 694 (1940); Bradley and Richardson, *ibid.*, **32**, 963 (1940); Bradley and Johnston, *ibid.*, **32**, 802 (1940); **33**, 86 (1941).

527. Brod, France, and Evans, *ibid.*, **31**, 114 (1939).

528. Ault, Cowan, Kass, and Jackson, *ibid.*, **34**, 1120 (1942).

529. Bauer and Liao, *Fette u. Seifen*, **47**, 250 (1940).

530. Starkweather, *J. Am. Chem. Soc.*, **56**, 1870 (1934).

531. De Nordiske Fabriker, Brit. Patent 127,814 (1919); De Nordiske Fabriker de-no-fa Aktieselskap, Brit. Patent 166,236 (1919).

532. Varrentrapp, *Ann.*, **35**, 196 (1840).

533. M. Saytzeff, C. Saytzeff, and A. Saytzeff, *J. prakt. Chem.* [2], **35**, 369 (1887); [2], **37**, 269 (1888).

534. Egorov, *J. Russ. Phys. Chem. Soc.*, **46**, 975 (1914).

535. Wagner, *Ber.*, **21**, 3347 (1888).

536. Eckert, *Monatsh.*, **38**, 1 (1917); *J. Chem. Soc.*, **112**, i, 317 (1917).

537. Le Sueur, *ibid.*, **79**, 1313 (1901).

538. Le Sueur and Withers, *ibid.*, **105**, 2800 (1914).

539. Nicolet and Jurist, *J. Am. Chem. Soc.*, **44**, 1136 (1922).

540. Linstead, *J. Chem. Soc.*, 2579 (1927); Eccott and Linstead, *ibid.*, 2153 (1929); Linstead, *ibid.*, 1603 (1930).

541. Linstead and Noble, *ibid.*, 614 (1934).

542. Scheiber, U. S. Patent 1,896,467 (1933).

543. Stiepel, U. S. Patent 1,429,114 (1922).

544. Moore, *Biochem. J.*, **31**, 138 (1937).

545. Kass, Miller, and Burr, *J. Am. Chem. Soc.*, **61**, 482 (1939).

546. Turpeinen, *ibid.*, **60**, 56 (1938).

547. Burr, U. S. Patent 2,242,230 (1941).

548. Mitchell and Kraybill, *J. Am. Chem. Soc.*, **64**, 988 (1942).

549. Turk and Boone, *Oil & Soap*, **21**, 321 (1944).

550. Mailhe, *Compt. rend.*, **173**, 658 (1921).

551. Mailhe, *ibid.*, **174**, 873 (1922).

552. Mailhe, *Bull. soc. chim.* [4], **31**, 681 (1922).

553. Mailhe, *Mat. grasses*, **14**, 6223 (1922).

554. Araki, *J. Chem. Soc. Japan*, **52**, 818 (1931).

555. Zelinsky and Lewina, *J. Applied Chem. (U.S.S.R.)*, **6**, 20 (1933).

556. Engler and Lehmann, *Ber.*, **30**, 2365 (1897).

557. Stadnikov and Ivanovskii, *Trans. Karpov Chem. Inst.*, No. **4**, 175 (1925).

558. Tanaka and Kuwata, *J. Faculty Eng. Tokyo Imp. Univ.*, **17**, 293 (1928).

559. Neuberg and Rosenberg, *Petroleum*, **3**, 831 (1908).

560. Spieckermann, *Z. Untersuch. Nahr.- u. Genussm.*, **27**, 83 (1914).

561. Hoog, *Arch. Hyg.*, **100**, 271 (1928).

562. Lind and Bardwell, *J. Am. Chem. Soc.*, **48**, 1556 (1926).

563. Bell, Goodman, and Whitehead, *Bull. Am. Assoc. Petroleum Geol.*, **24**, 1529 (1940).

564. Tiratsoo, *Petroleum*, **4**, 58 (1941).

565. Sheppard and Burton, *J. Am. Chem. Soc.*, **68**, 1636 (1946).

VII

THE FATTY ACID ESTERS

Since the fatty acids occur in nature as glycerides and to a much more limited extent as esters of the higher alcohols, it is quite common to consider the esters as a source rather than as derivatives of the fatty acids. The fatty acid esters, however, represent a very large group of compounds which comprises not only those which occur in nature but also the many esters which have been synthetically prepared. The latter constitute an important group of fatty acid derivatives, especially when we consider the large number of representatives of this type which have been synthesized and studied. These synthetic esters include the simple alkyl esters, the esters of aromatic alcohols, the esters of the polyhydric alcohols, and the more complex esters such as those of cellulose, starch, and allied compounds. This present chapter discusses the preparation and physical and chemical properties of many of these synthetic esters. Although much of the information presented herewith has a direct bearing upon the structure and properties of the naturally occurring fats and waxes, the primary purpose is to assemble and discuss the large amount of data which have been reported on the synthetic esters of the fatty acids.

The synthesis of any fatty acid ester in a state of purity generally resolves itself into two operations. First, the ester must be prepared by a satisfactory procedure, and secondly, it must be purified by separation from other esters which are present in the reaction mixture, such as esters of homologous acids or esters which possess a different degree of unsaturation. This latter step may be eliminated if the purification has been originally made through the acid, but since the esters generally lend themselves readily to separation, purification is generally accomplished through them rather than the acids.

THE SIMPLE ALKYL ESTERS

The fatty acid esters of the monohydric alkyl alcohols can be prepared by several procedures, two of the most important of which are the direct esterification of a fatty acid, or less frequently its anhydride, by reaction with an excess of the alcohol, generally in the presence of an acid catalyst, and the well-known method of ester interchange or alcoholysis. Alcoholysis consists of heating a triglyceride with an excess of an alcohol in the presence of either an acidic or a basic catalyst and is frequently used for the preparation of alkyl esters. Recourse to this method is often taken for the determination of the component acids present in the natural fats. The alkyl esters have also been obtained by the reaction of the fatty acid chlorides with alcohols and by the action of soap with alkyl halides; however, such methods are less frequently employed than direct esterification or alcoholysis.

Direct Esterification

Numerous examples of the preparation of the alkyl esters of the fatty acids by direct esterification procedures, employing an excess of alcohol in the presence of various catalysts, have been reported in the literature. For example, Ruhoff and Reid [1] have accomplished the preparation of a series of esters of the saturated acids by heating the acids with an excess of the alcohol in the presence of anhydrous hydrogen chloride. Thus, methyl pentadecanoate, ethyl myristate, and propyl tridecanoate are obtained by heating one mole of the acid with four moles of the alcohol containing 3–5% of anhydrous hydrogen chloride and 30% of anhydrous calcium chloride. Butyl laurate is prepared by heating one mole of lauric acid with three moles of anhydrous butanol containing 20% of anhydrous hydrogen chloride. After refluxing for some time the reaction mixture separates into two layers and the lower aqueous layer is discarded. The ester is washed with water to remove the excess of mineral acid and dried, the alcohol is removed by distillation, and the ester is distilled. The detailed procedure for the preparation of ethyl tridecanoate has been described by Ruhoff.[2] A convenient method for esterification consists of dissolving the acid in an excess of alcohol and saturating the solution with dry hydrogen chloride, during which process the ester separates as a layer which is washed and purified. Sulfuric acid and the various aromatic sulfonic acids are quite satisfactory catalysts for the preparation of esters of the saturated acids, although their use is not recommended for the esters of the highly unsaturated acids. Phosphoric acid has been suggested [3] as an esterification catalyst for the preparation of esters of unsaturated acids. The preparation of pure ethyl linoleate and pure ethyl linolenate by the simultaneous debromination and esterification of the respective tetrabromide and hexabromide has recently been described by McCutcheon.[4] The fatty acid esters of the higher alcohols can be obtained by heating the alcohols and acids even in the absence of catalysts. For example, Bellucci [5] has reported a 95% yield of cetyl palmitate by heating equimolecular amounts of the reactants in a slow stream of carbon dioxide at a temperature ranging from 230° to 270°.

Vapor-phase esterification can be employed conveniently for the preparation of esters of the lower acids; however, the difficulty of vaporizing the higher acids somewhat precludes the use of this method for obtaining their esters. The vapor-phase, high-temperature esterification of acids by excess alcohol in the presence of catalysts such as thoria or titania has been studied by Mailhe,[6] and the use of catalysts such as H_2SO_4, H_3PO_4, or $ZnCl_2$ on an inert carrier has been suggested.[7] Esters such as butyl butyrate have been prepared by the simultaneous hydrogenation and esterification of butyric acid in the presence of mixed oxide catalysts.[8] The direct conversion of nitriles into esters has been accomplished [9] by heating a mixture of the nitrile and alcohol under pressure in the presence of sulfuric acid.

It has previously been pointed out (Chapter IV) that the enzymatic hydrolysis of an ester is a reversible reaction. Although the biochemical synthesis of the alkyl esters is probably only of theoretical importance, it is interesting to note that castor bean lipase has been used as a catalyst for the preparation of methyl oleate and other esters.[10] The esterification of oleic acid with methanol in the presence of steapsin or pancreatin by a homogeneous phase reaction has been studied.[11]

Esterification reactions should be conducted under such conditions that the reaction is brought essentially to completion. This may be accomplished by the use of a large excess of the alcohol or by the removal of one of the products of the reaction. Such reactions are, therefore, generally conducted under conditions such that the water formed by the reaction is continuously removed from the reaction mixture. Most frequently the water is removed as an azeotropic mixture of water and the alcohol.[12] Mitchovitch [13] has prepared a series of esters by removal of the water as a ternary azeotropic mixture with ethanol and toluene.

The esters of the dicarboxylic acids can be prepared by direct esterification of the acids with excess of an alcohol in the presence of acid catalysts. Locquin and Elghozy [14] have described the preparation of diethyl adipate by the esterification of adipic acid with an excess of ethanol in the presence of toluene and hydrochloric acid, the water being removed as a ternary azeotropic mixture. The diethyl esters of suberic and azelaic acids have been obtained in high yields by a similar procedure.[15] The monoethyl esters of a number of dicarboxylic acids have been prepared by heating the diesters with an equimolecular amount of the free acids at 130° for four to six hours.[16]

The Kinetics of Esterification of the Fatty Acids

Since most esterification reactions involving the fatty acids are conducted under conditions in which the reactions are brought essentially to completion, the reaction velocity is a more important consideration than the equilibrium concentration. Influences of the solvent, the concentrations of the reactants, and the structures of the acid and alcohol upon the velocity of both catalyzed and uncatalyzed esterification reactions have been the subjects of a number of investigations. It has been stated by Hinshelwood and Legard [17] that esterification is always a catalytic process and is complicated kinetically by the fact that several of the molecular or ionic species may be exhibiting independent catalytic effects. In a consideration of the velocity equation

$$\frac{-d[\text{HX}]}{dt} = k_0[\text{HX}][\text{ROH}_2{}^+] + k_1[\text{HX}]^2$$

for reactions catalyzed by hydrogen chloride in the temperature range 0–60°, the first term so outweighs the second that k_0 can be determined directly from the Goldschmidt [18] equation,

$$kct = \left(1 + \frac{a}{r}\right) \log_e \frac{a}{a - x} - \frac{x}{r}$$

where a is the initial concentration of organic acid, c is that of hydrogen, x is the amount of acid esterified in time t, and r is a constant, the concentration and time units being expressed in moles per liter and in seconds, respectively. When the reaction is conducted at high temperatures (120–200°), k_1 may be evaluated by application of the equation [19] $kt = 1/(a - x) - 1/a$. That esterification reactions can be catalyzed by the presence of undissociated acid was indicated by Goldschmidt [20] in his studies on the velocity of esterification of a series of acids by absolute ethanol in the presence and absence of acid catalysts, the esterification rate being expressed by the equation $k = C[K_A\gamma + K_B(1 - \gamma)]$, where k is the velocity constant, γ the dissociation of the catalytic acid, C its concentration, and K_B and K_A the reaction constants for the undissociated and dissociated portions of the catalytic acid.

The esterification constants of substituted acrylic acids as compared to those of the corresponding saturated acids have been studied by Sudborough and Roberts,[21] who found that an acrylic acid is esterified much less readily than its saturated analog. No simple relationship was observed between the strength of the acids and their esterification constants. Later, it was reported [22] that a double bond in the α-position has an appreciable retarding effect, whereas its influence in the β- or γ-position is comparatively small, the esterification constants being of the same magnitude as those for the corresponding saturated acids.

It has been suggested that in esterification reactions it is actually the hydroxyl of the acid rather than the hydrogen which is replaced. The velocity constants of reactions in solution may be expressed by the modified Arrhenius equation $k = PZe^{-E/RT}$, Z being the actual rate of collision between molecules capable of reaction, P the probability that a collision will lead to reaction, and E the activation energy. The value of P approaches unity for ionic reactions but is much smaller for organic reactions, such as the esterification of the fatty acids. The functional relationships which exist between PZ and E have been the subject of several investigations by Fairclough and Hinshelwood,[23] and in a study of a number of esterification reactions Hinshelwood and Legard [17] arrived at the following conclusions: (1) for a series of alcohols, changes in rate are determined by variations in the activation energies; (2) for a series of acids, those which react most slowly correspond to the highest values of C; (3) in general, there is a correlation between large values of E and large values of P, and vice versa; and (4) on changing from a non-ionic catalyst to the hydrion, there is an increase of P of about 10^4, but differences between various non-ionic catalysts seem rather to depend upon the values of E itself. In 1939, Fairclough and Hinshelwood [24] studied the kinetics of the esterification of a series of fatty acids from acetic to behenic in an attempt to evaluate the effect of increased molecular weight and other factors upon the temperature-independent term PZ of the Arrhenius equation. The effect of increasing solvent density upon the value of Z was determined by recourse to a mechanical model originally proposed by Rabinowitch,[25] in which the molecules are represented by steel balls. When the balls representing the solvent and solute are of similar size, increase in the solvent density does not decrease the collision rate, since the number of repeated collisions increases at the expense of fresh collisions. A similar effect is noted when the solute balls are smaller than those representing the solvent. When the solute balls are larger, however, the solvent assumes a close-packed structure at high solvent densities, the solute being squeezed out with an attending increase in collision rate.

TABLE I

ESTERIFICATIONS IN ETHANOL

Acid	E	$\log PZ$	$k_{100} \times 10^6$
Acetic	15,200	3.69	5.70
Propionic	15,000	3.47	4.47
Butyric	14,800	3.18	3.00
Caproic	15,100	3.41	3.39
Pelargonic	14,900	3.34	3.80
Myristic	14,800	3.30	3.99
Palmitic	15,100	3.51	4.27
Behenic	15,100	3.51	4.27

Since esterification reactions can be catalyzed by the presence of undissociated acid, the esterification of fatty acids in excess of an alcohol is bimolecular with respect to the acid. Table I, taken from the data of Fairclough and Hinshelwood,[24] shows that k is proportional to PZ since the activation energies are constant within the limits of experimental error. The value k increases appreciably from butyric to behenic acid.

For esterifications in methanol catalyzed by hydrogen chloride, the values of PZ are essentially independent of the chain length of the acid, as shown by the data given in Table II. This was attributed to the fact that hydrions are not excluded by a close-packed solvent structure.

The course of the reaction in methanol was found to be described by the Goldschmidt equation, $kct = (1 + a/r) \log_e a/(a - x) - x/r$. The value of r varies with the temperature; for example, the following values were reported for pelargonic acid: 0.25 at 45°; 0.27 at 30°; 0.39 at 20°; and 0.32 at 0°. A series of esterification reactions employing cyclohexanol as the solvent indicated a small rise in the value of PZ with increase in molecular weight of the acid. It has been reported [26] that when equimolar mixtures of

stearic and oleic acids and of lauric and behenic acids are esterified
with ethanol, both acids enter evenly into the reaction.

TABLE II

ESTERIFICATIONS IN METHANOL

Acid (N/10)	E	log PZ	k_{20}
Acetic	12,450	7.955	0.0442
Propionic	11,600	6.960	0.0384
Butyric	11,800	7.183	0.0228
Caproic	11,700	7.073	0.0208
Pelargonic	11,300	6.750	0.0198
Palmitic	11,800	7.176	0.0221
Acetic N/2	10,800	6.710	0.0447

Alcoholysis

Ester interchange or alcoholysis is frequently employed for the
preparation of the alkyl esters of the fatty acids from their corresponding glycerides. The advantages of this method are obvious,
since it is not necessary to isolate the acids and the subsequent
purification can be made through the esters. As previously stated,
this method is often used for the determination of the component
acids of the naturally occurring glycerides. Haller [27] was among
the first to observe that the fats are converted into the corresponding esters and glycerol when heated with alcohols, such as methanol, in the presence of 1–2% of hydrochloric acid. Although all
the glycerides can undergo alcoholysis, those of low molecular
weight are more reactive, and it has been observed that fatty
substances which are soluble in alcohol are more readily alcoholyzed
than those which are insoluble. The use of solvents for the fat
generally increases the rate of alcoholysis. Acid catalysts, such as
sulfuric acid or benzenesulfonic acid, can be successfully employed.[28] Since the triglycerides are generally insoluble in alcohol,
the progress of the reaction may be followed by observing the
increasing solubility of the ester mixture, the reaction being completed when the mixture becomes completely homogeneous.
Castor oil is easily alcoholyzed owing to its solubility in alcohol,
and the esterification of castor oil by methyl, propyl, or isopropyl
alcohol yields the corresponding ester of ricinoleic acid together
with smaller amounts of other esters.[29] Elsdon [30] has studied the
alcoholysis of coconut oil by methanol in the presence of hydrochloric acid and has employed this method for the estimation of
the component acids.

The direct conversion of the fats into their ethyl esters has been shown to be a stepwise process,[31] since partially alcoholyzed mixtures contain both mono- and diglycerides together with the alkyl esters. Thus, the partial alcoholysis of 3000 g. of tristearin with ethanol in the presence of hydrochloric acid was observed to yield 100 g. of unchanged ester, 300 g. of distearin, 200 g. of monostearin, and 1200 g. of ethyl stearate. Reactions of alcoholysis are catalyzed by alkaline hydroxides, and it has been stated [32] that only small amounts of soaps are formed if anhydrous conditions are employed. Alcoholysis in the presence of alkaline hydroxides has also been observed [33] to proceed stepwise with the intermediate formation of both mono- and diglycerides. The preparation of alkyl esters by the alcoholysis of glycerides under pressure has been patented.[34] Detailed procedures for the preparation and purification of methyl myristate and palmitate by the alcoholysis of bayberry wax, and of ethyl caprylate, caprate, laurate, and myristate by the alcoholysis of coconut oil, have been published.[35] It must be borne in mind that ester interchange is characteristic of all the fatty acid esters and is not limited to the glycerides or waxes. As a means of preparing the alkyl esters, however, such reactions are generally confined to the glycerides because of their ready availability.

Purification of the Alkyl Esters

Mixtures of esters may be separated into their components either by crystallization or by distillation. Frequently a combination of both methods is employed for obtaining the pure esters from their mixtures. No general method can be recommended for the separation of mixtures of esters or for the purification of an individual ester, since the procedure required is largely dependent upon the components of the acid mixture. Fractional distillation offers a very satisfactory method for the separation of mixtures of esters of the saturated acids. Ester fractionation is a recognized method for the preparation of pure acids, since it is quite common to convert a mixture of acids to their methyl or ethyl esters, separate the esters by distillation, and reconvert the purified esters to acids. Since it is quite difficult to separate saturated and unsaturated esters containing the same number of carbon atoms by distillation, it is customary in such instances to employ an initial crystallization in order to remove the unsaturated esters from the mixture. For example, ethyl stearate can easily be separated from ethyl oleate and ethyl linoleate by fractional crystallization. Mixtures of esters of the unsaturated fatty acids of similar chain length can only be separated by fractional crystallization, and frequently repeated crystallizations in the same or different solvents are required. The separation and purification of an ester mixture is generally accomplished by a combination of crystallization and fractional distillation, particularly if such mixtures contain esters of both saturated and unsaturated acids.

The preparation of pure methyl oleate from the product of the alcoholysis of olive oil may be cited as an example of the many steps which are generally necessary in order to obtain pure esters of the unsaturated acids. Wheeler and Riemenschneider [36] employed the following steps in order to effect this separation: (1) fractional distillation of the methyl esters of the mixed acids of olive oil to remove palmitic and lower acids; (2) removal of most of the linoleic ester (in the filtrate) by crystallization from acetone (15 cc./g. of ester) at −60°; (3) precipitation of the bulk of the saturated esters from acetone (10 cc./g.) at −37°, and removal by filtration; (4) further elimination of methyl linoleate by two crystallizations from acetone (15 cc./g.) at −60°; (5) fractional distillation *in vacuo* to remove small amounts of remaining methyl palmitate; (6) two crystallizations from redistilled low-boiling petroleum ether (6 cc./g.) to remove the last traces of the linoleate.

Low-temperature fractional crystallization has been successfully employed for obtaining pure methyl ricinoleate from alcoholyzed castor oil. [37] The separation of the methyl or ethyl esters of the saturated fatty acids has been described by a number of investigators, [30, 38, 39, 40, 41, 42, 43, 44] and recently Wyman and Barkenbus [45] have described a process for the fractional distillation of small amounts of the methyl esters of the higher saturated acids. André [46] has reported that the fractional distillation of a mixture of methyl oleate and methyl linoleate gives only an imperfect separation. The use of fatty acid distillation methods in the analysis of fats has been ably reviewed by Longenecker. [47] The preparation of pure methyl linoleate by a chromatographic adsorption procedure employing aluminum oxide has recently been investigated. [48]

Properties of the Fatty Acid Esters of Monohydric Aliphatic Alcohols

The physical properties of the fatty acid esters have received almost as much study as those of the fatty acids themselves, and many of our present views on the structure of long-chain compounds have been developed through investigations upon the properties of these esters. It should be mentioned, however, that there are still many unanswered questions concerning the physical properties of the fatty acid esters, and that much more work is indicated. With the esters, as with the acids and most of their derivatives, we encounter polymorphism and, in certain series, alternation in properties, both of which phenomena can undoubtedly be rationally explained by molecular-structure studies. For obvious reasons, most of the data which have been reported on the physical properties of the fatty acid esters have been obtained on the methyl and ethyl esters of the saturated fatty acids. When a compound is capable of existing in two or more polymorphic forms we frequently find some confusion in the literature concerning certain of its physical properties, and it is only when the various polymorphic forms are clearly recognized that this situation can be clarified. Fortunately, with most of the fatty acid derivatives the stable or higher-melting form is easily realizable and is the one most frequently encountered. However, certain notable exceptions to this generalization have been observed and are discussed in later chapters. In considering the fatty acid esters it seems advisable, therefore, to discuss first the properties of the stable or higher-melting forms, particularly because of the usefulness of these data. It should be borne in mind that the subsequent discussion of the other polymorphic forms and the relationship between the molecular structure and physical properties of these esters is important; in fact, it forms an essential background which must be appreciated before we obtain any complete understanding of this group of compounds.

Esters of the fatty acids generally possess lower melting points than the acids themselves. In certain series the melting points alternate, the value depending upon whether the acid contains an even or odd number of carbon atoms. Esters of the lower molecular weight acids are liquids and frequently possess quite low freezing points. The esters of acids such as palmitic and stearic are crystalline solids, whereas those of the higher molecular weight acids are frequently waxy. Those of the high molecular weight alcohols and acids are found in nature in certain waxes, and synthetic esters prepared from the higher alcohols and the higher acids resemble waxes in appearance.

TABLE III *

PHYSICAL CONSTANTS OF METHYL AND ETHYL ESTERS OF SATURATED FATTY ACIDS

Acid	Methyl Ester				Ethyl Ester			
	M.P., °C.	B.P., °C.	d_4^t	n_D^t	M.P., °C.	B.P., °C.	d_4^t	n_D^t
Valeric	−91.0†	127.3	0.9097^{0}		−91.2†	$144.6_{736.5}$	0.8765^{20}	1.41537^{15}
Caproic	−71.0†	151.5	0.90327^{0} 0.88932^{15} 0.87528^{30}	1.40699^{15}	−67.5†	166–167	0.8890^{0} 0.8732^{20}	
Enanthic	−55.8†	173.8	0.89802^{0} 0.88459^{15} 0.8715^{30}	1.41334^{15}	−66.3†	188.55	0.88622^{0} 0.87297^{15} 0.85973^{30}	
Caprylic	−34	193–194 83_{15}	0.8942^{0}	1.4069^{45}	−43.2†	208.5	0.8842^{0}	1.41989^{15}
Pelargonic	−18	$213-214_{756}$	$0.8765^{17.5}$	1.4161^{46}	−36.7†	216–219	0.88156^{0} 0.86920^{15} 0.85693^{30}	1.42415^{15}
Capric		224 114_{15}		1.4220^{45}	−19.9†	243–245		1.42771^{15}
Undecanoic		123_{9-10}			−14.7†	140_{20}		
Lauric	5	141_{15}			−1.8†	163_{25}	0.8671^{19}	$1.43269^{12.9}_{\alpha}$
Tridecanoic					−4.8†	$163-165_{5}$		
Myristic	18.5	$155-157_{7}$		1.4281^{45}	12.3	$178-180_{20}$	0.8573^{25}	
Pentadecanoic	18.5	199_{30}	0.8616^{25}	1.4390^{20}	14	139_{4}		1.4362^{20}

Palmitic	1.4278^{50} 1.4200^{70}	$184.5\text{–}185.5_{10}$	25	1.4317^{45}	184_{12}	30.55
Margaric			25.7			29.7
Stearic	1.4320^{50} 1.4238^{70}	$152_{0.18}$	33.9	1.4346^{45}	215_{15}	39.1
Nonadecanoic		$166\text{–}168_{0.27}$	36.1			39.3
Eicosanoic		$177_{0.28}$	41.65			46.6
Heneicosanoic			44.5			47.6
Docosanoic		$184\text{–}185_{0.20}$	48.7			53.3
Tricosanoic		$198\text{–}199_{0.27}$	51.4			54.4
Tetracosanoic		$198\text{–}199_{0.24}$	54.8			58.4
Pentacosanoic			57.15			60.0
Hexacosanoic			60.2			63.45
Octacosanoic			64.6			67.5
Nonacosanoic			66.6			68.8
Triacontanoic			68.45			71.7
Dotriacontanoic			72.5			74.9
Tetratriacontanoic			75.4			77.9
Hexatriacontanoic			78.6			80.9
Octatriacontanoic			80.55			83.1
Hexatetracontanoic			90.5			91.0

* The values recorded in this table have been reported by Levene and Taylor, J. Biol. Chem., **59**, 905 (1924); Whitby, J. Chem. Soc., 1458 (1926); Deffet, Bull. soc. chim. Belg., **40**, 385 (1931); Bilterys and Gisseleire, ibid., **44**, 567 (1935); van Bellinghen, ibid., **47**, 640 (1938); Francis and Piper, J. Am. Chem. Soc., **61**, 577 (1939); Wyman and Barkenbus, Ind. Eng. Chem., Anal. Ed., **12**, 658 (1940); Ruhoff, Organic Syntheses, Coll. Vol. II, Blatt, editor, p. 292, John Wiley & Sons, New York (1943).

† Denotes freezing point.

All the fatty acid esters of the monohydric alcohols are quite soluble in organic solvents. The esters are, in general, more soluble in non-polar than in polar solvents; for example, most esters are more soluble in benzene or carbon tetrachloride than in ethanol or acetone. The higher the molecular weight of the ester the less its solubility in both polar and non-polar solvents, and the solubility of an ester in a specific solvent is in inverse ratio to its melting point. Thus the ethyl, propyl, and butyl esters of an acid will be somewhat more soluble than the methyl ester, because of the higher melting point of the latter. Unsaturation is accompanied by a greatly increased solubility especially in the non-polar solvents. The solubility behavior of the high molecular weight, waxy esters somewhat resembles that of the paraffins. Because of a reduced tendency towards hydrogen bonding, the solubility characteristics of an ester in an organic solvent are more predictable than those of an acid or many of its derivatives.

The melting or freezing points, boiling points, densities, and refractive indices are the most frequently recorded and useful constants of the fatty acid esters. The physical constants of the methyl and ethyl esters of the saturated fatty acids are compiled in Table III. The melting points recorded in this table correspond to the high-melting or stable form of the esters.

A number of fatty acid esters of the higher alcohols have been described in the literature. The physical constants of some representative esters of this type are shown in Table IV.

The melting or freezing points of the esters of a saturated acid generally decrease, with increase in molecular weight of the alcohol, to a minimum with the butyl ester. Further increase in the molecular weight of the alcohol yields esters of higher melting points. This is illustrated by the freezing points of several esters of heptanoic acid studied by Bilterys and Gisseleire,[49] the following values having been reported: methyl ester, $-55.8°$; ethyl, $-66.3°$; propyl, $-64.8°$; butyl, $-68.4°$; pentyl, $-49.5°$; hexyl, $-47.9°$; heptyl, $-33.3°$; and octyl, $-21.5°$. It is further illustrated by the melting points of the esters of palmitic and stearic acids as follows: (palmitic acid esters) methyl, $30.5°$; ethyl, $25°$; propyl, $20.4°$; butyl, $18.3°$; pentyl, $19.4°$; octyl, $22.5°$; (stearic acid esters) methyl, $39.1°$; ethyl, $33.9°$; propyl, $30.5°$; butyl, $27.5°$; pentyl, $30°$; octyl, $31.8°$.

Ruhoff and Reid[1] have prepared a series of isomeric esters containing sixteen carbon atoms, ranging from methyl pentadecanoate

TABLE IV *

PHYSICAL CONSTANTS OF HIGHER ALCOHOL ESTERS OF FATTY ACIDS

Acid	Ester	M.P.,°C.	B.P.,°C.	d_4^t	n_D^t
Butyric	Pentyl	−73.2 †			
	Hexyl	−78.0 †	207.88	0.85670^{30}	1.41875^{15}
	Heptyl	−57.5 †	225.87	0.85549^{30}	1.42279^{15}
	Octyl	−39.1 †	198.80	0.85492^{30}	1.42674^{15}
Valeric	Butyl	−92.8 †			
	Hexyl	−63.1 †	226.30	0.85524^{30}	1.42286^{15}
	Heptyl	−46.4 †	245.21	0.85426^{30}	1.42635^{15}
	Octyl	−42.3 †	261.6	0.85361^{30}	
Caproic	Propyl	−74.0 †	187.5	0.85872^{30}	1.41401^{15}
	Butyl	−63.1 †	207.74	0.85685^{30}	1.41877^{15}
	Pentyl	−50.0 †	226.16	0.85526^{30}	1.42280^{15}
	Hexyl	−55.25 †	245.43	0.85414^{30}	1.42637^{15}
	Heptyl	−34.4 †	260.97	0.85330^{30}	1.42934^{15}
	Octyl	−28.4 †	275.2	0.85259^{30}	1.43256^{15}
	Allyl		186–188		
Enanthic	Propyl	−64.8 †	207.94	0.85705^{30}	1.41894^{15}
	Butyl	−68.4 †	226.18	0.85553^{30}	1.42280^{15}
	Pentyl	−49.5 †	245.44	0.85427^{30}	1.42627^{15}
	Hexyl	−47.9 †	260.89	0.85327^{30}	1.42939^{15}
	Heptyl	−33.3 †	227.21	0.85277^{30}	1.43183^{15}
	Octyl	−21.5 †	290.75	0.85200^{30}	1.43488^{15}
Caprylic	Propyl	−46.2 †	226.43	0.85773^{30}	1.42351^{15}
	Butyl	−42.9 †	245.02	0.85479^{30}	1.42647^{15}
	Pentyl	−34.8 †	260.21	0.85345^{30}	1.43019^{15}
	Hexyl	−30.6 †	277.44	0.85270^{30}	1.43230^{15}
	Heptyl	−10.2 †	290.6	0.85204^{30}	1.43492^{15}
	Octyl	−15.1 †	306.8	0.85172^{30}	1.43698^{15}
	Allyl		225–230		
Pelargonic	Heptyl		162_{12}	0.8654_{15}^{15}	1.4361^{20}
Capric	Butyl	−20 †			
	Heptyl	−20.5 †	$170–172_{12}$	0.8652_{15}^{15}	1.4399^{20}
Undecanoic	Heptyl		168_3	0.8632_{15}^{15}	1.439^{20}
Lauric	Butyl	−4.8			
	Heptyl	−2.0 †	184_{12}	0.8635_{15}^{15}	1.441^{20}

* The values recorded in this table have been reported by Gascard, *Ann. chim.* [9], **15**, 332 (1921); Heiduschka and Ripper, *Ber.*, **56**, 1736 (1923); Lievens, *Bull. soc. chim. Belg.*, **33**, 122 (1924); Deulofeu, *J. Chem. Soc.*, 528 (1928); Bilterys and Gisseleire, *Bull. soc. chim. Belg.*, **44**, 567 (1935); Roger and Dvolaitskaya, *Recherches*, **1**, 79 (1937).

† Denotes freezing point.

TABLE IV (*Continued*)

PHYSICAL CONSTANTS OF HIGHER ALCOHOL ESTERS OF FATTY ACIDS

Acid	Ester	M.P.,°C.	B.P.,°C.	d_4^t	n_D^t
Myristic	Butyl	1.0			
	Heptyl		190_3	0.8621_{15}^{15}	1.4431^{20}
Palmitic	Butyl	27.5			
	Heptyl		205	0.8642_{15}^{15}	1.4481^{20}
	Octyl	22.5			1.4358^{50}
	Decyl	30			
	Dodecyl	41			
	Tetradecyl	48			
	Pentadecyl	55.5			
	Hexadecyl	56.5			1.4410^{70}
	Triacontyl	72			
Stearic	Butyl	27.5	$220\text{--}225_{25}$		
	Pentyl	30	360		
	Heptyl		216_3	0.8661_{20}^{20}	1.4505^{20}
	Octyl	31.8		1.4373^{50}	
	Hexadecyl	51.6			1.4398^{70}
	Heptadecyl	64.6			
	Hexacosyl	73			
	Triacontyl	76			

to pentadecyl formate, and have observed the variation in melting points and other properties which occur in such a series. This group is of interest in showing the effect of structure upon the physical properties of an ester. The boiling points reach a minimum with the symmetrical ester, octyl caprylate; however, the melting points and other properties show rather wide fluctuations. The physical constants reported by these authors for this series of esters are shown in Table V.

Gascard [50] has described the preparation and properties of several of the higher molecular weight esters, examples being myricyl melissate, m.p. 90.5°, and ceryl cerotate, and has reported that such esters resemble waxes in appearance. Brigl and Fuchs [51] have also undertaken the synthesis of several higher esters; however, the values reported for their constants are probably subject to some revision. Graves [52] has accomplished the preparation of esters such as lauryl laurate, m.p. 21°, and stearyl laurate, m.p. 37°, by reaction of the respective alcohols and acids. Pickard and Kenyon [53] have prepared a number of fatty acid esters of alcohols of the general formula MeCH(OH)R, in connection with their studies upon the dependence of rotatory power on chemical constitution. Somewhat later, Kenyon [54] prepared and studied a series of fatty acid esters of alcohols of the general formula EtCH(OH)R.

The reaction of acid chlorides on mercaptans yields thio esters, the preparation and properties of which have been described.[55]

TABLE V

PHYSICAL CONSTANTS OF ISOMERIC ESTERS

C Atoms in Alkyl Group	C Atoms in Acid	b_{30},°C.	M.P.,°C.	n_D^{20}	d_4^{25}
1	15	199.0	15.46	1.4390	0.8618
2	14	195.0	11.94	1.4362	0.8573
3	13	194.0	−5.74	1.4357	0.8555
4	12	194.0	−6.84	1.4354	0.8555
5	11	193.0	−21.17	1.4356	0.8560
6	10	193.0	−17.67	1.4351	0.8553
7	9	192.5	−15.54	1.4350	0.8553
8	8	192.5	−18.08	1.4352	0.8554
9	7	193.0	−11.14	1.4352	0.8552
10	6	193.0	−19.29	1.4353	0.8552
11	5	193.5	−23.14	1.4358	0.8560
12	4	194.5	−22.64	1.4353	0.8562
13	3	195.0	−0.42	1.4363	0.8574
14	2	197.0	14.00	1.4373	0.8581
15	1	201.5	13.69	1.4399	0.8618

The reported values for the physical constants of these thio esters are shown in Table VI.

Most of the esters of the unsaturated fatty acids are liquid at ordinary temperatures. Because of the comparatively greater difficulty in obtaining these acids in a state of purity, the constants which have been reported for their esters are probably not so reliable as those recorded for the esters of the saturated acids. Table VII shows some of the values which have been reported for esters of oleic and elaidic acids.

Chernoyarova [56] has prepared a series of esters of petroselinic acid and of 10- and 7-octadecenoic acids and has reported the following constants (b.p., d_4^{20}, n_D^{20}). Petroselinic acid esters: methyl, 196–197°$_8$, 0.8767, 1.45016; isopropyl, 192–194°$_{5-6}$, 0.8688, 1.45116; butyl, 202–204°$_{6-7}$, 0.8673, 1.45267; isoamyl, 216–217°$_{5-6}$, 0.8682,

1.45357; octyl, 236–239°$_{5-7}$, 0.8652, 1.45417. 10-Octadecenoic acid esters: propyl, 198°$_{10}$, 0.8702, 1.45187; butyl, 216–218°$_8$, 0.8657, 1.44956; amyl, 247–250°$_{15-16}$, 0.8670, 1.45257; octyl, 240–241°$_{6-7}$, 0.8642, 1.45367. 7-Octadecenoic acid esters: methyl, 193–195°$_8$, 0.8743, 1.45257; propyl, 205–208°$_{10}$, 0.8704, 1.45167; butyl, 219°$_{10}$, 0.8662, 1.45217; amyl, 220–222°$_8$, 0.8700, 1.45317. Methyl linoleate has been reported [48] to have the following physical con-

TABLE VI

PROPERTIES OF ESTERS OF ALIPHATIC THIO ACIDS

Ester	M.P. or B.P., °C.	d_4^{60}	n_D^{60}
Me thiolaurate	112–115$_1$	0.8734	1.4496
Et "	115–117$_1$	0.8645	1.4478
Pr "	126–128$_1$	0.8610	1.4478
Bu "	133–135$_1$	0.8595	1.4493
Me thiomyristate	34–35	0.8668	1.4507
Et "	134–136$_1$	0.8609	1.4488
Pr "	148–150$_1$	0.8568	1.4485
Bu "	149–151$_1$	0.8570	1.4501
Me thiopalmitate	44–45	0.8644	1.4521
Et "	172–175$_1$	0.8547	1.4513
Pr "	27–28	0.8559	1.4507
Bu "	29–30	0.8579	1.4505
Me thiostearate	50–51	0.8624	1.4526
Et "	38–39	0.8550	1.4514
Pr "	34–34.5	0.8508	1.4509
Bu "	31–32	0.8534	1.4529
Pr thioöleate	175–178$_1$	0.8643	1.4577

stants: $b_{0.05-0.1}$ 145–150°, n_D^{25} 1.4594; and the ethyl ester,[57] $b_{2.5}$ 175°, b_6 193.5°, $d_4^{15.5}$ 0.8846, d_4^{25} 0.8876, $n_D^{25.5}$ 1.4578, n_D^{30} 1.4542. McCutcheon [58] has observed the following constants for ethyl linolenate: $b_{2.5}$ 173°, $d_4^{15.5}$ 0.8958, d_4^{25} 0.8890; and Ault and Brown [59] have reported b_{1-2} 200–205° and n_D^{20} 1.4723 for methyl arachidonate.

A number of esters have been prepared from α-linoleic acid tetrabromide and from α-linolenic acid hexabromide, and their constants are of interest in the purification and identification of these products. The following melting points have been reported [60] for the esters of α-linoleic acid tetrabromide: methyl, 56–60°; ethyl, 58–60°; propyl, 45–50°; isopropyl, 50–52°; and allyl, 72–80°. Stanfield and Schierz [61] have prepared a series of esters of α-linolenic acid hexabromide and have reported the following melting points: methyl, 157–158°; ethyl, 151.5–152.5°; propyl, 144–146°; isopropyl, 141–143°; butyl, 143–143.1°; isobutyl, 136–138°; *tert*-butyl, 162.0–162.5°; amyl, 135.0–135.2°; hexyl, 132.6–132.8°; heptyl, 132.6–132.8°; and octyl, 128–129°. Values in

TABLE VII *

PHYSICAL CONSTANTS OF ESTERS OF OLEIC AND ELAIDIC ACIDS

Ester	M.P.,°C.	B.P.,°C.	d_{25}^{25}	n_D^t
Oleates				
Methyl	19.9	$212–213_{15}$	$0.8734_4^{19.9}$	1.4522^{20}
Ethyl		$216–217_{15}$	0.87019	1.44729^{25}
Propyl		$216–220_{14}$	0.86399	1.44719^{25}
Isopropyl		$223–224_{15}$	0.86438	1.44488^{25}
Butyl		$227–228.5_{10}$	0.86574	1.44799^{25}
Isobutyl		$226–227_{10}$	0.86487	1.44659^{25}
t-Butyl		$223–224.5_{10}$	0.88957	1.45819^{25}
Isoamyl		$223–224_{10}$	0.86516	1.44769^{25}
t-Amyl		$223–225.5_{10}$	0.88997	1.45512^{25}
Allyl		$219–220_{10}$	0.88125	1.45349^{25}
Heptyl		216_3	0.8694_{15}^{15}	1.4539^{20}
Elaidates				
Methyl		$213.5–215_{15}$	0.87025	1.44619^{25}
Ethyl		$217–218.5_{15}$	0.86645	1.44488^{25}
Propyl		$227–227.5_{15}$	0.86681	1.44538^{25}
Isopropyl		$224–225_{15}$	0.86218	1.44378^{25}
Butyl		$228–229_{10}$	0.86260	1.44649^{25}
Isobutyl		$227.5–228_{10}$	0.86073	1.44468^{25}
t-Butyl		$224–225_{10}$		
Isoamyl		$234–234.5_{10}$	0.86212	1.44599^{25}
t-Amyl		$225–226_{10}$		
Allyl		$219.5–221_{10}$	0.87616	1.45119^{25}

* The values recorded in this table have been reported by Koyama, *J. Chem. Soc. Japan*, **52**, 768 (1931); Plisov and Golendeev, *Rep. U.S.S.R. Fat and Margarine Inst.*, No. **2**, 3 (1935); Roger and Dvolaitskaya, *Recherches*, **1**, 79 (1937); Wheeler and Riemenschneider, *Oil & Soap*, **16**, 207 (1939).

agreement with some of the above have been reported by Vincente and West.[62] Methyl and ethyl brassidates have been stated[63] to melt at 34–35° and 29–30°, respectively. Methyl stearolate melts at −3° and boils at 204–206° at 20 mm.; the ethyl ester boils at 215–216° at 20 mm. The isoamyl and isobutyl esters of diiodobehenolic acid solidify at 6° and 14°, respectively.[64]

The most frequently encountered esters of the hydroxy acids are those of ricinoleic acid. Brown and Green[37] have prepared pure methyl ricinoleate by the low-temperature fractional crystallization of the methyl esters of castor oil fatty acids and have reported the following constants: m.p., $-4.5°$, n_D^{20} 1.4628, $[\alpha]_D^{27}$ 5.19° (Me_2CO). The following constants have been observed [65] for the ethyl ester: b_{2-3} 193–194°, d_{20}^{20} 0.9182, n_D^{25} 1.4595; and for its acetate, b_{2-3} 196° and n_D^{27} 1.452. The boiling points [29] of the isopropyl and isobutyl esters of ricinoleic acid are b_{11} 233–236° and b_{10} 239–240°, respectively. Physical constants [66] for the propyl ester are b_{13} 268°, d_4^{22} 0.9079, and n_D^{22} 1.4573; and for the heptyl ester, b_{10} 295°, d_4^{22} 0.8983, and n_D^{22} 1.4566. Mühle [67] has reported that ethyl ricinelaidate melts at 16° and that methyl and ethyl ricinstearolate boil at 225° and 230° at 12 mm., respectively. Ethyl diiodoricinstearolate, prepared either by the iodination of ethyl ricinstearolate or by the esterification of diiodoricinstearolic acid, melts at 31°.[68, 69] The melting points of the esters of dihydroxystearic acid prepared from ricinoleic acid [70] form two distinct melting point curves, one for the odd- and one for the even-membered esters, the hexyl ester exhibiting the lowest melting point. The following melting points were reported for these esters: methyl, 110°; ethyl, 106°; propyl, 100.6°; butyl, 93°; pentyl, 93.7°; hexyl, 92.2°; heptyl, 94.3°; octyl, 93.4°; nonyl, 95.4°; decyl, 94.9°; dodecyl, 95.6°; tetradecyl, 96.6°; hexadecyl, 97.4°; and octadecyl, 92.2°.

Any discussion of the esters of the hydroxy acids would be incomplete without reference to the various polyesters which result from the intermolecular esterification of the hydroxy acids. Comments have already been made upon the polyricinoleic acids which are obtained by the interesterification of ricinoleic acid. The various polyesters which result from the interesterification of the terminal hydroxy acids, however, are probably the most interesting examples of this class. Such polyesters are found in nature as the etholides and have been discussed previously. The synthesis of polyesters from ω-hydroxydecanoic acid was simultaneously investigated by Chuit and Hausser [71] and by Lycan and Adams,[72] the latter of whom reported the sole product obtained by heating ω-hydroxydecanoic acid in either the presence or the absence of catalysts to be chain polyesters of the general formula $HO(CH_2)_xCO_2[(CH_2)_xCO_2]_n(CH_2)_xCO_2H$. The polyesters are white powders which are soluble in many organic solvents but are completely insoluble in water and ether. The molecular weights ranged from 1000 to 9000 depending upon the time and conditions employed for the esterification. A twenty-two-membered, dimeric lactone of ω-hydroxydecanoic acid was prepared by the dry distillation of the product obtained by the action of acetic anhydride on potassium ω-hydroxydecanoate. Prolonged heating of the polyesters yields esters of quite high molecular weight which are tough, opaque solids becoming transparent at elevated temperatures.[73] These esters are capable of being drawn into threads. Carothers and Van Natta[74] have prepared polyesters from ω-hydroxydecanoic acid which range in molecular weight from 780 to 25,200, the melting points varying from 66–67° to 75–80°; d_4^{25}, 1.0957 to 1.0621; and n_D^{25}, 1.4494 to 1.4515. The influence of molecular weight on the physical properties of these polyesters was investigated by these authors. Strong, oriented fibers are obtained from those esters having molecular weights above 9330.

The preparation and properties of methyl 12-ketostearate, m.p. 42.5°, and of butyl 12-ketostearate have recently been described by Cox.[75]

Several esters of the cyclic acids have been prepared. Methyl hydnocarpate is a solid which melts at 8° and boils at 200–203° at 19 mm.; the ethyl ester boils at 211° at 19 mm.[76] The following physical constants have been reported [77,78,79,80] for the alkyl esters of chaulmoogric acid: methyl ester, m.p. 22°, b_{20} 227°, d_{25}^{25} 0.9119, $[\alpha]_D^{15}$ +50°; ethyl ester, b_{20} 230°, d_{15}^{15} 0.90741, $[\alpha]_D^{20}$ +50.7°; isoamyl ester, b_{20} 225°; octyl ester, b_0 214.6°; and allyl ester, b_5 222.3. Ethyl iododihydrochaulmoograte melts at 35–36°.[81] Chaulmoogryl chaulmoograte has been prepared [82] by the esterification of chaulmoogryl alcohol with chaulmoogric acid. The reduction of chaulmoogric acid by sodium in amyl alcohol yields both chaulmoogryl alcohol and chaulmoogryl chaulmoograte, m.p. 42°, $[\alpha]_D^{23}$ +55.4°.

Since the dicarboxylic acids possess two replaceable hydrogens, two series of esters are obtainable, depending upon whether one or both of the hydrogens are replaced. Esterification of the dicarboxylic acids is attended by a very substantial drop in melting points. The monoesters have higher melting points than the diesters, and the diethyl esters possess lower melting points than the dimethyl esters. It is interesting to note that although the melting points of the dicarboxylic acids and possibly of their monoesters fall upon two curves, the melting points of the diethyl esters fall upon a continuous curve.[83] It has been suggested [84] that the diethyl esters exist as single molecules, whereas the acids and the monoesters form double molecules. Table VIII shows the physical constants of some of the more important methyl and ethyl esters of the dicarboxylic acids.

TABLE VIII *

PHYSICAL CONSTANTS OF METHYL AND ETHYL ESTERS OF THE DICARBOXYLIC ACIDS

Acid	Methyl		Ethyl		Dimethyl		Diethyl	
	M.P., °C.	B.P., °C., d_4^t, n_D^t	M.P., °C.	B.P., °C., d_4^t, n_D^t	M.P., °C.	B.P., °C., d_4^t, n_D^t	M.P., °C.	B.P., °C., d_4^t, n_D^t
Adipic	3	b_{10} 162	28–29	d^{20} 1.081 n^{20} 1.4384	8.5		−21.4	b_{14} 130
Pimelic		b_1 146–150 d^{20} 1.047	10	b_{18} 181–182	−20.6 †	b_{11} 121–122	−23.8 †	b_{15} 139–141 d^{20} 0.99448
Suberic	10 †		21–22	b_{16} 186–188.5 d^{23} 1.037 n^{23} 1.4412	−3.1 †	b_9 130–131 d^{20} 1.0217 n^{20} 1.43408	−5.9 †	b_{320} 251–253 d^{20} 0.9822 n^{20} 1.43278
Azelaic			28–29	$b_{5.5}$ 178–179	−3.9		−18.5	b 291 d^{15} 0.9766
Sebacic	40–41	b_{20} 208	35	b_{15} 202–203	26.4	b_{20} 175 d^{28} 0.98818 n^{28} 1.43549	5.1	$b_{7.5}$ 158–159 d^{20} 0.96461 n^{20} 1.43589
Undecanedioic					31		16	
Dodecanedioic					33.2		20	

* The values recorded in this table have been reported by Mannich and Hancu, *Ber.*, **41**, 575 (1908); Blaise and Koehler, *Bull. soc. chim.* [4], **5**, 681 (1909); Fairweather, *Phil. Mag.* [7], **1**, 944 (1926); Normand, Ross, and Henderson, *J. Chem. Soc.*, 2632 (1926); Ceder, *Ann. Univ. Fennicae Aboensis, Series A2*, No. 4 (1926); Fourneau and Sabetay, *Bull. soc. chim.* [4], **45**, 834 (1929); Müller and Rölz, *Organic Syntheses*, **11**, 42 (1931); Meyer, *Helv. Chim. Acta*, **16**, 1291 (1933); Morgan and Walton, *J. Chem. Soc.*, 902 (1936).

† Denotes freezing point.

The following values have been reported [84, 85] for the melting points of the dimethyl and diethyl esters of some of the higher dicarboxylic acids: (C content of acids, m.p.) dimethyl esters: C_{13}, 33.2°; C_{14}, 43°; C_{15}, 43°; C_{16}, 51.6°; C_{17}, 52.3°; C_{18}, 60°; C_{19}, 60.2°; diethyl esters: C_{13}, 20°; C_{14}, 27°; C_{15}, 30°; C_{16}, 39°; C_{18}, 48.2°; C_{19}, 49.2°; C_{22}, 56°; C_{30}, 74°; C_{34}, 80°. Chuit [85] has determined the boiling points and densities of a number of the dimethyl and diethyl esters of the higher dicarboxylic acids, and the boiling points of the di-*tert*-butyl esters of the dicarboxylic acids from malonic to sebacic acid inclusive have been reported by Backer and Homan. [86] The following constants have been reported [12, 87] for the propyl and butyl esters of adipic acid: propyl, b_4 146°, d_4^{20} 1.0574, n_D^{20} 1.4401; butyl, b_4 155.5°, d_4^{20} 1.0377, n_D^{20} 1.4418; dipropyl, m.p. −20.25°, b_{16} 155°, d_4^{20} 0.9790, n_D^{20} 1.4314; dibutyl, m.p. −37.5°, b_4 145°, d_4^{20} 0.9652, n_D^{20} 1.4369.

Relationship between the Structure and Physical Properties of Fatty Acid Esters, Polymorphism

The zigzag arrangement of carbon atoms in an alkyl chain, the alternation in physical properties in the solid state, and the significance of polymorphism as evidenced by x-ray and thermal studies have been discussed in general terms in a previous chapter. The many investigations which have been made upon the methyl and ethyl esters of the fatty acids have not only contributed greatly to our knowledge of the esters themselves but have also afforded us a much better insight into the structure of long-chain compounds in general. It is largely by an appreciation of the structure of these esters as revealed by x-ray measurements that we are able to correlate the physical properties of their various polymorphic forms and to interpret many of the physical data which have been obtained concerning them.

In 1923, Shearer [88] observed that the increase in length per CH_2 group for the methyl, ethyl, octyl, and cetyl esters of palmitic acid is 1.22 Å, as compared to an increase of 2.0 Å per CH_2 group for the acids themselves. The measurements of the long spacings of these esters indicate that they exist as single molecules, thus being distinguished from the acids. Francis, Piper, and Malkin [89] have determined the long spacings of the ethyl esters of the saturated acids from palmitic to triacontanoic acid inclusive to be as follows: (C atoms in acid, long spacing in Å) 16, 22.9; 17, 24.6; 18, 25.8; 19, 26.8; 20, 27.6; 21, 29.2; 22, 30.1; 23, 31.36; 24, 32.1;

25, 33.5; 26, 34.6; 27, 35.8; 28, 37.0; 29, 38.0; 30, 39.2. Probably the most significant finding of these authors is that the measurements of the long crystal spacings of equimolar mixtures of these esters give values appreciably greater than those for either of the components. Thus an equimolar mixture of esters containing nineteen and twenty-two carbon atoms gives a spacing corresponding to a C_{24} ester, whereas a C_{22} and C_{24} ester mixture gives a spacing corresponding to a C_{26} ester. In a continuation of this study, Malkin [90] and others [91] found that the ethyl esters of the saturated acids exist in two modifications, one of which is stable only in the vicinity of the melting point. The transition of this metastable form is greatly retarded in the case of mixtures, and since its spacing is longer than that of the stable form the longer crystal spacings which are observed in equimolar mixtures of the ethyl esters are explainable. Previously melted samples of the pure esters which are held just below their melting points show the longer crystal spacings of the metastable form when examined by x ray, whereas pressed samples cooled to room temperature show the shorter spacing of the stable form. The spacings observed by Malkin for the two modifications of the ethyl esters from ethyl palmitate to hexacosanoate are shown in Table IX.

TABLE IX

LONG SPACINGS OF ETHYL ESTERS IN ÅNGSTRÖMS

No. of C Atoms in Acid

	16	17	18	19	20	21	22	23	24	25	26
Pressed	23.0	24.6	25.5	26.8	28.0	29.2	30.1	31.4	32.1	33.9	34.6
Melted	....	27.1	28.6	29.8	31.3	32.4	....	....	....	....	....

Differences in the spacings are due to the angle of tilt of the carbon chain with respect to the terminal group, the shorter spacings corresponding to an angle of 67°30′ and the longer to an angle of 90°. King and Garner [92] have stated that the angle of tilt is 64°26′ for the β-esters (tilted) which contain from twenty to twenty-six carbon atoms. Since the vertical modification is assumed in the vicinity of the melting point, we have an explanation of the previously confusing observation that the ethyl esters possess a tilted chain and yet do not exhibit alternation. The cooling curves of the ethyl esters from ethyl margarate upward show two distinct arrests, the liquid first solidifying to a transparent solid and then becoming opaque. These arrests are accompanied by changes in the crystal spacings as described above. It has been stated by Malkin that the transparent form of the ethyl esters is somewhat more stable for esters of the odd acids than for those of the even acids. Buckingham [93] has postulated that the freedom of movement of the hydrocarbon chains in the vertical forms is much greater than in the tilted forms, which accounts for the observation that the heats of crystallization per methylene group are much lower and the specific heats much higher in the former than in the latter modification. The thermal properties of the ethyl esters have been investigated by King and Garner,[92, 94] who reported that the ethyl esters of the even acids give two melting point curves which cross in the neighborhood of the twenty-carbon ester, the equations being as follows:

$$T_m = \frac{0.7630n + 0.63}{0.00179n + 0.01475} \quad \text{up to } n = 20$$

and

$$T_m = \frac{0.7081n - 3.28}{0.001796n - 0.0012} \quad \text{above } n = 20$$

The melting points of the ethyl esters of the odd acids are expressed by the equation

$$T_m = \frac{0.8389n - 5.58}{0.00224n - 0.00904}$$

The two equations for the even esters are occasioned by the fact that the melting point curves for the α- and β-forms cross in the neighborhood of the twenty-carbon ester, the α-modification of the higher members being stable at the melting point. Phillips and Mumford [95] have stated that both the cooling and the heating curves of ethyl esters of the fatty acids containing an odd number of carbon atoms show two distinct arrests, one at the setting point of the α-form and the other at the point at which this form changes reversibly into the opaque β-form, the α-form being stable between these two temperatures. The change is enantiotropic and in such esters the α- or transparent form is the stable form in contact with the melt. Only the cooling curves of the ethyl esters of the even acids up to C_{20} show two arrests, the change being monotropic, and the α-form of these esters is, therefore, unstable in the vicinity of the melting point. In the examination of the thermal properties of ethyl caprate, laurate, and stearate it was observed that only the β-form is readily obtainable. A later study [96] upon ethyl tridecanoate showed that it does not crystallize from the melt in the metastable, transparent α-form, but in the stable, opaque form before the α freezing point is reached. The β melting point and the α freezing point curves of the odd esters intersect just below ethyl pentadecanoate, the β melting points of the lower odd esters being below the α freezing point curve. Thus such esters, if polymorphic, will exhibit monotropy. In consideration of the above findings it appears that the ethyl esters fall into three categories, as follows: (1) for esters containing thirteen or less carbon atoms, the β- or opaque form is stable with the melt and the α-form is difficultly realizable; (2) for esters containing between thirteen and nineteen carbon atoms, the α-form of the uneven esters is stable in the vicinity of the melting point, whereas the α-form of the even esters is metastable; (3) for esters containing more than nineteen carbon atoms, the α-form of both even and odd esters is stable in the vicinity of the melting point. The polymorphic forms of the ethyl esters, their heats and temperatures of transition, and their relative ease of realization have been studied by van Bellinghen,[97] and the reader is referred to this article for an extensive treatment of the subject.

The melting points and heats of crystallization of the tilted, β-modifications yield an alternating series whereas those of the vertical, α-form are non-alternating. The thermal properties of the ethyl esters of the saturated fatty acids are shown in Table XXVI, Chapter V. The transition temperatures which have been reported for several of these esters are as follows: ethyl palmitate, $21°$; margarate, $9.5°$; stearate, $25.5–26.0°$; nonadecanoate, $24.3–24.7°$; eicosanoate, $32–33.5°$; and behenate, $34.5°$. It has been pointed out that the heats of crystallization of the even esters vary lineally with the number of carbon atoms, although it should be observed that there is a change of slope at $n = 20$, which has been attributed to a difference in the manner of orientation of the ester group in the crystal lattice.

The methyl esters, in contrast to the ethyl esters, crystallize in double molecules. This indicates that the methyl group has a binding power similar to, but probably much weaker than, that of the hydrogen of the acids. Malkin [90] has stated that this satisfactorily accounts for the fact that the methyl esters melt at higher temperatures than the corresponding ethyl esters. It might be mentioned, however, that this does not explain the fact that the melting points of the esters of a specific acid generally reach a minimum with the butyl ester, unless one admits of some degree of bonding in the ethyl and propyl esters. The methyl esters show evidence of polymorphism only with acids containing an odd number of carbon atoms, one of the forms being stable in the vicinity of the melting point. Table X shows the long spacings of the methyl esters of the saturated acids as reported by Malkin.[90]

TABLE X

LONG SPACINGS OF METHYL ESTERS IN ÅNGSTRÖMS

No. of C Atoms in Acid

	14	15	16	17	18	19	20	21	22	23
Pressed	38.8	41.8	43.2	46.5	47.8	51.2	56.2	55.6	56.7	60.4
Melted	38.8	23.6	43.3	26.0	47.8	28.4	....	30.9	....	....

It will be noted that the methyl esters of the even acids apparently exist in only one modification, which appears to be bimolecular. The esters of the odd acids exhibit two forms, the stable modification existing as double molecules and the unstable form as single molecules. Calculations of the angles of tilt indicate the chain to be inclined at 63° and 67°30′ for the even and odd stable forms, respectively, and at 75° for the metastable form of the esters of the odd acids. The cooling curves for the methyl esters of the odd acids show two arrests, the transition apparently being reversible. On the other hand, the cooling curves for the methyl esters of the even acids show only one arrest, an observation which is predictable from their crystal spacings. The heats of crystallization and specific heats of the methyl esters of several saturated acids containing an even number of carbon atoms are shown in Table XXVII, Chapter V. The thermal properties of most of the methyl esters of odd acids have not been investigated. The thermal constants of methyl nonadecanoate have been reported [94] to be as follows: heats of crystallization, vertical form, 10.24, tilted form, 14.74 kg. cal./g.-mol.; heat of transition, 4.63 kg. cal./g.-mol.; specific heats, liquid, 0.51, vertical form, 0.45 cal./g.; transition temperature, 31°; setting point, 38.64°. The fact that the heats of transition of the methyl esters are almost identical with those of the ethyl esters has been stated to be quite difficult of explanation, since the former apparently involves a change from a single to a double molecule whereas the latter takes place without any change in the degree of association. The melting points of the methyl esters of the even acids may be expressed by the equation $T_m = (1.083n - 4.15)/(0.002839n - 0.00185)$.

The crystal spacings of several of the mono- and diethyl esters of the dicarboxylic acids are shown in Table XV, Chapter V. The crystal spacings for the monoethyl esters of these acids indicate that there are two molecules between reflecting planes, whereas those of the diethyl esters contain only one molecule. The crystal spacings of the diethyl esters show a constant increment per methylene group.[84] It has previously been observed that the melting points of the diethyl esters of the dicarboxylic acids fall upon a continuous curve, an observation which is significant in view of the marked alternation exhibited by the acids.

Dielectric and Other Properties of Esters

The dielectric capacity of ethyl behenate has been reported[19] to fall upon solidification and also upon its transition from the α- to the β-form. Lewis and Smyth[98] have determined the polarization and dipole moments of ethyl undecanoate, ethyl palmitate, and ethyl stearate and have reported the dipole moments to be essentially identical for the three esters ($\mu \times 10^{18} = 1.88$). This value is similar to that previously observed[99] for ethyl acetate in benzene solution. It was concluded, therefore, that the long chains of these molecules do not hinder their free rotation in an externally applied electric field. The difference between the polarizations of a pure liquid ester and an ester at infinite dilution decreases with increasing chain length, indicating that long hydrocarbon chains reduce intermolecular action by dilution of the dipoles.

The Raman spectra for several methyl and ethyl esters of the saturated fatty acids have been reported.[100] Ellis[101] has determined the surface tension and parachor values for ethyl palmitate.

Binary and Ternary Systems of Esters

The studies which have been reported upon the binary and ternary systems of the fatty acid esters are of importance not only because the information contributes materially to our knowledge of these compounds but also because such studies are useful in ester separation and in the evaluation of the purity of individual esters. Smith[102] has shown that the system formed by the α-modifications of ethyl palmitate and ethyl stearate is an unbroken series of solid solutions possessing no maximum or minimum. Later, Phillips and Mumford[103] stated that binary systems of the ethyl esters, whether they involve even-even, even-odd, or odd-odd components, form systems similar to the above. This was soon confirmed by the studies of Carey and Smith [104] upon the systems ethyl palmitate-ethyl margarate and ethyl margarate-ethyl stearate. In their investigation of systems involving ethyl margarate, Phillips and Mumford [103] observed that its admixture with a lower homolog lowers its freezing point whereas admixture with a higher homolog raises it, and thus a ternary mixture may exhibit a freezing point similar to that of the pure ester. The temperature of the transition $\alpha \rightarrow \beta$, however, is lowered by the addition of either a higher or a lower homolog, as is also that of the reverse transition $\beta \rightarrow \alpha$. By determining the temperature at which the transition $\beta \rightarrow \alpha$ occurs, therefore, one can evaluate the purity of the ester. Thus, the transition $\beta \rightarrow \alpha$ for ethyl margarate occurs at 20.6°, the addition of an approximately 20% mole fraction of ethyl palmitate or ethyl stearate lowering the value to 16.0° or 18.8°, respectively. Systems involving both the α- and β-modifications of ethyl margarate with its odd homologs exist as a series of solid solutions without maxima or minima.[96] In the case of odd-even systems, however, the β-modifications apparently exist as solid solutions which exhibit a minimum. It was observed that in binary mixtures of ethyl margarate with its homologs the cooling curves show two arrests in the α-solid, thus indicating that the transition $\alpha \rightarrow \beta$ may proceed through an intermediate modification. Mumford and Phillips [96] have attempted to stabilize the α-forms of the lower esters by admixture with the higher homologs and have observed that the amount of the higher homolog required increases rapidly as the series is descended. Thus, α-ethyl myristate is stabilized by the addition of 3.5 mole % of ethyl palmitate, whereas α-ethyl laurate requires about 13 mole % of ethyl myristate. The amount of a lower homolog necessary for stabilization is much greater still; for example, α-ethyl myristate requires 36 mole % of ethyl laurate. In the system ethyl caprate-ethyl laurate the α-form was not realized. The α-forms of the two component esters give a continuous series of solid solutions irrespective of whether the components contain an odd or even number of carbon atoms. Although C_1 arrests were observed in the cooling curves, this form could not be isolated since it changes spontaneously in the case of ethyl margarate into the high-melting β-form. The system ethyl laurate-ethyl myristate as determined by Mumford and Phillips is shown in Fig. 1.

The system methyl palmitate-methyl stearate (Fig. 2) has been investigated by Guy and Smith,[105] who have observed that the opaque β-form becomes metastable near the middle of the system.

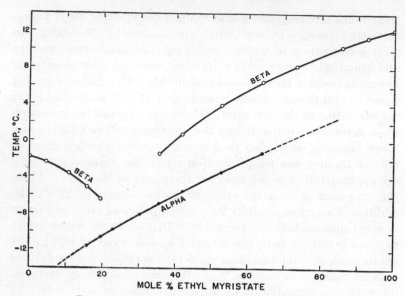

FIG. 1.   The system: ethyl laurate-ethyl myristate.

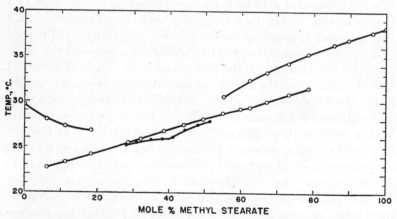

FIG. 2.   The system: methyl palmitate-methyl stearate.

The greater stability of the transparent α-form is evidence of the
weakness of the components in forming double molecules.   A
change in crystal lattice is indicated by a discontinuity in the
melting point curve between 50% and 60% of methyl stearate.
Mixtures which contain 25% to 90% of methyl palmitate crystallize in transparent needles or plates which when rubbed may

change into the opaque form. Attempts to locate the melting points of the opaque form in this region are shown in the figure by the filled circles. Near the extremes the mixtures first crystallize in transparent plates which soon become opaque. Compound formation is not evidenced in the figure; however, it is not excluded since the system has not been completed.

From consideration of the above it is evident that although considerable work has been done with these esters many moot points still remain. Association in the stable modification of the methyl esters, which is clearly evidenced by x-ray studies, has not been correlated with the thermal measurements, and the mechanisms of transitions and relative stabilities of the various polymorphic forms, both in the pure esters and in their mixtures, require further study.

Hydrolysis and Saponification of the Alkyl Esters

A kinetic study of the alkaline hydrolysis of several of the ethyl esters has been made by Evans, Gordon, and Watson.[106] From a consideration of their results on the basis of the equation $k = PZe^{-E/RT}$, it was shown that changes in the velocity of hydrolysis are due almost entirely to differences in the various energies of activation, E apparently varying in accordance with the inductive effect of the R group. In the alkaline hydrolysis of these esters it was observed that there is a gradual rise in the activation energy with increase in molecular weight of the ester. The values of k at several temperatures and of the activation energies of several of the ethyl esters investigated by these authors are shown in Table XI.

TABLE XI

ALKALINE HYDROLYSIS OF ESTERS IN 85% ETHANOL

Ethyl Ester	$k_{25} \times 10^3$	$k_{35} \times 10^3$	$k_{50} \times 10^3$	E (cal.)
Acetate	6.21	13.6	38.7	14,200
Propionate	3.63	8.31	24.7	14,500
Butyrate	1.72	3.94	12.2	15,000
Isobutyrate	0.801	1.84	5.72	14,500
Valerate	1.92	4.42	13.3	14,700
Isovalerate	0.427	1.02	3.34	15,700
Caproate	2.07	4.81	14.5	14,800
Enanthate	1.79	4.06	12.7	15,000
Caprylate	1.84	4.30	13.3	15,000

A subsequent investigation [107] of the alkaline hydrolysis of such esters in aqueous acetone confirmed the original observations that the velocity of hydrolysis varies with changes in E, the factor P rising with increase of E. It was noted that the velocity coefficients decrease steadily to a constant value at ethyl valerate. Since the velocity coefficient for this ester is close to that of ethyl enanthate, it is probably comparable with the coefficients of the higher esters. A comparison [108] of the rate constants of the saponification of ethyl laurate and ethyl butyrate has confirmed the statement that an increase in chain length beyond four carbon atoms does not have a measurable effect upon the velocity of saponification. The activating energy for the alkaline hydrolysis of these esters is appreciably lower in the acetone-water than in the ethanol-water system.

Acid hydrolysis of the alkyl esters evidently proceeds by a mechanism different from that of alkaline hydrolysis, since the activation energy is constant for the straight-chain esters.[107] The velocity of hydrolysis, however, decreases with increase in molecular weight of the ester. Smith and Steele [109] have subsequently observed that the rate of acid hydrolysis decreases slightly with increase in chain length of the esters and that substitution must take place in the α- or β-position to effect a substantial diminution in the rate constant. The reaction velocities at several temperatures and the activation energies for the acid hydrolysis of several esters as reported by Davies and Evans [107] are shown in Table XII.

TABLE XII

ACID HYDROLYSIS OF ESTERS IN 70% ACETONE

Ethyl Ester	$k_{24.8} \times 10^5$	$k_{35.0} \times 10^5$	$k_{44.7} \times 10^5$	E (cal.)
Acetate	4.47	10.9	24.7	16,200
Propionate	3.70	9.24	20.7	16,200
Butyrate	1.96	4.83	10.8	16,100
Valerate	1.79	4.45	10.2	16,500
Caproate	1.77	4.30	9.76	16,200
Enanthate	1.64	4.09	9.07	16,200
Caprylate	1.55	3.85	8.70	16,300

The mechanisms of the acid and alkaline hydrolyses of carboxylic esters as proposed by Lowry [110] are as follows:

Acid Hydrolysis

$$\underset{\substack{| \\ H-OH \; H^+}}{\overset{\displaystyle O}{\underset{\displaystyle \parallel}{R-C-OR'}}} \rightarrow \underset{\substack{| \\ H^+ \; OH \; H}}{\overset{\displaystyle O^-}{\underset{\displaystyle \overset{+}{|}}{R-C-OR'}}} \rightarrow \overset{\displaystyle O}{\underset{\displaystyle \parallel}{R-C-OH}} + R'OH + H^+$$

Alkaline Hydrolysis

$$\underset{\substack{| \\ OH^- \; H-OH}}{\overset{\displaystyle O}{\underset{\displaystyle \parallel}{R-C-OR'}}} \rightarrow \underset{\substack{| \\ OH \; H \; OH^-}}{\overset{\displaystyle O^-}{\underset{\displaystyle \overset{+}{|}}{R-C-OR'}}} \rightarrow \overset{\displaystyle O}{\underset{\displaystyle \parallel}{R-C-OH}} + R'OH + OH^-$$

In interpreting their results, Davies and Evans [107] have proposed a somewhat different mechanism. These authors have assumed that in alkaline hydrolysis the energy of activation is required for the process

$$\overset{\displaystyle O}{\underset{\displaystyle \parallel}{R-C-OEt}} + OH^- \rightarrow \underset{\substack{| \\ OH}}{\overset{\displaystyle O^-}{\underset{\displaystyle |}{R-C-OEt}}}$$

E is, therefore, the sum of the energies needed for the change $>\overset{\frown}{C}=O \rightarrow >\overset{+}{C}-\overset{-}{O}$ and for the approach of the hydroxyl ion. Attention was called to the findings of Pauling and Sherman [111] that the energy required for the change $C\overset{\frown}{=}O$ is quite small since the original ester resonates between the forms

R—C$\overset{\displaystyle O}{\underset{\displaystyle \diagdown \text{OEt}}{\diagup}}$ and R—C$\overset{\displaystyle O^-}{\underset{\displaystyle \overset{+}{\diagdown} \text{OEt}}{\diagup}}$. The activating energy, therefore,

is largely a function of the force required to overcome the repulsion between the ester molecule and the approaching ion. The initial and final states were depicted as follows:

$$RCO_2Et + O\overline{H} \rightarrow RCO\overline{O} + EtOH$$

It was pointed out that in the acid hydrolysis of the esters the energy of activation is needed mainly for bringing up the water molecule to the carbonyl carbon, the energy of activation being greater than that required for the alkaline hydrolysis. The initial and final states are represented as follows:

$$RCO_2Et + H^+ + HOH \rightarrow RCO_2H + EtOH + H^+$$

Salmi [112] has shown that the rate constants for the saponification of the methyl esters of butyric and the higher acids are comparable with the rates of esterification. Constants for the velocity of the acid hydrolysis of the methyl esters at 25° in the presence of 0.2080N HCl were reported by this author to be as follows: butyrate, 0.00423; valerate, 0.00441; caproate, 0.00410; and enanthate, 0.00412.

Miscellaneous Reactions of Alkyl Esters

Polymerizations involving the alkyl esters of the unsaturated acids do not differ fundamentally from those of the acids themselves. The polymerization of the methyl esters of certain highly unsaturated acids has been investigated by Kino.[113] The pyrolysis of the alkyl esters generally yields complex mixtures which contain unsaturated hydrocarbons. The formation of ethylenic hydrocarbons by the pyrolysis of esters in the presence of aluminum chloride has been investigated.[114]

THE FATTY ACID ESTERS OF AROMATIC OR CYCLIC ALCOHOLS

In contrast to the alkyl esters of the fatty acids, only a comparatively few esters of the aromatic or cyclic alcohols have been synthesized and characterized. One of the standard procedures for the preparation of aromatic esters of fatty acids is the action of the acyl chloride on the aromatic alcohol. Thus, phenyl oleate, an oil, has been obtained [115] by heating oleoyl chloride with phenol at 130–140°. Cresyl esters may be prepared by a similar procedure. Marangoni [116] has employed this method for the preparation of a number of esters of dihydric phenols and has reported the following melting points: resorcinyl dilaurate, 43–44.5°; dimyristate, 53°; dipalmitate, 62.5–63.5°; hydroquinyl dienanthate, 57–58°; dilaurate, 85–86°; dimyristate, 90–90.3°; dipalmitate, 94.5°; and distearate, 97°. Several aromatic esters of the dibasic acids have been synthesized by Marangoni; for example: diphenyl suberate, m.p. 70–71°; azelate, m.p. 59–60°; and sebacate, m.p. 65–66°. Hydroquinyl azelate and sebacate were described as white powders which decompose at 150°. Zanetti [117] has prepared esters of furfuryl alcohol and several of the lower molecular weight fatty acids by the action of the respective anhydrides on the alcohol. The following constants were reported for these esters: furfuryl propionate, b_1 59–60°, d_0^{20} 1.1085; butyrate, b_1 69–70°, d_0^{20} 1.0530; and valerate, b_1 82–83°, d_0^{20} 1.0284. A similar procedure was employed [118] for the preparation of α-tetrahydrofurfuryl butyrate (b_4 102–104°, d_0^{20} 1.012) and valerate (b_2 97–99°, d_0^{20} 0.999). The benzyl esters of several fatty acids have been obtained by Shonle and Row, [119] who reported the following physical constants for these compounds: benzyl laurate, m.p. 8.5°, b_{12} 209–211°, d_{25}^{25} 0.9457, n_D^{24} 1.4812; myristate, m.p. 20.5°, b_{11} 229–231°, d_{25}^{25} 0.9321, n_D^{24} 1.4903; palmitate, m.p. 36.0°, d_{25}^{38} 0.9136, n_D^{50} 1.4689; stearate, m.p. 45.8°, d_{25}^{50} 0.9075, n_D^{50} 1.4663; and oleate, b_7 237°, d_{25}^{25} 0.9330, n_D^{25} 1.4875. The synthesis of such esters by the action of sodium soaps and benzyl chloride was subsequently patented by Shonle and Row. [120]

The action of chaulmoogroyl chloride and α-naphthol results in a small yield of the α-naphthyl ester after heating for eight days at 100°; higher yields of the β-naphthyl ester, m.p. 49.5–51°, can be obtained by a similar procedure. [121] The phenyl esters of several iodo fatty acids have been described. [122] The preparation of fatty acid esters of cyclohexanol and mono- and dimethylcylcohexanol has been accomplished by the esterification of the respective components in the presence of small amounts of sulfuric acid. [123] The cyclopentyl esters of the aliphatic dibasic acids have been proposed [124] as plasticizers for synthetic resins, and p-cresyl caprylate has been suggested [125] as a perfume base. The sulfonation of the phenyl esters of the fatty acids has been stated [126] to yield wetting agents.

The phenacyl, p-chloro-, p-bromo-, and p-phenylphenacyl esters have often been suggested as characterizing derivatives for the monobasic [127, 128, 129, 130, 131, 132, 133, 134] and also the dibasic acids. [135, 136] Such esters are generally prepared by the action of the salts of the fatty acids on the respective phenacyl halides. The melting points of many of these esters are reported in Chapter IV. Price and Griffith [137] have recently reported the syntheses of the phenacyl, p-bromophenacyl, and p-nitrobenzyl esters of a number of α-hydroxy saturated acids.

The fatty esters of the terpene alcohols have been the subject of several investigations. The molecular rotatory powers of the menthyl esters of a number of the saturated acids have been studied by Hilditch,[138] and simultaneously Christopher and Hilditch [139] reported the results of an extensive investigation of the menthyl esters of a number of α-bromo saturated acids. In a later study, Brauns [140] reported the following physical constants for several of the menthyl esters: menthyl laurate, oil, d_4^{20} 0.8915, $[\alpha]_D^{20}$ -46.07; myristate, m.p. 21–22°, d_4^{20} 0.882, $[\alpha]_D^{20}$ -42.33; palmitate, m.p. 32°, d_4^{20} 0.8848, $[\alpha]_D^{20}$ -39.10; stearate, m.p. 38–39°, d_4^{45} 0.8665, $[\alpha]_D^{45}$ -36.60; and arachidate, m.p. 55°, d_4^{55} 0.8566, $[\alpha]_D^{55}$ -30.63. Menthyl stearate had been synthesized previously by Beckmann [141] in 1897. The preparation of menthyl oleate by the action of oleoyl chloride and menthol has been patented by Sulzberger.[142] The bornyl and isobornyl esters of the fatty acids have been the subject of several patents.[143, 144, 145, 146] Sobbe [147] has reported that bornyl palmitate melts at 67–68°.

SYNTHETIC ESTERS OF THE FATTY ACIDS AND THE POLYHYDRIC ALCOHOLS

No subject in fatty acid chemistry holds more interest than the preparation and study of the fatty acid esters of the polyhydric alcohols. The glycol esters, the mono-, di-, and triglycerides, and the esters of polyhydric alcohols such as mannitol have been and will continue to be a subject for research for many years. It is only natural that the synthetic glycerides have received the greater amount of this attention. As a result of work upon the preparation and study of glycerides of known constitution we have a better understanding of the structure and properties of the naturally occurring fats, which would in itself be ample justification for the many investigations which have been made in this field. The comparison of the natural with the synthetic glycerides has, undoubtedly, been the motivation behind much of the synthetic work which has been done upon this subject. Viewed in a purely isolated sense, however, the synthesis and study of these esters is a fascinating subject which will never be devoid of interest. This is shown by the facts that it has been only recently that reliable methods have been proposed for the synthesis of mixed glycerides, that many of the procedures formerly considered classical are now looked upon with suspicion, and that the physical chemistry of the glycerides has only been pioneered. The following pages contain a discussion of the synthesis, physical and chemical properties, polymorphism, and allied phenomena of the fatty acid esters of the glycols, glycerol, and other polyhydric alcohols. This consideration has, in so far as possible, been confined to pure compounds or to mixtures of known composition.

Fatty Acid Esters of the Glycols

The glycols form two series of esters, namely, the mono- and diesters, depending upon whether one or both of the hydroxyl groups are esterified. Esters of the symmetrical glycols differ from those of glycerol in that the esterification of one hydroxyl group can result in only one monoester; and likewise their diesters present only one structural possibility irrespective of whether the acidic groups are similar or dissimilar. The glycol esters can be obtained by direct esterification of the glycols with the fatty acids or their anhydrides, by the action of acid chlorides on the glycols, by the reaction of soaps with halohydrins or dihalides, or by other esterification methods which have been discussed previously. Many examples of the use of these various methods for the synthesis of the glycol esters are recorded in the literature. Stephenson [148] has described the preparation of the dipalmitate of ethylene glycol by the action of palmitoyl chloride on the glycol in the presence of pyridine. The preparation of ethylene distearate by the action of silver stearate [149, 150] or sodium stearate [151] on the dihalide has been described. Direct esterification is the most convenient procedure for the preparation of the simple diesters and possibly for the monoesters. Detailed directions for the preparation of both mono- and diesters of ethylene glycol with palmitic, margaric, and stearic acids have been published, together with procedures for their separation.[150, 152] The esters are separated by virtue of their relative solubilities in ethanol, the monoesters being appreciably more soluble than the diesters. For example, 1.829 g. of glycol monopalmitate dissolve in 100 g. of ethanol at $0°$ as compared to 0.018 g. of the dipalmitate. In direct esterification reactions the yield of diesters is generally much in excess of that of the monoesters. It has, however, been reported [153] that the yield of monoesters can be appreciably increased by employing solvents in which the glycol and the acid are mutually soluble. In a study of the direct esterification of ethylene glycol by mixtures of lauric, palmitic, and stearic acids with oleic acid it was observed [154] that the molar content of fully saturated esters approximates the square of the molecular content of saturated acid in the acid mixture, an observation which is in line with probability considerations. The velocities of esterification of ethylene glycol with valeric, caproic, and enanthic acids [155] in the presence of hydrochloric acid approximate that with butyric acid under similar conditions, the retarding effect of water being much less than for similar esterifications with ethanol. The physical constants which have been reported for several of the mono- and diesters of ethylene glycol are shown in Table XIII.

TABLE XIII

PHYSICAL CONSTANTS OF MONO- AND DIESTERS OF ETHYLENE GLYCOL

Ester	M.P.,°C.	B.P.,°C.	n_D^t	d_4^t
Butyrate		$98-100_{14}$	1.4303^{18}	1.0321^{18}
Pelargonate		$143-144_{14}$	1.4401^{18}	0.9618^{17}
Dilaurate	49			
Palmitate	51.5		$1.4411^{57.5}$	$0.8786^{60.5}$
Dipalmitate	68.7		$1.4378^{68.7}$	$0.8594^{72.9}$
Margarate	50.2		1.4440^{52}	
Dimargarate	65.5		1.4392^{67}	$0.8605^{67.1}$
Stearate	58.5		$1.4310^{58.5}$	0.8780^{60}
Distearate	75		1.4385^{75}	0.8581^{78}

The reaction between ethylene chlorohydrin and silver stearate first yields 2-chloroethyl stearate,[150] $ClCH_2CH_2OCOC_{17}H_{35}$, m.p. 48.5°, $n^{48.5}$ 1.4433, $d_4^{49.5}$ 0.9049. When this compound is heated for several hours at 140° with silver palmitate, the mixed glycol ester, ethylene palmitate stearate, m.p. 65°, n^{65} 1.4391, $d_4^{70.5}$ 0.8584 is formed.

Many fatty acid esters of glycols other than ethylene glycol have been described. Howe [152] has prepared the mono- and dipalmitates and -stearates of propylene glycol, $MeCH(OH)CH_2OH$, and the dipalmitate and mono- and 'distearates of trimethylene glycol, and has reported the following melting points for the latter compounds: dipalmitate, 56.2°; monostearate, 60.5°; and distearate, 64.7°. The preparation of esters of diethylene glycol, $O(CH_2CH_2OH)_2$, with fatty acids containing ten or more carbon atoms has been described.[156] Clayton and Reid [157] have prepared several esters of thiodiglycol, $S(CH_2CH_2OH)_2$, and the lower fatty acids, an example being the caproate, m.p. 7°, b_7 207°, n_D^{25} 1.0024, d_4^0 1.0198. Hansley [158] has obtained a series of fatty acid esters of sym-dialkylethylene glycols such as diundecylethylene glycol by reduction of the respective fatty acid acyloins and esterification of the resulting glycols. The oleic acid ester of β-methoxyethanol has been prepared by North [159] by the esterification of glycol monomethyl ether with oleic acid. The oxidation of the mono-esters of ethylene glycol for the production of the respective ester aldehydes has been described.[160] The continuous preparation of glycol esters by heating a mixture of the glycol and fatty acids under reduced pressure has been patented.[161]

Esterification of the glycols with dibasic acids yields polyesters of high molecular weight. Carothers and Arvin [162] have prepared a series of these polyesters by the esterification of dibasic acids with 5% excess of ethylene glycol at 175–185° for three hours and then at 200–250° under 0.2 mm. pressure for three hours, obtaining esters having molecular weights varying from 2300 to 5000. The melting points for these esters vary with the acid used and the molecular weight of the ester. Later, it was shown [73] that esters of much higher molecular weight can be obtained by prolonged heating of the reacting components in a molecular still or by heating in an inert atmosphere. The rate of polyesterification of deca-methylene glycol with adipic acid in the presence of p-toluene-sulfonic acid and of the alcoholysis of the polyesters with deca-methylene glycol has been investigated by Flory [163] by the application of viscosity measurements. The rate constant for the esterification was reported to be about eleven times that for the alcoholysis, the activation energies being 12,150 and 11,150 cal., respectively.

Synthetic Glycerides

Although the terms mono-, di-, and triglycerides are misleading as regards the actual structures of the compounds involved, they are universally accepted as designating the mono-, di-, and triesters of the fatty acids and glycerol. Since glycerol is a trihydric alcohol, various structural isomers are possible for the mono-, di-, and triesters, the only exception being a triglyceride in which the three acyl groups are similar. In order to designate the actual positions of ester groups within the glyceride molecule, the terms α, β, and α' have generally been employed. This terminology has quite a historical background; however, it is felt that the use of Greek letters in this instance leads to possible confusion with the designations of polymorphic modifications and of positions in the alkyl chain. In the following discussion, therefore, the positions will be designated as 1, 2, and 3 since it is felt that this method more simply defines the relative positions of the acyl groups within the glyceride.* The relationship between this terminology and the structure of the glyceryl radical is as follows:

$$
\begin{array}{c}
\text{H} \\
| \\
\text{H---C---} 1(\alpha) \\
| \\
\text{H---C---} 2(\beta) \\
| \\
\text{H---C---} 3(\alpha') \\
| \\
\text{H}
\end{array}
$$

In the older literature the term γ is frequently employed for $3(\alpha')$. A glance at the glyceryl radical shows that if the acyl groups are different the number of structural isomers possible increases with the number of such groups present. If the acyl groups are the same, however, the mono- and diglycerides can each exist as two isomers, whereas only one structure is possible for the triglyceride. For example, monostearin may exist as either 1- or 2-monostearin, and the diester may be either 1,2- or 1,3-distearin. The glycerides are quite frequently designated as "symmetrical" or "unsymmetrical," depending upon their molecular configurations.

METHODS OF PREPARATION

Many methods have been proposed for the synthesis of glycerides, some of which are applicable only to the preparation of the simple triglycerides, such as tristearin, whereas others are satisfactory for the synthesis of mixed glycerides of known constitution. The first procedure employed for the preparation of the glycerides was direct esterification. In 1854, Berthelot [164] obtained monostearin by heating glycerol and stearic acid in a sealed tube for twenty hours at 200°, continued heating resulting in the formation of distearin. The heating of monostearin with an excess of stearic acid yields tristearin. The direct esterification of the fatty acids and glycerol has been extensively studied and the method is frequently employed for the preparation of glyceride mixtures. With the exception of the simple triglycerides, however, direct esterification procedures are not satisfactory for the preparation of glycerides of definite constitution. Garner [165] has reported essentially theoretical yields of simple triglycerides by heating glycerol and fatty acids at 200° in the presence of carbon

* The writer is indebted to Dr. H. E. Longenecker for the suggestion that this terminology be employed.

dioxide. Zinc dust is frequently employed as a catalyst for this reaction. Steger and van Loon [166] have accomplished the complete esterification of glycerol with petroselinic and petroselidinic acids by heating the components for five hours at 180° under a partial pressure of carbon dioxide, zinc being present as a catalyst. The triglycerides of nonanoic, undecanoic, tridecanoic, and other acids have been prepared by a similar procedure.[167] Tripalmitin, tristearin, and triolein have been obtained [168] in 95–96% yields, by heating one mole of glycerol with three moles of acid at 30–40 mm. pressure for three hours at 180°, and finally for two to three hours at 240°. The synthesis of triolein by this procedure has been described in detail, [169] and it has been stated [170] that this process has been in commercial operation since 1891 for the preparation of this ester. When mixed acids are esterified with glycerol the product will consist of a mixture of the theoretically possible glycerides. It has been reported that the esterification of an equimolar mixture of stearic and oleic acids with the theoretical amount of glycerol for triglyceride preparation yields a product which contains approximately 20% of tristearin.[171]

When equimolecular amounts of a fatty acid and glycerol are esterified the product does not consist exclusively of the monoester, but contains appreciable quantities of both di- and triesters. The relative proportions of these esters depend upon the conditions employed for the esterification, and apparently to a considerable extent upon the particular acid involved. A study [168] of the reaction of one mole of glycerol with one of palmitic acid showed that di- and triglycerides are formed in substantial amounts in the initial stages, which indicates that they may be intermediate products in the formation of monoglycerides. A subsequent study [172] of the direct esterification of palmitic, stearic, and oleic acids with glycerol was stated to confirm the observation that monoglycerides are formed largely by the degradation of di- and triglycerides. The nature of the acid appears to influence the relative amounts of mono-, di-, and triglycerides formed under such conditions. Kawai and Nobori [173] have reported that one mole of lauric, stearic, or oleic acid is completely esterified by heating with glycerol for three hours at 230–240°; however, prolonged heating is necessary at 170–180°. The product formed from lauric or oleic acid consists chiefly of mono- and diglycerides, whereas that from stearic acid consists essentially of di- and triglycerides. The amount of triglyceride is greater in the product obtained at the lower reaction temperature. The esterification of equimolar proportions of acid and glycerol at 180° for several hours, followed by a further treatment at 240–245°, has been stated [174] to yield a high proportion of mono- and diglycerides to the exclusion of triglycerides. The relative amounts of mono- and dioleins obtained by the direct esterification of oleic acid with glycerol in the presence and absence of catalysts has been studied by Kawai,[175] who also observed [176] that the nature of the component acids present in an acid mixture influences the relative amounts of mono-, di-, and triglycerides formed. The preparation of mono- and distearin by the direct esterification of stearic acid with glycerol in the presence of sulfuric acid and the separation and purification of these products have been described in detail.[177] The relative rates of esterification of various saturated acids with glycerol have been the subject of several investigations by Kailan and coworkers.[178, 179] Hilditch and Rigg [153] have shown that the direct esterification of equimolar amounts of glycerol and fatty acids yields not only monoglycerides but also di- and triglycerides, and that the relative amounts of monoglycerides can be materially increased by employing a medium in which both the glycerol and the acid are soluble. They have patented [180] a process by which monoglycerides are prepared by direct esterification procedures in the presence of catalysts and phenolic solvents. Richardson [181] has suggested the use of dioxane as a solvent for the reaction.

The simple triglycerides may be prepared by the action of acid chlorides on glycerol in the presence of acid-binding agents. An example of this method is the preparation of tricaprylin by the action of caprylyl chloride and glycerol in the presence of either potassium hydroxide [182] or pyridine.[183] The action of acid chlorides on mono- and diglycerides of known constitution is often employed for the preparation of mixed glycerides.[184, 185]

One of the earliest methods proposed for the synthesis of mono- and diglycerides involves the reaction of glycerol halohydrins with the sodium, potassium, or silver salts of the fatty acids. Since it was supposed that the ester group attaches itself to the position originally occupied by the halogen, this reaction was considered reliable for the preparation of glycerides of known constitution. Both Krafft [186] and Guth [187] described the preparation of 1-monoglycerides by the reaction of 1-halohydrins with silver salts of the fatty acids, and Romburgh [188] studied a similar reaction with the alkali salts. The preparation of 1,3-distearin by the action of 1,3-dichlorohydrin and potassium stearate has been described.[189] The analogous reaction is not frequently employed for the preparation of the simple triglycerides, although Bömer and Limprich [190] reported the preparation of triheptadecanoin by the action of potassium heptadecanoate on 1,2,3-tribromopropane. The question of the reliability of such methods for the preparation of mono- and diglycerides is discussed shortly.

It is quite apparent that the synthesis of a mixed triglyceride of definite composition must involve reliable procedures for the preparation of the intermediate mono- or diglyceride, and that the subsequent reactions for the formation of the triglyceride must proceed without rearrangement. A recognition of this fact by workers in the field has resulted in many proposed methods for the synthesis of the mixed triglycerides, and although many of the earlier procedures are now known to be of doubtful value they certainly merit discussion. Prior to 1920, the most important methods were those developed by Grün and associates. In 1905, Grün [191] proposed the synthesis of symmetrical diglycerides by the action of fatty acids on glycerol disulfuric acid, and two years later Grün and Schacht [192] announced the preparation of symmetrical triglycerides by the action of acid chlorides or anhydrides on these diglycerides. The reactions involved are as follows:

$$
\begin{array}{cccc}
CH_2OH & CH_2OSO_3H & CH_2OCOR & CH_2OCOR \\
| & | & | & | \\
CHOH \xrightarrow{2H_2SO_4} & CHOH \xrightarrow{2RCO_2H} & CHOH \xrightarrow{R'COCl} & CHOCOR' \\
| & | & | & | \\
CH_2OH & CH_2OSO_3H & CH_2OCOR & CH_2OCOR
\end{array}
$$

Concurrently, Grün and Theimer [193] proposed the synthesis of unsymmetrical triglycerides by a somewhat similar reaction which first involves the preparation of an unsymmetrical diester of glycerol 1-chlorohydrin as follows:

$$
\begin{array}{cccc}
CH_2OH & CH_2OSO_3H & CH_2OCOR & CH_2OCOR \\
| & | & | & | \\
CHOH \xrightarrow{2H_2SO_4} & CHOSO_3H \xrightarrow{2RCO_2H} & CHOCOR \xrightarrow{R'CO_2K} & CHOCOR \\
| & | & | & | \\
CH_2Cl & CH_2Cl & CH_2Cl & CH_2OCOR'
\end{array}
$$

The above reactions were accepted as reliable for a number of years and many glycerides were synthesized by such procedures and their properties recorded in the literature. The work of Fischer and associates, however, proved such methods to be of questionable value in many instances. If a monoglyceride $RCOOCH_2CHOH-CH_2OH$ be treated with two moles of an acid chloride $R'COCl$ in quinoline, the product should be $RCOOCH_2CHOCOR'CH_2OCOR'$. A similar treatment of a diglyceride $CH_2OHCHOCOR'CHOCOR'$, obtained from $CHICHOCOR'CH_2OCOR'$ by the replacement of iodine by the hydroxyl group, should yield a triglyceride which is identical with the above. Fischer [194] reported that these reactions give products which are dissimilar, an observation which he attributed to the migration of an acyl group to form a 1,3-diglyceride during the replacement of the iodine by hydroxyl. The action of silver nitrite on 1-iododiglycerides is now an accepted method for the preparation of symmetrical diglycerides. Fischer considered that the shift of the acyl group could occur through the formation of a cyclic isomer, thus:

$$
\begin{array}{ccc}
\text{CH}_2\text{OCOR} & \text{CH}_2\text{OCOR} & \text{CH}_2\text{OCOR} \\
| & | & | \\
\text{CHOC} & \rightarrow \text{CH—O} \quad \text{R} & \rightarrow \text{CHOH} \\
| & | \quad \text{C} & | \\
\text{CH}_2\text{OH} & \text{CH}_2\text{—O} \quad \text{OH} & \text{CH}_2\text{OCOR}
\end{array}
$$

The formation of diglycerides from chlorohydrins is, therefore, not a simple exchange, but may be accompanied by a shift in the relative positions of the acyl groups; likewise the replacement of halogen by hydroxyl may be attended by a rearrangement. Fairbourne [195] has pointed out that migration of acyl groups appears to take place most readily when other reactions are in progress, as for example, in the elimination of a halogen atom from a glycerol molecule. Various mechanisms for these migrations have been suggested.[195, 196, 197] For example, Fairbourne, postulating the occurrence of the Hantzsch type of carboxyl group, has presented the following:

$$
\begin{array}{ll}
\text{R}'\text{C} \begin{cases} \text{O} \quad \text{CH}_2\text{—O} \\ \quad | \\ \text{O—CH} \quad \text{O} \end{cases} \text{CR} \rightarrow \text{R}'\text{C} \begin{cases} \text{O}\cdots\text{CH}_2\cdots\text{O} \\ \quad | \\ \text{O}\cdots\text{CH}\cdots\text{O} \end{cases} \text{CR} \rightarrow \\
\quad\quad | & \quad\quad\quad | \\
\quad\text{CH}_2\text{OCOR} & \quad\quad\text{CH}_2\text{OCOR}
\end{array}
$$

$$
\begin{array}{c}
\text{O—CH}_2 \quad \text{O} \\
\text{R}'\text{C} \qquad\qquad \text{CR} \\
\text{O} \quad \text{CH—O} \\
| \\
\text{CH}_2\text{OCOR}
\end{array}
$$

and

$$
\begin{array}{ll}
\text{RC} \begin{cases} \text{O} \quad \text{CH}_2\text{Br} \\ \quad | \\ \text{O—CH} \end{cases} & \text{RC} \begin{cases} \text{O}\cdots\text{CH}_2\cdots \\ \quad | \\ \text{O}\cdots\text{CH}\cdots \end{cases} \boxed{\text{Br}\cdot\text{Ag}}\text{—NO}_2 \rightarrow \\
\quad | & \quad | \\
\text{CH}_2\text{OCOR} & \text{CH}_2\text{OCOR}
\end{array}
$$

$$
\begin{array}{ll}
\text{O—CH}_2 & \text{CH}_2\text{OCOR} \\
\text{RC} & | \\
\text{O} \quad \text{CH}\cdot\text{NO}_2 \rightarrow & \text{CHOH} \\
\quad | & | \\
\text{CH}_2\text{OCOR} & \text{CH}_2\text{OCOR}
\end{array}
$$

This mechanism does not require the presence of a hydroxyl group, which is actively involved in Fischer's representation. Whatever the mechanism of this shift there are certain generalizations concerning it which have proved to be of value. It is known, for example, that in the monoglycerides the 1 position is favored, so that the migration 2 → 1 is frequently encountered whereas the reverse reaction does not take place. Likewise, migration in the diglycerides always proceeds toward the formation of the symmetrical 1,3-diglyceride. This is exemplified in direct esterification procedures, since 1-monoglycerides or 1,3-diglycerides are invariably formed.[153] It is thus apparent that the synthesis of 2-monoglycerides or 1,2-diglycerides presents appreciable difficulties, and since such syntheses involve special procedures their preparation is the subject of a later separate consideration. A similar sequence was followed by Daubert and King [198] in their recent review of the synthetic fatty acid glycerides.

The question of the reliability of many of the methods for the preparation of glycerides has led to an extensive restudy of several of the older methods. In a study of the course of the substitution reactions involving glycerol 1-iodohydrin and soap, Grün and Limpächer [199] reported that the product obtained by the action of potassium stearate consists essentially of 1-monostearin, together with free stearic acid and probably a distearoyl diglycerol. When silver stearate is employed, however, the primary reaction product is not 1-monostearin but stearic acid, glycidol, and stearoyl glycidol. This reaction, therefore, yields a heterogeneous mixture of glycerides of which 1-monostearin is only one of the components. Bömer and Limprich [189] have reported that some tristearin is formed along with 1-monostearin when glycerol 1-chlorohydrin is heated with potassium stearate.

The fact that the substitution of halogen by an ester or hydroxyl group frequently involves migration has rendered doubtful many of the previously accepted methods. Reactions such as those employed by Grün [200] for the preparation of 2-monoglycerides, involving the replacement of halogen by hydroxyl with silver nitrite, or that used by Renshaw [201] for the synthesis of 1,2-diglycerides, involving the action of lead soap on glycerol 1,2-dibromohydrin, undoubtedly led to erroneous conclusions regarding the structures of the resulting glycerides. The same errors are also inherent in the proposed synthesis of 2-monoglycerides by the action of lead soap on glycerol 2-chlorohydrin,[202] and in the method of Grün and

Theimer [193] for the preparation of 1,2-distearin by the action of silver nitrite on 1-chloro-2,3-distearin. Migration takes place in both instances, the former reaction yielding 1-monoglycerides and the latter 1,3-diglycerides. Methods for the synthesis of 1,3-diglycerides by the action of soaps on 1-chloro-3-acylglycerides cannot be considered in this category.[203]

In 1920, Fischer, Bergmann, and Bärwind [204] proposed the synthesis of 1-monoglycerides by the action of acid chlorides and acetone-glycerol (1,2-isopropylidene-glycerol) in the presence of acid-binding agents such as quinoline, the monoglyceride being obtained by the acid hydrolysis of the resulting product. Subsequent treatment with another acid chloride yields unsymmetrical mixed triglycerides. These reactions are as follows:

$$
\begin{array}{c}
CH_2OH \\
| \\
CHOH \\
| \\
CH_2OH
\end{array}
\xrightarrow{(CH_3)_2CO}
\begin{array}{c}
CH_2O \diagdown \diagup CH_3 \\
\qquad C \\
CHO \diagup \diagdown CH_3 \\
| \\
CH_2OH
\end{array}
\xrightarrow[\text{Quinoline}]{RCOCl}
\begin{array}{c}
CH_2O \diagdown \diagup CH_3 \\
\qquad C \\
CHO \diagup \diagdown CH_3 \\
| \\
CH_2OCOR
\end{array}
\xrightarrow{H_2O}
$$

$$
\begin{array}{c}
CH_2OH \\
| \\
CHOH \\
| \\
CH_2OCOR
\end{array}
\xrightarrow{2R'COCl}
\begin{array}{c}
CH_2OCOR' \\
| \\
CHOCOR' \\
| \\
CH_2OCOR
\end{array}
$$

The preparation of acetone-glycerol (and of acetone-glycerol chlorohydrin) has been studied by Fischer and Pfähler [205] and its structure was later verified by Hibbert and Carter.[197] The use of this reagent has proved to be satisfactory for the synthesis of the unsymmetrical triglycerides and it is frequently employed for their preparation. For example, Amberger and Bromig [206] have obtained 1-stearo-2,3-dipalmitin, and Averill, Roche, and King [207] have synthesized a number of 1-monoglycerides and unsymmetrical triglycerides by this method. Numerous descriptions of the preparation of glycerides by this procedure appear in the literature.[185, 208, 209, 210, 211, 212] The observation that the original acetone-glycerol ester is obtained when the monoglycerides prepared by this method are treated with acetone confirms their 1-structure. The direct formation of 1-monoglycerides by the oxidation of the corresponding esters of allyl alcohol [213] has been presented as further confirmation of the reliability of this method, as has the preparation of 1-monoglycerides through the use of 1-monosodium glyceroxide.[214, 215] The use of 1,2-benzylidene-glycerol, which is obtained as a by-product in the preparation of 1,3-benzylidene-glycerol,[216] offers an alternate procedure for the synthesis of 1-

monoglycerides, this reagent having been employed by Daubert and King [211] for the preparation of a number of 1-monoglycerides. From the above consideration it is evident that, owing to the tendency of a 2-acyl group to migrate to a terminal position, the synthesis of 2-monoglycerides, 1,2-diglycerides, and those products in which such compounds are intermediates must require quite specialized procedures. Methods which involve the direct esterification of glycerol 2-chlorohydrin by soap or the hydroxylation of 1,3-dichloroglycerol esters [193] yield 1-monoglycerides instead of the expected 2-monoglycerides. The identification of these products as 2-monoglycerides through their diphenylurethanes has been shown [195] to be based upon an erroneous assumption. In 1928, Helferich and Sieber [217] succeeded in preparing glycerol 2-monobenzoate and 2-mono(p-nitrobenzoate) by the hydrolysis of the 2-benzoyl- and the 2-(p-nitrobenzoyl)-1,3-triphenylmethyl (trityl) ethers of glycerol, the reaction apparently proceeding without migration of the benzoyl group. Several years later, Jackson and King [218] confirmed the observation that the acyl groups of the aromatic esters of glycerol do not undergo rearrangement. When this reaction was applied to the preparation of aliphatic 2-esters of glycerol, however, these authors obtained the 1-esters, and this shift of the acyl group in the aliphatic esters was later substantiated by Verkade, van der Lee, and Meerburg. [219]

Probably the first simple procedure for the preparation of the 2-glycerol esters of the fatty acids is that proposed by Bergmann and Carter, [216] which involves the catalytic reduction of 2-esters of 1,3-benzylidene-glycerol. For example, 2-monopalmitin is synthesized as follows:

$$\begin{array}{ccc}
\text{CH}_2\text{O} & \text{CH}_2\text{O} & \text{CH}_2\text{OH} \\
| \quad \diagdown & | \qquad \diagdown & | \\
\text{CHOH} \quad \text{CHC}_6\text{H}_5 \xrightarrow[\text{Pyridine}]{\text{C}_{15}\text{H}_{31}\text{COCl}} \text{CHOCOC}_{15}\text{H}_{31} \quad \text{CHC}_6\text{H}_5 \xrightarrow{\text{H}_2} \text{CHOCOC}_{15}\text{H}_{31} \\
| \quad \diagup & | \qquad \diagup & | \\
\text{CH}_2\text{O} & \text{CH}_2\text{O} & \text{CH}_2\text{OH}
\end{array}$$

The 2-esters of the even acids from capric to stearic with benzylidene-glycerol have been prepared by Stimmel and King, [220] and the 2-monoglycerides obtained by their reduction were described. The structure of 2-monopalmitin was confirmed by its conversion to 1,3-distearo-2-palmitin by reaction with stearoyl chloride. The relative stabilities of aromatic and aliphatic 2-monoglycerides have been the subject of several investigations. [197, 211, 220] It was observed that 2-monopalmitin is not materially changed when heated slightly above its melting point for one hour; however, a complete shift to the 1-isomer takes place after standing for twenty-four hours in 0.05N alcoholic hydrochloric acid or in 0.1N alcoholic ammonium hydroxide. Migration of the acyl group in glycerol-2-(p-bromobenzoate) requires 0.1N alcoholic hydrochloric acid, thus showing the greater stability of the aromatic esters.

Verkade and associates [221] have suggested a procedure for preparing 2-monoglycerides by reduction of the 2-acyl-1,3-ditrityl ethers of glycerol. This method was later verified by Daubert,[222] who prepared 2-monopalmitin and 2-monobutyrin by its use. The preparation of the 1,3-ditrityl ether of glycerol has been studied by Verkade and associates.[223]

As previously stated, the older methods which were proposed for the synthesis of 1,2-diglycerides generally yield the symmetrical 1,3-diglycerides. Many of these processes have been reinvestigated by Fairbourne [224] and have been shown to be attended by migration of an acyl group. The method employed by Whitby,[225] and later used by Thomson,[226] for the preparation of unsymmetrical diglycerides probably involves a migration. The same comments apply to many other procedures which have been proposed,[227, 228, 229] and the supposed method [184] for the differentiation between symmetrical and unsymmetrical glycerides, based upon their reactivities with thionyl chloride, has been shown to be unreliable. Among the earlier methods, that proposed by Abderhalden and Eichwald [230] is an exception to the above statement. Such procedures involve the use of hydroxypropylamine which has previously been resolved into its d- and l-isomers. Although this method is apparently satisfactory for the synthesis of 1,2-diglycerides, the tedious procedures involved render its successful application quite difficult. It has subsequently been investigated by Bergmann and associates.[216, 231, 232] The synthesis of the unsymmetrical aromatic diesters of glycerol has been successfully accomplished by Helferich and Sieber,[217, 233] but according to Daubert and King [234] the method employed is not satisfactory for the preparation of their aliphatic counterparts. The latter authors have investigated a procedure proposed by Verkade and associates [221] which involves the catalytic detritylation of 1,2-diacyl-3-trityl glycerols and have found it to be satisfactory for the preparation of unsymmetrical diglycerides. In their study of the preparation of 1,2-diglycerides, Daubert and King [234] have proposed a method, which has been stated to be reliable, based upon the reaction between 1-monosodium glyceroxide and benzylchloroformate, followed by esterification. The following reactions were stated to occur during this synthesis:

$$\begin{array}{ccc}
\text{CH}_2\text{ONa} & & \text{CH}_2\text{OOCOCH}_2\text{C}_6\text{H}_5 \\
| & \xrightarrow[\text{Benzene}]{\text{C}_6\text{H}_5\text{CH}_2\text{OCOCl}} & | & \xrightarrow[\text{Quinoline}]{\text{2RCOCl}} \\
\text{CHOH} & & \text{CHOH} \\
| & & | \\
\text{CH}_2\text{OH} & & \text{CH}_2\text{OH}
\end{array}$$

$$\begin{array}{ccc}
\text{CH}_2\text{OOCOCH}_2\text{C}_6\text{H}_5 & & \text{CH}_2\text{OH} \\
| & \xrightarrow[\text{Pt}]{\text{H}_2} & | \\
\text{CHOCOR} & & \text{CHOCOR} \\
| & & | \\
\text{CH}_2\text{OCOR} & & \text{CH}_2\text{OCOR}
\end{array}$$

The synthesis and study of optically active glycerides is a subject of considerable scientific interest, especially in view of the biological implications involved. In this present writing it is possible only to outline the general procedure employed in such syntheses, and the reader is referred to a recent review by Fischer and Baer[235] for a more complete treatment of this subject. A study of the glyceride molecule shows that all 1-monoglycerides, 1,2-diglycerides, and those 1,3-diglycerides which contain unlike substituents, as well as unsymmetrical triglycerides, are capable of appearing in enantiomorphic forms. Fischer and Baer have pointed out that two general methods for the synthesis of optically active glycerides are available. One of these consists of resolving an intermediate, from which the optically active glyceride is then obtained by esterification. The second method employs an optically active, naturally occurring compound which is converted without racemization to the desired optically active glyceride. An example of the former method is that employed by Abderhalden and Eichwald,[230, 236] who obtained optically active 1-mono- and 1,2-diglycerides by the use of compounds obtained from aminodibromopropane resolved by means of d-tartaric acid. Some pertinent steps in this synthesis are as follows:

$$\begin{array}{ccc}
\text{CH}_2 & & \text{CH}_2\text{NH}_2 \\
| \diagdown O & & | \\
\text{CH} \diagup & \rightarrow & \text{CHOH} \\
| & & | \\
\text{CH}_2\text{OH} & & \text{CH}_2\text{OH} \\
(-8.55°) & & (+17.70°) \\
\downarrow & & \downarrow \\
\text{CH}_2\text{OCOC}_3\text{H}_7 & & \text{CH}_2\text{OH} \\
| & & | \\
\text{CHOH} & & \text{CHOCOC}_3\text{H}_7 \\
| & & | \\
\text{CH}_2\text{OH} & & \text{CH}_2\text{OCOC}_3\text{H}_7 \\
d\text{-Monobutyrin} & & l\text{-Dibutyrin} \\
(+0.83°) & & (-1.10°)
\end{array}$$

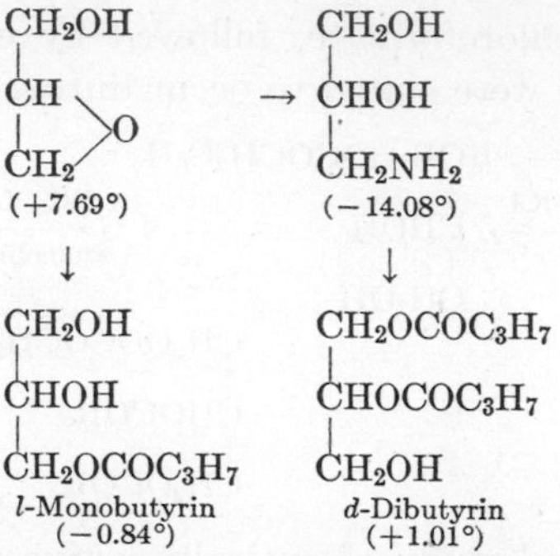

$$CH_2OH$$
$$|$$
$$CH$$
$$|\quad\diagdown O$$
$$CH_2\diagup$$
$$(+7.69°)$$

$$CH_2OH$$
$$|$$
$$\rightarrow CHOH$$
$$|$$
$$CH_2NH_2$$
$$(-14.08°)$$

$$\downarrow$$

$$CH_2OH$$
$$|$$
$$CHOH$$
$$|$$
$$CH_2OCOC_3H_7$$
l-Monobutyrin
$$(-0.84°)$$

$$\downarrow$$

$$CH_2OCOC_3H_7$$
$$|$$
$$CHOCOC_3H_7$$
$$|$$
$$CH_2OH$$
d-Dibutyrin
$$(+1.01°)$$

Grün and Limpächer [237] have resolved glycerides by fractional crystallization of the strychnine salts of their sulfuric esters, and Bergmann and Sabetay [238] resolved the 1-esters of aminopropylene glycol by the use of saccharic acid. The synthesis of optically active glycerides through naturally occurring compounds has recently been the subject of a series of studies by Baer and Fischer.[239] These authors first prepared d-acetone-glycerol and l-acetone-glycerol from d- and l-mannitol, respectively. For the preparation of the former, d-mannitol is first converted into 1,2,5,6-diacetone-d-mannitol, which is then split by means of lead tetraacetate into acetonated d-glyceraldehyde, the catalytic reduction of which yields d-acetone-glycerol. A similar procedure was employed for the preparation of l-acetone-glycerol, the l-mannitol being obtained from l-arabinose. The rotations of these compounds were found to be of equal magnitude ($\pm 12.6°$). The reactions for the preparation of d-acetone-glycerol are as follows:

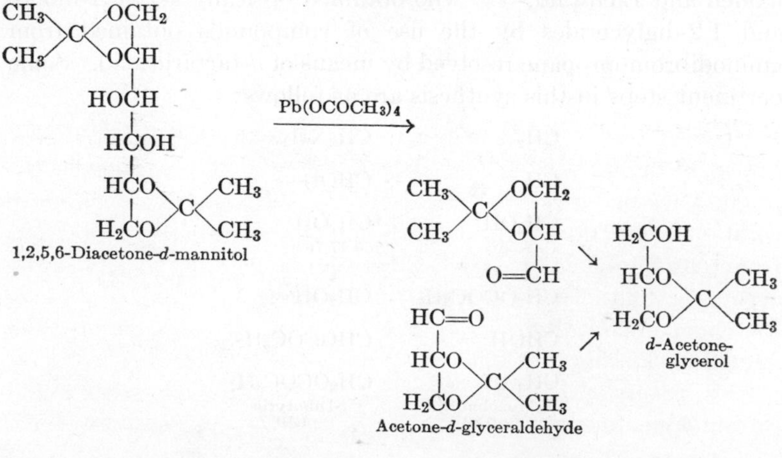

$$CH_3\diagdown\quad\diagup OCH_2$$
$$CH_3\diagup C\diagdown OCH$$
$$|$$
$$HOCH$$
$$|\qquad\qquad Pb(OCOCH_3)_4$$
$$HCOH\qquad\xrightarrow{\hspace{2cm}}$$
$$|$$
$$HCO\diagdown\quad\diagup CH_3$$
$$\qquad\quad C$$
$$H_2CO\diagup\quad\diagdown CH_3$$
1,2,5,6-Diacetone-d-mannitol

$$CH_3\diagdown\quad\diagup OCH_2$$
$$CH_3\diagup C\diagdown OCH$$
$$O{=}CH$$

$$HC{=}O$$
$$|$$
$$HCO\diagdown\quad\diagup CH_3$$
$$\qquad\quad C$$
$$H_2CO\diagup\quad\diagdown CH_3$$
Acetone-d-glyceraldehyde

$$H_2COH$$
$$|$$
$$HCO\diagdown\quad\diagup CH_3$$
$$\qquad\quad C$$
$$H_2CO\diagup\quad\diagdown CH_3$$
d-Acetone-
glycerol

The optically active glycerides were subsequently prepared according to the method of Fischer, Bergmann, and Bärwind,[204] by treatment of the acetone-glycerols with acid chlorides in pyridine followed by removal of the acetone group by hydrolysis. The specific rotations, $[\alpha]_D$, reported by Fischer and Baer [235] for several l-1-monoglycerides are as follows: l-1-monolaurin, $-3.76°$; l-1-monopalmitin, $-4.37°$; and l-1-monostearin, $-3.58°$. A detailed method for the preparation of l-acetone-glycerol from d-acetone-glycerol has been described by these authors. A further esterification of l-1-laurin, l-1-palmitin, and l-1-stearin yielded triglycerides which in spite of their asymmetry failed to show optical rotation. This is in contrast to the optical activity ($-19.9°$ in tetrachloroethane) exhibited by the aromatic triglyceride 1-(p-nitrobenzoyl)-2,3-dibenzoyl-glycerol. It was further found that active 1-monoglycerides containing aromatic radicals retain their activity over long periods of time, whereas active aliphatic 1-monoglycerides show an appreciable drop in activity when held at room temperature for a period of one year.

The first direct preparation of a pure, optically active diglyceride, d-1,2-distearin, was accomplished by Sowden and Fischer,[240] the following series of reactions being employed:

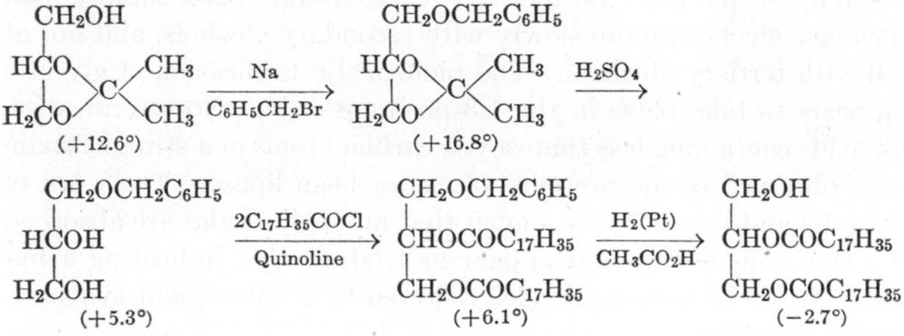

Fischer and Baer [235] have designated the optically active glycerides as the d- and l-forms, depending upon the rotation of the original acetone-glycerol. It is evident, however, that a change in rotation occurs during the substitution. This nomenclature differs from that employed by Abderhalden, who designated the glycerides according to the specific rotation exhibited. An explanation of the change of rotation during this sequence of reactions has been offered by Fischer and Baer.

Any discussion of the preparation of the glyceryl esters would certainly be incomplete without reference to the studies which have been made upon their biological synthesis. The great importance of this aspect of the subject is universally recognized and it is unfortunate that many of the investigations pertaining to it have been of an extremely empirical nature. It has been known for years that the hydrolysis of fats by enzymes is a reversible process, and that the synthesis of fats from glycerol and fatty acids is a biological reaction of vital significance in fat metabolism. Armstrong and Gosney,[241] for example, have conclusively demonstrated the reversibility of hydrolytic processes involving enzymes. Lombroso [242] has obtained triolein by the esterification of oleic acid and glycerol in the presence of pancreatic juice, the esterification still being incomplete after several weeks. It was believed that the synthesis and hydrolysis are brought about by a single enzyme present in the pancreatic juice and not by two separate enzymes. The esterifying properties of castor bean lipase have been noted by Dunlap and Gilbert,[243] and Ivanov [244] has observed that many ground seeds contain enzymes capable of both splitting and synthesizing glycerides. Morel and Velluz [245] have stated that the synthesizing power of ricinus seeds is due to the enzymatic activity of the cytoplasm of the seeds. Velluz [10] has studied the esterification of alcohols with fatty acids in the presence of castor bean lipase and has reported that reaction takes place rapidly with primary alcohols, more slowly with secondary alcohols, and not at all with tertiary alcohols. The biological esterification of glycerol appears to take place in the 1,3-positions only. No esterification of acids containing less than seven carbon atoms in a straight chain was observed in the presence of castor bean lipase. The work of Argyris and Frank [246] has shown that monoglycerides are absorbed by the animal body and appear as triglycerides, indicating a hydrolysis of the monoglycerides followed by a subsequent synthesis of triglycerides.

In the preceding pages we have discussed the various synthetic methods available for the preparation of glycerides of known structure and have attempted to differentiate between those methods which are trustworthy and those which are not. There are, of course, other methods which can be used for the preparation of glycerides and although such processes generally yield glyceride mixtures several of them are of practical significance. It is evident that the partial hydrolysis of a triglyceride can yield a mixture of mono- and diglycerides, and such methods have frequently been employed for their preparation. It has been shown,[247] for example, that the action of sulfuric acid on trilaurin yields, among other products, mono- and dilaurin. It has also been reported [248] that when trilaurin in cold ligroin solution is treated with three moles of sulfuric acid, sulfated esters result from which mono and di-laurin can be obtained by hydrolysis. Such methods, however, are satisfactory only for the preparation of mixtures of glycerides, and since complex reaction products are obtained the components are frequently quite difficult to separate.

The methods of alcoholysis and of ester interchange are often used for the preparation of glyceride mixtures. It has previously been shown that alcoholysis is one of the accepted methods for the preparation of the fatty acid esters of monohydric alcohols. Partial alcoholysis, on the other hand, is often used for the preparation of both mono- and diglycerides, and this procedure frequently presents a convenient method for the preparation of these compounds. Young and Black [249] have reported that the products obtained by the reaction of triglycerides with equal quantities of glycerol in the presence of trisodium phosphate consist essentially of 1-monoglycerides. Trilaurin, tripalmitin, and tristearin were observed to yield 1-monoglycerides by this procedure, and a similar reaction between glycol and its dipalmitate yields 2-hydroxyethyl palmitate. When oils such as hydrogenated fish oil, olive oil, or castor oil are heated with an excess of glycerol for one-half hour at 270–280°, the products consist of a mixture of mono- and di-glycerides. Catalysts such as MgO, CuO, and ZnO markedly lower the temperature required for the alcoholysis.[250] It has also been observed that the presence of metallic tin or zinc has a de-cidedly accelerating effect upon this reaction.[251] The influence of temperature, time, catalysts, and other factors upon the rate of reaction of glycerol with various triglycerides has been the subject of a recent investigation.[252] The formation of mixtures of di- and triglycerides by heating monoglycerides at high temperatures presents an interesting example of alcoholysis.[253]

The preparation of mixtures of mono- and diglycerides from tri-glycerides by methods resembling alcoholysis has been the subject of a number of patents. For example, sodium glyceroxide,[254] soaps,[255] and mixtures of soaps and alcoholates [255] have been sug-gested as catalysts for this reaction. Richardson and Eckey [256] have proposed the use of dioxane as a solvent for the fat and glycerol. Christensen [257] has proposed the preparation of mono- and diglycerides by the reaction of sodium glycerate and fatty acids, or by heating a mixture of glycerol and fatty acids in the presence of an alkali metal glycerate.

Ester interchange involving the various acyl groups of the glycerides is a well-known phenomenon. Such reactions are quite susceptible to catalysis and are probably quite closely allied to alcoholysis. Attempts have been made to associate this phenomenon with the various coordination forms possible for these esters. The heating of an equimolar mixture of tristearin and triolein at 280° for two hours results in ester interchange with the resulting formation of mixed glycerides,[258] and likewise the heating of tristearin with oleic acid results in an esterification of a fraction of the oleic acid. A similar interchange is observed between mixtures of fatty acids and esters of monohydric alcohols. Normann [259] has reported that the introduction of butyric acid into fats can be accomplished by heating mixtures of butyric acid and various fats and that mixed glycerides result when tributyrin and tristearin are heated. Such reactions are materially influenced by the presence of catalysts, sodium ethoxide, sulfonic acids, metals, and their compounds having been proposed.[260]

Mono- and diglycerides of the fatty acids are useful as emulsifying agents, and their sulfates [261] and phosphates [262] have been proposed as wetting agents.

Esters of Other Polyhydric Alcohols

The synthetic fatty acid esters of polyhydric alcohols which we have discussed have been confined essentially to those of the glycols and glycerol; however, several esters of mannitol and related compounds have been prepared and described. It is evident that the difficulties encountered in preparing pure esters of established structure increase with increase in complexity of the polyhydric alcohol. Stephenson [148] has reported the preparation of mannitol hexapalmitate, m.p. 64.5°, by the esterification of mannitol with palmitoyl chloride in the presence of pyridine, and a so-called mannitol fat has been obtained [263, 264] by the interaction of mannitol with triolein or tristearin. The reaction product of mannitol and triolein was considered to contain considerable amounts of mannitan dioleate and isomannide dioleate. The reaction between mannitol and olive oil has been studied by Irvine and Gilchrist [265] and the structure of the mannitol fat deduced through its methylated products. It was postulated that the reaction between mannitol and olive oil probably first results in the formation of mannitol dioleate, which is dehydrated to mannitan dioleate, and under more drastic conditions is further dehydrated to isomannide dioleate. As a result of this work it was considered that the probable structure of mannitol fat is as follows:

$$H_2C-\overset{\overset{\displaystyle OX}{|}}{C}-\overset{\overset{\displaystyle OX}{|}}{\underset{\underset{\displaystyle H}{|}}{C}}-\overset{\overset{\displaystyle H}{|}}{\underset{\underset{\displaystyle H}{|}}{C}}-\overset{\overset{\displaystyle H}{|}}{\underset{\underset{\displaystyle OH}{|}}{C}}-CH_2OH$$

(X = oleoyl radical)

The preparation of synthetic fats containing a methylglucoside residue has also been undertaken by these authors.[266]

Physical Properties of the Esters of Polyhydric Alcohols

(1) THE SIMPLE TRIGLYCERIDES

Polymorphism is a common phenomenon with all long-chain compounds, although in no other instance does it assume the dominant role that it does with the glycerides. The peculiar property of possessing multiple melting points which is exhibited by the glycerides makes it necessary to associate a melting point with a particular form, and the failure to recognize this necessity undoubtedly accounts for the fact that various authors have ascribed widely different melting points to supposedly pure samples of the triglycerides.

It was shown by Duffy [267] as early as 1853 that the stearin from mutton fat possesses at least three melting points, and the suggestion was made that isomeric stearins exist. Many years later, Guth [187] observed that if melted tristearin is rapidly cooled and then heated in a capillary tube, it melts at 55°, again solidifies, and then remelts at 71.5°. If the chilled sample is allowed to remain for some time at room temperature, it is transformed into the higher-melting, stable form. Smits and Bokhorst [268] ascribed this double melting point to the existence of two different crystalline modifications and observed that when the liquid is kept at a temperature between the two melting points the stable form slowly crystallizes. These findings were confirmed by Nicolet,[269] who reported that the stable form may be obtained directly by seeding, although the unstable form always appears if the temperature is

below 56°. Grün and Schacht [192] had previously observed that
the symmetrical triglycerides 2-lauro-1,3-distearin, 2-myristo-1,3-
dilaurin, and others exist in a low-melting form and a stable,
high-melting form, and that the stable modification can be rapidly
obtained from the unstable form by inoculation. These authors
considered such changes to involve isomerism rather than polymorphism. They observed that the transition is monotropic since
the stable form does not revert to the unstable form upon cooling.
It has been stated by Le Chatelier and Cavaignac [270] that if the
heating and cooling of a triglyceride be conducted slowly the melting and freezing points are approximately identical, an observation
which can be ascribed to the fact that such procedures permit of a
transition to the stable form. In spite of the early findings of
Duffy,[267] it was considered for many years that the triglycerides
exist in only two forms, the lower-melting, unstable form being
obtained upon rapid cooling and the higher-melting form either
by transformation or by direct solidification at higher temperatures. Because of the glasslike appearance of the lower-melting
form it has been described as liquid crystalline.[271] Bömer [272] has
considered the higher-melting form to be the only truly crystalline
phase, since it is always obtained upon crystallization of the
triglycerides from solvents. This viewpoint, however, was rendered untenable by the observation of Othmer [273] that trimyristin
and tristearin exhibit not two but three melting points and that
the various forms are polymorphic. The different forms of the
triglycerides of the even, saturated acids from acetic to stearic
acid inclusive were studied by Loskit,[274] who ascribed their occurrence to differences in the degree of polymerization. The existence
of at least three polymorphic forms of the triglycerides was likewise observed by Efremov [275] and by Weygand and Grüntzig,[276]
the last two believing that at least seven modifications are possible.
Joglekar and Watson,[277] on the other hand, recognized only two
forms of the triglycerides, considering them to be isomers rather
than polymorphs, and their observations were apparently substantiated by Rao and Jatkar [278] as late as 1935.

It is thus apparent that although it was realized for many years
that the triglycerides exist in various forms, the number of and the
relationship between these forms were matters of controversy, and
it became evident that a proper understanding of this relationship
could not be definitely obtained by visual observations or by

thermal data alone. Additional evidence was supplied in 1934 by the pioneer work of Clarkson and Malkin [279] upon the x-ray and thermal properties of the simple triglycerides. Their conclusive findings served to correlate the data then existing and to formulate the basis for our present views concerning the structure of the triglycerides. It was considered by certain authors that the polymorphism exhibited by triglycerides is similar to that previously

TABLE XIV

MELTING POINTS AND LONG CRYSTAL SPACINGS OF SIMPLE TRIGLYCERIDES

Triglyceride	Melting Points, °C.			Long Crystal Spacings, Å	
	β	α	γ	β	α
Tricaprin	31.5	18.0	−15	26.8	....
Triundecanoin	30.5	26.5	1.0	29.6	33.0
Trilaurin	46.4	35.0	15	31.2	35.6
Tritridecanoin	44.0	41.0	25	34.1	37.7
Trimyristin	57.0	46.5	33	35.8	41.2
Tripentadecanoin	54.0	51.5	40	38.9	42.9
Tripalmitin	65.5	56.0	45	40.6	45.6
Trimargarin	63.5	61.0	50	43.5	48.5
Tristearin	71.5	65.0	54.5	45	50.6
Triolein	4.9	−12	−32[282]	....	....
Trielaidin	41.5	37	15.5	44.1	....
Trierucin	32.5	25	6	51.1	55.0
Tribrassidin	57	43	36	53.6	60.9
Trilinolein	−12.9	−43[282]	....	....	....
Trilinolenin	−23[283]				

observed for the simple esters.[90, 102, 280] The three forms assumed by the simple triglycerides, therefore, are polymorphs, and are occasioned by differences in the angles of tilt of the hydrocarbon chains with reference to the terminal planes. As in the case of the other straight-chain compounds, the long crystal spacings of the tilted forms depend upon the number of carbon atoms and the angle of tilt, and their physical properties, such as melting points, form alternating series. The physical properties of the vertical form, on the other hand, are non-alternating. The melting points and long crystal spacings of the polymorphic forms of the simple triglycerides of the saturated acids from capric to stearic acid inclusive and of several unsaturated acids, as reported by Clarkson and Malkin [279] and by Meara,[281] are shown in Table XIV. The side spacings in Ångströms were observed to be as follows: β-form, even acids: 3.7, 3.9, 4.6, 5.3; odd acids: 3.65, 4.0, 4.6, 5.3; α- and γ-forms, 4.2.

When the melting points of these forms are plotted against the number of carbon atoms, those of the α- and γ-forms fall upon smooth curves and those of the β-forms alternate (Fig. 3).

The three forms of simple triglycerides, therefore, apparently resolve themselves into a stable or high-melting form, β, which

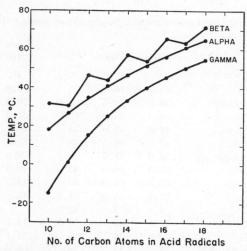

FIG. 3.   Melting points of polymorphic forms of simple triglycerides.

possesses inclined chains; an unstable, lower-melting form, α, containing vertical chains, and a low-melting form, γ, which has been considered to be non-crystalline. It has been suggested quite recently,[284] however, that all three of the polymorphic forms of tristearin are crystalline. In 1945, Lutton[285] published the results of an extensive investigation of the polymorphic behavior of tristearin and several of its homologs and although this work confirmed many of the previous observations of Clarkson and Malkin[279] certain essential differences were noted which have done much to clarify further our knowledge of the crystal structures of these compounds. Lutton verified the fact that the simple triglycerides exhibit monotropic trimorphism. The *gamma* form, originally described by Clarkson and Malkin as glassy, was observed to be non-existent. The lowest-melting form is, therefore, the *alpha* form. It was observed that the simple triglycerides exhibit an intermediate form which Malkin had actually described for several mixed triglycerides but which he had failed to recognize for the simple triglycerides. This form was designated as *beta prime*, and the name *beta* was retained for the highest-melting form. Thus, all three of the polymorphic forms of the simple triglycerides are crystalline and the glassy or *gamma* form does not exist. These findings do not detract from the importance of the original work; however, they modify our concept of the lower-melting forms. The revised nomenclature designates the three forms as *alpha*, *beta prime*, and *beta*, the melting points increasing in the order named. This nomenclature will be employed throughout the remainder of this discussion. The long spacings in Ångströms of the *alpha*, *beta prime*, and *beta* forms, respectively, of several triglycerides as reported by Lutton [285] are as follows: trilaurin, 35.5, 32.85, 31.15; trimyristin, 41.4, 37.65, 35.45; tripalmitin, 46.3, 42.3, 40.9; and tristearin, 50.6, 46.8, 45.15. The reported melting points of these respective forms are as follows: trilaurin, 14°, 34°, 43.9°; trimyristin, 32°, 44°, 55.5°; tripalmitin, 44°, 55.5°, 65.5°; and tristearin, 54°, 64°, 73.1°. The *alpha* form is obtained upon moderately rapid cooling since the higher-melting forms permit appreciable supercooling. The *beta prime* form is generally obtained by transformation of the *alpha* form; however, in many instances, its transformation to the *beta* form is quite rapid. The *beta* form is obtained either by transformation of the lower-melting, *beta prime* form, or by solvent crystallization.

A plot of the long crystal spacings obtained by Clarkson and Malkin [279] shows that they fall upon three straight lines; namely, β-odd, β-even, and α. In the case of the glycerides of odd acids a fourth form has been postulated. These x-ray data permitted a consideration of the crystal structures of the various polymorphic forms of the triglycerides. Since the long spacings indicate a length twice that of a single molecule, these authors have postulated a so-called tuning-fork structure for the triglycerides, the α-form consisting of vertical chains and the β-form of chains inclined at an angle of approximately 65°. The side spacings show a more complicated structure than that observed for most long-chain compounds and indicate a somewhat different arrangement for the glycerides of odd acids from those of even acids. The α-form contains chains free to rotate within fixed limits about the chain axes; the β- or tilted form contains chains fixed at an angle. The molecular configurations of the triglycerides proposed by Malkin and coworkers are shown in Fig. 4.

As in the case of other long-chain compounds which exhibit polymorphism, great care must be exercised in establishing the physical constants of the lowest-melting and intermediate forms since the transformation from an unstable to a stable form is often quite rapid. Clarkson and Malkin have stated that the nature of the solid separating from a molten glyceride depends on the initial temperature of the liquid, the rate of cooling, and the length of the acid chains. The α-form generally separates first, although very slow rates of cooling may result in a direct realization of the β-form. The observation of Weygand and Grüntzig [276] that at least seven different forms exist is explainable on the basis that variations in the rate of cooling result in a separation of mixtures of different forms. The transitions are much slower for the glycerides of the odd acids than for those of the even acids, and the stability of the α-form increases with increasing chain length. The α melting point is generally obtained by rapidly cooling the sample in a capillary tube and immediately immersing it in a bath at the temperature at which it just melts and solidifies, the proper temperature being ascertained by repeated trials. The melting point of the β'-form is obtained by the same procedure. The melting point of the β- or stable form is determined in the usual manner. It is quite important that small samples be employed (0.75–1.0 g.), since otherwise phase changes obscure the true melting points.

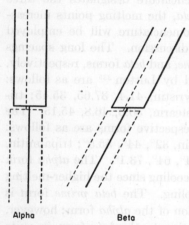

Alpha   Beta

FIG. 4. Molecular configurations of polymorphic forms of symmetrical triglycerides.

That the melting points of the various polymorphic forms of the triglycerides can be ascertained by a study of their cooling and heating curves has been shown by Nicolet [269] and later by Clarkson and Malkin,[279] and a very complete treatment of this subject can be found in a recent review by Ferguson and Lutton.[286] Heating curves for samples crystallized in the α-form show two distinct arrests, the first indicating the change $\alpha \to$ liquid attended by the transformation $\alpha \to \beta' \to \beta$, whereas the latter is the melting point of the β-form. If the sample is held for one hour above the α melting point the first arrest becomes less pronounced, and after holding for three hours only the latter arrest is observed. The microscopic appearance of the different forms of the triglycerides has been studied by several investigators [274, 276, 287] and has been reviewed by Ferguson and Lutton.[286]

Although many of the physical properties of the simple triglycerides have been mentioned in the above discussion, the literature contains many additional data. The melting points of the stable forms of tricaproin,[288] tricaprylin,[182] and trinonanoin [167] have been reported to be $-25°$, $9.8–10.1°$, and $8.7°$, respectively. Woolley and Sandin [289] have observed the melting points of the β'-, β-, and α-forms of trinonadecanoin to be $66.5–67°$, $70.5°$, and $60°$. The densities, d_4^t, and refractive indices, n_D^t, of the triglycerides of several saturated acids are as follows: tricaproin, 1.03424^{20}, 1.44268^{20}; tricaprylin, 0.9867^{25}, 1.44268^{20}; trilaurin, 0.8944^{20}, 1.44039^{20}; trimyristin, 0.8848^{60}, 1.44285^{60}; tripalmitin, 0.8657^{80}, 1.43807^{80}; and tristearin, 0.8621^{80}, 1.4396^{80}. The triglycerides are readily soluble in ether, carbon disulfide, chloroform, carbon tetrachloride, and benzene. The higher molecular weight glycerides possess limited solubilities in ethanol. The heats of crystallization of the α- and β-forms of tristearin and of the β-form of tripalmitin have been reported to be 44.2, 61.6, and 62.3 cal./g., respectively, and the heat of transition, 17.4 cal./g.[278] The average heat of transition for the simple triglycerides as obtained from heat of solution data was reported to be approximately 15 cal./g. The dielectric constants at several temperatures of liquid and β-tristearin have been reported.[290] Labrouste [291] and later Dervichian [292] have studied monomolecular films of the triglycerides. Binary systems of the triglycerides have recently been studied by Ravich and Vol'nova; [293] however, very little is known as yet concerning the binary and polycomponent mixtures of the glycerides. Efremov [275] has stated that such mixtures exhibit the polymorphic behavior characteristic of their components. Joglekar and Watson [277] have reported that the binary system tristearin-tripalmitin exhibits a eutectic for the stable modification. Mixtures of the naturally occurring glycerides have been investigated with inconclusive findings.[294]

(2) Symmetrical Mixed Triglycerides

Methods for the preparation of the symmetrical mixed triglycerides have been previously discussed. Triglycerides of this type have been synthesized and described by a number of investigators.[184, 185, 187, 192, 206, 207, 208, 295, 296] The thermal properties and crystal spacings of glycerides of this group have been studied by Malkin and Meara,[297] and most of our present-day knowledge concerning the polymorphic forms and crystal structure of these glycerides is based upon the comprehensive investigation made by these authors. The symmetrical mixed triglycerides of the even acids from capric to stearic were studied, and for purposes of discussion these compounds were divided into groups, depending upon the differences in chain lengths of the ester portions of the molecule. Thus, triglycerides in which the acyl groups differ by two carbon atoms, for example, 2-laurodimyristin or 2-myristodipalmitin, constitute one group; those in which the difference is four carbon atoms, 2-laurodipalmitin or 2-palmitodilaurin, comprise another group; and so on. Such groups were further subdivided depending upon whether the longer or shorter chain occupies the 2-position. The necessity for this classification will become apparent.

The thermal and x-ray data for the triglycerides of acids differing by two carbon atoms show four polymorphic forms, which Malkin designated as vitreous or γ, α, β', and β, the melting points increasing in the order named. Such triglycerides divide themselves into two groups, namely:

$$(a)\ C_n-\begin{matrix}C_{n+2}\\C_{n+2}\end{matrix} \quad \text{and} \quad (b)\ C_{n+2}-\begin{matrix}C_n\\C_n\end{matrix}$$

The long and side crystal spacings indicate the tuning-fork structure previously postulated for the simple triglycerides, adjacent molecules lying in reversed positions. The length of the unit cell is, therefore, twice that of the longest chain. The side spacings for groups (a) and (b) show characteristic differences. The stable form β possesses a chain tilted at 69°33' for group (a) and at 65°30' for group (b), the carbon-to-carbon distances being 1.18 and 1.147 Å, respectively. The α- and β'-modifications of group (a) were assumed to possess vertical chains, whereas the α-form of group (b) is vertical and the β'-form inclined at an angle of 70°55'. The transformation from one polymorphic form to another is more rapid for these glycerides than for the simple triglycerides. The members of group (a) were observed to solidify in the γ-form (except 2-capryldilaurin), whereas in group (b) only 2-stearodipalmitin solidifies in this form, the others assuming the α-form. The stable β-form is directly obtainable upon solvent crystallization. All the polymorphic forms of the corresponding members of groups (a) and (b), for example, myristodipalmitin and palmitodimyristin, possess nearly identical melting points.

The symmetrical triglycerides in which the acyl groups differ by four, six, and eight carbon atoms have also been examined by Malkin and Meara.[297] These can be grouped into several series, depending upon differences in the number of carbon atoms in the acyl groups and upon the relative positions of the longer and shorter groups as follows: (c) those in which the 2-acyl group contains four less carbon atoms than the 1- and 3-groups, e.g., 2-laurodipalmitin; (d) those in which it contains four more carbon atoms, e.g., 2-palmitodilaurin; (e) those in which it contains six less, e.g., 2-laurodistearin; and (f) those in which it contains six more, e.g., 2-stearodilaurin. A further group (g) comprising 2-stearodicaprin and 2-capryldistearin was also investigated. All these glycerides were observed to exist in four solid modifications, the velocity of transition decreasing with increasing chain length for members of the same group. A linear relationship between the lengths of the molecules and the long crystal spacings would not be observed due to the presence of the shorter chains. The long spacings observed for the β-form correspond to twice the length of a single molecule except for 2-palmitodilaurin and 2-stearodimyristin. This was attributed by Malkin and Meara to an acute angle of tilt of 41°18′ for the members of group (c), the increase in length per carbon atom being 0.83 Å. This transition from a single to a double structure, however, appears quite difficult of explanation at this time.

The melting points of the various forms of the symmetrical triglycerides as determined by Malkin and Meara are shown in Table XV.*

* To avoid confusion in the naming of glycerides containing caproic, caprylic, and capric acids, the following system of prefixes and suffixes is employed in this discussion:

Acid	Prefix	Suffix
caproic	caproyl-	-caproin
caprylic	caprylyl-	-caprylin
capric	capryl-	-caprin

TABLE XV

MELTING POINTS OF POLYMORPHIC FORMS OF SYMMETRICAL TRIGLYCERIDES

Melting Points, °C.

Glyceride	Vitreous (γ)	α	β'	β
Capryldilaurin	8	23	33	38.5
Laurodimyristin	24	35	45	50
Myristodipalmitin	37	46	55	60
Palmitodistearin	50	56	64	68
Laurodicaprin	6	25	34	37.5
Myristodilaurin	24	37	44	48
Palmitodimyristin	38	49	55	58.5
Stearodipalmitin	49	59	65	68
Capryldimyristin	16	37	40	43.5
Laurodipalmitin	34	47	50	53.5
Myristodistearin	47	56	59	62.5
Myristodicaprin	3	21	30	34
Palmitodilaurin	19	35	42.5	45.5
Stearodimyristin	33	47	53	55.5
Capryldipalmitin	20	42	48	51.5
Laurodistearin	36	52	58	60.5
Palmitodicaprin	6	27	36	40
Stearodilaurin	21	38	43	47
Stearodicaprin	5	34	40	44.5
Capryldistearin	30	47	53	57

2-Capryldilaurin, 2-caproyldistearin, 2-caprylyldistearin, and 2-capryldistearin have been observed [185, 208] to melt at 38.8°, 47.2°, 51.8°, and 56.2°, respectively. The following refractive indices, n_D^{70}, have been reported [185, 208, 298] for the symmetrical mixed triglycerides: 2-stearodilaurin, 1.44031; 2-stearodipalmitin, 1.44325; 2-laurodimyristin, 1.43901; 2-laurodipalmitin, 1.44044; 2-acetodipalmitin, 1.43749; 2-palmitodilaurin, 1.43980; 2-myristodilaurin, 1.43907; 2-caprylyldilaurin, 1.43643; 2-capryldilaurin, 1.43705; 2-acetodistearin, 1.43970; 2-caproyldistearin, 1.44019; 2-capryldistearin, 1.44153; 2-laurodistearin, 1.44222; 2-myristodistearin, 1.44300; 2-palmitodistearin, 1.44374.

The appreciable amount of work which has been done within recent years upon the symmetrical monoöleo disaturated triglycerides has served to advance our knowledge of the mixed triglycerides. The 2-oleo-1,3-diacyl triglycerides have been prepared [299] by the action of oleoyl chloride upon 1,3-diacyl glycerides, the following melting points having been reported: (acyl group,

m.p.) capryl, 5–6°; lauroyl, 14.5–15°; myristoyl, 26–27°; palmitoyl, 35.5–36°; and stearoyl, 42.5–43°. The structures of these
glycerides were proved by hydrogenation to the corresponding
2-stearo-1,3-diacyl triglycerides. Cooling and heating curves for
the 2-oleo-2,3-diacyl triglycerides have been obtained by Daubert
and Clarke [300] and the transition temperatures for the four polymorphic forms, γ, α, β′, and β, determined. The x-ray diffraction
analyses [301] of the symmetrical monoöleo disaturated triglycerides
have resulted in some interesting theories concerning their crystal
structure. Triglycerides containing an oleoyl radical in the
2-position were shown to possess long crystal spacings approximately three times those of the simple triglycerides, and this observation apparently forces an abandonment of the tuning-fork
structure for the glycerides of the former type. It has been
proposed that such glycerides possess an extended long-ordered
arrangement in which the unsaturated chains are aligned with
respect to each other. Such a structure may explain the appreciable melting-point difference which exists between a simple
triglyceride, such as tristearin, and its unsaturated counterpart,
2-oleo-1,3-distearin. That the presence of unsaturated fatty acid
radicals in the triglycerides is productive of a significant modification of the crystal structure of the saturated triglycerides has been
suggested by the work of Storkes and Germer [302] upon films of
various triglycerides upon polished nickel surfaces.

(3) THE UNSYMMETRICAL TRIGLYCERIDES

It has previously been pointed out that many of the earlier
methods for the preparation of the unsymmetrical triglycerides
actually yield symmetrical triglycerides or mixtures of glycerides,
so that the earlier constants reported for the unsymmetrical compounds are questionable. The unsymmetrical glycerides possess
lower melting points than their isomeric counterparts, although
in some instances the differences are quite small. They exhibit
four polymorphic forms, vitreous or γ, α, β′, and β, which are
quite similar to those observed for the symmetrical triglycerides.
The transition β′ → β is quite slow and the β-form separates
from solvents with difficulty. The crystal spacings as revealed
by x-ray measurements have been investigated by Carter and
Malkin,[303] who observed that the long crystal spacings and the
side spacings of the β-form are quite similar to those exhibited by
the simple triglycerides. The melting points of the various poly-

morphic forms of the saturated unsymmetrical triglycerides investigated by Carter and Malkin are shown in Table XVI.

Several saturated glycerides not shown in the following table have been synthesized and their melting points and refractive indices, n_D^{70}, reported:[185, 207, 208] 1-caprylyldilaurin, 28.4°, 1.43576; 1-capryldilaurin, 38.8°, 1.43705; 1-myristodilaurin, 42.8°, 1.43878;

TABLE XVI

MELTING POINTS OF POLYMORPHIC FORMS OF UNSYMMETRICAL TRIGLYCERIDES

Melting Points, °C.

Glyceride	Vitreous (γ)	α	β'	β
Capryldilaurin	5	26	31	35.5
Laurodimyristin	22	37	42	46.5
Myristodipalmitin	36	47.5	52	57
Palmitodistearin	50	57	61	65
Laurodicaprin	0	17.5	26	30
Myristodilaurin	19	33.5	39	43.5
Palmitodimyristin	34	45.5	50.5	54
Stearodipalmitin	46.5	55	59.5	62.5
Capryldimyristin	15	32	38	43.5
Laurodipalmitin	32	45	49.5	54
Myristodistearin	44	54	57.5	62
Myristodicaprin	3	20	31	34.5
Palmitodilaurin	20	33	43	46.5
Stearodimyristin	36	46	52	56
Capryldipalmitin	23	37	41	45.5
Laurodistearin	36	47	52	....
Palmitodicaprin	2	24	32	35
Stearodilaurin	20	31	41.5	45
Stearodicaprin	13	32	38	41
Capryldistearin	33	42.5	46	49

1-palmitodilaurin, 44.8°, 1.43965; 1-acetodipalmitin, 51–52°; 1-acetodistearin, 56.6°; 1-caproyldistearin, 42.7°, 1.43985; 1-caprylyldistearin, 47.6°, 1.44028; and 1-capryldistearin, 48.2°, 1.44058.

Prior to 1943, essentially no unsymmetrical triglycerides containing one or more unsaturated fatty acid chains had been described. This situation was occasioned not only by the difficulties inherent in their preparation but also by the unavailability of the unsaturated fatty acids in a state of purity sufficient to merit their adaptation to precise work. In 1943, Daubert and associates [304] described the synthesis of a series of 1-oleo-2,3-diacyl triglycerides the physical properties of which were reported to be as follows: (1-oleo-2,3-, m.p., n_D^{40}) dicaprin, 3–4°, 1.45185; dilaurin, 20.0°, 1.45322; dimyristin, 25.0°, 1.45458; dipalmitin, 34.5°, 1.45562; and distearin, 38.5°, 1.45700. The structures of these glycerides were proved by hydrogenation to the corresponding saturated triglycerides. The 1-elaido-2,3-diacyl triglycerides melt approximately 15° higher than the corresponding 1-oleo-2,3-diacyl triglycerides and approximately 20° lower than the corresponding fully saturated triglycerides. The following physical constants have been reported [305] for the 1-elaido-2,3-diacyl triglycerides: (1-elaido-2,3-, m.p., n_D^{45}) dicaprylin, 3.0°, 1.44786; dicaprin, 15.0°, 1.44895; dilaurin, 27.0°, 1.45023; and dimyristin, 39.5°, 1.45136. A series of dioleo monosaturated triglycerides has been prepared [306] by the action of oleoyl chloride upon saturated 1-monoglycerides. The following physical constants have been reported for these 1-acyl-2,3-dioleins: (1-acyl group, m.p., n_D^{35}) caproyl, −11.0 to −10.0°, 1.46114; caprylyl, −6.6 to −5.6°, 1.45998; capryl, −0.5 to 0.5°, 1.45941; lauroyl, 5.5–6.5°, 1.45932; myristoyl, 12.5–13.5°, 1.45995; palmitoyl, 18.0–19.0°, 1.46060; and stearoyl, 22.5–23.5°, 1.46190. It will be noted that, as in the case of the other triglycerides which contain unsaturated acid chains, the melting points increase with increase in the length of the saturated acid chains. Several 1-acyl-2,3-dielaidins have also been described the physical constants of which are as follows: (1-acyl group, m.p., n_D^{45}) capryl, 25.0°, 1.45391; lauroyl, 35.5°, 1.45507; and myristoyl, 40.0°, 1.45619. The 1-linoleo-2,3-diacyl triglycerides [307] possess lower melting points than the corresponding 1-oleo triglycerides. The following physical constants have been observed for the 1-linoleo-2,3-diacyl triglycerides: (1-linoleo-2,3-, m.p., n_D^{50}) dicaprylin, −13 to −12°, 1.45183; dicaprin, −1.0 to 0.0°, 1.45226; dilaurin, 15–16°, 1.45287; dimyristin, 20–21°, 1.45287; dipalmitin, 26–27°, 1.45385; and distearin, 32–33°, 1.45462. The 1-acyl-2,3-dilinoleins possess still lower melting points, their physical constants being as follows: (acyl group, m.p., n_D^{50}) lauroyl, −12 to −11°, 1.46895; myristoyl, −9 to −8°, 1.47010; palmitoyl, −4 to −3°, 1.47090; and stearoyl, 5–6°, 1.47193.

The triacid triglycerides constitute a very large group of compounds, their name being derived from the fact that three different fatty acid groups are attached to the glyceryl radical. Undoubtedly, many representatives of this type of triglyceride are present in the naturally occurring fats and oils. The synthesis of such compounds has been made possible by the observation of Verkade and van der Lee [308] that triphenylmethyl chloride (trityl chloride) reacts with 1-monoglycerides to yield 1-acyl-3-tritylglycerol, the esterification of which permits of the introduction of a second acyl group differing from the one originally present. Hydrolysis of this compound yields a 1,3-diglyceride into which a third acyl group may be introduced, thus yielding a triacid triglyceride. Verkade [309] has described an alternate method for the synthesis of triacid triglycerides which involves the removal of a trityl group from a 1,2-diacyl-3-trityl glyceride by hydrogenolysis, the reaction taking place without a migration of the acyl groups. Esterification of the product with a third acid chloride yields the desired triacid triglyceride. In 1945, Chen and Daubert [310] prepared a number of saturated triacid triglycerides and reported the melting points of their α-, β'-, and β-forms and also their solubilities in various organic solvents. The triacid triglycerides crystallize from certain solvents in the intermediate β'-form rather than in the higher-melting, stable β-form. This is contrary to the belief that it is always the highest-melting form which is obtained by solvent crystallization, and is an observation of considerable significance. A study of the x-ray diffraction data of the synthetic triacid triglycerides [311] shows that the long crystal spacings cannot be classified by the schematic arrangement proposed by Malkin for the simpler triglycerides. The results of this investigation indicated that a correlation may exist between the long crystal spacings and the molecular weights. The fact that two crystal forms may be obtained by solvent crystallization was definitely established, rapid crystallization favoring the formation of the β'-form and slow crystallization tending to produce the higher-melting β-form.

(4) The Diglycerides

The diglycerides are divided into two groups: the symmetrical or 1,3-diglycerides, and the unsymmetrical or 1,2-diglycerides. Many representatives of both of these groups have been synthesized and their physical constants reported. It has previously been pointed out that owing to a shift of the 2-acyl group to a terminal position many of the diglycerides formerly reported to be 1,2-diglycerides are actually the symmetrical 1,3-isomers. For this reason we do not have, as yet, many examples of 1,2-diglycerides of proven constitution, and the reader should accept with reservation the earlier physical constants which have been reported for these compounds. Very little information is available in the literature upon diglycerides containing acyl groups of different chain lengths, e.g., 1-lauro-3-myristin.

A number of symmetrical diglycerides were prepared by Averill, Roche, and King [207] in the course of their investigation of the triglycerides. In 1937, Malkin, el Shurbagy, and Meara [312] reported the results of their x-ray and thermal examinations of the symmetrical diglycerides from 1,3-dicaprin to 1,3-distearin, and the results of this study have afforded us an insight into the structure and thermal behavior of these compounds. It was reported as early as 1907 by Grün and Theimer [313] that the diglycerides

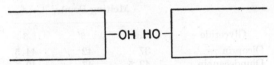

FIG. 5. Structure of diglycerides.

exhibit the phenomenon of double melting points previously observed with the triglycerides. The studies of Malkin and coworkers confirmed this observation and showed that the diglycerides are capable of existing in several polymorphic modifications. X-ray data showed that the diglycerides are built up of double molecules with the two hydrocarbon chains lying parallel on the same side of the glyceryl radical. The structure of the diglycerides as proposed by Malkin and associates is shown in Fig. 5.

The polymorphism exhibited by the symmetrical diglycerides was shown to be unusual in that three modifications of the diglycerides from 1,3-dicaprin to 1,3-dipentadecanoin were observed, whereas the higher diglycerides show only two modifications. The vitreous form appears to be absent except in the case of 1,3-dilaurin. The transition between the various forms was observed to be more rapid than that noted for the triglycerides and the above observations may be explainable on this basis. The three modifications observed for the lower diglycerides are α, β', and β, and for the higher, α and β. The side spacings of the lower members resemble those observed for the monoglycerides, whereas those of the higher members are characteristic of those observed for the triglycerides. The absence of the β'-form in the higher diglycerides was also borne out by a study of the thermal behavior of these compounds. The melting points for the various polymorphic forms of the symmetrical diglycerides as reported by Malkin and coworkers are shown in Table XVII.

The melting points and long crystal spacings of the β'- and β-forms indicate that the chains are tilted, the angles being calculated to be $72°12'$ and $66°30'$, respectively. These glycerides show a typical spherulite structure when solidified from the melt. 1,3-Diarachidin has been reported to melt at $75°$ and 1,3-diolein to be a liquid at room temperature.

TABLE XVII

MELTING POINTS OF POLYMORPHIC FORMS OF SYMMETRICAL DIGLYCERIDES

Melting Points, °C.

Glyceride	α	β'	β
Dicaprin	37	42	44.5
Diundecanoin	43.5	47	49
Dilaurin	49.5	54	56.5
Ditridecanoin	54.5	57	59.5
Dimyristin	60	63	65.5
Dipentadecanoin	63.5	66.5	68.5
Dipalmitin	68	....	72.5
Dimargarin	71.5	....	74.5
Distearin	74	....	78

Daubert and King [234] have synthesized 1,2-dipalmitin, m.p. $64°$, and 1,2-dimyristin, m.p. $59°$, by the action of 3-carbobenzyloxyglycerol on the respective acid chlorides, followed by hydrogenation. Optically active 1,2-diglycerides have been described by Sowden and Fischer,[240] who reported d-1,2-distearin, m.p. 74.5–$75°$, $[\alpha]_D$ $-2.7°$ in $CHCl_3$, and d-1,2-dipalmitin, m.p. 57–$57.5°$, $[\alpha]_D$ $-2.3°$ in $CHCl_3$. Verkade, Cohen, and Vroege [314] have prepared several 1,2-diglycerides through the trityl compounds and have reported that 1,2-distearin melts at 68.5–$69°$, 1-palmito-2-stearin at 60.5–$61°$, and 1-stearo-2-palmitin at 68.5–$69.5°$. Golendeev [315] has reported the synthesis of a series of 1,2-diglycerides through the allyl esters, the following physical constants having been observed: 1,2-dibutyrin, b_{19-20} 165–$167°$; 1,2-dipalmitin, m.p. 70–$73°$; and 1-stearo-2-palmitin, m.p. $73.4°$. The constants reported by this author are in question, since the possibility of a shift in position to yield 1,3-diglycerides was not rigidly eliminated.

Symmetrical diglycerides containing an oleoyl radical have been prepared by Daubert and Longenecker [316] by the hydrolysis of

1,2-diacyl-3-trityl glycerols, the reaction being accompanied by a shift of an acyl group from the 2-position to the 3-position. The following physical constants were reported for the 1-acyl-3-oleoyl diglycerides prepared by this procedure: (acyl group, m.p., n_D^{70}) lauroyl, 32°, 1.44335; myristoyl, 41.0°, 1.44155; palmitoyl, 40.0°, 1.44574; and stearoyl, 54.0°, 1.44690. A recent x-ray investigation [317] of several synthetic 1,3-diglycerides has shown that a straight-line relationship exists between the values of their long spacings and their molecular weights. The long spacings correspond to a double molecule, the glyceryl radical occupying approximately 8 Å. The structure of the diglycerides as originally proposed by Malkin and associates [312] was thus further confirmed by this investigation.

(5) THE MONOGLYCERIDES

It has previously been shown that although the 1-monoglycerides can be prepared easily by the method of Fischer, Bergmann, and Bärwind [204] and by several alternate procedures, the 2-monoglycerides are extremely difficult to synthesize. These authors observed that both 1-monostearin and 1-monopalmitin exist in two solid modifications, and later Rewadikar and Watson [318] confirmed the observation that such glycerides exist in two forms and exhibit the property of double melting. The extensive studies of Malkin and el Shurbagy [319] upon the thermal properties and crystal spacings of the 1-monoglycerides established that these compounds exhibit three modifications: a low-melting, α-form with vertical, rotating chains; an intermediate form, β′; and a high-melting, stable form, β, the last two possessing tilted chains. The melting points of the α-form, therefore, fall upon a continuous curve, whereas those of the β′- and β-forms fall upon alternating curves. The liquid glyceride solidifies in the α-form which then changes into the β′-form and finally into the stable β-form. The stable, high-melting form, β, is obtained directly by crystallization from solvents. The transition β′ → β is quite rapid for the lower members, e.g., 1-monocaprin; however, the higher members show an increasing stability of the intermediate β′-form. The melting points and phase transitions may be followed by means of heating and cooling curves taken over the proper temperature ranges as previously described for the triglycerides. Malkin and el Shurbagy have stated that the properties of these glycerides at points intermediate between arrests in the cooling curves resemble those of a

liquid crystalline state. The melting points of the various polymorphic forms of the saturated 1-monoglycerides as reported by
Malkin and el Shurbagy are shown in Table XVIII. The transition temperatures for the lower form vary from 8° for 1-mono-
caprin to 47.5° for 1-monostearin.

A recent x-ray study [321] of the crystal structures of the 1- and
2-monoglycerides indicates that the glycerol residues are similarly
oriented in these isomers. The angle of tilt of the β-form of the

TABLE XVIII

MELTING POINTS OF POLYMORPHIC FORMS OF 1-MONOGLYCERIDES

Melting Points, °C.

Monoglyceride	α	β'	β
Caprin	27	49	53
Undecanoin	36.5	52	56.5
Laurin	44	59.5	63
Tridecanoin	50	61	65
Myristin	56	67.5	70.5
Pentadecanoin	62	69	72
Palmitin	66.5	74	77
Margarin	70	74.5	77
Stearin	74	79	81.5
Arachidin	.....	.....	84.0 [320]

1-monoglycerides was calculated to be 58°41' and for the 2-mono-
glycerides 45°19'. This difference is such that a 1-monoglyceride
has approximately the same long spacing as a 2-monoglyceride
containing two more carbon atoms in the acid chain. It was
pointed out that this is in approximate agreement with the respective melting points; for example, 1-monolaurin melts at 63°
and 2-monomyristin at 61.5°.

The synthesis of pure 1-monoglycerides of unsaturated acids
has been accomplished only within the last few years. 1-Mono-
olein, m.p. 35.5°, n_D^{40} 1.46262, has been obtained [304] by the action of
oleoyl chloride upon acetone-glycerol in the presence of dry quinoline. 1-Monoelaidin, m.p. 58.5°, has been prepared [305] by a similar
procedure. This compound had been previously reported [322] to
melt at 44.8°, a value which is in fair agreement with that of the
β'-form, the melting points of the α-, β'-, and β-forms being 17.6°,
44.0°, and 58.5°, respectively. Izar [323] has described 1-monolinolein
as an oily liquid. The heating curves for 1-monolinolein [283] indi-

cate a melting point of $-22.8°$ for the β'-form and of $12.3°$ for the β-form. The β'- and β-forms of 1-monolinolenin melt at $-13.5°$ and $15.7°$, respectively. The higher melting point reported for 1-monolinolenin is of interest in view of its greater unsaturation.

The synthesis of the optically active, l-1-monoglycerides containing saturated acid chains varying from 2 to 18 carbon atoms with the exception of the 13, 15, and 17 members has been recently reported by Baer and Fischer.[324] The small rotation of these optically active monoglycerides is significant. It had been previously pointed out by Fischer, Bergmann, and Bärwind [204] that further esterification of the optically active monoglycerides is attended by a reduction of the optical activity to a still lower value. This affords an explanation of the fact that although many mixed triglycerides possess an asymmetric structure few naturally occurring fats and oils are optically active. The optical inactivity of the natural fats and oils may be explained by the fact that the rotations of the enantiomorphic forms of the triglycerides may be so small as to escape detection by the methods of measurement now available.

The first reliable synthesis of a 2-monoglyceride was accomplished by Bergmann and Carter,[216] who prepared 2-monopalmitin, m.p. $69°$, by the catalytic reduction of the palmitoyl ester of 1,3-benzylideneglycerol. The 2-monoglycerides of capric, lauric, myristic, palmitic, and stearic acids were subsequently prepared in a similar way by Stimmel and King,[220] who reported the following melting points and refractive indices, n_D^{70}, for these esters: 2-monocaprin, $40.4°$, 1.44045; 2-monolaurin, $51.1°$, 1.44240; 2-monomyristin, $61°$, 1.44420; 2-monopalmitin, $68.5°$, 1.44605; and 2-monostearin, $74.4°$, 1.44770. Daubert [222] has prepared 2-monopalmitin and 2-monobutyrin, b_4 $140-141°$, by the reduction of the respective 2-acyl-1,3-ditrityl ethers. It will be noted that the melting points of the symmetrical 2-monoesters are lower than those of the unsymmetrical 1-monoesters. The 2-monoglycerides are more soluble in organic solvents than the 1-isomers, the solubility of 2-monopalmitin in ethanol being 4.61 g. per 100 cc. in comparison to 4.09 g. for 1-monopalmitin. This greater solubility would, however, be predictable on the basis of their lower melting points, which also explains the greater solubilities of the unsymmetrical triglycerides as compared with their symmetrical isomers. The heats of combustion, $-\Delta U_R$, of 1- and 2-monopalmitin have been reported [325] to be, respectively, 2778.78 ± 0.36

and 2788.30 ± 0.67 kg. cal./mole at 25° and one atmosphere pressure.

(6) MISCELLANEOUS GLYCERIDES

A series of mixed glycerides of salicylic acid and fatty acids has been synthesized by Humnicki.[326] A number of mixed glycerides of amino acids and the fatty acids have been described in the literature,[327, 328] the reported melting points being quite high. The following are the melting points observed for several of these mixed esters: 1-glycyl-2,3-distearin, 170°; 1-glycyl-2,3-dipalmitin, 215°; 1-alanyl-2,3-distearin, 233°; 2-alanyl-1,3-dipalmitin, 216°; 1-leucyl-2,3-distearin, 150°; 1-leucyl-2,3-dipalmitin, 219°; and 1-alanyl-2,3-dipalmitin, 216°. It was stated that these mixed glycerides are soluble in water but insoluble in ligroin and other organic solvents. Mixed glycerides of aromatic and fatty acids have been described [218] and are frequently employed as intermediates in the preparation of aliphatic glycerides.

The glyceryl polyesters of dibasic acids such as those of adipic or sebacic acid have been stated [329] to be soft, stringy, flexible resins which become rubber-like upon gelation. Gelation occurs when approximately thirty mole per cent of the tetramer or higher polymer is present.

MISCELLANEOUS ESTERS OF THE FATTY ACIDS

There are several other groups of fatty acid esters which deserve mention because of their academic, biological, or commercial interest. The chemical and physical properties of some of these groups, for example, the cholesteryl and other steryl esters, are well defined, whereas with other types, such as the fatty acid esters of cellulose, our knowledge is still rather empirical.

Fatty Acid Esters of the Sterols

The fatty acid esters of cholesterol are of appreciable biological and physiochemical interest. Small amounts of cholesteryl palmitate and stearate are present in the blood and in the various animal fats and waxes. The biological function of the various cholesteryl esters is still not clearly understood. Cholesterol itself is levorotatory, conferring this property upon its various esters, the rotation decreasing with increasing length of the hydrocarbon chain. The physical properties of the cholesteryl esters are of exceptional interest because of their ability to assume a liquid-crystalline or mesomorphic state. In 1888, Reinitzer [330] observed that when solid cholesteryl benzoate is heated, it first forms a turbid liquid which upon further heating melts sharply to a clear liquid. Although these intermediate phases are pure liquids they exhibit certain properties intermediate between those of a solid and a liquid. This state has been defined as liquid crystalline, [331] although the term is somewhat misleading since this phase is not actually crystalline. Many years later, Friedel [332] proposed the more appropriate name mesomorphic state for this structure. The ability to assume the mesomorphic state is characteristic of the cholesteryl esters and has since been shown to be a common phenomenon with many long-chain compounds. There appear to be two types of mesomorphic phases, smectic and nematic. In the former of these phases the liquid flow is not normal but consists of a gliding movement in one plane, whereas in the latter phase the liquid flows readily and exhibits a threadlike structure and comparatively low viscosity. Certain of the cholesteryl esters yield a so-called cholesteric phase, which closely resembles the nematic phase but shows a distinct layer structure and exhibits color effects in polarized light, the molecular layers being much thicker than in the smectic phase. The cholesteryl esters from the formate to the myristate are capable of assuming this cholesteric phase, whereas those above the myristate assume the smectic state. The cholesteryl esters between cholesteryl caprylate and the myristate first yield a smectic liquid upon heating, then change into the cholesteric phase, and finally melt to yield a clear liquid. Such changes are reversible and are, therefore, observed both on cooling and on heating. With cholesteryl myristate, these transitions occur at 72°, 78°, and 83°, respectively. [333] The cholesteryl esters have been synthesized and studied by a number of investigators, [271, 334, 335, 336] and the more recent studies of Page and Rudy [337] not only constitute a compilation of the existing data but greatly expand our knowledge of the physical constants and behavior of these esters. The melting points of the cholesteryl esters tend to decrease with increasing chain length of the acid. It is quite interesting that only one melting point has been observed for cholesteryl laurate. The rotations, turbidity points, and melting points of the cholesteryl esters as reported by Page and Rudy are shown in Table XIX.

The cholesteryl esters are only sparingly soluble in ethanol at 20°; however, they are appreciably soluble in boiling ethanol. The lower members are quite soluble in acetone, the solubility decreasing rapidly with increase in molecular weight. With the exception of the diesters, they are easily soluble in ether. The cholesteryl

TABLE XIX

Physical Constants of Cholesteryl Esters

Ester	$[\alpha]_D^{20}$	Turbidity Point, °C.	Melting Point, °C.
Formate	−51.4	...	96
Acetate	−47.4	...	115
Propionate	−40.9	112	114
Butyrate	−36.3	103	111.5
Valerate	−34.0	92	94
Caproate	−34.0	85	101
Caprylate	−31.3	103	108
Caprate	−29.8	82	93
Laurate	−27.6	...	91
Myristate	−26.6	80	86
Palmitate	−25.1	78	90
Stearate	−24.3	78	82.5
Lignocerate	−18.7	87	89
Undecenoate	−28.3	79	83.5
Oleate	−23.4	...	44.5
Elaidate	−23.7	56	65.5
Petroselinate	−21.9	...	.....
Erucate	−20.8	44	48
Linoleate	−23.9	41	42
Linolenate	−24.3	49	74
Monoadipate	−30.6	...	144
Diadipate	−36.1	195	222
Monosuberate	−29.2	127	130
Disuberate	−34.9	...	179.5

esters are readily saponified by alcoholic sodium hydroxide solution, the ease of saponification increasing with increase in molecular weight. The esters of the vegetable sterols have been investigated by Heiduschka and Gloth,[338] who reported the palmitate, stearate, and oleate of stigmasterol to melt at 99°, 101°, and 44°, respectively.

Fatty Acid Esters of Plant Alcohols

Several esters of the plant pigments and other plant alcohols have been synthesized and described. Karrer and Ishikawa [339] have obtained the diesters of xanthophyll by treating this substance with acid chlorides in the presence of pyridine. The following melting points were reported for these esters: dipropionate, 138°; dibutyrate, 156°; divalerate, 128°; dicaprylate, 108°; and dipalmitate, 89°. Gossypyl hexapalmitate has been prepared by the condensation of gossypol with palmitoyl chloride.[340] The preparation of the fatty acid esters of the tocopherols has been patented.[341]

Fatty Acid Esters of the Carbohydrates

The carbohydrate esters of the fatty acids include esters of the sugars, starches, cellulose, and related substances. The cellulose esters of the lower aliphatic acids, such as cellulose acetate, and of inorganic acids, such as cellulose nitrate, are generally familiar to all chemists. Although the cellulose esters of the higher fatty acids are less well known, their film-forming properties are of such interest that the preparation and use of these esters has been the subject of a number of scientific investigations. A rather voluminous patent literature has been built around the higher fatty acid esters of cellulose and allied compounds. The cellulose esters of the higher fatty acids possess properties somewhat intermediate between those of cellulose and the fatty compounds, the specific properties depending upon the length of the alkyl chain of the acid and the number of acyl groups introduced into the cellulose molecule. In general, the monoesters resemble cellulose in appearance and are insoluble in organic solvents, whereas the di-, tri-, and polyesters are soluble in organic solvents and possess "fat-like" properties. Even the insoluble esters swell in organic solvents and the esters are obtained as somewhat brittle films upon removal of the solvent. When the acyl group or groups are removed by hydrolysis the original cellulose is generally regenerated, indicating that esterification is not accompanied by a profound change in the structure of the cellulose molecule. The monoesters generally decompose before melting; however, many of the polyesters melt over a temperature range, the melting being accompanied by some decomposition. Many examples of mixed cellulose esters, i.e., esters which contain two or more different acyl groups in the ester molecule, have been described in the literature. Such esters are prepared by the further esterification of a cellulose ester, by ester interchange, or by esterification of the cellulose with a mixture of acids, acid chlorides, or anhydrides.

The most frequently employed method for the preparation of cellulose esters is that proposed by Grün and Wittka,[342] which consists of treating the cellulose in benzene suspension with acyl chlorides, in the presence of pyridine or other acid acceptor. Cellulose monostearate, distearate, and dilaurate have been prepared by this procedure, the first of which was described as being almost insoluble in organic solvents and in copper oxide-ammonium hydroxide solution. It has been stated [343] that regenerated cellulose prepared from viscose cannot be esterified with the higher acid chlorides by this method because of the close union of the pyridine and cellulose brought about by the high acidity of the cellulose. Soluble cellulose esters of the higher fatty acids have been obtained by Gault and Ehrmann [344] by the action of acid chlorides on hydrocellulose in the presence of pyridine and toluene. The reaction yields not only the insoluble monoesters but also the more soluble diesters and the soluble triesters, the mixture being separated by virtue of these solubility characteristics. Mixed cellulose esters, such as laurodinitrocellulose or laurodiacetocellulose, have been obtained by the esterification of cellulose nitrate or acetate. Such esters have been described as completely soluble in aromatic solvents. Gault and Ehrmann [345] have stated that the esterification of cellulose nitrate proceeds with some difficulty and that the resulting esters are much less inflammable than the original cellulose nitrate. As previously stated, it has been reported [346] that all the monoesters of cellulose are insoluble in benzene, whereas the di- and triesters are appreciably soluble. In a study [347] of the caprylic acid esters of cellulose it was shown by x-ray measurements that the introduction of acyl groups up to sixty weight per cent does not alter the structure of the original cellulose. The preparation of esters from lignocellulose has been observed [348] to yield a mixture of products, the main components of which are the cellulose esters. The yields of mono-, di-, and triesters obtained by the action of acid chlorides on cellulose are dependent not only upon the relative proportions of the reactants employed but also upon the temperature and other reaction conditions.[349] The action of phosphorus halides on the cellulose esters has been investigated.[350]

The differences in the physical properties of the various mono-, di-, and triesters of cellulose can be illustrated [351] by a comparison of the various laurates. The monolaurate is obtained in the form of short fibers insoluble in benzene and decomposing at 190–200°;

the dilaurate forms fibrous granules melting with decomposition at 85–90°; and the trilaurate is a plastic mass which is elastic when hot, begins to soften at 90°, and is completely liquid at 170°. The latter two esters are quite soluble in organic solvents. The mono-, di-, and tripalmitates melt at 180°, 100°, and 80°, and the stearates at 180–190°, 85–89°, and 75°, respectively. The preparation of a soluble cellulose undecenoate and of the mono-, di-, and tricaproates of cellulose has been described.[352, 353] The treatment of cellulose xanthate and other cellulose derivatives with fatty acid chlorides has been investigated,[354] as has also the preparation of cellulose stearates [355] by the direct esterification of cellulose with stearic acid in the presence of monochloroacetic acid. The preparation of the soluble cellulose esters of the fatty acids has been reviewed by Gault and Ehrmann;[356] however, our knowledge of such compounds has been considerably expanded since this publication.

The patent literature contains many references to the preparation, properties, and uses of the cellulose esters of the higher fatty acids. In 1899, Weber and Cross [357] described the synthesis of cellulose butyrate by the action of butyryl chloride and butyric anhydride on cellulose in the presence of magnesium butyrate. This ester has also been obtained by the action of butyric acid or its anhydride on cellulose in the presence of sulfuric acid,[358] and it has been suggested [359] that the cellulose may first be impregnated with the catalyst and then esterified. A soluble cellulose butyrate has been obtained [360] by first soaking the cellulose in a mixture of sulfuric and butyric acids and then subjecting the product to the action of butyric anhydride. The esterification of cellulose by acid chlorides in the presence of organic bases and chlorinated solvents has been disclosed by Berthon,[361] and the use of temperatures of 140° or higher has been suggested [362] for carrying out esterification reactions involving cellulose. It has also been proposed [363] to employ temperatures below 110°, followed by a treatment of the reaction mixture at higher temperatures, for the preparation of soluble cellulose esters. The use of fatty acid anhydrides in the presence of sulfuric acid has been suggested [364] for such esterifications, and it has been stated [365] that free fatty acids may be employed in the presence of chloroacetic acid and phosphoric acid. It has been observed that soluble esters are produced when the insoluble cellulose esters are heated with chlorinated solvents in the presence of acidic or basic salts,[366] or with phosphorus oxy-

chlorides.[367] The same effect has been claimed [368] to be brought
about by heating the esters in a liquid medium containing pyridinium chloride.

The preparation of mixed cellulose esters has frequently been
described; for example, the action of a mixture of fatty acid
chlorides on cellulose yields mixed cellulose esters.[369, 370, 371] The
syntheses of mixed esters such as cellulose laurate phosphate,[372]
mixed esters of the higher and lower fatty acids,[373, 374, 375, 376] or mixed
cellulose-ricinoleate esters [377] have also been accomplished. Cellulose may be simultaneously esterified by the mixed acid chlorides
or the process may be carried out stepwise.[378] The preparation of
mixed esters by the action of high molecular weight acid anhydrides
on cellulose acetate has been described.[379] The use of magnesium
perchlorate as a catalyst for the preparation of mixed cellulose
esters has been proposed,[380] as has the combined use of this catalyst
and chloroacetic anhydride.[381] The simultaneous action of acetic
anhydride and halogenated organic acids in the presence of magnesium perchlorate yields mixed esters such as cellulose acetate-
2-bromostearate.[382] The sulfo derivatives of aliphatic hydrocarbons have been proposed [383] as catalysts for the esterification of
cellulose.

Many uses have been suggested for both the simple and the
mixed cellulose esters; for example, they can be employed for
waterproofing paper [384] or as a protective coating for metals.[385]
Where the films are too brittle it has been suggested [386] that they
be plasticized with the alkyl esters of the fatty acids, such as ethyl
stearate.

The starch esters of the higher fatty acids are closely allied to
those of cellulose and are prepared by generally similar methods.
Karrer and Zega [387] have obtained starch hexapalmitate, sintering
at 54° and melting at 75°, $[\alpha]_D^{18}$ 53.54°, and starch hexastearate,
sintering at 69° and melting at 86°, $[\alpha]_D^{18}$ 49.38°, by the action of
the respective acid chlorides on starch. The yields were observed
to be much higher than with cellulose; however, these authors
succeeded in preparing cellulose hexastearate, sintering at 83°
and melting at 118°, $[\alpha]_D^{18}$ −0.79°. The preparation of the fatty
acid esters of starch by the action of acid chlorides in the presence
of pyridine or other acid acceptors is the subject of several patents.[388, 389, 390] The products are described as odorless, non-inflam-
mable, and soluble in organic solvents.

The fatty acid esters of the sugars have many of the properties of the glyceryl esters. Such esters can be obtained by the action of acid chlorides on the sugars in the presence of acid-binding agents. Hess and Messmer [391] have prepared the pentapalmitoyl, pentastearoyl, and pentaoleoyl esters of glucose, the octapalmitoyl and octastearoyl esters of sucrose, the hendecapalmitoyl and hendecastearoyl esters of raffinose, and other esters of the sugars and fatty acids. Some of the physical constants which have been reported for these sugar esters are as follows: pentacaproylglucose, $b_{0.01}$ 240–245°; pentapalmitoylglucose, m.p. 65–67°; pentastearoylglucose, m.p. 70–71°; octapalmitoylsucrose, m.p. 54–55°; octastearoylsucrose, m.p. 57°; and hendecapalmitoyl- and hendecastearoylraffinoses, m.p. 43° and 63°, respectively. As previously stated, such esters resemble the glycerides more closely than they resemble the carbohydrate esters. Bloor [392] has shown that the glucose esters are readily assimilated in the animal body. The preparation of the fatty glucosides has been studied by Gilchrist,[393] and more recently Noller and Rockwell [394] have prepared a series of alkylglucosides. The alkylglucosides melt over appreciable temperature ranges, the observed values being as follows: hexyl, 88–91°; octyl, 65–99°; nonyl, 65–118°; decyl, 75–130°; dodecyl, 77–137°. The alkylglucoside tetraacetates melt at lower temperatures and over a much more limited range. Among the interesting uses for the esters of the sugars and the fatty acids may be mentioned that suggested by Rosenthal and Lenhard,[395] who proposed the use of esters of sucrose and highly unsaturated acids as drying oils.

References

1. Ruhoff and Reid, *J. Am. Chem. Soc.*, **55**, 3825 (1933).
2. Ruhoff, *Organic Syntheses*, **16**, 35 (1936).
3. Bannister, U. S. Patent 1,796,231 (1931).
4. McCutcheon, *Organic Syntheses*, **22**, 75, 82 (1942).
5. Bellucci, *Chem.-Ztg.*, **35**, 669 (1911).
6. Mailhe, *ibid.*, **35**, 485, 507 (1911).
7. Durrans and Ellis, Can. Patent 211,664 (1921).
8. Goldschmidt and Littmann, U. S. Patent 1,997,172 (1935).
9. Spiegel, *Ber.*, **51**, 296 (1918).
10. Velluz, *Bull. soc. chim. biol.*, **16**, 909 (1934).
11. Bailly, *J. chim. phys.*, **16**, 28 (1918).
12. Contzen-Crowet, *Bull. soc. chim. Belg.*, **35**, 165 (1926).
13. Mitchovitch, *Bull. soc. chim.* [5], **4**, 1661 (1937).

14. Locquin and Elghozy, *ibid.* [4], **41**, 445 (1927).
15. Sugasawa, *J. Pharm. Soc. Japan*, No. **550**, 1044 (1927).
16. Fourneau and Sabetay, *Bull. soc. chim.* [4], **43**, 859 (1928).
17. Hinshelwood and Legard, *J. Chem. Soc.*, 587 (1935).
18. Goldschmidt and Udby, *Z. physik. Chem.*, **60**, 728 (1907).
19. Rolfe and Hinshelwood, *Trans. Faraday Soc.*, **30**, 935 (1934).
20. Goldschmidt, *Z. physik. Chem.*, **94**, 233 (1920).
21. Sudborough and Roberts, *J. Chem. Soc.*, **87**, 1840 (1905).
22. Sudborough and Thomas, *ibid.*, **91**, 1033 (1907).
23. Fairclough and Hinshelwood, *ibid.*, 538, 1573 (1937); 236 (1938).
24. Fairclough and Hinshelwood, *ibid.*, 593 (1939).
25. Rabinowitch, *Trans. Faraday Soc.*, **33**, 1225 (1937).
26. Toyama, Ishikawa, and Akiyama, *J. Soc. Chem. Ind., Japan*, **37**, S.b. 193 (1934).
27. Haller, *Compt. rend.*, **143**, 657 (1906).
28. Haller and Youssoufian, *ibid.*, **143**, 803 (1906).
29. Haller, *ibid.*, **144**, 462 (1907).
30. Elsdon, *Analyst*, **38**, 8 (1913).
31. Grün, Wittka, and Kunze, *Chem. Umschau*, **24**, 15 (1917).
32. Toyama, Tsuchiya, and Ishikawa, *J. Soc. Chem. Ind., Japan*, **36**, S.b. 230 (1933).
33. Toyama and Tsuchiya, *ibid.*, **36**, S.b. 232 (1933).
34. Hansley, U. S. Patent 2,177,407 (1939).
35. Sauer, Hain, and Boutwell, *Organic Syntheses*, **20**, 67 (1940).
36. Wheeler and Riemenschneider, *Oil & Soap*, **16**, 207 (1939).
37. Brown and Green, *J. Am. Chem. Soc.*, **62**, 738 (1940).
38. Bull, *Ber.*, **39**, 3570 (1906).
39. Haller, *Compt. rend.*, **146**, 259 (1908).
40. Holland, *J. Ind. Eng. Chem.*, **3**, 171 (1911).
41. Smedley, *Biochem. J.*, **6**, 451 (1912).
42. Armstrong, Allan, and Moore, *J. Soc. Chem. Ind.*, **44**, 63T (1925).
43. Ueno and Iwai, *J. Soc. Chem. Ind., Japan*, **38**, S.b. 602 (1935).
44. Lepkovsky, Feskov, and Evans, *J. Am. Chem. Soc.*, **58**, 978 (1936).
45. Wyman and Barkenbus, *Ind. Eng. Chem., Anal. Ed.*, **12**, 658 (1940).
46. André, *Compt. rend.*, **176**, 686 (1923).
47. Longenecker, *Oil & Soap*, **17**, 53 (1940).
48. Swift, Rose, and Jamieson, *ibid.*, **20**, 249 (1943).
49. Bilterys and Gisseleire, *Bull. soc. chim. Belg.*, **44**, 567 (1935).
50. Gascard, *Ann. chim.* [9], **15**, 332 (1921).
51. Brigl and Fuchs, *Z. physiol. Chem.*, **119**, 280 (1922).
52. Graves, U. S. Patent 1,944,887 (1934).
53. Pickard and Kenyon, *J. Chem. Soc.*, **105**, 830 (1914).
54. Kenyon, *ibid.*, **105**, 2226 (1914).
55. Ralston, Segebrecht, and Bauer, *J. Org. Chem.*, **4**, 502 (1939).
56. Chernoyarova, *J. Gen. Chem. (U.S.S.R.)*, **9**, 178 (1939).
57. McCutcheon, *Can. J. Research*, **16B**, 158 (1938).
58. McCutcheon, *ibid.*, **18B**, 231 (1940).
59. Ault and Brown, *J. Biol. Chem.*, **107**, 615 (1934).
60. de Santos and West, *Philippine J. Sci.*, **34**, 199 (1927).

61. Stanfield and Schierz, *J. Am. Chem. Soc.*, **54**, 4356 (1932).
62. Vincente and West, *Philippine J. Sci.*, **36**, 73 (1928).
63. Meyer, *Monatsh.*, **22**, 415 (1901).
64. Wingler, U. S. Patent 1,688,100 (1928).
65. Brady, *J. Am. Chem. Soc.*, **61**, 3464 (1939).
66. van Alphen, *Rec. trav. chim.*, **44**, 1064 (1925).
67. Mühle, *Ber.*, **46**, 2091 (1913).
68. Riedel, Ger. Patent 303,052 (1914).
69. Boedecker, U. S. Patent 1,381,057 (1921).
70. Ishikawa and Kuroda, *Science Reports Tokyo Bunrika Daigaku*, Sec. A, **3**, 265 (1939).
71. Chuit and Hausser, *Helv. Chim. Acta*, **12**, 463 (1929).
72. Lycan and Adams, *J. Am. Chem. Soc.*, **51**, 3450 (1929).
73. Carothers and Hill, *ibid.*, **54**, 1557 (1932).
74. Carothers and Van Natta, *ibid.*, **55**, 4714 (1933).
75. Cox, U. S. Patents 2,180,730 (1939); 2,227,823 (1941).
76. Power and Barrowcliff, *J. Chem. Soc.*, **87**, 884 (1905).
77. Power and Gornall, *ibid.*, **85**, 851 (1904).
78. Barrowcliff and Power, *ibid.*, **91**, 557 (1907).
79. Herrera-Batteke and West, *Philippine J. Sci.*, **31**, 161 (1926).
80. Herrera and Guevara, *Univ. Philippines Nat. and Applied Sci. Bull.*, **4**, 332 (1935).
81. Dean, Wrenshall, and Fujimoto, *U. S. Pub. Health Service, Pub. Health Bull., No. 168*, 28 (1927).
82. Kariyone and Sugahara, *J. Pharm. Soc. Japan*, **59**, 18 (1939).
83. Fairweather, *Phil. Mag.* [7], **1**, 944 (1926).
84. Normand, Ross, and Henderson, *J. Chem. Soc.*, 2632 (1926).
85. Chuit, *Helv. Chim. Acta*, **9**, 264 (1926).
86. Backer and Homan, *Rec. trav. chim.*, **58**, 1048 (1939).
87. Timmermans, *Bull. soc. chim. Belg.*, **36**, 502 (1927).
88. Shearer, *J. Chem. Soc.*, **123**, 3152 (1923).
89. Francis, Piper, and Malkin, *Proc. Roy. Soc. (London)*, **128A**, 214 (1930).
90. Malkin, *J. Chem. Soc.*, 2796 (1931).
91. Phillips and Mumford, *ibid.*, 1732 (1931).
92. King and Garner, *ibid.*, 1449 (1934).
93. Buckingham, *Trans. Faraday Soc.*, **30**, 377 (1934).
94. King and Garner, *J. Chem. Soc.*, 1372 (1936).
95. Phillips and Mumford, *ibid.*, 898 (1932).
96. Mumford and Phillips, *Rec. trav. chim.*, **52**, 181 (1933).
97. van Bellinghen, *Bull. soc. chim. Belg.*, **47**, 640 (1938).
98. Lewis and Smyth, *J. Am. Chem. Soc.*, **62**, 1529 (1940).
99. Smyth and Walls, *ibid.*, **53**, 527 (1931).
100. Kohlrausch, Köppl, and Pongratz, *Z. physik. Chem.*, **22B**, 359 (1933).
101. Ellis, *J. Chem. Soc.*, 1697 (1932).
102. Smith, *ibid.*, 802 (1931).
103. Phillips and Mumford, *Rec. trav. chim.*, **52**, 175 (1933).
104. Carey and Smith, *J. Chem. Soc.*, 635 (1933).
105. Guy and Smith, *ibid.*, 615 (1939).
106. Evans, Gordon, and Watson, *ibid.*, 1439 (1938).

107. Davies and Evans, *ibid.*, 339 (1940).
108. Levenson and Smith, *J. Am. Chem. Soc.*, **62**, 1556 (1940).
109. Smith and Steele, *ibid.*, **63**, 3466 (1941).
110. Lowry, *J. Chem. Soc.*, 2554 (1927).
111. Pauling and Sherman, *J. Chem. Phys.*, **1**, 606 (1933).
112. Salmi, *Ann. Acad. Sci. Fennicae*, A **48**, No. 4 (1937); *Ber.*, **72B**, 1767 (1939).
113. Kino, *Sci. Papers Inst. Phys. Chem. Research Tokyo*, **29**, 31 (1936).
114. Gault and Beloff, *Bull. soc. chim.* [5], **5**, 295 (1938).
115. Sulzberger, U. S. Patent 970,662 (1910).
116. Marangoni, *Atti ist. Veneto sci.*, Pt. *2*, **97**, 209 (1937–38) [*C. A.*, **34**, 6934 (1940)].
117. Zanetti, *J. Am. Chem. Soc.*, **47**, 535 (1925).
118. Zanetti, *ibid.*, **50**, 1821 (1928).
119. Shonle and Row, *ibid.*, **43**, 361 (1921).
120. Shonle and Row, U. S. Patent 1,553,271 (1925).
121. de Santos and West, *Philippine J. Sci.*, **43**, 409 (1930).
122. Farben-vorm. F. Bayer and Co., Ger. Patent 233,327 (1910).
123. Kusama, Jap. Patent 95,687 (1932).
124. Evans and Scheibli, U. S. Patent 2,237,729 (1941).
125. Bollmann, U. S. Patent 1,813,607 (1931).
126. Oranienburger Chemische Fabrik A.-G., Ger. Patent 666,626 (1938).
127. Rather and Reid, *J. Am. Chem. Soc.*, **41**, 75 (1919); **43**, 629 (1921).
128. Judefind and Reid, *ibid.*, **42**, 1043 (1920).
129. Hann, Reid, and Jamieson, *ibid.*, **52**, 818 (1930).
130. Drake and Bronitsky, *ibid.*, **52**, 3715 (1930).
131. Moses and Reid, *ibid.*, **54**, 2101 (1932).
132. Kimura, *J. Soc. Chem. Ind., Japan*, **35**, S.b. 221 (1932).
133. Lundquist, *J. Am. Chem. Soc.*, **60**, 2000 (1938).
134. Kass, Nichols, and Burr, *ibid.*, **64**, 1061 (1942).
135. Drake and Sweeney, *ibid.*, **54**, 2059 (1932).
136. Kelly and Kleff, *ibid.*, **54**, 4444 (1932).
137. Price and Griffith, *ibid.*, **63**, 1767 (1941).
138. Hilditch, *J. Chem. Soc.*, **101**, 192 (1912).
139. Christopher and Hilditch, *ibid.*, **101**, 202 (1912).
140. Brauns, *J. Am. Chem. Soc.*, **42**, 1478 (1920).
141. Beckmann, *J. prakt. Chem.* [2], **55**, 14 (1897).
142. Sulzberger, U. S. Patent 969,420 (1910).
143. Chem. Fabrik von Heyden A.-G., Ger. Patent 184,635 (1905).
144. Weizmann, Ger. Patent 207,155 (1907).
145. Verley, Urbain and Feige, Ger. Patent 207,156 (1907).
146. Schindelmeiser, Ger. Patent 229,190 (1909).
147. Sobbe, *J. prakt. Chem.* [2], **77**, 510 (1908).
148. Stephenson, *Biochem. J.*, **7**, 429 (1913).
149. Wurtz, *Ann. chim. phys.* [3], **55**, 400 (1859).
150. Ruttan and Roebuck, *Trans. Roy. Soc. Can.* [3], **9**, Sec. **III**, 1 (1915).
151. Ayres and Haabestad, Can. Patent 286,077 (1929).
152. Howe, *Trans. Roy. Soc. Can.* [3], **12**, Sec. **III**, 13 (1918).
153. Hilditch and Rigg, *J. Chem. Soc.*, 1774 (1935).

154. Bhattacharya and Hilditch, *ibid.*, 901 (1931).
155. Kailan and Schachner, *Monatsh.*, **52**, 23 (1929).
156. Calvert, U. S. Patent 1,807,304 (1931).
157. Clayton and Reid, *J. Am. Chem. Soc.*, **64**, 908 (1942).
158. Hansley, U. S. Patent 2,025,684 (1935).
159. North, U. S. Patent 2,010,560 (1935).
160. Halasz and Rovira, *Bull. soc. chim.* [5], **8**, 185 (1941).
161. I. G. Farbenind. A.-G., Ger. Patent 548,370 (1928).
162. Carothers and Arvin, *J. Am. Chem. Soc.*, **51**, 2560 (1929).
163. Flory, *ibid.*, **62**, 2261 (1940).
164. Berthelot, *Ann. chim. phys.* [3], **41**, 432 (1854); *Chimie Organique Fondée sur la Synthèse*, Vol. 2, Mallet-Bachelier Imprimeur-Libraire, Paris (1860).
165. Garner, *J. Soc. Chem. Ind.*, **47**, 278T (1928).
166. Steger and van Loon, *Rec. trav. chim.*, **46**, 703 (1927).
167. Verkade, van der Lee, and Meerburg, *ibid.*, **51**, 850 (1932).
168. Bellucci, *Gazz. chim. ital.*, **42**, II, 283 (1912).
169. Bellucci and Manzetti, *Atti accad. Lincei* [5], **20**, I, 125 (1911).
170. Gianoli, *Seifensieder-Ztg.*, **39**, 578 (1911).
171. Tsuchiya and Akiyama, *J. Soc. Chem. Ind., Japan*, **37**, S.b. 195 (1934).
172. Bellucci, *Gazz. chim. ital.*, **42**, II, 283 (1912).
173. Kawai and Nobori, *J. Soc. Chem. Ind., Japan*, **43**, S.b. 59 (1940).
174. Kawai and Nobori, *ibid.*, **43**, S.b. 170 (1940).
175. Kawai, *ibid.*, **43**, S.b. 220 (1940).
176. Kawai, *ibid.*, **43**, S.b. 428 (1940).
177. Veikhertz, *Khim. Farm. Prom.*, 284 (1932).
178. Kailan and Raupenstrauch, *Monatsh.*, **45**, 485 (1924).
179. Kailan and Ulicny, *ibid.*, **61**, 169 (1932).
180. Hilditch and Rigg, Brit. Patent 440,888 (1936).
181. Richardson, U. S. Patent 2,251,692 (1941).
182. Herschberg, *J. Am. Chem. Soc.*, **61**, 3587 (1939).
183. Hartwell, *Am. J. Path.*, **16**, 313 (1940).
184. Heiduschka and Schuster, *J. prakt. Chem.* [2], **120**, 145 (1929).
185. McElroy and King, *J. Am. Chem. Soc.*, **56**, 1191 (1934).
186. Krafft, *Ber.*, **36**, 4339 (1903).
187. Guth, *Z. Biol.*, **44**, 78 (1903).
188. Romburgh, *Rec. trav. chim.*, **1**, 186 (1882).
189. Bömer and Limprich, *Z. Untersuch. Nahr.- u. Genussm.*, **25**, 354 (1913).
190. Bömer and Limprich, *ibid.*, **23**, 641 (1912).
191. Grün, *Ber.*, **38**, 2284 (1905).
192. Grün and Schacht, *ibid.*, **40**, 1778 (1907).
193. Grün and Theimer, *ibid.*, **40**, 1792 (1907).
194. Fischer, *ibid.*, **53B**, 1621 (1920).
195. Fairbourne, *J. Chem. Soc.*, 369 (1930).
196. Grün, *Ber.*, **54B**, 290 (1921).
197. Hibbert and Carter, *J. Am. Chem. Soc.*, **51**, 1601 (1929).
198. Daubert and King, *Chem. Rev.*, **29**, 269 (1941).
199. Grün and Limpächer, *Ber.*, **59B**, 690, 695 (1926).
200. Grün, *ibid.*, **43**, 1288 (1910).
201. Renshaw, *J. Am. Chem. Soc.*, **36**, 537 (1914).

202. Brash, *J. Soc. Chem. Ind.*, **46**, 481T (1927).
203. Grün and von Skopnik, *Ber.*, **42**, 3750 (1909).
204. Fischer, Bergmann, and Bärwind, *ibid.*, **53B**, 1589 (1920).
205. Fischer and Pfähler, *ibid.*, **53B**, 1606 (1920).
206. Amberger and Bromig, *Biochem. Z.*, **130**, 252 (1922).
207. Averill, Roche, and King, *J. Am. Chem. Soc.*, **51**, 866 (1929).
208. Robinson, Roche, and King, *ibid.*, **54**, 705 (1932).
209. Verkade and van der Lee, *Proc. Acad. Sci. Amsterdam*, **37**, 812 (1934).
210. Converse and Shaw, *Proc. S. Dakota Acad. Sci.*, **17**, 31 (1937).
211. Daubert and King, *J. Am. Chem. Soc.*, **60**, 3003 (1938).
212. Black and Overley, *ibid.*, **61**, 3051 (1939).
213. Fairbourne and Foster, *J. Chem. Soc.*, 3146 (1926).
214. Fairbourne and Toms, *ibid.*, **119**, 1035 (1921).
215. Fairbourne and Foster, *ibid.*, **127**, 2759 (1925).
216. Bergmann and Carter, *Z. physiol. Chem.*, **191**, 211 (1930).
217. Helferich and Sieber, *ibid.*, **175**, 311 (1928).
218. Jackson and King, *J. Am. Chem. Soc.*, **55**, 678 (1933).
219. Verkade, van der Lee, and Meerburg, *Rec. trav. chim.*, **54**, 716 (1935).
220. Stimmel and King, *J. Am. Chem. Soc.*, **56**, 1724 (1934).
221. Verkade, van der Lee, de Quant, and Zuydewijn, *Proc. Acad. Sci. Amsterdam*, **40**, 580 (1937).
222. Daubert, *J. Am. Chem. Soc.*, **62**, 1713 (1940).
223. Verkade, van der Lee, and Meerburg, *Rec. trav. chim.*, **56**, 613 (1937).
224. Fairbourne, *J. Chem. Soc.*, 1151, 2232 (1929); Fairbourne and Cowdrey, *ibid.*, 129 (1929).
225. Whitby, *Trans. Roy. Soc. Can.* [3], **13**, Sec. III, 255 (1919).
226. Thomson, *ibid.* [3], **20**, Sec. V, 445 (1926).
227. Delaby and Dubois, *Compt. rend.*, **187**, 767 (1928).
228. Weizmann and Haskelberg, *ibid.*, **189**, 104 (1929).
229. Humnicki and Lunkiewicz, *Bull. soc. chim.* [4], **45**, 422 (1929).
230. Abderhalden and Eichwald, *Ber.*, **48**, 1847 (1915).
231. Bergmann, Brand, and Dreyer, *ibid.*, **54B**, 936 (1921).
232. Bergmann, *Z. physiol. Chem.*, **137**, 27 (1924); Bergmann and Sabetay, *ibid.*, **137**, 46 (1924).
233. Helferich and Sieber, *ibid.*, **170**, 31 (1927).
234. Daubert and King, *J. Am. Chem. Soc.*, **61**, 3328 (1939).
235. Fischer and Baer, *Chem. Rev.*, **29**, 287 (1941).
236. Abderhalden and Eichwald, *Ber.*, **47**, 1856 (1914); **48**, 113 (1915); **51**, 1308 (1918).
237. Grün and Limpächer, *ibid.*, **60B**, 255 (1927).
238. Bergmann and Sabetay, *Z. physiol. Chem.*, **137**, 46 (1924).
239. Baer and Fischer, *J. Biol. Chem.*, **128**, 463, 475, 491 (1939).
240. Sowden and Fischer, *J. Am. Chem. Soc.*, **63**, 3244 (1941).
241. Armstrong and Gosney, *Proc. Roy. Soc. (London)*, **88B**, 176 (1914).
242. Lombroso, *Arch. farm. sper.*, **14**, 429 (1912).
243. Dunlap and Gilbert, *J. Am. Chem. Soc.*, **33**, 1787 (1911).
244. Ivanov, *Ber. deut. botan. Ges.*, **29**, 595 (1911).
245. Morel and Velluz, *Bull. soc. chim. biol.*, **10**, 478 (1928).
246. Argyris and Frank, *Z. Biol.*, **59**, 143 (1912).

247. van Eldik Thieme, *Proc. Acad. Sci. Amsterdam*, **10**, 855 (1908).
248. van Eldik Thieme, *J. prakt. Chem.* [2], **85**, 284 (1912).
249. Young and Black, *J. Am. Chem. Soc.*, **60**, 2603 (1938).
250. Tsuchiya and Akiyama, *J. Soc. Chem. Ind., Japan*, **36**, S.b. 233 (1933).
251. Kawai and Yamamoto, *ibid.*, **43**, S.b. 219 (1940).
252. Blagonravova, Antipova, Savvina, and Svetlichnaya, *J. Applied Chem.* (*U.S.S.R.*), **14**, 102 (1941).
253. Grün, *Chem. Umschau*, **32**, 225 (1925).
254. Edeler and Richardson, Can. Patent 340,803 (1934).
255. Edeler and Richardson, Can. Patents 340,804–5 (1934).
256. Richardson and Eckey, U. S. Patent 2,251,693 (1941).
257. Christensen, U. S. Patents 2,022,493–4 (1935).
258. Toyama, *J. Soc. Chem. Ind., Japan*, **42**, S.b. 218 (1939).
259. Normann, *Chem. Umschau*, **30**, 250 (1923).
260. van Loon, Brit. Patent 249,916 (1924).
261. N. V. Chemische Fabriek Servo and M. D. Rozenbroek, Fr. Patent 821,731 (1937).
262. Hoffman-LaRoche and Co. A.-G., Ger. Patent 708,074 (1935).
263. Lapworth and Pearson, *Biochem. J.*, **13**, 296 (1919).
264. Halliburton, Drummond, and Cannon, *ibid.*, **13**, 301 (1919).
265. Irvine and Gilchrist, *J. Chem. Soc.*, **125**, 10 (1924).
266. Irvine and Gilchrist, *ibid.*, **125**, 1 (1924).
267. Duffy, *ibid.*, **5**, 197 (1853).
268. Smits and Bokhorst, *Proc. Acad. Sci. Amsterdam*, **15**, 681 (1912); *J. Chem. Soc.*, **104**, i, 157 (1913).
269. Nicolet, *J. Ind. Eng. Chem.*, **12**, 741 (1920).
270. Le Chatelier and Cavaignac, *Compt. rend.*, **156**, 589 (1913).
271. Jaeger, *Rec. trav. chim.*, **25**, 334 (1906).
272. Bömer, *Z. Untersuch. Nahr.- u. Genussm.*, **14**, 90 (1907).
273. Othmer, *Z. anorg. Chem.*, **91**, 209 (1915).
274. Loskit, *Z. physik. Chem.*, **134**, 135 (1928).
275. Efremov, *Ann. inst. polytech. Oural*, **6**, 155 (1927).
276. Weygand and Grüntzig, *Z. anorg. allgem. Chem.*, **206**, 304, 313 (1932).
277. Joglekar and Watson, *J. Indian Inst. Sci.*, **13A**, 119 (1930).
278. Rao and Jatkar, *J. Indian Chem. Soc.*, **12**, 574 (1935).
279. Clarkson and Malkin, *J. Chem. Soc.*, 666 (1934).
280. Malkin, *Trans. Faraday Soc.*, **29**, 977 (1933).
281. Meara, in *The Chemical Constitution of Natural Fats*, Hilditch, p. 350, John Wiley & Sons, New York (1940).
282. Wheeler, Riemenschneider, and Sando, *J. Biol. Chem.*, **132**, 687 (1940).
283. Daubert and Baldwin, *J. Am. Chem. Soc.*, **66**, 997 (1944).
284. Bailey, Jefferson, Kreeger, and Bauer, *Oil & Soap*, **22**, 10 (1945).
285. Lutton, *J. Am. Chem. Soc.*, **67**, 524 (1945).
286. Ferguson and Lutton, *Chem. Rev.*, **29**, 355 (1941).
287. Reimer and Will, *Ber.*, **18**, 2011 (1885).
288. Eisenstein, *Chem. Umschau*, **27**, 3 (1920).
289. Woolley and Sandin, *J. Am. Chem. Soc.*, **57**, 1078 (1935).
290. Bhide and Bhide, *J. Univ. Bombay*, **7**, Pt. 3, 97 (1938).
291. Labrouste, *Ann. phys.* [9], **14**, 164 (1920).

292. Dervichian, *J. Chem. Phys.*, **7**, 931 (1939).
293. Ravich and Vol'nova, *Compt. rend. acad. sci. U.R.S.S.*, **37**, 59 (1942).
294. van Roon, *Chem. Weekblad*, **27**, 498 (1930).
295. Kreis and Hafner, *Ber.*, **36**, 2766 (1903).
296. Grün and Schacht, *ibid.*, **40**, 1778 (1907).
297. Malkin and Meara, *J. Chem. Soc.*, 103, 1141 (1939).
298. Averill, Roche, and King, *J. Am. Chem. Soc.*, **52**, 365 (1930).
299. Jackson, Daubert, King, and Longenecker, *ibid.*, **66**, 289 (1944).
300. Daubert and Clarke, *ibid.*, **66**, 690 (1944).
301. Filer, Sidhu, Daubert, and Longenecker, *ibid.*, **68**, 167 (1946).
302. Storkes and Germer, *J. Chem. Phys.*, **5**, 131 (1937).
303. Carter and Malkin, *J. Chem. Soc.*, 577, 1518 (1939).
304. Daubert, Fricke, and Longenecker, *J. Am. Chem. Soc.*, **65**, 2145 (1943).
305. Daubert, *ibid.*, **66**, 290 (1944).
306. Daubert, Spiegl, and Longenecker, *ibid.*, **65**, 2144 (1943).
307. Daubert and Baldwin, *ibid.*, **66**, 1507 (1944).
308. Verkade and van der Lee, *Rec. trav. chim.*, **55**, 267 (1936).
309. Verkade, *ibid.*, **62**, 393 (1943).
310. Chen and Daubert, *J. Am. Chem. Soc.*, **67**, 1256 (1945).
311. Filer, Sidhu, Chen, and Daubert, *ibid.*, **67**, 2085 (1945).
312. Malkin, el Shurbagy, and Meara, *J. Chem. Soc.*, 1409 (1937).
313. Grün and Theimer, *Ber.*, **40**, 1792 (1907).
314. Verkade, Cohen, and Vroege, *Rec. trav. chim.*, **59**, 1123 (1940).
315. Golendeev, *J. Gen. Chem. (U.S.S.R.)*, **6**, 1841 (1936).
316. Daubert and Longenecker, *J. Am. Chem. Soc.*, **66**, 53 (1944).
317. Sidhu and Daubert, *ibid.*, **68**, 2603 (1946).
318. Rewadikar and Watson, *J. Indian Inst. Sci.*, **13A**, 128 (1930).
319. Malkin and el Shurbagy, *J. Chem. Soc.*, 1628 (1936).
320. Sidhu and Daubert, *J. Am. Chem. Soc.*, **68**, 1975 (1946).
321. Filer, Sidhu, Daubert, and Longenecker, *ibid.*, **66**, 1333 (1944).
322. Börner and Kappeller, *Fette u. Seifen*, **44**, 340 (1937).
323. Izar, *Biochem. Z.*, **60**, 320 (1914).
324. Baer and Fischer, *J. Am. Chem. Soc.*, **67**, 2031 (1945).
325. Clarke and Stegeman, *ibid.*, **62**, 1815 (1940).
326. Humnicki, *Bull. soc. chim.* [4], **45**, 275 (1929).
327. Weizmann and Haskelberg, *Compt. rend.*, **189**, 104 (1929).
328. Weizmann and Haskelberg, *Bull. soc. chim.* [4], **51**, 59 (1932).
329. Kienle and Petke, *J. Am. Chem. Soc.*, **63**, 481 (1941).
330. Reinitzer, *Monatsh.*, **9**, 421 (1888).
331. Lehmann, *Z. physik. Chem.*, **4**, 462 (1889).
332. Friedel, *Ann. phys.* [9], **18**, 273 (1922).
333. Fürth and Sitte, *Ann. Physik* [5], **30**, 388 (1937).
334. White, *J. Physiol. Proc.*, **38**, vi (1908).
335. Gaubert, *Compt. rend.*, **149**, 608 (1909).
336. Prins, *Z. physik. Chem.*, **67**, 689 (1909).
337. Page and Rudy, *Biochem. Z.*, **220**, 304 (1930).
338. Heiduschka and Gloth, *Arch. Pharm.*, **253**, 415 (1915).
339. Karrer and Ishikawa, *Helv. Chim. Acta*, **13**, 709, 1099 (1930).
340. Gil'tburg, *Masloboĭno Zhirovoe Delo*, **12**, 546 (1936).

341. Hoffman-LaRoche and Co., Brit. Patent 536,602 (1941).

342. Grün and Wittka, *Z. angew. Chem.*, **34**, 645 (1921).

343. Shettle, Klyuchkin, and Kogan, *J. Applied Chem. (U.S.S.R.)*, **7**, 976 (1934).

344. Gault and Ehrmann, *Bull. soc. chim.* [4], **39**, 873 (1926).

345. Gault and Ehrmann, *Caoutchouc & gutta-percha*, **24**, 13748 (1927); **25**, 13868 (1928).

346. Sakurada and Nakashima, *Sci. Papers Inst. Phys. Chem. Research Tokyo*, **7**, 153 (1927).

347. Nowakowski, *Roczniki Chem.*, **15**, 68 (1935).

348. Solechnik, *Lesokhim. Prom.*, **3**, No. 4, 12 (1934) [*C. A.*, **29**, 4935 (1935)].

349. Gault and Ehrmann, *Caoutchouc & gutta-percha*, **23**, 13312, 13888 (1926); **24**, 13453 (1927).

350. Pringsheim, Lorand, and Ward, *Cellulosechem.*, **13**, 119 (1932).

351. Gault and Ehrmann, *Caoutchouc & gutta-percha*, **24**, 13532 (1927).

352. Gault and Urban, *Compt. rend.*, **179**, 333 (1924).

353. Gault and Ehrmann, *Caoutchouc & gutta-percha*, **24**, 13706 (1927).

354. Sakurada and Nakashima, *Sci. Papers Inst. Phys. Chem. Research Tokyo*, **6**, 197 (1927).

355. Shettle and Klyuchkin, *J. Applied Chem. (U.S.S.R.)*, **7**, 558 (1934).

356. Gault and Ehrmann, *Compt. rend.*, **177**, 124 (1923).

357. Weber and Cross, U. S. Patent 632,605 (1899).

358. Esselen and Mork, U. S. Patent 1,425,581 (1922).

359. A. D. Little, Inc., Brit. Patent 182,820 (1921).

360. Esselen and Mork, U. S. Patent 1,425,580 (1922).

361. Berthon, U. S. Patent 1,553,924 (1925).

362. I. G. Farbenind. A.-G., Brit. Patent 283,181 (1927).

363. Hagedorn and Hingst, U. S. Patent 1,940,589 (1933).

364. Angla, U. S. Patent 1,909,798 (1933).

365. Hiatt and Crane, U. S. Patent 2,254,652 (1941).

366. I. G. Farbenind. A.-G., Fr. Patent 644,636 (1927).

367. I. G. Farbenind. A.-G., Brit. Patent 292,929 (1927).

368. Hagedorn and Hingst, U. S. Patent 1,931,844 (1933).

369. I. G. Farbenind. A.-G., Ger. Patent 483,999 (1924).

370. Berthon, U. S. Patent 1,651,990 (1927).

371. Staud and Beeton, Brit. Patent 344,151 (1929).

372. I. G. Farbenind. A.-G., Ger. Patent 511,208 (1926).

373. Clarke and Malm, U. S. Patent 1,704,282 (1929).

374. Malm, U. S. Patent 1,946,632 (1934).

375. Kodak A.-G., Ger. Patent 629,518 (1936).

376. Kodak Ltd., Brit. Patent 527,973 (1940).

377. Hagedorn, U. S. Patent 1,966,757 (1934).

378. I. G. Farbenind. A.-G., Ger. Patent 597,924 (1934).

379. Kodak-Pathé, Fr. Patent 667,556 (1929).

380. Clarke, Malm, and Stinchfield, Brit. Patent 287,880 (1927).

381. Clarke and Malm, Brit. Patent 304,278 (1928).

382. Kodak-Pathé, Fr. Patent 667,557 (1929).

383. Soc. des usines chim. Rhône-Poulenc, Fr. Patent 689,244 (1930).

384. Mitchell, U. S. Patent 2,193,831 (1940).

385. Fordyce and Hiatt, U. S. Patent 2,170,016 (1939).
386. Kodak-Pathé, Fr. Patent 778,961 (1935).
387. Karrer and Zega, *Helv. Chim. Acta*, **6**, 822 (1923).
388. I. G. Farbenind. A.-G., Ger. Patent 484,242 (1923).
389. Soc. de Stéarinerie et Savonnerie de Lyon, Brit. Patent 208,685 (1923).
390. Cantor, U. S. Patent 2,147,241 (1939).
391. Hess and Messmer, *Ber.*, **54B**, 499 (1921).
392. Bloor, *Orig. Com. 8th Intern. Congr. Appl. Chem.*, **19**, 29 (1912).
393. Gilchrist, *Rept. Brit. Assoc. Advancement Sci.*, 357 (1922).
394. Noller and Rockwell, *J. Am. Chem. Soc.*, **60**, 2076 (1938).
395. Rosenthal and Lenhard, U. S. Patent 1,739,863 (1929).

VIII

THE NITROGEN-CONTAINING DERIVATIVES
OF THE FATTY ACIDS

Few, if any, series of derivatives of naturally occurring or synthetic substances possess the intrinsic academic and commercial interest which is to be found in the nitrogen-containing derivatives of the fatty acids. An interesting consideration regarding such compounds is the wide range of physical and chemical properties which characterizes the various representatives of this class. Such derivatives range from the comparatively neutral, waxlike amides on the one hand, to the highly basic amines on the other, the salts of which possess marked surface active properties. The nitrogen-containing derivatives of the fatty acids embrace a very large number of compounds which, for the purposes of this discussion, have been divided into three general types. The first of these, the amides, substituted amides, and related compounds, comprise a large group, many of the representatives of which possess characteristic and distinctive properties. The second group, the nitriles, are important intermediate products, whereas the last group, the amines, constitute an important series of organic bases from which are obtained the amine salts, the quaternary ammonium compounds, and many other chemicals which are proving to be of increasing scientific interest.

THE AMIDES, SUBSTITUTED AMIDES, AND RELATED
DERIVATIVES OF THE FATTY ACIDS

The fatty amides, $RCONH_2$, are related to the fatty acids in that the hydroxyl group of the acid is replaced by an amino group. The substitution of alkyl, aryl, or other groups for one or both of the amino hydrogens yields the substituted amides of which many representatives have been described in the literature. The latter can be prepared directly from the acids or their derivatives by reaction with amines, or they may be obtained by substitution reactions involving the hydrogens of the amino group.

Preparation of Amides

A variety of methods have been proposed and investigated for the preparation of the amides and substituted amides of the fatty acids. The oldest of such methods, and one which is still extensively used, involves the dehydration of an ammonium or amine salt of a fatty acid. Acid amides, such as oxamide, were prepared by Dumas as early as 1830 by the dry distillation of the corresponding salts. Later, Hofmann [1] found that the higher amides, such as stearamide, can be obtained simply by heating the ammonium salts of the fatty acids, and Menschutkin [2] prepared a series of amides by heating the sodium salts of the fatty acids with ammonium chloride. Stearamide was first prepared by Carlet [3] by heating ethyl stearate with an alcoholic solution of ammonia; however, Meyer [4] later showed this reaction to be reversible. Modifications of these methods have been employed by other investigators [5, 6, 7] for the preparation of fatty acid amides, and many subsequent studies have been made relative to the rates of decomposition of the ammonium or amine salts, the optimum conditions for such reactions, and the equilibria involved. Fundamentally, such procedures involve simply the dehydration of the ammonium or amine salts of the fatty acids by the following reaction:

$$RCO_2NH_4 \rightleftarrows RCONH_2 + H_2O$$

Since the amide may lose a further molecule of water to form the nitrile, it is necessary that the proper reaction conditions be employed in order to obtain high yields of the amide. Dehydration procedures are especially adaptable to the preparation of the high molecular weight substituted amides, an example being the formation of N-octadecylacetamide by heating octadecylammonium acetate. [8] The decomposition of a number of salts of octadecylamine and dodecylamine to form the corresponding amides has recently been studied. [9] An illustration of this procedure is the preparation of N-octadecylstearamide by heating octadecylammonium stearate at 225–250° for a period of 15–30 minutes in an atmosphere of nitrogen, the yield being 98%.

In the preparation of the higher molecular weight amides it is quite apparent that the formation and dehydration of the ammonium soaps may be conducted simultaneously. This may be accomplished by passing ammonia into the heated acids contained in a closed vessel, the water and excess ammonia being removed continuously. Such processes form the basis of several early patents.[10,11] Mitchell and Reid,[12] in their study of the preparation of amides by passing ammonia gas through the heated acids in such a manner that the water is continuously removed, concluded that the reaction velocity becomes appreciably slower with increasing molecular weight of the acids. They reported that no amide was obtained from palmitic or stearic acid at 125° or 190°. High yields of the lower molecular weight amides were, however, reported by these authors, and it has subsequently been shown that their conclusions with reference to the preparation of palmitamide and stearamide were erroneous. Dimethyl amides result when the fatty acids are similarly treated with dimethylamine, the yields being comparable to those of the unsubstituted amides. A series of saturated amides of high purity has recently been prepared[13] by this method, the procedure employed being as follows:

Ammonia was passed through the acids at 190–210° for 10–14 hours to obtain the amides. The crude product was poured into water while still hot to remove excess ammonia and any ammonium soap which was formed. The product was then dissolved in tetrachloromethane, washed free of fatty acid with alcoholic potassium hydroxide, and recrystallized from acetone until a constant freezing point was obtained.

Anilides are similarly obtained by heating the fatty acids with aniline, added dropwise, for 2–3 hours at 150-170°. The use of surface catalysts such as silica gel to promote amide formation has been suggested,[14,15] and Nill[16] has described the preparation of stearanilide by passing the preheated vapors of aniline through stearic acid maintained at a temperature of 235°. Bruson[17] has obtained a series of amides containing seven or more carbon atoms by heating a mixture of the acids and urea at temperatures ranging from 180° to 250°, and D'Alelio and Reid[18] have reported that pure amides may be obtained by using approximately 0.5 mole of urea per mole of aliphatic monocarboxylic acid and operating at temperatures not exceeding 160°. The preparation of a number of amides of both mono- and dicarboxylic acids is described in this last patent. Temperatures of 170–180° are employed for the synthesis of the diamides.

One of the earliest methods for the preparation of amides consists of treating acid chlorides with dry ammonia or an amine. This procedure was first employed by Liebig in 1832 and has subsequently been used for the preparation of a wide variety of both substituted and unsubstituted amides. Among the first descriptions of its use for the synthesis of amides of the higher fatty acids may be mentioned the preparations of caproamide by Henry,[19] of caprylamide, undecanamide, undecenamide, and stearamide by Aschan,[20] and of a series of saturated amides by Krafft and Stauffer.[21] The preparation of stearamide by this method has been described by Orton,[22] who also reported that low yields of amides are obtained from the dicarboxylic acids by its use. The method is especially adaptable to the preparation of amides of high purity and was employed by Guy and Smith [23] for the preparation of palmitamide and stearamide, which were used in their physicochemical studies of these compounds. Substituted amides such as N,N-dimethylcaproamide and N,N-dimethylcaprylamide have been prepared [24] by adding acid chlorides dropwise to a concentrated aqueous solution of an amine. The synthesis of stearanilide and of N,N-diphenyl amides by the action of acid chlorides on aniline or diphenylamine has been described.[13] In the former instance, aniline is added dropwise to stearoyl chloride maintained at a temperature below 50°, whereas the N,N-diphenyl amides are obtained by heating the appropriate acid chlorides with diphenylamine for 2–4 hours at 135–145°.

The ammonolysis of fats or of other esters of the fatty acids is one of the recognized methods for the preparation of both substituted and unsubstituted amides. Such processes bear a close similarity to ordinary hydrolytic reactions, the ammonia functioning as $H^+ NH_2{}^-$. In these reactions, therefore, the NH_2 group corresponds to the hydroxyl of water, the ammonolysis of an ester being represented thus:

$$RCO_2R' + HNH_2 \rightarrow RCONH_2 + R'OH$$

Reactions of this type were first investigated with amines such as aniline, the action of which resembles that of anhydrous ammonia. When fats are heated with aniline in sealed tubes at 230° for five hours, they are partially converted to anilides and glycerol,[25] and de'Conno [26] has stated that these anilides may be separated by fractional distillation. The preparation of amides by the action of ammonia on fats involves the principles inherent in the use of aniline or other amines; however, it appears to have been studied only comparatively recently. In 1934, Oda [27] reported that fats are quantitatively converted into amides and glycerol when heated under pressure with liquid ammonia for one hour at 65°. Catalysts such as ammonium chloride have a promoting effect upon reactions of this type. A Russian patent [28] issued in 1937 discloses the preparation of amides by the treatment of fats with liquid ammonia at 20–40° under a pressure of 8–15 atmospheres, in the presence of catalysts such as ammonium salts of inorganic acids or metallic amides. Increase of temperature, the addition of ammonium chloride, or the presence of an emulsifier increases the velocity of the ammonolysis.[29] It was reported, however, that the reaction proceeds faster with gaseous ammonia at 100° under a pressure of 60 atmospheres than in liquid ammonia. The ammonolysis of oils and fats by the action of liquid ammonia in the presence of ammonium salts has been shown [30] to result in essentially quantitative yields of amides and glycerol. The preparation of amides by the action of liquid ammonia on fats, acid chlorides, or fatty acids has been described in the patent literature.[31] The amidation of aliphatic esters by treatment at 100° under pressure with aqueous solutions of aliphatic amines has also been described.[32]

The partial hydrolysis of nitriles yields amides according to the following reaction:

$$RCN + H_2O \rightarrow RCONH_2$$

This reaction may be accomplished by treatment of the nitriles with concentrated hydrochloric acid, sulfuric acid, or glacial acetic acid at low temperatures. The amide precipitates as a white solid. The preparation of capramide from caprinitrile by this method has been described as follows: [13]

Highly purified caprinitrile (10 g.) was poured into concentrated sulfuric acid (200 ml.) and left for 24 hours. The addition product thus formed was then hydrolyzed by pouring the mixture over a large excess of ice, and the amide which precipitated was filtered and recrystallized from acetone.

Nitriles are converted into amides by treatment with hydrogen peroxide in alkaline solution, the action proceeding with the liberation of oxygen.[33] An interesting method for the preparation of amides consists of heating mixtures of fatty acids and potassium thiocyanate.[34, 35] Hofmann,[1] however, has reported that the yields obtained by this method are small, and the procedure has not been extensively employed for the preparation of the higher amides.

The preparative methods which have been discussed are of rather general adaptability. Procedures such as the action of gaseous ammonia or amines on acids or acid chlorides are particularly suited to the laboratory preparation of these compounds, but the choice of a method is largely optional. A number of specialized methods have been described in the literature for the preparation of amides, and such procedures will be discussed when specific amides are considered.

Physical Properties of the Amides of Fatty Acids

No series of aliphatic compounds offers more of a challenge to the physical chemist than do the amides. Present-day theories as to their structure and physical behavior are controversial, and contradictory observations can apparently be presented against every rational explanation of their behavior. Statements as to their structure cannot be accepted with any pretense of finality and the present tentative conclusions will have to be verified by many more detailed and exacting studies. It is for this reason that the amides are of unusual interest, and the many observations which have been reported relative to their physical and chemical behavior should be carefully considered.

Quite unlike other series of aliphatic compounds, the amides do not exhibit the gradation in physical properties in the solid state which characterizes most homologous series. The relatively high melting points of the amides together with their unusual solubility characteristics have long been attributed to some form of molecular association.

Most of the work bearing upon the structure of the amides has been confined to those containing six or less carbon atoms; however, it is reasonable to assume that such investigations have a direct bearing upon the structure of the higher molecular weight amides. It is evident that the monomeric amides may possess at least two tautomeric structures, the keto form $RCONH_2$ and the enol form $RC:(NH)OH$, and that these two structures may be in dynamic equilibrium either in the monomeric state or in relation to a polymer. Earlier workers were too much inclined to assume that the amides must possess a fixed structure, either the keto or the enol form, and many papers have been published in support of one or the other. The keto structure of the amides was questioned in 1868 by Wanklyn and Schenk,[36] who suggested the structure

$NH:C(NH_2)OH$ for carbamide, and later by Rathke,[37] who proposed the formula $NH:C(NH_2)SH$ for thiocarbamide. A few years later, it was suggested [38] that benzamide has the structure $NH:C(C_6H_5)OH$ and not $NH_2COC_6H_5$. The work of Auwers and associates [39] showed the amides to be associated in benzene solution, and since association was at that time supposedly dependent upon the presence of a hydroxyl group the enol structure for the amides was assumed. This contention, however, was later modified by Auwers,[40] who postulated that the trivalent nitrogen atom may be involved in amide association. In an attempt to distinguish between the keto and enol structures for the amides, Meldrum and Turner [41] determined their molecular weights by the ebullioscopic method in a series of solvents, confirming the fact that the amides are associated in solution. Their results were in substantial agreement with the Nernst-Thomson theory that association is greater in non-polar solvents. These authors, however, did not consider that their results substantiated the enol structure for amides and suggested that the trivalent nitrogen or the oxygen atom of the group —$CONH_2$ may be responsible for the association. The prior work of several investigators [42, 43, 44, 45, 46, 47] which purported to favor the keto structure $RCONH_2$ for the amides was mentioned in support of their contention. Arguments to the contrary, however, have been presented by several workers.[48, 49] In a further study of the structure of the amides and substituted amides, Meldrum and Turner [50] observed that the extent of association decreases with increasing molecular weight, that the presence of phenyl groups decreases association, and that the substitution of both amino hydrogens yields substances of normal molecular size. Thus aromatic amides are less strongly associated than aliphatic amides, whereas the anilides show less tendency towards association than the corresponding amides. It also appears that the presence of an amino hydrogen in the amide molecule is a prerequisite to its association, since substances such as N-methylacetanilide are apparently incapable of forming associated molecules. Mascarelli and Benati [51] had previously shown that the substitution of both hydrogens attached to the amide nitrogen yields compounds which are not associated. A necessary conclusion from these observations is that the association of the amides cannot be explained merely by the presence of the trivalent nitrogen atom. The quite high molecular weights of the amides in water, in spite of the high dielectric constant of the latter, have been cited [52] as representing an apparent exception to the Nernst-Thomson theory.

The concept of hydrogen bonding [53, 54] has done much to explain association and has rendered somewhat questionable the ordinary ebullioscopic and cryoscopic methods for molecular weight determination. More recent work [55] has pointed out the strong hydrogen-bonding characteristics of the amide nitrogen atom. In their studies of the amides and sulfonamides, Chaplin and Hunter [56] emphasized that the dependence of association upon the presence of the amidic hydrogen atom clearly points to hydrogen bonding as the cause of association. They have suggested that the bonded hydrogen atom is shared between the nitrogen atom of one amide group and the oxygen atom of another.

Association of the amides may result in either linear or cyclic polymers involving either the keto or the enol form. The dissociation of these polymers into monomers can yield the amide, the imino alcohol, or mixtures of these, the course depending upon environmental conditions. Thus, intermolecular hydrogen bonding involving resonating forms may explain both association and the tautomeric behavior of the amide molecule. In their studies of the hydrogen-bonding characteristics of the amides, Copley, Zellhoefer, and Marvel [57] have suggested the formation of linear polymers, an example of which is the following:

$$\cdots O \quad \overset{\overset{\displaystyle R}{|}}{\underset{|}{\overset{\|}{C}}} \quad N-H\cdots O \quad \overset{H}{\underset{\overset{\|}{\underset{R}{C}}}{|}} \quad N-H\cdots O \quad \overset{\overset{\displaystyle R}{|}}{\underset{|}{\overset{\|}{C}}} \quad N-H\cdots$$

It was pointed out, however, that linear polymerization, as in the case of the alcohols, yields compounds of low melting point, whereas the melting points of the amides are unusually high, and that association of the amides exclusively through the enol form would involve a rearrangement equivalent to ionization of a hydrogen atom,[58] an occurrence rather improbable in a non-polar solvent. The x-ray investigations of Henderson [59] have indicated that the amides are associated as cyclic dimers, two resonating structures of which were proposed by Copley, Zellhoefer, and Marvel,[57] thus:

$$R-C\overset{O---H-N}{\underset{N-H---O}{}}C-R \qquad R-C\overset{O-H--N}{\underset{N---H-O}{}}C-R$$

These authors have further stated that the properties of amides may possibly be explained by a type of association brought about by the fusion of dimers, the structure of the resulting polymer being represented as follows:

$$R-C\overset{O---H-N}{\underset{N-H---O}{}}C-R$$
$$R-C\overset{O---H-N}{\underset{N-H---O}{}}C-R$$

The high dielectric constants and dipole moments which have been reported [60, 61, 62, 63] for the amides argue against a symmetrical cyclic structure, since such configurations would bring about a neutralization of the dipole moments. However, it has been stated [57] that the values observed for these constants may be explained by assuming the presence of an appreciable amount of monomer. Pauling and Sherman [64] have pointed out the resonating nature of the unsubstituted amides, the excited form being $R-C\overset{O^-}{\underset{NH_2}{}}^+$ with a moment of approximately 10, and Kumler and Porter [62] have added that it is also reasonable to assume that resonance occurs in substituted amides. They expressed the opinion that the unsubstituted amides do not exist to a large extent in the iminohydroxy form. Studies of the infrared absorption spectra [58, 65] and of the ultraviolet absorption [66] testify to the tautomeric nature of the amides, and the presence of the enol isomer is evidenced by their chemical behavior.[38, 48, 49, 67] The significance of hydrogen bonding in explaining the physical properties of the amides has been pointed out by Lassettre [68] and the many investigators previously cited.

From the above discussion it is evident that much is yet to be learned concerning the actual structure of the amides. Structures formulated upon hydrogen bonding and resonating forms can explain many of the observations relative to the observed association characteristics and tautomeric nature of the amides, but certain facts appear to be at variance with all proposed structures. The possibility of an asymmetric cyclic structure in which amide molecules are combined as side chains [13] may perhaps warrant further investigation.

The melting and freezing points of the unsubstituted amides of the saturated acids are unusual in several respects, and we do not as yet have a satisfactory explanation for their behavior. It is subsequently shown that such irregularities are not confined to the melting points, but manifest themselves in solubility characteristics and other physico-chemical behaviors. Most homologous series of aliphatic compounds show a well-defined trend in melting points, the values falling to a minimum in the vicinity of the compound containing five carbon atoms and then rising with increasing molecular weight, the differences between successive members becoming less as the series is ascended. This generalization applies to both alternating and non-alternating series.

The melting points of the amides alternate from even to odd members in the sense that they can be plotted upon two generally similar curves. In both the odd and the even series the melting points rise abruptly from the initial member, then fall irregularly to a minimum which occurs at seven carbon atoms in the odd series and at ten carbon atoms in the even (Fig. 1). Wide fluctuations, therefore, occur in the melting points of the lower molecular weight members of this series. On the other hand, the similarity in melting points of the higher members is quite striking, large differences in molecular weight having little effect upon the melting points. For example, caprylamide freezes only 3.8° lower than stearamide. Substitution of an amino hydrogen brings about a profound change in the melting point curves. Robertson [69] has shown that the melting points of both even and odd anilides fall to a minimum at the eighth and ninth members, respectively, the fall being extremely abrupt between propionanilide and valeranilide in the odd series and between caproanilide and caprylanilide

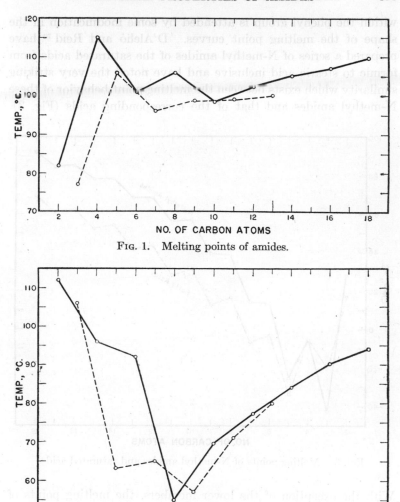

FIG. 1.   Melting points of amides.

FIG. 2.   Melting points of anilides.

in the even (Fig. 2).   The effect of substitution in the phenyl group
of the anilides upon the melting point curves was studied by
Robertson, who observed that the *p*-toluidides show an extremely
rapid initial drop, followed by a slight fall in the even series and a
slight rise in the odd.   In every series examined (*o*-toluidides,
o-bromo-*p*-toluidides,   and   2,4,6-tribromoanilides),   substitution

within the phenyl group is attended by some modification in the shape of the melting point curves. D'Alelio and Reid [70] have prepared a series of N-methyl amides of the saturated acids from formic to stearic acid inclusive and have noted the very striking similarity which exists between the melting point behavior of these N-methyl amides and that of the corresponding acids (Fig. 3).

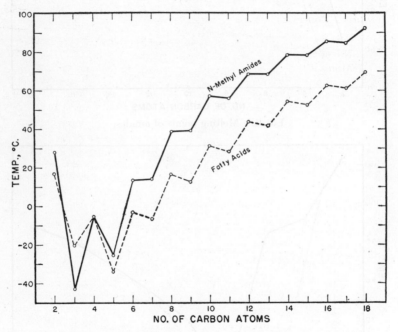

FIG. 3.   Melting points of N-methyl amides and saturated acids.

With the exception of the lower members, the melting points of the anilides are lower than those of the amides. The very low melting points of the lower N-methyl amides when compared to those of either the amides or the anilides are extremely note-worthy and suggest a fundamental difference in physical structure. However, with increase in molecular weight the melting points of the N-methyl amides and the anilides approach each other quite closely.

Many investigators have reported melting point or freezing point data for the amides [1, 12, 13, 21, 69, 71, 72, 73, 74, 75, 76, 77] and for the anilides.[23, 26, 78, 79, 80, 81, 82, 83] The currently accepted values, together with the melting points of the N-methyl amides as reported by D'Alelio and Reid,[70] are compiled in Table I.

Other constants for the N-methyl amides are: N-methylpropionamide, b_{90} 146°, n_D^{20} 1.4345, d_4^{25} 0.9304; N-methylbutyramide, b_{90} 156°, n_D^{20} 1.4365, d_4^{25} 0.0108; N-methylvaleramide, b_{90} 169°,

TABLE I

MELTING POINTS OF AMIDES, ANILIDES, AND N-METHYL AMIDES OF
SATURATED ACIDS

No. of C Atoms in Chain	Melting Points, °C.		
	Amides	Anilides	N-Methyl Amides
2	82	112	28
3	77	106	−43.0
4	115	96	−5.2
5	106	63	−25.5
6	101	92	13.6
7	96.05 *	65	14.0
8	105.9 *	55	38.9
9	98.8 *	57	39.1
10	98.5 *	69.5 *	57.3
11	99	71	56.0
12	102.4 *	77.2 *	68.4
13	100	80	68.2
14	105.1 *	84	78.4
15	....	....	78.3
16	107.0 *	90.2 *	85.5
17	....	....	84.8
18	109.7 *	94	92.1
20	108	....	....
22	111–112	101–102	....

* Denotes freezing point.

n_D^{20} 1.4401, d_4^{20} 0.933; N-methylcaproamide, b_{90} 183°, n_D^{20} 1.4431, d_4^{25} 0.8925; N-methylenanthamide, b_{15} 151°, n_D^{20} 1.4450, d_4^{25} 0.8869; N-methylcaprylamide, b_{15} 161.5°; and N-methylpelargonamide, b_{15} 175°.

The melting points of the amides and the anilides as reported by Robertson [69] are shown plotted against the number of carbon atoms in Figs. 1 and 2. The distinct difference in the curves formed by these two series of compounds is quite evident.

Figure 3 shows the melting point curve of the N-methyl amides as determined by D'Alelio and Reid [70] compared to that of the corresponding acids. The close similarity in these two curves, as pointed out by these authors, is apparent.

Only a few reliable values for the physical properties of amides of the unsaturated acids are available in the literature. Oleamide has been reported to melt at 75–76° [20] and elaidamide at 93–94°.[84] Erucamide melts at 82.5–83°, erucanilide at 65.5–66°, and brassidamide at 94°.[81] The amide of ricinoleic acid melts at 66° and the amide and anilide of chaulmoogric acid [85] at 104° and 89°, respectively.

The dibasic acids form two series of amides, the mono- and the diamides. The monoamides of the lower dibasic acids are quite water soluble; the diamides of these acids possess limited solubilities in water. The following are some of the physical constants which have been reported for the amides of the dibasic acids: adipic acid, monoamide,[86] m.p. 125–130°, diamide,[87] m.p. 220°; suberic acid,[86] monoamide, m.p. 125–127°, diamide, m.p. 216°; azelaic acid,[86] monoamide, m.p. 93–95°, diamide, m.p. 175–176°; sebacic acid,[86] monoamide, m.p. 170°, diamide, m.p. 210°. Hill and Carothers [88] have prepared a number of mono- and dianilides of the dicarboxylic acids and have reported the following values for their melting points: (acid, m.p. of monoanilide, m.p. of dianilide) pimelic, 108–109°, 155–156°; suberic, 128–129°, 186–187°; azelaic, 107–108°, 186–187°; undecanedioic, 112.5–113°, 160–161°; dodecanedioic, 123°, 170–171°; brassylic, 118.5–119.5°, 160–161°; tetradecanedioic, 124–125°, 169.5–170°; octadecanedioic, 128–129°, 162–163°. Barnicoat [89] has prepared the p-bromoanilides, o-toluidides, and p-toluidides of several of the dibasic acids. A number of substituted amides of the monocarboxylic fatty acids have been prepared by Robertson [69] in a study of the physical constants of such compounds. The melting points of the p-toluidides, o-toluidides, and β-naphthyl amides as reported by this author are shown in Table II.

Several other series of substituted amides have been synthesized by Robertson [69] and also by de'Conno,[26] some of the reported melting points being as follows: α-naphthyl amides—myristic 110°, palmitic 112.8°, stearic 110.8°, arachidic 99°, oleic 60°, erucic 73°; p-bromoanilides—caproic 105°, enanthic 98°, caprylic 108°, pelargonic 100°, capric 102°, undecanoic 102°, lauric 104°, myristic 107°, palmitic 110°, stearic 114°; p-hydroxyanilides—myristic 113°, palmitic 131°, stearic 132°, arachidic 115°, oleic 80°, erucic 114°; p-methoxyanilides—myristic 101.5°, palmitic 108°,

stearic 104°, arachidic 106°, oleic 67°, erucic 85°; p-ethoxyanilides
—myristic 108°, palmitic 109°, stearic 110°, arachidic 111°, oleic
72°, erucic 87°; o-bromo-p-toluidides—caproic 84°, enanthic 90°,
caprylic 78°, pelargonic 86°, capric 82°, undecanoic 91°, lauric 85°,
tridecanoic 95°, myristic 89°, stearic 97°; 2,4,6-tribromoanilides—
caproic 136°, enanthic 134°, caprylic 131°, pelargonic 131°, capric
129°, undecanoic 129°, lauric 126°, myristic 124°; α-bromo-β-

TABLE II

MELTING POINTS OF SUBSTITUTED AMIDES OF THE SATURATED ACIDS

Melting Points, °C.

Acid	p-Toluidide	o-Toluidide	β-Naphthyl Amide
Acetic	153	110	132
Propionic	126	87	...
Butyric	75	79	125
Valeric	74	70	112
Caproic	73	71	107
Enanthic	80	68	101
Caprylic	70	69	103
Pelargonic	84	73	103
Capric	78	76	104
Undecanoic	80	78	...
Lauric	87	83	106
Tridecanoic	88	85	107
Myristic	93	88	108
Palmitic	98	..	...
Stearic	102	97	112

naphthyl amides—caproic 120°, enanthic 111°, caprylic 104°,
pelargonic 103°, capric 102°, lauric 99°, myristic 100°, stearic 106°.
Several p-xenyl amides have been prepared by Gilman and Ford [90]
by heating the acids in sealed tubes with equimolar quantities of
p-xenylamine. The following melting points were reported for
these compounds: lauric, 146°; myristic, 143°; palmitic, 142°; and
stearic, 143°.

An interesting series of N-octadecyl and N-dodecyl amides of
the saturated acids has recently been obtained by Hunter [9] by
the pyrolysis of the corresponding salts of octadecyl- and dodecylamine, the method employed being similar to that previously used
by Hunter, Harber, and Gilman. [8] The following melting points
were reported for the N-octadecyl amides ($RCONHC_{18}H_{37}$):

formic, 68–68.5°; acetic, 78–78.5°; propionic, 77–77.5°; butyric, 76–76.5°; valeric, 76–76.5°; caproic, 78–78.5°; caprylic, 79–79.5°; capric, 83–83.5°; lauric, 87.5–88°; myristic, 89–89.5°; palmitic, 91.5–92°; stearic, 95.5–96°; and for the N-dodecyl amides ($RCONHC_{12}H_{25}$): acetic, 53–54°; propionic, 53–53.5°; lauric, 77–77.5°; myristic, 84–85°; palmitic, 82.5–83°; and stearic, 85–85.5°. It is noteworthy that these compounds do not show the wide fluctuations in melting points exhibited by the unsubstituted amides and that the melting points, with the exception of those of the first members, increase regularly with increase in carbon content of the amide chain.

Several other series of monosubstituted amides have been prepared and described; for example, the N-isobutyl amides of the following saturated acids have been obtained by Asano:[74] caprylic, b_7 154–155°; pelargonic, b_6 162°, m.p. 37–38°; capric, b_6 171°, m.p. 37–38°; undecanoic, m.p. 51°; and lauric, m.p. 51°. D'Alelio and Reid[91] have prepared the N-(2-hydroxyethyl) and N-(2-hydroxypropyl) amides of the saturated acids by reaction of the respective ethyl esters with 2-aminoethanol and 1-amino-2-propanol. The following melting points were reported for the higher N-(2-hydroxyethyl) amides: (number of C atoms in acid, m.p.) 6, 46°; 7, 53.6°; 8, 63.2°; 9, 71.6°; 10, 77.1°; 11, 84.8°; 12, 78.2°; 13, 91.8°; 14, 87.4°; 15, 97.0°; 16, 94.4°; 17, 99.2°; 18, 96.1°. It was observed that the plot of the melting points of the N-(2-hydroxyethyl) amides against the carbon content of the amide chain is essentially the reverse of that of the N-methyl amides. N-cyclopentyllauramide and N-cyclopentylstearamide have been reported[92] to melt at 55–56° and 67–68°, respectively, and N-cyclopentylundecenamide was reported to boil at 175–181° under 4 mm. pressure. The vanillyl amides of a number of the saturated acids have been prepared by the action of the acid chlorides on vanillylamine, and their physical properties have been recorded.[93] The melting points and solubilities of a number of amides of the general formula $C_2H_4(NHCOR)_2$, where R is a straight-chain radical, have been reported,[94] the melting points varying from about 150° to 190°, depending upon the length of the alkyl chain.

Substitution of both hydrogen atoms of the amide nitrogen generally results in a lowered melting point and in a more rational behavior as regards the relationships among the members of any specific series. Several early studies [95, 96, 97] on the preparation and properties of the N,N-dimethyl amides have been described, although the physical properties of the higher members of this series have not been reported. Mitchell and Reid [12] and later Ruhoff and Reid [24] have prepared a series of dimethyl amides of the lower acids by reaction of the acids with dimethylamine, the latter authors reporting the physical constants of the amides from N,N-dimethylformamide to N,N-dimethylcaprylamide inclusive. The following constants were observed: (m.p., b_{100}, d_4^{25}, n_D^{25}) N,N-dimethylvaleramide, $-51°$, 141.0°, 0.8962, 1.4419; N,N-dimethylcaproamide, $-42°$, 158.0°, 0.8896, 1.4430; N,N-dimethylenanthamide, $-19°$, 172.5°, 0.8854, 1.4450; and N,N-dimethylcaprylamide, $-21°$, 187.0°, 0.8810, 1.4471. An interesting observation regarding these amides is that they form azeotropic mixtures with the corresponding acids, the mixtures having boiling points 4–5° above those of the amides. Several N,N-diphenyl amides have been prepared [13] by the action of the acid chlorides on diphenylamine, the following freezing points having been observed: N,N-diphenylcapramide, 47.5°; N,N-diphenyllauramide, 57.0°; N,N-diphenylpalmitamide, 69.5°; and N,N-diphenylstearamide, 72.3°. The melting points of the N,N-di(2-hydroxyethyl) amides of several of the fatty acids are as follows: [91] undecanoic, 45.3°; myristic, 47.9°; pentadecanoic, 50.9°; palmitic, 65.1°; heptadecanoic, 67–69°; and stearic, 69.7°.

The solubility behavior of the amides, particularly the unsubstituted amides, shows certain anomalies which are difficult of explanation. It has recently been shown [13] that, unlike other series of aliphatic compounds, the solubilities of amide series in certain solvents do not present an orderly arrangement but appear to be distributed almost randomly. In benzene, ethyl acetate, and 2-butanone, for example, lauramide is, in general, more soluble than capramide, and palmitamide more soluble than myristamide, whereas in cyclohexane myristamide is less soluble than stearamide, and caprylamide is the least soluble compound investigated. In the more polar solvents, such as methanol, nitroethane, and acetonitrile, the solubilities decrease with increasing molecular weight, although the intervals between the curves are not uniform. The substituted amides, on the other hand, show an orderly sequence of solubility in all solvents. The solubilities of the amides, N-phenyl amides and N,N-diphenyl amides in various solvents as determined by Ralston, Hoerr, and Pool [13] are compiled in Table III.

TABLE III
Solubilities of Amides of Saturated Acids at 30°C.*

Grams per 100 g. Solvent

No. of C Atoms in Amide †	Benzene	Tetrachloro-methane	Acetone	Methanol	95% Ethanol	Aceto-nitrile
8	0.6	0.4	7.8	53.0	32.8	5.4
10	0.8	0.2	3.8	15.2	12.0	1.4
12	1.0	0.4	3.4	12.4	11.4	0.9
14	0.4	<0.1	1.0	2.7	3.8	0.6
16	0.4	0.1	0.8	1.2	1.5	0.3
18	0.4	<0.1	0.5	0.7	0.8	0.2
10φ	67(110) ‡	52(110)	93	70.1	81	18.0
12φ	14.7(56)	14.0(43)	12.5	11.1	22.3	3.0
16φ	2.2	1.2	3.3	0.8	2.2	0.7
18φ	1.5	0.5	2.0	0.2	1.2	0.5
10φφ	329	310	735	200	275	252
12φφ	179	147	192	81	53	75
16φφ	81	44.7	45.5	5.6	5.0	5.8
18φφ	65	30.1	10.6	3.9	2.6	2.4

* Solubility data for these compounds in benzene, cyclohexane, tetrachloromethane, ethyl acetate, butyl acetate, acetone, 2-butanone, methanol, 95% ethanol, 2-propanol, butanol, nitroethane, and acetonitrile at a number of temperatures have been reported,[13] and the reader is referred to the original article for these data.

† φ = C_6H_5.

‡ Values in parentheses are for unstable forms.

Figure 4 illustrates the solubility relationships of the amides in a non-polar solvent (cyclohexane), and Fig. 5 in a polar solvent (acetonitrile).[13]

The melting point curves of binary mixtures of palmitamide-stearamide and of palmitanilide-stearanilide have been investigated by Guy and Smith [23] and are shown in Fig. 6. The curves indicate the presence of equimolar compounds with non-congruent melting points, the compounds forming eutectics with the lower-melting components. The similarity of these curves to those formed by binary acid mixtures is striking.

The thioamides, $RCSNH_2$, are closely related structurally to the amides. Kindler [98] has shown that the lower molecular weight thioamides can be prepared by the thiohydrolysis of nitriles, and more recently several of the higher molecular weight thioamides have been obtained [99, 100] by the action of alcoholic solutions of ammonium sulfide on nitriles in a steel bomb at 160°, the reaction being as follows:

$$RC{:}N + H_2S \xrightarrow{NH_3} RCSNH_2$$

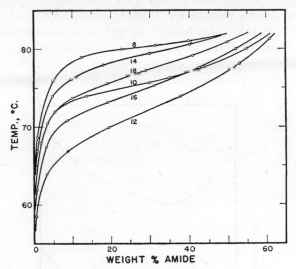

FIG. 4. Solubilities of amides in cyclohexane.

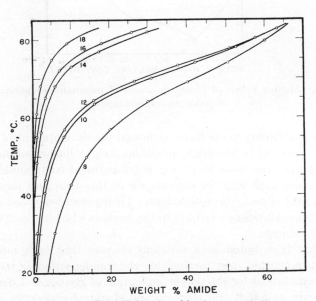

FIG. 5. Solubilities of amides in acetonitrile.

The following melting points were reported [99] for the higher molecular weight thioamides: thiolauramide, 82–83°; thiomyristamide, 87–88°; thiopalmitamide, 93–94°; and thiostearamide, 96–97°. Reduction of the thioamides by metallic sodium in alcohol yields the corresponding amines, whereas pyrolysis results in a loss of hydrogen sulfide with the formation of nitriles.

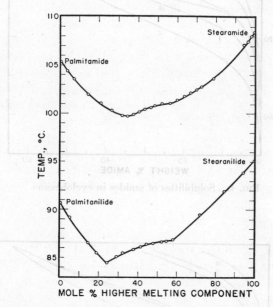

Fig. 6. Melting points of binary mixtures of palmitamide-stearamide and of palmitanilide-stearanilide.

The last twenty years have witnessed the development of a very intense interest in the high molecular weight linear polymers resulting from reactions involving polyfunctional compounds. The polyamides rank high in importance in this field and have been the subject of many investigations. Their present-day commercial importance stands as a tribute to the workers who have contributed to this subject.

It has been noted in a previous chapter that high molecular weight polyesters are formed by the condensation of terminal hydroxy acids or by the polyesterification of glycols and dicarboxylic acids, and that the physical and chemical properties of such compounds are dependent not only upon the nature of the reacting components but also upon the conditions employed for their preparation. A large variety of polyesters can thus be prepared, the properties of which vary over a wide range. It is evident that amide formation between polyfunctional compounds will generally resemble polyesterification, in that molecules of large size can be formed. In 1930, Carothers and Berchet [101] showed that 6-amino-caproic acid reacts both intra- and intermolecularly, producing 20–30% of a seven-membered lactam together with 80–70% of an undistillable polyamide. The separation of the lactam from the polyamide may be accomplished by vacuum distillation of the former. Partial hydrolysis of the polyamide with hydrochloric acid yields polyaminocaproylaminocaproic acids, the polyamide evidently being built upon the structural unit $-NH(CH_2)_5CO-$. Molecular weight determinations indicated the polyamide to be formed from at least ten molecules of the amino acid. That it is a true condensation polymer was proved by the fact that the lactam will not polymerize under the conditions resulting in polyamide formation and also that no lactam can be obtained by prolonged heating of the polyamide. It was pointed out by Carothers and Berchet that the tendency towards polyamide formation is critical as regards the chain length of the reactant, since 7-amino-heptanoic acid yields polyamide exclusively, whereas 4-aminobutyric and 5-aminovaleric acids have been shown [102,103] to yield predominantly the five- and six-membered lactams. The higher amino acids, such as 11-aminoundecanoic acid, have been stated [104] to yield only polyamides. The linear polyamides are much less soluble and fusible than the polyesters and are appreciably harder and tougher. Treatment in a molecular still brings about a further increase in molecular weight, attended by a greater insolubility in most organic solvents. Carothers and Hill [105] have prepared mixed polyester-polyamides by the condensation of trimethylene glycol, octadecanedioic acid, and 6-aminocaproic acid, obtaining tough, elastic solids the properties of which were intermediate between those of the polyesters and those of the polyamides. Solubility characteristics indicated that such polymers are polyester-polyamides rather than simple mixtures of the two, the molecules containing the following structural units: $-NHRCO-$, $-OR'O-$, and $-COR''CO-$. Such products are capable of being drawn into filaments. In 1939, Carothers and Graves [106] described a process whereby polyamides such as polyhexamethylenadipamide may be obtained by the condensation of diamines with dibasic acids. The preparation of polyamides by heating ω-

aminocarboxylic acids in the presence of inert solvents has been patented,[107, 108] as has the condensation of dibasic acids such as adipic, pimelic, suberic, azelaic, and sebacic acids with tetra-, penta-, hexa-, deca-, trideca-, and octadecamethylenediamines.[109] Polyamides prepared by the condensation of aromatic diamines with aliphatic dicarboxylic acids have also been prepared.[110] The mechanical production of artificial fibers from linear condensation superpolymers has been described in detail by Carothers and Hill [111] and is the subject of several patents.[112, 113] It is of interest to note that these studies have formed the basis for the development of the synthetic fiber now marketed under the trade name of nylon.*

Polyamides prepared from dimerized acids and diamines such as ethylenediamine have been the subject of considerable recent interest, although they have not been extensively described in the literature at this writing.

Chemical Properties of the Fatty Acid Amides

The amides undergo many chemical reactions and have been used as the starting point for the synthesis of a large number of derivatives. The aliphatic amides are essentially neutral, the basic properties of the amino group being counterbalanced by the acyl group. Their tautomeric nature, however, is evidenced by the fact that they are reactive with a number of reagents.

Hydrolysis of the amides results in the formation of the corresponding acids, the reaction being the reverse of that encountered during their formation from the acids and ammonia. Crocker and Lowe [114] have determined by conductivity methods the velocity of hydrolysis of the amides in the presence of hydrochloric acid or sodium hydroxide, and have reported that the reactions are bimolecular, the temperature coefficient being quite large in the case of the acid hydrolysis. It was observed that the order of relative reactivities is approximately the same for each temperature and decreases in the order formamide, propionamide, acetamide, caproamide, and valeramide. In the alkaline hydrolysis the reaction is evidently one of direct substitution of the hydroxyl for the amido group. Because of the insolubilities and high melting points of the higher amides, their hydrolysis in the presence of

* The reader is referred to *Collected Papers of Wallace Hume Carothers on High Polymeric Substances,* Mark and Whitby, editors, Vol. I, Interscience Publishers, Inc., New York (1940).

bases can be completed only under pressure. However, the high molecular weight amides can be quantitatively hydrolyzed by refluxing with constant-boiling hydrochloric acid for several hours. Amides may be converted to the corresponding acids by the action of nitrous acid, the reaction being similar to that which takes place between nitrous acid and primary amines. Stearanilide has been shown [115] to form hydrates of undetermined composition; however, the substitution of the remaining amido hydrogen, as in N-methylstearanilide or N,N-diphenylstearamide, prevents hydration.[116]

The pyrolysis of amides results in their dehydration with the formation of nitriles, a similar result being obtained when the amides are treated with dehydrating agents such as phosphorus pentoxide or phosphorus pentachloride. Such reactions are discussed in detail under the methods of preparation of the high molecular weight nitriles.

Hydrogenation of the amides yields mixtures of the corresponding primary and secondary amines. Adkins and Wojcik [117] have described the reduction of heptanamide, lauramide, and other amides in dioxane under 100–300 atmospheres of hydrogen pressure at 175–250°, in the presence of copper-chromium oxide catalysts. Yields of 40–70% of the corresponding primary amines and of 25–50% of the secondary amines were reported. Substituted amides such as N-cyclohexyllauramide give 70–95% of secondary or tertiary amines. The reduction of lauramide, myristamide, and palmitamide under 203–210 atmospheres of hydrogen in the presence of a $CuO-Cr_2O_3-BaO$ catalyst yields products which consist essentially of the corresponding secondary amines together with small amounts of the primary amines.[77] The preparation of dioctyl-, didecyl-, and dioctadecylamines by the hydrogenation of caprylamide, capramide, and stearamide has been described,[77] a temperature of 250–270° and a pressure of 180–200 atmospheres being required. It was suggested that the amide be dissolved in at least three times its weight of dioxane. The reduction of lauranilide, myristanilide, and palmitanilide by a similar procedure has been reported [83] also to yield the corresponding secondary amines.

In 1881, Hofmann [118] investigated the action of amides with halogens in strong alkaline solution, the reaction involving a migration with the ultimate formation of an amine. This important reaction, which bears the name of the original investigator, is generally familiar to all organic chemists. When two moles of acetamide are treated with one mole of sodium hypobromite, the product is N-methyl-N'-acetylurea, the reaction being as follows:

$$2CH_3CONH_2 + NaBrO \rightarrow CO\Big\langle{}^{NHCH_3}_{NHCOCH_3} + NaBr + H_2O$$

It was observed that this compound reacts with water to yield acetic acid, ammonia, methylamine, and carbon dioxide, according to the reaction

$$CO\Big\langle{}^{NHCH_3}_{NHCOCH_3} + 2H_2O \rightarrow CH_3CO_2H + CH_3NH_2 + NH_3 + CO_2$$

A study of the products of pyrolysis of the substituted urea led to an explanation of the formation of the amine through a rearrangement, the products of pyrolysis being methyl isocyanate and acetamide as follows:

$$CO\Big\langle{}^{NHCH_3}_{NHCOCH_3} \rightarrow CH_3CNO + CH_3CONH_2$$

In a subsequent study, Hofmann [119] prepared the N,N-dibromo amide by the action of two moles of bromine and sodium hydroxide on one mole of the amide. The reaction of equimolecular quantities of the N,N-dibromo amide and the amide yields the monobromo amide. When two molecules of monobromoacetamide are treated with one molecule of hydrochloric acid, the bromine is replaced with the formation of N-chloroacetamide and acetamide. The later extensive investigations of Hofmann [120] upon the action of halogens with amides in alkaline solution form the basis of our present-day knowledge of this reaction. The action of one mole of bromine with one mole of an amide first yields the N-bromo amide, which loses hydrogen bromide in the presence of alkali to give a product which rearranges to form an alkyl isocyanate. The hydrolysis of the isocyanate yields an amine, the sequence of reactions in the case of butyramide being as follows:

(I) $$C_3H_7CONH_2 + Br_2 \xrightarrow{\text{NaOH}} C_3H_7CONHBr + HBr$$

(II) $$C_3H_7CONHBr + NaOH \longrightarrow C_3H_7NCO + NaBr + H_2O$$

(III) $$C_3H_7NCO + H_2O \longrightarrow C_3H_7NH_2 + CO_2$$

The formation of the alkyl acyl substituted ureas probably results from the reaction of the intermediate alkyl isocyanate with unchanged amide. Hofmann has shown that treatment of the bromo amide with sodium carbonate instead of sodium hydroxide permits of the isolation of alkyl isocyanatos and also N,N'-dialkyl substituted ureas, which are probably formed by the interaction of the alkyl isocyanate with the amine, as follows:

$$RNCO + RNH_2 \rightarrow \begin{array}{c} RNH \\ RNH \end{array}\!\!\!>\!\!CO$$

Although reactions of the type described by Hofmann are satisfactory for the preparation of the lower molecular weight amines, the yield of amines of molecular weight higher than that of amylamine is extensively reduced by side reactions. Nitrile formation is one of the foremost of such reactions and is invariably encountered when high molecular weight amides are so treated; the use of an excess of halogen increases the amount of nitrile formed. It was first considered that the nitriles result from dehydration of the amides, but a later investigation [121] showed them to contain one carbon atom less than the starting amide. The formation of nitriles is, therefore, probably a secondary reaction resulting from the dehydrogenation of the amine by the addition of bromine and its removal as hydrogen bromide.

In the course of his investigations, Hofmann prepared and described a number of substituted ureas obtained by the action of alkaline bromine solutions on the amides, the list including the following ureas: ethyl propionyl, m.p. 100°; propyl butyryl, m.p. 99°; isobutyl valeryl, m.p. 102°; pentyl caproyl, m.p. 97°; hexyl enanthyl, m.p. 97°; heptyl caprylyl, m.p. 86°; octyl pelargonyl, m.p. 97°; nonyl capryl, m.p. 101°; and heptadecyl stearoyl, m.p. 112°. The preparation by the Hofmann reaction of the alkylamines from methylamine to nonylamine inclusive and of heptadecylamine has been described.[122] In 1897, Jeffreys [123] confirmed the fact that only small yields of the higher amines result by the Hofmann reaction, it being necessary, in the case of heptadecylamine, to isolate and rearrange the heptadecyl octadecanoyl urea. Distillation of the bromo amides with lime had previously been shown [124] to result in higher yields of the amines of intermediate molecular weight, such as heptylamine; however, this method is not satisfactory for the preparation of the higher homologs. It was observed by Lengfeld and Stieglitz [125] that alkyl-urethans result from the action of sodium methylate in methanol on bromo amides, and the saponification of these high molecular weight urethans was shown by Jeffreys [123] to result in substantial yields of the high molecular weight amines.

The memorable researches of Stieglitz and associates [126] upon the rearrangement of nitrogen-containing compounds have established the fact that such rearrangements involve the intermediate presence of a monovalent nitrogen atom, and that only nitrogen compounds which lose constituents and form such intermediates are capable of rearrangement.*

The mechanism proposed by Stieglitz for the formulation of isocyanates during the Hofmann rearrangement is as follows:

$$RC\underset{N<_Y^X}{\overset{O}{\diagup}} \rightarrow RC\underset{N<}{\overset{O}{\diagup}} + XY \rightarrow R-N=C=O + XY$$

Many of the chemical reactions of the high molecular weight amides have been described in the patent literature. Such reactions have been studied with a view to the commercial utilization of the resulting products, and the high molecular weight amides are the starting point for the synthesis of a number of wetting agents, dye assistants, high-melting waxes, and other products. In a consideration of the voluminous patent literature which has developed around the amide derivatives, it is apparent that although many of the procedures suggested result in comparatively simple products, in many instances complex reactions are involved which leave the identity of the final product in considerable doubt. Many of the patents in this field, therefore, are only of interest in showing a trend toward the utilization of the amides and contribute little to our knowledge of the chemistry of these compounds. In the following discussion an attempt has been made to select that literature which best illustrates the general reactions of the amides and which leaves the reader with a general knowledge of the properties and uses of the amide derivatives. The higher molecular weight amides are unquestionably a series of compounds which will receive considerable future attention.

The water-resistant properties of the higher amides make their inclusion in various waterproofing formulations a subject of interest. The use of the high molecular weight amides such as behen-

* See Porter, *Molecular Rearrangements*, Chemical Catalog Co., New York (1928); Blatt, *Chem. Rev.*, **12**, 215 (1933).

amide in wax compositions has been patented,[127] and the diamides, R'CONHRNHCOR', have been stated [128] to be useful as waxes and coating materials. Amides may be emulsified by the use of sulfonated oleic acid or similar materials,[129] sulfuric esters of amides and N-substituted amides are used for treating textiles,[130] and amides prepared from polyhydroxy amines and acids have been proposed as wetting agents.[131]   The basically substituted carboxylic acid amides have been suggested as dye assistants.[132]   Bousquet and Salzberg [133] have stated that amides containing a heterocyclic radical possess insecticidal properties, and the monoisobutyl amide of 10-undecenoic acid has been proposed as the active ingredient of a fly spray.[134]   Amides prepared from amino carboxylic acids and aromatic carboxylic acids have been suggested [135] as wetting agents.

The sulfonation of the amides and their derivatives has resulted in the preparation of a number of water-soluble compounds which possess surface active properties. Sulfonation of both substituted and unsubstituted amides has been described,[136] and it has been claimed that the products function as wetting agents. Somewhat similar products are obtained [137] by the action of high molecular weight acyl chlorides on methylaminomethanesulfonic acid. The sulfonation of amides prepared from conjugated acids has been described,[138] as well as the sulfonation of substituted oleamides such as N-propyloleamide.[139]   Substituted amides of ethers or thioethers, of the general formulas $ROCH_2CONR_1R_2$ and $RSCH_2CONR_1R_2$, where R is a long-chain hydrocarbon radical and R_1 and R_2 are hydrogen or hydrocarbon radicals, have been synthesized and proposed as wetting agents.[140]   The reaction of high molecular weight amides with chlorosulfonic acid has been investigated,[141] and the sulfonation of substituted aliphatic diamides has been described,[142] as has the sulfonation of amides prepared from fatty acids and diethylenetriamine.[143]   The sulfonation of a number of substituted amides has been described by Rosenhauer.[144]

Details for the chlorination of stearamide have recently been described,[145] the product melting at 67–68°. The action of sulfuric acid and its salts or the alkali sulfites on the halogen-containing substituted amides has been employed for the preparation of wetting agents. For example, amides such as the N-methylbromoethyl amide of palmitic acid,[146] or the N-octadecyl amide of chloroacetic acid,[147, 148] yield wetting agents when treated with sodium sulfite, the compound formed in the latter case having the structure $CH_2(SO_3H)CONHC_{18}H_{37}$. The action of thiosulfates on amides of the general formula $RCONR'R''$, where R is a halogenated hydrocarbon radical, yields surface active compounds,[149] an example being the action of $ClCH_2CONHC_{11}H_{23}$ with $Na_2S_2O_3$ to yield $NaSO_3SCH_2CONHC_{11}H_{23}$. Sulfonated amides have been prepared by the action of sulfonated acids, e.g., sulfonated oleic acid, with amines such as 2-aminoethanol.[150] Katzman [151] has described the preparation of sulfonated ethylene diamides of the general formula $RCONHCH_2CH_2NHCOCH_2CHCO_2M$, in which

$$SO_3M$$

M is an alkali metal or an ammonium radical. The sulfonation of chlorinated anilides, such as the anilide of chlorostearic acid, has been stated [152] to produce water-soluble products having surface active properties. A number of water-soluble derivatives have been synthesized by the sulfonation of N-acyl substituted high molecular weight amides.[153, 154] The sulfonation of N-(ethoxyphenyl)stearamide, $C_{17}H_{35}CONHC_6H_4OC_2H_5$, has been described,[155] the sulfonation taking place in the benzene ring. Moyer [156] has investigated the action of higher fatty amides with sulfur in the presence of liquid sulfur dioxide. The N-substituted chloroacetamides have been employed for the preparation of a number of amido derivatives, the following reactions having been investigated: [157]

$$ClCH_2CONHC_{11}H_{23} + \begin{cases} Ba(OH)_2 \rightarrow HOCH_2CONHC_{11}H_{23} \\ NaOC_6H_5 \rightarrow C_6H_5OCH_2CONHC_{11}H_{23} \\ NaCO_2CH_3 \rightarrow CH_3CO_2CH_2CONHC_{11}H_{23} \\ NaSH \rightarrow HSCH_2CONHC_{11}H_{23} \\ Na_2S_x \rightarrow C_{11}H_{23}NHCOCH_2S_xCH_2CONHC_{11}H_{23} \\ C_2H_5SH \rightarrow C_2H_5SCH_2CONHC_{11}H_{23} \\ Na_2S_2O_3 \rightarrow NaSO_3SCH_2CONHC_{11}H_{23} \end{cases}$$

The reactions of secondary amines with fatty acids containing halogen, hydroxyl, or nitrogen-containing groups yield products which can be sulfonated or sulfated to give surface active chemicals.[158] Piggott [159] has proposed the preparation of amides of the general formula $RCONHX$, where X is a polyhydroxyhydrocarbon radical, such as N-(trihydroxy-*tert*-butyl)stearamide, and has stated that their sulfuric or phosphoric esters possess surface active properties. The mixed boric and sulfuric acid esters of the N-(hydroxyethyl) amides of high molecular weight have been reported [160] to be water soluble.

Amides react with alkali metals in inert solvents such as benzene, the metal apparently attaching itself to the nitrogen atom. The preparation of such compounds and their reaction with substances such as chloroethanesulfonic acid or p-(chloromethyl)benzenesulfonic acid has been described. [161]

The action of amides with chlorinated ethers has been extensively investigated. The reaction of equimolar amounts of stearamide or lauramide with dichlorodimethyl ether, $(ClCH_2)_2O$, followed by treatment of the resulting product with pyridine, has been studied, [162] and softening agents suitable for treating textiles are claimed from the reaction of stearamide with two moles of dichlorodimethyl ether followed by treatment with thiourea. [163] The reaction of amides with chloromethyl ethyl ether has been stated [164] to proceed as follows:

(I) $2RCONH_2 + ClCH_2OC_2H_5 \rightarrow RCONHCH_2NHCOR + C_2H_5OH + HCl$

(II) $RCONHCH_2NHCOR + 2ClCH_2OC_2H_5 \rightarrow$

$$RC\!\!\begin{array}{c} \nwarrow O \\ | \\ NCH_2Cl \\ | \\ CH_2 \\ | \\ NCH_2Cl \\ | \\ RC \searrow O \end{array} + 2C_2H_5OH$$

Wetting agents are obtained when these products are treated with thiourea or pyridine. [165] The amides prepared by the reaction of stearic acid with one or two molar equivalents of diethanolamine are soft waxes [166] which, when treated with ethylene chlorohydrin in the presence of chlorinated hydrocarbons, yield products suitable for treating textiles. The reaction between amides, such as stearamide, and monomeric glyoxal, CHOCHO, has recently been investigated. [167] It has been stated that water-soluble products are obtained when amides such as ricinoleamide are treated with the condensation products of the glycols and maleic anhydride. [168] The methylation of the amides with dimethyl sulfate has recently been studied. [169]

Paraskova [170] has investigated the reaction of diamides with Grignard reagents and has reported that, when bis(N,N-diethyl)-sebacamide, $Et_2NCO(CH_2)_8CONEt_2$, is heated with ethylmagnesium bromide and the product hydrolyzed, ketones are obtained, the main product in this instance consisting of 3,12-tetradecanedione and 3-diethylamino-3-ethyl-12-tetradecanone.

The amides are reactive with ethylene oxide, the products ranging from high-melting, waxy materials to water-dispersible substances depending upon the mole proportion of ethylene oxide employed. Orthner and Keppler [171] have obtained wetting agents by the reaction of N-hydroxyalkyl amides with several mole proportions of ethylene oxide. The reaction product of ethylene oxide and ricinoleamide has been stated to possess surface active properties.[172] The action of the high molecular weight amides with ethylene oxide has been the subject of several patents.[173, 174, 175, 176]

Amides are reactive with formaldehyde or its polymers yielding the corresponding methylol derivatives, which are important chemical intermediates. In many of the reactions involving these intermediates, the methylol compounds are not isolated, since most of these reactions are extremely involved and their actual course is frequently in doubt. The fact that practically all the work reported upon such compounds appears in the patent literature is evidence of their potential commercial importance. These products have been suggested for such purposes as wetting agents, detergents, waxes, insecticides, dye intermediates, and many others. N-methylolstearamide is best prepared by heating stearamide in benzene solution with paraformaldehyde and pulverized potassium carbonate, the reaction proceeding smoothly and yielding a product which melts at about 115°.[177] When the reaction between the amides and formaldehyde is conducted in the presence of acids, there are generally obtained [178] higher-melting products which probably contain substantial amounts of methylene diamides. The following reactions of stearamide illustrate the formation of the above products:

$$C_{17}H_{35}C\underset{NH_2}{\overset{O}{<}} + HCHO \rightarrow C_{17}H_{35}C\underset{NHCH_2OH}{\overset{O}{<}}$$
Methylolstearamide

$$2C_{17}H_{35}C\underset{NH_2}{\overset{O}{<}} + HCHO \rightarrow C_{17}H_{35}\overset{O}{\overset{\|}{C}}NHCH_2NH\overset{O}{\overset{\|}{C}}C_{17}H_{35} + H_2O$$
Methylenedistearamide

Esters of the methylol amides have been prepared [179] by the reaction of acid anhydrides with methylol amides; for example, the acetate of methylolstearamide results from the treatment of the methylol amide with acetic anhydride. Methylol ethers of the general formula $RCONHCH_2OR'$ are obtained [180] by the reaction of methylol amides with alcohols in the presence of acidic catalysts, e.g., sulfuric acid, phosphorus oxychloride. The preparation of a number of water-soluble products having surface active properties by the action of amides and formaldehyde in the presence of organic bases has been described. Such products result when amides are treated with formaldehyde in the presence of acetic acid and tetramethylenediamine,[181] or when the acetate of methylolstearamide is condensed with pyridine,[182] the product in the latter instance being stearamidomethylpyridinium acetate. The product of the reaction of methylolstearamide with urea is a solid, waxy mass which melts at 194–210°.[183] Bruson [184] has studied the reaction of amides with formaldehyde in the presence of bases such as diethylamine or diethanolamine, and water-soluble compounds have been stated [185] to result when such reactions are conducted in the presence of cyclic bases and sulfur dioxide. In the latter instance an N-methylol sulfite is first formed, this then reacting with the base. Somewhat similar reactions have been described [186] in which the bases employed are N-substituted amines of the benzene or naphthalene series. Compounds of the general formula $RCONHCH_2SO_3Na$ have been reported [187] to result from the reaction of bisulfite addition products of formaldehyde with amides, and it has been claimed [188] that similar products are formed by the action of sodium bisulfite and the N-methylol amides. The reaction of sulfuric acid with the product formed by the condensation of amides with formaldehyde in the presence of glacial acetic acid yields high-melting waxes.[178]

Sulfonation of the methylol amides and of many of their derivatives yields a variety of water-soluble products; for example, the amide formed by treating castor oil with 2-aminoethanol yields a wetting agent when treated with formaldehyde and sulfonated.[189,190] A number of Swiss patents have been issued disclosing the preparation of high-melting waxes and wetting agents useful in the textile industry, obtained by various condensations involving methylollauramide or methylolstearamide. Such reactions include the condensation of methylollauramide with the sulfonyl chloride of benzoic acid in the presence of pyridine,[191] with thioglycolic acid in the presence of acetic anhydride,[192] with glycerol mercaptan in the presence of an acid,[193] and with sodium mercaptoethanesulfonate in the presence of an acid.[194] The reaction of methylollauramide with chloroacetamide followed by treatment of the product with pyridine yields a diamide [195, 196] of the structure $C_{11}H_{23}CNHCH_2NHCCH_2NC_5H_5$. Wetting agents have been

$$\underset{O}{\overset{\parallel}{C}} \qquad \underset{O}{\overset{\parallel}{C}} \underset{Cl}{\overset{\mid}{C}}$$

obtained from methylolstearamide by condensation with chloroacetamide in the presence of trimethylamine or pyridine,[197] with N,N'-diethylthiourea in the presence of acids,[198] and with thioglycolic acid in the presence of glacial acetic acid.[199] The product in the latter instance has the formula $C_{17}H_{35}CONHCH_2SCH_2$-$CO_2H$. The product of the condensation of methylolstearamide and benzamide in the presence of dioxane and hydrochloric acid is a high-melting wax.[200] Wetting agents result when stearamide is treated with N,N'-dimethylolurea,[201] with the sodium salt of N-methylolacetamidesulfonic acid,[202] or with N-methylolchloroacetamide in glacial acetic acid followed by treatment with trimethylamine.[203] The reaction of stearamide and paraformaldehyde in the presence of amines such as N-methylmorpholine has been reported [204] to yield water-soluble compounds. High molecular weight N-methylol amides condense with alkoxybenzenes and similar compounds in the presence of catalysts such as zinc chloride, the reaction being as follows: [205, 206]

$$RCONHCH_2OH + C_6H_5OR' \rightarrow RCONHCH_2C_6H_4OR' + H_2O$$

Sulfonation of the resulting products renders them water dispersible. Substituted amides, such as N-methylstearamide, react with formaldehyde in the presence of hydrochloric acid to yield the corresponding N-methyl-N-chloromethyl derivatives,[207] which can be further condensed with a number of substances to yield wetting agents. A series of derivatives of N-methylol amides have been prepared by Baldwin and Walker [208] by reaction of the N-methylol amides with sodium pyrosulfate in the presence of pyridine or other bases. It has been stated [209] that resins are obtained when the amides or thioamides of polyamino carboxylic acids are condensed with formaldehyde.

Fibers can be rendered water repellent by impregnation with amides followed by treatment with formaldehyde,[210] and it has been claimed that a further treatment with sodium dihydrogen phosphate is beneficial. A process whereby fibers are coated with N-heptadecyl-N-octadecylurea followed by treatment with gaseous formaldehyde has been stated [211] to impart high water-repellent properties.

The Preparation and Properties of Compounds Structurally Related to the Amides

The amidines, $RC(:NH)NH_2$, are related to the amides in that the oxygen of the amide group is replaced by an imino group. In contrast to the amides, the unsubstituted amidines are strongly basic and are generally encountered as their salts. The early work of Pinner and Klein [212] upon the transformation of nitriles into imino ethers and thence to amidines showed that when benzonitrile is treated with anhydrous isobutyl alcohol in the presence of hydrochloric acid the hydrochloride of the isobutyl imino ether results as follows:

$$C_6H_5CN + C_4H_9OH + HCl \rightarrow C_6H_5C\begin{array}{l} \diagup NH \cdot HCl \\ \diagdown OC_4H_9 \end{array}$$

The amidine is formed by the action of ammonia on the imino ether, thus:

$$C_6H_5C\begin{array}{l} \diagup NH \cdot HCl \\ \diagdown OC_4H_9 \end{array} + NH_3 \rightarrow C_6H_5C\begin{array}{l} \diagup NH \cdot HCl \\ \diagdown NH_2 \end{array} + C_4H_9OH$$

The formation of imino ethers and amidines from nitriles by the above procedure is a general reaction, only some ortho-substituted aromatic nitriles and certain halogen-substituted nitriles being unreactive.[213] In their study of the nitrogen derivatives of the higher fatty acids, Eitner and Wetz [214] prepared the hydrochlorides of the isobutyl ethers of laurimide, myristimide, palmitimide, and stearimide, with melting points at 65–66°, 69–70°, 73°, and 77–78°, respectively. These compounds were described as white, microcrystalline, very hygroscopic powders which are extremely soluble in ethanol and difficultly soluble in ether. The hydrochloride of the diisobutyl ether of sebacimide is totally insoluble in ether. Treatment of the hydrochlorides of the isobutyl imino ethers with alcoholic solutions of ammonia yields the corresponding amidine hydrochlorides, the melting points being as follows: lauramidine-·HCl, 128–129°; myristamidine·HCl, 176–177°; palmitamidine-·HCl, 217° (decomp.); and stearamidine·HCl, 244–245° (decomp.). The higher amidine hydrochlorides are soluble in ethanol but difficultly soluble in ether. The free bases, obtained by the action of sodium ethylate on alcoholic solutions of the hydrochlorides, are white, crystalline masses which readily absorb carbon dioxide.

Hill and Rabinowitz [215] have described the preparation of valer-imido methyl ether hydrochloride and several of its derivatives, the procedure for the preparation of this compound being as follows:

One molecular equivalent each of valeronitrile and methanol are dissolved in an equal weight of dry ether. The solution is cooled and dry hydrogen chloride is passed in until 1.25 molecular equivalents have been absorbed. After standing overnight the precipitated hydrochloride is filtered off and washed with ether.

A yield of 80% was reported. The free imino ether is obtained from the hydrochloride by treatment with potassium carbonate in ether. The reaction of the imino ether hydrochloride with two moles of p-ethoxyaniline (p-phenetidine) proceeds as follows:

$$C_4H_9C\underset{OCH_3}{\overset{NH \cdot HCl}{\diagdown}} + 2H_2NC_6H_4OC_2H_5 \rightarrow$$

$$C_4H_9C\underset{NHC_6H_4OC_2H_5}{\overset{NC_6H_4OC_2H_5}{\diagdown}} + CH_3OH + NH_4Cl$$

Condensation of the above product with phenyl isocyanate results in a substitution of the remaining amido hydrogen by the group $CONHC_6H_5$. The reaction of valeramidine with one mole of p-phenetidine yields the imino-substituted derivative.

$$\overset{NR'}{\underset{\|}{}}$$

Substituted amidines, $RCNR''R'''$, where R', R'', and R''' are hydrogen, alkyl, acyl, or some other radical, may be prepared either by substitution of the imino or amido hydrogens of the amidines or by reaction of imino ethers with amines. Many representatives of this type of compound have been described in the patent literature, and they are frequently mentioned as chemical intermediates. The reaction of substituted amidines with alkylating or acylating agents has been described,[216, 217] and these products have been proposed as wetting agents. Pyman and Levene [218] have studied the preparation of amidines of the general formula $R_1R_2N(CH_2)_nC(:NH)NH_2$, such as 11-(diethylamino)-undecanamidine or 12-(dibutylamino)dodecanamidine, by the reaction of the corresponding terminally substituted amino nitriles with hydrochloric acid in alcoholic solution followed by treatment with ammonia. The compounds were isolated as the dipicrates. Diamidines of the dibasic acids have been prepared [219] from the corresponding dinitriles by formation of the diimino ethyl ethers followed by treatment of the product with alcoholic ammonia. The following melting points were reported for the diamidine salts: heptane-1,7-diamidinium chloride, 218–219°, picrate, 249–250° (decomp.); nonane-1,9-diamidinium sulfate, 310–315° (decomp.), picrate, 260–261°; decane-1,10-diamidinium picrate, 249–250°; undecane-1,11-diamidinium picrate, 245–246°; dodecane-1,12-diamidinium chloride, 174–175°, picrate, 227–228°; tridecane-1,13-diamidinium picrate, 192–193°.

The amidoximes, $RC(:NOH)NH_2$, result from the action of hydroxylamine on nitriles and are related to the amidines, the imino hydrogen being replaced by a hydroxyl group. Eitner and Wetz [214] have prepared several of the higher molecular weight amidoximes by the action of hydroxylamine hydrochloride on the respective nitriles in the presence of sodium carbonate. The high molecular weight amidoximes are soluble in ethanol and chloroform but are difficultly soluble in ether. The following melting points have been reported for these compounds: lauramidoxime, 92–92.5°; myristamidoxime, 97°; palmitamidoxime, 101.5–102°; and stearamidoxime, 106–106.5°.

Hydroxamic acids, RCONHOH, are prepared by the action of hydroxylamine hydrochloride on fatty acid esters in the presence of sodium hydroxide. The hydroxamic acids of the fatty acids were obtained by Inoue and Yukawa [220] by the above method, and the following melting points were reported: acetic, 88°; propionic, 92.5–93°; butyric, liquid; caproic, 63.5–64°; caprylic, 78.5–79°; capric, 88–88.5°; lauric, 94°; myristic, 98–98.5°; palmitic, 102.5°; stearic, 106.5–107°; behenic, 109°; and arachidic, 112.5°. The melting points of the hydroxamic acids of oleic, linoleic, and linolenic acids are 61°, 41–42°, and 37–38°, respectively. The saturated hydroxamic acids are insoluble in petroleum ether.

The hydrazides of the fatty acids result from the action of hydrazine hydrate on the fatty esters.[221, 222] For example, lauric acid hydrazide, m.p. 104.5°, is formed by heating ethyl laurate with hydrazine hydrate for 1.5 hours at 130°.[223] Palmitic acid hydrazide, m.p. 111°, stearic acid hydrazide, m.p. 112–114°, and oleic acid hydrazide, m.p. 110–112°, may be similarly prepared. The phenyl hydrazides [224, 225] of lauric, myristic, palmitic, oleic, and elaidic acids melt at 105°, 108°, 110.5°, 91.3°, and 98–99°, respectively. The acid azides, $RCON_3$, of several of the saturated acids have been described as thick oils.[223]

The fatty acid piperidides are easily obtained by condensation of the acids with piperidine, thus:

$$C_5H_{10}NH + HO_2CR \rightarrow C_5H_{10}NCOR + H_2O$$

It has been observed that the piperidides of pelargonic acid and 2-nonenoic acid are violently pungent, those of capric, undecanoic, and 10-undecenoic acids weakly pungent, and that of myristic acid tasteless. The following physical constants have been reported [226] for some of the fatty acid piperidides: caprylic, b_4 144°; pelargonic, b_{13} 184–187°; 2-nonenoic, b_4 167°; capric, b_{12} 193–194°; undecanoic, b_7 187–189°; 10-undecenoic, b_6 185–186°; lauric, b_3 185–187°; and myristic, b_3 206–207°, m.p. 28°.

Stendal [227] has described the preparation of the ureides of the fatty acids by the action of urea on the ethyl esters, and has reported the following melting points: caprylic, 191.3°; capric, 187°; stearic, 176.8°; arachidic, 172°; undecenoic, 175°; oleic, 161°; and erucic, 161.5°. These ureides are hydrolyzed by potassium hydroxide solution to yield the potassium salts of the corresponding acids.

The high molecular weight acyl-, diacyl-, and alkylsulfanilamides, which have recently been synthesized, are of considerable pharmacological interest. A logical nomenclature for the substituted sulfanilamides has been suggested.[228] The nitrogens are differentiated by superscripts: N^1 referring to substituents on the amide nitrogen and N^4 to substituents on the amino nitrogen in the sulfanilamide nucleus, $\rangle N\langle\bigcirc\rangle SO_2N\langle$. N^1-acylsulfanilamides have been synthesized [229] by the action of acyl halides on N^4-acetylsulfanilamides in the presence of dry pyridine, followed by removal of the acetyl group by treatment with sodium hydroxide, and subsequent acidification of the resulting salt. The following N^1-acylsulfanilamides were obtained by this method: (N^1-substituent, m.p.) hexanoyl, 129.2–129.9°; heptanoyl, 121.8–123.6°; octanoyl, 101.0–103.0°; decanoyl, 119–121°; undecanoyl, 112.5–114.5°; dodecanoyl, 127–128.5°; tetradecanoyl, 113.5–117.7°; octadecanoyl, 98–102°; 9-octadecenoyl, liquid. The corresponding N^1-acyl-N^4-acetyl derivatives which were prepared possess higher melting points than the above. N^1-dodecanoyl-N^4-dodecanoylsulfanilamide melts at 144.0–145.0°. N^1-dodecanoylsulfanilamide was found to be effective against certain infections and to arrest the spread of tuberculosis in cavies. The solubility in water decreases on ascending the series, the reverse being noted for the solubility in fats. The following N^1-alkylsulfanilamides have been synthesized and characterized:[230] octyl, m.p. 114–119.5°; dodecyl, m.p. 118–124°; octadecyl, m.p. 127–130°; and 9-octadecenyl, m.p. 118–122.5°.

The imidazoles, particularly the 2-alkylbenzimidazoles, and their various derivatives constitute an important class of nitrogen-containing aliphatic compounds. The imidazoles are formed by the action of aromatic diamines with carboxylic acids, the reaction for the formation of the benzimidazoles being as follows:

$$\text{(benzene ring)}\begin{array}{c}NH_2\\NH_2\end{array} + \begin{array}{c}HO\\O\end{array}CR \rightarrow \text{(benzene ring)}\begin{array}{c}NH\\N\end{array}CR + 2H_2O$$

The 2-alkylbenzimidazoles can be formed by the condensation of aliphatic aldehydes with o-phenylenediamine in the presence of cupric salts,[231] and Graenacher and Ackermann [232] have stated that substituted benzimidazoles and also naphthimidazoles are formed when o-phenylenediamine or naphthylenediamines are condensed with glycerides in the presence of reducing agents. The imidazoles are basic, forming salts with strong acids. They are generally isolated as their picrates, which possess limited solubilities in water. A number of 2-alkylbenzimidazoles have been prepared from the saturated acids by Seka and Müller,[233] and more recently Pool, Harwood, and Ralston [234] have prepared a series of 2-alkylbenzimidazoles from 2-methylbenzimidazole to 2-heptadecylbenzimidazole inclusive. These authors have suggested their use as derivatives for the identification of the aliphatic acids. The melting points and mixed melting points of these derivatives have been recorded previously, in Table VI, Chapter IV. Benzimidazoles of the monocarboxylic acids have subsequently been prepared by several investigators.[235, 236]

Polymethylenedibenzimidazoles have been synthesized by Shriner and Upson,[237] by heating two moles of o-phenylenediamine with one mole of dibasic acid at 125–135° in the presence of hydrochloric acid as a catalyst, the reaction proceeding as follows:

$$2\,\text{(benzene ring)}\begin{array}{c}NH_2\\NH_2\end{array} + (CH_2)_n(CO_2H)_2 \rightarrow \text{(benzene ring)}\begin{array}{c}NH\\N\end{array}C - (CH_2)_n - C\begin{array}{c}NH\\N\end{array}\text{(benzene ring)} + 4H_2O$$

The products were described as white solids which melt with decomposition at high temperatures. They readily form dihydrochlorides.

The 2-alkylbenzimidazoles and related compounds, such as the naphthimidazoles, have been suggested as the starting point for the preparation of emulsifying agents, wetting agents, and other materials of similar function. Alkylation of the 2-alkylbenzimidazoles with esters of high molecular weight alcohols and chloroacetic acid, or with halogenated ethers, such as octadecyl chloromethyl ether, yields imidazolium compounds which have been reported to be water soluble.[238] Surface active chemicals have been stated to result when 2-heptadecylbenzimidazole is treated with benzaldehyde in the presence of boric acid as a condensing agent,[239] with the addition product of N-methylolchloroacetamide and trimethylamine,[240] with benzaldehyde followed by sulfonation [241] or treatment with ethyl chloride,[242] or when it is treated with benzaldehyde, hydrogenated, and then condensed with ethyl chloride.[243] Products useful as dispersing agents are obtained when 2-heptadecylbenzimidazole is condensed with methyl chloride and methanol under pressure at 140–150°, or when 2-heptadecenylbenzimidazole is condensed under similar conditions with ethylene chlorohydrin and methanol.[244] 1-Methyl-2-heptadecylbenzimidazole yields similar products when subjected to the above reaction.[245] The condensation of 2-methylbenzimidazole with lauroyl chloride or dodecanol followed by sulfonation yields water-soluble products,[246] and it has also been observed [247] that water-soluble compounds result when 1-hydroxyethyl-2-benzimidazolium chloride is treated with low molecular weight alcohols. The sulfonation of 2-heptadecylnaphthimidazole and similar compounds has been investigated.[248]

The imidazolines possess the cyclic structure of the imidazoles. The parent ring

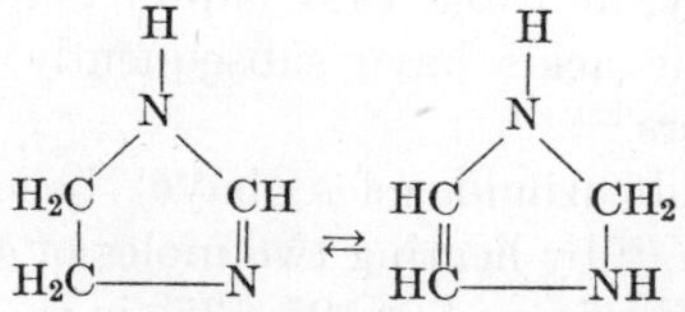

$$
\begin{array}{ccc}
\overset{\displaystyle H}{\underset{|}{N}} & & \overset{\displaystyle H}{\underset{|}{N}} \\
H_2C \diagup \quad \diagdown CH & & HC \diagup \quad \diagdown CH_2 \\
H_2C \!\!-\!\!-\!\!-\!\! N & \rightleftarrows & HC \!\!-\!\!-\!\!-\!\! NH
\end{array}
$$

differs from that of the imidazoles in that it contains two additional hydrogen atoms. Imidazolines which possess high molecular weight substituents have been the subject of several investigations, the results of which are contained in the patent literature. A process for the synthesis of substituted imidazolines by the condensation of diamines such as ethylenediamine with the fatty acids has been disclosed by Waldmann and Chwala,[249] the reaction taking place in the presence of acid salts and proceeding as follows:

$$\begin{array}{c} CH_2NH_2 \\ | \\ CH_2NH_2 \end{array} + HO_2CR \rightarrow \begin{array}{c} CH_2-N \\ | \quad\quad\quad >C-R + 2H_2O \\ CH_2-N \\ \quad\quad | \\ \quad\quad H \end{array}$$

Such reactions are readily accomplished by the use of the hydrochloride of monoacetylated ethylenediamine and the fatty acids.[250] N-substituted imidazolinium halides are obtained by condensing N,N'-disubstituted ethylenediamines with the fatty acids, an example being the condensation of N,N'-dibenzylethylenediamine with stearic acid in the presence of hydrochloric acid, to yield 2-heptadecyl-1,3-dibenzylimidazolinium chloride as follows:[251]

$$\begin{array}{c} CH_2\langle\rangle \\ | \\ H_2C-NH \\ | \quad\quad + C_{17}H_{35}CO_2H + HCl \rightarrow \\ H_2C-NH \\ | \\ CH_2\langle\rangle \end{array} \quad\quad \begin{array}{c} CH_2\langle\rangle \\ | \\ H_2C-N \\ | \quad\quad >C-C_{17}H_{35} + 2H_2O \\ H_2C-N-Cl \\ | \\ CH_2\langle\rangle \end{array}$$

The treatment of such products with sulfonating agents yields water-soluble compounds. Surface active compounds are also produced when 2-alkylimidazolines are treated with compounds such as 1-chloro-2-hydroxypropanesulfonic acid.[252] The use of the substituted imidazolines as wetting agents has been patented.[253] The dehydrogenation of the 2-alkylimidazolines in the presence of metallic catalysts and hydrogen acceptors has been stated to yield imidazoles, which can subsequently be treated with hydrogen halides to produce wetting agents.[254]

Several other classes of nitrogen-containing cycloaliphatic derivatives have been described and are worthy of mention. One of the most important of these, the phthalimides, results from the condensation of amines with phthalic acid or phthalic anhydride, the reaction in the latter instance being illustrated by the formation of dodecylphthalimide as follows:

$$\begin{array}{c} \langle\rangle \overset{C}{\underset{C}{\diagup}} \overset{O}{\underset{O}{\diagdown}} O + H_2NC_{12}H_{25} \rightarrow \langle\rangle \overset{C}{\underset{C}{\diagup}} \overset{O}{\underset{O}{\diagdown}} NC_{12}H_{25} + H_2O \end{array}$$

Dodecylphthalimide

Treatment of the phthalimides with strong alkalies results in their partial hydrolysis to monosubstituted amides, thus:

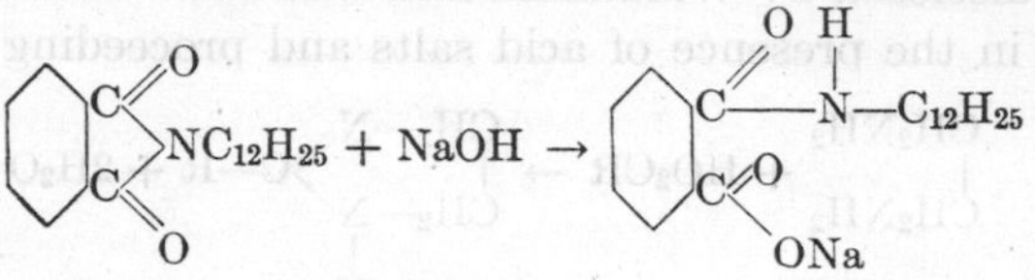

The preparation of polymethylenediphthalimides by the reaction of compounds such as 1,10-diiododecane with two moles of potassium phthalimide has been described by v. Braun,[255] decamethylenediphthalimide being formed as follows:

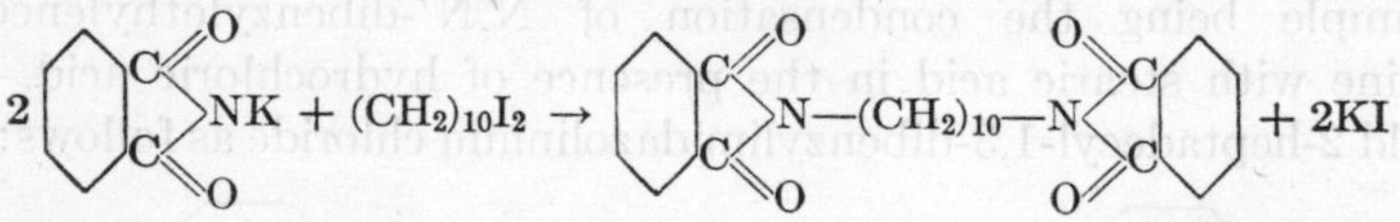

A yield of 75% of this compound, melting at 136°, was reported.

Cyclic imines have been obtained by the cyclization of α-halo-ω-aminoalkanes, $X(CH_2)_nNH_2$, in the presence of alkalies.[256] For example, 1-bromo-16-aminohexadecane, when heated for five days at 73° in aqueous isopropyl alcohol containing sodium hydroxide, gives 45% of hexadecamethylenimine and 24% of 1-hydroxy-16-aminohexadecane. Pentadeca-, tetradeca-, and tridecamethylenimines are similarly prepared. It was observed that the formation of nine- to twelve-membered cyclic imines is quite difficult, as indicated by an unsuccessful attempt to obtain the twelve-membered imine and a yield of only 5% for the eleven-membered compound. Pentadecamethylenimine was reported to possess a strong local anesthetic action; however, its hydrochloride and acetate are local irritants. Methylation of the cyclic imines yields the N-methyl derivatives, which are liquid at ordinary temperatures.

THE ALIPHATIC NITRILES

The nitriles, $RC:N$, are important chemical intermediates for the synthesis of a wide variety of aliphatic compounds. The reactivity of the nitrile molecule is occasioned by the presence of the unsaturated nitrogen atom, the nitriles as a class being characterized by many additive reactions which make them one of the important and interesting series of aliphatic derivatives.

Preparation of Nitriles

The formation of nitriles by the dehydration of amides was described over a century ago by Wöhler and Liebig [257] and has since been the subject of many investigations. Phosphorus pentoxide is the dehydrating agent most frequently employed, although other agents are often used and recommended. In 1869, Henry [258] described a method for the preparation of nitriles by the dehydration of amides with phosphorus pentasulfide, and the preparation of butyronitrile, valeronitrile, and capronitrile was accomplished by this procedure. A number of years later, Krafft and Stauffer [21] obtained lauronitrile, myristonitrile, and stearonitrile by the action of phosphoric anhydride on the respective amides, the boiling points of these nitriles being subsequently determined by Krafft and Weilandt.[259] Dehydrating agents such as carbonyl chloride [260] have been suggested for the preparation of nitriles from amides, and Boehner and Andrews [261] have studied the decomposition of amides into nitriles by heating them in the presence of aluminum oxide, pumice, glass, or graphite at temperatures between 250° and 300°. It was also observed that nitriles result when amides are passed in the vapor phase over aluminum oxide, the optimum temperature being 425°.[262]

Since the amide is an intermediate in the preparation of nitriles from the fatty acids, it is evident that nitriles may be formed directly from the fatty acids and ammonia at high temperatures without the actual isolation of the amides. The direct formation of nitriles from the fatty acids may be accomplished in either the vapor or the liquid phase. The studies which have been made upon the latter method have been very helpful in explaining the mechanism of nitrile formation. The formation of small amounts of nitriles during the preparation of amides from the fatty acids was observed by Mitchell and Reid,[12] the amount of nitrile being markedly increased if the reaction takes place in the presence of zinc chloride. The liquid-phase conversion of fatty acids to nitriles has been studied by Ralston, Pool, and Harwood,[263] who observed that when the fatty acids are heated in a stream of ammonia at a temperature of about 300° and the resulting water is continuously removed from the reaction mixture, a complete conversion of the fatty acids to nitriles is obtained. It had formerly been supposed that the mechanism of the liquid-phase formation of nitriles from fatty acids by their reaction with ammonia involved a stepwise dehydration, the ammonium soap losing a molecule of water to form the amide and the amide losing a molecule of water to form the nitrile. A study [264] of the mechanisms of the formation of nitriles from amides has shown that the reaction is not one of simple dehydration, since the pyrolysis of an amide yields equimolecular quantities of a nitrile and a fatty acid. Thus, when stearamide is heated above its decomposition temperature the product consists of equimolar quantities of stearic acid and stearonitrile, showing that two molecules of the stearamide have entered into the reaction, one being converted to the nitrile and the other to the acid. It was postulated that the water formed by the dehydration of one molecule of amide serves to hydrolyze a second molecule, as expressed by the following equilibria:

$$\underset{\text{(I)}}{RCO_2H} + NH_3 \rightleftarrows \underset{\text{(II)}}{RCO_2NH_4} \underset{+H_2O}{\overset{-H_2O}{\rightleftarrows}} \underset{\text{(III)}}{RCONH_2} \underset{+H_2O}{\overset{-H_2O}{\rightleftarrows}} RCN$$

The peculiar physical properties of the amides which have been attributed to their tautomeric nature and association have already been discussed. It is interesting to note that the above reaction may be explained by rupture of a heterocyclic ring, and it is highly probable that detailed studies of nitrile formation may yield some clue to the actual molecular structure of the amides.

A consideration of the above mechanism shows that when the fatty acids are heated in a continuous stream of ammonia at a temperature above the decomposition point of the amides, a series of reactions results in which the amides are alternately formed and decomposed, the amount of acid progressively decreasing and the amount of nitrile increasing until a quantitative conversion is obtained. Such reactions take place either in the presence or in the absence of contact catalysts and are accelerated by the removal of water during the process. It has been claimed [265] that nitriles are formed when fatty acids or amides are heated with ammonia under pressure, the reaction being catalyzed by thoria or alumina.

When the fatty acids or their esters are passed in the vapor phase with ammonia over contact catalysts, at temperatures around 400°, they are rapidly converted to nitriles. Since the temperatures employed are much above the point of stability of the ammonium soaps, the actual mechanism of nitrile formation in the vapor phase is not known. Among the first to employ the vapor-phase method were Weidel and Ciamician,[266] who obtained capronitrile by passing a mixture of ammonia and caproic acid vapor over red-hot pumice. The preparation of aromatic nitriles by passing the vapors of aromatic carboxylic acids mixed with ammonia over thoria was investigated by Mailhe,[267] and it was subsequently shown [268] that aliphatic nitriles are formed when the esters of aliphatic acids are similarly treated. The preparation of oleonitrile by passing a mixture of ammonia and methyl oleate over heated alumina has been described by Mailhe,[269] who made the following statements relative to the optimum temperature.

The temperature at which the reaction takes place is relatively high. It varies between 480–490° for thoria and 500° for alumina, the thermometer being laid in the trough which supports the catalytic tube. The reaction begins successfully at the lower temperature, around 450°, but under these conditions the reaction is incomplete and a part of the ester remains unchanged or the decomposition stops entirely at the amide stage.

The catalysts generally employed are alumina or thoria, although it has been stated [270] that silica gel is more effective than either of these oxides. Titania is also frequently suggested as a satisfactory contact catalyst for this conversion. Mailhe [271] has observed that when the vapors of amides are passed over reduced nickel catalysts, carbon monoxide is split off and the resulting amine is dehydrogenated to a nitrile containing one carbon atom less than the starting amide. The direct conversion of acid chlorides into nitriles has been investigated,[272] it having been observed that when the vapors of acid chlorides mixed with ammonia are passed over dehydrating catalysts at 490–500° the corresponding nitriles are produced in substantial yields, the reaction being as follows:

$$RCOCl + NH_3 \rightarrow RCN + H_2O + HCl$$

It appears logical to assume that an amide is formed as an intermediate product during this reaction. High yields of nitriles are obtained [273] when the vapors of aliphatic aldehydes and ammonia are passed over thoria at 220°, and it has also been observed [274] that primary and secondary aliphatic amines are dehydrogenated in the presence of nickel with the formation of a mixture of nitriles, ethylenic hydrocarbons, and hydrogen. When equimolar mixtures of organic esters and primary amines are passed over dehydrating catalysts at 500°, nitriles, alcohols, and unsaturated hydrocarbons are formed.[275] The preparation of nitriles by passing the vapors of fatty acids or their esters together with ammonia over dehydrating catalysts heated to 320–420° has been patented.[276, 277] Unsaturated nitriles may be prepared by passing the vapors of hydroxy acids, such as ricinoleic acid or hydroxystearic acid, over catalysts in the presence of ammonia at temperatures between 300° and 450°, the dehydration within the alkyl chain proceeding simultaneously with nitrile formation.[278] The use of aluminum phosphate as a dehydrating catalyst has been suggested [279] for the vapor-phase formation of nitriles from the fatty acids or their esters.

The preparation of dinitriles from diamides or dicarboxylic acids can be accomplished by essentially the same procedures which have been developed for the preparation of the mononitriles; however, owing to the polyfunctional nature of the dicarboxylic acids and their amides, side reactions are more frequently encountered. Greenewalt and Rigby [280] have obtained nitriles such as sebaconitrile by heating the respective amides in a stream of ammonia at a temperature of about 250°. Ammonium molybdate was suggested as a suitable catalyst. The preparation of adiponitrile by heating adipamide with acetic anhydride in the presence of cobalt or nickel acetate has been disclosed, and this nitrile has also been obtained by passing ammonia through adipic acid at 300° in the presence of phosphates.[281] The preparation of adiponitrile by heating the diamide in the presence of ammonium molybdate has been studied,[282] and it was reported that the optimum temperature for the reaction is between 220° and 230°. The liquid-phase formation of dinitriles by the action of ammonia on the dicarboxylic acids is catalyzed by the presence of phosphoric acid or its esters.[283] The vapor-phase reaction between adipic acid and ammonia for the preparation of adiponitrile has been studied,[284] the vapors being passed over a dehydrating catalyst at 320–400°. Catalysts which contain both boron and phosphorus are effective in promoting this reaction.[285, 286]

The synthesis of nitriles by the reaction of alkyl halides with inorganic cyanides is one of the oldest and most conventional methods for their preparation. Since this process results in a nitrile which contains one carbon atom more than the parent alkyl compound, it is frequently employed for the synthesis of odd-carbon-membered acids and other aliphatic derivatives. The alkali cyanides are most generally employed to effect this synthesis, the heavy metal cyanides such as mercuric, silver, zinc, and other cyanides frequently yielding isonitriles or mixtures of isonitriles with nitriles. Isonitrile formation is especially pronounced when the shorter-chained alkyl halides are treated with the heavy metal cyanides. The preparation of high molecular weight nitriles by treating alkyl iodides with alcoholic solutions of potassium cyanide has been described in detail by Levene and Taylor.[287] Heptadecanenitrile has been obtained[288] by the action of potassium cyanide on hexadecyl iodide, and the synthesis of tridecane-, pentadecane-, and heptadecanenitrile by the action of potassium cyanide on dodecyl, tetradecyl, and hexadecyl iodides has been described.[289] Optically active nitriles, such as d-amyl cyanide, $EtCHMeCH_2CN$, have been obtained by treating the corresponding iodide with potassium cyanide.[290] The dinitriles can be prepared in good yields by the treatment of dihalo compounds with alcoholic solutions of potassium cyanide. Detailed procedures for the preparation of 1,10-dicyanodecane and 1,12-dicyanododecane from 1,10-diiododecane and 1,12-diiodododecane have been published,[291] and v. Braun and Danziger[292] have described the synthesis of 1,5-dicyanopentane, 1,7-dicyanoheptane, 1,9-dicyanononane, and 1,11-dicyanoundecane by a similar procedure.

Several other methods for the synthesis of the aliphatic nitriles have been proposed. The action of excess bromine in alkaline solution on the aliphatic amides or amines, first investigated by Hofmann,[121] yields nitriles which contain one carbon atom less than the parent compound. This reaction can be conveniently employed for the synthesis of the odd-carbon-membered nitriles. Aldoximes lose a molecule of water in the presence of dehydrating agents, such as acetic anhydride, to form the corresponding nitriles, thus:

$$RCH:NOH \rightarrow RC:N + H_2O$$

Mixtures of nitriles and amides are formed when aliphatic acids are treated with the alkali salts of thiocyanic acid.[34] The splitting of phenylhydrazones in the presence of catalysts such as cuprous chloride yields a mixture of nitriles and amines[293] according to the reaction

$$C_6H_5NHN:CHR \rightarrow C_6H_5NH_2 + RCN$$

Although high yields of nitriles have been obtained by this method, the reaction is of only theoretical interest for the preparation of the higher molecular weight nitriles, owing to the difficulty of obtaining the higher aldehydes in a state of purity.

Physical Properties of the Aliphatic Nitriles

The aliphatic nitriles possess lower melting and boiling points than the corresponding acids. The higher members of the series are low-melting solids. They possess a characteristic odor which reaches a maximum at valeronitrile; myristonitrile and its higher homologs are odorless. The aliphatic nitriles are non-toxic, and relatively large amounts can be consumed without ill effects.

TABLE IV

MELTING POINTS OF ALIPHATIC NITRILES

No. of C Atoms	M.P., °C.
4	−112.6
5	−96.0
6	−79.4
8	−45.6
9	−34.2
10	−14.46 *
12	4.02 *
14	19.25 *
16	31.40 *
18	40.88 *
20	48.5–49.5
22	53.5–54.5
25	58–59
26	61–62

* Denotes freezing point.

The lower molecular weight aliphatic nitriles possess very low melting points, the values rising first abruptly and then more gradually as the series is ascended. Table IV shows the reported melting points of some of the saturated aliphatic nitriles.

Levene and Taylor [287] have reported double melting points for several of the higher molecular weight nitriles; however, this observation has not been verified and may have been occasioned by the presence of impurities.

The saturated nitriles can be distilled under reduced pressure without undergoing decomposition and the lower members can be distilled at atmospheric pressure. Lauronitrile and its higher homologs undergo some decomposition when distilled at atmospheric pressure. The boiling points of the saturated nitriles containing from six to eighteeen carbon atoms inclusive have recently been determined [289] at a number of pressures under equilibrium conditions. The reported values are compiled in Table V.

TABLE V

BOILING POINTS OF n-ALKYL NITRILES

No. of C Atoms	°C. at Following Pressures in Millimeters									
	1	2	4	8	16	32	64	128	256	512	760
6	.....	.....	.....	44.7	57.0	71.6	87.8	106.1	126.4	149.9	164.8
7	.....	.....	48.5	61.1	74.7	89.9	106.8	125.8	147.1	171.3	186.9
8	41.1	52.0	64.0	77.3	91.6	107.3	124.7	143.9	166.1	191.2	206.8
9	55.0	66.1	79.0	92.4	107.1	123.3	141.2	160.2	183.5	209.3	225.9
10	69.6	81.1	93.7	107.6	122.3	138.8	157.2	177.8	201.0	227.4	244.1
11	82.9	94.8	107.8	121.8	137.1	154.1	172.7	193.5	216.7	248.7	260.8
12	95.8	107.3	120.1	134.4	150.1	167.4	186.7	208.1	232.4	259.4	276.7
13	107.6	119.8	133.2	148.1	164.2	181.7	201.3	222.9	247.2	275.5	292.8
14	118.9	131.6	145.4	160.4	177.1	194.8	214.7	237.1	261.7	298.3	306.9
15	130.5	143.6	157.6	172.7	189.2	207.2	227.4	250.2	275.4	304.3	322.1
16	142.3	155.0	168.6	183.9	200.5	218.8	239.2	267.2	287.4	316.2	334.2
17	152.3	164.9	179.1	194.8	211.9	230.4	251.3	274.0	299.6	328.2	346.7
18	161.3	174.6	189.0	204.5	221.7	240.8	261.4	284.6	311.4	339.8	357.4

The vapor pressures of the saturated aliphatic nitriles at various temperatures are shown in Fig. 7.

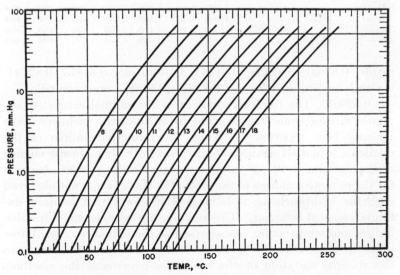

FIG. 7. Vapor pressures of n-alkyl nitriles.

The vapor tensions and latent heats of evaporation of the saturated nitriles from acetonitrile to caprylonitrile have been reported,[294] and the densities of the aliphatic nitriles which are liquid at ordinary temperatures have been published by Merckx, Verhulst, and Bruylants [295] and also by Daragan.[296] The former reported the following densities for the liquid nitriles: (d_4^0, d_4^{15}, d_4^{30}) valeronitrile, 0.81636, 0.80348, 0.79060; capronitrile, 0.82171, 0.80942, 0.79711; enanthonitrile, 0.82524, 0.81348, 0.80176; caprylonitrile, 0.82871, 0.81739, 0.80586; pelargononitrile, 0.83180, 0.82061, 0.80947; caprinitrile, 0.83429, 0.82322, 0.81243; undecane-

TABLE VI

REFRACTIVE INDICES (n_D^t) OF NORMAL ALIPHATIC NITRILES

Nitrile	20.0°	25.0°	30.0°	35.0°	40.0°	45.0°	50.0°	55.0°	65.0°	75.0°
Butyro-	1.3842	1.3820	1.3798	1.3773	1.3754	1.3729	1.3706	1.3862	1.3636	1.3590
Valero-	1.3972	1.3950	1.3929	1.3908	1.3887	1.3864	1.3843	1.3820	1.3774	1.3727
Capro-	1.4069	1.4049	1.4028	1.4008	1.3986	1.3966	1.3944	1.3921	1.3878	1.3834
Enantho-	1.4144	1.4124	1.4104	1.4083	1.4064	1.4044	1.4022	1.4000	1.3960	1.3817
Caprylo-	1.4204	1.4183	1.4164	1.4145	1.4124	1.4104	1.4085	1.4063	1.4021	1.3980
Pelargono-	1.4254	1.4235	1.4216	1.4197	1.4176	1.4157	1.4137	1.4115	1.4075	1.4035
Capri-	1.4296	1.4276	1.4256	1.4237	1.4218	1.4199	1.4180	1.4159	1.4119	1.4080
Undecane-	1.4330	1.4312	1.4293	1.4273	1.4254	1.4236	1.4217	1.4197	1.4156	1.4118
Lauro-	1.4360	1.4341	1.4322	1.4304	1.4286	1.4267	1.4248	1.4227	1.4188	1.4149
Tridecane-	1.4387	1.4368	1.4349	1.4330	1.4312	1.4294	1.4275	1.4254	1.4216	1.4177
Myristo-	1.4410	1.4392	1.4373	1.4354	1.4335	1.4317	1.4398	1.4279	1.4240	1.4202
Pentadecane-	......	1.4413	1.4395	1.4376	1.4356	1.4338	1.4320	1.4300	1.4261	1.4224
Palmito-	......	......	......	1.4396	1.4377	1.4358	1.4340	1.4318	1.4281	1.4244
Margaro-	......	......	......	......	1.4392	1.4373	1.4355	1.4336	1.4298	1.4260
Stearo-	......	......	......	......	......	1.4389	1.4370	1.4351	1.4313	1.4276

nitrile, 0.83621, 0.82538, 0.81464; lauronitrile, 0.83815, 0.82744, 0.81682; tridecanenitrile, —, 0.82937, 0.81885; myristonitrile, —, —, 0.82067. The refractive indices of the normal saturated aliphatic nitriles from butyronitrile to stearonitrile inclusive have recently been reported.[297] When the refractive indices of the nitriles are plotted against temperature, a rather abrupt change of slope occurs at 40–45°, a phenomenon similar to that observed for the refractive indices of the acids.[298] This effect is not observed with the hydrocarbons, it having been shown that heptane exhibits a normal behavior. This relationship between the refractive indices and temperature was ascribed to the influence of the latter upon the orientation of the dipoles, since at elevated temperatures the thermal agitation of the molecules overcomes the restraint imposed by dipole interaction. The refractive indices of the nitriles are shown in Table VI.

Binary mixtures of the saturated aliphatic nitriles exhibit polymorphism, and the liquid mixtures are also mesomorphic over an appreciable range of temperature and composition. The recently investigated system palmitonitrile-stearonitrile [299] is shown in Fig. 8.

It will be noted that all mixtures of palmitonitrile and stearonitrile exist in two modifications. The low melting, unstable form, α, the liquidus curve of which is shown by the line $ACDB$, is the one first obtained on cooling. This modification shows the forma-

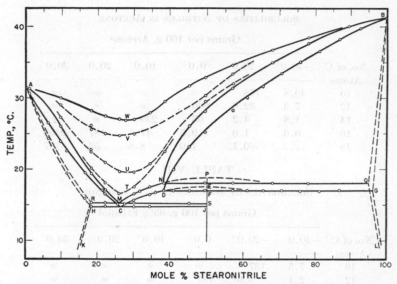

FIG. 8. The system: palmitonitrile-stearonitrile.

tion of an equimolar compound with an incongruent melting point E and a eutectic C at $14.78°$ which contains 26.3 mole % of stearonitrile. The curve $AMNB$ is the liquidus for the β or stable modification, and its similarity to that shown by the α-form is apparent. It is quite interesting to note that the stable form does not go immediately to an isotropic liquid on heating but assumes a series of mesomorphic states as indicated by the transition curves T, U, V, and finally W. Above the line W, the mixtures exist as isotropic liquid. No evidence of polymorphism of the pure components was observed. This is not surprising, however, since it is rather generally accepted that an unstable form of an aliphatic compound is rendered relatively more stable in mixtures.

An extensive investigation of the solubilities of the even-carbon-membered aliphatic nitriles containing from ten to eighteen carbon

atoms has recently been published.[300] In general, the solubilities
of the nitriles decrease with increasing polarity of the solvent, and
in a specific solvent the solubilities decrease regularly with increasing molecular weight of the nitriles. The nitriles form eutectic
mixtures with the non-polar solvents (benzene, cyclohexane, and
tetrachloromethane), the eutectic between lauronitrile and ben-

TABLE VII

SOLUBILITIES OF NITRILES IN ACETONE

Grams per 100 g. Acetone

No. of C Atoms	−40.0°	−20.0°	0.0°	10.0°	20.0°	30.0°
10	40.8	478	∞	∞	∞	∞
12	7.3	32.6	660	∞	∞	∞
14	1.8	4.2	63	239	∞	∞
16	0.3	1.0	9.5	47.8	187	2450
18	....	≈0.1	1.0	8.8	53	197

TABLE VIII

SOLUBILITIES OF NITRILES IN 95% ETHANOL

Grams per 100 g. 95% Ethanol

No. of C Atoms	−40.0°	−20.0°	0.0°	10.0°	20.0°	30.0°
10	7.5	137	∞	∞	∞	∞
12	2.4	5.6	181	∞	∞	∞
14	1.2	2.2	8.7	59	∞	∞
16	0.6	0.7	1.7	5.1	33.3	1000
18	≈0.2	0.3	0.5	0.9	4.5	35.7

zene, for example, containing 51.1% nitrile and freezing at −14.8°.
That between lauronitrile and cyclohexane contains 19.9% nitrile
and freezes at −15.1°, and that between lauronitrile and tetrachloromethane contains 7.9% nitrile and freezes at −27.9°. The
nitriles are more soluble in benzene than in cyclohexane or tetrachloromethane. They are, in general, less soluble in the slightly
polar solvents (trichloromethane, ethyl ether, glacial acetic acid,
ethyl acetate, butyl acetate) than in the non-polar solvents. The
nitriles are less soluble in acetone than in butanone, and are less
soluble in methanol, 95% ethanol, isopropyl alcohol, and butanol
than in any of the solvents mentioned above. They possess
limited solubilities in acetonitrile and nitroethane. Tables VII
and VIII show the solubilities of the nitriles in acetone and 95%

ethanol, and their solubility curves in benzene and ethyl ether are shown in Figs. 9 and 10. The nitriles show evidences of appreciable hydrogen-bonding tendencies [301, 302] which markedly influence their solubility characteristics. They possess relatively high dipole moments. [303, 304]

Very few reliable constants are available for the unsaturated nitriles. Bruylants and Ernould [304] have reported the following values for the hexenenitriles: $trans$-2-hexenenitrile, b_{755} 164–165°, d_4^{20} 0.82535, n_D^{20} 1.43408; cis-2-hexenenitrile, b_{757} 149.5°, d_4^{20} 0.82331, n_D^{20} 1.43157. The 2-heptenenitriles have been prepared by Vandewyer [305] and also by de Hoffmann, [306] the latter of whom reported the following physical constants: cis-2-heptenenitrile, $b_{12.5}$ 60.2–60.4°, d_4^{15} 0.82960, d_4^{30} 0.81754, n_D^{15} 1.43849, n_D^{20} 1.43205; $trans$-2-heptenenitrile, b_{15} 67.8°, d_4^{15} 0.83088, d_4^{30} 0.81875, n_D^{15} 1.44292, n_D^{30} 1.43668. Cis- and $trans$-2-undecenenitriles have the following constants: [307] cis-, b_{10} 119.7–119.9°, d_4^{20} 0.83255, n_D^{20} 1.44816; $trans$-, b_{10} 127.9–128.1°, d_4^{20} 0.83359, n_D^{20} 1.45146. Elaidonitrile freezes at about −1° and boils at 213–214° under 16 mm. pressure. [308] The physical constants of a number of the 2-alkenenitriles have been tabulated by Bruylants. [309]

Chemical Properties of the Aliphatic Nitriles

Hydrolysis of the nitriles proceeds through the amides to the carboxylic acids, the reaction being the reverse of that which takes place during the formation of nitriles from the carboxylic acids. The lower molecular weight nitriles can be hydrolyzed completely by refluxing with aqueous or alcoholic solutions of alkali hydroxides. [310, 311] The rate of hydrolysis of the higher members is appreciably accelerated by conducting the reaction under pressure. The catalytic hydrolysis of nitriles by steam has been studied by Mailhe, [312] who showed that when the vapors of nitriles mixed with steam are passed over thorium oxide or aluminum oxide at about 420°, complete hydrolysis occurs with the formation of the corresponding acids. The preparation of caproic acid from capronitrile by this procedure was described.

The velocity of both the alkaline and the acid hydrolyses of the lower molecular weight nitriles has been the subject of several investigations. Since such hydrolytic reactions probably proceed stepwise, two equilibria are involved, as follows: nitrile $\xrightarrow{k_1}$ amide $\xrightarrow{k_2}$ acid, the equilibrium constants and the relative rates of attainment of equilibrium being functions of the conditions employed

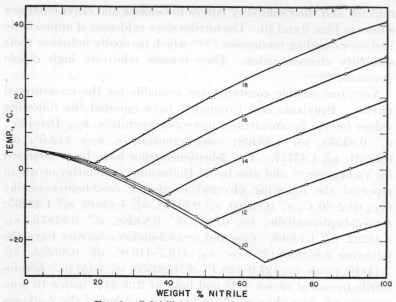

FIG. 9.   Solubilities of nitriles in benzene.

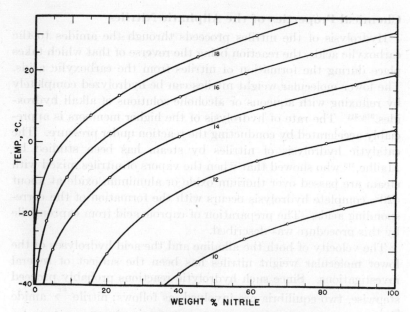

FIG. 10.   Solubilities of nitriles in ethyl ether.

for the hydrolysis. It is evident that if the rate of hydrolysis of the amide k_2 is rapid in comparison to that of nitrile hydrolysis k_1, the latter will be determinative as regards the overall reaction rate. If, on the other hand, the reverse is encountered, the former will be determinative, and the reaction may be stopped at the amide stage. The rate of amide hydrolysis may, of course, be studied independently by starting with the amide.[313] In their study of the rates of hydrolysis of a series of low molecular weight nitriles including acetonitrile and propionitrile, Krieble and Noll [314] observed that the rates of hydrolysis with hydrochloric acid increase rapidly with increasing concentration of the acid, the increase being approximately proportional to the increase in the square of the mean ion activity. Sulfuric acid was reported to be a much poorer catalyst than hydrochloric acid. The rate of hydrolysis of propionitrile in concentrated solutions of mineral acids has been extensively studied by Winkler and associates.[315, 316, 317, 318] It was observed that for acid concentrations between $1N$ and $4N$ the rate of amide hydrolysis is much greater than that of nitrile hydrolysis ($>100:1$). At higher acid concentrations either the relative rates are comparable or the amide hydrolysis is slower, depending upon the particular acid employed. The range of reaction rates exhibited in various concentrations of sulfuric acid is quite wide, the velocity of nitrile hydrolysis increasing and that of amide hydrolysis decreasing with increasing acid concentration. It was stated, for example, that with $10.00N$ sulfuric acid the ratio of the velocities of the nitrile and amide hydrolyses is about $1:30$, whereas at $18.86N$ the ratio is $10:1$. In their study of the hydrolysis of nitriles in glacial acetic acid-concentrated sulfuric acid mixtures, however, Karvé and Gharpure [319] reported insignificant amide formation over an acid concentration range from $16.34N$ to $26.21N$. This can probably be explained on the basis of a modified solubility effect. The reduction in the rate of amide hydrolysis is quite evident with concentrated sulfuric acid solutions, since when nitriles are dissolved in this reagent a quantitative conversion to the corresponding amide is obtained. Since the nitriles are easily purified by distillation, their reaction with concentrated sulfuric acid offers a convenient method for the preparation of amides.[13] In their studies of the hydrolysis of nitriles in concentrated solutions of mineral acids, Winkler and associates [315, 316, 317, 318] observed that at lower acid concentrations the velocities of hydrolysis in the various acids are essentially similar; however, at higher concentrations the catalytic effect decreases in the order: hydrochloric acid, sulfuric acid, hydrobromic acid, nitric acid. It was stated that such differences may be accounted for by specific differences in the PZ and E factors of the Arrhenius equation, a decrease in activation energy with increasing acid concentration being typical.

Nitriles are converted to acids in good yields by heating with 100% phosphoric acid;[320] however, with 93.5% phosphoric acid the nitriles remain practically unchanged.[321] Hantzsch[322] has stated that nitriles dissolve in strong acids to yield true salts, which in certain instances slowly change to amides. The reaction kinetics have been studied by von Peskoff and Meyer.[323]

Alkaline hydrolysis is much more frequently employed than acid hydrolysis for the preparation of the high molecular weight acids from nitriles. Levene and Taylor[287] have accomplished the hydrolysis of the higher molecular weight nitriles by prolonged boiling with an excess of 50% aqueous sodium hydroxide solution, the acids being obtained by subsequent acidification of the resulting soap. Alkaline hydrolysis of the nitriles is very often employed as one of the steps in synthetic procedures involving high molecular weight aliphatic compounds, since when the reaction is conducted under pressure at about 150° a very rapid and complete hydrolysis results. Kinetic studies[324] upon the alkaline hydrolysis of propionitrile indicate that the rate is dependent upon the rate of formation of the intermediate amide, the relative rates of the hydrolysis of propionitrile and propionamide being approximately 1 : 10. The reaction rate is apparently independent of the alkali concentration, although Reitz[325] has reported a decrease above $0.8N$. Subsequent investigations, however, have failed to confirm this finding. The activation energy for the alkaline hydrolysis of propionitrile is materially less (5000 cal.) than that for the acid hydrolysis. The independence of the rate of alkaline hydrolysis upon alkali concentration suggests a somewhat different mechanism from that encountered in acid hydrolysis.

Nitriles may be converted directly to esters by treatment with alcohols under pressure in the presence of acid catalysts. It has been reported[326] that the best conditions for the preparation of ethyl esters from nitriles include treatment with one mole of concentrated sulfuric acid and ten parts of ethanol at 130–140° in a pressure vessel, concentrated sulfuric acid apparently being preferable to hydrochloric acid for this purpose. The thiohydrolysis of nitriles by alkaline sulfide solutions yields the corresponding thio-amides,[99, 100] which have been discussed previously.

Nitriles react with hydrogen chloride in alcoholic solution to form imino ethers [213] from which amidines may be obtained [214] by treatment with alcoholic solutions of ammonia. The preparation and properties of compounds of this type have been discussed earlier in this chapter.

Imino chlorides result from the direct addition of hydrogen chloride to the nitriles. These may be reduced to aldimines, the hydrolysis of which yields aldehydes as follows: [327]

$$RC:N \xrightarrow{HCl} RCCl:NH \xrightarrow{H_2} RCH:NH \xrightarrow{H_2O} RCHO + NH_3$$

Caprylonitrile, myristonitrile, palmitonitrile, and stearonitrile yield the corresponding aldehydes by hydrolysis of their aldimines. The aldimines may be prepared easily by treating nitriles with an ether solution of hydrogen chloride in the presence of anhydrous stannous chloride, the aldimine separating as aldimine stannic chloride, $(RCH:NH \cdot HCl)_2SnCl_4$. The steam distillation of these complexes was stated to give the aldehydes in high yields. The more recent work of Williams [328] has indicated that this process gives small yields of the higher aldehydes.

The reaction of aliphatic nitriles with Grignard reagents offers a very satisfactory procedure for the preparation of the higher molecular weight ketones, the addition product first formed being hydrolyzed to yield ketones as follows:

(I) $RC:N + R'MgX \rightarrow RR'C:NMgX$

(II) $RR'C:NMgX + 2HCl + H_2O \rightarrow RR'CO + MgXCl + NH_4Cl$

Baerts [329] has reported that butyronitrile and ethylmagnesium bromide yield 40% of ethyl propyl ketone, side reactions resulting in some formation of 3-ethyl-3-hexanol and 2-butyrylbutyronitrile. The action of adiponitrile with ethylmagnesium bromide yields 1-imino-2-cyanocyclopentane and 3,8-decanedione.[330] Ketones have been obtained [331] by the action of organomagnesium compounds on brominated nitriles. The amides likewise react with Grignard reagents to form ketones, Ryan and Nolan [332] having obtained α-naphthyl heptadecyl ketone by the action of the corresponding Grignard reagent on stearamide. They have also prepared α-naphthyl pentadecyl ketone and p-tolyl pentadecyl ketone from palmitamide by similar procedures. Ralston and Christensen [333] have described the preparation of a number of high molecular weight ketones by the action of Grignard reagents on nitriles and have established their identity by comparison with the products obtained by Friedel-Crafts reactions. The following procedure was employed for the preparation of ketones from nitriles by the Grignard method:

The magnesium complex was prepared and the corresponding nitrile added dropwise and refluxed until the Grignard reagent was used up, as evidenced by a negative color test. . . . The reaction mixtures were hydrolyzed by 10 per cent hydrochloric acid. Satisfactory yields were obtained—for example, 67.0 per cent, in the synthesis of p-diphenyl heptadecyl ketone, and 61.5 per cent in the case of p-diphenyl undecyl ketone.

The color test referred to above is that devised by Gilman and Schulze.[334]

Amides result from the action of alkaline solutions of hydrogen peroxide on nitriles, the reaction taking place with a liberation of oxygen.[33] The nitriles undergo many additive reactions, an example of which is the addition of hydroxylamine.[214, 335, 336] When the aliphatic nitriles are treated with metallic sodium, substituted aminopyridines are formed from the condensation of three moles of nitrile.[337, 338, 339] The addition of bromine to aliphatic nitriles yields 2-bromo nitriles [307, 340, 341] which, when treated with organic bases, lose hydrogen bromide to yield 2-alkenenitriles. The 2-alkenenitriles possess a conjugated unsaturated system and consequently show 1,4-addition reactions.

The preparation of amino nitriles by the action of liquid ammonia on hydroxy nitriles has been disclosed,[342] an example being the preparation of 6-aminocapronitrile from 6-hydroxycapronitrile. Amino acids result from the hydrolysis of these amino nitriles. The preparation of the amino nitriles by various procedures has been investigated by Luten.[343] Unsaturated nitriles may be polymerized in either the presence or the absence of catalysts [344] to yield dimers or higher polymers, and these products may be hydrolyzed to polycarboxylic acids [345] or hydrogenated to polyamines.[346] Probably the most important reaction of the long-chain nitriles is their reduction or catalytic hydrogenation to amines. Such reactions are discussed later in this chapter.

A distinctive characteristic of the aliphatic nitriles, differentiating them from other high molecular weight, polar aliphatic compounds, is that they can be thermally cracked without loss or modification of their polar group.[264] If the fatty acids and ammonia are caused to react at temperatures above the thermal stability point of the nitriles, the processes of nitrile formation and cracking proceed simultaneously, cracked nitrile mixtures being obtained directly. Amines such as methylamine or aniline may be employed instead of ammonia, a mixture of cracked anilides resulting in the latter instance. The aliphatic nitriles may be cracked in either the vapor or the liquid phase, the former method consisting of passing the vapors over various catalysts at temperatures between 450° and 600°, and the latter of heating them in a closed vessel at approximately 420°. The products consist of a mixture of straight-chain saturated and unsaturated nitriles and hydrocarbons. These cannot be separated by distillation, since the boiling points of the resulting nitriles will correspond to those of the hydrocarbons of greater chain lengths. A separation may be effected, however, by converting the nitriles in the cracked mixture either to acids or to amines and separating these from the hydrocarbons by washing with aqueous alkaline or acid solution. Various procedures have been developed for the direct separation of the nitriles and hydrocarbons in such mixtures, one of the most effective of which [347] consists of passing the cracked mixtures over silica gel, which adsorbs both hydrocarbons and nitriles. Washing with petroleum ether removes the hydrocarbons, the nitriles being subsequently removed by heating the silica gel in a stream of ammonia. The use of preferential solvents brings about an efficient separation of the nitriles and hydrocarbons from the mixture of cracked products. It was found that the nitriles are easily soluble in 75% aqueous methanol, whereas the hydrocarbons are insoluble. However, 85% methanol forms a homogeneous solution containing alcohol, water, nitriles, and hydrocarbons. Glacial acetic acid containing a small percentage of water dissolves the nitriles but not the hydrocarbons. When the cracked mixtures are treated with aqueous solutions of phenols, three layers are formed, the upper consisting of the hydrocarbons, the lower of water, and the middle of phenol, water, and nitriles. The nitriles may be removed from this layer by treatment with aqueous sodium hydroxide solutions. Amines, such as aniline, have also been found to function as preferential solvents for such mixtures. The pyrolysis of aliphatic nitriles and the separation of the resulting products have been the subject of an extensive investigation,[264] and the general processes involved have been patented.[348, 349, 350]

The fact that the aliphatic nitriles can be cracked to yield mixtures of shorter-chained saturated and unsaturated nitriles together with saturated and unsaturated hydrocarbons is quite significant, since it means that the high molecular weight nitriles can function as the starting material for the synthesis of a wide variety of aliphatic compounds. Such mixtures contain only straight-chain components and the unsaturated bonds are generally present in terminal positions. The rather wide availability of the higher fatty acids makes such processes of more than usual interest.

Several uses have been proposed for the higher molecular weight nitriles aside from their function as chemical intermediates. The aliphatic nitriles containing from ten to fourteen carbon atoms inclusive are highly repellent to insects, and their use as agricultural insect repellents has been proposed.[351] They impart the property of "oiliness" to petroleum lubricants.[352] It has been observed that mixtures of aliphatic nitriles and mineral oil function as penetrating oils,[353] and their use in motor fuels has been suggested.[354] The reaction products of aliphatic nitriles with phosphorus pentasulfide or sulfur monochloride have been proposed as "extreme-pressure" lubricants.[355] The lower molecular weight nitriles are effective flotation agents for certain metallic ores,[356] and the dinitriles are also useful for this purpose.[357] The use of nitriles as plasticizers for synthetic elastomers and various plastic materials is a subject of recent interest.

THE HIGH MOLECULAR WEIGHT ALIPHATIC AMINES AND RELATED COMPOUNDS

The amines may be considered as substituted ammonias, in which one or more hydrogens of the ammonia are replaced by hydrocarbon radicals. The aliphatic amines are classed as primary, RNH_2, secondary, $RR'NH$, or tertiary, $RR'R''N$, depending upon whether one, two, or three hydrogens are replaced. The R groups present in the secondary and tertiary amines may, of course, be alike or different, and as a consequence a very large number of representatives of this class of compounds is theoretically possible. The mixed amines which contain a long-chain hydrocarbon group together with one or more aromatic radicals attached to the nitrogen also constitute an important group of compounds. Being basic, the amines form salts with acids, the chemical and physical properties of which have been and will continue to be the subjects of many scientific investigations. The wide gradation in properties and the characteristic and often unique physical behavior exhibited by the high molecular weight aliphatic amines and their salts impart to them an interest unexcelled by any other group of aliphatic compounds.

Preparation of Amines

Many methods have been proposed for the synthesis of the high molecular weight amines. Only a few of the suggested procedures have withstood the test of time; others, because they involve difficultly obtainable intermediates or because they result in complex reaction mixtures, are of historical interest only. One of the earliest methods employed for the preparation of primary amines is that suggested by Hofmann,[358] who obtained hexadecylamine by the reaction of 1-iodohexadecane with an alcoholic solution of ammonia under pressure. It was recognized, however, that this procedure yields not only primary amines, but also substantial amounts of secondary and tertiary amines which, in the case of the higher molecular weight compounds, are difficult to separate. The reaction has been conveniently employed for the synthesis of the lower molecular weight amines such as ethylamine, and van Renesse [359] has reported satisfactory yields of octyl- and dioctyl-amine by the action of alcoholic ammonia on 1-iodoöctane at 100°. The reaction of aqueous ammonia with alkyl halides has been suggested as a method for the preparation of secondary amines,[360] the reaction being conducted at about 120° to 170° with an excess of ammonia. The preparation of didecyl-, didodecyl-, ditetradecyl-, and dioctadecylamines by this procedure was described. Mixed secondary amines such as N-methyldecyl-, N-methyldodecyl-, N-methyltetradecyl-, N-butyltetradecyl-, and N-methyloctadecyl-amines are obtained [361] when alkyl halides are treated with the lower primary amines. Alcohols constitute the main by-product when the alkyl halides are treated with ammonium hydroxide.[362] It has been claimed [363] that wetting agents can be obtained by the treatment of chlorinated paraffins with lower molecular weight amines followed by treatment with sulfuric acid. The preparation of amines from petroleum hydrocarbons has been described,[364] the process involving chlorination of the hydrocarbons followed by treatment of the product with aqueous ammonia under pressure.

The use of liquid instead of aqueous ammonia for the preparation of amines from the alkyl halides offers an interesting modification, recent experiments having indicated that this procedure may be satisfactorily employed for the preparation of many of the high molecular weight amines. The investigations of v. Braun [365] upon the reaction of liquid ammonia with the alkyl halides show that the relative yields of primary amines are materially increased with increase in molecular weight of the alkyl halide. The product from the reaction of 1-bromopentane contains 10% pentylamine and 80% dipentylamine; 1-bromoöctane gives approximately equal amounts of primary and secondary amines, and the product from 1-bromododecane consists of 90% primary amine. When equal amounts of 1-chlorododecane and liquid ammonia are heated at 75–80° for 90 hours, 28–33% of didodecylamine is obtained.[366] Only 35% of the halide reacts after 170 hours at 45°, but higher temperatures materially increase the reaction rate. A subsequent investigation [367] has shown that although this method is satisfactory for the preparation of certain high molecular weight primary amines, it is not applicable for amines which contain twenty or more carbon atoms because of the insolubility of the higher alkyl halides in liquid ammonia. Such halides, however, are quite soluble in anhydrous amines such as methylamine, dimethylamine, and similar compounds, and the method is therefore satisfactory for the synthesis of secondary or tertiary amines which contain one long-chain alkyl group. For example, docosylamine is obtainable only in traces, but N,N-dimethyldocosylamine can be prepared in quantitative yields. A study [368] of the amination of alkyl halides by sodium amide in liquid ammonia showed that the products consist of primary, secondary, and tertiary amines together with olefins. The yield of primary amines increases with increase in molecular weight for the lower members, the highest yield (74%) being obtained from 1-bromohexane. The alkyl chlorides are not so reactive under these conditions as the bromides and show a greater amount of olefin formation. Amination takes place only with those compounds which contain primary halogens, the action of liquid ammonia on 2-bromopentane and 2-bromo-2-methyl-butane yielding only olefins. The addition of water was observed to increase the amount of secondary amines formed in all cases. The reaction of 1-chloroalkanes with liquid ammonia and the lower amines has been extensively studied by Westphal and Jerchel,[369] who observed that smooth reactions are obtained by the use of liquid ammonia-ethanol mixtures. Under such conditions the main product is the secondary amine, the yield of primary amine increasing and that of tertiary amine decreasing with increasing chain length. 1-Chloroöctane under these conditions yields 11% of primary and 22% of tertiary amine, whereas 1-chlorohexadecane gives 24% of primary and no tertiary amine. The yield of didodecylamine from 1-chlorododecane was reported to be 80–85%. The secondary alkylamines are obtained exclusively when 1-chloroöctane and its higher homologs are treated with methylamine. The 1-chloroalkanes form tertiary amines readily by reaction with secondary amines such as dimethyl- or diethylamine. For example, an 86% yield of N,N-diethyldodecylamine is obtained from 1-chlorododecane and diethylamine. Secondary amines such as dibenzylamine give high yields of tertiary amines when treated with the 1-chloroalkanes. Tertiary amines such as trimethylamine act slowly with the 1-chloroalkanes to give quaternary ammonium salts, the preparation of which is discussed later in this chapter.

The action of ammonia or alkylamines on the aliphatic alcohols is commonly employed for the preparation of the lower molecular weight amines, and it has received considerable attention as a method for the synthesis of the higher amines. That the reaction is not simply one of dehydration, but one involving the formation of chemical intermediates, has been indicated by the several studies made upon its mechanism. The preparation of aliphatic amines from alcohols is not new, since it was first proposed by Berthelot [370] almost a hundred years ago. This investigation, which involved the reaction of ammonium chloride with methanol, was later repeated by Weith,[371] who reported the formation of only small amounts of primary, secondary, and tertiary amines. The preparation of the aliphatic amines up to and including octylamine was accomplished in 1884 by heating alcohols in a sealed tube with an excess of ammonium zinc chloride.[372]

Interest in the preparation of amines from alcohols was revived by the investigations of Sabatier upon contact catalysts, and it was observed that amines are the chief products formed when alcohols and ammonia are passed simultaneously over dehydrating catalysts at elevated temperatures. Sabatier and Mailhe [373] obtained dimethylamine together with a little trimethylamine when methanol and ammonia were passed over thorium dioxide at 300–350°. It had previously been shown [374] that primary amines are formed when alcohols and ammonia are passed over tungstic oxide at 360°. This investigation indicated that amine formation can be accomplished at temperatures below those at which excessive dehydration of the alcohols to olefins is encountered.

Mono-, di-, and triethylamines together with ethylene and diethyl ether are obtained [375] when ethanol and ammonia are passed over aluminum oxide at 330–350°, this temperature having been stated to be optimum for amine formation from these materials. Somewhat later, Dorrell [376] found that 300° is an optimum temperature for such reactions. The alkylation of ammonia in the presence of various catalysts has been studied by Brown and Reid, [377] who reported silica gel to be the most effective and blue tungstic oxide the least effective of the catalysts investigated. The preparation of hexadecylamine and octadecylamine from the corresponding alcohols by reaction with ammonia under high pressure in the presence of thorium dioxide has been accomplished, [378] it being stated that maximum yields of the amines are obtained at 380°. A study [379] of the preparation of high molecular weight amines from alcohols and ammonia at atmospheric pressure showed that the conversion of 1-dodecanol at 300° yields 6.6% dodecylamine, 5.5% didodecylamine, and less than 0.5% tridodecylamine when silica gel is used as the catalyst. At 350° under the same conditions substantially higher yields are obtained: 7.5% dodecyl-, 23.5% didodecyl-, and 8.0% tridodecylamine. 1-Octadecanol and ammonia at 360° give 54% of a mixture of primary, secondary, and tertiary amines. A 36% conversion of oleyl alcohol is obtained at 350° in the presence of aluminum oxide. In an earlier patent [380] it was claimed that by employing a high ratio of alcohol to ammonia, secondary amines are preferentially formed. Covert [381] has described the preparation of a series of hexadecylamines by the action of ammonia or amines on dicapryl alcohol. The use of metallic hydrogenation catalysts to increase the relative proportions of primary amines has been suggested, [382, 383] and it has also been stated [384] that primary amine formation is favored if aluminum oxide catalysts, coated with metallic oxides such as chromium or nickel oxide, are employed. The preparation of high molecular weight secondary and tertiary amines has been accomplished by treating alcohols with low molecular weight amines under high pressure in the presence of dehydrating catalysts. [385, 386] The application of high pressures materially increases the rate of alkylation of ammonia by high molecular weight alcohols. [387] The preparation of high molecular weight tertiary amines by the action of the lower secondary amines on substances which reduce to alcohols has been disclosed, the reaction being accomplished in the presence of hydrogen and hydrogenating catalysts.[388] The use of oxides or salts of iron or copper for promoting the reaction of ammonia or amines with high molecular weight alcohols has been proposed.[389]

The formation of secondary and tertiary amines by the action of alcohols with primary and secondary amines in the presence of dehydrogenating catalysts has been studied by Adkins and associates [390, 391, 392, 393] and also by Kindler,[394] and in 1939 Schwoegler and Adkins [395] published the results of their studies upon the mechanism of amine formation by this reaction. Since tertiary alcohols do not react under such conditions, it was assumed that the alcohol is initially dehydrogenated to an aldehyde or a ketone, which then reacts with the amine to yield a product which is readily hydrogenated to the higher amine, the reactions involved being as follows:

$$\text{(I)} \qquad R_2CHOH \rightarrow R_2CO + H_2$$

$$\text{(II)} \qquad R_2CO + R'NH_2 \rightarrow R_2C{\overset{\displaystyle OH}{\underset{\displaystyle NHR'}{\big<}}}$$

$$\text{(III)} \qquad R_2C{\overset{\displaystyle OH}{\underset{\displaystyle NHR'}{\big<}}} + H_2 \rightarrow R_2CHNHR' + H_2O$$

The optimum conditions for the preparation of a number of amines by this procedure were ascertained by these authors. That aldehydes and ketones may be intermediates in this synthesis is shown by the observation of Mignonac [396] that the hydrogenation of ammoniacal solutions of aldehydes or ketones yields amines, and also by the observation that high yields of amines can be obtained by the hydrogenation of aldehyde-ammonia complexes in organic solvents.[397] The preparation of primary amines by passing the vapors of aldehydes mixed with ammonia and hydrogen over hydrogenating catalysts has been patented,[398] and various procedures have been disclosed whereby aldehydes and ketones may be converted into amines by hydrogenating processes in the presence of ammonia.[399, 400, 401, 402] It has been claimed that high molecular weight amines are formed by the action of ammonia under pressure on high molecular weight esters in the presence of hydrogen and a hydrogenating catalyst, an example being the preparation of octadecyl- and dioctadecylamines by the action of hydrogen and ammonia on ethyl stearate.[403]

The formation of amines by the reduction of aldoximes, ketoximes, and related compounds has occupied the attention of a number of investigators.[404, 405, 406, 407, 408] It was shown by Goldschmidt,[409] for example, that high yields of heptylamine can be obtained by the reduction of enanthaldoxime, and Krafft [410] showed that tetradecylamine results from the reduction of myristaldoxime. In 1923, v. Braun and coworkers [411] suggested that primary amines are the initial product of the catalytic hydrogenation of aldoximes and that the resulting secondary amines are formed by a subsequent reaction involving the primary amines and the aldimines or ketimines as follows:

(I) $RCH{=}NOH \xrightarrow{H_2} RCH{=}NH \xrightarrow{H_2} RCH_2NH_2$

(II) $RCH_2NH_2 + RCH{=}NH \xrightarrow{-NH_3} RCH{=}NCH_2R \xrightarrow{H_2} (RCH_2)_2NH$

The catalytic hydrogenation of a number of oximes under high pressure has been accomplished by Winans and Adkins,[397] who have obtained 62% of pentylamine and 27% of dipentylamine by the hydrogenation of valeraldoxime, and 61% of heptylamine and 20% of diheptylamine by the hydrogenation of heptaldoxime. The preparation of heptylamine by the reduction of heptaldoxime with sodium and ethanol has been described in detail.[412] Paul [413] has stated that in the presence of metallic nickel the aldoximes are hydrogenated to a mixture of primary and secondary amines; however, the ketoximes are rapidly reduced to the corresponding primary amines. Hydrogenation of oximes has been stated to result in high yields of primary amines if the hydrogenation is conducted under high partial pressures of ammonia in the presence of catalysts such as tungstic oxide, tungstic sulfide, or nickel tungstate.[414]

The formation of amines by the action of bromine in alkaline solution on the amides has been discussed previously in this chapter. Although this method has been extensively investigated, the occurrence of side reactions, chiefly nitrile formation, with the higher molecular weight compounds precludes the use of this method as an acceptable procedure for the preparation of the higher molecular weight amines.

The reduction of nitriles by either chemical or catalytic means is the procedure most frequently employed for the preparation of the high molecular weight primary and secondary amines, and such methods have been shown to be satisfactory for both laboratory and commercial preparation of the long-chain amines. The reduction of nitriles may be accomplished either by the use of nascent hydrogen under acidic or alkaline conditions or by catalytic hydrogenation procedures. The higher molecular weight nitriles were first reduced to amines by the use of metallic sodium and alcohol, the reaction yielding nearly quantitative amounts of primary amines. These are generally isolated as their salts, such as the hydrochlorides, from which the free amines are obtained by treatment with alkali hydroxides.

The fact that the nitriles combine with four atoms of hydrogen to form primary amines was discovered in 1862 by Mendius,[415] and since then several investigators have contributed to our knowledge of this reaction. Among the first to apply such procedures to the preparation of the higher amines were Krafft and Moye,[416] who prepared hexadecylamine by the reduction of palmitonitrile with sodium in ethanol. The amine was isolated as the hydrochloride and analyzed as the double salt of its hydrochloride and platinum chloride, $(C_{16}H_{33}NH_2HCl)_2PtCl_4$. Treatment of the hydrochloride with potassium hydroxide produced the free amine. A secondary amine, N-ethylhexadecylamine, was obtained by treatment of the hexadecylamine with ethyl iodide followed by liberation of the free amine by the use of potassium hydroxide. The tertiary amine, N,N-diethylhexadecylamine was obtained by the action of 1-iodohexadecane and diethylamine. The preparation of dodecylamine and tetradecylamine by reduction of the respective nitriles was later described by Krafft,[410] and the reduction of enanthonitrile to heptylamine by sodium and ethanol was reported several years later.[417] The various steps in the conversion of palmitic acid to hexadecylamine have been published in detail by Teunissen.[418] Although the reduction of nitriles to amines by the use of sodium and alcohol offers a feasible method for their preparation, the large excess of sodium required to effect the reduction together with the fact that the reaction mixtures become extremely viscous has retarded the commercial adaptation of such procedures. A method developed by Harwood,[419] in which the sodium is initially dispersed in toluene, has been shown to reduce greatly the amount of sodium required and to offer a quite satisfactory procedure for both the laboratory and the commercial reduction of the long-chain nitriles. This method results in almost theoretical yields of the primary amines and is especially useful for the preparation of the unsaturated amines, such as octadecenyl-amine from oleonitrile. The preparation of dodecylamine from lauronitrile by this modified method proceeds as follows:

Twenty grams of sodium are suspended in 300 g. of toluene. The suspension is heated to boiling under a reflux and 36 g. of lauronitrile mixed with 65 g. of 1-butanol and 300 g. of toluene are slowly added. The reaction mixture is then heated for one-half hour at 60° with stirring, after which time it assumes a jelly-like consistency. After completion of the reaction, 300 g. of water are added in order to react with the excess sodium and to decompose the alcoholate. Two layers are formed and the aqueous layer is discarded. The other layer is then acidified and the 1-butanol and toluene removed by distillation. The amine is then obtained by making the mixture alkaline and distilling.

Octadecylamine is prepared from stearonitrile by substantially the same procedure.

Any alcohol may be employed; however, the use of butanol has been found to give satisfactory results. It has subsequently been found that the acidification step is not necessary and that the amine may be obtained directly by distillation of the reaction mixture after the addition of water and removal of the aqueous layer. The reduction of the dinitriles to diamines has been studied by Ladenburg,[420] and the preparation of 1,9-diaminononane by reduction of the corresponding dinitrile has been described in detail.[292]

The reduction of nitriles by acidic methods has been proposed for the preparation of the lower molecular weight amines, an example being the reduction of butyronitrile to butylamine by the use of zinc and sulfuric acid.[421] Such methods have, to the author's knowledge, not been employed for the synthesis of the higher molecular weight aliphatic amines.

The catalytic hydrogenation of nitriles to amines has been an interesting subject since the initial work of Sabatier upon catalytic hydrogenations. Such hydrogenations are generally conducted in the liquid phase in the presence of metallic nickel under moderate hydrogen pressures. The products consist of primary and secondary amines, the relative amounts of these products being quite dependent upon the conditions employed for the hydrogenation. Many of the procedures yield high percentages of secondary amines; in fact, Rupe and Glenz [422] have reported that although the reduction of capronitrile by means of sodium and ethanol yields hexylamine the product of the catalytic hydrogenation of capronitrile consists essentially of dihexylamine. The mechanism of the formation of secondary amines during the hydrogenation of nitriles has been studied by Adkins and associates.[391, 395] Secondary amines may result from the loss of a molecule of ammonia from two molecules of primary amine, thus:

$$2RNH_2 \rightarrow R_2NH + NH_3$$

This reaction may take place in either the presence or the absence of catalysts, and since prolonged heating partially converts primary amines to secondary amines, heat undoubtedly plays a part in secondary amine formation during catalytic hydrogenation. Secondary amines may result directly from catalytic hydrogenations by the reaction of one molecule of imine with one of primary amine, the former being postulated as an intermediate in the hydrogenation. The reactions involved are as follows:

(I) $$RCN + H_2 \rightarrow RCH{=}NH$$

(II) $$RCH{=}NH + RCH_2NH_2 \rightarrow \overset{H}{\underset{HNCH_2R}{R\overset{|}{C}NH_2}}$$

(III) $$\overset{H}{\underset{HNCH_2R}{R\overset{|}{C}NH_2}} + H_2 \rightarrow RCH_2NHCH_2R + NH_3$$

Another possible explanation [423] for the presence of secondary amines in the hydrogenation products involves the formation of a complex between one molecule of primary amine and one of nitrile, to form a compound which loses ammonia upon hydrogenation and is converted to a secondary amine as follows:

(I) $$RCN + RCH_2NH_2 \rightarrow \underset{H-N-CH_2R}{R-C{=}NH}$$

(II) $$\underset{H-N-CH_2R}{R-C{=}NH} + 2H_2 \rightarrow RCH_2NHCH_2R + NH_3$$

In all the above reactions it is observed that ammonia is one of the products of secondary amine formation, and it is logical to assume that if the hydrogenation is conducted in the presence of high partial pressures of ammonia, secondary amine formation will be minimized. It has been shown [395] that hydrogenation of butyronitrile and capronitrile in the presence of ammonia at 125°, with a Raney nickel catalyst, yields 90–95% of the respective primary amines with less than 5% of the secondary amines. The preparation of high molecular weight amines by the liquid-phase hydrogenation of nitriles under high partial pressures of ammonia or of non-aromatic amines has been described in several patents.[424, 425] The use of catalysts containing cobalt has been suggested,[426, 427] and it has also been proposed [428] to conduct such hydrogenations in the presence of oxide or sulfide catalysts, such as the oxides or sulfides of tungsten or molybdenum. It has been observed [429] that a substantial increase in the proportion of primary to secondary amines formed during the hydrogenation of nitriles will result if the hydrogenation is conducted in the presence of several per cent of water and a small amount of an alkaline-reacting substance such as sodium hydroxide. If the hydrogenation is conducted at temperatures between 200° and 250°, with a continuous or intermittent venting of the gaseous phase, secondary amine formation is greatly favored.[430] The type of catalyst employed materially influences the ratio of primary to secondary amines obtained during hydrogenation, catalysts such as nickel formate, acetate, or oxalate favoring secondary amine formation.[431] Details of the procedures employed for the preparation of primary amines by the catalytic hydrogenation of nitriles have been published by several investigators.[423, 432, 433, 434] The preparation of secondary amines by heating the respective primary amines for 5–6 hours at 200° in the presence of Raney nickel catalyst has been described,[435] as has also the synthesis of tertiary amines by heating the secondary amines with the appropriate haloalkane followed by liberation of the amines.[436]

The catalytic hydrogenation of dinitriles to diamines has been the subject of a number of patents. Howk [437] has described the preparation of several diamines, such as octamethylenediamine and decamethylenediamine, by the liquid-phase hydrogenation of the corresponding dinitriles with hydrogen and ammonia under high pressures in the presence of nickel catalysts. It was later stated [438] that cobalt catalysts are superior to nickel catalysts, since the former yield smaller amounts of imines and secondary amines. The vapor-phase hydrogenation of adiponitrile results in substantial yields of hexamethylenimine together with hexamethylenediamine and other products. [439] Vapor-phase hydrogenation of dinitriles with a mixture of hydrogen and ammonia has been patented,[440] as has also a process whereby the dinitriles are hydrogenated in the presence of low molecular weight primary amines.[441]

Primary and secondary amines result from the catalytic hydrogenation of amides. For example, Sabatier and Mailhe [442] obtained propylamine by hydrogenation of propionamide in the presence of nickel at 230° or of copper at 260–280°. The hydrogenation of lauramide and enanthamide under 250 atmospheres of hydrogen at 175–250° in the presence of a copper-chromium oxide catalyst yields 40–70% of primary amines and 25–50% of secondary amines.[117] It has also been reported that high yields of amines are obtained by the hydrogenation of ammonium laurate under similar conditions. The high-pressure hydrogenation of amides in the presence of oxide catalysts and solvents such as dioxane has been described.[443, 444] Lauramide, when subjected to high-pressure hydrogenation in the presence of nickel catalysts at temperatures between 200° and 280°, yields both dodecyl- and didodecylamines.[445] Since the hydrogenation of amides to amines has been discussed previously the reader is referred to this earlier description of such processes for further details.

The reduction of the low molecular weight nitroparaffins yields primary amines; however, such reactions have not been attempted for the synthesis of the higher molecular weight amines. Züblin [446] obtained butylamine by reduction of 1-nitrobutane with zinc and hydrochloric acid, and Worstall [447] has prepared hexylamine by reducing 1-nitrohexane with iron and acetic acid. Heptylamine, octylamine,[448] and nonylamine have been obtained by a similar procedure.

Although the above-described processes constitute the most important procedures proposed for the preparation of the high molecular weight amines, there are worthy of mention a number of methods which are quite satisfactory for the synthesis of certain types of amines. Mixed secondary amines containing both an aryl group and a long-chain alkyl group are prepared by the decarboxylation of 2-substituted fatty acids, an example being the decarboxylation of 2-anilino acids to form N-phenylalkylamines. The slow distillation of 2-anilinostearic acid yields N-phenylheptadecylamine,[449] and N-phenylpentadecylamine and N-phenyltridecylamine can be prepared similarly from 2-anilinopalmitic and 2-anilinomyristic acids, respectively. The decarboxylation of 2-anilinostearic acid is conveniently accomplished in the presence of an inert diluent such as paraffin, the resulting amine being recovered by diluting the reaction mixture with ether and extracting with dilute hydrochloric acid.[450, 451] Buck and Baltzly [452] have described a process whereby primary amines may be converted to secondary amines with a minimum of side reactions. In this procedure the primary amine is condensed with benzaldehyde to yield a Schiff's base which is then catalytically reduced to the corresponding N-benzylalkylamine. The addition of a haloalkane yields the hydrohalide of a N-benzyldialkylamine, the free amine from which is catalytically reduced to a secondary amine. The reactions are as follows:

$$C_6H_5CHO + H_2NR \rightarrow C_6H_5CH{=}NR \xrightarrow{H_2} C_6H_5CH_2NHR \xrightarrow{R'X}$$

$$C_6H_5CH_2NRR'HX \xrightarrow{NaOH} C_6H_5CH_2NRR' \xrightarrow{H_2} RR'NH + C_6H_5CH_3$$

Primary and secondary amines may easily be methylated to tertiary amines by treatment with formaldehyde and formic acid,[453] the reactions being represented as follows:

$$R_2NH + CH_2O + HCO_2H \rightarrow R_2NCH_3 + CO_2 + H_2O$$

Such reactions are quite applicable to high molecular weight amines, and the methylation of a number of high molecular weight primary and secondary amines by this procedure has recently been described.[454]

The action of ammonia at high pressure in the presence of dehydrating catalysts has been stated [455] to be effective in converting either secondary or tertiary amines to primary amines. It has been observed [456] that catalysts such as manganese oxide promote primary amine formation from the lower molecular weight secondary and tertiary amines. The utility of this process for the preparation of the high molecular weight primary amines is somewhat questionable.

Physical Constants of the Aliphatic Amines and Their Salts

The Primary Amines

The lower molecular weight, saturated aliphatic amines are liquids at ordinary temperatures, and their higher homologs are low-melting solids. Since the primary amines react readily with carbon dioxide, great care must be exercised in the determination of their physical constants and in the evaluation of their physical behavior. The primary amines react readily with acids to form salts, most of which are appreciably soluble in water. In solution, such salts function as cationic electrolytes, the long hydrocarbon chain being in the positive or cationic portion of the molecule, as distinguished from the soaps, alkyl sulfates and sulfonates, and the usual colloidal electrolytes. In the following discussion of the physical properties of amines and their salts, it is hoped to leave the reader not only with a general knowledge of their physical properties but also with an appreciation of the interesting surface active properties exhibited by solutions of cationic electrolytes. The studies which have been and will be made upon the behavior of solutions of cationic electrolytes can contribute many funda-

TABLE IX

FREEZING POINTS OF PRIMARY AMINES AND THEIR ACETATES

No. of C Atoms	Freezing Points, °C.	
	Amine	Acetate
10	16.11	....
12	28.32	68.5–69.5
13	.....	66.0–67.5
14	38.19	74.5–76.0
15	.....	75.0–76.5
16	46.77	80.0–81.5
17	.....	81.5–82.5
18	53.06	84.0–85.0
22	67 *	....

* Denotes melting point.

mental facts to our general knowledge of surface activity and solution phenomena.

The freezing points [434, 457] of the higher molecular weight amines and their acetates are shown in Table IX.

The boiling points of the n-alkyl primary amines at pressures varying from 1 mm. to 760 mm. have recently been reported [433] (Table X).

TABLE X

BOILING POINTS OF n-ALKYL PRIMARY AMINES

No. of C Atoms	°C. at Following Pressures in Millimeters										
	1	2	4	8	16	32	64	128	256	512	760
6	.....	.....	.....	.....	.....	47.7	62.5	79.1	98.1	119.4	132.7
7	.....	.....	.....	.....	53.8	67.3	81.8	99.8	119.7	143.4	156.9
8	.....	35.2	46.6	58.9	72.1	86.6	102.8	121.1	141.5	164.9	179.6
9	.....	51.5	62.9	75.6	89.4	104.8	122.2	141.2	162.8	187.3	202.2
10	56.3	66.9	78.4	91.2	105.6	121.4	138.8	158.3	180.2	204.9	220.5
11	69.0	80.3	91.9	105.1	120.0	136.7	155.3	175.7	198.4	224.9	241.6
12	81.4	93.5	106.3	120.5	135.2	152.3	171.2	191.8	214.9	242.1	259.1
13	97.0	108.0	120.8	134.9	150.6	167.8	186.7	207.4	230.9	258.2	275.7
14	109.2	120.9	133.6	147.8	163.4	181.4	201.1	222.9	246.6	274.2	291.2
15	120.5	132.3	145.5	160.1	176.3	194.6	214.5	236.9	261.7	289.7	307.6
16	131.8	143.9	157.6	172.7	189.4	207.9	228.2	250.7	275.8	304.6	322.5
17	143.2	155.0	168.6	183.9	200.6	219.3	239.7	262.3	288.1	317.6	335.9
18	153.2	166.1	180.0	195.5	212.3	232.0	.....	.....	.....	.....	348.8

The values contained in Table X are thought to be not more than 2° from the true boiling points and most of them to be considerably within this range. The higher amines undergo some decomposition when distilled at atmospheric pressure. Figure 11 shows the vapor-pressure curves of the normal primary amines.[433] The recorded boiling points of the n-alkyl primary amines show

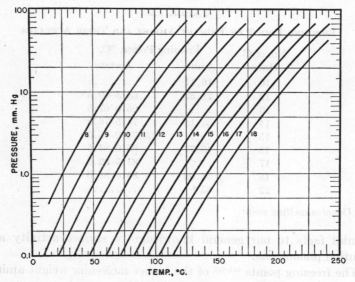

Fig. 11.   Vapor pressures of n-alkyl amines.

that they can easily be separated by means of an efficient fractionating column.

The acetates and hydrochlorides are the best known of the high molecular weight amine salts. Both the acetates and the hydrochlorides of the primary aliphatic amines are solids. The melting points which have been reported for the latter are, in many instances, so high that it is believed they represent decomposition points rather than true melting points. The fatty acid salts of octadecylamine, excluding the formate, decrease in melting point to octadecylammonium caproate, after which they show a substantial increase. The following melting points have been reported [9] for the fatty acid salts of octadecylamine: formate, 78.5–79.5°; acetate, 84.5–85°; propionate, 78.5–79°; butyrate, 71–71.5°; valerate, 60–61°; caproate, 55–56°; caprylate, 57.5–58°; caprate, 62–62.5°; laurate, 68–69°; myristate, 78–78.5°; palmitate, 85–85.5°; stearate,

89.5–90.9°. The corresponding salts of dodecylamine melt at lower temperatures; for example: acetate, 67–68°; propionate, 56–57°; myristate, 72.5–73°; palmitate, 72–73°; and stearate, 69–70°.

A degree of caution must be exercised in reporting the physical constants and behavior of aliphatic compounds, since, as previously pointed out, polymorphism and inapparent structural differences must be carefully considered in any discussion of such properties. Although the melting points reported in the literature for aliphatic compounds generally refer to stable forms of proved composition, recent work has shown that this is not always true. Studies on the amines and their salts have shown that polymorphism exerts a very dominant influence, and in many instances a series of salts may be formed between an amine and an acid. Recently, Davidson, Sisler, and Stoenner,[458] in an investigation of the acetic acid-ammonia system, showed the existence of five solid compounds. The system octadecylamine-acetic acid [459] exhibits two compounds, $C_{18}H_{37}NH_2 \cdot HC_2H_3O_2$ and $C_{18}H_{37}NH_2 \cdot 2HC_2$-$H_3O_2$, each of which exists in three polymorphic modifications. It thus appears that the ability of the amines to form salts decreases with increasing molecular weight of the amine. This is in agreement with the observation [460] that the degree of hydration of octadecylamine is less than that of dodecyl- or octylamine, since octadecylamine forms a mono- and a dihydrate whereas dodecylamine forms a tetrahydrate and octylamine a hexahydrate. The system octadecylamine-acetic acid [459] is shown in Fig. 12.

This figure shows the formation of two stable compounds ($C_{18}H_{37}NH_2 \cdot HC_2H_3O_2$ and $C_{18}H_{37}NH_2 \cdot 2HC_2H_3O_2$). The former melts at 84.4°, whereas the latter decomposes at 60.8° and forms a meritectic system at B with a submerged maximum at C. The compound $C_{18}H_{37}NH_2 \cdot 2HC_2H_3O_2$ and acetic acid form a eutectic at 14.2° which contains 96.6 mole per cent of acetic acid. Octadecylamine and the monoacetate form a monotectic system. The diacetate shows three modifications: a stable form and two metastable forms indicated by the curves DEF and GH. The monoacetate also shows a stable form and the two metastable forms indicated by the curves JK and LM. Transformations of the unstable form of the monoacetate to the stable form between 1 and 57 mole per cent of acetic acid are so rapid that equilibrium temperatures were not observed.

The free amines form a series of hydrates, the degree of hydration and the stability of the hydrates decreasing with increasing molecular weight of the amines. Bidet [461] first recognized the fact that the aliphatic amines form stable hydrates and succeeded in isolating several crystalline hydrates of hexyl- and isohexylamine. Phase diagrams for the systems octylamine-water, dodecylamine-water, and octadecylamine-water have been established,[460] it being observed that all the systems are qualitatively similar, the degree of hydration decreasing with increasing molecular weight. The lower amines and their hydrates are more soluble in water than the hydrates of the higher amines. Of the three systems, octylamine-water is the only one in which there is an isotropic region extending over the entire range of concentration. The hydrates of the higher amines pass through one or more mesomorphic states before their melting or decomposition temperatures are reached. The system dodecylamine-water shown in Fig. 13 illustrates the behavior of the higher amines in water, the comments of the authors upon this system being as follows:

. . . On this diagram A represents the freezing point of dodecylamine (28.0°). Area 1 is isotropic solution. Three hydrates are formed, one having a composition of $(C_{12}H_{25}NH_2)_3 \cdot 2H_2O$, another $C_{12}H_{25}NH_2 \cdot 2H_2O$ and the third $C_{12}H_{25}NH_2 \cdot 4H_2O$. The lowest hydrate exists as a crystalline solid below 24.4° (F), while above this temperature it breaks down to a mixture of higher hydrate and solution. The dihydrate exists as crystalline solid below 15.4° (H), while between this temperature and 35.5° it exists as a smectic type of liquid crystal. At 35.5° the mesomorphic hydrate begins to liquefy, while at 36.5° (C) this mixture of hydrate and solution changes to isotropic solution. The dodecylamine tetrahydrate exists as crystalline solid below 14.0° (R), while above this temperature it exists as a smectic type of liquid crystal, changing to a form of the nematic type at 34.2° (P) and to another form of the latter type at 38.0° (O). At 48.0° (M) the tetrahydrate decomposes.

The equilibrium between dodecylamine and its dihydrate is similar to that between octylamine and its hexahydrate. Dodecylamine precipitates out of the isotropic solution (area 1) along AB, while the dihydrate freezes out along BC, giving a eutectic at B. Thus areas 2 and 3 consist of two phase mixtures, solid amine and solution, and solid dihydrate and solution, respectively. Below EBF (area 4) the system consists of a heterogeneous mixture of crystals of dodecylamine and its dihydrate.

Area 5 of this diagram is similar to area 5 of the octylamine-water system. Again the solid solution consists of a microscopically homogeneous mesomorphic mixture of amine and amine hydrate. As

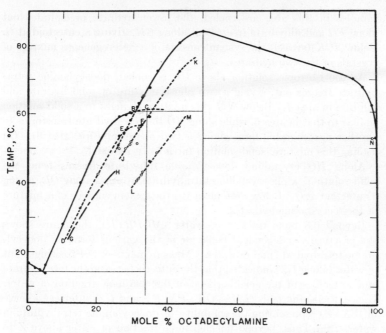

FIG. 12. The system: octadecylamine-acetic acid.

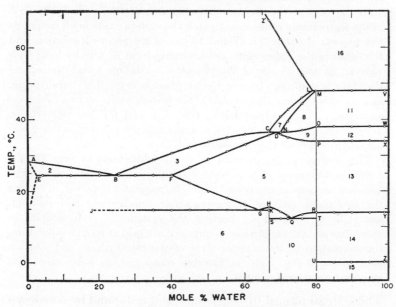

FIG. 13. The system: dodecylamine-water.

samples in this area are cooled, the lower hydrate precipitates out along FG and dihydrate freezes out along GH, giving a eutectoid at G. Below JGK (area 6) the system consists of a heterogeneous mixture of crystals of the two hydrates.

As the isotropic solution above CL is cooled, dodecylamine tetrahydrate freezes out, giving a two phase mixture of solid hydrate and solution in area 7. Below NM this mixture changes to a solid solution similar to that in area 5, while along NO the tetrahydrate transforms to another mesomorphic form giving a two phase mixture (area 9). On cooling this mixture, solid solution (area 5) is obtained.

Along HQ crystalline dodecylamine dihydrate freezes from the solid solution, while crystalline tetrahydrate appears along QR, giving a eutectoid at Q. Below SQT (area 10) the system consists of a mixture of these crystalline hydrates.

Beyond 0.8 mole fraction of water ($MOPRTU$), the figure shows the practically independent behavior of the various forms of dodecylamine tetrahydrate and of water. Measurements of the freezing point of water (along UZ) indicated that the eutectic between the tetrahydrate and water lies in the neighborhood of 0.99995 mole fraction of water. Hence, the isothermals (LMV, OW, PX, RY and UZ) intersect a curve ($VWXYZ$) representing the solubility of dodecylamine tetrahydrate in water. . . . Thus, beyond 0.99995 mole fraction of water above Z to 0.0°, the system exists as isotropic solution.

In the part of the diagram between $Z'LMOPRTU$ and $VWXYZ$ in the temperature range investigated the system exists in all regions as two phases. In areas 11, 12 and 13 one of the phases is solution, and the other is the appropriate mesomorphic form of tetrahydrate (*vide supra*). In area 14 one of the phases is crystalline tetrahydrate, and the other is solution. In area 15 one phase is crystalline tetrahydrate, and the other is ice. Above LMV the system exists as two conjugate solutions. . . . The lines LMV, OW, PX and RY are isothermals. Their depression with increasing concentration is well within the experimental accuracy of their measurement.

The portion of the diagram in the neighborhood of area 12 is a region of formation of a fibrous, curd-like solid of hydrated amine. This is a metastable compound which is frequently obtained on cooling the two phase mixture of mesomorphic tetrahydrate and solution, and is never obtained on heating the system. . . . If samples in which this metastable product is obtained are held at room temperature, transformation to the smectic form of the tetrahydrate and solution takes place slowly. The metastable compound, in some cases, has remained for several months.

The systems formed by octylamine and water and by octadecylamine and water are quite similar to that described above, with the exception that octylamine forms two hydrates, $(C_8H_{17}NH_2)_2 \cdot 3H_2O$ and $C_8H_{17}NH_2 \cdot 6H_2O$, and octadecylamine forms $(C_{18}H_{37}NH_2)_3 \cdot H_2O$ and $C_{18}H_{37}NH_2 \cdot 2H_2O$.

The solubilities of decylamine, dodecylamine, tetradecylamine, hexadecylamine, and octadecylamine in fourteen organic solvents have recently been determined.[434] The amines do not exhibit the

TABLE XI

SOLUBILITIES OF PRIMARY AMINES IN ACETONE

Grams per 100 g. Acetone

No. of C Atoms	−20.0°	0.0°	20.0°	30.0°	40.0°	50.0°
10	6.6	54	∞	∞	∞	∞
12	0.3	8.1	226	∞	∞	∞
14	...	0.1	15.5	228	∞	∞
16	...	....	0.1	4.7	445	∞
18	...	....	......	0.1	3.7	17.0

TABLE XII

SOLUBILITIES OF PRIMARY AMINES IN 95% ETHANOL

Grams per 100 g. 95% Ethanol

No. of C Atoms	−40.0°	−20.0°	0.0°	20.0°	30.0°	40.0°	50.0°
10	8.5	9.1	350	∞	∞	∞	∞
12	2.0	14.1	115	660	∞	∞	∞
14	...	1.5	30.2	218	660	∞	∞
16	...	...	3.0	83	239	770	∞
18	...	...	0.1	7.2	75	280	1630

marked correlation between solubility and polarity of solvent which is shown by other aliphatic compounds. They form eutectics with the non-polar solvents benzene, cyclohexane, and tetrachloromethane. The solubilities of the amines in benzene are shown in Fig. 14. The amines are more soluble in chloroform than in ethyl ether, ethyl acetate, or butyl acetate. Although they are appreciably soluble in alcohols (methanol, ethanol, 2-propanol, 1-butanol), they are less soluble in these solvents than in chloroform. They are more soluble in 2-butanone than in acetone, and the higher members possess limited solubilities in acetonitrile. The solubilities of the amines in acetone and in 95% ethanol are shown in Tables XI and XII.

The behavior of the salts of the high molecular weight amines in water typifies that of cationic electrolytes. In a study of their behavior, phase diagrams are of importance for defining generally the nature of the system over the entire concentration range. However, in view of the colloidal nature of such solutions, these diagrams tell us little concerning the actual physical state of the substances in solution. On the other hand, a study of the osmotic and electrical properties of these solutions has given us many data from which to formulate theories relative to actual structures. The systems dodecylammonium chloride-water and octadecylammonium chloride-water have been studied in some detail,[462] the salts functioning as typical colloidal electrolytes. The former system exhibits both a stable and a metastable form, whereas in the latter only one form is observed. The behavior of the acetates of dodecylamine and octadecylamine was subsequently studied,[463] and later Hoerr and Ralston [464] reported complete data for the system dodecylammonium acetate-water. This system is shown in Fig. 15, and the description of the system as given by these authors is as follows:

. . . A represents the freezing point of dodecylammonium acetate (69.3°) and K that of water. Area 1 is clear, isotropic solution. Two hydrates are found, a tetrahydrate (m.p. 129.0°) and an eicosahydrate (m.p. 86.0°).

The eutectic between dodecylammonium acetate and its tetrahydrate is represented by B. Areas 2 and 3 are two phase mixtures. Area 5 is a region of microscopically homogeneous material in a mesomorphic state. This region is analogous to the solid solutions of metallic systems and is physically identical with the corresponding phases of the amine-water systems. . . . Area 4 consists of a mixture of acetate crystals and the solid solution phase of concentration on curve EN. A eutectoid between the acetate and water is represented by N. Area 6 consists of a mixture of crystals of these components. F represents a eutectic between the tetrahydrate and the eicosahydrate. After passing through a narrow two phase region upon cooling, samples containing mixtures of these two hydrates become physically identical with other samples in area 5. J represents a eutectic between the eicosahydrate and water.

Dodecylammonium formate and propionate show a behavior in water quite similar to that exhibited by the acetate. The formate forms an eicosahydrate (m.p. 99.6°), and the propionate two hydrates, a tetrahydrate (m.p. 77.0°) and a triacontahydrate (m.p.

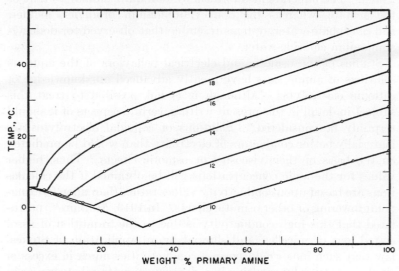

FIG. 14. Solubilities of amines in benzene.

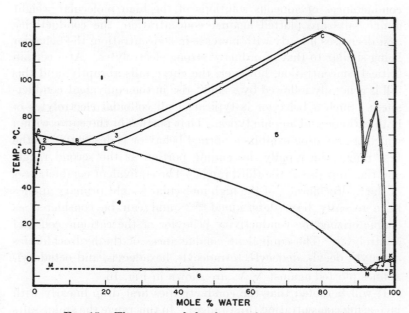

FIG. 15. The system: dodecylammonium acetate-water.

24.8°). The butyrate also forms a system quite similar to that of the acetate, whereas the dodecylammonium bromide-, iodide-, and phosphate-water systems resemble that observed for dodecylammonium chloride-water.

Studies of the osmotic and electrical behaviors of the aqueous solutions of amine salts have greatly advanced our knowledge of cationic electrolytes. Although it is not possible to treat this subject in detail in this present writing, certain aspects of it should certainly be considered.* Solutions of colloidal electrolytes are materially better conductors of electricity than would be predicted on the basis of their viscosity or osmotic effects. Thus, higher values for the ionic concentrations will be obtained if the calculations are based upon conductivity values rather than upon freezing-point lowering or other osmotic effects. In 1913, McBain [465] postulated that this high conductivity is due to the formation of associated ions or micelles, and showed by an application of Stokes' law that such ions would possess conductivities much in excess of single ions, thereby resulting in a disproportionation between ordinary osmotic effects and conductivity effects. When the equivalent conductances of aqueous solutions of the high molecular weight amine salts are plotted against concentration, the conductivity first decreases linearly with increase in concentration, the behavior being similar to that of ordinary strong electrolytes. At a certain critical concentration, however, the curve falls abruptly, and this fall is generally followed by a slight rise in the equivalent conductances. Such a behavior is typical of all colloidal electrolytes of both cationic and anionic types. That portion of the curve within which the solution exhibits a normal behavior is designated as the first range, the rapidly descending portion as the second range, and the later rise as the third range. The equivalent conductances of the hydrochlorides of the high molecular weight primary amines have recently been determined [466, 467] and can be considered as characterizing the conductivity behavior of the cationic colloidal electrolytes. The equivalent conductances of the hydrochlorides of octyl-, decyl-, dodecyl-, tetradecyl-, hexadecyl-, and octadecyl-amines plotted against $\sqrt{N_v}$ are shown in Fig. 16.

It will be noted that the conductivities first drop linearly with increasing concentration (first range). In this range the amine salts

* For a fuller discussion the reader is referred to Ralston, *Ann. N. Y. Acad. Sci.*, **46**, 351 (1946).

function as ordinary electrolytes, and the observed values are approximately those calculated from the Onsager equation. The conductivities then drop abruptly (second range), the critical point occurring at a lower concentration the higher the molecular weight

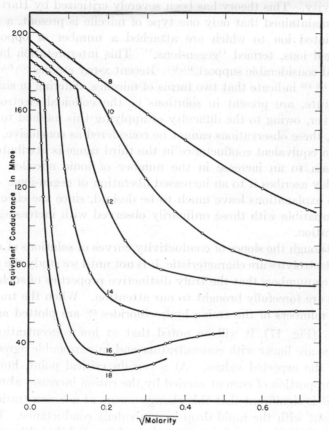

FIG. 16.   Equivalent conductances of primary amine hydrochlorides.

of the amine salt. The negative slopes of the curves also increase decidedly with increase in molecular weight. In the case of the above salts the critical points occur at the following concentrations (N_v): C_{10}, 0.04; C_{12}, 0.013; C_{14}, 0.004; C_{16}, 0.0008; and C_{18}, 0.0003. This decrease in equivalent conductance has been attributed by McBain and coworkers [468] and also by Lottermoser and Püschel,[469] to the formation of large micelles of low conductivity (lamellar micelles) which are spontaneously formed and which overshadow the effect of the highly conducting ionic micelles. Such a theory, therefore, postulates the presence of two types of micelles: the ionic micelle, which is a highly conducting, associated ion; and a lamellar micelle or neutral colloid, which possesses a feeble conductivity. This theory has been severely criticized by Hartley,[470] who maintained that only one type of micelle is present, a large, associated ion to which are attached a number of oppositely charged ions, termed "gegen-ions." This interpretation has received considerable support.[471, 472] Recent x-ray studies [473, 474, 475, 476, 477, 478, 479, 480] indicate that two forms of micelles, differing in size and structure, are present in solutions of the colloidal electrolytes; however, owing to the difficulty of applying this method to solutions, these observations cannot be considered as conclusive. The rise in equivalent conductance in the third range is attributed by McBain to an increase in the number of ionic micelles, while Hartley ascribes it to an increased liberation of gegen-ions. Both these explanations leave much to be desired, since the effects are incompatible with those ordinarily observed with increasing concentration.

Although the slopes of conductivity curves of solutions of colloidal electrolytes are characteristic, it is not until we study the transference numbers that the truly distinctive properties of such solutions are forcefully brought to our attention. When the transference numbers of the amine hydrochlorides [481] are plotted against $\sqrt{N_v}$ (Fig. 17), it will be noted that at low concentration the values are linear with concentration and in reasonable agreement with the expected values. At a certain critical point, however, the proportion of current carried by the cation increases abruptly, and it is significant that this change occurs at a concentration coincident with the rapid drop in equivalent conductance. In the third range the transference numbers drop slightly, although for the higher amine salts they still retain their abnormally high values. At infinite dilution the cationic transference numbers increase with increasing molecular weight; however, beyond the critical concentration the transference numbers for the amine hydrochlorides increase in the order C_8, C_{10}, C_{18}, C_{16}, C_{12}, C_{14}, thus indicating a maximum effect for the C_{14} salt. The rapid rise in transference numbers has been attributed to a spontaneous formation of both ionic and lamellar micelles, the presence of the latter accounting for the decreased conductivity and that of the former for the increased transference numbers. Others have maintained that the high transference numbers are due to the attachment of gegen-ions. That the formation of ionic micelles is not a spontaneous effect is shown by the fact that the transference numbers, even in very dilute solutions and well within the first range, are materially higher than the calculated values, thus indicating that the association in aqueous solution of ions possessing long hydrocarbon chains

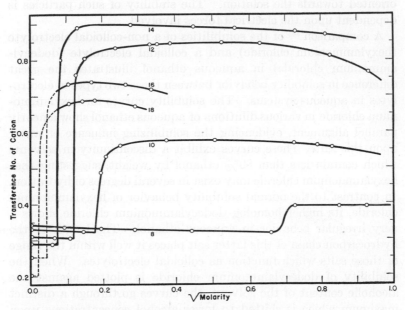

FIG. 17. Cationic transference numbers of primary amine hydrochlorides.

is a normal rather than an abnormal behavior. Increase in temperature increases the equivalent conductances, although it does not change the general nature of the curves or materially alter the position of the critical point.

Various significant changes in the physical behavior of solutions of colloidal electrolytes occur coincident with the critical point. The second range is characterized by greatly increased solubilities of the amine salts, the solubilities increasing enormously over very small temperature ranges. A similar phenomenon was found for the alkyl sulfonates by Tartar and Wright,[471] who also observed [472] a break in the density and viscosity curves at this point. A possible explanation for the changes which occur at the critical point is that they manifest a solubility effect by representing the point at which the true solubility of the electrolyte is exceeded. Owing to the electrical forces involved and to the widely different internal pressures between solvent and solute, the system does not separate into two distinct phases, but forms one visibly homogeneous phase. This consists of solution and associated molecules, the dispersed phase consisting of a number of particles whose polar groups are oriented towards the solution. The stability of such particles is dependent upon the electrical forces involved.

A comparison [482] of the solubilities of a non-colloidal electrolyte (hexylammonium chloride) and a colloidal electrolyte (dodecyl-ammonium chloride) in aqueous ethanol illustrates the great difference in solubility behavior between these two types of electrolytes in aqueous systems. The solubility curves for hexylammonium chloride in various dilutions of aqueous ethanol show a nearly parallel alignment, evidencing the solubilizing influence of water upon this salt. These curves exhibit a discontinuity in solvents which contain less than 80% ethanol by weight, suggesting that hexylammonium chloride may exist in several degrees of hydration. In contrast to the normal solubility behavior of hexylammonium chloride, its higher homolog dodecylammonium chloride shows a very irregular behavior in aqueous ethanol. The length of the hydrocarbon chain of this latter salt places it well within the range of those salts which function as colloidal electrolytes. When the solubility of dodecylammonium chloride is plotted against the alcoholic content of the solvent, the curves go through a distinct maximum which is shifted to lower alcohol concentrations upon elevation of the temperature. Thus, at 60° the solubility of this salt in a solvent containing approximately 40 weight per cent of ethanol is nearly twice that in either pure water or pure ethanol. The electrical behaviors of hexylammonium and dodecylammonium chlorides in aqueous ethanol are characteristically different.[483] The addition of ethanol to aqueous solutions of the hexylammonium chloride lowers the conductivities at all concentrations. With the dodecylammonium chloride such additions are attended by a rise in both the specific and the equivalent conductancy values in the concentrated solutions and by an irregular decrease in the less-concentrated solutions. The critical point for micelle formation is shifted towards higher concentrations by the addition of ethanol, and such additions are accompanied by a lowering of the cationic transference numbers. Such effects are attributable to the presence of associated particles in solutions of dodecylammonium chloride. High concentrations of ethanol inhibit micelle formation in solutions of dodecylammonium chloride, an effect which has also been noted with solutions of sodium dodecyl sulfate.[484]

In a study of the surface tensions [485] of films of alkylammonium chlorides over various subphases, it was noted that time effects of long duration occur below the critical concentration for micelle formation. Pressure-area isothermals for films of octadecylam-

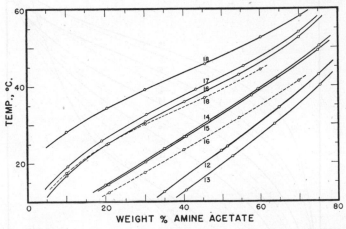

FIG. 18.   Solubilities of primary alkylammonium acetates in 95% ethanol.

monium chloride on a $0.01N$ hydrochloric acid subphase show that at large areas per molecule the films are vapor expanded, but that increased pressure produces condensed films. Pressure-area isothermals at 25.0° for octadecylamine spread on the following $0.01N$ acids have been determined: hydrochloric, hydrobromic, hydriodic, perchloric, nitric, sulfuric, chromic, and phosphoric. The films on the chromic acid subphase are completely condensed, those on nitric and sulfuric acids are expanded at low pressures, and those on the other acids are expanded at all pressures. Increase of temperature causes the films of octadecylammonium chloride to become more expanded. It was observed that films of octadecylammonium acetate are too soluble to permit their investigation by means of the film balance; however, docosylammonium acetate could be examined by this procedure.

The alkylammonium acetates are quite soluble in 95% ethanol and in benzene.[457] Figure 18 shows the solubility curves of the acetates from dodecylammonium acetate to octadecylammonium acetate inclusive, in 95% ethanol. It will be noted that the salts of the even-carbon-membered amines form one series and those of the uneven another. Since the intervals between the curves in the first series are less than those in the second, the curves are apparently in disorder. For example, heptadecylammonium acetate is less soluble than hexadecylammonium acetate, whereas pentadecyl-

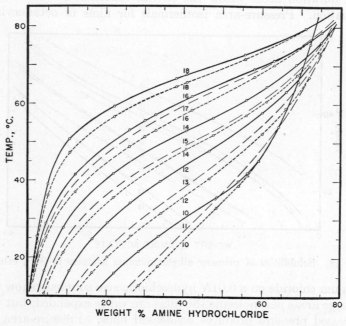

FIG. 19.   Solubilities of primary alkylammonium chlorides in 95% ethanol.

ammonium acetate is more soluble than tetradecylammonium acetate and tridecylammonium acetate is more soluble than dodecylammonium acetate. The acetates of both hexadecyl- and octadecylamine exhibit polymorphism, the solubilities of the more soluble metastable forms being indicated by the broken lines. The unstable form is obtained by rapid chilling and may be kept indefinitely at low concentrations. The alkylammonium acetates are less soluble in anhydrous benzene than in 95% ethanol, but the solubility curves are in the same order. No polymorphism is evidenced in benzene solution, both hexadecyl- and octadecylammonium acetates appearing in only one form. In a recent study [486] of the solubilities of the primary amine hydrochlorides in

95% ethanol, it has been observed that the salts containing an even number of carbon atoms exist in two modifications, whereas only one form is present for those with an uneven number of carbon atoms, thus indicating either that the latter are not polymorphic or that the transition of the unstable form is so rapid that it could not be recognized by the procedure employed. The solubilities in 95% ethanol of the amine hydrochlorides from decyl- to octadecyl-ammonium chloride inclusive are shown in Fig. 19. In this figure the solid lines refer to the solubilities of the stable forms and the broken lines to those of the metastable forms.

The solubilities of a number of salts of dodecylamine, such as the iodide, bromide, phosphate, formate, propionate, butyrate, and acid sulfate, in 95% ethanol and in benzene have been reported.[464] From the work which has already been done on the primary amines and their salts, it is evident that their physical properties present a complex but interesting study in which polymorphism, surface activity, and colloidal phenomena are important factors.

THE SECONDARY AMINES

The secondary amines fall naturally into two groups, the symmetrical secondary amines, in which the hydrocarbon groups are similar, and the unsymmetrical secondary amines. Examples of the former are dioctylamine, didodecylamine, and dioctadecylamine, and of the latter, N-methyldodecylamine, N-ethyloctadecylamine, and N-phenyloctadecylamine. The secondary amines possess higher melting and boiling points than the primary amines containing the same alkyl group, and only the lower members can be distilled without decomposition. They react readily with carbon dioxide to form carbamates, and the same caution must be employed in the determination of their physical constants as with the primary amines. Many of the reported melting points for the lower molecular weight secondary amines are apparently too high.[77, 372] The freezing and melting points of the symmetrical secondary amines from dihexyl- to dioctadecylamine inclusive are shown in Table XIII.[487]

It will be noted that the secondary amines below ditetradecyl-amine exist in two polymorphic forms, the unstable form being realized upon freezing.

The lower-melting form is designated as the α-modification and the higher-melting form as the β-modification. A plot of these freezing and melting points shows that the values fall upon two curves which intersect at ditetradecylamine. The melting and freezing points of the higher members fall upon a continuation of the curve formed by the melting points of the β- or high-melting form of the lower homologs. It is significant that the melting points of the polymorphic forms of the alcohols intersect at 1-

TABLE XIII

FREEZING AND MELTING POINTS OF SYMMETRICAL SECONDARY AMINES

Amines	F.P., °C.	M.P., °C.	
Dihexyl	−13.06	−13.06	α
		1.2	β
Diheptyl	2.7	2.7	α
		15.5	β
Dioctyl	14.62	14.62	α
		26.7	β
Dinonyl	25.0	25.0	α
		34.5	β
Didecyl	32.60	32.60	α
		41.5	β
Diundecyl	40.5	40.5	α
		47.0	β
Didodecyl	46.95	46.95	α
		51.8	β
Ditridecyl	53.5	53.5	α
		56.5	β
Ditetradecyl	60.62	60.62	
Dipentadecyl	63.3	63.3	
Dihexadecyl	67.03	67.03	
Diheptadecyl	69.6	69.6	
Dioctadecyl	72.3	72.3	

tetradecanol, which contains half as many carbon atoms as ditetradecylamine. This indicates that the R groups in the secondary amines may lie parallel and that such compounds do not possess a linear structure. The behavior of didodecylamine is typical of that of the lower secondary amines. Upon cooling, this compound begins to freeze at 46.95° in the form of small, transparent crystals which, if heated rapidly, will melt at this temperature. If the temperature is kept constant at the freezing point for several minutes, however, this amine transforms to a dense, opaque, crystalline mass which melts at 51.8°. This transformation in the case of dihexylamine, dioctylamine, and didecylamine apparently requires the presence of a small amount of impurity, since very pure samples of these compounds melt and freeze at the lower temperatures. This presents an outstanding exception to the generalization that the presence of an impurity stabilizes a metastable, lower-melting form.

The presence of the nitrogen atom in the middle of the chain does not impart any unusual solubility characteristics to the secondary amines. They are, in general, somewhat more soluble in organic solvents than are the primary amines of corresponding chain length.[435] This is attributed to the fact that the polar groups in the middle of the chain cause the melting points to be considerably lower than those of the primary amines of the same carbon content. In similarity to other polar aliphatic compounds, the secondary amines form eutectics with the non-polar solvents benzene, cyclohexane, and tetrachloromethane. Among these solvents they are most soluble in benzene and least soluble in tetrachloromethane. The compositions and temperatures of the eutectics formed by the α- and β-forms of dioctylamine in these solvents are as follows: (α- values, β- values) benzene, 41.6% amine at $-1.5°$, 36.7% at $-0.4°$; cyclohexane, 17.5% at $-7.6°$, 12.7% at $-2.8°$; tetrachloromethane, 1.6% at $-23.9°$, 0.7% at $-23.4°$. Eutectics for the higher amines are located at much lower concentrations. The symmetrical secondary amines are very soluble in chloroform and somewhat less soluble in ethyl ether, ethyl acetate, and butyl acetate. They are more soluble in 2-butanone than in acetone, and become progressively more soluble in the alcohols with increase in molecular weight of the solvent. Such amines show a marked correlation between solubility and polarity of solvent, being difficultly soluble in the highly polar solvents. The solubilities of the secondary amines in 95% ethanol and in acetone are shown in Tables XIV and XV.[435]

TABLE XIV

SOLUBILITIES OF SECONDARY AMINES IN 95% ETHANOL

Grams per 100 g. 95% Ethanol

No. of C Atoms	$-10.0°$	$10.0°$	$30.0°$	$40.0°$	$50.0°$	$60.0°$
16	4.6	63	∞	∞	∞	∞
24	...	0.2	19.5	185	3350	∞
26	...	....	4.5	43.1	655	∞
28	...	....	0.4	7.8	233	almost ∞
30	...	....	....	1.8	66	1640
36	...	....	....	.....	≈ 0.1	4.9

TABLE XV

SOLUBILITIES OF SECONDARY AMINES IN ACETONE

Grams per 100 g. Acetone

No. of C Atoms	0.0°	20.0°	30.0°	40.0°	50.0°	56.1°
16	1.9	625	∞	∞	∞	∞
24	...	...	1.8	18.7	3900	∞
26	...	...	<0.1	5.2	505	almost ∞
28	...	...	.....	1.1	22.5	900
30	...	...	.....	<0.1	6.4	310
36	...	...	.....	.....	0.1	2.0

Figure 20 shows the solubility curves for several of the secondary amines in 1-butanol.

The secondary amines are stronger bases than the primary amines; however, salt formation is more difficult with the former owing to their reduced solubilities in water. Few constants have

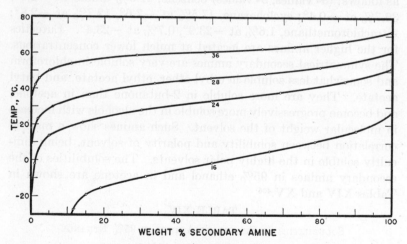

FIG. 20.   Solubilities of secondary amines in 1-butanol.

been reported for the salts of the secondary amines since the higher members are generally purified and characterized as the free amines. A comparison of the equivalent conductances at infinite dilution and of the ionization constants of many of the primary and secondary amines has recently been made [488] and the reported values are shown in Table XVI.

TABLE XVI

IONIZATION CONSTANTS OF THE ALIPHATIC AMINES IN WATER AT 25°

Amine	Λ_0	Concn. Range Investigated, moles/liter	$K_B \times 10^{-4}$
Butyl	235	0.0004–0.073	4.1
Isobutyl	235	.0008– .057	2.7
Amyl	232	.0008– .049	4.3
Isoamyl	232	.0008– .040	4.0
Hexyl	229	.0008– .046	4.4
Dihexyl	214	.0008– .030	10.2
Heptyl	226	.0008– .022	4.6
Octyl	223	.0008– .016	4.5
Dioctyl	208	.0008– .014	10.2
Nonyl	220	.0008– .015	4.4
Decyl	217	.0008– .012	4.4
Undecyl	214	.0008– .011	4.3
Dodecyl	211	.0008– .011	4.3
Didodecyl	197	.0008– .011	9.9
Tridecyl	208	.0008– .011	4.3
Ditridecyl	193	.0008– .008	9.9
Tetradecyl	205	.0008– .008	4.2
Pentadecyl	202	.0008– .008	4.1
Dipentadecyl	187	.0008– .008	10.0
Hexadecyl	199	.0008– .008	4.1
Heptadecyl	196	.0008– .008	4.0
Octadecyl	193	.0008– .008	4.0
Dioctadecyl	180	.0008– .008	9.9
Docosyl	180	.0008– .008	4.0

The reports of physico-chemical data for the unsymmetrical secondary amines have largely been confined to a recording of the melting and boiling points for such amines and some of their salts. Westphal and Jerchel [369] have reported the boiling points of several N-methylalkylamines, the observed values being as follows: methylhexyl-, b_{755} 80–110°; methyloctyl-, b_3 60–65°; methyldodecyl-, $b_{1.5}$ 108–110°; and methylhexadecylamine, b_1 147–150° (HCl salt, m.p. 169–170°). Several N-arylalkylamines have been prepared by Le Sueur,[449] who reported the following physical constants: phenyltridecyl-, m.p. 23–24° (HCl salt, m.p. 94.5–95.5°); phenylpentadecyl-, m.p. 34–35° (HCl salt, m.p. 97.5°); and phenylheptadecylamine, m.p. 42–43° (HCl salt, m.p. 99–100°).

The cyclic imines prepared by Ruzicka and associates [256,489,490] are low-melting solids which form stable salts with acids. Some of the constants reported for these cyclic imines are as follows: hexamethylenimine, b_{720} 130–134° (HCl salt, m.p. 230–232°); octamethylenimine, b_{17} 69°, d_4^{20} 0.8905; tridecamethylenimine, $b_{0.05}$ 65°, m.p. 38–39°; tetradecamethylenimine, $b_{0.05}$ 97–98°, m.p. 47–48°; hexadecamethylenimine, m.p. 58–59°, d_4^{72} 0.8470; and heptadecamethylenimine, m.p. 64–66°, d_4^{72} 0.8435.

THE TERTIARY AMINES

Like the secondary amines, the tertiary amines can be divided into the two groups, symmetrical and unsymmetrical. The symmetrical tertiary amines possess lower freezing points than the symmetrical secondary amines containing the same alkyl group; for example, dioctadecylamine freezes at 72.3° whereas trioctadecylamine freezes at 54.0°. Trioctylamine freezes at −34.0° and tridodecylamine at 15.7°. The solubilities of the symmetrical tertiary amines decrease abruptly with increasing polarity of the solvent.[436] Their solubilities appear to be comparable to those of the secondary amines containing an equivalent number of carbon atoms. Thus, the curves for trioctylamine in the moderately polar solvents are very similar to those for didodecylamine. They possess limited solubility in methanol, 95% ethanol, and 2-propanol, the solubilities decreasing with increasing molecular weight of the amine. The tertiary amines are extremely soluble in the non-polar solvents benzene, cyclohexane, and tetrachloromethane and form eutectics with these solvents. The percentage of amine in the eutectic mixture decreases enormously with increase in molecular weight of the amine. For example, the eutectic between trioctylamine and benzene contains 91.0% amine, the eutectic temperature being 38.5°, whereas that with tridodecylamine contains 42.5% amine at 0.3° and that with trioctadecylamine contains 0.2% amine at 5.5°. The solubilities of the symmetrical tertiary amines in organic solvents may be illustrated by those of tridodecylamine (Table XVII).[436]

The N-methyldialkylamines possess materially lower melting points than the corresponding symmetrical dialkylamines. The following constants have been reported for the N-methyldialkylamines: [369] methyldihexylamine, b_{12} 118°; methyldidodecylamine, $b_{1.5}$ 201°, m.p. 15–16°; and methyldihexadecylamine, b_1 269–271°. The N,N-dimethylalkylamines are either liquids or low-melting solids, some of the constants of which are as follows: [369, 491, 492] dimethylpentyl, b_{755} 122–130°; dimethylhexyl, b_{766} 146–147° (pic-

TABLE XVII
SOLUBILITIES OF TRIDODECYLAMINE *

Grams Amine per 100 g. Solvent

Solvent	−20.0°	−10.0°	0.0°	10.0°	20.0°	30.0°	40.0°
Benzene	...	.....	.....	570	∞	∞	∞
Cyclohexane	...	.....	.....	570	∞	∞	∞
Tetrachloromethane	6.3	16.5	43.2	188	∞	∞	∞
Trichloromethane	7.6	26.8	106	490	∞	∞	∞
Ethyl ether	4.2	13.5	54	315	∞	∞	∞
Ethyl acetate	...	0.2	1.0	≈850	∞	∞	∞
Butyl acetate	1.5	3.9	11.4	900	∞	∞	∞
Acetone	...	.....	.....	0.1	1.4	2.2	3.4
2-Butanone	...	.....	0.5	9.8	∞	∞	∞
Methanol	...	.....	.....	<0.1	0.3	0.5	1.2
95% Ethanol	...	.....	.....	.....	0.2	0.7	1.5
2-Propanol	...	.....	<0.1	2.7	15.3	23.9	58
1-Butanol	...	<0.1	1.5	25.5	∞	∞	∞

* ∞ with all solvents above 17.9° except as otherwise noted.

rate, m.p. 100°); dimethylheptyl, b_{760} 170° (picrate, m.p. 75°); dimethyloctyl, b_{760} 191° (picrate, m.p. 72°); dimethylhexadecyl, b_1 138°; and dimethyldocosyl, $b_{0.6}$ 190°, m.p. 44°. Several N,N-diethylalkylamines have been reported,[367,493] examples being diethylhexadecylamine, $b_{0.4}$ 161°; diethyltridecylamine, b_{12} 169°; and diethyldodecylamine, b_2 122–124°. N,N-dibenzyldodecylamine boils at 219–220° at 2 mm. and its hydrochloride melts at 101°. Buck and Baltzly [452] have reported constants for several N-benzyldialkylamines as follows: (alkyl groups, b.p.) methylbutyl, b_{16} 113°; methylpentyl, b_{15} 126°; methyldodecyl (HCl salt, m.p. 133–134°); ethylbutyl, b_{13} 115–116°; ethylpentyl, b_8 117–121°; and butylpentyl, b_9 145–146°.

MISCELLANEOUS AMINES

The aliphatic α,ω-diamines are much more soluble in ethanol and water than the monoamines. They readily form salts with acids, two series of which are possible. The dihydrochlorides melt with decomposition at relatively high temperatures. The following freezing points have been reported [292,494,495,496,497,498] for the α,ω-diamines: 1,4-diaminobutane, 23–24°; 1,6-diaminohexane, 34.2°; 1,7-diaminoheptane, 28–29°; 1,8-diaminoöctane, 50–52°; 1,9-diaminononane, 37–37.5°; 1,10-diaminodecane, 61.5°; 1,11-diamino-undecane, 58°; 1,12-diaminododecane, 66–67°. Several ω-hydroxy amines have been described.[256] These compounds possess relatively high melting points; for example, 16-hydroxyhexadecylamine melts at 90–91°, and 13-hydroxytridecylamine melts at 84°.

Chemical Properties of the High Molecular Weight Aliphatic Amines

In general, the high molecular weight aliphatic amines exhibit the reactions of the lower members of the series. Since, however, different reaction conditions are frequently indicated for the higher molecular weight compounds, it often appears that qualitative distinctions can be shown between the reactions of the higher amines and those of their lower homologs. The most characteristic reaction of the amines is salt formation, and the physical properties of a number of these salts have previously been discussed. Many of these amine salts can easily be dehydrated to the corresponding amides as has been shown earlier in this chapter. Acylating agents yield substituted amides.

The primary and secondary amines react readily with carbon dioxide to form alkyl carbamates. With carbon disulfide in cold alcohol or ether solution, the amines form alkylammonium N-alkyldithiocarbamates,[499] which on heating lose hydrogen sulfide to form dialkylthioureas as follows:

$$2RNH_2 + CS_2 \rightarrow SC\diagup{\overset{\displaystyle SH\cdot H_2NR}{\diagdown NHR}}$$

$$SC\diagup{\overset{\displaystyle SH\cdot H_2NR}{\diagdown NHR}} \rightarrow (RNH)_2CS + H_2S$$

If the reaction with primary amines is conducted at high dilutions in the presence of heavy metal salts, alkyl isothiocyanates result in satisfactory yields, the decomposition of the intermediate alkylammonium N-alkyldithiocarbamate proceeding thus:

$$SC\diagup{\overset{\displaystyle SH\cdot H_2NR}{\diagdown NHR}} \rightarrow RNCS + H_2S + RNH_2$$

Dioleylthiourea melts at 67–69°, whereas the isothiocyanate is a liquid, $b_{0.4}$ 200–210°. The reaction of the aliphatic amines with sulfur dioxide is apparently somewhat complex. Michaelis[500] has shown that an equimolar addition product of aniline and sulfur dioxide results from the action of phenyl isocyanate, aniline, and water. Later it was observed [501] that the aliphatic amines react directly with sulfur dioxide to form compounds having a 1:1 ratio of amine to sulfur dioxide. These are white, crystalline compounds which lose sulfur dioxide when exposed to the atmosphere. In 1935, Hill and Fitzgerald [502] determined the vapor pressures of the system pentylamine-sulfur dioxide, the results indicating the formation of a white, metastable compound with an amine:sulfur dioxide ratio of 1:½, and of a stable, yellow compound with a 1:1 ratio. The heats of formation of the stable compounds for pentyl- and heptylamine were 3500 and 6400 cal., respectively, which are much lower than those calculated for the aromatic amine-sulfur dioxide complexes.

The primary and secondary aliphatic amines yield complex mixtures when treated with strong oxidizing agents. The oxidation of primary amines, such as heptylamine, by means of persulfuric or permanganic acid, has been stated [503] to yield hydroxamic acids, the reaction having been proposed for the qualitative detection of amines. Although ammonia forms a peroxide, $(NH_4)_2O_2$, when treated with an ether solution of hydrogen peroxide at low temperatures,[504] the action of oxidizing agents on the high molecular weight primary and secondary aliphatic amines has received little attention. It has been claimed that the oxidation of secondary amines with alcoholic solutions of hydrogen peroxide yields hydroxylamines, the oxidation of N-methyldodecylamine being cited as an example.[505] The tertiary amines form stable oxides, $R_1R_2R_3NO$, when treated with oxidizing agents, the preparation and properties of many of these amine oxides having been rather extensively described in the patent literature. The oxidation of N,N-dimethyldodecylamine, N,N-dimethylhexadecylamine, N-hexadecylpiperidine, and 4-dimethylamino-1-laurophenone with oxidizing agents such as Caro's acid, hydrogen peroxide, or ozone yields the corresponding amine oxides, many of which are water soluble.[506] Details have been given for the preparation of amine oxides from N,N-dimethyldodecylamine,[507] N-methyl-N-dodecylcyclohexylamine,[508] N-ethyl-N-dodecylcyclohexylamine,[509] and N-ethyl-N-octadecenylcyclohexylamine.[510] The amine oxides have been suggested as wetting agents for the treatment of textiles, and it has also been stated [511] that they function as detergents. Wetting agents have also been prepared by treating the lower molecular weight amine oxides with high molecular weight alkylating agents.[512] Such products are less basic than the original amines but are still capable of salt formation. The oxidation products of alkylated ethylenediamines have been described.[513] Wetting agents are obtained when compounds such as 2-(dimethylamino)-stearic acid are subjected to the action of oxidizing agents.[514] The kinetics of the oxidation of tertiary amines has been studied.[515]

The reaction of amines with nitrous acid has long been a standard procedure for distinguishing between primary, secondary, and tertiary amines. When primary amines are treated with this reagent they yield alcohols, together with other products, nitrogen being evolved. The secondary amines, on the other hand, yield nitrosoamines, and the tertiary amines are unreactive. The reactions of primary and secondary amines with nitrous acid proceed as follows:

(I) $RNH_2 + HNO_2 \rightarrow ROH + N_2 + H_2O$

(II) $RR'NH + HNO_2 \rightarrow RR'NNO + H_2O$

Although the lower molecular weight primary amines react according to equation (I), the action with the higher primary amines is more complicated, since isomeric alcohols and olefins are formed along with the primary alcohols. Thus, propylamine yields 1- and 2-propanol together with propene when treated with nitrous acid.[516, 517, 518] Tertiary butyl alcohol and isobutylene are formed by the action of isobutylamine with nitrous acid.[519] Among the products formed from butylamine and nitrous acid are 1- and 2-butanol, 2-methyl-1-propanol, butenes, and dibutylnitrosoamine.[421, 520, 521] In 1932, Whitmore and Langlois [522] made an extensive investigation of the action of nitrous acid on butylamine, the reaction being conducted in aqueous solution in the presence of the calculated amount of hydrochloric acid. The following products were identified in the reaction mixture: 1-butanol, 25.0%; 2-butanol, 13.2%; 1-chlorobutane, 5.2%; 2-chlorobutane, 2.8%; and butenes, 36.5%. Since the reaction was conducted under conditions in which dehydration or esterification of the alcohol was improbable, and since it did not appear that the olefins are intermediates, it was postulated that the decomposition of the amine nitrite results in the intermediate formation of butyl and hydroxy radicals, the subsequent and probably almost instantaneous reaction of which yields the observed products. The synthesis of the higher molecular weight alcohols by the reaction of nitrous acid on the amines has been described,[523] the following procedure having been employed for the preparation of 1-dodecanol:

Dodecylamine (48 g.) is dissolved in about 300 grams of 95% ethanol, 60 grams of concentrated hydrochloric acid is added and the solution cooled to 0°. Sodium nitrite (50 g.) dissolved in 100 cc. of water is then added, the mixture allowed to stand for one hour and then refluxed for an additional hour. Excess water (600–650 g.) is then added, precipitating the 1-dodecanol, which is then washed free of acid and fractionated.

The hydrogenation of nitriles to amines and their conversion to alcohols may be accomplished without isolation of the amines. Substantial quantities of olefins and chloroalkanes are generally present in the reaction products of the higher amines and nitrous acid in the presence of hydrochloric acid.

The degradation of amines may be accomplished by heating their salts at temperatures above their decomposition points, in the presence or absence of catalysts. The tertiary amines may be progressively converted to secondary amines and then to primary amines by such procedures. Trimethylammonium chloride yields dimethylammonium chloride, trimethylamine, and 1-chlorobutane when heated to 295°, and higher temperatures finally result in the formation of some methylamine.[524] The salts of the higher molecular weight amines, however, yield mainly monoölefins when heated above their decomposition points. Grün[525] has described the preparation of olefins by pyrolysis of the secondary N-aryl-alkylamines in the presence of zinc chloride; N-undecylaniline, for example, yields undecene. Salts of the primary amines also yield monoölefins when heated to temperatures of 300° to 400°. Mc-Corkle[526] has disclosed the continuous preparation of olefins from primary amines by dropping the amine upon heated phosphoric acid in a closed vessel, the olefin being continuously removed while the phosphoric acid is regenerated through decomposition of the resulting ammonium metaphosphate.

The reaction of the high molecular weight amines with alkylene oxides leads to a variety of products the compositions and properties of which are dependent upon the particular amine involved, the mole proportions of the reactants, and the conditions used to effect the condensations. The general type of reaction encountered can best be illustrated by the well-known condensation of ammonia with ethylene oxide, first investigated by Wurtz[527] in 1859. Aminoethanols are produced thus:

$$CH_2\!\!-\!\!\!-\!\!CH_2 + NH_3 \rightarrow CH_2OH$$
$$\diagdown O \diagup \qquad\qquad CH_2NH_2$$

2-Hydroxyethylamine

$$CH_2 \overline{\quad\quad} CH_2 + CH_2OH \rightarrow HOCH_2CH_2$$
$$\diagdown O \diagup \quad\quad CH_2NH_2 \quad\quad\quad NH$$
$$HOCH_2CH_2$$

Di(2-hydroxyethyl)amine

$$CH_2 \overline{\quad\quad} CH_2 + HOCH_2CH_2 \quad\quad HOCH_2CH_2$$
$$\diagdown O \diagup \quad\quad\quad\quad NH \rightarrow HOCH_2CH_2 \overline{\quad} N$$
$$HOCH_2CH_2 \quad\quad\quad HOCH_2CH_2$$

Tri(2-hydroxyethyl)amine

The condensation of ethylene oxide with the low molecular weight primary, secondary, and tertiary amines has been the subject of a number of investigations.[528, 529, 530, 531, 532] In 1932, Horne and Shriner [533] made an extensive study of the condensation of ethylene oxide with diethylamine, the results of which are of exceptional interest since they comprise not only an isolation of the primary reaction products but also a study of the secondary condensation products. The equations given by these authors exemplify the type of chain reaction typical of ethylene oxide, and since cyclic polymerization was prevented by the presence of the tertiary amino group an isolation of the products was possible. The reaction of diethylamine with an excess of ethylene oxide proceeds as follows:

$$(C_2H_5)_2NH + CH_2 \overline{\quad} CH_2 \rightarrow (C_2H_5)_2NCH_2CH_2OH \xrightarrow{\quad CH_2 \overline{\quad} CH_2 \quad}$$
$$\diagdown O \diagup \quad\quad\quad\quad\quad\quad\quad\quad\quad\quad \diagdown O \diagup$$

$$(C_2H_5)_2NCH_2CH_2OCH_2CH_2OH \xrightarrow{\quad CH_2 \overline{\quad} CH_2 \quad}$$
$$\diagdown O \diagup$$

$$(C_2H_5)_2NCH_2CH_2OCH_2CH_2OCH_2CH_2OH \xrightarrow{\left(\begin{array}{c} CH_2 \overline{\quad} CH_2 \\ \diagdown O \diagup \end{array} \right)_n}$$

$$(C_2H_5)_2NCH_2CH_2(OCH_2CH_2)_xOH$$

It was subsequently shown [534] that the number of $-OCH_2CH_2-$ groups contained in such products may be quite large, fifty or more, the ethylene oxide being capable of adding to each newly formed hydroxyl group. Reactions similar to the above are obtained with the higher molecular weight amines, the initial product being the hydroxy amino compound, which is capable of further condensation with ethylene oxide at both the amino and the hydroxyl groups. The preparation of water-dispersible products by the condensation of ethylene oxide with high molecular weight aliphatic compounds containing an active hydrogen has been described,[535] and it has been stated [173] that products of a similar nature are obtained when high molecular weight amines are condensed with the polyglycols obtained from ethylene oxide or its homologs. The action of ethylene oxide on the high molecular weight tertiary amines yields quaternary ammonium bases.[536] Compounds of the general formula $R_1R_2R_3NOH(C_nH_{2n}O)_xH$ have been obtained [537] by the condensation of ethylene oxide with the oxides of tertiary amines. The preparation of wetting agents by treatment of ethylene oxide or its homologs with tertiary amines in which one of the R groups is a long-chain hydrocarbon radical and another is a polyhydroxyalkyl group has been described.[538] Water-dispersible products are obtained by treating primary amines successively with propylene and ethylene oxides, or with epichlorohydrin and ethylene oxide.[539] In the earlier work upon alkylene oxide-amine condensations, it was shown that the presence of a small amount of water is necessary to catalyze the reaction. Recently, Schwoegler [540] has observed that, if the reaction is conducted at an elevated temperature (100–150°) and the ethylene oxide is added slowly, a smooth condensation results in the absence of water.

As previously stated, the product obtained by the condensation of an amine with an alkylene oxide depends, to a large extent, upon the mole proportions of the reactants employed. With the higher amines those products which contain a low molecular ratio of alkylene oxide to amine are generally waxlike solids, whereas those with higher proportions of alkylene oxide possess lower melting points and a greater water solubility. Although a considerable amount of work has been reported upon reactions involving the higher amines and the alkylene oxides, it is evident that the actual composition of the intermediate and end products is, in many instances, quite uncertain. The assumption that such reactions proceed similarly to those observed for the lower amines appears reasonable, although more work is required concerning the structures and properties of the intermediate and final products before conclusive statements are justified. Compounds which possess many of the properties of amine-alkylene oxide condensates have been obtained by reaction of the amines with glycidol.[541] The preparation of water-dispersible compounds with the glycides has also been described.[542]

The action of sulfonating agents on the high molecular weight secondary and tertiary amines yields products which function as wetting agents,[543] and an imposing number of surface active chemicals have been synthesized by such reactions. Among the most important of these products are the sulfuric esters of the secondary or tertiary amines which contain one or more long alkyl chains together with one or more hydroxyalkyl groups. Thus, the treatment of N-hydroxyethyldioctylamine with sulfuric acid yields the sulfuric ester, the sodium salt of which is water soluble.[544] Compounds with similar properties may be obtained by treating the sodium salts of the sulfuric esters of low molecular weight hydroxyalkylamines, such as $NH_2CH_2CH_2OSO_3Na$, with high molecular weight acylating agents such as stearoyl chloride,[545] or by the action of acylating agents on lower molecular weight hydroxyalkylamines followed by sulfonation of the resulting products.[546] The partial esterification of amines such as tri(2-hydroxyethyl)amine with high molecular weight acids or acid chlorides has been accomplished,[547] and the treatment with sulfuric acid or sulfonating agents of the secondary amines which contain hydroxyalkyl radicals has been described in detail.[548] Water-soluble derivatives result from the sulfonation of tertiary amines or quaternary ammonium compounds which contain a benzyl radical.[549] Calcott and Clarkson [550] have studied the condensation of high molecular weight amines with halohydrins. Compounds which possess marked water solubilities can be prepared [551] by condensing primary amines with glycerol monochlorohydrin; for example, the reaction of two moles of this reagent with one mole of dodecylamine yields N,N-di(2,3-dihydroxypropyl)dodecylamine, $(CH_2OHCHOHCH_2)_2NC_{12}H_{25}$. The tetrasulfuric ester of this amine and its sodium salt are extremely water soluble and possess detergent properties. Water-soluble products of interest as wetting agents have been obtained by the sulfonation of unsaturated secondary amines such as N-methyloctadecenylamine or N-benzyloctadecenylamine.[552]

The primary amines are reactive with ethyl malonate, it having been reported [553] that pentyl-, octyl-, and dodecylamine react at essentially the same rates with this reagent.

The salts of the high molecular weight amines form double salts with many of the heavy metals. Most of these double salts are of well-defined composition and several have been employed for the isolation and identification of the higher amines. For example, the double salts of the alkylammonium chlorides and platinic chloride were employed by Hofmann [554] and also by Krafft and Moye [416] for the characterization of a number of the high molecular weight amines. A yellow, crystalline double salt of dodecyl-ammonium chloride and cupric chloride, $CuCl_2 \cdot 2(C_{12}H_{25} \cdot HCl)$, has recently been described.[555] Goebel and Walker [556] have investigated the alkylammonium metallo nitrites, and have prepared double salts such as decylammonium cobalti hexanitrite, $(C_{10}H_{21}NH_3)_3Co(NO_2)_6$, tetradecylammonium nickel hexanitrite, and octadecylammonium cadmium tetranitrite, and have suggested their use as corrosion inhibitors.

The high molecular weight amines form coordination complexes with the salts of the heavy metals, many of these compounds being quite stable and possessing well-defined melting points. Such compounds are undoubtedly similar in structure to the well-known ammino derivatives of the metallic salts, the amines being held by auxiliary valences and forming a complex ion with the metal. The number of amine molecules contained in the complex apparently decreases rapidly with increase in molecular weight of the amine. Copper chloride and ammonia form a series of complexes, up to and including one with a coordination number of six, hexammino-cupric chloride, $[Cu(NH_3)_6]Cl_2$. Probably the best known of these ammino-cupric chloride complexes is tetrammino-cupric chloride, $[Cu(NH_3)_4]Cl_2$. Straumanis and Cirulis [557] found that a higher ratio of amine to metal can be obtained with methylamine than with its higher homologs ethyl-, propyl-, and butylamine, although the stability of the complexes increases with increasing boiling point of the amine. A 1:4 complex of beryllium chloride and butylamine rapidly decomposes to a 1:2 complex when washed with ether.[558] The complexes of the higher amines which have so far been prepared show a coordination number of two. Most of these complexes are insoluble in cold water and are decomposed in boiling water; many of them are quite soluble in organic solvents. The following ammino-metallic complexes have been prepared from the higher molecular weight amines: [555] bisdodecyl-ammino-cupric chloride, $Cu[C_{12}H_{25}NH_2]_2Cl_2$, blue crystals, m.p. 128°; bisdodecylammino-cupric acetate, $Cu[C_{12}H_{25}NH_2]_2(OAc)_2$, purple clusters, m.p. 86°; bisdodecylammino-silver nitrate, $Ag[C_{12}H_{25}NH_2]_2NO_3$, white flakes, m.p. 75° (decomp.); bisdodecyl-ammino-zinc chloride, $Zn[C_{12}H_{25}NH_2]_2Cl_2$, white flakes, m.p. 135–136°; bisdodecylammino-zinc bromide, $Zn[C_{12}H_{25}NH_2]_2Br_2$, white crystals, m.p. 137–140°; bisdodecylammino-cadmium chloride, $Cd[C_{12}H_{25}NH_2]_2Cl_2$, white crystals, m.p. 141–142°; bisdodecyl-ammino-mercuric chloride, $Hg[C_{12}H_{25}NH_2]_2Cl_2$, white crystals, m.p. 155–156° (decomp.); bisoctadecylammino-cupric chloride, $Cu[C_{18}H_{37}NH_2]_2Cl_2$, blue crystals, m.p. 126°; bisoctadecylammino-cupric acetate, $Cu[C_{18}H_{37}NH_2]_2(OAc)_2$, purple clusters, m.p. 95.5–96°; bisdioctylammino-cupric chloride, $Cu[(C_8H_{17})_2NH]_2Cl_2$, blue crystals, m.p. 126–127°. Attempts to prepare complexes between the high molecular weight tertiary amines and metallic salts have, so far, not been successful. A spectrophotometric study [559] of the system dodecylamine-cupric acetate has shown that this compound is highly dissociated in solution. This investigation failed to establish the presence of alkylammino-cupric complexes with an amine-metal ratio higher than two to one.

Uses of the High Molecular Weight Amines and Their Derivatives

The surface active properties of the amine salts and many of the derivatives which have been synthesized from the high molecular weight amines indicate their usefulness as wetting, emulsifying, and dispersing agents. Many of the recent uses which have been proposed for the higher amine salts are worthy of mention. The amine salts are effective flotation agents for the froth-flotation separation of minerals.[560] In such processes the amine salts generally differ from the anionic type of flotation agent in that they preferentially float silica or other oxides. In the froth-flotation separation of calcium phosphate from silica by the use of amine salts, it is, therefore, the silica or gangue mineral which floats, thus reversing the usual flotation process.[561, 562] The amine salts can be used to bring about a flotation separation of potassium chloride from sodium chloride, the former appearing in the concentrate and the latter in the tailings.[563] Oxide and sulfide minerals can be floated from gangue minerals by the use of salts of high molecular weight, unsaturated primary amines.[564] Mixtures of high molecular weight amine salts and nitriles are extremely effective flotation agents for the separation of a number of mineral mixtures.[565] In many instances a pretreatment of the ore with a strongly alkaline solution decreases the amount of amine reagent required and increases its specificity.[566] A theoretical study of the function of high molecular weight amine salts as flotation agents has been made by Wark.[567]

Aqueous solutions of the higher amine salts possess high bactericidal properties, such effects appearing to bear a marked correlation to their surface active properties. Those salts which function as normal electrolytes over an appreciable range of concentration possess feeble bactericidal properties, whereas those which exhibit micelle formation at low concentrations are highly bactericidal. Although the structure of an amine salt bears a distinct relationship to its specificity against certain organisms, it can be stated that, in general, all the water-soluble salts of the higher amines possess a high degree of effectiveness against bacteria. The quaternary ammonium compounds are of particular interest as bactericides, and considerable work has been done in correlating their structure with this property. These quaternary ammonium compounds are discussed later in this chapter. One of the earlier references to the bactericidal properties of the amine salts and the quaternary ammonium compounds is the French Patent 782,930, issued to I. G. Farbenind. A.-G.,[568] in which it was disclosed that salts such as dodecylammonium chloride, N-ethyldodecylammonium chloride, and many quaternary ammonium compounds which contain at least one long-chain hydrocarbon group are highly bactericidal. The fungicidal properties of the amine derivatives, particularly those which contain a sulfur atom, have also been disclosed.[569] The bactericidal and fungicidal properties of the amines and their derivatives have been the subject of a rather extensive patent literature.

The amine salts are strongly adsorbed upon siliceous surfaces, and this property has been made the basis of several interesting industrial applications. When a siliceous aggregate is coated with a cation-active compound, the affinity of the aggregate for asphalt or similar materials is greatly increased, so that the aggregate will not "work out" of such mixtures.[570] A similar effect may be obtained by dissolving the amine or its salt in the asphalt. Siliceous building materials may be made more resistant to the passage of water by treatment with aqueous solutions of cation-active compounds.[571] The plasticity of lime, plaster of Paris, and allied materials is improved by the addition of small amounts of cation-active compounds.[572]

The high molecular weight primary and secondary amines are lethal to insects, the effect being at a maximum with octyl- and decylamine in the primary series and with dihexyl- and dioctylamine in the secondary series.[573] The higher primary and secondary amines are essentially devoid of this property, as are also those amine salts which have so far been investigated.

Other uses which have been suggested for the amines or their derivatives are as follows: the waterproofing of cellulose, cotton, rayon, and similar textiles;[574] the rendering of textile products uncrushable;[575] the treatment of textiles in conjunction with formaldehyde or formaldehyde-producing substances;[576] the dyeing of textiles;[577, 578] the compounding of varnishes and enamels;[579, 580] the preservation of latex;[581] the production of foaming agents[582] and emulsifying agents;[583, 584, 585] the clarification of water;[586] the improvement of the plasticity of clay;[587] and the sterilization of liquids.[588]

From the above it is apparent that many uses have been suggested for the cation-active compounds, and, in view of their unusual physical behavior, it is safe to predict that continued study will greatly enlarge this list.

THE QUATERNARY AMMONIUM COMPOUNDS

Although the quaternary ammonium compounds have been known for some time, they have been so extensively studied during the past few years that one is almost justified in the belief that they constitute a new class of nitrogen-containing derivatives. The quaternary ammonium salts can be defined as tetra-substituted ammonium salts, $RR'R''R'''NX$, and the quaternary ammonium bases as tetra-substituted ammonium hydroxides. It was initially considered that the R groups of the quaternary ammonium compounds must consist of carbon-containing radicals; however, an expansion of the literature upon this subject has forced a modification of this concept, as will presently be shown. The quaternary nitrogen may be joined to one or more nitrogen, oxygen, or other atoms, and the quaternary ammonium compounds frequently possess extremely complex structures. The quaternary ammonium compounds are often referred to as "invert soaps"; however, this term does not differentiate them from phosphonium, sulfonium, and similar types of compounds, and is not illuminative as regards their structure. All the quaternary ammonium compounds have one property in common: the quaternary nitrogen is pentavalent and appears in the positive portion of the molecule. They are, therefore, typical cationic electrolytes, and their physical behavior parallels that previously described for such substances.

Those quaternary ammonium compounds which contain one or more high molecular weight alkyl groups constitute a very important class of nitrogen-containing fatty acid derivatives. Obviously, the number of such compounds theoretically possible is extremely large, and many representatives of this type of derivative have been prepared and described. All such compounds bear a structural similarity, although they vary widely in complexity. All the R groups may be straight-chain hydrocarbon radicals of equal or unequal length; one or more of the R groups may be aromatic radicals; the quaternary nitrogen atom may be part of a heterocyclic ring; one or more of the R groups may contain attached polar groups or be interrupted by a nitrogen, sulfur, or other atom; or the R groups may be other than carbon-containing radicals. The quaternary ammonium compounds which fall within the category of fatty derivatives must contain at least one long alkyl or alkenyl chain which constitutes an integral part of the molecule. Although it is not possible to discuss in detail here all the high molecular weight quaternary ammonium compounds which have been described, we will consider a sufficient number of representatives of the various types to illustrate their modes of synthesis and general characteristics.

The most general procedure for the preparation of the simple quaternary ammonium compounds consists of the reaction of a tertiary amine with an alkyl ester, an example being the preparation of triethylhexadecylammonium iodide by the reaction of N,N-diethylhexadecylamine with ethyl iodide.[416] In such procedures it is evident that the long-chain hydrocarbon group may be incorporated into the quaternary ammonium compound by two methods. The long-chain group may be initially attached to the nitrogen atom of the tertiary amine, as in the above example, or a low molecular weight amine may be treated with a high molecular weight haloalkane. An alternate synthesis of the above compound would, therefore, be the treatment of triethylamine with 1-iodohexadecane.[589] The choice of procedure depends largely upon the compound in question and upon the relative ease of preparation and availability of the starting materials. Triethylhexadecylammonium iodide, mentioned above, is quite representative of quaternary ammonium salts of this type. It melts at 179–181° and is soluble in both warm water and ethanol but insoluble in ether. When treated with moist silver oxide it yields triethylhexadecylammonium hydroxide.

Recent interest in the bactericidal properties of the quaternary ammonium salts and related substances has resulted in the preparation and study of a large number of such compounds. Among these are the methyldialkylbenzylammonium salts,[590] which are obtained by the reaction of N-methyldialkylamines with halomethylbenzenes, the following having been described: methyldibutylbenzylammonium chloride, prepared by heating MeBu$_2$N and C$_6$H$_5$CH$_2$Cl for 15 minutes at 110°, m.p. 181°; methyldihexylbenzylammonium chloride, m.p. 58°; methyldioctylbenzylammonium chloride, m.p. 96°; and methyldihexadecylbenzylammonium chloride, m.p. 99°. Methylethyldidodecylammonium iodide melts at 149°, and the corresponding nitrate has been described as a colorless oil melting at 14°. The methosulfates are obtained by the action of dimethyl sulfate on the tertiary amines. Dimethyldihexylammonium methosulfate forms hygroscopic needles, m.p. 35°, and dimethyldihexadecylammonium methosulfate melts at 129–130°. The bactericidal activity of the methyldialkylbenzylammonium compounds towards most of the organisms investigated was found to be at a maximum with the dioctyl derivative. Westphal and Jerchel [369] have observed that the higher 1-chloroparaffins do not yield quaternary ammonium compounds when heated with low molecular weight amines. The formation of quaternary ammonium compounds by reaction of the higher 1-chloroparaffins and amines can, however, be brought about within narrow temperature ranges. For example, dimethyloctylbenzylammonium chloride is obtained by heating N,N-dimethylbenzylamine with 1-chloroöctane in ethanol for 24 hours at 105°, and dimethyldodecylbenzylammonium chloride is similarly obtained in 90% yield by heating N,N-dimethylbenzylamine with 1-chlorododecane for 45 hours at 90°. Higher temperatures greatly reduce the yield, and at 175° no quaternary ammonium salt is obtained. High yields of trimethyloctylammonium chloride, m.p. 70°, dimethylhexadecylbenzylammonium chloride, m.p. 58°, and trimethyldodecylammonium chloride are obtained at reaction temperatures around 100°, in the presence of ethanol. Such reactions do not yield quaternary ammonium compounds in the absence of solvents, or in water, benzene, or acetone. Tertiary amines such as triethyl- or tributylamine react slowly with the higher chloroparaffins, and the yields of quaternary ammonium compounds from such reactions are small. The bactericidal properties of the quaternary ammonium compounds were pointed out by Domagk [591] and have been described in several patents.[592] The high activity of quaternary ammonium halides which contain two lower molecular weight alkyl groups, a long-chain alkyl group, and a benzyl radical attached to the quaternary nitrogen has been disclosed.[593] Such compounds are designated as "Zephirols." Shelton [594] has recently described the synthesis of a number of quaternary ammonium compounds which contain a hexadecyl radical attached to the quaternary nitrogen. Examples of these are trimethylhexadecylammonium bromide, iodide, or chloride; triethylhexadecylammonium nitrate; and methylhexadecylpyridinium bromide.

The synthesis of isomeric trimethyldodecoxyphenylammonium methosulfates has been described,[595] the *ortho*, *meta*, and *para* compounds melting at 102–104°, 82–83°, and 118–120°, respectively. The preparation of the *o*-isomer is accomplished as follows:

The potassium salt of *o*-nitrophenol is heated with 1-chlorododecane in the presence of zinc chloride. The resulting ether is then reduced by hydrogen in the presence of platinum to *o*-aminophenyl dodecyl ether, which is treated with two moles of dimethyl sulfate to give *o*-(N,N-dimethylamino)phenyl dodecyl ether. This is then converted to the methosulfate by heating with dimethyl sulfate for two hours at 120°.

Quaternary ammonium salts which contain a methallyl group, $CH_2=C(CH_3)CH_2—$, together with a high molecular weight alkyl or alkenyl group containing from eight to twenty carbon atoms, are obtained by treatment of tertiary amines with methallyl chloride.[596] Examples of these are dimethyldodecylmethallylammonium chloride and 9-octadecenyldimethylmethallylammonium chloride. Quaternary ammonium compounds containing a stearoyl group have been described, an example being the product obtained by the action of diethyl sulfate or other low molecular weight dialkyl sulfate or haloalkane on amines such as N-(*p*-dimethylaminobenzyl)octadecanamide.[597] The preparation of quaternary urea derivatives has been disclosed, the compounds being obtained by the action of dimethyl sulfate on N-(*p*-dimethylaminophenyl)-N-heptadecylurea, and a series of patents [598] has been issued disclosing the preparation of quaternary ammonium compounds from N-stearoylurea.

The reaction of chlorobenzene with N-alkyl substituted anilines, such as N-dodecylaniline, followed by alkylation of the product with dimethyl sulfate, has been employed [599] to prepare high molecular weight quaternary ammonium salts which contain a phenyl group. The methylation or ethylation of N-octadecylaniline with dimethyl or diethyl sulfate yields phenyldialkyloctadecylammonium metho- or ethosulfates, which have been described as water-soluble, waxlike compounds.[600] Quaternary ammonium salts which contain a chlorophenyl group have been prepared,[601] an example being dimethylchlorobenzyloctylammonium bromide, obtained by the reaction of the tertiary amine with 1-bromoöctane. The alkylation of the reaction products of N,N-dialkylanilines and high molecular weight methylol amides yields quaternary ammonium salts.[602] Somewhat similar compounds have also been described by Wolf.[603] Niederl and Weingarten [604] have studied the preparation of quaternary ammonium salts containing a naphthyl radical, an example being dimethylheptadecyl-β-naphthylammonium iodide, m.p. 106°. Diamines which contain a tertiary amino group and an acylamino group, such as N,N-diethyl-N'-octadecenoylethylenediamine, are reactive with alkylating agents to form quaternary ammonium compounds.[605] Piggott and Woolvin [606] have described the preparation of quaternary ammonium compounds by the action of 1-haloalkanes and allied compounds on the higher alkyl esters of p-dimethylaminobenzoic acid.

In addition to the numerous examples which have been reported of the preparation of quaternary ammonium salts by the action of alkyl or aryl halides on the tertiary amines, it has also been shown that other compounds which contain reactive halogens can be condensed with the tertiary amines to produce quaternary ammonium derivatives. Thus, the α-halo ethers are reactive with tertiary amines to form quaternary ammonium salts,[607] and the esters of α-halo acids react in a similar manner.[608, 609] The latter may be illustrated by the reaction of N,N-dimethyloctadecylamine with butyl 2-bromolaurate, or by the reaction between N,N-dimethyldodecylamine and ethyl chloroacetate.

The treatment of N-(1-phenyldodecyl)dimethylaminoacetamide with benzyl chloride yields a water-soluble quaternary ammonium salt.[610] Bock and Houk [611] have recently described high molecular weight quaternary ammonium salts which contain an aldehydo group, and Bock [612] has disclosed the preparation of quaternary ammonium salts by the reaction of tertiary aminomethyl amides with halomethyl esters of primary or secondary alcohols. An example of the latter product is N-stearamidomethyl-N-ethoxymethyl-N-dimethylammonium chloride.

High molecular weight quaternary ammonium compounds in which the quaternary nitrogen constitutes a portion of a heterocyclic ring are prepared by procedures similar to those previously described. They may also be obtained by reactions involving simultaneous cyclization and alkylation. Hexadecylpyridinium bromide can be prepared by heating 1-bromohexadecane with pyridine at moderate temperatures. Fawcett and Gibson [613] have studied the effect of pressure upon the rate of formation of hexadecylpyridinium bromide at 40°, 50°, and 60°, and of hexadecylpyridinium chloride at 100°. It was found that the reaction rate is accelerated by pressures up to 3000 kg./cm.^{2}, after which it is essentially constant. Even at the higher pressures the reaction is not complete after 200 hours.

A series of quaternary ammonium compounds has been prepared by Macovski [614] by the action of 1-iodohexadecane on cyclic tertiary amines, the following having been described: hexadecylpyridinium iodide, m.p. 101°; hexadecylquinolinium iodide, m.p. 99°; and hexadecylisoquinolinium iodide, m.p. 75°. These salts were reported to be relatively insoluble in water. They are converted by boiling with alcoholic silver chloride into their corresponding, more soluble chlorides, which melt at 110°, 114°, and 95°, respectively. Quaternary nicotinium salts have been obtained by the action of 1-haloalkanes such as 1-bromododecane or -octadecane on nicotinic acid, and it has been stated that such products function as insecticides.[615] The N-methyl-3-, -6-, and -8-dodecoxyquinolinium methosulfates have been synthesized by Kuhn and Westphal [616] and their bactericidal properties determined. Ethersubstituted quinolinium compounds which contain a benzyl group are obtained by the action of benzyl chloride on the substituted quinolines. Thus 6-hexoxyquinoline is heated with benzyl chloride to prepare 6-hexoxybenzylquinolinium chloride, m.p. 160°. 6-Dodecoxybenzylquinolinium chloride, m.p. 182–183°; 7-dodecoxybenzylquinolinium chloride, m.p. 188–189°; 6-dodecoxybenzylhydroxyquinolinium chloride, m.p. 167–168°; and 6-hexylthiobenzylquinolinium chloride are similarly prepared. The quaternary piperidinium salts are obtained by heating N-alkylpiperidines with alkyl or aryl halides, and the preparation of the following has been described:[617] N-benzyl-N-decylpiperidinium chloride, N-benzyl-N-dodecylpiperidinium chloride, N-crotyl-N-octadecylpiperidinium bromide, N-methyl-N-dodecylpiperidinium bromide, and N-geranyl-N-dodecylpiperidinium chloride.

A series of dipiperidinium salts has recently been synthesized by Niederl and Lanzilotti [618] by the action of bromoalkanes on methylenedipiperidine and benzaldipiperidine. The N,N'-dialkylmethylenedipiperidinium dibromides prepared by this procedure are as follows: diheptyl, m.p. 178°; dioctyl, m.p. 162°; ditetradecyl, m.p. 183°; and dihexadecyl, m.p. 176°. The following melting points were reported for the N,N'-dialkylbenzaldipiperidinium dibromides: diheptyl, 177°; dioctyl, 165°; ditetradecyl, 181°; and dihexadecyl, 179°. The dipiperidines were obtained by condensing formaldehyde or benzaldehyde with two moles of piperidine. Quaternary ammonium compounds which contain the nitrogen as part of a heterocyclic ring are obtained by treating pyridine, N-alkylpyridines, or quinoline with the sulfuric esters of high molecular weight alcohols,[619, 620] the products in the case of pyridine having the general formula

$$\langle \!\!\! \bigcirc \!\!\! N \!\!\! \begin{array}{c} R \\ SO_4H \end{array}$$

Esters of α-halo acids, such as dodecyl chloroacetate, react with cyclic tertiary amines such as pyridine to form quaternary ammonium derivatives,[621] and the α-bromo acids, such as α-bromostearic acid, also react with the cyclic tertiary amines to form quaternary ammonium compounds.[622] The preparation of a number of quaternary ammonium compounds by the reaction of α-halo acids with pyridine has been described.[623]

Cyclization is frequently employed as a means of synthesizing the quaternary ammonium salts. For example, N-(4-bromobutyl)-diethylamine is easily converted to the pyrrolidinium derivative as follows:[624]

$$BrCH_2CH_2CH_2CH_2N(C_2H_5)_2 \rightarrow \begin{array}{c} CH_2\!\!-\!\!CH_2 \\ | \qquad \qquad N(C_2H_5)_2 \\ CH_2\!\!-\!\!CH_2 \quad Br \end{array}$$

Littmann and Marvel [625] have prepared bromo tertiary amines of the general formula $Br(CH_2)_nN(CH_3)_2$, where n has a value of 4, 5, 6, or 7, and have reported that they undergo ring closure to yield cyclic quaternary ammonium salts. Thus, N,N-dimethylpyrrolidinium bromide results from the cyclization of N-(4-bromobutyl)dimethylamine, N,N-dimethylpiperidinium bromide is obtained from N-(5-bromopentyl)dimethylamine (yield 63%), and N,N-dimethylhexamethyleniminium bromide from N-(6-bromo-hexyl)dimethylamine. These cyclic quaternary nitrogen compounds are solids which melt at relatively high temperatures. In a subsequent investigation [626] of the quaternary ammonium salts obtained from N-(ω-bromoheptyl)dimethylamine and its octyl, nonyl, and docyl homologs, it was shown that the main reaction of those bromo amines containing from seven to ten carbon atoms inclusive in the long chain is one of linear polymerization, which results in the formation of long-chain quaternary ammonium salts of the following structure:

$$\left[Br\!-\!(CH_2)_n\!-\!\underset{\underset{CH_3}{|}}{\overset{\overset{CH_3}{|}}{N}}\!-\! \left[(CH_2)_n\!-\!\underset{\underset{CH_3}{|}}{\overset{\overset{CH_3}{|}}{N}} \right]_x \!-\!(CH_2)_n\!-\!\underset{\underset{CH_3}{|}}{\overset{\overset{CH_3}{|}}{N}} \right] Br_{x+1}$$

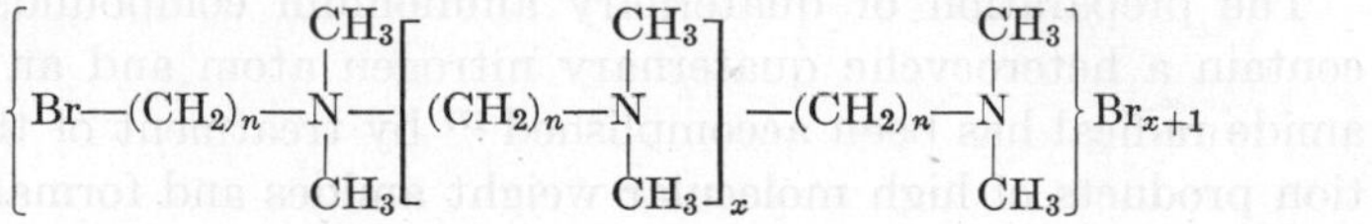

Such substances are described as hygroscopic materials which vary from resinous gums through glasslike products to amorphous solids. The observed molecular weights range from 3350 to 28,000.

Quaternary ammonium salts which contain a mixed heterocyclic ring have been prepared. For example, Hart and Niederl [627] have described several quaternary ammonium derivatives of the long-chain ethers of thiazoline phenols. Other examples of mixed heterocyclic quaternary ammonium salts are the N-ethyl- and N-ethylol-N-alkylmorpholinium salts,

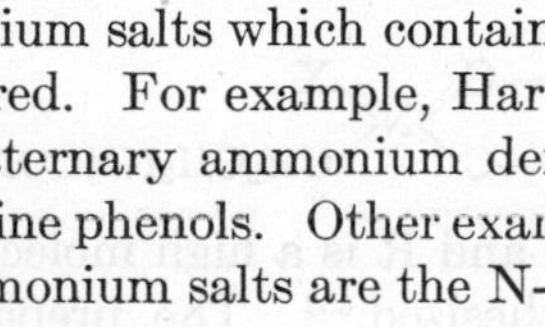

$$\left[O \underset{CH_2CH_2}{\overset{CH_2CH_2}{\diagdown\diagup}} N \underset{R}{\overset{R}{\diagup\diagdown}} \right] X$$

which are obtained by the action of N-ethyl- or N-ethylolmorpholine on bromoalkanes.[628] The following morpholinium bromides have been synthesized by this procedure: N-ethyl-N-dodecyl, m.p. 201°; N-ethyl-N-tetradecyl, m.p. 203°; N-ethyl-N-hexadecyl, m.p. 207°; N-ethylol-N-dodecyl, m.p. 92°; N-ethylol-N-tetradecyl, m.p. 95°; and N-ethylol-N-hexadecyl, m.p. 97°. The symmetrical dimorpholinium salts have recently been synthesized [629] by the action of bromoalkanes with methylenedimorpholine or benzaldimorpholine. The N,N'-dialkyl-4,4'-methylenedimorpholinium dibromides have the following structure:

$$\left[O \underset{CH_2CH_2}{\overset{CH_2CH_2}{\diagdown\diagup}} \underset{R}{\overset{}{N}}\!-\!CH_2\!-\!\underset{R}{\overset{}{N}} \underset{CH_2CH_2}{\overset{CH_2CH_2}{\diagup\diagdown}} O \right] Br_2$$

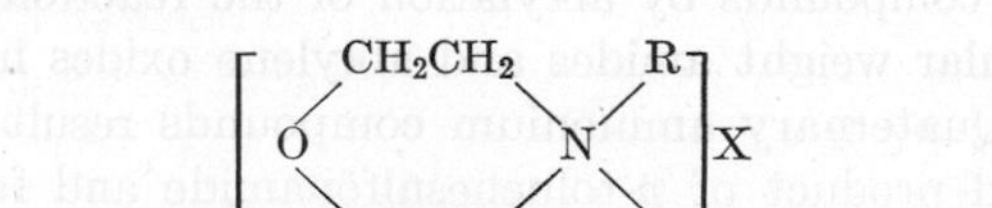

The dibutyl, diheptyl, dioctyl, ditetradecyl, and dihexadecyl derivatives melt at relatively high temperatures (141–180°) with decomposition. The corresponding benzal derivatives have the following melting points: N,N'-dibutyl, 174°; -diheptyl, 153°; -dioctyl, 156°; -ditetradecyl, 175°; and -dihexadecyl, 178°. Dimorpholinium salts have been obtained by treating dimorpholinylethane, prepared by the condensation of *sym*-di(chloroethyl) ether and methylenediamine, successively with a high molecular weight ester and dimethyl sulfate.[630]

The preparation of quaternary ammonium compounds which contain a heterocyclic quaternary nitrogen atom and an alkylol amide radical has been accomplished [177] by treatment of the reaction products of high molecular weight amides and formaldehyde with pyridine salts and allied compounds. Details of the preparation of N-(stearamidomethyl)pyridinium acetate and similar compounds have been described by Shipp.[631] Compounds of the general formula

$$\begin{matrix} -C \\ \diagdown \\ -C \end{matrix} N \diagdown \begin{matrix} X \\ CH_2CH_2NHCOR \end{matrix}$$

where X is a halogen and R is a high molecular weight alkyl radical, have been synthesized.[632] The preparation of quaternary ammonium compounds by alkylation of the reaction products of high molecular weight amides and alkylene oxides has been disclosed.[633] Quaternary ammonium compounds result by treating the acylated product of *p*-toluenesulfonamide and formaldehyde with pyridine.[634] Quaternary ammonium compounds which contain alkoxymethylene radicals can be obtained by the action of halomethoxyalkanes on tertiary amines of the general formula $ROCH_2NR_1R_2$, where R is a high molecular weight alkyl group and R_1 and R_2 are either short alkyl chains or the hydrocarbon portion of a heterocyclic ring.[635] Alkylene chlorohydrins are reactive with the heterocyclic nitrogen bases to yield products whose alkylation results in quaternary ammonium derivatives.[636] The preparation of oxalates of quaternary ammonium compounds which contain a pyridinium or quinolinium group substituted by an alkoxymethylene, $—CH_2OR$, where R is a long-chain hydrocarbon radical, has been described,[637] and the use of the oxalates or other salts of such quaternary ammonium compounds for treating cellulose and allied materials has been suggested.[638]

The action of sulfonating agents on quaternary ammonium compounds has been studied,[639] and it has been claimed that wetting agents are obtained by treating certain quaternary ammonium compounds with organic sulfonic acids. Piggott [640] has suggested the preparation of wetting agents by the sulfonation of such compounds as dimethylhexadecylbenzylammonium chloride. The synthesis of sulfur-containing ammonium compounds which contain at least one long-chain hydrocarbon radical has been investigated.[641]

Considerable experimental work has been done within recent years upon those quaternary ammonium compounds which contain at least one long hydrocarbon radical and in which the quaternary nitrogen atom is attached to other than carbon atoms. In such compounds the quaternary nitrogen may or may not be contained in a heterocyclic ring. Examples of the latter type are the azonium salts recently described by Westphal.[642] Trihexylazonium chloride,

$$
\begin{array}{c}
C_6H_{13} \\
C_6H_{13}-\overset{+}{N} \\
C_6H_{13}
\end{array}
\begin{array}{c}
NH_2 \\
\\
\bar{C}l
\end{array}
$$

is obtained in a 15% yield by heating 1-chlorohexane, hydrazine, and ethanol for 16 hours at 150°. It melts at 65° and is extremely soluble in water. N,N-dimethyl-N-dodecylazonium iodide, m.p. 126°, is prepared by the treatment of N-methyl-N-dodecylhydrazine with methyl iodide. The following compounds are synthesized in a similar manner: N-methyl-N-ethyl-N-dodecylazonium bromide, m.p. 82°; N-methyl-N-allyl-N-dodecylazonium chloride and bromide (not crystalline); N,N-dimethyl-N-hexadecylazonium methosulfate, m.p. 99–100°; N,N-dimethyl-N-hexadecylazonium iodide, m.p. 163–164.5°; and N-methyl-N-ethyl-N-hexadecyl-azonium bromide, m.p. 94°. Benzotriazolium bromides have been synthesized by the action of 1-bromoalkanes on potassium benzotriazole, 1,3-dioctylbenzotriazolium bromide and 1,3-didodecyl-benzotriazolium bromide having been obtained by this procedure.[643] These compounds have the general formula

$$
\begin{array}{c}
N \diagdown R \\
\overset{+}{N} \diagup N \\
| \\
R \quad Br^-
\end{array}
$$

1-Dodecylbenzotriazole yields 1-dodecyl-3-methylbenzotriazolium methosulfate, m.p. 25°, when treated with dimethyl sulfate. The action of bromoethane on 1-dodecyl- and 1-hexadecylbenzotriazole yields quaternary ammonium compounds. 1-Dodecyl-4-ethyl-1,2,4-triazolium bromide, m.p. 150–152°,

$$\begin{array}{c} N\!\!=\!\!CH \\ | \\ H_{25}C_{12}N\!\!-\!\!CH \end{array}\!\!\!>\!\!N\!\!<\!\!\begin{array}{c} C_2H_5 \\ \\ Br^- \end{array}$$

has been prepared by the action of bromoethane on 1-dodecyl-triazole. The high bactericidal activity of such compounds has led to their further study and to the synthesis of quaternary ammonium compounds which contain more than three nitrogen atoms in the heterocyclic ring.[644] A representative of this type of compound is 2,3-diphenyl-5-undecyltetrazolium chloride,

$$C_{11}H_{23}C\!\!<\!\!\begin{array}{c} N\!\!-\!\!NC_6H_5 \\ | \\ N\!\!=\!\!\overset{+}{N}C_6H_5 \\ | \\ \overset{-}{Cl} \end{array}$$

which is prepared as follows: dodecanal is condensed with phenyl-hydrazine and the resulting phenylhydrazone is treated with benzenediazonium chloride. The resulting formazane is cyclized with lead tetraacetate to give 2,3-diphenyl-5-undecyltetrazolium acetate, which is converted to the chloride by treatment with hydrochloric acid. The reactions involved are as follows:

$$C_{11}H_{23}C\!\!<\!\!\begin{array}{c} O \\ \\ H \end{array} + H_2NNHC_6H_5 \rightarrow C_{11}H_{23}C\!\!<\!\!\begin{array}{c} NNHC_6H_5 \\ \\ H \end{array}\xrightarrow{C_6H_5NNCl}$$

$$C_{11}H_{23}C\!\!<\!\!\begin{array}{c} NNHC_6H_5 \\ \\ N\!\!=\!\!NC_6H_5 \end{array}\xrightarrow{PbAc_4} C_{11}H_{23}C\!\!<\!\!\begin{array}{c} N\!\!-\!\!NC_6H_5 \\ | \\ N\!\!=\!\!\overset{+}{N}C_6H_5 \\ | \\ \overset{-}{Ac} \end{array}\xrightarrow{HCl}$$

$$C_{11}H_{23}C\!\!<\!\!\begin{array}{c} N\!\!-\!\!NC_6H_5 \\ | \\ N\!\!=\!\!\overset{+}{N}C_6H_5 \\ | \\ \overset{-}{Cl} \end{array}$$

Several compounds of this type have been synthesized, and their bactericidal properties have been reported to be equal or superior to the dimethylbenzylalkylammonium halides (Zephirols).

The pyrolysis of quaternary ammonium compounds yields ethylenic hydrocarbons and tertiary amines. The distillation of butyltrimethylammonium hydroxide, for example, yields 1-butene and N,N-dimethylbutylamine.[491] When similarly treated, hexyl-trimethylammonium hydroxide gives 1-hexene (5%) and N,N-dimethylhexylamine (73%); heptyltrimethylammonium hydroxide yields 1-heptene, 1-heptanol, and N,N-dimethylheptylamine; octyltrimethylammonium hydroxide yields 1-octene, 1-octanol, and N,N-dimethyloctylamine; and hexadecyltrimethylammonium hydroxide yields 1-hexadecene, 1-hexadecanol, and N,N-dimethylhexadecylamine. The quaternary bases of the diamines yield unsaturated hydrocarbons, unsaturated tertiary amines, and saturated ditertiary amines when heated above their decomposition temperatures.[645] In an investigation of the mechanism of decomposition of quaternary ammonium compounds, Hanhart and Ingold [646] have pointed out that the hydrogen atom eliminated for olefin formation is the one attached to a carbon atom which occupies a β-position with reference to the nitrogen atom, the liberated electron moving to the nitrogen atom. The formation of alcohols during the decomposition is probably a reaction competitive with olefin formation. The relative proportions of olefins and tertiary amines formed during such decompositions are materially influenced by the presence of carbon dioxide, the amount of olefin being greatly decreased when the decomposition is brought about in its presence.[647] The addition of alkali increases the rate of decomposition of the quaternary bases, but does not, in general, influence the relative proportions of the resulting products. The quaternary ammonium salts decompose with the formation of olefins, haloalkanes or other esters, and tertiary amines, the decomposition generally requiring more drastic conditions than necessary with the quaternary bases.

The physico-chemical behavior of the quaternary ammonium compounds which contain at least one long-chain hydrocarbon group parallels that of the high molecular weight alkylamine salts. The equivalent conductance curves [648] of octyl-, decyl-, dodecyl-, and hexadecyltrimethylammonium bromides show downward breaks at critical concentrations, thus evidencing micelle formation. The critical points occur at lower concentrations with increasing length of the alkyl chain. Butyl- and hexyltrimethylammonium bromides exhibit no discontinuities in their equivalent conductance curves, and of the compounds examined only hexadecyltrimethylammonium bromide shows an increase in its equivalent conductance at higher concentrations. The electrical behavior of the so-called double-long-chain salts is of unusual interest. Examples of such compounds are octyltrimethylammonium octanesulfonate and decyltrimethylammonium decanesulfonate, the equivalent conductances of the aqueous solutions of which have been determined.[649] Such salts form micelles at concentrations much below those of the corresponding single-long-chain salts.

Many uses have been proposed for the long-chain quaternary ammonium salts. Their bactericidal properties are rapidly becoming well recognized and they will undoubtedly be extensively used as disinfecting and preserving agents. Certain of the quaternary ammonium salts possess fungicidal properties.[650] These compounds have also been suggested for use in detergents,[651] fire-extinguishing foams,[652] the saponification of cellulose esters,[653] wetting agents,[654, 655, 656] and flotation agents.[560, 563]

References

1. Hofmann, *Ber.*, **15**, 977 (1882).
2. Menschutkin, *ibid.*, **17**, 846 (1884).
3. Carlet, *Bull. soc. chim.* [1], **1**, 73 (1859).
4. Meyer, *Ber.*, **22**, 24 (1889).
5. Dessaignes and Chautard, *J. pharm. chim.* [3], **13**, 241 (1848).
6. Chiozza, *Ann.*, **91**, 102 (1854).
7. Felletár, *Jahresber. Fortschr. Chem.*, 624 (1868).
8. Hunter, Harber, and Gilman, *Proc. Iowa Acad. Sci.*, **47**, 263 (1940).
9. Hunter, *Iowa State College J. Sci.*, **15**, 223 (1941).
10. Chem. Werke Hansa, Ger. Patent 189,477 (1906).
11. Kösters and Ottemann, Brit. Patent 6,731 (1907); U. S. Patent 915,680 (1908).
12. Mitchell and Reid, *J. Am. Chem. Soc.*, **53**, 1879 (1931).
13. Ralston, Hoerr, and Pool, *J. Org. Chem.*, **8**, 473 (1943).
14. I. G. Farbenind. A.-G., Fr. Patent 757,867 (1934).
15. Reppe and Keyssner, U. S. Patent 2,013,108 (1935).
16. Nill, U. S. Patent 1,659,150 (1928).
17. Bruson, U. S. Patent 1,989,968 (1935).
18. D'Alelio and Reid, U. S. Patent 2,109,941 (1938).
19. Henry, *Ber.*, **2**, 494 (1869).
20. Aschan, *ibid.*, **31**, 2344 (1898).
21. Krafft and Stauffer, *ibid.*, **15**, 1728 (1882).
22. Orton, *J. Chem. Soc.*, **79**, 1351 (1901).
23. Guy and Smith, *ibid.*, 615 (1939).
24. Ruhoff and Reid, *J. Am. Chem. Soc.*, **59**, 401 (1937).
25. de'Conno and Biazzo, *Rend. accad. sci. Napoli*, **21**, III, 322 (1915); *J. Chem. Soc.*, **110**, i, 788 (1916).
26. de'Conno, *Gazz. chim. ital.*, **47**, I, 93 (1917).
27. Oda, *Sci. Papers Inst. Phys. Chem. Research Tokyo*, **24**, No. 510, 171 (1934).
28. Shatenshteïn, Russ. Patent 50,964 (1937).
29. Shatenshteïn and Izrailevich, *J. Applied Chem.* (*U.S.S.R.*), **11**, 967 (1938).
30. Balaty, Fellinger, and Audrieth, *Ind. Eng. Chem.*, **31**, 280 (1939).

31. Hund and Rosenstein, U. S. Patent 2,070,991 (1937).
32. Henke and Zartman, U. S. Patent 2,058,013 (1936).
33. Radziszewski, *Ber.*, **18**, 355 (1885).
34. Letts, *ibid.*, **5**, 669 (1872).
35. Schulze, *J. prakt. Chem.* [2], **27**, 512 (1883).
36. Wanklyn and Schenk, *J. Chem. Soc.*, **21**, 31 (1868).
37. Rathke, *Ber.*, **14**, 1774 (1881).
38. Tafel and Enoch, *ibid.*, **23**, 103 (1890).
39. Auwers, *Z. physik. Chem.*, **12**, 689 (1893); **15**, 33 (1894); **23**, 449 (1897).
40. Auwers, *ibid.*, **30**, 529 (1899).
41. Meldrum and Turner, *J. Chem. Soc.*, **93**, 876 (1908).
42. Claisen, *Ann.*, **287**, 360 (1895).
43. Hantzsch and Voegelen, *Ber.*, **34**, 3142 (1901).
44. Auwers, *ibid.*, **34**, 3558 (1901).
45. Hantzsch and Dollfus, *ibid.*, **35**, 226 (1902).
46. Schmidt, *ibid.*, **36**, 2459 (1903).
47. Fawsitt, *Proc. Roy. Soc. Edinburgh*, **25**, 51 (1904).
48. Claisen and Meyerowitz, *Ber.*, **22**, 3273 (1889).
49. Pinner, *ibid.*, **25**, 1434 (1892).
50. Meldrum and Turner, *J. Chem. Soc.*, **97**, 1605 (1910).
51. Mascarelli and Benati, *Gazz. chim. ital.*, **39**, II, 642 (1909).
52. Meldrum and Turner, *J. Chem. Soc.*, **97**, 1805 (1910).
53. Latimer and Rodebush, *J. Am. Chem. Soc.*, **42**, 1419 (1920).
54. Huggins, *J. Org. Chem.*, **1**, 407 (1936).
55. Zellhoefer, Copley, and Marvel, *J. Am. Chem. Soc.*, **60**, 1337 (1938).
56. Chaplin and Hunter, *J. Chem. Soc.*, 1114 (1937).
57. Copley, Zellhoefer, and Marvel, *J. Am. Chem. Soc.*, **60**, 2666 (1938).
58. Buswell, Rodebush, and Roy, *ibid.*, **60**, 2444 (1938).
59. Henderson, *Proc. Roy. Soc. Edinburgh*, **48**, 20 (1928).
60. Zahn, *Physik. Z.*, **33**, 525 (1932).
61. Devoto, *Gazz. chim. ital.*, **63**, 495 (1933).
62. Kumler and Porter, *J. Am. Chem. Soc.*, **56**, 2549 (1934).
63. Kumler, *ibid.*, **57**, 600 (1935).
64. Pauling and Sherman, *J. Chem. Phys.*, **1**, 606 (1933).
65. Freymann and Freymann, *Bull. soc. chim.* [5], **4**, 944 (1937).
66. Ramart-Lucas and Grunfeld, *ibid.* [5], **4**, 478 (1937).
67. Titherley, *J. Chem. Soc.*, **71**, 460 (1897); **79**, 391 (1901).
68. Lassettre, *Chem. Rev.*, **20**, 259 (1937).
69. Robertson, *J. Chem. Soc.*, **93**, 1033 (1908); **115**, 1210 (1919).
70. D'Alelio and Reid, *J. Am. Chem. Soc.*, **59**, 109 (1937).
71. Rowney, *Ann.*, **79**, 236 (1851).
72. Masino, *ibid.*, **202**, 172 (1880).
73. Fournier, *Bull. soc. chim.* [4], **5**, 920 (1909).
74. Asano, *J. Pharm. Soc. Japan*, No. **480**, 97 (1922).
75. Garner and Rushbrooke, *J. Chem. Soc.*, 1351 (1927).
76. Deffet, *Bull. soc. chim. Belg.*, **40**, 385 (1931).
77. Ueno and Takase, *J. Soc. Chem. Ind., Japan*, **42**, S.b. 409 (1939); **44**, S.b. 29 (1941).
78. Pebal, *Ann.*, **91**, 138 (1854).

79. Hell and Jordanoff, *Ber.*, **24**, 936 (1891).
80. Curtius and Dellschaft, *J. prakt. Chem.* [2], **64**, 419 (1901).
81. Toyama, *J. Soc. Chem. Ind., Japan*, **25**, 1053 (1922).
82. Bruni and Levi, *Giorn. chim. ind. applicata*, **7**, 447 (1925).
83. Ueno, Takase, and Tajima, *J. Soc. Chem. Ind., Japan*, **44**, S.b. 58 (1941).
84. Emeljanoff and Albitzkiĭ, *J. Russ. Phys. Chem. Soc.*, **31**, 106 (1899).
85. Herrera-Batteke, *Philippine J. Sci.*, **32**, 35 (1927).
86. Étaix, *Ann. chim.* [7], **9**, 356 (1896).
87. Henry, *Compt. rend.*, **100**, 943 (1885); *J. Chem. Soc.*, **48**, 886 (1885).
88. Hill and Carothers, *J. Am. Chem. Soc.*, **55**, 5023 (1933).
89. Barnicoat, *J. Chem. Soc.*, 2926 (1927).
90. Gilman and Ford, *Iowa State Coll. J. Sci.*, **13**, 135 (1939).
91. D'Alelio and Reid, *J. Am. Chem. Soc.*, **59**, 111 (1937).
92. Arnold and Austin, U. S. Patent 2,151,369 (1939).
93. Ford-Moore and Phillips, *Rec. trav. chim.*, **53**, 847 (1934).
94. Tucker, *J. Am. Chem. Soc.*, **57**, 1989 (1935).
95. Franchimont, *Rec. trav. chim.*, **2**, 329 (1883); Franchimont and Klobbie, *ibid.*, **6**, 247 (1887); Franchimont and Rouffaer, *ibid.*, **13**, 331 (1894).
96. Verley, *Bull. soc. chim.* [3], **9**, 690 (1893).
97. Tiffeneau and Fuhrer, *ibid.* [4], **15**, 162 (1914).
98. Kindler, *Ann.*, **431**, 187 (1923).
99. Ralston, Vander Wal, and McCorkle, *J. Org. Chem.*, **4**, 68 (1939).
100. Ralston, U. S. Patent 2,168,847 (1939).
101. Carothers and Berchet, *J. Am. Chem. Soc.*, **52**, 5289 (1930).
102. Schotten, *Ber.*, **21**, 2235 (1888).
103. Gabriel, *ibid.*, **22**, 3335 (1889).
104. Carothers, *Chem. Rev.*, **8**, 353 (1931).
105. Carothers and Hill, *J. Am. Chem. Soc.*, **54**, 1566 (1932).
106. Carothers and Graves, U. S. Patent 2,163,584 (1939).
107. E. I. du Pont de Nemours and Co., Brit. Patent 461,236 (1937).
108. Carothers, U. S. Patent 2,130,523 (1938).
109. E. I. du Pont de Nemours and Co., Brit. Patent 461,237 (1937).
110. Triggs, Brit. Patent 525,516 (1940).
111. Carothers and Hill, *J. Am. Chem. Soc.*, **54**, 1579 (1932).
112. Carothers, U. S. Patents 2,130,948 (1938); 2,157,116 (1939); 2,188,332 (1940); Can. Patent 379,253 (1939).
113. E. I. du Pont de Nemours and Co., Brit. Patent 501,197 (1939).
114. Crocker, *J. Chem. Soc.*, **91**, 593 (1907); Crocker and Lowe, *ibid.*, **91**, 952 (1907).
115. Toms, *Nature*, **145**, 227 (1940).
116. Toms, *ibid.*, **146**, 560 (1940).
117. Adkins and Wojcik, *J. Am. Chem. Soc.*, **56**, 247 (1934).
118. Hofmann, *Ber.*, **14**, 2725 (1881).
119. Hofmann, *ibid.*, **15**, 407 (1882).
120. Hofmann, *ibid.*, **15**, 752, 762 (1882).
121. Hofmann, *ibid.*, **17**, 1406 (1884).
122. Hofmann, *ibid.*, **15**, 762 (1882).
123. Jeffreys, *ibid.*, **30**, 898 (1897).
124. Hoogewerff and Van Dorp, *Rec. trav. chim.*, **6**, 373 (1887).

125. Lengfeld and Stieglitz, *Am. Chem. J.*, **15**, 504 (1893); **16**, 370 (1894).
126. Lengfeld and Stieglitz, *ibid.*, **16**, 370 (1894); Stieglitz, *ibid.*, **18**, 751 (1896); **29**, 49 (1903); Stieglitz and Earle, *ibid.*, **30**, 399, 412 (1903).
127. Schirm, U. S. Patent 2,054,638 (1936).
128. Berchet, U. S. Patent 2,132,388 (1938).
129. I. G. Farbenind. A.-G., Brit. Patent 328,075 (1929).
130. H. Th. Böhme A.-G., Ger. Patent 595,173 (1934).
131. Soc. pour l'ind. chim. à Bâle, Fr. Patent 771,614 (1934).
132. Schirm, U. S. Patent 2,186,769 (1940).
133. Bousquet and Salzberg, U. S. Patent 2,166,118 (1939).
134. Bousquet, U. S. Patents 2,166,119–20 (1939).
135. Balle and Schild, U. S. Patent 2,215,367 (1940).
136. Guenther, Münz, and Haussmann, U. S. Patent 1,932,176 (1933).
137. Guenther and Haussmann, U. S. Patent 1,932,177 (1933).
138. I. G. Farbenind. A.-G., Fr. Patent 710,960 (1931).
139. I. G. Farbenind. A.-G., Ger. Patent 640,581 (1937).
140. Henkel et Cie. G.m.b.H., Ger. Patent 675,723 (1939).
141. I. G. Farbenind. A.-G., Brit. Patent 506,049 (1939).
142. I. G. Farbenind. A.-G., Brit. Patent 499,130 (1939).
143. I. G. Farbenind. A.-G., Ger. Patent 663,808 (1938).
144. Rosenhauer, U. S. Patents 2,120,512, 2,139,037 (1938).
145. Orthner and Jacobs, U. S. Patent 2,365,431 (1944).
146. I. G. Farbenind. A.-G., Fr. Patent 814,166 (1937).
147. I. G. Farbenind. A.-G., Brit. Patent 382,718 (1932).
148. Guenther, Holsten, and Saftien, U. S. Patent 1,932,178 (1933).
149. Henkel et Cie. G.m.b.H., Ger. Patent 619,299 (1935).
150. Robinson and Webber, U. S. Patent 2,329,086 (1943).
151. Katzman, U. S. Patent 2,239,720 (1941).
152. I. G. Farbenind. A.-G., Brit. Patent 390,840 (1933).
153. Guenther, Haussmann, and Münz, U. S. Patent 1,932,179 (1933).
154. Guenther, Münz, and Haussmann, U. S. Patent 1,932,180 (1933).
155. Imperial Chemical Industries Ltd., Fr. Patent 797,631 (1936).
156. Moyer, U. S. Patent 2,195,188 (1940).
157. Henkel et Cie. G.m.b.H., Fr. Patent 770,539 (1934).
158. I. G. Farbenind. A.-G., Brit. Patent 499,022 (1939).
159. Piggott, Brit. Patent 414,403 (1934).
160. Katz, Brit. Patent 538,859 (1941).
161. I. G. Farbenind. A.-G., Brit. Patent 378,002 (1932); Ger. Patent 664,309 (1938).
162. Soc. pour l'ind. chim. à Bâle, Swiss Patents 213,378, 214,784 (1941).
163. Soc. pour l'ind. chim. à Bâle, Swiss Patent 211,657 (1941).
164. Graenacher and Sallmann, U. S. Patent 2,338,178 (1944).
165. Graenacher, Sallmann, and Albrecht, U. S. Patent 2,338,177 (1944).
166. Weisberg and Corman, U. S. Patent 2,266,136 (1941).
167. Beck, U. S. Patent 2,297,864 (1942).
168. De Groote and Keiser, U. S. Patent 2,363,047 (1944).
169. Mauersberger, U. S. Patent 2,329,406 (1943).
170. Paraskova, *Compt. rend.*, **198**, 1701 (1934).
171. Orthner and Keppler, U. S. Patent 2,002,613 (1935).

172. De Groote and Keiser, U. S. Patent 2,300,555 (1942).
173. Schoeller and Wittwer, U. S. Patents 1,970,578 (1934); 2,085,706 (1937).
174. De Groote and Keiser, U. S. Patent 2,226,119 (1940).
175. I. G. Farbenind. A.-G., Ger. Patent 729,286 (1942).
176. Hentrich and Kirstahler, U. S. Patent 2,345,121 (1944).
177. Baldwin, Walker, and Imperial Chemical Industries Ltd., Brit. Patent 475,170 (1937).
178. I. G. Farbenind. A.-G., Fr. Patent 792,589 (1936).
179. Shipp, U. S. Patent 2,232,485 (1941).
180. Engelmann, U. S. Patent 2,361,185 (1944).
181. Balle, Rosenbach, and Dittus, U. S. Patent 2,210,442 (1940).
182. Shipp, U. S. Patent 2,146,408 (1939).
183. Soc. pour l'ind. chim. à Bâle, Swiss Patent 210,976 (1940).
184. Bruson, U. S. Patent 1,952,008 (1934).
185. I. G. Farbenind. A.-G., Fr. Patent 799,093 (1936); Brit. Patent 466,853 (1937).
186. Cusa and Imperial Chemical Industries Ltd., Brit. Patent 531,691 (1941).
187. Yamashita and Yoshizaki, U. S. Patent 2,313,695 (1943).
188. I. G. Farbenind. A.-G., Indian Patent 26,032 (1939).
189. Alframine Corp., Brit. Patent 515,882 (1939).
190. Mauersberger, U. S. Patent 2,186,464 (1940).
191. Soc. pour l'ind. chim. à Bâle, Swiss Patent 210,958 (1940).
192. Soc. pour l'ind. chim. à Bâle, Swiss Patent 210,959 (1940).
193. Soc. pour l'ind. chim. à Bâle, Swiss Patent 210,960 (1940).
194. Soc. pour l'ind. chim. à Bâle, Swiss Patent 210,962 (1940).
195. Soc. pour l'ind. chim. à Bâle, Brit. Patent 533,220 (1941).
196. Sallmann and Albrecht, U. S. Patent 2,279,497 (1942).
197. Soc. pour l'ind. chim. à Bâle, Swiss Patent 209,637 (1940).
198. Soc. pour l'ind. chim. à Bâle, Swiss Patent 213,553 (1941).
199. Soc. pour l'ind. chim. à Bâle, Swiss Patent 208,530 (1940).
200. Soc. pour l'ind. chim. à Bâle, Swiss Patent 210,978 (1940).
201. Soc. pour l'ind. chim. à Bâle, Swiss Patent 210,977 (1940).
202. Soc. pour l'ind. chim. à Bâle, Swiss Patent 210,975 (1940).
203. Soc. pour l'ind. chim. à Bâle, Swiss Patent 210,974 (1940).
204. I. G. Farbenind. A.-G., Brit. Patent 486,026 (1938).
205. Imperial Chemical Industries Ltd., Fr. Patent 848,101 (1939).
206. Baldwin, Piggott, Statham, and Imperial Chemical Industries Ltd., Brit. Patent 508,477 (1939); Baldwin, Piggott, and Statham, U. S. Patents 2,237,296, 2,259,602 (1941).
207. Baldwin and Piggott, U. S. Patent 2,131,362 (1938).
208. Baldwin and Walker, U. S. Patent 2,146,392 (1939).
209. I. G. Farbenind. A.-G., Brit. Patent 424,076 (1935).
210. Hubert, Heisenberg, Steindorff, and Orthner, U. S. Patent 2,211,976 (1940).
211. I. G. Farbenind. A.-G., Brit. Patent 463,300 (1937).
212. Pinner and Klein, Ber., 10, 1889 (1877).
213. Pinner, ibid., 23, 2917 (1890).
214. Eitner and Wetz, ibid., 26, 2840 (1893).
215. Hill and Rabinowitz, J. Am. Chem. Soc., 48, 732 (1926).

216. Geigy A.-G., Brit. Patent 498,090 (1939).
217. Martin and Zaeslin, U. S. Patent 2,211,280 (1940).
218. Pyman and Levene, Brit. Patent 518,575 (1940).
219. Easson and Pyman, *J. Chem. Soc.*, 2991 (1931).
220. Inoue and Yukawa, *J. Agr. Chem. Soc. Japan*, **16**, 504 (1940).
221. Falciola and Mannino, *Ann. chim. applicata*, **2**, 351 (1014).
222. Falciola, *Gazz. chim. ital.*, **50**, I, 162 (1920).
223. Curtius, *J. prakt. Chem.* [2], **89**, 508 (1914).
224. Veselý and Haas, *Chem. Listy*, **21**, 351 (1927).
225. van Alphen, *Rec. trav. chim.*, **44**, 1064 (1925).
226. Asano and Kanematsu, *J. Pharm. Soc. Japan*, No. **531**, 375 (1926).
227. Stendal, *Compt. rend.*, **196**, 1810 (1933).
228. Crossley, Northey, and Hultquist, *J. Am. Chem. Soc.*, **60**, 2217 (1938).
229. Crossley, Northey, and Hultquist, *ibid.*, **61**, 2950 (1939).
230. Crossley, Northey, and Hultquist, *ibid.*, **62**, 532 (1940).
231. I. G. Farbenind. A.-G., Ger. Patent 676,196 (1939).
232. Graenacher and Ackermann, U. S. Patent 2,031,037 (1936).
233. Seka and Müller, *Monatsh.*, **57**, 97 (1931).
234. Pool, Harwood, and Ralston, *J. Am. Chem. Soc.*, **59**, 178 (1937).
235. Brown and Campbell, *J. Chem. Soc.*, 1699 (1937).
236. Bloom and Day, *J. Org. Chem.*, **4**, 14 (1939).
237. Shriner and Upson, *J. Am. Chem. Soc.*, **63**, 2277 (1941).
238. Graenacher and Ackermann, U. S. Patents 2,053,822, 2,056,449 (1936).
239. Soc. pour l'ind. chim. à Bâle, Brit. Patent 490,774 (1938).
240. Soc. pour l'ind. chim. à Bâle, Swiss Patent 208,534 (1940).
241. Soc. pour l'ind. chim. à Bâle, Swiss Patent 214,093 (1941).
242. Soc. pour l'ind. chim. à Bâle, Swiss Patent 214,096 (1941).
243. Soc. pour l'ind. chim. à Bâle, Swiss Patent 214,097 (1941).
244. Soc. pour l'ind. chim. à Bâle, Brit. Patent 451,500 (1936).
245. Soc. pour l'ind. chim. à Bâle, Swiss Patent 208,534 (1940).
246. Soc. pour l'ind. chim. à Bâle, Swiss Patents 177,815–18 (1935); Brit. Patent 439,261 (1935).
247. Soc. pour l'ind. chim. à Bâle, Swiss Patents 179,659–60 (1935).
248. Soc. pour l'ind. chim. à Bâle, Fr. Patent 754,626 (1933).
249. Waldmann and Chwala, Brit. Patent 479,491 (1938); U. S. Patent 2,155,877 (1939).
250. Waldmann and Chwala, U. S. Patent 2,155,878 (1939).
251. Waldmann and Chwala, Fr. Patents 796,917 (1936); 811,423 (1937).
252. Waldmann and Chwala, U. S. Patent 2,154,922 (1939).
253. I. G. Farbenind. A.-G., Fr. Patent 836,873 (1939).
254. Graenacher and Meyer, U. S. Patent 2,226,057 (1940); Ger. Patent 703,899 (1941).
255. v. Braun, *Ber.*, **42**, 4541 (1909).
256. Ruzicka, Salomon, and Meyer, *Helv. Chim. Acta*, **20**, 109 (1937).
257. Wöhler and Liebig, *Ann.*, **3**, 249 (1832).
258. Henry, *Ber.*, **2**, 305, 494 (1869).
259. Krafft and Weilandt, *ibid.*, **29**, 1316 (1896).
260. Greenhalgh and Imperial Chemical Industries Ltd., Brit. Patent 488,036 (1938); U. S. Patent 2,206,351 (1940).

261. Boehner and Andrews, *J. Am. Chem. Soc.*, **38**, 2503 (1916).
262. Boehner and Ward, *ibid.*, **38**, 2505 (1916).
263. Ralston, Pool, and Harwood, U. S. Patent 2,061,314 (1936).
264. Ralston, Harwood, and Pool, *J. Am. Chem. Soc.*, **59**, 986 (1937).
265. Herold and von der Horst, Ger. Patent 704,494 (1941).
266. Weidel and Ciamician, *Ber.*, **13**, 65 (1880).
267. Mailhe, *Compt. rend.*, **166**, 36 (1918).
268. Mailhe, *ibid.*, **166**, 121 (1918).
269. Mailhe, *Bull. soc. chim.* [4], **27**, 226 (1920); *Ann. chim.* [9], **13**, 183 (1920).
270. Mitchell and Reid, *J. Am. Chem. Soc.*, **53**, 321 (1931).
271. Mailhe, *Bull. soc. chim.* [4], **37**, 1394 (1925).
272. Mailhe, *ibid.* [4], **23**, 380 (1918).
273. Mailhe and de Godon, *Compt. rend.*, **166**, 215 (1918).
274. Mailhe and de Godon, *ibid.*, **165**, 557 (1917).
275. Mailhe, *ibid.*, **170**, 813 (1920).
276. I. G. Farbenind. A.-G., Brit. Patent 416,631 (1934); Fr. Patents 781,444, 785,622 (1935).
277. Nicodemus and Wulff, U. S. Patent 2,177,619 (1939).
278. Nicodemus and Wulff, U. S. Patent 2,037,389 (1936).
279. I. G. Farbenind. A.-G., Brit. Patent 451,594 (1936).
280. Greenewalt and Rigby, U. S. Patent 2,132,849 (1938).
281. Société des usines chimiques Rhône-Poulenc, Brit. Patents 532,938, 537,954 (1941).
282. Korshak and Pakhomov, *J. Applied Chem. (U.S.S.R.)*, **14**, 632 (1941).
283. Fluchaire and Iavorsky, U. S. Patent 2,273,633 (1942).
284. E. I. du Pont de Nemours & Co., Brit. Patent 494,236 (1938).
285. Arnold and Lazier, U. S. Patent 2,200,734 (1940).
286. E. I. du Pont de Nemours & Co., Brit. Patent 535,187 (1941).
287. Levene and Taylor, *J. Biol. Chem.*, **59**, 905 (1924).
288. Becker, *Ann.*, **102**, 209 (1857).
289. Ralston, Selby, and Pool, *Ind. Eng. Chem.*, **33**, 682 (1941).
290. Marckwald and Nolda, *Ber.*, **42**, 1583 (1909).
291. v. Braun, *ibid.*, **42**, 4541 (1909).
292. v. Braun and Danziger, *ibid.*, **45**, 1970 (1912).
293. Arbusow, *ibid.*, **43**, 2296 (1910).
294. Heim, *Bull. soc. chim. Belg.*, **42**, 467 (1933).
295. Merckx, Verhulst, and Bruylants, *ibid.*, **42**, 177 (1933).
296. Daragan, *ibid.*, **44**, 597 (1935).
297. Dorinson and Ralston, *J. Am. Chem. Soc.*, **66**, 361 (1944).
298. Dorinson, McCorkle, and Ralston, *ibid.*, **64**, 2739 (1942).
299. Hoffman, Hoerr, and Ralston, *ibid.*, **67**, 1542 (1945).
300. Hoerr, Binkerd, Pool, and Ralston, *J. Org. Chem.*, **9**, 68 (1944).
301. Copley, Zellhoefer, and Marvel, *J. Am. Chem. Soc.*, **61**, 3550 (1939).
302. Copley, Ginsberg, Zellhoefer, and Marvel, *ibid.*, **63**, 254 (1941).
303. Ostwald, *Kolloid-Z.*, **45**, 56 (1928).
304. Bruylants and Ernould, *Bull. classe sci. Acad. roy. Belg.* [5], **17**, 1174 (1931).
305. Vandewyer, *Bull. soc. chim. Belg.*, **44**, 376 (1935).
306. de Hoffmann, *ibid.*, **44**, 435 (1935).

307. van Caillie, *ibid.*, **44**, 438 (1935).
308. Krafft and Tritschler, *Ber.*, **33**, 3580 (1900).
309. Bruylants, *Acad. roy. Belg.*, *Classe sci.*, *Mém.*, **14**, No. 7, 78 pp. (1936).
310. Frankland and Kolbe, *Ann.*, **65**, 288 (1848).
311. Adams and Marvel, *J. Am. Chem. Soc.*, **42**, 310 (1920).
312. Mailhe, *Compt. rend.*, **171**, 245 (1920).
313. Taylor, *J. Chem. Soc.*, 2741 (1930).
314. Krieble and Noll, *J. Am. Chem. Soc.*, **61**, 560 (1939).
315. Rabinovitch and Winkler, *Can. J. Research*, **20B**, 73 (1942).
316. Rabinovitch, Winkler, and Stewart, *ibid.*, **20B**, 121 (1942).
317. McLean, Rabinovitch, and Winkler, *ibid.*, **20B**, 168 (1942).
318. Rabinovitch and Winkler, *ibid.*, **20B**, 221 (1942).
319. Karvé and Gharpure, *J. Univ. Bombay*, **8**, Pt. 3, 139 (1939).
320. Berger and Olivier, *Rec. trav. chim.*, **46**, 600 (1927).
321. Olivier, *ibid.*, **48**, 568 (1929).
322. Hantzsch, *Ber.*, **64**, 667 (1931).
323. von Peskoff and Meyer, *Z. physik. Chem.*, **82**, 129 (1913).
324. Rabinovitch and Winkler, *Can. J. Research*, **20B**, 185 (1942).
325. Reitz, *Z. physik. Chem.*, **183A**, 371 (1939).
326. Spiegel, *Ber.*, **51**, 296 (1918).
327. Stephen, *J. Chem. Soc.*, **127**, 1874 (1925).
328. Williams, *J. Am. Chem. Soc.*, **61**, 2248 (1939).
329. Baerts, *Bull. soc. chim. Belg.*, **31**, 421 (1922).
330. Compère, *ibid.*, **44**, 523 (1935).
331. Trunel, *Compt. rend.*, **197**, 453 (1933).
332. Ryan and Nolan, *Proc. Roy. Irish Acad.*, **30B**, 1 (1913).
333. Ralston and Christensen, *Ind. Eng. Chem.*, **29**, 194 (1937).
334. Gilman and Schulze, *J. Am. Chem. Soc.*, **47**, 2002 (1925).
335. Tiemann, *Ber.*, **17**, 126 (1884).
336. Nordmann, *ibid.*, **17**, 2746 (1884).
337. Frankland and Kolbe, *Ann.*, **65**, 269 (1848).
338. Bayer, *Ber.*, **2**, 319 (1869).
339. von Meyer, *J. prakt. Chem.* [2], **22**, 261 (1880); [2], **27**, 152 (1883); [2], **37**, 396 (1888); [2], **39**, 188 (1889).
340. Merckx and Bruylants, *Bull. classe sci. Acad. roy. Belg.* [5], **19**, 681 (1933).
341. Gavriloff, *ibid.* [5], **19**, 815 (1933).
342. Gesellschaft für Kohlentechnik m.b.H., Brit. Patent 436,692 (1935).
343. Luten, *J. Org. Chem.*, **3**, 588 (1939).
344. Ralston, U. S. Patent 2,175,092 (1939).
345. Ralston, U. S. Patent 2,162,971 (1939).
346. Ralston and Vander Wal, U. S. Patent 2,178,522 (1939).
347. Pool, U. S. Patent 2,107,904 (1938).
348. Ralston, U. S. Patents 1,991,955–6 (1935).
349. Ralston, Pool, and Harwood, U. S. Patents 2,033,536–7 (1936).
350. Ralston and Pool, U. S. Patents 2,133,007 (1938); 2,145,802–4 (1939).
351. Ralston and Barrett, *Oil & Soap*, **18**, 89 (1941); U. S. Patent 2,280,850 (1942).
352. Ralston, Pool, and Harwood, U. S. Patent 2,053,045 (1936).
353. Ralston, Pool, and Harwood, U. S. Patent 2,053,046 (1936).

354. Conquest, U. S. Patent 2,135,327 (1938).
355. Ralston, U. S. Patents 2,116,472, 2,125,853 (1938).
356. Harwood and Pool, U. S. Patent 2,166,093 (1939).
357. Ralston and Pool, U. S. Patent 2,175,093 (1939).
358. Hofmann, *Ann.*, **73,** 91 (1850).
359. van Renesse, *ibid.*, **166,** 80 (1873).
360. I. G. Farbenind. A.-G., Ger. Patent 648,088 (1937).
361. I. G. Farbenind. A.-G., Fr. Patent 784,599 (1935).
362. I. G. Farbenind. A.-G., Brit. Patent 437,530 (1935).
363. I. G. Farbenind. A.-G., Brit. Patent 359,001 (1930).
364. Profft, U. S. Patent 2,305,830 (1942).
365. v. Braun, *Ber.*, **70B,** 979 (1937).
366. Wibaut, Heierman, and Wagtendonk, *Rec. trav. chim.*, **57,** 456 (1938).
367. v. Braun and Klar, *Ber.*, **73B,** 1417 (1940).
368. Shreve and Burtsfield, *Ind. Eng. Chem.*, **33,** 218 (1941).
369. Westphal and Jerchel, *Ber.*, **73B,** 1002 (1940).
370. Berthelot, *Ann. chim.* [3], **38,** 38 (1853).
371. Weith, *Ber.*, **8,** 458 (1875).
372. Merz and Gasiorowski, *ibid.*, **17,** 623 (1884).
373. Sabatier and Mailhe, *Compt. rend.*, **153,** 1204 (1911).
374. Sabatier and Mailhe, *ibid.*, **148,** 898 (1909).
375. Smolenski and Smolenski, *Roczniki Chem.*, **1,** 232 (1921); *J. Chem. Soc.*, **122,** i, 234 (1922).
376. Dorrell, *J. Chem. Soc.*, **127,** 2399 (1925).
377. Brown and Reid, *J. Phys. Chem.*, **28,** 1067 (1924).
378. Shinozaki and Kubo, *J. Agr. Chem. Soc. Japan*, **13,** 1 (1937).
379. Arnold, U. S. Patent 2,078,922 (1937).
380. Arnold, U. S. Patent 1,799,722 (1931).
381. Covert, U. S. Patent 2,160,058 (1939).
382. Alexander Wacker Ges. für elektrochemische Ind. G.m.b.H., Fr. Patent 687,398 (1929).
383. Olin and McKenna, U. S. Patent 2,365,721 (1944).
384. Goshorn, U. S. Patent 2,349,222 (1944).
385. I. G. Farbenind. A.-G., Fr. Patent 779,913 (1935).
386. Smeykal, U. S. Patent 2,043,965 (1936).
387. Deutsche Hydrierwerke A.-G., Ger. Patent 611,924 (1935).
388. I. G. Farbenind. A.-G., Fr. Patent 780,028 (1935).
389. I. G. Farbenind. A.-G., Fr. Patent 767,771 (1934).
390. Adkins and Cramer, *J. Am. Chem. Soc.*, **52,** 4349 (1930).
391. Winans and Adkins, *ibid.*, **54,** 306 (1932).
392. Paden and Adkins, *ibid.*, **58,** 2487 (1936).
393. Hill and Adkins, *ibid.*, **60,** 1033 (1938).
394. Kindler, *Ann.*, **485,** 113 (1931).
395. Schwoegler and Adkins, *J. Am. Chem. Soc.*, **61,** 3499 (1939).
396. Mignonac, *Compt. rend.*, **172,** 223 (1921).
397. Winans and Adkins, *J. Am. Chem. Soc.*, **55,** 2051 (1933).
398. Reppe, U. S. Patent 1,762,742 (1930).
399. Vanderbilt, U. S. Patent 2,219,879 (1940).
400. Olin and Schwoegler, U. S. Patent 2,278,372 (1942); Olin, U. S. Patent 2,278,373 (1942).

401. Clark and Wilson, U. S. Patent 2,319,848 (1943).
402. Olin and McKenna, U. S. Patent 2,367,366 (1945).
403. I. G. Farbenind. A.-G., Fr. Patent 761,952 (1934).
404. Mailhe, *Bull. soc. chim.* [3], **33**, 962 (1905).
405. Mailhe and Murat, *ibid.* [4], **9**, 464 (1911).
406. Wassiljew, *Ber.*, **60B**, 1122 (1927).
407. Hartung, *J. Am. Chem. Soc.*, **50**, 3370 (1928); **53**, 2248 (1931).
408. Skita and Keil, *Ber.*, **65B**, 424 (1932).
409. Goldschmidt, *ibid.*, **20**, 728 (1887).
410. Krafft, *ibid.*, **23**, 2360 (1890).
411. v. Braun, Blessing, and Zobel, *ibid.*, **56**, 1988 (1923).
412. Lycan, Puntambeker, and Marvel, *Organic Syntheses*, Coll. Vol. 2, Blatt, editor, p. 318, John Wiley & Sons, New York (1943).
413. Paul, *Bull. soc. chim.* [5], **4**, 1121 (1937).
414. I. G. Farbenind. A.-G., Ger. Patent 621,629 (1935).
415. Mendius, *Ann.*, **121**, 129 (1862).
416. Krafft and Moye, *Ber.*, **22**, 811 (1889).
417. Forselles and Wahlforss, *ibid.*, **25R**, 636 (1892).
418. Teunissen, *Rec. trav. chim.*, **46**, 208 (1927).
419. Harwood, U. S. Patent 2,122,644 (1938).
420. Ladenburg, *Ber.*, **18**, 2956 (1885).
421. Linnemann and v. Zotta, *Ann.*, **162**, 3 (1872).
422. Rupe and Glenz, *Helv. Chim. Acta*, **5**, 937 (1922).
423. Ralston, *Oil & Soap*, **17**, 89 (1940).
424. I. G. Farbenind. A.-G., Fr. Patent 773,367 (1934); Brit. Patents 438,793, 439,274 (1935).
425. Schmidt, U. S. Patent 2,160,578 (1939).
426. I. G. Farbenind. A.-G., Ger. Patent 648,297 (1937).
427. Schmidt, U. S. Patent 2,165,515 (1939).
428. I. G. Farbenind. A.-G., Fr. Patent 781,960 (1935); Ger. Patent 621,629 (1935).
429. Young and Christensen, U. S. Patent 2,287,219 (1942).
430. Young, U. S. Patent 2,355,356 (1944).
431. Pool and Potts, U. S. Patent 2,358,030 (1944).
432. Harber and Gilman, *Proc. Iowa Acad. Sci.*, **44**, 125 (1937).
433. Ralston, Selby, Pool, and Potts, *Ind. Eng. Chem.*, **32**, 1093 (1940).
434. Ralston, Hoerr, Pool, and Harwood, *J. Org. Chem.*, **9**, 102 (1944).
435. Hoerr, Harwood, and Ralston, *ibid.*, **9**, 201 (1944).
436. Ralston, Hoerr, and Du Brow, *ibid.*, **9**, 259 (1944).
437. Howk, U. S. Patent 2,166,150 (1939).
438. Howk, U. S. Patent 2,166,152 (1939).
439. Lazier, U. S. Patent 2,200,282 (1940).
440. E. I. du Pont de Nemours & Co., Fr. Patent 851,748 (1940).
441. Signaigo, U. S. Patent 2,166,183 (1939).
442. Sabatier and Mailhe, *Ann. chim.* [8], **16**, 70 (1909).
443. Röhm and Haas Co., Brit. Patent 425,927 (1935).
444. Adkins, U. S. Patent 2,143,751 (1939).
445. Lazier, U. S. Patent 2,187,745 (1940).
446. Züblin, *Ber.*, **10**, 2083 (1877).
447. Worstall, *Am. Chem. J.*, **21**, 218 (1899).

448. Eichler, *Ber.*, **12**, 1879 (1879).
449. Le Sueur, *J. Chem. Soc.*, **97**, 2433 (1910).
450. H. Th. Böhme A.-G., Fr. Patent 785,004 (1935); Brit. Patent 443,863 (1936).
451. Grün, U. S. Patent 2,104,421 (1938).
452. Buck and Baltzly, *J. Am. Chem. Soc.*, **63**, 1964 (1941).
453. Clarke, Gillespie, and Weisshaus, *ibid.*, **55**, 4571 (1933).
454. Kirby, U. S. Patent 2,366,534 (1945).
455. I. G. Farbenind. A.-G., Brit. Patent 425,486 (1935).
456. Olin and Deger, U. S. Patent 2,192,523 (1940).
457. Harwood, Ralston, and Selby, *J. Am. Chem. Soc.*, **63**, 1916 (1941).
458. Davidson, Sisler, and Stoenner, *ibid.*, **66**, 779 (1944).
459. Pool, Harwood, and Ralston, *ibid.*, **67**, 775 (1945).
460. Ralston, Hoerr, and Hoffman, *ibid.*, **64**, 1516 (1942).
461. Bidet, *Compt. rend.*, **158**, 876 (1914).
462. Ralston, Hoffman, Hoerr, and Selby, *J. Am. Chem. Soc.*, **63**, 1598 (1941).
463. Ralston, Hoerr, and Hoffman, *ibid.*, **63**, 2576 (1941).
464. Hoerr and Ralston, *ibid.*, **64**, 2824 (1942).
465. McBain, *Trans. Faraday Soc.*, **9**, 99 (1913).
466. Ralston, Hoerr, and Hoffman, *J. Am. Chem. Soc.*, **64**, 97 (1942).
467. Ralston and Hoerr, *ibid.*, **64**, 772 (1942).
468. McBain, Laing, and Titley, *J. Chem. Soc.*, **115**, 1279 (1919).
469. Lottermoser and Püschel, *Kolloid-Z.*, **63**, 175 (1933).
470. Hartley, *Aqueous Solutions of Paraffin Chain Salts*, Hermann et Cie., Paris (1936).
471. Tartar and Wright, *J. Am. Chem. Soc.*, **61**, 539 (1939).
472. Wright and Tartar, *ibid.*, **61**, 544 (1939).
473. Thiessen and Spychalski, *Z. physik. Chem.*, **156A**, 435 (1931).
474. Hess and Gundermann, *Ber.*, **70B**, 1800 (1937).
475. Hess, Philippoff, and Kiessig, *Kolloid-Z.*, **88**, 40 (1939).
476. Stauff, *Naturwissenschaften*, **27**, 213 (1939); *Kolloid-Z.*, **89**, 224 (1939); **96**, 244 (1941).
477. Kiessig and Philippoff, *Naturwissenschaften*, **27**, 593 (1939).
478. Philippoff, *Kolloid-Z.*, **96**, 255 (1941).
479. Kiessig, *ibid.*, **98**, 213 (1942).
480. Ross, *J. Phys. Chem.*, **46**, 414 (1942).
481. Hoerr and Ralston, *J. Am. Chem. Soc.*, **65**, 976 (1943).
482. Ralston and Hoerr, *ibid.*, **68**, 851 (1946).
483. Ralston and Hoerr, *ibid.*, **68**, 2460 (1946).
484. Ward, *Proc. Roy. Soc. (London)*, **176A**, 412 (1940).
485. Hoffman, Boyd, and Ralston, *ibid.*, **64**, 498, 2067 (1942).
486. Sedgwick, Hoerr, and Ralston, *J. Org. Chem.*, **10**, 498 (1945).
487. Hoerr, Harwood, and Ralston, *ibid.*, **11**, 199 (1946).
488. Hoerr, McCorkle, and Ralston, *J. Am. Chem. Soc.*, **65**, 328 (1943).
489. Ruzicka, Goldberg, Hürbin, and Boekenoogen, *Helv. Chim. Acta*, **16**, 1323 (1933).
490. Ruzicka, Hürbin, Goldberg, and Furter, *ibid.*, **18**, 659 (1935).
491. v. Braun, *Ann.*, **382**, 1 (1911).
492. Clarke, *J. Chem. Soc.*, **103**, 1689 (1913).

493. Westphal, *Ber.*, **74B**, 1365 (1941).
494. Ladenburg, *ibid.*, **19**, 780 (1886).
495. Phookan and Krafft, *ibid.*, **25**, 2252 (1892).
496. v. Braun and Müller, *ibid.*, **38**, 2203 (1905).
497. Neuberg, *Z. physiol. Chem.*, **45**, 110 (1905).
498. Naegeli and Lendorff, *Helv. Chim. Acta*, **15**, 49 (1932).
499. Wagner-Jauregg, Arnold, and Rauen, *Ber.*, **74B**, 1372 (1941).
500. Michaelis, *ibid.*, **24**, 745 (1891).
501. Michaelis and Storbeck, *Ann.*, **274**, 187 (1893); Michaelis, *ibid.*, **274**, 200 (1893).
502. Hill and Fitzgerald, *J. Am. Chem. Soc.*, **57**, 250 (1935).
503. Bamberger, *Ber.*, **36**, 710 (1903).
504. D'Ans and Wedig, *ibid.*, **46**, 3075 (1913).
505. I. G. Farbenind. A.-G., Fr. Patent 786,334 (1935).
506. Soc. pour l'ind. chim. à Bâle, Brit. Patent 437,566 (1935); Fr. Patent 786,911 (1935).
507. Soc. pour l'ind. chim. à Bâle, Swiss Patent 175,351 (1935).
508. Soc. pour l'ind. chim. à Bâle, Swiss Patent 181,444 (1936).
509. Soc. pour l'ind. chim. à Bâle, Swiss Patent 182,592 (1936).
510. Soc. pour l'ind. chim. à Bâle, Swiss Patent 183,587 (1936).
511. Soc. pour l'ind. chim. à Bâle, Swiss Patent 178,364 (1935).
512. I. G. Farbenind. A.-G., Ger. Patent 664,425 (1938).
513. Guenther and Saftien, U. S. Patent 2,169,976 (1939).
514. Engelmann, U. S. Patent 2,159,967 (1939).
515. Berkenheïm and Gostev, *J. Gen. Chem. (U.S.S.R.)*, **3**, 385 (1933).
516. Siersch, *Ann.*, **144**, 137 (1867).
517. Linnemann, *ibid.*, **161**, 15 (1872); *Ber.*, **10**, 1111 (1877).
518. Meyer and Forster, *ibid.*, **9**, 535 (1876).
519. Linnemann, *Ann.*, **162**, 12 (1872).
520. Meyer, Barbieri, and Forster, *Ber.*, **10**, 130 (1877).
521. Rây and Rakshit, *J. Chem. Soc.*, **101**, 141 (1912).
522. Whitmore and Langlois, *J. Am. Chem. Soc.*, **54**, 3441 (1932).
523. Ralston, Pool, and Harwood, U. S. Patent 2,086,239 (1937).
524. Vincent, *Compt. rend.*, **85**, 667 (1877).
525. Grün, U. S. Patent 2,101,314 (1937).
526. McCorkle, U. S. Patent 2,355,314 (1944).
527. Wurtz, *Ann. chim. phys.* [3], **55**, 400 (1859).
528. Demole, *Ann.*, **173**, 123 (1874).
529. Roithner, *Monatsh.*, **15**, 665 (1894).
530. Knorr and Matthes, *Ber.*, **34**, 3482 (1901); Matthes, *Ann.*, **315**, 104 (1901).
531. Knorr and Brownsdon, *Ber.*, **35**, 4470 (1902).
532. Gabel, *ibid.*, **58**, 577 (1925).
533. Horne and Shriner, *J. Am. Chem. Soc.*, **54**, 2925 (1932).
534. Headlee, Collett, and Lazzell, *ibid.*, **55**, 1066 (1933).
535. Ulrich, Nüsslein, and Körding, U. S. Patent 1,923,178 (1933).
536. Ulrich and Ploetz, U. S. Patent 2,127,476 (1938).
537. Ulrich, U. S. Patent 2,185,163 (1939).
538. Piggott, Brit. Patent 420,066 (1934).

539. Schuette and Wittwer, U. S. Patent 2,174,760 (1939).
540. Schwoegler, U. S. Patent 2,337,004 (1943).
541. I. G. Farbenind. A.-G., Brit. Patent 419,588 (1934).
542. I. G. Farbenind. A.-G., Fr. Patent 751,744 (1933).
543. I. G. Farbenind. A.-G., Fr. Patent 849,019 (1939).
544. I. G. Farbenind. A.-G., Brit. Patent 512,022 (1939).
545. I. G. Farbenind. A.-G., Ger. Patent 633,334 (1936).
546. I. G. Farbenind. A.-G., Ger. Patent 612,686 (1935).
547. I. G. Farbenind. A.-G., Ger. Patent 546,406 (1928).
548. Henkel et Cie. G.m.b.H., Fr. Patent 774,087 (1934).
549. Piggott, Brit. Patent 419,942 (1934).
550. Calcott and Clarkson, U. S. Patent 2,060,851 (1936).
551. Ralston and Harwood, U. S. Patent 2,229,307 (1941).
552. Zerweck and Gofferje, U. S. Patent 2,086,690 (1937).
553. Grunfeld, *Compt. rend.*, **194**, 893 (1932).
554. Hofmann, *Ber.*, **15**, 762 (1882).
555. Broome, Ralston, and Thornton, *J. Am. Chem. Soc.*, **68**, 67 (1946).
556. Goebel and Walker, U. S. Patent 2,274,058 (1942).
557. Straumanis and Cirulis, *Z. anorg. allgem. Chem.*, **230**, 65 (1936); **234**, 17 (1937).
558. Fricke and Röbke, *ibid.*, **170**, 25 (1928).
559. Broome, Ralston, and Thornton, *J. Am. Chem. Soc.*, **68**, 849 (1946).
560. Lenher, U. S. Patent 2,132,902 (1938).
561. Phosphate Recovery Corp., Fr. Patent 831,743 (1938).
562. Tartaron, U. S. Patent 2,222,728 (1940).
563. Kirby, U. S. Patent 2,088,325 (1937).
564. Ralston and Pool, U. S. Patent 2,267,307 (1941).
565. Corley, Ralston, and Segebrecht, U. S. Patent 2,298,281 (1942).
566. Ralston and Segebrecht, U. S. Patent 2,313,360 (1943).
567. Wark, *J. Phys. Chem.*, **40**, 661 (1936).
568. I. G. Farbenind. A.-G., Fr. Patent 782,930 (1935).
569. I. G. Farbenind. A.-G., Fr. Patent 44,640 (1935).
570. Dohse and Spoun, U. S. Patent 2,191,295 (1940).
571. Ralston and Vander Wal, U. S. Patent 2,317,301 (1943).
572. Ralston and Hoffman, U. S. Patent 2,320,010 (1943).
573. Ralston, Barrett, and Hopkins, *Oil & Soap*, **18**, 11 (1941).
574. I. G. Farbenind. A.-G., Brit. Patent 467,166 (1937).
575. I. G. Farbenind. A.-G., Fr. Patent 777,426 (1935).
576. I. G. Farbenind. A.-G., Brit. Patent 426,956 (1935).
577. Deutsche Hydrierwerke A.-G., Fr. Patent 782,802 (1935).
578. I. G. Farbenind. A.-G., Fr. Patent 783,008 (1935).
579. I. G. Farbenind. A.-G., Fr. Patent 826,646 (1938).
580. Hovey and Hodgins, U. S. Patent 2,230,326 (1941).
581. I. G. Farbenind. A.-G., Fr. Patent 787,466 (1935).
582. I. G. Farbenind. A.-G., Fr. Patent 716,560 (1931).
583. I. G. Farbenind. A.-G., Brit. Patents 358,114, 359,001 (1930).
584. Soc. pour l'ind. chim. à Bâle, Swiss Patent 183,444 (1936).
585. Vanderbilt, U. S. Patent 2,281,177 (1942).
586. Ralston and Pool, U. S. Patent 2,315,734 (1943).

587. Ralston and Hoffman, U. S. Patent 2,320,009 (1943).
588. Ralston and Hopkins, U. S. Patent 2,247,711 (1941).
589. Reychler, *Kolloid-Z.*, **13**, 252 (1913).
590. Kuhn, Jerchel, Westphal, Möller, and v. Czernucki-Hrebeljanowitsch, *Ber.*, **73B**, 1095 (1940).
591. Domagk, *Deut. med. Wochschr.*, **61**, 829 (1935).
592. I. G. Farbenind. A.-G., Ger. Patents 627,880, 638,005 (1936); 680,599, 681,850, 682,393, 682,441, 685,321 (1939).
593. Domagk, U. S. Patent 2,108,765 (1938).
594. Shelton, U. S. Patents 2,295,504–5 (1942).
595. Kuhn and Jerchel, *Ber.*, **73B**, 1100 (1940).
596. Bruson, U. S. Patent 2,191,922 (1940).
597. J. R. Geigy A.-G., Swiss Patent 199,452 (1938).
598. J. R. Geigy A.-G., Swiss Patents 206,594 (1939); 207,299, 207,300–3 (1940).
599. J. R. Geigy A.-G., Fr. Patent 842,299 (1939); Brit. Patent 509,542 (1939).
600. J. R. Geigy A.-G., Swiss Patents 211,790, 211,792 (1941).
601. I. G. Farbenind. A.-G., Fr. Patent 806,662 (1936); Ger. Patent 685,321 (1939).
602. Cusa and Imperial Chemical Industries Ltd., Brit. Patent 531,691 (1941).
603. Wolf, Ger. Patent 703,501 (1941).
604. Niederl and Weingarten, *J. Am. Chem. Soc.*, **63**, 3534 (1941).
605. Soc. pour l'ind. chim. à Bâle, Ger. Patent 559,500 (1928).
606. Piggott and Woolvin, U. S. Patent 2,202,864 (1940).
607. Schirm, Ger. Patent 704,388 (1941).
608. I. G. Farbenind. A.-G., Fr. Patent 806,790 (1936).
609. Balle and Eisfeld, U. S. Patent 2,087,565 (1937).
610. J. R. Geigy A.-G., Swiss Patent 212,562 (1941).
611. Bock and Houk, U. S. Patent 2,276,149 (1942).
612. Bock, U. S. Patent 2,282,702 (1942).
613. Fawcett and Gibson, *J. Chem. Soc.*, 396 (1934).
614. Macovski, *Bull. soc. chim.* [5], **3**, 498 (1936).
615. Oakeshott, U. S. Patent 2,048,885 (1936).
616. Kuhn and Westphal, *Ber.*, **73B**, 1105 (1940).
617. Hahl, Taub, and Leuchs, U. S. Patent 2,152,047 (1939).
618. Niederl and Lanzilotti, *J. Am. Chem. Soc.*, **66**, 844 (1944).
619. H. Th. Böhme, Fr. Patent 753,189 (1933).
620. Bertsch and Stober, U. S. Patent 2,104,728 (1938).
621. Henkel & Cie. G.m.b.H., Ger. Patent 657,055 (1938).
622. Soc. pour l'ind. chim. à Bâle, Swiss Patent 179,654 (1935).
623. Soc. pour l'ind. chim. à Bâle, Swiss Patents 179,661–7 (1935).
624. Marvel, Zartman, and Bluthardt, *J. Am. Chem. Soc.*, **49**, 2299 (1927).
625. Littmann and Marvel, *ibid.*, **52**, 287 (1930).
626. Lehman, Thompson, and Marvel, *ibid.*, **55**, 1977 (1933).
627. Hart and Niederl, *ibid.*, **63**, 945 (1941).
628. McGreal and Niederl, *ibid.*, **63**, 1476 (1941).
629. Niederl and Kenney, *ibid.*, **66**, 840 (1944).
630. J. R. Geigy A.-G., Swiss Patent 206,717 (1939).
631. Shipp, U. S. Patent 2,146,408 (1939).

632. Haack, U. S. Patent 2,242,211 (1941).
633. I. G. Farbenind. A.-G., Fr. Patent 806,819 (1936); Brit. Patent 465,200 (1937).
634. Flores and Essers, Brit. Patent 507,687 (1939).
635. Bock, U. S. Patent 2,204,653 (1940).
636. Gränacher, U. S. Patent 2,089,602 (1937).
637. Piggott, Brit. Patent 488,869 (1938); U. S. Patent 2,146,406 (1939).
638. Evans, Piggott, Salkeld, Reynolds, Walker, and Woolvin, Brit. Patent 495,025 (1938).
639. I. G. Farbenind. A.-G., Brit. Patent 499,203 (1939).
640. Piggott, U. S. Patent 2,075,958 (1937).
641. Soc. pour l'ind. chim. à Bâle, Swiss Patent 211,245 (1940).
642. Westphal, Ber., 74B, 1365 (1941).
643. Kuhn and Westphal, ibid., 73B, 1109 (1940).
644. Kuhn and Jerchel, ibid., 74B, 941 (1941).
645. v. Braun, Ann., 386, 273 (1912).
646. Hanhart and Ingold, J. Chem. Soc., 997 (1927).
647. v. Braun, Teuffert, and Weissbach, Ann., 472, 121 (1929).
648. Scott and Tartar, J. Am. Chem. Soc., 65, 692 (1943).
649. Scott, Tartar, and Lingafelter, ibid., 64, 698 (1943).
650. I. G. Farbenind. A.-G., Fr. Patent 771,746 (1934).
651. I. G. Farbenind. A.-G., Fr. Patent 824,493 (1938).
652. Henkel & Cie. G.m.b.H., Ger. Patent 650,919 (1937).
653. Schlack, U. S. Patent 2,144,202 (1939).
654. Hailwood and Todd, Brit. Patent 393,276 (1933).
655. Hunsdiecker and Vogt, Brit. Patent 421,862 (1935).
656. Whittaker and Wilcock, Brit. Patent 501,020 (1939).

IX

THE ALCOHOLS AND THEIR ESTERS, THE ETHERS, MERCAPTANS, SULFIDES, SULFONATES, AND RELATED COMPOUNDS

THE ALCOHOLS

The aliphatic alcohols, excluding the sterols, possess the general formula ROH. The R group may be either a straight-chain saturated radical or it may contain one or more unsaturated bonds. Only the higher primary alcohols which contain six or more carbon atoms, together with certain high molecular weight dihydric alcohols and a few of the polyhydric alcohols, are included in this discussion.

The fatty alcohols occupy a unique position among the fatty acid derivatives in that they are of both natural and synthetic origins. Their occurrence as esters in many of the animal, vegetable, and marine lipoids and waxes removes them from the category of purely synthetic derivatives. Our familiarity with the animal and vegetable waxes extends as far back as our knowledge of the fats themselves. The advent of catalytic hydrogenation, on the other hand, and the adaptability of such processes to the synthesis of the higher alcohols from the acids or their esters have served to place them among the most important of the synthetic fatty derivatives. The active interest which now exists in the fatty alcohols and in the products derived from them is directly dependent upon their present ready availability from synthetic sources.

Although the naturally occurring wax esters have ceased to be an important source of most of the higher aliphatic alcohols, the presence of these alcohols in such products is a subject which is certainly not devoid of interest. In the following discussion, therefore, we will first consider the natural occurrence of the higher alcohols, bearing in mind, however, that most of these alcohols have now been synthesized and can be prepared in large amounts

from the corresponding acids. The close parallelism which exists
between the structures of the naturally occurring alcohols and
acids is noteworthy. For example, the saturated alcohols consist
largely of straight-chain compounds which contain an even number
of carbon atoms, one of the most abundant of these being hexadecanol, which finds its counterpart in palmitic acid. One apparent
distinction between the occurrences of the alcohols and the acids
is that alcohols of quite high molecular weight, C_{24} and higher,
predominate in many of the vegetable waxes and in insect waxes.
These are, however, frequently associated with acids of similar
chain length. The naturally occurring unsaturated alcohols are
closely related to the acids, the double bonds generally occupying
positions similar to those occupied in the acids. Thus, the most
abundant of the unsaturated acids, oleic acid, possesses the same
alkenyl chain as the widely distributed oleyl alcohol. This structural similarity suggests a common origin. In general, it can be
stated that the occurrence of the higher alcohols in the natural
waxes and in certain lipoid materials presents a biological problem
of great interest which is well worth more study.

The saturated alcohols of intermediate molecular weight, from
dodecanol to octadecanol inclusive, occur as esters in certain
animal oils, chiefly those of marine origin. Such alcohols are
present in rather appreciable amounts in the head, jaw, and blubber
oils of the sperm whale and other marine animals. The saturated
alcohols which have been isolated from such sources include
dodecanol, tetradecanol, hexadecanol, and octadecanol, hexadecanol occurring in by far the largest amounts. It is significant that
all these naturally occurring alcohols contain a normal hydrocarbon chain and possess an even number of carbon atoms.

The presence of hexadecanol in sperm head oil was first established by Chevreul [1] in 1817, and the waxy portion of this and allied
oils, which is commonly designated as spermaceti, has long been
a source of this alcohol. Spermaceti, which constitutes approximately 11% of crude sperm oil, consists largely of hexadecyl palmitate, the esters of lower and higher homologs of hexadecanol being
present in much smaller amounts. André and François [2] have
reported that the head oil of the sperm whale contains large
amounts of hexadecanol together with smaller quantities of tetradecanol and octadecanol. It has been estimated [3] that hexadecanol
forms approximately 40% of the alcohols present in sperm head
oil and 25% of the alcohols in sperm blubber oils. Its presence in
Arctic sperm blubber oils has been established,[4] and it apparently

occurs in very significant amounts (60%) in porpoise head oil. Dodecanol and tetradecanol are present as esters in the head and jaw oils of marine mammals, the former appearing only in traces and the latter generally constituting a minor component.[5] Ueno and Koyama[6] have stated that traces of octanol and decanol are present in sperm blubber oil in addition to small amounts of dodecanol. Tetradecanol comprises about 8% of the alcohols of sperm head oil[2,3] and is present in porpoise head oil.[7] Octadecanol is found as a minor component, 5% or less, in the various blubber oils[3,7,8] and in sperm head oil.[2,3] Alcohols of higher molecular weight than octadecanol, such as eicosanol, are probably present in traces in such oils. With the exception of hexadecanol, none of the higher alcohols is available from the marine oils in sufficient amounts to be of practical significance.

The higher aliphatic alcohols, tetracosanol and its higher homologs, occur as their fatty acid esters in the vegetable and insect waxes, many of which waxes consist essentially of such esters together with varying amounts of hydrocarbons. In several of the vegetable waxes one alcohol frequently appears in great preponderance, whereas in other waxes the alcohols consist of mixtures comprising three or more components. The latter is particularly true in the case of the insect waxes. Owing to the fact that the higher alcohols are not easily separated from one another, considerable disagreement has appeared in the earlier literature concerning the identity and structure of the higher alcohols from such sources. Cognizance of this situation was taken in 1921 by Gascard,[9] who attributed these differences of interpretation to the difficulty of obtaining the alcohols in a state of purity. Later, Chibnall and others[10] urged the discontinuance of the use of the common names for the alcohols, such as ceryl, montanyl, myricyl or mellissyl, and others, since such names have been associated with substances now known to be mixtures. The use of scientific names eliminates any question as to the identity of the alcohols and is employed in our discussion except when historical considerations demand otherwise.

One of the most important of the vegetable waxes, carnauba wax, contains esters of the normal aliphatic alcohols ranging from tetracosanol to tetratriacontanol. Cotton wax, palm wax, and flax wax also contain mixtures of esters of the higher alcohols. Failure to appreciate the fact that several alcohols, rather than a single alcohol, are present in these waxes has led to many disagreements among investigators.[11,12] As previously stated, however, several of the vegetable waxes actually do appear to contain a preponderance of one alcohol. For example, sugar cane wax and alfalfa wax contain large amounts of triacontanol, wheat wax contains octacosanol, and the wax from cocksfoot grass contains hexacosanol.

The presence of esters of the higher alcohols in beeswax was first pointed out by Brodie,[13] and the subject of the identity of these alcohols has been a matter of considerable controversial discussion.[12, 14, 15] The erroneous conclusion has frequently been advanced that those alcohols which are present in the insect waxes contain an uneven number of carbon atoms. All the insect waxes, Chinese insect wax, psylla wax, beeswax, and others, contain mixtures of even-carbon-membered alcohols, hexacosanol and triacontanol apparently being among the major alcohols present.

The mineral waxes, such as montan wax, which is obtained by the extraction of peat or allied materials, contain appreciable amounts of the higher alcohols.[16] Since such materials are probably of vegetable origin, the presence of these higher alcohols is not surprising. Small quantities of normal aliphatic alcohols are present in wool wax,[17] the unsaponifiable portion of which consists mainly of cholesterol.

The unsaturated alcohols which occur in natural products are quite closely related structurally to the naturally occurring unsaturated fatty acids. Thus, as has been stated before, it is significant that the most abundant of the unsaturated alcohols, 9-octadecenol or oleyl alcohol, is structurally related to oleic acid. Oleyl alcohol was first recognized by Tsujimoto [18] as a constituent of sperm oils, and its presence in such oils was later confirmed by Toyama.[8, 19] The wide distribution of this alcohol in the fish and marine mammal oils has been pointed out by Toyama.[20] Oleyl alcohol has been stated to constitute 66–70% of the alcohols of sperm body oil [3] and 30% of the alcohols of porpoise head oil.[7] A number of other mono- and polyethenyl alcohols have been identified in the naturally occurring fats and waxes. 5-Tetradecenol (physeteryl alcohol) and 9-hexadecenol (zoömaryl alcohol) have been isolated from sperm head oil;[21] decenol has been identified in sperm blubber oil,[6] and two highly unsaturated alcohols, $C_{20}H_{33}OH$ and $C_{22}H_{35}$-OH, have also been isolated from the latter oil.[22] Ethylenic alcohols of low molecular weight are apparently present in certain plant waxes.

Of the alcohols which are associated with the natural oils, none has occasioned more biological interest than the dihydric ether alcohols, chimyl, batyl, and selachyl alcohols. Such alcohols are present in the unsaponifiable portion of certain marine oils, particularly the liver oils, in some of which they occur in appreciable amounts. Attention was first directed to these alcohols by Tsujimoto and Toyama [23] in their studies of the unsaponifiable fraction of fish liver oils, in which oils they occur as their diesters.[24] Weidemann [25] in 1926 showed that such alcohols are split by hydriodic acid, and two years later Heilbron and Owens [26] observed that batyl alcohol yields octadecyl iodide when similarly treated. Subsequent investigations [27,28,29] showed batyl alcohol to be 2,3-dihydroxypropyl octadecyl ether, the naturally occurring alcohol being dextro-rotatory. Selachyl alcohol differs from batyl alcohol in having a double bond in the 9-position, and chimyl alcohol is a homolog of batyl alcohol. The accepted formulas and melting points of these alcohols are as follows: chimyl alcohol, $CH_3(CH_2)_{15}$-$OCH_2CH(OH)CH_2(OH)$, 60.5–61.5°; batyl alcohol, $CH_3(CH_2)_{17}$-$OCH_2CH(OH)CH_2(OH)$, 70–71°; selachyl alcohol, $CH_3(CH_2)_7$-$CH:CH(CH_2)_8OCH_2CH(OH)CH_2(OH)$. These three alcohols are generally found together, selachyl alcohol usually occurring in the largest amount and chimyl alcohol in the smallest. Lovern [30] has postulated that such alcohols are formed by the partial hydrogenation of glyceride molecules, since they are present in substantial amounts (37%) in rat-fish liver oil, an essentially non-glyceride oil. The relationship of these alcohols to the glycerides and the wax esters is a matter of biological interest and will undoubtedly receive further study.

The esters of the higher alcohols may be saponified by essentially the same procedures as are applied to the glycerides. Boiling with alcoholic potassium hydroxide rapidly saponifies the esters present in spermaceti and other waxes, the higher alcohols being obtained by diluting the alcoholic soap solutions with water. Owing to the limited water solubilities of the higher alcohols in comparison to glycerol, the commercial saponification of their higher esters presents certain difficulties not experienced with the glycerides. Whereas glycerol is readily removed in the aqueous layer, the higher alcohols appear in the fat or soap phase and are, therefore, difficult to separate. Many of the proposed procedures for the commercial preparation of the higher alcohols from spermaceti and the vegetable and insect waxes involve saponification procedures which yield water-insoluble soaps from which the alcohols may be separated with ease. One of the most important

of these processes [31] consists of heating spermaceti with an excess
of calcium oxide containing a small amount of water. The product
is heated in a still to remove the water, and the higher alcohols are
then distilled from the calcium soaps. The distillation is preferably
accomplished under reduced pressure. Yields of 40 to 45% of
hexadecanol from crude spermaceti have been claimed for this
process. The separation of higher alcohols from the insoluble soaps
may also be accomplished by filtration,[32] centrifugation, or the use
of selective solvents. Separation of the alcohols by the centrifugation of a refrigerated solution of the soaps and alcohols diluted with
solvents has been proposed,[33] and many novel processes have been
patented for the separation of the higher alcohols from spermaceti
or allied substances. Such procedures include hydrolysis or
saponification followed by extraction of the alcohols with petroleum
ether; [34] dry saponification followed by removal of the alcohols with
superheated steam; [35] drying of the saponified mixture followed by
solvent extraction; [36] reduction of the esters with sodium and
alcohol followed by a separation of the resulting alcohols; [37, 38]
hydrogenation followed by saponification and extraction; [39] extraction of the saponified mixture with liquid sulfur dioxide; [40] and
azeotropic distillation.[41] Hexadecanol may be prepared by the
saponification of spermaceti with aqueous potassium hydroxide
followed by the addition of pyridine, which is a preferential solvent
for the alcoholic component.[42] Mixtures of potassium soaps and
higher alcohols have been separated by extraction with chlorinated
hydrocarbon solvents.[43]

The separation of the saturated from the unsaturated alcohols
may be accomplished by the use of preferential solvents, liquid
sulfur dioxide [44] and carbon disulfide [45] having been proposed for
this purpose. The purification of the waxes by removal of the
resinous material with benzene prior to saponification has been
suggested.[46]

Preparation of the Higher Alcohols

The synthesis of the higher aliphatic alcohols has been studied
for many years, and this work has resulted in a gradual abandonment of the long and tedious procedures formerly employed for
their preparation. The more recent catalytic processes which
have been developed have removed the higher alcohols from the
category of comparatively rare chemicals and have established
them as industrially important compounds.

One of the earliest procedures for the synthesis of the alcohols [47] consists of treating the silver salts of the fatty acids with iodine, the alcohol being obtained by the saponification of the resulting ester. The preparation of pentadecanol by the action of iodine on silver palmitate [48] proceeds as follows:

$$2C_{15}H_{31}CO_2Ag + I_2 \rightarrow 2AgI + CO_2 + C_{15}H_{31}CO_2C_{15}H_{31}$$

$$C_{15}H_{31}CO_2C_{15}H_{31} + H_2O \rightarrow C_{15}H_{31}OH + C_{15}H_{31}CO_2H$$

It will be noted that the resulting alcohol contains one less carbon atom than the original acid.

Alcohols are the major product formed by the reduction of aldehydes with nascent hydrogen, although the difficulty of obtaining the higher aldehydes in reasonable yields and in a state of purity greatly reduces the value of this procedure. The preparation of the alcohols from the corresponding aldehydes was probably first accomplished by Bouis and Carlet,[49] who obtained heptyl acetate by the reduction of enanthaldehyde with zinc and acetic acid. The saponification of the ester yields heptanol. This reaction was later repeated [50] using sodium amalgam and dilute sulfuric acid as the reducing agents. Krafft [51] obtained decanol, dodecanol, tetradecanol, hexadecanol, and octadecanol by the reduction of their respective aldehydes with zinc and acetic acid. The aldehydes were obtained by heating the barium salts of the fatty acids with barium formate. The preparation of alcohols by this method is not employed commercially because of the lack of feasible methods for the synthesis of the aldehydes; however, the process still retains considerable interest, as evidenced by the more recent proposals to form and reduce the aldehydes simultaneously.[52] In such processes the calcium soap of the fatty acid is heated with calcium formate in the presence of a suitable solvent, hydrogen, and a catalyst, at elevated temperatures and pressures. It has subsequently been observed [53] that the calcium soap of the acid may be replaced by an alkali soap, an example being the preparation of octadecanol by heating sodium stearate, calcium formate, and a solvent in the presence of hydrogen and a catalyst at elevated pressures.

The reduction of the esters of the fatty acids in an alkaline medium, first proposed by Bouveault and Blanc,[54] offers a satisfactory procedure for the laboratory preparation of the higher alcohols and has been employed on a limited scale for their commercial synthesis. The method consists of adding an excess of metallic sodium to an alcoholic solution of an ester, the reaction being as follows:

$$RCO_2R' + (4H) \rightarrow RCH_2OH + R'OH$$

Prior to the development of catalytic hydrogenation, sodium reduction was generally employed for the synthesis of the higher alcohols. Meyer and Reid [55] have reported the preparation of the normal aliphatic alcohols from decanol to octadecanol by reduction of the esters of the corresponding acids with metallic sodium and butanol, the yields ranging from 81 to 87%. The reduction of ethyl caproate by sodium and ethanol is a satisfactory method for the preparation of hexanol.[56] Methyl myristate is easily reduced to tetradecanol by sodium and butanol.[57] α,ω-Diols are obtained by reduction of the dialkyl esters of dibasic acids, Chuit and Hausser [58] having reported the following yields of α,ω-diols by reduction of the corresponding dimethyl esters with sodium and absolute ethanol: 1,15-pentadecanediol, 56.5%; 1,16-hexadecanediol, 55%; 1,18-octadecanediol, 41.6%; 1,19-nonadecanediol, 33.3%; 1,20-eicosanediol, 33.6%; and 1,21-heneicosanediol, 23.5%. The diols from 1,9-nonanediol to 1,16-hexadecanediol had been synthesized earlier by the same procedure.[59] Yields of 60 to 90% of the higher alcohols result from the reduction of the triglycerides with sodium and ethanol.[60] The reduction of alkyl esters to alcohols by sodium in butanol has been patented,[61] and it was later stated that such procedures are quite satisfactory for the preparation of higher alcohols from naturally occurring triglycerides such as coconut oil.[62] Branched-chain alcohols are obtained by reducing the corresponding ethyl esters,[63] ethyl 2-ethylpalmitate yielding 2-ethyl-1-hexadecanol, and ethyl 2-octylcaprate yielding 2-octyl-1-decanol. Activated aluminum in absolute alcohol may be employed for the reduction of the alkyl esters, providing catalysts such as zinc chloride, copper chloride, or metallic zinc are present.[64] The reduction of the marine animal waxes, such as spermaceti, with sodium and the lower alcohols has been proposed [65] for the preparation of the higher alcohols.

Nascent hydrogen is effective only for the reduction of polar groups, and consequently sodium-alcohol reductions and similar processes offer convenient methods for the preparation of the unsaturated alcohols. Details have been published [66] for the reduction of butyl oleate to oleyl alcohol, and the process is of general adaptability for the reduction of such esters to alcohols. The recommended procedure is as follows: *

A 5-l. round-bottomed flask is fitted with a wide-bore Y adapter and two wide-bore reflux condensers. Three liters of anhydrous butyl alcohol . . . and 507 g. (1.5 moles) of butyl oleate . . . are placed in the flask, and 180 g. (7.8 gram atoms) of clean sodium, cut in approximately 2.5-cm. cubes, is added in one lot and the flask connected to the condensers. The reaction is rather sluggish at first, requiring about one-half hour to reach the boiling point of the butyl alcohol . . . , but then becomes quite vigorous. With two condensers no difficulty is encountered in taking care of the reflux, but, if the reaction becomes too vigorous or excessive foaming occurs, wet towels should be placed on the flask until the reaction is again under control. . . . Toward the end of the reaction the flask is placed on a heated sand bath and gentle refluxing maintained until all the sodium has reacted. The heating is stopped temporarily, 160 cc. of water is added gradually through the condenser, and the solution is again refluxed gently for one hour. . . . At the end of this time the heating is stopped and 1.2 l. of water is added. The flask is well shaken and the mixture allowed to separate into two layers. The lower aqueous layer of sodium hydroxide is siphoned off and discarded. . . .

About 200 g. of solid sodium chloride . . . is added to the flask, and the butyl alcohol is removed by steam distillation. . . . The alcohol layer is separated while still hot . . . , transferred to a 1-l. beaker, and heated on a hot plate with stirring until the temperature reaches about 160°. By this time all the water is removed and foaming has stopped. . . . The hot liquid is transferred to a 1-l. Claisen flask having a 25-cm. fractionating side arm, and distilled at 3 mm. After a small fore-run of 5–10 g., the main fraction boils at 177–183°/3 mm. and amounts to 330–340 g. (82–84 per cent of the theoretical amount).

Butanol is much preferable to ethanol since the procedure is less dangerous and less time-consuming. Esters of the highly unsaturated acids are easily reduced to the corresponding alcohols, a yield of 70–72% of linoleyl alcohol having been reported from the reduction of methyl linoleate with sodium and butanol.[67] The reduction of methyl linoleate with sodium in ethanol gives a 45% yield of linoleyl alcohol with no apparent reduction of the double bonds.[68] The sodium reduction of the esters of the dienoic acids is apparently attended by some shifting of the double bonds toward a conjugated position, since studies of the molecular refraction and absorption curves of the linoleyl alcohol obtained by the reduc-

* The reader should consult the original for detailed precautions.

tion of methyl linoleate show it to be a mixture of 9,12- and 10,12-octadecadien-1-ols.[69]

A modification of the Bouveault and Blanc procedure, suggested by Prins,[70] has been reported to give higher yields of the alcohols in many instances. The modification, in general, consists of dissolving the ester in ether and then placing the solution over aqueous sodium acetate. Sodium strips are added and acetic acid is dropped in slowly, care being exercised to maintain the ether layer either neutral or slightly acid. The ether layer is rotated slowly by stirring during the process. Ethyl caprylate yields 90% of 1-octanol when so treated. The method has been found to be satisfactory for the preparation of chaulmoogryl alcohol from ethyl chaulmoograte.[71] Low yields of chaulmoogryl alcohol are obtained by the reduction of chaulmoogric acid with sodium in amyl alcohol.[72]

The large excess of metallic sodium required for reduction of the fatty esters to alcohols has long been a deterring factor in the commercial acceptance of this process. It has been proposed [73] to conduct this reduction with close to the theoretical amount of sodium by suspending the sodium in a hydrocarbon solvent, such as xylene, then adding to this suspension the ester to be treated, together with the alcohol and more hydrocarbon solvent. Such a process has been stated to be adaptable to the reduction of the alkyl esters, the glycerides, and the waxes. The reduction of the higher esters by sodium and an alcohol in the presence of an aliphatic ether has been proposed,[74] an example being the preparation of ricinoleyl alcohol by the reduction of methyl ricinoleate in the presence of *tert*-butyl alcohol and an aliphatic ether.

The higher molecular weight primary, secondary, and tertiary alcohols can be prepared by the Grignard method, and recourse to this procedure is often advisable, particularly for the preparation of certain tertiary alcohols. The synthesis of primary alcohols by this method is accomplished by treating an alkylmagnesium halide with formaldehyde, the product being subsequently hydrolyzed. The reactions are as follows:

$$\text{RMgBr} + \text{HCHO} \rightarrow \text{H}_2\text{C} \underset{\text{R}}{\overset{\text{OMgBr}}{\diagup}} \xrightarrow{\text{HOH}} \text{RCH}_2\text{OH} + \text{MgBr(OH)}$$

Hexadecylmagnesium bromide gives a 53% yield of 1-heptadecanol, and heptadecylmagnesium bromide a 64% yield of 1-octadecanol by the above procedure.[75] The reaction of the higher aldehydes with Grignard reagents yields secondary alcohols, thus:

$$\text{RCHO} + \text{R'MgX} \rightarrow \text{RCH}\underset{\text{R'}}{\overset{\text{OMgX}}{\diagdown}} \xrightarrow{\text{HOH}} \text{RR'CHOH} + \text{MgX(OH)}$$

An example of the above reaction is the preparation of 2-methyl-1-decanol by the action of heptanal on isobutylmagnesium bromide.[76] Ketones react with Grignard reagents to yield tertiary alcohols, thus:

$$\text{R}_2\text{CO} + \text{R'MgX} \rightarrow \text{R}_2\text{C}\underset{\text{R'}}{\overset{\text{OMgX}}{\diagdown}} \xrightarrow{\text{HOH}} \text{R}_2\text{R'COH} + \text{MgX(OH)}$$

The reaction of esters and acid chlorides with Grignard reagents is similar to that of the ketones. In such reactions it is possible that ketones are first formed, the chlorine of the acid chloride or the alkoxy group of the ester replacing the alkyl group of the Grignard reagent. This method is frequently used for the preparation of high molecular weight tertiary alcohols. Korshak[77] has synthesized 1,1-dihexadecyl-1-octadecanol, $(C_{16}H_{33})_2C_{18}H_{35}OH$, by the action of two moles of hexadecylmagnesium bromide on one mole of ethyl stearate, and has also prepared 1,1-diphenyl-1-octadecanol from two moles of phenylmagnesium bromide and one of ethyl stearate. Phenylmagnesium bromide when treated with stearone yields 18-phenyl-18-pentatriacontanol. 3-Methyl-3-do-decanol is obtained by the action of ethyl bromide and magnesium on 2-undecanone.[78] Ryan and Dillon[79] have prepared a series of tertiary alcohols by the action of Grignard reagents on esters of palmitic and stearic acids. The tertiary alcohols so prepared include 1,1-dimethyl-, 1,1-diethyl-, and 1,1-diphenyl-1-hexadecanol, and 1,1-dimethyl-, 1,1-diethyl-, 1,1-dipropyl-, and 1,1-diphenyl-1-octadecanol. The production of tertiary alcohols by the action of Grignard reagents on the naturally occurring glycerides and waxes has been described,[80] it being claimed that the reaction proceeds smoothly in the presence of ethers or other inert solvents and a small amount of a tertiary amine.

The production of the higher alcohols by the catalytic hydrogenation of the esters of the fatty acids or of the fatty acids themselves is a comparatively recent development. Since the higher alcohols are intermediates in the hydrogenation of the fatty acids or their esters, the final products being hydrocarbons, it follows that their successful preparation by this procedure depends upon the use of preferential catalysts and the application of rather specific reaction conditions. The catalysts ordinarily employed for the hydrogenation of ethylenic bonds, such as metallic nickel or cobalt, are not satisfactory in general for the preparation of the higher alcohols, since they yield hydrocarbons rather than the desired alcohols, under the high temperatures and pressures involved. The catalysts which have been found to be satisfactory for this reduction can be broadly described as mixed oxides which function only under high pressures and at relatively high temperatures. Such catalysts exhibit a high degree of specificity for the reduction of carboxy and carbalkoxy groups. Many of them do not catalyze the hydrogenation of unsaturated carbon-to-carbon linkages to any material extent, and the further reduction of the hydroxyl group of the alcohol does not occur appreciably under the optimum conditions for alcohol formation.

The initial disclosures for the preparation of higher alcohols by catalytic hydrogenation confine themselves to the reduction of the alkyl esters of the fatty acids to the corresponding alcohols. Patents issued to H. Th. Böhme A.-G. in 1930–1936 [81] disclose the preparation of 1-dodecanol from ethyl laurate, by hydrogenation at 300–400° under 100–200 atmospheres in the presence of a finely divided metallic copper catalyst. Hydrogenation of the fatty esters to alcohols in the presence of oxide catalysts was also disclosed in 1930.[82] The hydrogenation of the acids themselves offers a more practical method for the commercial preparation of the higher alcohols, since the process of esterification is thereby avoided. This was soon realized, and a patent issued to I. G. Farbenind. A.-G.[83] disclosed the vapor- or liquid-phase hydrogenation of aliphatic or cycloaliphatic mono- and polycarboxylic acids to the corresponding alcohols. These hydrogenations were conducted under high hydrogen pressures in the presence of salts or oxides of metals such as copper, nickel, iron, cobalt, or silver, or of free metals of the second to fourth groups of the periodic system. The alcohols so obtained may be esterified with fatty acids for the preparation of synthetic waxes. Metallic copper upon kieselguhr has been proposed [84] as a catalyst for the hydrogenation of fatty acids to alcohols, and compounds which reduce to metallic copper under reducing conditions are effective in promoting such hydrogenations. For example, the fatty acids or their esters are reduced to alcohols in the presence of copper carbonate at 315° under 140 atmospheres hydrogen.[85] The copper catalyst may be prepared by the addition of sodium carbonate to a solution of copper acetate, the precipitated carbonate being washed and reduced in a stream of hydrogen at 190–200°.[86] Copper soaps have been employed as catalysts for such hydrogenations,[87] and the hydrogenation of the copper soaps themselves has been reported [88] to give good yields of the higher alcohols. The zinc, lead, manganese, cobalt, and mercury soaps of the higher acids have also been suggested as catalysts.[89] A study [90] of the effects of various catalysts upon the high-pressure hydrogenation of the fatty acids or their esters showed that hydrogenations in the presence of metallic nickel under 200 atmospheres pressure, at temperatures above 350°, yield hydrocarbons with the same number of carbon atoms as the original acids. When metallic copper is used as the catalyst at temperatures not exceeding 320°, the corresponding alcohols are formed. Mixed catalysts, such as copper chromite, zinc and copper chromates, or nickel and copper zincates, were observed to be effective catalysts for the preparation of alcohols. Temperatures above 400° result in hydrocarbon formation irrespective of the catalyst employed. The hydrogenation of ethyl oleate in the presence of a copper chromate catalyst at 270–280° yields 80–90% of 1-octadecanol.[91] This alcohol is obtained in 17% yield by the hydrogenation of castor oil in the presence of a cobalt catalyst under 200 atmospheres pressure at 220°. The use of large amounts of catalyst reduces the pressure required to bring about the reduction.

The metallic chromites and closely allied compounds are apparently the most effective catalysts for the hydrogenation of the acids or their esters to the corresponding alcohols. A 97.5% yield of dodecanol was reported by Adkins and Folkers [92] to result from the hydrogenation of 0.13 mole of ethyl laurate in the presence of three grams of copper chromite at 250° and 220 atmospheres. Ethyl myristate yields 98.5% of the theoretical amount of tetradecanol when similarly treated. The preparation of the copper chromite catalyst has been described by Adkins and Connor.[93] In 1932, Lazier [94] described the hydrogenation of the fatty acids to higher alcohols by passing such compounds in the liquid phase over catalysts consisting preferably of the chromites of hydrogenating metals. Temperatures between 300° and 400° were observed to be optimum, and pressures above 100 atmospheres were generally employed. Glycerides may also be reduced to alcohols by hydrogenation in the presence of cadmium-copper-zinc chromate catalysts,[95b] which are quite preferential for the hydrogenation of the ester group. A second hydrogenation with metallic nickel is used if saturated alcohols are desired. The hydrogenation of esters in the presence of composite catalysts which may contain one hydrogenating metal or its oxide with or without promoters, such as the oxides of manganese, zinc, magnesium, or chromium, has been described.[96] The reduction of compounds which contain the oxide of a hydrogenating metal and an ammonium chromate yields active catalysts, an example being the catalyst prepared by decomposing $Ni_2O(NH_4)_2(CrO_4)_2$ and reducing the product in hydrogen.[97]

Although it has been observed that mixed oxide catalysts, and particularly the chromites of hydrogenating metals, are effective catalysts for the hydrogenation of acids and esters to alcohols, it has also been found that the presence of small amounts of other materials greatly increases their activities. Such substances are generally referred to as promoters. The addition of ferric oxide, for example, to a copper-chromium oxide catalyst has been observed to reduce materially the amount of unchanged ester in the hydrogenated product.[98, 99] Compounds of barium, calcium, and magnesium have also been found to increase the activity of metallic chromite catalysts.[100] The presence of barium in a copper chromite catalyst exerts a decided promoting effect, and a mixture of barium and copper chromites is frequently used as a catalyst. The preparation of this catalyst has been described by Lazier and Arnold,[101] the procedure employed being as follows:

A mixture of 26 g. (0.1 mole) of C.P. barium nitrate and 800 cc. of distilled water is warmed to 70°. After solution is complete 218 g. (0.9 mole) of C.P. cupric nitrate trihydrate is added and the mixture stirred at 70° until a clear solution results. . . .

A solution of ammonium chromate is prepared by dissolving 126 g. (0.5 mole) of C.P. ammonium dichromate in 600 cc. of distilled water and adding 150 cc. of 28 per cent aqueous ammonia (sp. gr. 0.9). . . . The warm solution of the nitrates is stirred (hand stirring is adequate) while the ammonium chromate solution is poured into it in a thin stream. Stirring is continued for a few minutes, after which the reddish brown precipitate of copper barium ammonium chromate is collected . . . and pressed in a 16-cm. Büchner funnel, and dried at 110°. This dry precipitate is placed in a loosely covered nickel pan . . . , or one or two small porcelain casseroles covered with watch glasses, and heated in a muffle furnace for one hour at 350–450°. . . . At this point the yield of chromite should be about 160 g. The ignition residue is pulverized in a mortar to break up any hard lumps that may be present . . . and then transferred to a 2-l. beaker containing 1.2 l. of 10 per cent acetic acid. After being stirred for ten minutes the mixture is allowed to settle. After about ten minutes, two-thirds or more of the spent acid solution is decanted and replaced by 1.2 l. of fresh 10 per cent acetic acid, and the extraction is repeated. The residue is washed by repeating the extraction procedure four times with 1.2 l. of distilled water each time. . . . The insoluble portion is collected by filtering with suction on a Büchner funnel, dried at 110°, and ground in a mortar to a fine black powder. The yield is 130–140 g.

Many other catalytic combinations have been proposed, some of the most important of which are as follows: mixed cadmium and copper chromites;[102] cadmium-copper-zinc chromite;[103] Ni, Co, Cu, Fe, Pt, Pd, or their oxides mixed with acidic oxides such as those of chromium, aluminum, molybdenum, or tungsten;[104] mixtures of nickel, copper, or cobalt with magnesium oxide;[105] and mixtures of zinc and copper.[106] Komori[107] has compared the efficiencies of the chromates of magnesium, cadmium, mercury, strontium, cobalt, and manganese and has reported that the cadmium and cobalt salts are the most active of this group.

The preparation of the higher unsaturated alcohols by the hydrogenation of unsaturated acids or their esters offers many points of interest. The catalytic reduction of unsaturated acids in the presence of copper-cadmium catalysts yields the corresponding unsaturated alcohols.[108] The hydrogenation of oleic acid or cottonseed oil over a mixed catalyst consisting of the chromites of zinc, copper, and cadmium yields a mixture of saturated and unsaturated alcohols.[109] Komori[110] has reported that the hydrogenation of erucic acid in the presence of zinc chromite yields large amounts of 1-docosenol together with much smaller amounts of 1-docosanol and 1-docosene. The ethyl esters of rice oil fatty acids, when hydrogenated in the presence of an iron chromite catalyst at 320° under 120 atmospheres, give an 80% yield of unsaturated alcohols.[111] Although ferric oxide is less active than ferric chromite, the use of 50% of this catalyst yields 75% of the theoretical amount of unsaturated alcohols. The use of cadmium chromate mixed with molybdic oxide has been suggested for the preparation of highly unsaturated alcohols.[112] The hydrogenation of the ethyl ester of erucic, oleic, or linoleic acid in the presence of a zinc-chromium oxide catalyst produces the unsaturated alcohol in high yields.[113] Highly unsaturated alcohols are also formed by the hydrogenation of soybean oil in the presence of this catalyst, which is prepared by heating ammonium zinc chromate at 450°, or by hydrogenation in the presence of a mixture of chromium trioxide and zinc oxide at 550°. It has been postulated that the hydrogenation of a glyceride in the presence of this catalyst involves an initial hydrolysis.[114]

Sauer and Adkins [115] have compared the effects of various catalysts on the relation between the rate of hydrogenation of ethylenic linkages and the rate of hydrogenation of carbalkoxy groups. In the hydrogenation of the alkyl esters of oleic acid, zinc-chromium oxide is active towards the carbalkoxy group, yielding unsaturated alcohols; copper-chromium oxide gives saturated alcohols, thus showing activity towards both the carbalkoxy group and the ethylenic bond; and copper-molybdenum oxide yields the saturated ester, thereby indicating a preferential hydrogenation of the ethylenic bond. Zinc-vanadium oxide and zinc-molybdenum oxide are inferior to zinc-chromium oxide for the hydrogenation of the carbalkoxy group.

The partial hydrogenation of a fatty acid or ester frequently yields substantial amounts of esters of the higher molecular weight alcohols, the esters resulting from the esterification by the remaining fatty acids of the alcohols formed during the reaction. For example, Sauer and Adkins [115] observed that the reduction of butyl oleate at 283–300° for eleven hours, in the presence of a zinc-chromium oxide catalyst, gives 63–65% of octadecenol; however, when the reduction is continued only for eight hours, the product contains 46% of octadecenol and 34% of octadecenyl oleate. The hydrogenation of ethyl oleate at 300° for five hours, in the presence of a zinc-vanadium oxide catalyst, gives 55% of octadecenyl oleate, whereas a copper-vanadium oxide catalyst at 275° for five hours gives 63% of octadecyl stearate. In general, weak hydrogenating catalysts give high yields of esters, either saturated or unsaturated depending upon the specificity of the catalyst employed. Unsaturated esters are obtained when unsaturated acids are hydrogenated in the presence of metallic oxide catalysts containing metalloids of the fourth, fifth, or sixth group of the periodic system.[116] Copper-chromium oxide catalysts whose activities have been reduced by the addition of sulfur or phosphorus compounds have been proposed for the preparation of the higher esters.[117]

Schmidt [91] has observed that the chief product of the hydrogenation of castor oil in the presence of a cobalt catalyst is 1,12-octadecanediol, and it has been reported [118] that hydrogenation of ricinoleic acid, ethyl ricinoleate, or castor oil in the presence of the chromites of cadmium, copper, and zinc yields this diol as the main product. Dihydric alcohols, such as 1,4-butanediol, are obtained by the hydrogenation of the esters of the corresponding dicarboxylic acids.[119]

The general procedure employed for the hydrogenation of acids or esters to alcohols consists of passing these substances in the liquid phase over the catalyst, the system being under high hydrogen pressure. Many modifications of this method have been suggested. Green,[120] for example, has proposed a process whereby the alcohols are removed as soon as they are formed, in order to prevent their further reduction.

The production of secondary alcohols has been accomplished by the hydrogenation of metallic soaps.[121] The catalytic hydrogenation of ketones yields secondary alcohols, catalysts such as the chromates, molybdates, tungstates, or uranates of copper, zinc, or cadmium generally being employed to effect such reductions. Aldehydes such as oleyl aldehyde yield the corresponding unsaturated alcohols when similarly treated.[122, 123] High-melting waxes are obtained by the high-pressure hydrogenation of ketones in the presence of iron catalysts.[124] Secondary alcohols result when mixtures of calcium acetate and calcium soaps are treated with hydrogen under high pressure in the presence of a copper catalyst and a solvent.[121] The hydrogenation of anhydrides of the fatty acids in the presence of catalysts such as copper chromite yields high molecular weight alcohols.[125] Mixed anhydrides such as that of boric and stearic acids are preferably employed in this process. High molecular weight secondary alcohols have been obtained by first converting the acids to methyl alkyl ketones and then hydrogenating these ketones at 100° under 40 atmospheres pressure in the presence of a nickel catalyst.[126] The hydrogenation of oxidized petroleum hydrocarbons has been reported to yield higher alcohols.[127] The high molecular weight ethers when hydrogenated at 150–250 atmospheres hydrogen pressure in the presence of a nickel catalyst yield higher alcohols.[128] For example, dodecyl benzyl ether when so treated is converted into toluene and 1-dodecanol.

The carboxylic acids and their esters are reduced to alcohols by the action of hydrogen activated by the silent electric discharge,[129] it having been claimed that high yields of 1-dodecanol are obtained by the reduction of ethyl laurate under these conditions. Such processes have not, as yet, proved to be of commercial significance.

The hydration of olefins is a well-known procedure for the preparation of the lower molecular weight alcohols. Such reactions take place in the presence of sulfuric acid or other acidic catalysts, the addition product being subsequently or simultaneously hydrated to yield the desired alcohols. These processes, however, are not very satisfactory for the preparation of the higher alcohols because of the tendency of the higher olefins to polymerize in the presence of sulfuric acid.[130] The preparation of higher alcohols by hydration of high molecular weight olefins in the presence of metallic sulfates or concentrated sulfuric acid has been patented.[131] The synthesis of 1,10-octadecanediol by the hydration of oleyl alcohol has been studied by Seck and Dittmar.[132] Low yields of 1,10-octadecanediol are obtained by the use of concentrated sulfuric acid followed by hydrolysis of the addition product; however, 50% yields of the glycol result from the use of glacial acetic acid mixed with dilute sulfuric acid. The reaction of potassium acetate and acetic acid on 1,10-dibromoöctadecane gives fair yields of the glycol, whereas the use of silver acetate and acetic acid results in a quantitative conversion. The hydrogenation of 10-hydroxystearic acid gives low yields of 1,10-octadecanediol. Glycols such as 1,10- and 1,12-octadecanediol are partially dehydrated to the unsaturated primary alcohols when heated at 250–300° in the presence of oxide catalysts.[133]

Alcohol mixtures result from the condensation of carbon monoxide and hydrogen in the presence of catalysts. Effective catalysts for this reaction are the salts of silver, copper, or zinc and an acidic oxide, together with an alkali or alkaline-earth oxide.[134] The preparation of alcohols from methanol to 1-octanol by the action of carbon monoxide and hydrogen in the presence of mixed oxide catalysts has been the subject of an extensive investigation.[135] Higher alcohols have been obtained from carbon monoxide and hydrogen by first oxidizing the condensation product and then hydrogenating the oxidized material in the presence of a copper chromite catalyst.[136] Alcohols from 1-propanol to 1-nonanol inclusive have been prepared by passing the vapors of methanol and ethanol mixed with hydrogen over catalysts consisting of magnesium oxide mixed with small amounts of heavy metal oxides.[137]

High molecular weight ethynyl carbinols of the general formula $RR'C(OH)C\vdots CH$, where R and R' are long-chain hydrocarbon radicals, result from the action of metal acetylides on high molecular weight ketones in the presence of liquid ammonia. The alcohol is obtained by hydrolysis of the condensation product.[138] The treatment of the fatty acids or their esters with formaldehyde followed by hydrogenation of the resulting condensation products has been stated to yield higher alcohols.[139] Preparation of higher alcohols by deamination of high molecular weight amines has been discussed previously (Chapter VIII).

Physical Properties of the High Molecular Weight Aliphatic Alcohols

The straight-chain primary alcohols possess lower melting and boiling points than the corresponding acids. 1-Dodecanol and its lower homologs are liquid at room temperature. The lower alcohols have sharp, pungent odors; those of intermediate molecular weight have pleasant, rather fruity odors; the higher alcohols, 1-tetradecanol and its higher homologs, are odorless.

The freezing points, boiling points, refractive indices, and densities of the 1-alkanols from 1-butanol to 1-hexatriacontanol are shown in Table I.

TABLE I

PHYSICAL PROPERTIES OF 1-ALKANOLS

Alcohol	F.P., °C.	B.P., °C.	n_D^{20}	d_4^{20}
Butanol	....	117.4	1.39931	0.80978
Pentanol	−79 *	138	1.40994	0.8144
Hexanol	−51.6 *	157.2	1.41790	0.8186
Heptanol	−34.1 *	176.3	1.42410	0.8219
Octanol	−16.3 *	194.5	1.42920	0.8246
Nonanol	−5	215	1.43347	0.8274
Decanol	6.88	120_{12}	1.43682	0.8297
Undecanol	15.85	131_{15}	1.4392^{23}	0.8334^{23}
Dodecanol	23.95	150_{20}	......	0.8309^{24}
Tridecanol	30.03	$155-156_{15}$	......	......
Tetradecanol	38.26	$170-173_{20}$	......	0.8236^{38}
Pentadecanol	43.9	....	......	......
Hexadecanol	49.62	190_{15}	......	0.8105^{60}
Heptadecanol	53.9	....	......	......
Octadecanol	57.98	210_{15}	......	0.8124^{59}
Nonadecanol	61.65	$166-167_{0.32}$		
Eicosanol	65.5 *	220_3		
Heneicosanol	68.5 *	$178_{0.4}$		
Docosanol	70.6	$180_{0.22}$		
Tricosanol	74 *	$191-193_{0.7}$		
Tetracosanol	74.8	$210_{0.40}$		
Pentacosanol	79 *	$214-216_{0.36}$		
Hexacosanol	78.8			
Octacosanol	82.25			
Nonacosanol	84.1			
Triacontanol	86.3			
Dotriacontanol	88.9			
Tetratriacontanol	91.6			
Hexatriacontanol	92.6			

* Denotes melting point.

The fatty alcohols crystallize in double molecules which are joined at their hydroxyl groups. Their long crystal spacings, therefore, relate to twice the length of a single molecule. When the melting points of the saturated aliphatic alcohols are plotted against the number of carbon atoms, the lower members show an appreciable alternation; however, this alternation becomes negligible for the higher members. The melting points of 1-dodecanol and its higher homologs apparently fall upon a continuous curve. This difference between the higher and lower alcohols must be related to a difference in structural configuration. It is known that alternation is characteristic of those series whose members possess tilted chains and that those series in which the members have vertical chains do not exhibit this property. In a study of the thermal properties of the higher alcohols, Meyer and Reid [55] noted decided arrests in the cooling curves of the alcohols 1-tridecanol to 1-octadecanol inclusive, below their freezing points. An arrest in the cooling curve of 1-hexadecanol below its freezing point had previously been reported.[140] Such cooling curves, therefore, show two arrests, one at the solidification point of the alcohol and another at a transition point in the solid state. A visual change in the crystal form takes place at this second arrest, the transparent crystals which first appear becoming white and amorphous. This transition takes place a few degrees below the melting point. The second arrest was not observed for pure 1-dodecanol or its lower homologs. In 1934, Phillips and Mumford,[141] in a study of the dimorphism of the higher alcohols, observed that the freezing point curve of the transparent α-form of the alcohols intersects the melting point curve of the opaque β-form in the vicinity of the C_{13} alcohol. 1-Dodecanol and its lower homologs first solidify in the transparent α-form, which is then transformed, on standing, into the higher-melting, opaque β-form. In the case of 1-dodecanol the freezing point of the α-form is 21.6°, and the melting point of the β-form is 23.8°. In such instances the change from the α- to the β-form is monotropic. Since the freezing point curve of the α-forms and the melting point curve of the β-forms cross in the vicinity of the C_{13} alcohol, a different thermal behavior is observed for 1-tetradecanol and its higher homologs. Such alcohols solidify in the α-form but change enantiotropically into the β-form on cooling. Thus the alcohols from 1-tetradecanol upward melt in the α-form. The transition arrests which appear on cooling exhibit alternation, in that those of the even members are on a higher curve than those of the odd members. On heating, such arrests are obtained only in the case of the odd alcohols. The transition temperatures ($\alpha \rightarrow \beta$) obtained on cooling 1-tetradecanol and its higher homologs have been reported to be as follows: C_{14}, 35.0 ± 0.2°; C_{15}, 38.9 ± 0.1°; C_{16}, 45.0 ± 0.2°; C_{17}, 47.3 ± 0.1°; C_{18}, 53.6 ± 0.2°; and C_{19}, 54.0 ± 0.2°. Transitions in the heating curves for the odd alcohols appear at the following temperatures: C_{15}, 42.5°; C_{17}, 51.2°; and C_{19}, 58°. Malkin [142] has determined the long crystal spacings of the alcohols from 1-dodecanol to 1-pentacosanol inclusive, and has reported that the odd alcohols always possess vertical chains, whereas the stable form of the even alcohols contains a chain tilted at an angle of 55°40′. The latter form of the higher alcohols changes into the vertical modification somewhat below the point of fusion. His conclusion that the vertical form is characteristic of the odd alcohols was, however, questioned by Phillips and Mumford [141] on the basis that a transition from the α-transparent form (vertical) to the β-opaque form (tilted) is obtained for both the odd and the even alcohols which contain fourteen or more carbon atoms. Wilson and Ott [143] have suggested that such a transition may be from a vertical rotating chain (α-form) to a vertical non-rotating chain (β-form), a transition which would not involve a change in apparent chain length or a difference in the angle of tilt. The changes in side spacings which accompany changes in rotation were investigated by Malkin,[144] who observed two main spacings (3.7 and 4.2 Å) for the β-form of the C_{15}, C_{17}, and C_{19} alcohols, but only one (4.2 Å) for the α-form, thus indicating that the $\alpha \rightarrow \beta$ transition of the odd alcohols does not necessarily involve a transition from a vertical to a tilted chain. Considerable support has been obtained for this contention by other independent investigators. Bernal [145] has observed a hexagonal, rotating form for crystals of 1-dodecanol at 16–24°, the distance between the chains being 4.76 Å. X-ray data indicate a hexagonal cell containing two molecules which form a double layer and lie on triad axes, the molecules rotating about their long axes. 1-Hexadecanol was observed to have an inclined double-layer structure. Baker and Smyth [146] have made an extensive investigation by the dielectric constant method of the possible rotation of long-chain molecules in the solid state. The dielectric constant of 1-hexadecanol rises sharply upon solidification. It was observed, however, that the α-form, which exists between the freezing point and the transition point, shows the dielectric behavior of a viscous liquid. It was therefore concluded that the alcohol molecules in the α-form possess a freedom of rotation which decreases with falling temperatures. It was pointed out that this is consistent with the lower density of the α-form. The long crystal spacings of the even alcohols from 1-octadecanol to 1-tetratriacontanol have been determined by Francis, Collins, and Piper [147] and are recorded in Chapter V. The melting points of mixtures of 1-hexacosanol and 1-octacosanol have been reported by Piper, Chibnall, and Williams.[148]

The structure of the liquid state of the primary saturated alcohols presents many points of interest. Stewart [149] has stated that although there is substantial agreement that the molecules of aliphatic alcohols lie generally parallel, the suggestion has been made that there is no transverse space relationship of the polar pairs. It was concluded, however, that the polar groups in the alcohols have a three-space relation in the liquid state. The absence of alternation in the liquid state is evidenced by the facts that the heats of combustion and also the molecular volumes of the liquid alcohols form continuous series and that the refractive increments are essentially constant. The following heats of combustion Q_v and Q_p (in kg. cal. 15°), have been reported by Verkade and Coops [150] for some of the 1-alkanols: 1-butanol, 638.3, 639.5; 1-pentanol, 794.1, 795.6; 1-hexanol, 950.1, 951.9; 1-heptanol, 1106.4, 1108.4; 1-octanol, 1262.7, 1265.0; 1-nonanol, 1418.3, 1420.9; 1-decanol, 1573.9, 1576.9. The average Δ_{CH_2} is 156.3 kg. cal. 15°. The molecular volumes (cc.) and Δ_{CH_2} (cc.) for these alcohols at 35.6° are as follows: C_4, 92.76, —; C_5, 109.56, 16.80; C_6, 126.34, 16.78; C_7, 143.09, 16.75; C_8, 159.76, 16.67; C_9, 176.36, 16.60; C_{10}, 192.95, 16.59; C_{11}, 209.55, 16.60; and C_{12}, 226.15, 16.60.

The liquid alcohols are highly associated, the association probably taking place by means of hydrogen bonding (O—H—O).[151,152, 153,154] Verkade and Coops [150] have stated that the degree of association of the higher alcohols apparently decreases for the higher members of the series. Since the heats of combustion increase by constant increments, it was suggested that the heats of association must be quite small, since otherwise it is necessary to assume that the molecular heat of association increases as the series is ascended.

The dipolar absorption bands [155] of 1-octanol show that the absorption maxima for frequencies 5, 10.5, 18, and 26 m. lie between 30° and −40°, the temperature decreasing with increasing frequency. When the alcohol is slowly cooled to −43°, it is transformed into a white, glassy mass and the absorption bands for the above frequencies disappear. When the temperature is returned to $-35°$, the absorption reappears but shows two maxima. For 1-hexadecanol in the temperature range of 50° to 100°, the shorter the wavelength the more the maximum is displaced toward the higher temperatures. From a comparison of the absorption bands of 1-hexadecanol with those of other alcohols, it is apparent that with increasing number of carbon atoms the absorption maximum occurs at higher temperatures. The continuous absorption spectrum of the higher alcohols in the vapor state has been investigated,[156] and it was reported that the dissociation energy of the C—OH bond varies from 133.6 to 152.5 kg. cal./mole for the series CH_3OH to $n\text{-}C_{12}H_{25}OH$.

Owing to the fact that the high molecular weight unsaturated alcohols are difficult to prepare in a state of high purity, few reliable constants for such compounds have been reported in the literature. The melting points are appreciably lower than those of their saturated counterparts, and most of the ethylenic alcohols which contain eighteen or less carbon atoms are liquid at ordinary temperatures. Several terminally unsaturated primary alcohols containing an uneven number of carbon atoms have been prepared and described.[157] The following physical constants were reported for these alcohols: 10-undecenol, f.p. $-2°$, b_3 122°; 11-dodecenol, b_{11} 138°, d_4^{15} 0.840; 12-tridecenol, b_9 149–150°, d_4^{15} 0.845; and 14-pentadecenol, m.p. 32–33°, b_{10} 170–172°. Oleyl alcohol, cis-9-octadecen-1-ol, has been described [158] as an oily liquid which solidifies at about 2° and boils at 208–210° at 15 mm. Other constants for this alcohol are: b_3 177–183°, d_4^{20} 0.8489, and n_D^{20} 1.4607.[66] Its trans isomer, elaidyl alcohol, is a solid, m.p. 36–37°, b_{18} 216°, d_4^{40} 0.8388, and n_D^{40} 1.4552. Erucyl alcohol, cis-13-docosen-1-ol, melts at 34.4–35.5° and boils at 240.5–241.5° at 10 mm. Linoleyl alcohol, prepared by the reduction of methyl linoleate by sodium in dry butanol, melts at $-5°$ to $-2°$ and has d_4^{20} 0.8612 and n_D^{20} 1.4782.[67] According to Kass, Miller, and Burr,[159] the linoleyl alcohol so prepared, as shown by its molecular refraction, contains 10,12-octadecadien-1-ol in addition to 9,12-octadecadien-1-ol. A linoleyl alcohol obtained by the reduction of methyl linoleate with sodium in anhydrous ethanol showed a freezing point below $-16°$ and n_D^{23} 1.4698.[68] The bromination of this alcohol yields a tetrabromide which melts at 87.3°. Linolenyl alcohol, prepared by the reduction of methyl linolenate, is a colorless, oily liquid, n_D^{23} 1.4792. Chaulmoogryl alcohol is a solid which melts at 36°.

The branched-chain alcohols melt at appreciably lower temperatures than the isomeric normal alcohols. Thus 1-ethyl-1-hexadecanol melts at 15° and 1-octyl-1-decanol at −8°.[63] An interesting series of isomeric hexadecanols having the general formula $RR'CHCH_2OH$ has been prepared by Cox and Reid.[160] The observed melting points are as follows: (R, R', m.p.) H, $C_{14}H_{29}$, 49.3°; CH_3, $C_{13}H_{27}$, 12–13°; C_2H_5, $C_{12}H_{25}$, −0.2°; C_3H_7, $C_{11}H_{23}$, 5.5°; C_4H_9, $C_{10}H_{21}$, −14.5 to −14°; C_5H_{11}, C_9H_{19}, −9 to −8°; C_6H_{13}, C_8H_{17}, −30 to −26°; C_7H_{15}, C_7H_{15}, −25 to −18°.

A series of high molecular weight tertiary alcohols have been prepared by Ryan and Dillon [79] by the action of Grignard reagents on high molecular weight esters. The following melting points were observed: 2-methyl-2-heptadecanol, 35°; 3-ethyl-3-octadecanol, 34–35°; 1,1-diphenylhexadecanol, 47–48°; 2-methyl-2-nonadecanol, 44–45°; 4-propyl-4-heneicosanol, 28–30°; and 1,1-diphenyloctadecanol, 58°.

The higher molecular weight α,ω-glycols, $HO(CH_2)_xOH$, which have been synthesized [58, 59, 161, 162] by the reduction of the dimethyl esters of the corresponding dicarboxylic acids, possess the following melting points: (C atoms, m.p.) 9, 45.8°; 10, 77.2°; 11, 62–62.5°; 12, 80.8°; 13, 76.4–76.6°; 14, 84.8°; 15, 88°; 16, 91.4°; 17, 96–96.5°; 18, 98.6–99°; 19, 101°; 20, 103°; 21, 105–105.5°; and 22, 105.3–105.5°. The 1,12-octadecanediol which is obtained by the catalytic reduction of ricinoleic acid [118] melts at 66–67°.

The solubilities of 1-decanol, 1-dodecanol, 1-tetradecanol, 1-hexadecanol, and 1-octadecanol in a large number of organic solvents have recently been investigated.[163] The solubility behavior of the alcohols in organic solvents is quite similar to that of the nitriles and the fatty acids. They form eutectics with the non-polar solvents benzene, cyclohexane, and tetrachloromethane, the compositions and temperatures of which are shown in Table II.

The alcohols are quite soluble in ethyl ether, the solubilities in this solvent exceeding those in the non-polar solvents and in other slightly polar solvents such as trichloromethane, ethyl acetate, and butyl acetate. The solubilities of the alcohols in ethyl ether are shown in Table III.

The alcohols are quite soluble in the moderately polar solvents acetone and 2-butanone. In the lower alcohols (methanol, 95% ethanol, 2-propanol, and 1-butanol), the higher alcohols become

TABLE II

EUTECTICS FORMED BY ALCOHOLS

		No. of C Atoms				
Solvent		10	12	14	16	18
Benzene	Wt. % Alcohol	38.0	23.9	6.5	1.7	0.8
	Temp.	$-7.5°$	$2.5°$	$5.2°$	$\approx 5.5°$	$\approx 5.5°$
Cyclohexane	Wt. % Alcohol	29.3	15.8	5.6	1.4	0.4
	Temp.	$-10.8°$	$-0.9°$	$4.8°$	$6.0°$	$6.5°$
Tetrachloro-methane	Wt. % Alcohol	5.7	1.1	0.1	.....	.....
	Temp.	$-25.2°$	$-23.3°$	$-23.0°$	.....	.....

TABLE III

SOLUBILITIES OF ALCOHOLS IN ETHYL ETHER

No. of C Atoms	Grams per 100 g. Ethyl Ether					
	$-40.0°$	$-20.0°$	$0.0°$	$20.0°$	$30.0°$	$34.5°$
10	8.0	38.9	520	∞	∞	∞
12	1.4	5.3	44.2	960	∞	∞
14	0.1	1.2	9.3	100	380	1180
16	...	0.1	3.0	26.1	76	123
18	...	....	0.5	7.7	26.4	46

more soluble at lower temperatures as the molecular weight of the solvent increases; however, at higher temperatures the relative solubilities are reversed and the alcohols are almost as soluble in methanol as in the non-polar or slightly polar solvents. The solubilities of the higher alcohols in acetone and 95% ethanol are shown in Tables IV and V respectively.

TABLE IV

SOLUBILITIES OF ALCOHOLS IN ACETONE

No. of C Atoms	Grams per 100 g. Acetone					
	$-20.0°$	$0.0°$	$10.0°$	$20.0°$	$30.0°$	$40.0°$
10	13.6	335	∞	∞	∞	∞
12	1.6	12.9	75	1150	∞	∞
14	<0.1	2.4	8.7	38.6	340	∞
16	.....	0.1	1.3	6.7	30.9	290
18	.....	.....	0.1	1.1	7.0	41.4

TABLE V

SOLUBILITIES OF ALCOHOLS IN 95% ETHANOL

Grams per 100 g. 95% Ethanol

No. of C Atoms	−40.0°	−20.0°	0.0°	20.0°	30.0°	40.0°
10	7.1	43.6	1150	∞	∞	∞
12	0.6	4.2	52	2120	∞	∞
14	...	0.4	6.4	105	630	∞
16	...	....	1.8	15.9	89	430
18	...	....	0.2	5.0	22.2	120

The solubilities of the alcohols in the highly polar solvents nitroethane and acetonitrile are so limited that the systems exist as two immiscible solutions over considerable ranges of concentrations. It is very interesting, however, that the range of immiscibility becomes smaller with increasing molecular weights of the

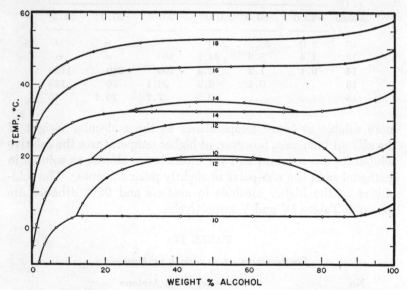

FIG. 1. Solubilities of alcohols in nitroethane.

alcohols. This is strikingly illustrated in Fig. 1, which shows the solubilities of the alcohols in nitroethane, in which the immiscible range is absent for both 1-hexadecanol and 1-octadecanol.

Although the solubility behavior of the alcohols is considered by many to be greatly influenced by molecular association, it is apparent that this phenomenon alone is not sufficient to explain all of their observed solubility characteristics.

Chemical Properties of the High Molecular Weight Aliphatic Alcohols

The most characteristic reaction of the alcohols is esterification. Such reactions are discussed later in this chapter and the properties of the high molecular weight aliphatic esters of both inorganic and organic acids are considered in some detail.

Oxidative reactions involving the higher primary alcohols first yield aldehydes, which are then further oxidized to the corresponding acids. For example, the oxidation of 1-heptanol yields heptanoic acid with the probable intermediate formation of heptanal.[164] The incomplete oxidation of the higher alcohols with potassium dichromate and sulfuric acid yields significant amounts of high molecular weight esters together with other products.[165,166,167] High yields of aldehydes are produced [168] by passing the lower alcohols, mixed with a limited amount of air, over a metallic catalyst, although unsatisfactory yields of the higher aldehydes are obtained by this procedure. It has been stated,[169] however, that if an excess of the alcohol vapors mixed with air be passed over a silver catalyst at reduced pressures (20 to 40 mm.) at 230–300°, high yields of the corresponding aldehydes result. For example, an 80% yield of 1-dodecanal has been obtained from dodecanol by this method.

The oxidation of primary alcohols to the corresponding acids may be accomplished by treatment with anhydrous sodium or potassium hydroxide at elevated temperatures (240–250°), hydrogen being evolved.[170] Although the higher alcohols yield soaps of the corresponding acids together with hydrogen when heated with alkali hydroxides, those alcohols which contain less than seven carbon atoms are also partly dehydrated to the corresponding olefins when so treated.[171]

Hydrogenation of the aliphatic alcohols yields saturated hydrocarbons. These are frequently formed in significant amounts during the preparation of alcohols by the high-pressure hydrogenation of the fatty acids or their esters. Such hydrocarbons result from further hydrogenation of the alcohols. For example, the hydrogenation of fats at 350° under 200 atmospheres pressure, in the presence of nickel, yields appreciable amounts of saturated hydrocarbons. The hydrogenation of esters in the presence of mixed oxide catalysts at temperatures above 400° results in the further hydrogenation of the resulting alcohols to saturated hydrocarbons.[90]

The thermal decomposition of the higher alcohols is a subject of appreciable interest, inasmuch as the initial decomposition can proceed in two directions. Such decompositions involve either a dehydrogenation of the alcohol with the formation of an aldehyde, thus:

$$RCH_2OH \rightarrow RCHO + H_2$$

or a dehydration to yield an olefin, thus:

$$RCH_2CH_2OH \rightarrow RCH{=}CH_2 + H_2O$$

The type of decomposition encountered is largely determined by the reaction conditions and by the presence of various catalytic materials. Generally, secondary reactions take place so that the final product is frequently quite heterogeneous. A study [172] of the non-catalytic decomposition of a number of the lower molecular weight alcohols at constant pressure and at temperatures between 300° and 525° showed that reactions of dehydration and subsequent polymerization, and reactions of dehydrogenation followed by the splitting off of carbon monoxide or by polymerization, proceed simultaneously. The non-volatile products of the dry distillation of 1-hexadecanol contain large amounts of unsaturated hydrocarbons.[173] The free-energy change for the dehydration of 1-alkanols has been stated [174] to conform approximately to the equation

$$\Delta F = 15,100 - 1410n - 25.6T$$

where n is the number of carbon atoms and T is in degrees Kelvin.

Subsequent studies upon the effect of high temperatures on the alcohols have shown that the nature of the resulting decomposition is materially influenced by various catalysts. Dehydrating catalysts such as aluminum oxide, thorium oxide, phosphoric acid, and other oxide catalysts greatly favor reactions of dehydration, whereas metallic catalysts such as nickel or copper promote dehydrogenation reactions. When 1-hexadecanol is passed over an aluminum oxide catalyst at 325–350°, the product consists almost exclusively of 1-hexadecene, the reaction apparently being one of dehydration.[175] On the other hand, when the decomposition is conducted in the presence of zinc oxide, the gaseous phase consists largely of hydrogen and the product contains substantial amounts of polymerized hexadecanal. It is, therefore, apparent that under such conditions zinc oxide promotes the dehydrogenation reaction. Chromium trioxide and also ferric oxide bring about both dehydration and dehydrogenation, as indicated by an analysis of both the solid and the gaseous products. Activated aluminum oxide is the contact catalyst most frequently employed for the dehydration of the higher alcohols to olefins, and dehydrations in the presence of this catalyst probably yield the normal olefins and not branched-chain olefins as has been reported.[176] Thus, the dehydration of 2-octanol in the presence of alumina yields a mixture of 1-octene and 2-octene with a minimum of branched-chain isomers.[177] 1-Heptene has been shown [178] to be the principal product of the dehydration of 1-heptanol over activated alumina at 380–400°. Likewise, the dehydration of 1-hexanol and 1-octanol over aluminum oxide at 350° yields the corresponding 1-alkenes as the main products.[179] The higher alcohols are dehydrated by treatment with phosphoric acid at elevated temperatures. For example, a mixture of 1-octene and 2-octene results when 2-octanol is dropped into anhydrous phosphoric acid heated to 225°.[180] Although it has been stated that a similar treatment of 1-octanol yields pure 1-octene, Whitmore and Herndon [181] have reported that the dehydration of this alcohol by means of heated phosphoric acid involves a rearrangement with the formation of a mixture of 1-octene and 2-octene in the approximate ratio of 2:1. 2-Octanol under such conditions yields a 1:4 ratio of 1-octene and 2-octene. A comparison of the dehydrating activities [182] of zinc chloride, phosphoric acid, and sulfuric acid for the conversion of 2-octanol into octenes has indicated that sulfuric acid is the most effective catalyst.

When the higher primary alcohols are passed over reduced nickel catalysts at 250° under 100–200 atmospheres of hydrogen, the liquid product consists essentially of the next lower saturated hydrocarbon, its formation being attributed to hydrogenolysis.[183] Undecane, tridecane, and heptadecane have been prepared by this method. The formation of these saturated hydrocarbons, however, does not necessarily involve hydrogenolysis, since it has been shown [184] that undecane is formed by the dehydrogenation of 1-dodecanol in the presence of metallic nickel, irrespective of whether the reaction is conducted in an atmosphere of hydrogen or nitrogen. The isolation of some dodecanal from the reaction product indicates that undecane results from a cleavage of carbon monoxide from dodecanal, the reaction proceeding as follows:

$$C_{12}H_{25}OH \rightarrow C_{11}H_{23}CHO + H_2$$
$$C_{11}H_{23}CHO \rightarrow C_{11}H_{24} + CO$$

In a study of the decomposition of 1-heptanol in the presence of nickel at 220°, Böeseken and van Senden [185] obtained high yields of hexane together with heptanal and some unchanged 1-heptanol. When the decomposition was conducted in the presence of carbon dioxide, the product contained both hexane and 1-hexene, the latter probably resulting from pyrolysis of the aldehyde into 1-hexene, hydrogen, and carbon monoxide. When 1-octanol is passed in the vapor phase at elevated temperatures over zinc chloride, a vigorous reaction results with the formation of octenes and lower olefins. The presence of aldehydes in the product indicates that both dehydration and dehydrogenation are encountered.[186] The decomposition of the higher alcohols in the presence of mixed catalysts, the components of which exert independent action, has been made the subject of an interesting study.[187] The pyrolysis of the higher alcohols in the presence of mixed dehydrating and dehydrogenating catalysts first yields olefins, the further dehydrogenation of which forms polyolefins. When alcohols are passed over an alumina-chromium oxide catalyst, a simultaneous dehydration and dehydrocyclization is encountered with the formation of aromatic hydrocarbons. It was reported that benzene and toluene are obtained from 1-hexanol and 1-heptanol, respectively, whereas 1-octanol gives a mixture of aromatic hydrocarbons. Since dehydration occurs at lower temperatures (200–300°) than dehydrogenation and cyclization (450°), the reaction was conducted at the higher temperature.

Alcohols react with isocyanates to form urethans, which are esters of substituted carbamic acids. Since these urethans are quite easily prepared and are definitely crystalline, they are frequently used as identifying derivatives for the higher alcohols. The method of preparation generally consists of heating the alcohol with a slight excess of an isocyanate and crystallizing the resulting urethan from the appropriate solvent. The reaction of 1-dodecanol with phenyl isocyanate is illustrative of the preparation of the urethans, thus:

$$C_6H_5N{=}C{=}O + HOC_{12}H_{25} \rightarrow C_6H_5NHCO_2C_{12}H_{25}$$

The phenyl urethans have long been employed for the identification of the higher alcohols. It has been found, however, that the α-naphthyl urethans [188, 189] and the substituted phenyl urethans such as the *p*-nitrophenyl urethans [190] and the 3,5-dinitrophenyl urethans [191] are equally satisfactory derivatives. The melting points of the phenyl, α-naphthyl, and 3,5-dinitrophenyl urethans of some of the more important higher alcohols are shown in Table VI.

TABLE VI

MELTING POINTS OF URETHANS OF PRIMARY ALIPHATIC ALCOHOLS

Melting Points, °C.

Alcohol	Phenyl Urethan	α-Naphthyl Urethan	3,5-Dinitrophenyl Urethan
Butanol	57	71	64
Hexanol	42	59	58
Heptanol	68	62	47
Octanol	74	66	61
Nonanol	62	..	52
Decanol	60	71	57
Undecanol	62	..	62
Dodecanol	..	80	..
Pentadecanol	72	..	..
Hexadecanol	73	82	..
Octadecanol	80	..	88
10-Undecenol	54.5–55	..	..
Elaidyl alcohol	55	71	

o-, *m*-, and *p*-Nitrophenyl urethans have been prepared from several of the higher alcohols, the list including: (alcohol, m.p. of urethan) *o*-nitrophenyl urethans: 1-octanol, 44°; 1-nonanol, 34°; 1-undecanol, 37°; *m*-nitrophenyl urethans: 1-octanol, 63°; 1-nonanol, 66°; 1-undecanol, 56°; *p*-nitrophenyl urethans: 1-hexanol, 103°; 1-heptanol, 102°; 1-nonanol, 104°; 1-undecanol, 99.5°. The *p*-xenyl urethans of several of the lower molecular weight alcohols have also been prepared.[192] It has been stated that the 4′-iodobiphenylyl urethans,[193] prepared by heating the alcohols with 4′-iodobiphenylyl isocyanate, are quite satisfactory derivatives for the identification of the higher primary alcohols. The following melting points were reported for these compounds: (alcohol, m.p. of urethan) methanol, 191°; ethanol, 200–200.5°; 1-propanol, 189°; 1-butanol, 173–174°; 1-pentanol, 166.5°; 1-hexanol, 156°; 1-heptanol, 150–151°; 1-octanol, 148–149°; 1-nonanol, 148.5–149°; 1-decanol, 147°; 1-undecanol, 146.5°; 1-dodecanol, 146°; 1-tridecanol, 144–144.5°; 1-tetradecanol, 142–143°; 1-pentadecanol,

141.5°; 1-hexadecanol, 138–138.5°; 1-heptadecanol, 138.5°; and 1-octadecanol, 137.5°.

Carbamates of the higher alcohols are prepared by heating the lower esters of carbamic acid with the alcohols. Thus, the action of ethyl carbamate with 1-octadecanol yields octadecyl carbamate with the evolution of ethanol.[194]

Several aromatic esters of the higher alcohols have been proposed as derivatives for their identification. Malone and Reid [195] have prepared the 3,5-dinitrobenzoates of the normal alcohols from methanol to 1-decanol by the procedure of Reichstein.[196] Such esters show an alternation in the melting points of the odd and even members, the following values having been reported: (ester, m.p.) propyl, 73.0°; butyl, 62.5°; pentyl, 46.4°; hexyl, 58.4°; heptyl, 46.9°; octyl, 60.8°; nonyl, 52.2°; and decyl, 56–57°. The 3,5-dinitrobenzoates of several of the lower molecular weight alcohols have been prepared and their optical properties investigated.[197] The p-nitrobenzoates have been obtained by the action of the alcohols on p-nitrobenzoyl chloride in the presence of sodium hydroxide.[198]

The higher alcohols can be made to enter into a variety of condensation reactions. They may be condensed, for example, with ethylene oxide to form high molecular weight ether alcohols which are useful as wetting agents.[199] Mixtures of the condensation product of ethylene oxide and oleyl alcohol with substances such as N-(2-hydroxyethyl)dodecylamine have been stated to function as wetting agents.[200] 1-Hexadecanol has been condensed successively with ethylene oxide and propylene oxide and the resulting product sulfonated to increase its water solubility.[201] The higher alcohols have been condensed with lower aldehydes such as formaldehyde in the presence of hydrogen halides to yield products which may be further treated for the preparation of a variety of water-soluble derivatives.[202] The acyl derivatives of sugars, such as pentaacetylglucose, may be condensed with the higher alcohols in the presence of dehydrating agents for the preparation of glucosides. Such products have been sulfonated and the neutralized products have been stated to possess high wetting properties.[203]

ESTERS OF THE HIGHER ALCOHOLS

Esters of Inorganic Acids

The esterification of the higher aliphatic alcohols by inorganic acids or allied compounds yields the corresponding alkyl or alkenyl esters, many of which are of considerable academic and commercial importance. Such compounds include the high molecular weight alkyl or alkenyl halides, sulfates, phosphates, thiocyanates, and many others. A number of representatives of this class of compounds have been prepared and their properties described.

The alkyl or alkenyl halides are formed from the high molecular weight alcohols by replacement of the hydroxyl group by a halogen. The reactions employed do not differ fundamentally from those used for the preparation of the lower molecular weight halides, although the higher alcohols generally react much more slowly and consequently require somewhat more vigorous conditions for their complete esterification. The action of the phosphorus halides upon the higher molecular weight alcohols has been extensively employed for the preparation of the corresponding halides. The action of the phosphorus chlorides or bromides on the higher molecular weight alcohols is generally attended by the formation of secondary products with a resultant lowering in the yield of the desired halide. Satisfactory yields of the higher alkyl chlorides have been obtained by the action of phosphorus trichloride and zinc chloride on higher alcohols.[204] The presence of zinc chloride increases the yields of alkyl chlorides from the alcohols and phosphorus pentachloride, although this reagent is not satisfactory for the preparation of 1-chlorohexadecane. Thionyl chloride also converts the higher alcohols into the corresponding chlorides, the reaction proceeding in either the presence or the absence of a solvent such as benzene. The reaction of the higher alcohols with phosphorus iodides presents somewhat of a contrast to the above, these reactions generally proceeding very smoothly and giving high yields of the desired iodides. Such reactions are generally accomplished by heating the dry alcohol with a mixture of red phosphorus and iodine, the time and temperature required varying with the particular alcohol. An 85% yield of 1-iodohexadecane from 1-hexadecanol has been reported by the use of this procedure,[205] and it has frequently been employed for the synthesis of the long-chain iodoalkanes.[206]

The preparation of the haloalkanes by esterification of the corresponding alcohols with halogen acids is an old and well-known process. In the case of the higher alcohols, some unsaturated hydrocarbons are formed along with the halides when the alcohols are refluxed with constant-boiling hydrobromic acid.[207] Norris and associates [208] have studied the influence of the structure of an alcohol upon its reactivity with constant-boiling hydrobromic acid.

Relatively poor yields are obtained with the primary alcohols, whereas the secondary alcohols give better yields and the tertiary alcohols high yields of the halides. The reaction takes place much more slowly with increasing molecular weight of the alcohols, and a large excess of the acid is required. However, the addition of sulfuric acid to the reaction mixture permits of the application of this method to the preparation of the higher molecular weight bromides.[209] The higher alkyl bromide separates as a layer which is removed immediately in order to avoid decomposition. The preparation of lauryl bromide has been described as follows: *

In a 250 cc. round-bottomed flask are placed 70 g. of HBr (48%), 22 g. of conc. H_2SO_4, and 40 g. of lauryl alcohol. The mixture is boiled under a reflux condenser for five to six hours. The solution is diluted with water and the bromide layer is separated, washed once with a little cold conc. H_2SO_4, then with water, and finally with dilute sodium carbonate solution. The product is distilled under reduced pressure. The yield is 49 g. (91% of the theoretical).

The preparation of 1-bromododecane, -tetradecane, and -octadecane by a substantially similar procedure has been described in detail.[210, 211] Guyer and others [212] have studied the effects of temperature and various catalysts upon the esterification of 1-hexadecanol by the halogen acids. Both zinc chloride and zinc sulfate were observed to be effective catalysts for the esterification of the alcohol with hydrochloric acid. The activity of the former was attributed to the formation of a complex, $ROH \cdot 2ZnCl_2$, which then reacts with the acid to form a chloroalkane. Cadmium chloride is less catalytic than zinc chloride, and sulfuric acid, sodium sulfate, and copper sulfate were reported to be without effect. Hydrogen bromide reacts readily at 140–150° with 1-hexadecanol in the absence of a catalyst, and a quantitative yield of 1-iodohexadecane results when the alcohol is heated with 55% aqueous hydrogen iodide for two hours, the final temperature being 120°. These halides are also formed when hexadecyl stearate is similarly treated. The iodoalkanes are obtained when alkali metal iodides are treated with chloroalkanes in organic solvents.[213] The preparation of 1-iodoöctane by the action of sodium iodide on 1-chloroöctane in tetrahydrofurfural has been described.

The 1-chloroalkanes are liquids which are insoluble in water, but appreciably soluble in most organic solvents. The following

* Excerpted from Kamm and Marvel, *Organic Syntheses*, Coll. Vol. 1, Gilman, editor, pp. 27–28, John Wiley & Sons, New York (1932).

physical constants have been reported [204] for several of these esters: (number of C atoms, b.p., d_4^t, n_D^t) 6, 135–136°, 0.8759^{20}, 1.42364^{20}; 7, 159.0–159.5°, 0.8741^{20}, 1.42844^{20}; 8, 179–180°, 0.8745^{20}, 1.43424^{20}; 9, 98–100_{23}°, 0.8679^{20}, 1.43692^{20}; 10, 105–$105.5_{15.5}$°, 0.8696^{20}; 16, —, 0.8384^{20}, 1.45477^{20}, m.p. 13°.

Meyer and Reid [55] have stated that the 1-bromoalkanes have almost the same melting points as the hydrocarbons from which they are derived, thus indicating that a terminal bromine atom has approximately the same effect upon the melting point as a terminal hydrogen. The 1-bromoalkanes form an unusual series in that the melting point curve of those which contain an odd number of carbon atoms, above C_{13}, is higher than the melting point curve of those which contain an even number. Since the cooling curves show only a single halt, which occurs at the freezing point, it was concluded that they do not exhibit polymorphism. The melting points of the 1-bromoalkanes from 1-bromodecane to -octadecane inclusive are as follows: (C content, m.p.) 10, −29.26°; 11, −13.15°; 12, −9.60°; 13, 5.94°; 14, 5.67°; 15, 18.63°; 16, 17.54°; 17, 28.40°; 18, 27.35°. Niemann and Wagner [57] have reported the following freezing points for the 1-bromoalkanes: C_{14}, 5.5°; C_{16}, 17.8°; and C_{18}, 27.4°.

The 1-iodoalkanes possess somewhat higher melting points than the corresponding bromo derivatives. For example, Simon [214] has reported 1-chloropentane to melt at −99°, 1-bromopentane at −95.25°, and 1-iodopentane at −85.0°. The boiling points increase materially from the chloro to the iodo compounds, thus: 1-chloropentane, 108.35°; 1-bromopentane, 129.70°; and 1-iodopentane, 157.00°. The densities likewise increase, as follows: (d_4^{15}) 0.88657, 1.22367, and 1.52384. In 1932, Smith [206] called attention to the discordant values reported for the freezing point of supposedly pure samples of 1-iodohexadecane, the values varying from 21.15° [215] to 22.5°,[193] and he suggested that this may be explained by a diminution of the rate of crystallization occasioned by small amounts of impurities. His study of the binary system 1-iodohexadecane:1-iodoöctadecane showed such mixtures to be polymorphic, since the transparent crystals which first form change rapidly to a higher-melting, opaque modification. The binary system shows the formation of an equimolar compound of the two iodides, the compound possessing a non-congruent melting point and apparently forming a eutectic with the lower-melting component. Although the pure components did not exhibit polymorphism, sufficient information was obtained to show that the mixtures exist in at least two polymorphic forms. Somewhat later, Francis, Collins, and Piper [147] showed the higher 1-iodo-alkanes (C_{22}–C_{30}) to exist in α- and β-forms, the latter of which is stable and melts several degrees higher than the former. The crystal spacings of the β-form as shown by x rays were also determined. The molecular rotations and the dipole characteristics of 1-chlorodecane, -dodecane, and -hexadecane have been investigated.[216]

The unsaturated alcohols react with hydrobromic acid to give the corresponding bromo compounds together with some of the dibromo compounds. Thus, 10-undecenol, $CH_2:CH(CH_2)_8CH_2OH$, when treated with hydrobromic acid, yields 1-bromo-10-undecene, b_8 117–118°, d_{15} 1.070, along with a smaller quantity of 1,10-dibromoundecane, b_8 164–165°.[157] If the reaction is prolonged the latter product is obtained in appreciable yields. The action of hydrobromic acid on 12-tridecen-1-ol yields 1-bromo-12-tridecene, b_8 141–143°, d_{15} 0.8795, and 1,12-dibromotridecane, b_8 185°, d_{15} 1.217. 14-Pentadecen-1-ol gives the 1-bromoalkene, b_8 164–166°, d_{15} 1.009, and 1,14-dibromopentadecane when similarly treated.

The polymethylene glycols, $HO(CH_2)_xOH$, when treated with hydrobromic acid yield the corresponding dibromo compounds with the intermediate formation of the bromohydrins. Chuit and Hausser [58, 59, 217] have prepared a number of bromohydrins and dibromides and have reported the following physical constants: $Br(CH_2)_9OH$, m.p. 33.5°, b_2 125–126°; $C_9H_{18}Br_2$, b_2 121°, d_{15} 1.145; $Br(CH_2)_{10}OH$, b_8 153.5°, d_{15} 1.188; $C_{10}H_{20}Br_2$, m.p. 27.4°, b_9 161.1–162.4°, d_{30} 1.335; $C_{11}H_{22}Br_2$, b_{12} 179°, d_{15} 1.332; $C_{12}H_{24}Br_2$, m.p. 36.8°, b_8 177–178°; $C_{13}H_{26}Br_2$, m.p. 8–10°, b_9 185–187°, d_{15} 1.276; $C_{14}H_{28}Br_2$, m.p. 50.4°, b_8 190–192°; $Br(CH_2)_{15}OH$, m.p. 59–60°; $C_{15}H_{30}Br_2$, m.p. 15°, b_{15} 215–225°; $C_{16}H_{32}Br_2$, m.p. 56.2–56.7°; $C_{17}H_{34}Br_2$, m.p. 38–38.4°; $C_{18}H_{36}Br_2$, m.p. 63.5–64°, $b_{1.5}$ 205–207°; $C_{19}H_{38}Br_2$, m.p. 46.2–46.5°, $b_{1.5}$ 210–211°; $C_{20}H_{40}Br_2$, m.p. 67.4–68°, b_2 220–222°; $C_{21}H_{42}Br_2$, m.p. 52.5–53°, $b_{2.5}$ 226–228°. It will be noted that the melting points of these dibromides alternate from even to odd member, the alternation becoming less the higher the molecular weight. The preparation of the higher polymethylene dibromides from the glycols by converting a lower glycol to the dibromide and thence to the nitrile, hydrolyzing the nitrile to its corresponding dicarboxylic acid, and reducing its ester to a glycol, is a process which involves many steps and must be repeated several times in order to obtain the higher members of the series. In 1909, v. Braun [218] suggested a procedure whereby the lower dibromide is treated with sodium phenolate to yield the bromoether $Br(CH_2)_xOPh$. This ether is then subjected to the Wurtz reaction and thereby converted into the diether $PhO(CH_2)_{2x}OPh$, which is then split with a hydrohalide to yield the desired polymethylene dihalide. In a subsequent work,[219] it was observed that the phenoxy group of the higher members resists cleavage. However, conversion of the diphenoxy derivatives to the corresponding cycloaliphatic compounds by catalytic hydrogenation yields the dicyclohexyl ethers, which are easily cleaved. The preparation of 1,12-dibromododecane from adipic acid has been described in detail.[220]

The high molecular weight fluoroalkanes are prepared by the reaction of metallic fluorides or hydrogen fluoride on haloalkanes. Such reactions frequently yield appreciable amounts of olefins and other products along with the fluoro compounds. For example, the reaction of 1-iodobutane with mercurous fluoride in a copper flask gives somewhat more than 50% of 1-fluorobutane, $b_{745.8}$ 31.95°, d_{15} 0.7824, together with a mixture of butenes.[221] 1-Bromo-hexane and mercurous fluoride yield 1-fluorohexane, b_{755} 93.15°, d_{15} 0.8052, n_D^{20} 1.3747, together with hexenes and a little 2-fluoro-hexane. The action of silver silicofluoride, Ag_2SiF_6, or of mercuric silicofluoride, $HgSiF_6$, on 1-iodoöctane yields both 1-fluoroöctane and octenes. Higher yields of the former result from the use of silver fluoride.[222] It has been stated [223] that the use of hydrogen fluoride is preferable to that of silver fluoride for the preparation of the higher fluoroalkanes. The 1-fluoroalkanes can be distilled without decomposition, which distinguishes them from the fluoro-isoalkanes. They are quite resistant to the action of alkali hydroxides, but they react with concentrated sulfuric acid in the cold with the liberation of hydrogen fluoride. The following physical constants have been reported for several of the higher molecular weight 1-fluoroalkanes: -pentane, m.p. $< -80°$, b 62.8°, d_{20} 0.7880; -heptane, m.p. $-73°$, b_{755} 119°, d_2 0.8029; -octane, b_{750} 142.5°, d_{21} 0.8036; -decane, b 183.5°, $d_{0.2}$ 0.792; -hexadecane, b 287.5°, $d_{7.5}$ 0.809.

The chloro-, bromo-, and iodoalkanes are quite reactive and are frequently employed as intermediates for the preparation of high molecular weight compounds. Replacement of the halogen atom by a cyanide group is a common procedure for the synthesis of

higher nitriles and acids.[157] The haloalkanes may be hydrolyzed
to the corresponding alcohols. They lose hydrogen halide when
heated with organic bases. For example, 1-iodohexane is converted into a mixture of isomeric hexenes when heated with quinoline.[56] The Friedel-Crafts alkylation of benzene by 1-bromo-
octadecane yields 50% of 1-phenyloctadecane with no evidence of
polyalkylation or lateral rearrangement.[224] However, it has been
reported [225] that the reaction of 1-bromoöctadecane with ethyl
5-bromo-2-furoate gives a 46% yield of ethyl 4-*tert*-butyl-5-bromo-
2-furoate. 1-Bromohexadecane, -tetradecane, and -dodecane yield
the corresponding 1-phenylalkanes when treated with benzene in
the presence of aluminum chloride.[226] A detailed study of the reaction between 1-bromododecane and benzene showed that, in addition to 1-phenyldodecane, small amounts of isomeric phenyldodecanes are formed.

The Wurtz-Fittig reaction is frequently used for the preparation
of high molecular weight hydrocarbons from the haloalkanes.
Such reactions yield either aliphatic hydrocarbons or alkyl-substituted hydrocarbons depending upon the reacting components
employed. For example, 1-iodoöctadecane and iodobenzene give
substantial yields of 1-phenyloctadecane.[224, 227] Hydrocarbons with
the same number of carbon atoms as the haloalkanes have been
synthesized by treating iodoalkanes with sodium amalgam in the
presence or absence of a solvent. When the haloalkanes are
treated with sodium or potassium in boiling xylene, hydrocarbons
containing double the number of carbon atoms are obtained in
appreciable yields.[9, 215]

The high molecular weight chloro-, bromo-, and iodoalkanes
react with magnesium to yield the well-known Grignard reagents.
The conditions for the preparation of the higher alkyl Grignard
reagents do not differ essentially from those employed for those of
lower molecular weight. The higher primary bromo- and iodoalkanes react quite readily with magnesium; however, the chloroalkanes react much more slowly. The higher alkylmagnesium
chlorides are frequently quite difficult to prepare. Marvel,
Gauerke, and Hill [228] have synthesized the alkylmagnesium chlorides, bromides, and iodides up to and including the octyl derivatives, and have treated these reagents with the corresponding
mercuric halides to obtain alkylmercuric halides. The latter are
well-crystallized compounds which are useful in the identification
of the haloalkanes. The preparation of a number of high molecular

weight organometallic compounds, particularly those containing magnesium or lithium, has been described,[229] and it was reported that compounds such as octadecylmagnesium bromide can be obtained in yields as high as 95%. Webster and Schaefer [75] have prepared hexadecyl- and heptadecylmagnesium bromides and have obtained 1-heptadecanol and 1-octadecanol by treatment of these compounds with formaldehyde. The action of magnesium on the α,ω-dihaloalkanes yields not only the expected dimagnesium halides, but the magnesium also exerts a condensation effect similar to that of the Wurtz reaction. Magnesium completely dissolves in a solution of 1,6-dibromohexane and ether at $-14°$; if, however, the ether is replaced by toluene and the mixture is heated for six hours at 120°, a 30% yield of 1,12-dibromododecane results. A smaller yield of 1,12-diiodododecane is obtained from 1,6-diiodohexane. 1,7-Dibromoheptane gives a 20% yield of 1,14-dibromotetradecane, but pure 1,20-dibromoeicosane could not be isolated from the reaction mixture of magnesium and 1,10-dibromodecane.[230] The dibromoparaffins react with sodiomalonic ester to yield esters of the type

$$\begin{array}{c} CH_2(CH_2)_x \\ | \\ CH_2(CH_2)_x \end{array}\!\!\!\!\!>\!\!C(CO_2Et)_2$$

from which the corresponding dicarboxylic acids can readily be obtained.[231]

The haloalkanes may be identified as the S-alkylisothiourea picrates,[232] which are prepared by the reaction of the halo compounds with thiourea followed by conversion of the resulting S-alkylthiourea halides to the corresponding picrates, the reactions being as follows:

$$HS-C\!\!\!<^{NH_2}_{NH} + RX \rightarrow RSC\!\!\!<^{NH_2}_{NH}\cdot HX \xrightarrow{HOC_6H_2(NO_2)_3}$$

$$RSC\!\!\!<^{NH_2}_{NH}\cdot HOC_6H_2(NO_2)_3 + HX$$

The melting points of several of these picrates have been reported [233] to be as follows: butyl, 177°; pentyl, 154°; hexyl, 157°; heptyl, 142°; octyl, 134°; and hexadecyl, 137°.

The alkyl thiocyanates have been obtained by the action of sodium or potassium thiocyanate on the haloalkanes, or by the treatment of lead mercaptides with cyanogen chloride.[234] Allen [235] has prepared a series of alkyl thiocyanates by refluxing one mole of the bromoalkane with 1.5 moles of potassium thiocyanate in 340 cc. of ethanol for two hours, and has reported the following physical constants for these esters: (ester, b.p., d_4^{25}, n_D^{25}) octyl, 141–142$_{19}$°, 0.9149, 1.4642; nonyl, 156–157$_{19}$°, 0.9091, 1.4649; decyl, 154–155$_{15}$°, 0.9047, 1.4652; undecyl, 160–161$_{10}$°, 0.9007, 1.4653; dodecyl, 170–172$_{10}$°, 0.8958, 1.4657; tridecyl, 173–176$_7$°, 0.8935, 1.4661. The alkyl thiocyanates are insoluble in water but are readily soluble in ether, benzene, absolute methanol and ethanol, carbon tetrachloride, and ethyl acetate. The solubility in alcohol decreases with increasing molecular weight. 1-Methylheptyl thiocyanate has been synthesized by Rose and Haller.[236] The alkyl thiocyanates have been used extensively as insecticides.[237, 238]

The high molecular weight alkyl sulfates are represented by two groups of esters, the neutral esters R_2SO_4 and the acid esters RSO_3OH. Salts of the latter type are extensively employed as wetting agents and detergents and are among the more important derivatives of the fatty acids.

Several methods have been proposed for the preparation of the dialkyl sulfates; however, most of the suggested procedures have been shown to give quite low yields when applied to the higher members of the series. The action of sulfuric acid on the higher alcohols generally yields acid sulfates, together with smaller amounts of ethers and other products. The oxidation of alkyl sulfites by the method proposed by Voss and Blanke [239] gives quite low yields when applied to the higher molecular weight sulfites. The reaction of the alkyl chlorosulfonates with the sodium alcoholates [240, 241, 242] likewise gives low yields of the higher alkyl sulfates. The action of the alkyl chlorosulfonates with the alkyl sulfites [243] offers a satisfactory procedure for the synthesis of the higher alkyl sulfates. The application of this method to the preparation of the higher sulfates has been studied by Barkenbus and Owen,[244] who considered the two main reactions to be as follows:

(I) $(RO)_2SO + ClSO_2OCH_2CH_2R' \rightarrow$

$$(RO)_2SO_2 + R'CH{=}CH_2 + HCl + SO_2$$

(II) $(RO)_2SO + ClSO_2OR' \rightarrow (RO)_2SO_2 + SO_2 + R'Cl$

The physical constants of the dialkyl sulfates as reported by these authors are listed in Table VII.

TABLE VII

PHYSICAL CONSTANTS OF DIALKYL SULFATES

R Group	B.P., °C.	M.P., °C.	d_{25}^{25}	n_D^{25}
Butyl	97.4$_3$	....	1.0591	1.4210
Pentyl	117.0$_{2.5}$	....	1.0265	1.4270
Hexyl	125.3$_2$	....	1.0039	1.4344
Heptyl	146.6$_{1.5}$	11.4	0.9819	1.4362
Octyl	166.1$_2$	20.3	0.9661	1.4408
Nonyl	....	41.9–42.1		
Decyl	....	37.6–37.8		
Dodecyl	....	48.4–48.5		
Tetradecyl	....	57.8–58.0		
Hexadecyl	....	66.2–66.3		
Octadecyl	....	70.2–70.7		

The long-chain alkyl hydrogen sulfates have been extensively investigated during recent years. Interest in these compounds largely centers around the facts that they are appreciably soluble in water and that their alkali metal salts, such as sodium dodecyl sulfate (Gardinol), possess marked surface active properties. Such compounds are extensively employed as wetting agents and detergents, their advantage over the soaps lying in the fact that their aqueous solutions are quite stable in hard waters. The preparation and the many uses of these compounds have been the subjects of a number of patents. The use of the higher alkyl hydrogen sulfates and their salts as wetting agents and detergents is a comparatively recent development. Among the earlier patents in this field is one issued to H. Th. Böhme A.-G.,[245] which called attention to the wetting and emulsifying properties of the higher alkyl sulfuric acids.

The higher alkyl hydrogen sulfates may be prepared by a variety of methods, the most important of which consists of treating the alcohols at low temperatures with concentrated sulfuric acid or chlorosulfonic acid. The preparation of alkyl hydrogen sulfates by the esterification of a number of the higher alcohols, or of various mixtures of alcohols such as those derived from coconut or palm oil fatty acids, with concentrated sulfuric acid, has been described.[246] Oleyl alcohol when so treated gives the sulfuric ester of 1,9-octadecanediol. The velocity of esterification of oleyl alcohol by sulfuric acid has been studied in some detail.[247] The removal of excess sulfating agent may be accomplished by adding lower molecular weight alcohols or esters such as glyceryl mono-sulfate to the sulfated alcohols.[248] The surface active properties of dodecyl hydrogen sulfate, its higher homologs, and their derivatives are quite pronounced, and solubility considerations have resulted in a centering of interest around the dodecyl ester. The most abundant source of such compounds is the fatty alcohols obtained by the hydrogenation of coconut oil acids, and it has been proposed [249] to remove the lower alcohols from such mixtures and sulfate the remaining alcohols, 1-dodecanol and its higher homologs, for the preparation of wetting agents.

The alkyl hydrogen sulfates can be obtained by the action of chlorosulfonic acid on the higher alcohols in the presence of organic bases such as pyridine,[250] or by the action of chlorosulfonic acid on alcohols in the presence of inert solvents.[251] Sulfuric esters may be obtained by the reaction of either saturated or unsaturated alcohols with the addition product of chlorosulfonic acid or sulfur trioxide and a tertiary base.[252] The esterification of the unsaturated alcohols, such as oleyl alcohol, with sulfonating agents in the presence of organic bases has been investigated,[253] as has the preparation of compounds such as the pyridine salt of dodecyl or octadecyl sulfate.[254] These last compounds have been stated to possess surface active properties.

The alkyl hydrogen sulfates are easily converted to their sodium salts, the detergent properties of which are well known. The salts can be prepared directly from the higher alcohols by neutralization of the esters formed during the process of sulfation, without an actual isolation of the intermediate esters.[255] The preparation of a number of these high molecular weight sodium alkyl sulfates has been described,[249] and details have also been given for the preparation of water-soluble salts of the sulfuric esters of 2-nonadecanol and related compounds.[256] Various processes for the preparation of salts of the alkyl sulfuric acids have been suggested, one of which proposes to atomize the alcohol and a solid sulfating agent into a reaction vessel.[257] The direct preparation of the ammonium salts of the alkyl sulfuric acids has been accomplished by treatment of the higher alcohols with aminosulfonic acid, NH_2SO_3H, an example being the synthesis of ammonium octadecyl sulfate by the action of this reagent on 1-octadecanol.[258]

Many uses have been suggested for the alkyl sulfuric acids and their alkali metal salts, and most of the patents which relate to their preparation have suggested their use as wetting agents and detergents.[245, 246, 249] Mixtures of the sodium alkyl sulfates and alkali phosphates have been stated to possess good cleansing properties,[259] and mixtures of the sodium alkyl sulfates with various organic sulfates and water-soluble inorganic alkali salts have been claimed to possess excellent cleansing properties.[260] Treatment of the alkyl hydrogen sulfates with sodium sulfite produces superior wetting agents,[261] and their action with halogenating agents yields emulsifying and cleansing agents.[262] The use of the alkyl hydrogen sulfates as addends to flotation agents has been suggested,[263] and mixtures of sodium alkyl sulfates with the higher alcohols[264] or with mineral oils[265] have been proposed as flotation agents. The sodium alkyl sulfates have been stated to function as stabilizing agents for rubber latex.[266] They prevent adhesion between the contacting surfaces during the process of vulcanization of rubber articles.[267] Cory and Langford[268] have investigated the use of sodium alkyl sulfates as insecticides and have found them to be valuable emulsifying agents for insecticidal oils. Sodium dodecyl sulfate, which was the most lethal to insects of the salts investigated, possesses a toxicity comparable to that of potassium laurate; however, high concentrations of sodium alkyl sulfates cannot be used in insecticidal compositions because of excessive plant injury. Mixtures of the sodium alkyl sulfates and pyrethrins are active mosquito larvicides.

The alkyl hydrogen sulfates and their salts may be identified as their S-benzylthiuronium derivatives, prepared by the reaction of the esters with S-benzylthiuronium chloride.[269] This reagent can easily be obtained by the reaction of benzyl chloride with thiourea.[270, 271] The reaction between the alkyl hydrogen sulfates and S-benzylthiuronium chloride proceeds as follows:

$$C_6H_5CH_2SC(NH_2)_2Cl + ROSO_3H \rightarrow ROSO_3(NH_2)_2CSCH_2C_6H_5 + HCl$$

The following melting points have been reported for these derivatives: propyl, 111.5–112.5°; butyl, 100–101°; pentyl, 85–86°; hexyl, 85–86°; heptyl, 77–79°; octyl, 42–70°(?); decyl, 73–75°; dodecyl, 74–76°; tetradecyl, 87–88°.

Stenhagen[272] has studied the monolayers of sodium docosyl sulfate on $M/25$ phosphate buffer and on $0.01N$ HCl. A strong interaction between the head groups was indicated by the fact that the monolayers solidify on both substrates at a pressure of a few dynes and a molecular area of 26 sq. Å. The monolayers are quite stable and show little tendency to dissolve.

The high molecular weight esters of the phosphorus acids and their salts possess properties somewhat similar to the sulfates; however, such esters are not so well known as the sulfates or the acid sulfates. Hexadecyl dihydrogen phosphate, first prepared by Biehringer,[273] has been synthesized by Plimmer and Burch [274] by heating phosphorus oxychloride, $POCl_3$, and 1-hexadecanol in chloroform for two hours over a water bath. The reaction mixture is poured into water and neutralized with barium hydroxide, yielding barium monohexadecyl phosphate, from which the acid ester, m.p. 72°, is obtained by acidification. Prolonged heating of the reaction mixture yields some dihexadecyl phosphoryl chloride, from which the dihexadecyl ester can readily be obtained. When 1-hexadecanol and phosphorus oxychloride are boiled under a reflux condenser the sole product is 1-hexadecene; however, gradually adding the oxychloride to 1-hexadecanol on a water bath yields trihexadecyl phosphate, m.p. 61°. This ester may also be obtained by heating an ether solution containing an excess of 1-hexadecanol with phosphorus pentoxide. Hexadecylchloroethylphosphoric acid, m.p. 54.5°, is obtained by the action of 2-chloroethylphosphoryl dichloride and 1-hexadecanol.[275] Compounds related to the phosphatides are formed by the treatment of such esters with liquid ammonia.

The alkyl esters of pyrophosphoric acid, $H_4P_2O_7$, have been prepared by heating the higher alcohols with pyrophosphoric acid.[276] Graves [277] has described the preparation of a number of the mixed alkyl esters of the phosphorus acids, such as dodecyl octadecenyl hydrogen phosphate, and has proposed the use of such esters as plasticizers and addends to lubricants. The heavy metal salts of these esters are catalysts for the oxidation of drying oils. Mixed phosphoric and sulfuric acid esters have been prepared from the dihydric alcohols, such as ricinoleyl alcohol, by esterification of one hydroxyl group with phosphoric acid, and of the other group with sulfuric acid.[278] These products are used as washing and emulsifying agents. The preparation of the higher alkyl esters of boric acid and of silicic acid has been studied, and such esters have been stated to function as plasticizers.[279] The incorporation of the alkyl esters of silicic acid into the nitrocellulose plastics markedly reduces the inflammability of the latter.

Esters of Organic Acids—The Synthetic Waxes

The esters of higher molecular weight alcohols and fatty acids range in physical properties from the crystalline acetates to the waxy esters of the higher acids. The latter are well known as components of the natural waxes.

The acetates of higher alcohols may be prepared by treatment of the alcohols with acetic anhydride in the presence of fused sodium acetate. The melting points of the higher acetates are quite close to those of the ethyl esters with which they are isomeric. The acetates of the higher alcohols present an interesting case of polymorphism. Meyer and Reid [55] have reported two fusion points for hexadecyl and octadecyl acetates and for the acetates of the odd alcohols 1-undecanol, 1-tridecanol, and 1-pentadecanol. The melting points and transition temperatures of the acetates from decyl to octadecyl have been reported by these authors. The cooling curves of these acetates are unusual in that the curves fall until the α- or metastable form begins to crystallize, remain flat during the crystallization of this form, rise abruptly when solidification is completed to the fusion point of the β-form, again remain flat for an appreciable time interval, and finally fall again. If the sample is agitated during the crystallization of the α-form, the temperature rises immediately to the β- freezing point. Phillips and Mumford [141] have made an extensive investigation of the dimorphism of the acetates and have assembled the available thermal data relative to the polymorphic forms. The acetates of the even alcohols from C_{12} to C_{18} exhibit monotropic dimorphism, the transparent α-form changing into the opaque β-form. With the acetates of the lower alcohols C_{12} and C_{14}, the α-form is realizable only by admixture. The acetates of the uneven alcohols exhibit three polymorphic forms, the transparent α-form first changing into an opaque β-form, the change being monotropic for the lower and enantiotropic for the higher members. This β-form then changes monotropically and slowly into a still higher-melting β_2-form. The transition $\alpha \rightarrow \beta$ for the even acetates is quite rapid; however, the transformation $\beta \rightarrow \beta_2$ for the odd acetates is quite slow, the final temperature reached being lower than the melting point. The melting and freezing points of the acetates [141] are recorded in Table VIII, and the relationship of the various forms [55] is shown in Fig. 2.

Physical constants for acetates not included in Table VIII have been reported as follows: hexyl, b 169.2°, d_0^0 0.8902; heptyl, b 195°, d_0^0 0.8891; oleyl,[20] d_4^{20} 0.8704, n_D^{20} 1.4515; and tetracosyl,[280] m.p. 57°. Chuit [59] has prepared several of the glycol diacetates: $C_{11}H_{22}(OAc)_2$, b_{13} 181–183°, d_{15} 0.964; $C_{12}H_{24}(OAc)_2$,

TABLE VIII

MELTING AND FREEZING POINTS OF n-ALKYL ACETATES, °C.

(Tr = temp. of transition; ↓ = from cooling curve; ↑ = from heating curve)

No. of C Atoms in Alcohol	α-Form	β-Form (odd)	β-Form (even) β_2-Form (odd)
10	....	....	−15.05
11	....	−12.59	−9.27
12	−16.7	....	1.13
			1.3 *
13	....	2.44	7.03
14	3.3	....	14.0
15	11.4	14.7	18.5
			20.35 *
16	18.5	....	24.12
			24.2 *
17	24.6	Tr ↓ ca. 10.5	30.25 *
		Tr ↑ 21.5	
18	30.25	....	31.95
			32.85 *
19	35.35	Tr ↓ ca. 14	37.6 *
		Tr ↑ 27.2	
20	....	....	40 ± 0.5 *

* Denotes melting point.

b_{10} 189–190°, m.p. 36°; $C_{15}H_{30}(OAc)_2$, m.p. 36°; and $C_{16}H_{32}$-$(OAc)_2$, m.p. 47.2°.

Wetting agents have been obtained by sulfonation of the phenoxyacetic acid esters of the higher alcohols [281] and by the action of hyposulfurous acid on the higher alcohol esters of chloroacetic acid.[282]

The esters of the higher acids may be prepared by direct esterification with the acids or their anhydrides. The melting and boiling points of these esters increase with increasing molecular weight. The physical constants of a series of isomeric esters each of which contains sixteen carbon atoms, ranging from methyl pentadecanoate to pentadecyl formate, have been determined by Ruhoff and Reid.[283] The reported values are shown in Table V, Chapter VII. The physical properties of a number of the fatty acid esters of 1-decanol have been determined and the following values reported: [284, 285] propionate, b_8 123.9–124.3°, d_4^{20} 0.8639; butyrate,

b_8 134.8–135°, d_4^{20} 0.8617; caproate, b_{15} 219.0–219.1°, m.p. 9.7°, d_4^{20} 0.8586; and palmitate, m.p. 30°.

The higher molecular weight esters are waxlike solids. A number of them have been isolated from natural sources; however, the physical constants reported for these compounds are subject to some question because of the difficulty of separating such esters

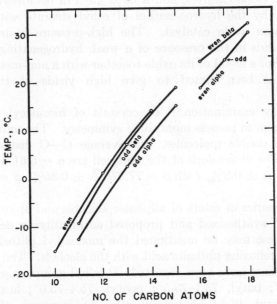

FIG. 2.   Melting points of polymorphic forms of n-alkyl acetates.

from their lower and higher homologs. Hexadecyl palmitate, m.p. 53.5°, has been prepared by Krafft [286] by the esterification of 1-hexadecanol with palmitic acid, and also by the action of palmitoyl chloride on the alcohol. The octadecyl ester, m.p. 59°, was obtained in a similar manner. The syntheses of docosyl behenate, m.p. 75°, and tetracosyl tetracosanoate, m.p. 75.9°, have been described.[280]   Gascard [9] has synthesized pentadecyl palmitate, m.p. 55.5°, and heptadecyl stearate, m.p. 64.7°, by a method originally proposed by Simonini [47] and subsequently employed by Panics,[48] which involves treatment of the silver salts of the respective acids with iodine. Hexacosyl stearate, m.p. 73°, and triacontyl stearate, m.p. 76°, have been obtained by direct esterification of their components.

High molecular weight esters are formed as intermediate products during the hydrogenation of fatty acids to alcohols, the proper choice of a catalyst and reaction conditions frequently resulting in substantial yields of such esters. Sauer and Adkins [115] obtained a 34% yield of octadecenyl oleate, b 272°, n_D^{25} 1.4618, by the high-pressure hydrogenation of butyl oleate in the presence of a zinc-chromium oxide catalyst, and a 63% yield of octadecyl stearate, m.p. 62°, by the hydrogenation of ethyl stearate with a zinc-molybdenum oxide catalyst. The high-pressure hydrogenation of fatty acids in the presence of a weak hydrogenating catalyst, consisting of a metal or its oxide together with a non-metallic compound, has been stated to give high yields of the higher esters.[116]

An x-ray examination [287] of crystals of hexadecyl palmitate showed them to possess monoclinic symmetry. The unit cell contains two double molecules, the average C—C distance being 1.27 Å. The dimensions of the unit cell are a = 5.61 Å ± 0.5%, b = 7.415 Å ± 0.2%, $c \sin \beta$ = 77.875 Å ± 0.35%, β = 61.3° ± 0.8%.

Several series of esters of aliphatic alcohols and aromatic acids have been synthesized and proposed as identifying derivatives. Among these may be mentioned the monoalkyl phthalates, obtained by refluxing phthalic acid with the alcohols. The following melting points have been reported: [288] (alkyl group, m.p.) propyl, 54.1–54.4°; butyl, 73.1–73.5°; pentyl, 75.4–75.6°; hexyl, 24.6–25.4°; heptyl, 16.5–17.5°; octyl, 21.5–22.5°; nonyl, 42.4–42.6°; decyl, 37.8–38.0°; undecyl, 43.8–44.1°; dodecyl, 50.2–50.4°; tridecyl, 52.4–52.7°; tetradecyl, 59.8–60.0°; pentadecyl, 60.3–60.5°; hexadecyl, 66.7–66.9°; heptadecyl, 66.6–66.8°; octadecyl, 72.4–72.6°; nonadecyl, 70.8–71.0°; eicosyl, 77.1–77.3°. The esters of 3-nitrophthalic acid possess much higher melting points, although they do not show so great a difference between the melting points of adjacent members as shown in the above series.[289]

THE HIGH MOLECULAR WEIGHT ALIPHATIC ETHERS

The high molecular weight ethers constitute an important group of derivatives which can be prepared from the higher alcohols. Such ethers are characterized by the presence of at least one long-chain hydrocarbon group and are represented by a large number of both symmetrical and unsymmetrical compounds. Many of the unsymmetrical ethers have been used as intermediates for the preparation of wetting agents and allied compounds.

The higher ethers may be prepared by processes generally applicable to the synthesis of their lower homologs. Senderens [290] has studied the synthesis of several of the higher alkyl symmetrical ethers such as dibutyl, diheptyl, and di-sec-octyl ethers, which can be obtained by the action of sulfuric acid on the respective alcohols. Olefin formation is pronounced when the higher alcohols are converted into ethers by this process, but may be retarded by a reduction in the amount of sulfuric acid employed. Dihexadecyl ether, m.p. 55°, has been prepared by this method.

The most frequently employed and satisfactory procedure for the synthesis of the higher ethers consists of treating alcoholates with haloalkanes or -alkenes, the reaction proceeding as follows:

$$RONa + R'X \rightarrow ROR' + NaX$$

This method is applicable to the synthesis of all types of higher molecular weight ethers, as for example the symmetrical and unsymmetrical dialkyl ethers, the mono- and polyethers of the glycols and glycerol, the alkyl aromatic ethers, and many others. Examples of the synthesis of the symmetrical dialkyl ethers by this procedure include the preparation of dihexadecyl ether by the action of 1-iodohexadecane and sodium hexadecoxide,[291] and the preparation of diheptyl ether by heating 1-iodoheptane with sodium heptoxide.[292] Dioctyl ether, b 286–287°, has been prepared by heating 1-iodoöctane with sodium octoxide in a sealed tube at 100°.[293] Gascard [9] has obtained didotriacontyl ether, m.p. 92°, by a similar procedure. The physical properties of the higher symmetrical dialkyl ethers whose alkyl groups contain an even number of carbon atoms are as follows: dioctyl ether, m.p. $-7°$, b 291.7°, d_{17}^{17} 0.805, n_D^{20} 1.4329; didecyl ether, m.p. 16°, b_6 170–180°, d_4^{20} 0.819, n_D^{20} 1.4418; didodecyl ether, m.p. 33°, b_1 190–195°, d_4^{33} 0.8147; ditetradecyl ether, m.p. 38.40°, b_4 238–248°, d_4^{45} 0.8127; dihexadecyl ether, m.p. 54°, d_4^{54} 0.8117; and dioctadecyl ether, m.p. 58–60°. These ethers are described [294] as ranging from colorless liquids to white, crystalline, waxlike solids which are insoluble in water, slightly soluble in 2-propanol, methanol, and glacial acetic acid, and soluble in acetone, ether, and benzene. The crystal structure of dihexadecyl ether has been investigated by Kohlhaas,[287, 295] who observed that this compound crystallizes in small, rhombic plates with profile angles of 73.7° and 106.4°. The crystal cell contains four molecules and has the dimensions $a = 5.571$ Å $\pm$ 0.2%, $b = 7.452$ Å $\pm$ 0.2%, $c \sin \beta = 78.19$ Å $\pm$ 0.4%, $\beta = 63.07°$ $\pm$ 0.5%.

Many representatives of the unsymmetrical dialkyl ethers have been prepared and their properties described. Ethyl heptyl ether, b_{748} 165°, has been synthesized by the action of sodium ethoxide on 1-iodoheptane,[296] or by heating 1-iodoheptane with alcoholic potassium hydroxide.[297] Propyl heptyl ether, b 187.6°, and butyl heptyl ether, b 205.7°, have been similarly prepared. The following alkyl octyl ethers have been described: methyl octyl,[54] b 173°; ethyl octyl,[291, 292] b 189.2°; propyl octyl, b 207°; butyl octyl, b 225.7°; and heptyl octyl, b 278.8°. Ethers containing a decyl radical have been obtained [284, 285] by the action of 1-iododecane on sodium ethoxide and its homologs, the following having been described: ethyl decyl ether, b 223.5–224°, b_8 99.6–99.8°, d_4^{20} 0.7942; propyl decyl, b 242.5°, b_{15} 122.5°, d_4^{20} 0.7973; butyl decyl, d_4^{20} 0.8009; and didecyl, $b_{15.5}$ 196°, d_4^{20} 0.8187. Ethyl hexadecyl ether,[298] f.p. 20°, and ethyl dotriacontyl ether,[9] m.p. 72°, have been synthesized. A series of ethers which contain a heptyl radical have been prepared [299] by the action of 1-bromoheptane on alcohols in the presence of sodamide. Methyl octyl ether, b 158°, has been obtained by the action of dimethyl sulfate on the magnesium alkoxide;[300] however, a considerable amount of octene is simultaneously formed, and the reaction is not successful for the preparation of ethyl octyl ether.

Vinyl alkyl ethers have been obtained by the action of acetylene on the liquid alcohols at temperatures between 120° and 180° in the presence of metallic sodium or a highly alkaline medium,[301, 302] the following having been described: vinyl octyl ether, b_5 75°; vinyl decyl ether, b_4 110°; vinyl dodecyl ether, b_4 120°; vinyl tetradecyl ether, b_4 140–145°; vinyl oleyl ether, b_2 170–175°; and vinyl octadecyl ether, b_{10} 190°. The last was hydrogenated to ethyl octadecyl ether, b_{10} 190°. Price and Dumbrow [303] have described the preparation of a series of methallyl ethers, such as methallyl dodecyl, methallyl hexadecyl, methallyl octadecyl ethers, and related compounds, the sulfonation of which was stated to yield surface active agents.

The unsymmetrical dialkyl ethers have frequently been suggested as intermediates for the preparation of wetting agents and allied chemicals. For example, surface active agents have been obtained [304] by the action of sulfonating or sulfating agents on ethers of the formula ROR', in which R is an unsaturated straight-chain group containing at least eight carbon atoms and R' is an alkyl group which contains one to five carbon atoms. The high molecular weight ethers which contain a halomethyl group, such as dodecyl chloromethyl ether, octadecyl chloromethyl ether, and dodecyl bromomethyl ether, have been proposed as intermediates for the synthesis of wetting agents. The reaction of such ethers with aminocarboxylic acids in the presence of acid-accepting agents,[305] or with sodium chloroacetate,[306] has been described. The chloromethyl ethers and similar compounds are reactive with tertiary bases to yield surface active products.[307]

High molecular weight ethers in which one of the R groups is a hydroxy- or polyhydroxyalkyl radical and the other is a long-chain hydrocarbon radical are compounds of unusual interest. The esterification of the hydroxyl group or groups of such ethers by sulfuric acid or other acids permits of the formation of surface active compounds, a large number of which have been described in the patent literature. Ethers of this type are generally prepared by reaction of the higher molecular weight alcohols with the chloro-hydrins of glycerol or the glycols. Thus, dodecyl 2,3-dihydroxy-propyl ether or its chloro derivatives can be prepared by the con-densation of 1-dodecanol and glycerol epichlorohydrin in the presence of a small amount of sulfuric acid.[308] The sodium salts of the sulfuric esters of this or similar ethers are water soluble and are useful as wetting and emulsifying agents. The preparation of high molecular weight alkyl 2,3-dihydroxypropyl ethers by the condensation of the fatty alcohols with glycerol α-chlorohydrin is a recognized method for the synthesis of such compounds.[309] Ethers which contain hydroxyalkyl radicals may also be obtained by condensation of esters of the higher alcohols, such as 1-chloro-dodecane, with alkoxides of the glycols or glycerol, or by condens-ing such esters with glycols or glycerol in a highly alkaline me-dium.[310, 311] Examples have been given of the preparation of 2-hydroxyethyl dodecyl ether, b_{15} 170–174°; 2,3-dihydroxypropyl dodecyl ether, b_3 198°; and its tetradecyl, b_3 206–207°, hexadecyl, b_1 205–206°, and octadecyl, b_2 215–220°, homologs.

The β-ethers of glycerol are prepared by condensation of the alkali metal derivative of alkylidene or aralkylidene glycerol with an alkyl ester. Thus, 1,3-dihydroxypropyl-2 hexadecyl ether is prepared by treating 1,3-benzylidene glycerol with sodium, and

condensing the product with 1-iodohexadecane, the reaction being
as follows:[312]

$$
\begin{array}{c}
CH_2O \\
| \\
CHOH \quad CHC_6H_5 \\
| \\
CH_2O
\end{array}
\xrightarrow{Na}
\begin{array}{c}
CH_2O \\
| \\
CHONa \quad CHC_6H_5 \\
| \\
CH_2O
\end{array}
\xrightarrow{C_{16}H_{33}I}
$$

$$
\begin{array}{c}
CH_2O \\
| \\
CHOC_{16}H_{33} \quad CHC_6H_5 \\
| \\
CH_2O
\end{array}
\xrightarrow{HCl}
\begin{array}{c}
CH_2OH \\
| \\
CHOC_{16}H_{33} \\
| \\
CH_2OH
\end{array}
$$

The monoalkyl ethers of ethylene glycol and trimethylene glycol
have been synthesized and described.[313] High molecular weight
ethers have also been prepared from the polyglycols and the haloalkanes,[314] and the reaction of these ethers with ethylene oxide has
been studied.[315] Schmidt and Meyer [316] have described the preparation of a large number of monoalkyl ethers of polyhydroxy compounds, such as the monoalkyl ethers of pentaerythritol [tetra-
hydroxymethylmethane, $C(CH_2OH)_4$], mannitol, sorbitol, and
allied polyhydroxy compounds. The alkyl ethers of cellulose have
been prepared [317] by reaction of partially acylated cellulose with
haloalkanes in the presence of alkalies.

A number of water-soluble compounds have been obtained from
the hydroxy ethers. For example, surface active agents result
from their sulfation or sulfonation,[318] and the halogenation of these
products for the preparation of textile assistants has been suggested.[319] The dihydroxy ethers prepared from glycerol and the
high molecular weight chloroalkanes may be treated with chloroacetyl chloride and then with sodium sulfate to produce water-
soluble derivatives,[320] and the monohydroxy ethers obtained from
the glycols may be similarly treated. Wetting agents may be
prepared from the monoalkyl ethers of the glycols by esterifying
the free hydroxyl group with a dibasic acid and converting the
resulting compound to its alkali metal salt.[321]

The many representatives of the mixed alkyl aromatic ethers
which have been synthesized testify to a considerable interest in
compounds of this type. The preparation of ethers from the monohydric phenols and structurally similar compounds is generally
accomplished by heating a haloalkane with the alkali metal derivative of the phenol, or by reaction with the phenol itself in a highly
alkaline medium. Examples of mixed ethers which have been

prepared include phenyl decyl ether,[284, 285] m.p. 8–10°, b_{15} 178°, obtained by the action of 1-iododecane on sodium phenoxide; phenyl heptadecyl ether, m.p. 42°; p-tolyl dodecyl ether, m.p. 23.5°; and p-, m-, and o-tolyl hexadecyl ethers, m.p. 42.5°, 35°, and 21.5°, respectively, which are obtained by the action of bromoalkanes on the phenols in the presence of alcoholic potassium hydroxide.[322] Several 2-naphthyl alkyl ethers have been prepared by refluxing the bromoalkanes with 2-naphthol in half-normal alcoholic potassium hydroxide, and the following melting points have been reported for these ethers: [323] 2-naphthyl undecyl ether, 55–56°; tridecyl, 61–62°; pentadecyl, 66–67°; and heptadecyl, 70–71°. The p-nitrophenyl alkyl ethers have been synthesized in high yields by the reaction of potassium p-nitrophenoxide with haloalkanes dissolved in ketones, and the following values have been reported for their melting and boiling points: [324] (alkyl group, b.p., m.p.) hexyl, b_5 172–174°, —; heptyl, b_5 184–185°, —; octyl, b_5 196–197°, 24°; nonyl, b_7 206–207°, 20°; decyl, —, 41°; undecyl, —, 30°; and dodecyl, —, 53°.

Benzyl ethers may be prepared by the reaction of benzyl chloride on the various sodium alkoxides, an example being the preparation of benzyl dodecyl ether, b 180–182°, n_D^{20} 1.4820, d_{25}^{25} 0.8938, by the reaction of benzyl chloride with sodium dodecoxide.[128] Such ethers have also been obtained by the reaction of benzyl chloride with the respective alcohols in the presence of aluminum and an acid-binding agent, octadecyl benzyl ether, hexadecyl benzyl ether, and oleyl benzyl ether having been thus prepared.[325, 326]

The high molecular weight alkyl aromatic ethers have been proposed as intermediates for the preparation of surface active chemicals, an example being the sulfonation of phenyl alkyl or naphthyl alkyl ethers to yield wetting agents.[327] These sulfonated ethers may be alternatively prepared by the etherification of the phenol- or naphtholsulfonic acids. Wetting agents may be obtained [328] by sulfonation of the benzyl aliphatic ethers, such as dodecyl, hexadecyl, or octadecyl benzyl ether. Sulfonation of the allyl ethers of the alkylphenols, for example, allyl dodecylphenyl ether, allyl octadecylphenyl ether, and similar compounds, gives surface active agents.[329] The sulfonation of a number of mixed aliphatic aromatic ethers and the general properties of the resulting products have been described.[330, 331] Such sulfonated products are generally employed as their sodium salts, which, in many instances, are extremely water soluble.

Etherification of those aromatic compounds which contain two or more hydroxyl groups yields several series of compounds. For example, either one or both of the hydroxyl groups of a dihydric phenol may be etherified, yielding either mono- or diethers. The diethers may be subdivided into the symmetrical diethers, in which the alkyl groups are similar, and the unsymmetrical diethers, in which the alkyl groups are dissimilar. The monoalkyl ethers of the dihydric phenols can be prepared by heating a haloalkane with a slight excess of the phenol in a highly alkaline medium or with the sodium derivative of the phenol. Such ethers are generally purified by crystallization of their sodium salts. The melting points of several of the monoethers of the polyhydric phenols are as follows: [323] pyrocatechol monoheptadecyl ether, 43°; resorcinol monopentadecyl ether, 52–53°; resorcinol monoheptadecyl ether, 62°; hydroquinol monoundecyl ether, 78°; hydroquinol monotridecyl ether, 82°; hydroquinol monopentadecyl ether, 85–86°; and hydroquinol monoheptadecyl ether, 91–92°. Holt [332] has described the preparation of a series of mixed ethers containing a long-chain hydrocarbon radical and an alicyclic radical which contains a hydroxy or alkoxy substituent. Examples of such ethers are hydroxycyclohexyl octadecyl ether, b_1 208–225°, and hydroxycyclohexyl 9-octadecenyl ether, b_1 180–215°.

The symmetrical dialkyl ethers of the dihydric phenols may be obtained by refluxing the phenols with a slight excess of a haloalkane in alcoholic sodium or potassium hydroxide solution. Hartley [322] has described the preparation of the dioctyl ethers of o-, m-, and p-dihydroxybenzenes, the ethers melting at 23.5°, 37.5°, and 56°, respectively. The dialkyl ethers of o-dihydroxybenzene have the following melting points: [323] diundecyl, 43°; ditridecyl, 50–51°; dipentadecyl, 56–57°; and diheptadecyl, 62°. Those of m-dihydroxybenzene and of p-dihydroxybenzene possess higher melting points which are, respectively: diundecyl, 56°, 76°; ditridecyl, 64–65°, 81°; dipentadecyl, 68–69°, 85°; and diheptadecyl, 75°, 91°.

The diethers may be obtained by refluxing the sodium salts of the monoethers of the phenols with haloalkanes in alcohol, and such methods are advantageously employed for the synthesis of those diethers which contain dissimilar alkyl groups. Hartley [322] has reported the following melting points for a number of the diethers of resorcinol prepared by this method: (alkyl groups, m.p.) C_6, C_6, $12.5°$; C_8, C_6, $15°$; C_8, C_8, $37.5°$; C_{10}, C_6, $27°$; C_{12}, C_4, $29.5°$; C_{14}, C_2, $30.5°$; C_{10}, C_8, $31°$; C_{12}, C_6, $34°$; C_{14}, C_4, $34°$; C_{16}, C_2, $37.5°$; C_{12}, C_{12}, $60°$; C_{16}, C_{16}, $71.5°$.

The dialkyl ethers of p-azoxyphenol,

RO<____>N=N<____>OR

have been synthesized [324] from the p-nitrophenyl ethers by the method originally proposed by Elbs,[333] and the alkyl ethers of p-azophenol have been obtained by the action of iodoalkanes on p-azophenol in the presence of potassium hydroxide and methanol. The melting points reported are, respectively: dihexyl, 81°, 102°; diheptyl, 74°, 102°; dioctyl, 76°, 98°; dinonyl, 77°, 103°; didecyl, 78°, —; diundecyl, 78°, —; and didodecyl, 82°, 106°. The p-alkoxybenzaldehydes and the dialkyl ethers of p-azomethynephenol have also been prepared and described by Weygand and Gabler.[324] Mixed ethers of the general formula ROR'X, where R is an alkyl group, R' is an aromatic or hydroaromatic radical, and X is an acidic group, have been synthesized and proposed as intermediates for the preparation of wetting agents.[334] Bruson [335] has described the synthesis of a number of β-chloroalkoxyalkyl ethers of the monohydric phenols.

Ethers which contain one or more higher alkyl groups show, in general, the reactions of their lower homologs. Van Duzee and Adkins [128] have studied the hydrogenation and hydrogenolysis of several of the higher alkyl ethers in the presence of metallic nickel, and have observed that benzyl dodecyl ether yields 1-dodecanol and toluene when subjected to such conditions. The cleavage of the higher ethers with hydrogen bromide has been the subject of several detailed studies.[219, 220]

THE SULFUR-CONTAINING DERIVATIVES OF THE FATTY ACIDS

The Aliphatic Mercaptans

The aliphatic mercaptans or thioalcohols, RSH, are either liquids or low-melting solids, the melting points of which are decidedly lower than those of the corresponding alcohols. Although the lower members of the series possess distinctly unpleasant odors, the higher members are essentially odorless.

The aliphatic mercaptans are generally prepared from the halo-alkanes or other alkyl esters, and several methods have been proposed for their synthesis. Such processes include the action of alkali metal hydrosulfides on the haloalkanes, the action of the haloalkanes with thiourea in the presence of alkaline hydroxides, and the reduction of the dialkyl disulfides. Many examples of the preparation of the higher molecular weight alkyl mercaptans by the above procedures have been reported in the literature. However, few detailed studies of the preparation of the higher alkyl mercaptans have been described until comparatively recently, the earlier literature being confined mainly to the synthesis of individual members of the series. Among the earlier mercaptans described are 1-pentanethiol,[336] 1-hexanethiol,[337] 1-heptanethiol,[338] and 1-octanethiol.[339] In 1932, Ellis and Reid [340] prepared a number of 1-alkanethiols from the corresponding bromo compounds by their reaction with potassium hydrosulfide in alcoholic solution. The method included saturating an alcoholic solution of potassium hydroxide with hydrogen sulfide and adding the bromoalkane slowly to this solution while agitating with a stream of hydrogen sulfide. The reaction product contained some unchanged bromoalkane which was removed by distillation. Murray [341] has reported that some dialkyl disulfide is produced together with the mercaptan when 1-iodohexadecane reacts with potassium hydrosulfide in ethanol. A study [342] of the preparation of dodecane-, hexadecane-, and octadecanethiol from the corresponding iodoalkanes showed that high yields require not only an excess of the hydrosulfide but also precautions against loss of hydrogen sulfide during the reaction. It was recommended that the reaction be conducted in an autoclave at 120–130° for two to three hours, and it was further pointed out that the reacting components must be kept quite dry. The preparation of 1-hexadecanethiol by the action of sodium hydrosulfide on 1-iodohexadecane has been described,[343] the procedure employed being to treat the iodo compound with a solution of sodium in absolute ethanol saturated with hydrogen sulfide. Fore and Bost [344] have prepared the 1-alkanethiols from tridecane- to nonadecanethiol inclusive by the action of an alcoholic solution of potassium hydrosulfide on the respective 1-bromoalkanes.

The action of the 1-bromoalkanes with thiourea, followed by treatment of the resulting S-alkylisothiourea hydrobromides with sodium hydroxide, offers a very satisfactory procedure for the synthesis of pure 1-alkanethiols.[345] The reactions involved are as follows:

$$S=C(NH_2)_2 + RBr \rightarrow RSC\diagup^{NH}_{\diagdown NH_2} \cdot HBr$$

$$2RSC\diagup^{NH}_{\diagdown NH_2} \cdot HBr + 2NaOH \rightarrow 2RSH + NH_2C\cdot NHCN + 2NaBr + 2H_2O$$
$$\underset{NH}{\overset{\|}{}}$$

A 79–83% yield of the theoretical amount of 1-dodecanethiol from 1-bromododecane was obtained by the use of the method, and comparable yields of 1-heptane-, 1-octane-, 1-nonane-, 1-undecane-, 1-dodecane-, and 1-octadecanethiol were also reported. 1-Dodecanethiol has also been prepared by the action of alkali hydroxides on the salts of S-dodecylthiourea.[346] Noller and Gordon [347] have synthesized the 1-alkanethiols from 1-nonane- to 1-tetradecanethiol inclusive by reductions of the corresponding dialkyl disulfides with zinc and sulfuric acid. The dialkyl disulfides were refluxed with an approximately 50% aqueous sulfuric acid solution to which zinc dust was added in small portions until the reduction was complete. The synthesis of the alkanethiols by such procedures is the subject of several patents.[348, 349] It has been stated [350] that high molecular weight mercaptans can be prepared by passing the vapors of the corresponding alcohols mixed with hydrogen sulfide over dehydrating catalysts at elevated temperatures. Thus, 1-octadecanethiol results when the vapors of 1-octadecanol together with hydrogen sulfide are passed over zirconium oxide, or octadecene-1-thiol is formed when octadecen-1-ol and hydrogen sulfide are passed over aluminum oxide.

The alkyl hydroselenides, RSeH, can be obtained by the action of alkali metal hydroselenides on haloalkanes. Butyl hydroselenide has been prepared by this procedure.[351]

The values which have been reported for the physical constants of the 1-alkanethiols are compiled in Table IX. It will be noted that the melting points of the lower members of the series alternate, the odd members possessing the higher melting points.

The aliphatic mercaptans readily form metallic derivatives, the mercaptides, which are structurally related to the alkoxides. These mercaptides are much more easily formed than the corresponding derivatives of the alcohols, and they are frequently employed as intermediates for the preparation of other sulfur-containing alkyl derivatives. The sodium mercaptides can be prepared

TABLE IX

PHYSICAL CONSTANTS OF 1-ALKANETHIOLS

Mercaptan	M.P., °C.	B.P., °C.	d_4^{25}	n_D^{25}
Methanethiol	−123.1	....	0.85991	......
Ethanethiol	−147.3	....	0.83147	1.4270
1-Propanethiol	−113.3	....	0.83572	1.4351
1-Butanethiol	−115.9	....	0.83651	1.4401
1-Pentanethiol	−75.7	....	0.83750	1.4440
1-Hexanethiol	−81.3	....	0.83826	1.4473
1-Heptanethiol	−43.4	174–176	0.83891	1.4498
1-Octanethiol	−49.2	198–200 98–100_{22}	0.83956	1.4519
1-Nonanethiol	−20.2	200–220 98–100_{15}	0.84015	1.4537
1-Decanethiol	−26	88–91_2	0.8410_{20}^{20}	1.45367^{20}
1-Undecanethiol	......	103–104_3	0.8432_{20}^{20}	1.45816^{20}
1-Dodecanethiol	−7.5	153–155_{24}	0.8450_{20}^{20}	1.45886^{20}
1-Tridecanethiol	......	162–166_{22}	0.8468_{20}^{20}	1.45906^{20}
1-Tetradecanethiol	6.5	176–180_{22}	0.8484_{20}^{20}	1.46005^{20}
1-Hexadecanethiol	18	123–$128_{0.5}$		
1-Octadecanethiol	25	170–175_4		

by treating the mercaptans with the theoretical quantity of sodium hydroxide dissolved in a small amount of water,[352] or by the action of sodium hydroxide on the mercaptans dissolved in an organic solvent. The lead mercaptides are readily prepared by the action of soluble lead salts on the mercaptans. Fore and Bost [344] have described the preparation and properties of a series of higher alkyl lead mercaptides obtained by treating an alcoholic solution of the mercaptan with alcoholic lead acetate. The lead mercaptides are yellow solids which melt without appreciable decomposition. The melting point differences between the various higher alkyl lead mercaptides are not great, as shown by the following values: tridecyl, 100°; tetradecyl, 104–105°; hexadecyl, 106–107°; heptadecyl, 108–109°; octadecyl, 110–111°; and nonadecyl, 112–114°.

The alkanethiols decompose to yield alcohols, sulfides, and olefins when heated to high temperatures with aqueous alkaline solutions, the reaction rate apparently decreasing with increasing molecular weight of the mercaptans.[353] The alkanethiols are very reactive chemically, and can be employed as the starting point for the synthesis of a number of sulfur-containing fatty acid derivatives.

The Aliphatic Sulfides, Sulfoxides, Sulfones, Dialkyl Disulfides, and Related Compounds

The alkyl sulfides or thioethers, $RR'S$, are structurally related to the ethers, but they differ decidedly from the latter in that they are readily oxidized to sulfoxides, $RR'SO$, and sulfones, $RR'SO_2$. The high molecular weight alkyl sulfides can be prepared by reaction of the mercaptans or mercaptides with alkylating or acylating agents. They have also been obtained by the action of the higher alcohol esters with alkali metal sulfides; however, such reactions frequently yield mixtures of the sulfides and mercaptans. Several other procedures have been proposed for the synthesis of the alkyl sulfides.

Those sulfides which are derivatives of the higher fatty acids are characterized by the presence of at least one long-chain hydrocarbon group. Like the ethers they may be divided into symmetrical and unsymmetrical compounds depending upon whether the R groups are similar or dissimilar. A number of examples of the preparation of the symmetrical sulfides by the action of potassium or sodium sulfide on the haloalkanes have been described. For example, dibutyl sulfide has been obtained by the action of 1-iodobutane with potassium sulfide.[354] Diheptyl sulfide,[338] dioctyl sulfide,[293] and dihexadecyl sulfide [291] have been prepared similarly. The synthesis of alkyl sulfides by heating haloalkanes with the metallic sulfides has been patented.[355] An alternate procedure for the synthesis of the symmetrical sulfides is to treat an alkali metal mercaptide with the corresponding haloalkane.

The following physical constants have been reported for the symmetrical dialkyl sulfides: [294] (m.p., b.p., d_4^t, n_D^t) dipentyl, $-51.33°$, $230.1°$, —, —; dioctyl, $0.5°$, $180_{10}°$, 0.8419_{17}^{17}, 1.4606^{26}; didecyl, $22°$, $205-206_4°$, 0.831^{25}, $1.4569^{33.5}$; didodecyl, $40-40.5°$, $260-263_4°$, 0.8275^{40}, —; ditetradecyl, $49-50°$, —, 0.8258^{50}, —; dihexadecyl, $57-58°$, —, 0.8253^{60}, —; dioctadecyl, $68-69°$, —, 0.8148^{20}, —.

Many examples of the preparation of the unsymmetrical sulfides have been published in both the academic and the patent literature. These compounds include sulfides in which both R groups are aliphatic and those in which one R group is aliphatic and the other aromatic. Examples of the former type are ethyl dodecyl sulfide, m.p. $-6°$ to $-5°$, b_{18} $167-171°$; and ethyl hexadecyl sulfide, m.p. $19°$, b_{12} $201-205°$. These compounds are obtained by dissolving ethyl mercaptan in a small amount of aqueous alkali, adding a little ethanol, and treating the solution with the respective 1-iodoalkane.[352] Bost and associates [356, 357] have synthesized the 1-alkylthio-2,4-dinitrobenzenes and have proposed their use as identifying derivatives for the mercaptans. These thioethers are readily prepared by reaction of the respective sodium mercaptides with 1-chloro-2,4-dinitrobenzene in alcoholic solution. They form light yellow plates or needles which possess sharp melting points. The following 1-alkylthio-2,4-dinitrobenzenes have been described: [344, 356, 357] (alkyl group, m.p.) hexyl, 74°; heptyl, 82°; octyl, 78°; nonyl, 86°; decyl, 85°; undecyl, 90°; dodecyl, 89°; tridecyl, 94.0–94.5°; tetradecyl, 93.5–94.0°; hexadecyl, 95.5–96.0°; heptadecyl, 98.5–99.0°; octadecyl, 97.0–97.5°; and nonadecyl, 99.5–100°.

The condensation of alkali metal mercaptides with chlorohydrins yields mixed thioethers which contain hydroxy groups. Such compounds are frequently proposed as intermediates for the preparation of wetting agents and detergents.[358, 359] Thus, the action of 1-hexadecanethiol with ethylene chlorohydrin in alkaline solution yields 2-hydroxyethyl hexadecyl sulfide, and 1-hexadecanethiol and glycerol α-monochlorohydrin yield 2,3-dihydroxypropyl hexadecyl sulfide. The preparation of 2,3-dihydroxypropyl dodecyl sulfide, m.p. 53°, by a similar procedure has been described.[360, 361] A number of these hydroxy sulfides have been synthesized by Bennett and Gudgeon [362] by the action of potassium methyl sulfide on the chlorohydrins, the following ω-hydroxyalkylthiomethanes having been described: 7-hydroxyheptyl, b_{10} 133–134°; 8-hydroxyoctyl, b_{10} 135–138°; 9-hydroxynonyl, m.p. 22°; 10-hydroxydecyl, m.p. 25°; 12-hydroxydodecyl, m.p. 49°; 14-hydroxytetradecyl, m.p. 38°; 16-hydroxyhexadecyl, m.p. 54–56°; 18-hydroxyoctadecyl, m.p. 62°. The above hydroxy sulfides were converted into their chloro analogs and an attempt made to obtain large-ring monosulfides by ring closure. Those which contain seven to twelve carbon atoms in the hydroxyalkyl group yield polysulfides; however, evidence of ring closure was obtained with the higher members.

Compounds which contain readily exchangeable halogen atoms, such as the α-halo acids and their salts, react with the mercaptides to form mixed thioethers. A variety of such compounds have been prepared and proposed as intermediates for the synthesis of wetting agents, examples being 2-(dodecylthio)acetic acid, which is obtained by the reaction of sodium dodecyl sulfide with monochloroacetic acid, and 2-(ethylthio)stearic acid, from 2-chlorostearic acid and sodium ethyl sulfide.[363, 364] The preparation and properties of a number of compounds of this type have been described.[365] Urquhart and Connor [366] have discussed the preparation of 2-(heptylthio)acetic acid by the action of sodium chloroacetate on sodium heptyl sulfide. Surface active chemicals have also been obtained by the condensation of amino carboxylic acids with sulfides which contain a reactive halogen, such as chloromethyl dodecyl sulfide.[367]

Jones and Reid [368] have studied the addition of sulfur, hydrogen sulfide, or mercaptans to unsaturated hydrocarbons. The addition of hydrogen sulfide is effected by heating the olefin and hydrogen sulfide in a steel bomb for ten hours at 180° in the presence of a small amount of sulfur. The mercaptan which is first formed rapidly adds to a second mole of the alkene to form a sulfide. In their study of the addition of mercaptans to olefins, they observed that the presence of peroxides influences the direction of addition, 1-octene and ethanethiol yielding ethyl octyl sulfide if the addition takes place in the presence of peroxides. These authors prepared a number of sulfides by the reaction of mercaptans with terminally unsaturated hydrocarbons and identified the products by comparing them with sulfides obtained by the action of mercaptides with 1-bromoalkanes. The melting points reported for these sulfides are: 1-phenylthioundecane, 33.8°; 1-phenylthiotridecane, 43.9°; 1-phenylthiopentadecane, 51.1°; 1-phenylthioheptadecane, 57.6°; 1-phenylthiononadecane, 60.5°; 1-p-tolylthioundecane, 29.8°; 1-p-tolylthiotridecane, 40.2°; 1-p-tolylthiopentadecane, 48.8°; 1-p-tolylthioheptadecane, 55.8°; 1-p-tolylthiononadecane, 59.5°; 1-β-naphthylthioundecane, 46.8°; 1-β-naphthylthiotridecane, 54.5°; 1-β-naphthylthiopentadecane, 60.9°; 1-β-naphthylthioheptadecane, 66.2°; 1-β-naphthylthiononadecane, 70.0°; 1-dodecylthioundecane, 37.2°; 1-dodecylthiotridecane, 39.8°; 1-dodecylthiopentadecane, 49.2°; 1-dodecylthioheptadecane, 52.1°; and 1-dodecylthiononadecane, 53.2°. The addition of 1-tridecene to dimercaptans of the general formula $HS(CH_2)_nSH$ yields the disulfides $C_{13}H_{27}$-$S(CH_2)_nSC_{13}H_{27}$, and Jones and Reid [368] have prepared the members of this series of disulfides in which n varies from two to eighteen. The addition of 1-dodecanethiol to 1-allylthiododecane gives the symmetrical disulfide $C_{12}H_{25}S(CH_2)_3SC_{12}H_{25}$, m.p. 47°, which is identical with that obtained by the action of 1-bromododecane on trimethylenedithiol.

Compounds of the general formula $RSCH_2CH_2(OCH_2CH_2)_x$-OCH_2CH_2OH are obtained by condensation of the aliphatic mercaptans with ethylene oxide,[369] and the condensation product of 1-dodecanethiol and five moles of ethylene oxide, the probable formula of which is $C_{12}H_{25}SCH_2CH_2(OCH_2CH_2)_3OCH_2CH_2OH$, has been proposed as a wetting agent. The action of ethylene oxide with the thioethers, such as 2,3-dihydroxypropyl dodecyl sulfide, has also been investigated.[370, 371] The reaction of mercaptans with 3-substituted-1,2-epoxypropanes yields a variety of surface active chemicals.[372, 373]

The high molecular weight alkyl sulfides have been used as intermediates for the preparation of many high molecular weight sulfur-containing derivatives. They readily form addition products with metallic salts such as mercuric chloride, the addition products often melting without appreciable decomposition. The dialkyl sulfides are reactive with haloalkanes or related compounds to yield alkylsulfonium compounds $(RR'R''S)^+X^-$,[374, 375] which possess many of the physical properties of the quaternary nitrogen compounds. Bost and Everett [352] have prepared several of the higher alkylsulfonium halides by reaction of the dialkyl sulfides with alkyl halides, ethyl hexadecyl sulfide and methyl bromide yielding methylethylhexadecylsulfonium bromide, m.p. 77°. With methyl iodide the corresponding sulfonium iodide, m.p. 73°, is obtained. Methylethyldodecylsulfonium iodide, m.p. 65°, was similarly prepared. Methylethylhexadecylsulfonium nitrate, m.p. 61°, has been obtained by the action of silver nitrate on the corresponding iodide. It was reported that solvents which possess high dielectric constants favor the reaction for sulfonium halide formation, methanol being the best solvent investigated. The preparation of a number of sulfonium compounds which contain at least one long-chain alkyl group has been described.[376] The list includes dodecylbenzylmethylsulfonium methosulfate, m.p. 70–71°, 2-palmitoxyethyl-p-tolylmethylsulfonium methosulfate, m.p. 54–55°, S,S'-didodecyl-S,S'-dimethylethylenedisulfonium dimethosulfate, m.p. 155–156°, and others. The use of the higher alkylsulfonium compounds such as dimethyldodecylsulfonium bromide and dimethylhexadecylsulfonium iodide as wetting agents has been suggested.[377]

The aliphatic sulfides are easily oxidized to sulfoxides which can, by the use of stronger oxidizing agents, be further oxidized to sulfones. Hunter [378] has prepared a number of sulfoxides and sulfones from the symmetrical dialkyl sulfides, the former being obtained by the action of dilute nitric acid and the latter by the use of hydrogen peroxide in acetic acid or by the use of fuming nitric acid. The reported melting points of the sulfoxides, R_2SO, and the sulfones, R_2SO_2, so obtained are as follows: (R, sulfoxide m.p., sulfone m.p.) dodecyl, 89–90°, 94.5–95.5°; tetradecyl, 95–96°, 99.5–100°; hexadecyl, 97–98°, 100–100.5°; octadecyl, 99–100°, 105.5–106.5°. Diheptyl sulfoxide and sulfone freeze at 70° and 80°, respectively.[338]

Many unsymmetrical sulfones have been synthesized and described. A very satisfactory procedure for the synthesis of the dialkyl sulfones consists of adding a saturated aqueous solution of potassium permanganate to a glacial acetic acid solution of the sulfide.[379] For example, 1-(ethylthio)dodecane yields 1-(ethylsulfonyl)dodecane, m.p. 78.5°, and 1-(ethylthio)hexadecane yields 1-(ethylsulfonyl)hexadecane, m.p. 88°, when so treated.[352] A similar treatment of the 1-alkylthio-2,4-dinitrobenzenes gives the corresponding sulfones. These sulfones are described as snow-white, crystalline-to-waxy solids which possess the following melting points: [344, 356, 357] (alkyl group, m.p.) hexyl, 97°; heptyl, 101°; octyl, 98°; nonyl, 92°; decyl, 93°; undecyl, 97°; dodecyl, 101°; tridecyl, 101.5°; hexadecyl, 105°; heptadecyl, 106.5°; and octadecyl, 107.5°. The oxidation of the 2-alkylthio acids yields the corresponding alkylsulfonyl acids,[366] an example being the oxidation of heptylthioacetic acid to heptylsulfonylacetic acid, m.p. 95.5–96°, by the use of hydrogen peroxide in glacial acetic acid.

High molecular weight alkyl sulfides which contain hydroxyalkyl groups have been oxidized to the corresponding sulfones, the sulfonation of which has been proposed for the preparation of wetting and emulsifying agents.[380] Examples have been given of the preparation of 1-(2-hydroxyethylsulfonyl)dodecane, 1-(2,3-dihydroxypropylsulfonyl)dodecane and similar products. Vinyl sulfones of the general formula $R(SO_2CH:CH_2)_x$, where R is a long-chain alkyl group, have been described,[381, 382] and it has been proposed to treat such sulfones with monosodium sulfite to produce surface active chemicals. Sulfones such as 1-(hexadecylsulfonyl)-4-chlorobenzene, m.p. 66–68°, are reactive with secondary amines to yield a variety of compounds which are useful as wetting agents.[383]

The dialkyl disulfides, RSSR′, are obtained in high yields by the oxidation of mercaptans or mercaptides with iodine, sulfuryl chloride, or other mild oxidizing agents. The higher molecular weight mercaptans are very readily oxidized to disulfides, and it has been observed [342] that considerable conversion of 1-dodecane-, 1-hexadecane-, and 1-octadecanethiol to the corresponding disulfides occurs upon exposure to air at ordinary temperatures. Examples of the synthesis of didodecyl, dihexadecyl, and dioctadecyl disulfides by oxidation of their alcoholic solutions with iodine have been published. [342] Fore and Bost [344] have described the preparation of dialkyl disulfides by treatment of the lead mercaptides suspended in glacial acetic acid with a slight excess of iodine. The reaction mixture is diluted with water, the precipitated disulfides and lead iodide are removed by filtration, and the lead iodide is separated by washing the precipitate with aqueous potassium iodide, which converts it to the soluble double iodide. Oxidation of the so-called Bunte salts [384] (sodium alkyl thiosulfates) with iodine [385] or hydrogen peroxide [386] yields dialkyl disulfides. Westlake and Dougherty [387] have synthesized dibutyl, diheptyl, dioctyl, didodecyl, and dioctadecyl disulfides by the use of this method. It is not necessary to isolate the intermediate sodium alkyl thiosulfate, since it may be oxidized directly to the disulfide. The higher molecular weight dialkyl disulfides are odorless, crystalline compounds which are slightly soluble in cold ethanol and acetone. The following constants have been reported for these disulfides: dibutyl, b_3 90–100°; diheptyl, b_5 143–147°; dioctyl, b_5 178–183°; didodecyl, m.p. 33.5–34°; ditridecyl, m.p. 43.5–44°; ditetradecyl, m.p. 45.5–46°; dihexadecyl, m.p. 53.5–54°; diheptadecyl, m.p. 59.5–60°; dioctadecyl, m.p. 62.0–62.5°; and dinonadecyl, m.p. 68.5–69°.

Oxidation of the dialkyl disulfides yields sulfonic acids as the final product, with the probable intermediate formation of dialkyl disulfones. [342] Reduction of the dialkyl disulfides with zinc dust and acetic acid or other reducing agents yields the corresponding mercaptans.

The Alkanesulfonic Acids and Related Compounds

The high molecular weight alkanesulfonic acids and their salts have been the subject of many investigations as regards both their synthesis and their chemical and physical properties.

The pure higher alkanesulfonic acids are generally obtained by treatment of mercaptans or mercaptides with strong oxidizing agents. The preparation of 1-hexadecanesulfonic acid was accomplished by Reychler [388] by the oxidation of 1-hexadecanethiol with an aqueous solution of potassium permanganate, and separation of the sulfonate as the lead salt. The free acid was obtained by treatment of this salt, suspended in ethanol, with hydrogen sulfide. A subsequent investigation [389] showed that this method results in low yields of the sulfonic acid. In a continuation of the study of the preparation of higher alkanesulfonic acids from mercaptans, [342] it was observed that either the mercaptans or the disulfides are smoothly oxidized by powdered potassium permanganate in acetic acid or acetone, or by chromic anhydride in acetic acid, to give high yields of the corresponding sulfonic acids. These were isolated as their lead salts, which were then suspended in water and decomposed by the addition of hydrochloric acid, the higher alkanesulfonic acids being "salted out" upon addition of mineral acid. Such an oxidation was stated to be more satisfactory than the use of aqueous potassium permanganate, and the use of hydrochloric acid to be preferable to that of hydrogen sulfide. The oxidative reactions with either the mercaptans or the disulfides gave substantial amounts of a neutral compound which was thought to be composed largely of disulfones. In a detailed investigation of the oxidation of 1-hexadecancthiol with potassium permanganate, Flaschenträger and Wannschaff [343] observed that 2,2-di(hexadecylthio)propane, m.p. 53°,

$$\begin{array}{c} CH_3 \\ \diagdown \\ CH_3 \end{array} C \begin{array}{c} SC_{16}H_{33} \\ \diagup \\ \diagdown SC_{16}H_{33} \end{array}$$

is formed together with potassium hexadecanesulfonate when the oxidation is conducted in acetone. When, however, water or acetic acid is employed as the solvent, dihexadecyl disulfide is one of the reaction products.

Fewer secondary products and higher yields of alkanesulfonic acids are apparently obtained by oxidation of mercaptans, mercaptides, or disulfides with nitric acid than by oxidation with the other oxidizing agents so far investigated. Murray [341] has reported that the oxidation of 1-hexadecanethiol or dihexadecyl disulfide by means of fuming nitric acid gives a 98% yield of the corresponding alkanesulfonic acid. 1-Hexadecanesulfonic acid has been obtained [390] by the oxidation of 1-hexadecanethiol with 50% nitric acid. The sulfonic acid was separated as the lead salt, which was converted into the free acid and lead chloride by dry hydrogen chloride in 2-propanol. The higher alkyl lead mercaptides are also readily oxidized to the corresponding lead sulfonates by the action of 50% nitric acid.[347] The following yields of lead sulfonates have been obtained by oxidation of the lead mercaptides: nonane-, 16.7%; decane-, 75.5%; undecane-, 83.0%; dodecane-, 76.0%; tridecane-, 58.0%; and tetradecane-, 68.5%. The oxidation of alkyl polysulfides with oxidizing agents such as hypohalous acids yields the corresponding alkanesulfonates.[391]

A number of allyl-type sulfonates have been prepared [392] by the oxidation of mercaptans in which the thiol group is directly attached to a tertiary carbon atom joined directly to an alkenyl radical. Such compounds may be oxidized to sulfonic acids by the use of nitric acid, hydrogen peroxide, or other strong oxidizing agents.

The action of sulfites on the haloalkanes is a very successful method for the preparation of the low molecular weight alkanesulfonic acids. This reaction was first proposed by Strecker [393] in 1868. In her study of the preparation of hexadecanesulfonic acid, Norris [389] stated that this method is not satisfactory for the preparation of the higher alkanesulfonic acids, and other investigators have supported this statement. However, such reactions have been stated in the patent literature to be adaptable to the preparation of these higher acids,[394, 395] and examples have been given of the preparation of dodecanesulfonic acid by the action of dodecyl hydrogen sulfate with sodium sulfite under pressure. In 1935, Reed and Tartar [396] obtained approximately 70% yields of the sodium alkanesulfonates by heating the corresponding bromoalkanes with aqueous sodium sulfite under pressure for nine hours at 180–200°. The even-carbon-membered sodium alkanesulfonates from sodium octanesulfonate to sodium octadecanesulfonate were obtained by this method. More recently, Latimer and Bost [397] have reported the synthesis of a number of alkanesulfonic acids by the action of the bromoalkanes with ammonium sulfite, the sulfonic acids being isolated as their barium salts. Alkanesulfonic acids have also been obtained by the action of alkali sulfites on the higher alcohol esters of halogenated acids, such as hexadecyl chloroacetate.[398]

The high molecular weight alkanesulfonic acids are soaplike solids which are quite hygroscopic and readily form hydrates and other solvates. They are extremely difficult to prepare in a state of high purity. Since they are highly acidic they readily form salts, many of which are very water soluble and function as colloidal electrolytes. The reported melting points of several of the higher alkanesulfonic acids [347] are shown in Table X.

Several identifying derivatives have been proposed for the alkanesulfonic acids. The benzylanilinium alkanesulfonates, for example, have been observed [347] to be nonhygroscopic and to possess sharp melting points which are as follows: (alkane- group, m.p.) nonane-, 90.5–91.0°; decane-, 84.0–84.5°; undecane-, 84.6–84.7°; dodecane-, 91.0–91.2°; tridecane-, 87.5–88.0°; tetradecane-, 82.5–82.7°. The phenylhydrazine salts of the lower alkanesulfonic

TABLE X

MELTING POINTS OF ALKANESULFONIC ACIDS

No. of C Atoms	M.P., °C. Monohydrate	M.P., °C. Anhydrous
9	.....	46
10	.....	46.5
11	40–41	49
12	43–45	52
13	48–49	58
14	55–56	65.5
16	.....	53–54 [390]

acids [397] melt as follows: (alkane- group, m.p.) butane-, 114–115°; pentane-, 108–108.2°; hexane-, 101–101.6°; heptane-, 100–100.5°; and octane-, 90–90.5°.

The surface active properties of the alkanesulfonic acids and their water-soluble salts have long been a subject of interest and have formed the basis of a number of detailed investigations. Reychler [388, 399] first pointed out that sodium hexadecanesulfonate is surface active and possesses many of the properties of an ordinary soap. Later, Norris [389] observed that hexadecanesulfonic acid functions as a hydrogen soap and that its solutions possess a behavior characteristic of solutions of colloidal electrolytes. Investigations of the electrical behavior [390, 400, 401] of solutions of the alkanesulfonic acids showed that the lower members of the series function as strong electrolytes but that the higher members, from heptanesulfonic acid upward, show a behavior analogous to that observed for solutions of the higher soaps. When the equivalent conductance is plotted against $\sqrt{N_v}$, the curves fall linearly with concentration up to a certain critical concentration. At this point the curves fall abruptly to a minimum, after which an appreciable rise is evidenced. This phenomenon has been attributed to the formation of associated particles and is characteristic of the behavior of colloidal electrolytes. The higher the alkane group of the sulfonic acid, the lower is the critical concentration for micelle formation. The equivalent conductances of several of the alkanesulfonic acids are shown in Fig. 3.

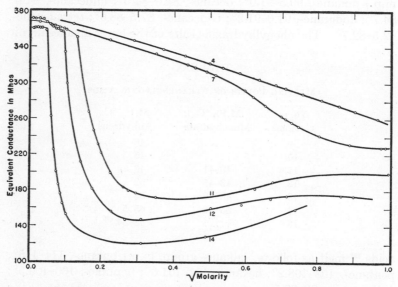

FIG. 3.   Equivalent conductances of alkanesulfonic acids.

The solubilities of the salts of the alkanesulfonates parallel those of other colloidal electrolytes in that they increase greatly at the critical concentration for micelle formation. Murray and Hartley [402] observed such a behavior for the sodium, lithium, and potassium salts of 1-hexadecanesulfonic acid. The most comprehensive work on the solubilities of the salts of the higher alkanesulfonic acids is that of Reed and Tartar,[403] who have reported the solubilities of the calcium, magnesium, and sodium salts of the alkanesulfonic acids from 1-octanesulfonic acid to 1-octadecanesulfonic acid. The reported solubilities of these salts in water are shown in Table XI.

The extremely low solubilities of the calcium and magnesium salts are significant. It will be noted that the solubilities of the sodium salts decrease greatly with increase in the chain length. The conductivity behavior of solutions of the sodium alkanesulfonates parallels that of solutions of the free sulfonic acids.[403] The interfacial tensions between benzene and solutions of the sodium alkanesulfonates show characteristic changes with time. The cupric, magnesium, zinc, aluminum, thallium, nickel, manganous, ferrous, and cobalt salts of 1-hexadecanesulfonic acid are water soluble, whereas the calcium, strontium, barium, ferric, silver, and lead salts are insoluble.[343] The solubilities of the lithium, sodium, and potassium salts of 1-hexadecanesulfonic acid are as follows:

TABLE XI

SOLUBILITIES OF SALTS OF 1-ALKANESULFONIC ACIDS

Grams per 100 g. Water

No. of C Atoms	Ca salt		Mg salt		Na salt	
	25°	60°	25°	60°	25°	60°
8	......	......	......	......	74.40	......
10	0.155	0.260	0.268	......	4.55	......
12	.011	.033	.033	48.0	0.253	>48
14	.0014	.005	.0035	0.016	.041	38.8
16	.0005	.0013	.0012	.006	.0073	6.49
18	.0006	.0007	.0010	.003	.0010	0.131

(salt, sol. in mg./100 cc. water at 22°) Li, 30.4; Na, 18.4; and K, 15.2.

A number of higher alkyl derivatives of the aromatic sulfonic acids have been described. Sekera and Marvel [404] have prepared the alkyl esters of p-toluene- and p-bromobenzenesulfonic acids, and have proposed their use as alkylating agents. The melting points of these esters are as follows: (p-toluenesulfonates, m.p.) dodecyl, 30°; tetradecyl, 35°; hexadecyl, 49°; octadecyl, 56°; (p-bromobenzenesulfonates, m.p.) decyl, 43-44°; dodecyl, 49°; tetradecyl, 51.5°; hexadecyl, 60°; and octadecyl, 64-65°. Details of the preparation of dodecyl p-toluenesulfonate have been published.[405] Meals and Gilman [226] have prepared p-dodecyl-2-naphthalenesulfonanilide and the five isomers formed by varying the position of attachment to the dodecane portion in their study of the reliability of mixed-melting-point determinations with structurally similar compounds.

The patent literature contains a number of examples of the preparation of higher alkyl-substituted aromatic sulfonic acids. Flett [406] has synthesized compounds such as sodium dodecylhydroxybenzenesulfonate and has proposed their use as detergents. Higher alkyl-substituted sulfonated phenols have been condensed with the higher alcohols in the presence of condensing agents such as zinc chloride, and details have been given for the preparation of many nuclear alkyl-substituted sulfonated phenols and allied compounds.[407] Their use as emulsifying and suspending agents has been proposed.[408] The higher nuclear alkyl-substituted naphthalenesulfonates have likewise been described.[409] Thomas [410] has prepared the salts of several alkyl-substituted aromatic polysulfonic acids, such as disodium tetradecylnaphthalenedisulfonate and disodium decylanthracenedisulfonate. Condensation products of the higher aliphatic sulfides with aromatic sulfonic acids and a lower primary aliphatic alcohol have been described.[411] Such products include dimethylhexadecylsulfonium p-toluenesulfonate, diethyldodecylsulfonium β-naphthalenesulfonate, and similar compounds. The cycloaliphatic sulfonic derivatives such as sodium cyclohexanesulfonate can be condensed with high molecular weight acid chlorides, e.g., octadecenoyl chloride, for the preparation of surface active compounds.[412]

The fact that compounds which contain a sulfonic acid group together with a long-chain hydrocarbon radical are surface active and function as colloidal electrolytes has resulted in an extensive patent literature pertaining to derivatives of this type. A number of fatty compounds have been treated with sulfonating agents for the preparation of water-soluble products. Some of the reactions described yield true sulfonic acids or their salts; however, others undoubtedly give heterogeneous mixtures consisting of sulfates and sulfonates together with other products. True sulfonic acids may be obtained by the action of sulfonating agents on olefins, and it has been proposed to treat the higher olefins [413, 414, 415] or the higher unsaturated alcohols such as octadecen-1-ol [416, 417] with sulfonating agents for the preparation of wetting agents. The action of sulfonating agents with the higher saturated alcohols probably yields sulfates as the major components, although such products are frequently of heterogeneous composition. Many examples of the action of sulfonating agents with the higher alcohols and the use of the resulting products as wetting agents are to be found in the patent literature.[418, 419, 420, 421, 422] The action of sulfonating agents with chlorinated alcohols has been described,[423] and wetting agents have been prepared by condensation of the sodium soaps with salts of the chloroalkanesulfonates such as sodium chloromethane-sulfonate,[424] or by the action of sulfonating agents on the higher hydroxyalkyl sulfides.[425] Surface active chemicals have also been obtained by the action of sulfonating agents on the higher alkyl borates [426] or other esters.[427] Waldmann and Chwala [428] have described the preparation of a number of sulfonated higher aliphatic amino ethers and have suggested their use as wetting agents. Condensation of fatty alcohols with sulfuryl chloride or the sodium salt of sulfanilic acid produces surface active chemicals.[429] Several detergent compositions have been proposed which comprise mixtures of the alkyl sulfates and sulfonates.[430]

Other Sulfur-Containing Aliphatic Derivatives

Although the mercaptans, sulfides, sulfonates, and allied compounds constitute the most important of the higher alkyl sulfur-containing derivatives, several other types of sulfur compounds merit mention.

The magnesium alkylsulfinates, $(RSO_2)_2Mg \cdot 2H_2O$, containing from three to sixteen carbon atoms inclusive have been synthesized [431] by the action of dry sulfur dioxide on the respective alkylmagnesium bromides. These compounds are white powders which are insoluble in ethanol. The lower members are slightly soluble in hot water, but the higher members are quite insoluble. The sodium alkylsulfinates, $RSO_2Na \cdot 2H_2O$, are water soluble and yield solutions which resemble those of the higher soaps. Sodium alkylsulfinates are reactive with haloalkanes to yield sulfones, and a series of 1,2-dialkylsulfonylethanes, $(RSO_2CH_2-)_2$, has been prepared by reaction of the sodium alkylsulfinates with 1,2-dibromoethane. Several alkylsulfonylethanes, $RSO_2C_2H_5$, have also been prepared by this procedure.

Salts of the higher alkylxanthates, $ROCS_2M$, where R is a higher alkyl radical and M is an alkali metal, have been obtained by the action of higher alcohols with carbon disulfide in the presence of alkali metal hydroxides.[432] It was stated that such compounds function as vulcanization accelerators, and their use as wetting agents has been proposed.[433] The higher alkylxanthicformates and their higher alcohol esters have been synthesized by the action of phosgene on the alkylxanthates.[434] Such compounds have been stated to be vulcanization accelerators and to possess parasiticidal activity. The condensation products of chloromethoxyhexadecane with thiourea [435] and with the alkali metal salts of hyposulfurous acid or sulfanilic acid [436] have been described.

The higher alkylthiobenzothiazoles have been synthesized by the reaction of sodium mercaptobenzothiazole with haloalkanes.[437] For example, 2-hexadecylthiobenzothiazole is obtained by the reaction of sodium mercaptobenzothiazole with 1-bromohexadecane:

$$\text{[benzothiazole]}N{=}\overset{S}{\underset{|}{C}}SNa + C_{16}H_{33}Br \rightarrow \text{[benzothiazole]}N{=}\overset{S}{\underset{|}{C}}SC_{16}H_{33} + NaBr$$

Such compounds can be further treated with chloroalkanes or other esters for the preparation of the corresponding quaternary ammonium derivatives. Sulfonated derivatives of the alkyl-substituted indoles have been synthesized and described.[438]

Pseudo-thiohydantoins, $RSC\underset{\diagdown N\text{---}C=O}{\overset{\diagup NH\text{---}CHR}{\diagdown|}}$, result from the reaction of α-bromo acids with thiourea, and the following 5-alkyl-pseudo-thiohydantoins have been described:[439] (alkyl group, m.p.) butyl, 183°; decyl, 182.5°; dodecyl, 180.5°; tetradecyl, 176.5°; and hexadecyl, 175°. Their hydrolysis yields α-mercapto acids which have the following boiling or melting points: 2-mercaptocaproic acid, b 234°; 2-mercaptolauric acid, 59°; 2-mercaptomyristic acid, 66°; 2-mercaptopalmitic acid, 72–73°; and 2-mercaptostearic acid, 80°.

HIGHER ALKYL DERIVATIVES OF PHOSPHORUS AND ARSENIC

The higher alkyl derivatives of phosphorus and arsenic have not been extensively investigated; however, the phosphonium and arsonium compounds have occasioned interest owing to their similarity in physical behavior to the quaternary ammonium compounds. Jerchel [440] has recently prepared a number of phosphonium and arsonium halides which contain a long-chain alkyl group and has studied their physical behavior and bactericidal properties. Octyltriethylphosphonium iodide, $C_8H_{17}(C_2H_5)_3PI$, is obtained by the reaction of 1-iodoöctane with triethylphosphine.[441] The dodecyl and hexadecyl homologs are prepared in a similar manner. The condensation of benzyldimethylphosphine with 1-iodoöctane, -dodecane, or -hexadecane yields the corresponding benzylalkyldimethylphosphonium iodides. The use of 1-chloroalkanes yields the corresponding phosphonium chlorides. The structurally related arsonium compounds may be likewise prepared from the alkylarsines and the haloalkanes. The dimethylalkylarsines are obtained by the action of dimethyliodoarsine, $(CH_3)_2AsI$, with alkylmagnesium halides. The following alkyldimethylarsines have been prepared and described: octyldimethylarsine, b_{11} 102–104°; dodecyldimethylarsine, b_{10} 149–150°; and hexadecyldimethylarsine, b_{11} 200–202°. The melting points of a number of the higher alkylphosphonium and -arsonium halides as reported by Jerchel [440] are shown in Table XII.

TABLE XII

Melting Points of Alkylphosphonium and -arsonium Halides

Halide	M.P., °C.
Phosphonium	
Octyltriethyl—iodide	94
Dodecyltriethyl—iodide	110
Hexadecyltriethyl—iodide	125
Dodecyldimethylbenzyl—chloride	176
Hexadecyldimethylbenzyl—chloride	189
Octyldimethylbenzyl—iodide	72
Dodecyldimethylbenzyl—iodide	49
Hexadecyldimethylbenzyl—iodide	66
Arsonium	
Octyltriethyl—iodide	68–70
Dodecyltriethyl—iodide	98
Hexadecyltriethyl—iodide	114
Octyldimethylbenzyl—chloride	144–146
Dodecyldimethylbenzyl—chloride	159–161
Hexadecyldimethylbenzyl—chloride	181–183
Octyldimethylbenzyl—iodide	71
Dodecyldimethylbenzyl—iodide	72
Hexadecyldimethylbenzyl—iodide	69

Many of these compounds are water soluble, and such solutions undoubtedly parallel those of the quaternary ammonium compounds in physical behavior.

References

1. Chevreul, *Ann. chim. phys.* [2], **7**, 155 (1817).
2. André and François, *Compt. rend.*, **183**, 663 (1926).
3. Hilditch and Lovern, *J. Soc. Chem. Ind.*, **48**, 365T (1929).
4. Toyama, *Chem. Umschau*, **32**, 113 (1925).
5. Gill and Tucker, *Oil & Fat Industries*, **7**, 101 (1930).
6. Ueno and Koyama, *J. Chem. Soc. Japan*, **57**, 1 (1936); *Bull. Chem. Soc. Japan*, **11**, 394 (1936).
7. Lovern, *Biochem. J.*, **28**, 394 (1934).

8. Toyama, *J. Soc. Chem. Ind., Japan*, **30**, 527 (1927).
9. Gascard, *Ann. chim.* [9], **15**, 332 (1921).
10. Chibnall, Piper, Pollard, Williams, and Sahai, *Biochem. J.*, **28**, 2189 (1934).
11. Heiduschka and Gareis, *J. prakt. Chem.* [2], **99**, 293 (1919).
12. Gascard, *Compt. rend.*, **170**, 1326 (1920).
13. Brodie, *Ann.*, **67**, 180 (1848); **71**, 144 (1849).
14. Gascard, *Compt. rend.*, **170**, 886 (1920).
15. Damoy, *J. pharm. chim.* [7], **29**, 148 (1924).
16. Ryan and Dillon, *Sci. Proc. Roy. Dublin Soc.* [2], **12**, 202 (1909).
17. Salomone, *Boll. laniera*, **44**, 199 (1930).
18. Tsujimoto, *J. Soc. Chem. Ind., Japan*, **24**, 41 (1920); *Chem. Umschau*, **32**, 127 (1925).
19. Toyama, *Chem. Umschau*, **29**, 237 (1922).
20. Toyama, *ibid.*, **31**, 13 (1924).
21. Toyama and Tsuchiya, *J. Chem. Soc. Japan*, **56**, 1072 (1935).
22. Toyama and Akiyama, *ibid.*, **56**, 1316 (1935).
23. Tsujimoto and Toyama, *Chem. Umschau*, **29**, 27, 35, 43 (1922); Toyama, *ibid.*, **29**, 237, 245 (1922); **31**, 13, 61, 153 (1924).
24. André and Bloch, *Compt. rend.*, **195**, 627 (1932).
25. Weidemann, *Biochem. J.*, **20**, 685 (1926).
26. Heilbron and Owens, *J. Chem. Soc.*, 942 (1928).
27. Knight, *Biochem. J.*, **24**, 257 (1930).
28. Davies, Heilbron, and Owens, *J. Chem. Soc.*, 2542 (1930).
29. Davies, Heilbron, and Jones, *ibid.*, 165 (1933); 1232 (1934).
30. Lovern, *Biochem. J.*, **31**, 755 (1937).
31. Axelrad and Hochstadter, U. S. Patent 1,290,870 (1919).
32. Schrauth, U. S. Patent 1,962,941 (1934).
33. Porter and Brewster, U. S. Patent 1,452,388 (1923).
34. Youtz, U. S. Patent 1,814,654 (1931).
35. Sexton and Ward, Brit. Patent 398,807 (1933); U. S. Patent 2,021,926 (1935).
36. I. G. Farbenind. A.-G., Brit. Patent 304,150 (1928).
37. Rosser and Swann, U. S. Patent 2,070,318 (1937).
38. Henke and Benner, U. S. Patent 2,070,597 (1937).
39. Deutsche Hydrierwerke A.-G., Fr. Patent 699,945 (1930); Ger. Patent 588,201 (1933).
40. I. G. Farbenind. A.-G., Brit. Patent 366,025 (1930).
41. I. G. Farbenind. A.-G., Fr. Patent 711,789 (1931); Ger. Patent 583,323 (1933).
42. Mihalovici and Bors, *Curierul Farm.*, **8**, No. 6, 1 (1938).
43. Gottfried and Ulzer, *Chem. Umschau*, **33**, 141 (1926).
44. Reid, U. S. Patent 2,004,131 (1935).
45. Grote, Hundsdörfer, and Moos, U. S. Patent 2,113,960 (1938).
46. I. G. Farbenind. A.-G., Fr. Patent 690,958 (1930).
47. Simonini, *Monatsh.*, **13**, 320 (1892); **14**, 81 (1893).
48. Panics, *ibid.*, **15**, 9 (1894).
49. Bouis and Carlet, *Ann.*, **124**, 352 (1862).
50. Grimshaw and Schorlemmer, *Ber.*, **6**, 596 (1873).

51. Krafft, *ibid.*, **16**, 1714 (1883).
52. H. Th. Böhme A.-G., Brit. Patent 381,476 (1932); Ger. Patent 586,067 (1933).
53. H. Th. Böhme A.-G., Brit. Patent 385,488 (1932); Fr. Patent 734,864 (1932).
54. Bouveault and Blanc, *Compt. rend.*, **136**, 1676 (1903); **137**, 60 (1903); *Bull. soc. chim.* [3], **31**, 666, 672 (1904).
55. Meyer and Reid, *J. Am. Chem. Soc.*, **55**, 1574 (1933).
56. Zelinsky and Prschevalsky, *J. Russ. Phys. Chem. Soc.*, **40**, 1105 (1908).
57. Niemann and Wagner, *J. Org. Chem.*, **7**, 227 (1942).
58. Chuit and Hausser, *Helv. Chim. Acta*, **12**, 850 (1929).
59. Chuit, *ibid.*, **9**, 264 (1926).
60. Mitchovitch and Stefanovitch, *Compt. rend.*, **205**, 386 (1937).
61. H. Th. Böhme A.-G., Ger. Patent 547,640 (1929).
62. H. Th. Böhme A.-G., Ger. Patent 557,515 (1929).
63. Brunner and Wiedemann, *Monatsh.*, **66**, 438 (1935).
64. Loshakov and Alvin-Gutzatz, Russ. Patent 31,431 (1933).
65. Imperial Chemical Industries Ltd., Brit. Patent 417,383 (1934).
66. Reid, Cockerille, Meyer, Cox, and Ruhoff, *Organic Syntheses*, Coll. Vol. 2, Blatt, editor, p. 468, John Wiley & Sons, New York (1943).
67. Turpeinen, *J. Am. Chem. Soc.*, **60**, 56 (1938).
68. Kass and Burr, *ibid.*, **62**, 1796 (1940).
69. Kass, Miller, and Burr, *ibid.*, **61**, 482 (1939).
70. Prins, *Rec. trav. chim.*, **42**, 1050 (1923).
71. Dewar, *U. S. Pub. Health Service, Pub. Health Bull.*, No. *168*, 33 (1927).
72. Power and Gornall, *J. Chem. Soc.*, **85**, 851 (1904).
73. Scott and Hansley, U. S. Patent 2,019,022 (1935).
74. E. I. du Pont de Nemours & Co., Fr. Patent 810,983 (1937).
75. Webster and Schaefer, *Proc. S. Dakota Acad. Sci.*, **19**, 124 (1939).
76. Petrov, Sumin, Meerovich, Kudrina, and Tikhonova, *J. Gen. Chem.* (*U.S.S.R.*), **9**, 2144 (1939).
77. Korshak, *ibid.*, **9**, 1470 (1939).
78. Saytzeff with Unanoff, *J. Russ. Phys. Chem. Soc.*, **43**, 351 (1911).
79. Ryan and Dillon, *Proc. Roy. Irish Acad.*, **29B**, 235 (1912); *J. Chem. Soc.*, **104**, i, 583 (1913).
80. Henkel & Cie. G.m.b.H., Fr. Patent 776,319 (1935); Brit. Patent 422,804 (1935).
81. H. Th. Böhme A.-G., Brit. Patent 356,606 (1930); Fr. Patent 708,286 (1930); Böhme Fettchemie G.m.b.H., Ger. Patent 639,527 (1936).
82. I. G. Farbenind. A.-G., Fr. Patent 689,713 (1930).
83. I. G. Farbenind. A.-G., Brit. Patent 356,731 (1930).
84. H. Th. Böhme A.-G., Brit. Patent 358,869 (1930); Fr. Patent 718,394 (1931).
85. Böhme Fettchemie G.m.b.H., Ger. Patents 642,518 (1937); 648,510 (1937).
86. Böhme Fettchemie G.m.b.H., Ger. Patent 617,542 (1935).
87. Nippon Chissohiryô K. K., Japan. Patent 102,105 (1933).
88. Ueno and Komatsu, *J. Soc. Chem. Ind., Japan*, **41**, S.b. 62 (1938).
89. Schrauth and Böttler, U. S. Patent 2,023,383 (1935).

90. Schrauth, Schenck, and Stickdorn, *Ber.*, **64B**, 1314 (1931).
91. Schmidt, *ibid.*, **64B**, 2051 (1931).
92. Adkins and Folkers, *J. Am. Chem. Soc.*, **53**, 1095 (1931).
93. Adkins and Connor, *ibid.*, **53**, 1091 (1931).
94. Lazier, U. S. Patent 1,839,974 (1932).
95. E. I. du Pont de Nemours & Co., Brit. Patent 399,848 (1933).
96. Lazier, Brit. Patent 385,625 (1933).
97. Lazier, U. S. Patent 1,964,000 (1934).
98. Chemische Fabrik vorm. Sandoz, Swiss Patent 178,814 (1935); Brit. Patent 440,934 (1936).
99. Guyer, U. S. Patent 2,110,483 (1938).
100. Adkins, Folkers, and Connor, U. S. Patent 2,091,800 (1937).
101. Lazier and Arnold, *Organic Syntheses*, Coll. Vol. 2, Blatt, editor, p. 142, John Wiley & Sons, New York (1943).
102. E. I. du Pont de Nemours & Co., Brit. Patent 397,938 (1933).
103. E. I. du Pont de Nemours & Co., Brit. Patent 399,848 (1933).
104. Imperial Chemical Industries Ltd. and Stanley J. Green, Brit. Patent 433,549 (1935).
105. Schiller, U. S. Patent 2,121,367 (1938).
106. Deutsche Hydrierwerke A.-G., Ger. Patent 670,832 (1939).
107. Komori, *J. Soc. Chem. Ind., Japan*, **42**, S.b. 246 (1939).
108. Böhme Fettchemie G.m.b.H., Fr. Patent 819,255 (1937); Brit. Patent 479,642 (1938).
109. Lazier, U. S. Patent 2,094,127 (1937).
110. Komori, *J. Soc. Chem. Ind., Japan*, **43**, S.b. 122 (1940).
111. Komori, *ibid.*, **43**, S.b. 428 (1940).
112. Komori, Japan. Patent 137,780 (1940).
113. Komori, *J. Soc. Chem. Ind., Japan*, **42**, S.b. 46 (1939).
114. Sinozaki and Sumi, *J. Agr. Chem. Soc. Japan*, **14**, 1113, 1117, 1123, 1129 (1938).
115. Sauer and Adkins, *J. Am. Chem. Soc.*, **59**, 1 (1937).
116. H. Th. Böhme A.-G., Brit. Patent 441,096 (1936).
117. Normann and Schuckmann, U. S. Patent 2,126,367 (1938).
118. Lazier, U. S. Patent 2,094,611 (1937).
119. Lazier, U. S. Patent 2,040,944 (1936).
120. Green, U. S. Patent 2,080,419 (1937).
121. H. Th. Böhme A.-G., Ger. Patent 580,139 (1933).
122. I. G. Farbenind. A.-G., Brit. Patent 398,982 (1933).
123. Schmidt, Huttner, and Kaeb, U. S. Patent 2,009,948 (1935).
124. I. G. Farbenind. A.-G., Brit. Patent 410,087 (1934).
125. Hintermaier, U. S. Patent 1,987,558 (1935).
126. I. G. Farbenind. A.-G., Ger. Patent 589,946 (1933).
127. Luther and Dietrich, U. S. Patent 2,048,662 (1936).
128. Van Duzee and Adkins, *J. Am. Chem. Soc.*, **57**, 147 (1935)
129. H. Th. Böhme A.-G., Fr. Patent 728,893 (1931).
130. Brooks and Humphrey, *J. Am. Chem. Soc.*, **40**, 822 (1918).
131. N. V. de Bataafsche Petroleum Maatschappij, Fr. Patents 729,765 (1931); 730,829 (1932).
132. Seck and Dittmar, *Chem. Umschau*, **39**, 226 (1932).

133. H. Th. Böhme A.-G., Brit. Patent 421,218 (1934).
134. Patart, Brit. Patent 250,563 (1925).
135. Bocharova and Dolgov, *Compt. rend. acad. sci. U.R.S.S.*, **3**, 115·(1934).
136. Hentrich, Lainau, and Kaiser, U. S. Patent 2,151,106 (1939).
137. Deutsche Gold- und Silber-Scheideanstalt vormals Roessler, Brit. Patent 381,185 (1932).
138. Ralston, U. S. Patent 2,203,363 (1940).
139. Armour and Co., Brit. Patent 458,391 (1936).
140. Phillips and Mumford, *J. Chem. Soc.*, 1732 (1931).
141. Phillips and Mumford, *ibid.*, 1657 (1934).
142. Malkin, *J. Am. Chem. Soc.*, **52**, 3739 (1930).
143. Wilson and Ott, *J. Chem. Phys.*, **2**, 231 (1934).
144. Malkin, *J. Chem. Soc.*, 726 (1935).
145. Bernal, *Nature*, **129**, 870 (1932); *Z. Krist.*, **83**, 153 (1932).
146. Baker and Smyth, *J. Am. Chem. Soc.*, **60**, 1229 (1938).
147. Francis, Collins, and Piper, *Proc. Roy. Soc. (London)*, **158A**, 691 (1937).
148. Piper, Chibnall, and Williams, *Biochem. J.*, **28**, 2175 (1934).
149. Stewart, *Proc. Iowa Acad. Sci.*, **43**, 268 (1936).
150. Verkade and Coops, *Rec. trav. chim.*, **46**, 903 (1927).
151. Errera and Mollet, *Nature*, **138**, 882 (1936).
152. Wolf, *Trans. Faraday Soc.*, **33**, 179 (1937).
153. Buswell, Deitz, and Rodebush, *J. Chem. Phys.*, **5**, 84, 501 (1937).
154. Zellhoefer, Copley, and Marvel, *J. Am. Chem. Soc.*, **60**, 1337 (1938).
155. Cavallaro, *Ricerca Sci.*, **8**, I, 424 (1937); **8**, II, 124 (1937).
156. Hukumoto, *Nature*, **134**, 538 (1934).
157. Chuit, Boelsing, Hausser, and Malet, *Helv. Chim. Acta*, **10**, 113 (1927).
158. Willstätter and Mayer, *Ber.*, **41**, 1475 (1908).
159. Kass, Miller, and Burr, *J. Am. Chem. Soc.*, **61**, 482 (1939).
160. Cox and Reid, *ibid.*, **57**, 1801 (1935).
161. Lespieau, *Compt. rend.*, **187**, 605 (1928).
162. Shiina, *J. Soc. Chem. Ind., Japan*, **42**, S.b. 147 (1939).
163. Hoerr, Harwood, and Ralston, *J. Org. Chem.*, **9**, 267 (1944).
164. Schorlemmer, *Ann.*, **161**, 263 (1872).
165. Zincke, *ibid.*, **152**, 1 (1869).
166. Franchimont and Zincke, *ibid.*, **163**, 193 (1872).
167. Bouveault, *Bull. soc. chim.* [3], **31**, 1306 (1904).
168. Moureu and Mignonac, *Compt. rend.*, **170**, 258 (1920).
169. Moureu and Mignonac, *ibid.*, **171**, 652 (1920).
170. Dumas and Stass, *Ann.*, **35**, 129 (1840).
171. Guerbet, *Compt. rend.*, **153**, 1487 (1911).
172. Herndon and Reid, *J. Am. Chem. Soc.*, **50**, 3066 (1928).
173. Araki, *J. Chem. Soc. Japan*, **52**, 818 (1931).
174. Francis, *Ind. Eng. Chem.*, **20**, 283 (1928).
175. Sandonnini and Bezzi, *Atti accad. Lincei* [6], **12**, 154 (1930).
176. Goldwasser and Taylor, *J. Am. Chem. Soc.*, **61**, 1751, 1762 (1939).
177. Egloff, Morrell, Thomas, and Bloch, *ibid.*, **61**, 3571 (1939).
178. Appleby, Dobratz, and Kapranos, *ibid.*, **66**, 1938 (1944).
179. Komarewsky, Uhlick, and Murray, *ibid.*, **67**, 557 (1945).
180. Waterman and te Nuyl, *Rec. trav. chim.*, **51**, 533 (1932).

181. Whitmore and Herndon, *J. Am. Chem. Soc.*, **55**, 3428 (1933).
182. Kao and Chang, *Science Repts. Natl. Tsing Hua Univ.*, **Ser. A, 4,** 35 (1937) [*C.A.*, **31**, 6189 (1937)].
183. Wojcik and Adkins, *J. Am. Chem. Soc.*, **55**, 1293 (1933).
184. Gault, Palfray, and Hsu, *Compt. rend.*, **209**, 999 (1939).
185. Böeseken and van Senden, *Rec. trav. chim.*, **32**, 23 (1913).
186. Gerassimov and Glushnev, *Compt. rend. acad. sci. U.R.S.S.* [2], **29,** 462 (1940).
187. Komarewsky, Riesz, and Thodos, *J. Am. Chem. Soc.*, **61**, 2525 (1939).
188. Neuberg and Kansky, *Biochem. Z.*, **20**, 445 (1909).
189. Bickel and French, *J. Am. Chem. Soc.*, **48, 747** (1926).
190. Shriner and Cox, *ibid.*, **53**, 1601 (1931).
191. Hoeke, *Rec. trav. chim.*, **54**, 505 (1935).
192. Morgan and Pettet, *J. Chem. Soc.*, 1124 (1931).
193. Kawai and Tamura, *J. Chem. Soc. Japan*, **52**, 77 (1931).
194. I. G. Farbenind. A.-G., Ger. Patent 565,319 (1931).
195. Malone and Reid, *J. Am. Chem. Soc.*, **51**, 3424 (1929).
196. Reichstein, *Helv. Chim. Acta*, **9**, 799 (1926).
197. Bryant, *J. Am. Chem. Soc.*, **54**, 3758 (1932).
198. Henstock, *J. Chem. Soc.*, 216 (1933).
199. I. G. Farbenind. A.-G., Fr. Patent 727,202 (1931).
200. I. G. Farbenind. A.-G., Fr. Patent 770,804 (1934).
201. Schuette and Wittwer, U. S. Patent 2,174,761 (1939).
202. Deutsche Hydrierwerke A.-G., Fr. Patent 742,897 (1933).
203. Bertsch and Rauchalles, U. S. Patent 2,049,758 (1936).
204. Clark and Streight, *Trans. Roy. Soc. Can.* [3], **23**, Sec. III, 77 (1929).
205. Hartman, Byers, and Dickey, *Organic Syntheses*, Coll. Vol. 2, Blatt, editor, p. 322, John Wiley & Sons, New York (1943).
206. Smith, *J. Chem. Soc.*, 737 (1932).
207. Michael and Leupold, *Ann.*, **379**, 263 (1911); Michael and Zeidler, *ibid.*, **393**, 81 (1912).
208. Norris, *Am. Chem. J.*, **38**, 627 (1907); Norris, Watt, and Thomas, *J. Am. Chem. Soc.*, **38**, 1071 (1916).
209. Kamm and Marvel, *ibid.*, **42**, 299 (1920); *Organic Syntheses*, Coll. Vol. 1, Gilman, editor, p. 27, John Wiley & Sons, New York (1932).
210. Ruhoff, Burnett, and Reid, *J. Am. Chem. Soc.*, **56**, 2784 (1934).
211. Reid, Ruhoff, and Burnett, *Organic Syntheses*, Coll. Vol. 2, Blatt, editor, p. 246, John Wiley & Sons, New York (1943).
212. Guyer, Bieler, and Hardmeier, *Helv. Chim. Acta*, **20**, 1462 (1937).
213. Schirm, Hueter, and Engelbrecht, U. S. Patent 2,277,359 (1942).
214. Simon, *Bull. soc. chim. Belg.*, **38**, 47 (1929).
215. Delcourt, *ibid.*, **40**, 284 (1931).
216. Fischer and Klages, *Physik. Z.*, **40**, 721 (1939).
217. Chuit and Hausser, *Helv. Chim. Acta*, **12**, 463 (1929).
218. v. Braun, *Ber.*, **42**, 4541 (1909).
219. v. Braun and Kamp, *ibid.*, **70B**, 973 (1937).
220. v. Braun and Friedrich-Liebenberg, *ibid.*, **70B**, 1598 (1937).
221. Desreux, *Bull. classe sci. Acad. roy. Belg.* [5], **20**, 457 (1934).
222. Paternò and Spallino, *Atti accad Lincei* [5], **16**, II, 160 (1907); *Gazz. chim. ital.*, **37**, II, 309 (1907).

223. Swarts, *Bull. soc. chim. Belg.*, **30**, 302 (1921).
224. Gilman and Turck, *J. Am. Chem. Soc.*, **61**, 478 (1939).
225. Gilman and Turck, *ibid.*, **61**, 473 (1939).
226. Meals and Gilman, *Proc. Iowa Acad. Sci.*, **48**, 250 (1941).
227. Krafft, *Ber.*, **19**, 2982 (1886).
228. Marvel, Gauerke, and Hill, *J. Am. Chem. Soc.*, **47**, 3009 (1925).
229. Hoyt and Gilman, *Proc. Iowa Acad. Sci.*, **45**, 133 (1938).
230. Müller and Schütz, *Ber.*, **71B**, 689 (1938).
231. Franke and Hankam, *Monatsh.*, **31**, 177 (1910).
232. Brown and Campbell, *J. Chem. Soc.*, 1699 (1937).
233. Levy and Campbell, *ibid.*, 1442 (1939).
234. The Grasselli Chemical Co., Brit. Patent 431,064 (1935).
235. Allen, *J. Am. Chem. Soc.*, **57**, 198 (1935).
236. Rose and Haller, *ibid.*, **58**, 2648 (1936).
237. Heckert, U. S. Patent 1,808,893 (1931).
238. The Grasselli Chemical Co., Fr. Patent 773,852 (1934).
239. Voss and Blanke, *Ann.*, **485**, 258 (1931).
240. Bushong, *Am. Chem. J.*, **30**, 212 (1903).
241. Levaillant and Simon, *Compt. rend.*, **169**, 854 (1919).
242. Levaillant, *ibid.*, **188**, 261 (1929).
243. Levaillant, *ibid.*, **197**, 648 (1933).
244. Barkenbus and Owen, *J. Am. Chem. Soc.*, **56**, 1204 (1934).
245. H. Th. Böhme A.-G., Brit. Patent 308,824 (1928).
246. Bertsch, U. S. Patents 1,968,793–5 (1934).
247. Matumoto, *Repts. Chem. Research, Prefectural Inst. Advancement Ind., Tokyo*, No. **3**, 28 (1940) [*C.A.*, **35**, 7938 (1941)].
248. Chemische Fabrik vorm. Sandoz, Swiss Patent 177,938 (1935).
249. Bertsch, U. S. Patent 2,114,042 (1938).
250. Soc. pour l'ind. chim. à Bâle, Brit. Patent 390,023 (1933).
251. Carbide and Carbon Chemicals Corp., Fr. Patent 789,405 (1935).
252. Imperial Chemical Industries Ltd. and A. J. Hailwood, Brit. Patent 391,435 (1933).
253. Siebenbürger, U. S. Patent 2,060,254 (1936).
254. Bertsch, U. S. Patent 2,256,877 (1941).
255. H. Th. Böhme A.-G., Brit. Patent 358,612 (1929).
256. Guenther, Haussmann, Nusslein, Schuette, and Schoeller. U. S. Patent 2,229,649 (1941).
257. Mills and Wood, U. S. Patent 2,214,254 (1940).
258. I. G. Farbenind. A.-G., Ger. Patent 558,296 (1930); Brit. Patent 382,945 (1932).
259. Deutsche Hydrierwerke A.-G., Ger. Patent 623,403 (1935).
260. Bertsch and Stober, Ger. Patent 696,904 (1940).
261. I. G. Farbenind. A.-G., Fr. Patent 716,705 (1931).
262. Deutsche Hydrierwerke A.-G., Brit. Patent 400,986 (1933).
263. H. Th. Böhme A.-G., Fr. Patent 755,895 (1933).
264. Lenher, U. S. Patent 2,012,609 (1935).
265. Lenher, U. S. Patent 2,116,727 (1938).
266. Imperial Chemical Industries Ltd., Fr. Patent 765,022 (1934).
267. Weller, U. S. Patent 2,015,207 (1935).
268. Cory and Langford, *J. Econ. Entomol.*, **28**, 257 (1935).

269. Bair and Suter, *J. Am. Chem. Soc.*, **64**, 1978 (1942).
270. Donleavy, *ibid.*, **58**, 1004 (1936).
271. Chambers and Watt, *J. Org. Chem.*, **6**, 376 (1941).
272. Stenhagen, *Trans. Faraday Soc.*, **36**, 496 (1940).
273. Biehringer, *Ber.*, **38**, 3974 (1905).
274. Plimmer and Burch, *J. Chem. Soc.*, 279 (1929).
275. Christensen, *J. Biol. Chem.*, **135**, 399 (1940).
276. Böhme Fettchemie G.m.b.H., Ger. Patent 619,019 (1935).
277. Graves, U. S. Patent 2,005,619 (1935).
278. Oranienburger Chemische Fabrik A.-G., Ger. Patent 664,514 (1938).
279. Graves and Werntz, U. S. Patent 2,053,474 (1936).
280. Brigl and Fuchs, *Z. physiol. Chem.*, **119**, 280 (1922).
281. J. R. Geigy A.-G., Swiss Patents 165,401–2 (1934).
282. J. R. Geigy A.-G., Swiss Patents 165,403–4 (1934).
283. Ruhoff and Reid, *J. Am. Chem. Soc.*, **55**, 3825 (1933).
284. Talvitie, *Ann. Acad. Sci. Fennicae*, No. 16, **26A**, 1 (1927).
285. Komppa and Talvitie, *J. prakt. Chem.* [2], **135**, 193 (1932).
286. Krafft, *Ber.*, **16**, 3018 (1883).
287. Kohlhaas, *Z. Krist.*, **98**, 418 (1938).
288. Goggans and Copenhaver, *J. Am. Chem. Soc.*, **61**, 2909 (1939).
289. Dickinson, Crosson, and Copenhaver, *ibid.*, **59**, 1094 (1937).
290. Senderens, *Compt. rend.*, **176**, 813 (1923); **179**, 1015 (1924); **181**, 698 (1925).
291. Fridau, *Ann.*, **83**, 1 (1852).
292. Dobriner, *ibid.*, **243**, 1 (1888).
293. Möslinger, *ibid.*, **185**, 49 (1877).
294. *Aliphatic Derivatives*, The Connecticut Hard Rubber Co., New Haven, Conn.
295. Kohlhaas, *Ber.*, **73B**, 189 (1940).
296. Cross, *Ann.*, **189**, 1 (1877).
297. Welt, *Ber.*, **30**, 1493 (1897).
298. Becker, *Ann.*, **102**, 219 (1857).
299. Roger and Dvolaitskaya, *Recherches*, **1**, 13 (1937).
300. Cerchez, *Bull. soc. chim.* [4], **43**, 762 (1928).
301. I. G. Farbenind. A.-G., Ger. Patent 584,840 (1933).
302. Reppe, U. S. Patent 1,959,927 (1934).
303. Price and Dumbrow, U. S. Patent 2,241,421 (1941).
304. Böhme Fettchemie G.m.b.H., Ger. Patent 652,433 (1937).
305. Orthner, Balle, Rosenbach, and Bonstedt, U. S. Patent 2,217,846 (1940).
306. Rosenbach and Balle, U. S. Patent 2,283,764 (1942).
307. Deutsche Hydrierwerke A.-G., Fr. Patent 743,594 (1933).
308. Deutsche Hydrierwerke A.-G., Ger. Patent 635,903 (1936).
309. J. R. Geigy A.-G., Swiss Patent 162,732 (1933).
310. Henkel & Cie. G.m.b.H., Fr. Patents 751,923 (1933); 768,554 (1934).
311. Elbel, U. S. Patent 2,028,654 (1936).
312. Imperial Chemical Industries Ltd. and Baldwin, Heilbron, and Jones, Brit. Patent 436,143 (1935).
313. Schöller and Nüsslein, U. S. Patent 2,164,431 (1939).
314. Henkel & Cie. G.m.b.H., Fr. Patent 788,663 (1935).

315. I. G. Farbenind. A.-G., Fr. Patent 770,804 (1934).
316. Schmidt and Meyer, U. S. Patent 1,959,930 (1934).
317. Haskins and Ellsworth, U. S. Patent 2,102,205 (1937).
318. Imperial Chemical Industries Ltd. and Baldwin, Bunbury, and Heilbron, Brit. Patent 436,209 (1935).
319. I. G. Farbenind. A.-G., Brit. Patent 394,043 (1933).
320. J. R. Geigy A.-G., Swiss Patents 165,385 to 165,400 (1934).
321. I. G. Farbenind. A.-G., Fr. Patent 800,079 (1936).
322. Hartley, J. Chem. Soc., 1828 (1939).
323. Mehta, Mehta, and Thosar, J. Indian Chem. Soc., Ind. & News Ed., 4, 170 (1941) [C.A., 36, 4486 (1942)].
324. Weygand and Gabler, J. prakt. Chem. [2], 155, 332 (1940).
325. Imperial Chemical Industries Ltd., Fr. Patent 749,402 (1933).
326. Baldwin and Davidson, U. S. Patent 1,999,315 (1935).
327. Deutsche Hydrierwerke A.-G., Ger. Patent 535,338 (1928).
328. Imperial Chemical Industries Ltd. and Hailwood and Baldwin, Brit. Patent 378,454 (1932).
329. Michel and Buschmann, Ger. Patent 707,023 (1941).
330. I. G. Farbenind. A.-G., Fr. Patent 798,728 (1936).
331. Rohm and Haas Co., Brit. Patent 505,769 (1939)
332. Holt, U. S. Patent 2,197,105 (1940).
333. Elbs, Z. Elektrochem., 7, 141 (1900).
334. I. G. Farbenind. A.-G., Ger. Patent 634,037 (1936).
335. Bruson, U. S. Patent 2,098,203 (1937).
336. Pexsters, Bull. classe sci. Acad. roy. Belg. [4], 8, 796 (1906).
337. Pelouze and Cahours, Jahresber., 523 (1863).
338. Winssinger, ibid., 1280 (1887).
339. Kahn, Bull. soc. chim. Roumania, 5, 70 (1923).
340. Ellis and Reid, J. Am. Chem. Soc., 54, 1674 (1932).
341. Murray, J. Chem. Soc., 739 (1933).
342. Collin, Hilditch, Marsh, and McLeod, J. Soc. Chem. Ind., 52, 272T (1933).
343. Flaschenträger and Wannschaff, Ber., 67B, 1121 (1934).
344. Fore and Bost, J. Am. Chem. Soc., 59, 2557 (1937).
345. Urquhart, Gates, and Connor, Organic Syntheses, 21, 36 (1941).
346. Backer, Terpstra, and Dijkstra, Rec. trav. chim., 51, 1166 (1932).
347. Noller and Gordon, J. Am. Chem. Soc., 55, 1090 (1933).
348. Henkel & Cie. G.m.b.H., Fr. Patent 751,117 (1933).
349. Elbel and Kirstahler, U. S. Patent 2,031,529 (1936).
350. I. G. Farbenind. A.-G., Brit. Patent 454,668 (1936).
351. Tschugaeff, Ber., 42, 49 (1909).
352. Bost and Everett, J. Am. Chem. Soc., 62, 1752 (1940).
353. Billheimer and Reid, ibid., 52, 4338 (1930).
354. Grabowsky and Saytzeff, Ann., 171, 251 (1874).
355. Salzberg, U. S. Patent 2,085,452 (1937).
356. Bost, Turner, and Norton, J. Am. Chem. Soc., 54, 1985 (1932).
357. Bost, Turner, and Conn, ibid., 55, 4956 (1933).
358. Imperial Chemical Industries Ltd., Fr. Patent 786,625 (1935).
359. Baldwin and Piggott, U. S. Patent 2,100,297 (1937).
360. Elbel and Kirstahler, U. S. Patent 1,987,526 (1935).

361. Henkel & Cie. G.m.b.H., Ger. Patent 671,546 (1939).
362. Bennett and Gudgeon, *J. Chem. Soc.*, 1891 (1938).
363. Henkel & Cie. G.m.b.H., Fr. Patent 748,460 (1933).
364. Elbel and Müller, U. S. Patent 2,050,169 (1936).
365. Henkel & Cie. G.m.b.H., Brit. Patent 403,882 (1934).
366. Urquhart and Connor, *J. Am. Chem. Soc.*, **63**, 1483 (1941).
367. Orthner, Balle, Rosenbach, and Bonstedt, U. S. Patent 2,217,846 (1940).
368. Jones and Reid, *J. Am. Chem. Soc.*, **60**, 2452 (1938).
369. I. G. Farbenind. A.-G., Fr. Patent 780,144 (1935).
370. I. G. Farbenind. A.-G., Brit. Patent 437,590 (1935).
371. Kuhlmann, Fr. Patent 794,830 (1936).
372. Kirstahler, U. S. Patent 2,078,856 (1937).
373. Schuette, Schoeller, and Wittwer, U. S. Patent 2,129,709 (1938).
374. von Oefele, *Ann.*, **132**, 82 (1864).
375. Cahours, *ibid.*, **135**, 352 (1865).
376. Chemische Fabrik von Heyden A.-G., Fr. Patent 810,437 (1937).
377. Böhme Fettchemie G.m.b.H., Ger. Patent 671,882 '' 939).
378. Hunter, *Iowa State Coll. J. Sci.*, **15**, 215 (1941).
379. Bost and Conn, *Ind. Eng. Chem.*, **23**, 93 (1931).
380. Henkel & Cie. G.m.b.H., Fr. Patent 762,405 (1934); Ger. Patent 685 241 (1939).
381. I. G. Farbenind. A.-G., Brit. Patent 446,992 (1936).
382. Ufer, U. S. Patent 2,103,879 (1937).
383. Martin and Hirt, U. S. Patent 2,207,021 (1940).
384. Bunte, *Ber.*, **7**, 646 (1874).
385. Price and Twiss, *J. Chem. Soc.*, **91**, 2021 (1907); **93**, 1395, 1401 (1908).
386. Price and Twiss, *ibid.*, **95**, 1489 (1909).
387. Westlake and Dougherty, *J. Am. Chem. Soc.*, **64**, 149 (1942).
388. Reychler, *Bull. soc. chim. Belg.*, **27**, 110 (1913).
389. Norris, *J. Chem. Soc.*, **121**, 2161 (1922).
390. McBain and Williams, *J. Am. Chem. Soc.*, **55**, 2250 (1933).
391. Schirm, U. S. Patent 1,966,187 (1934).
392. de Simo and O'Connor, U. S. Patent 2,243,331 (1941).
393. Strecker, *Ann.*, **148**, 90 (1868).
394. Deutsche Hydrierwerke A.-G., Fr. Patent 711,210 (1930).
395. I. G. Farbenind. A.-G., Brit. Patent 360,539 (1930); Fr. Patent 716,705 (1931).
396. Reed with Tartar, *J. Am. Chem. Soc.*, **57**, 570 (1935).
397. Latimer and Bost, *ibid.*, **59**, 2500 (1937).
398. Imperial Chemical Industries Ltd., Fr. Patent 735,211 (1932).
399. Reychler, *Bull. soc. chim. Belg.*, **27**, 217, 300 (1913); *Kolloid-Z.*, **12** 277 (1913); **13**, 252 (1913).
400. McBain and Betz, *J. Am. Chem. Soc.*, **57**, 1905 (1935).
401. McBain, Dye, and Johnston, *ibid.*, **61**, 3210 (1939).
402. Murray and Hartley, *Trans. Faraday Soc.*, **31**, 183 (1935).
403. Reed and Tartar, *J. Am. Chem. Soc.*, **58**, 322 (1936).
404. Sekera and Marvel, *ibid.*, **55**, 345 (1933).
405. Marvel and Sekera, *Organic Syntheses*, **20**, 50 (1940).
406. Flett, U. S. Patent 2,205,946 (1940).

407. Flett, U. S. Patents 2,205,947–8 (1940).
408. Flett, U. S. Patent 2,205,950 (1940).
409. Eitelman and Flett, U. S. Patent 2,221,933 (1940).
410. Thomas, U. S. Patent 2,210,962 (1940).
411. N. V. de Bataafsche Petroleum Maatschappij, Fr. Patent 840,778 (1939); Dutch Patent 47,715 (1940).
412. I. G. Farbenind. A.-G., Ger. Patent 657,404 (1938).
413. I. G. Farbenind. A.-G., Brit. Patent 358,583 (1930).
414. Beller and Owen, U. S. Patent 2,149,265 (1939).
415. Günther and Haussmann, Ger. Patent 705,179 (1941).
416. H. Th. Böhme A.-G., Brit. Patent 317,039 (1928).
417. Wolter, U. S. Patent 2,231,979 (1941).
418. Deutsche Hydrierwerke A.-G., Ger. Patent 542,048 (1928).
419. H. Th. Böhme A.-G., Brit. Patent 351,452 (1929); Fr. Patent 38,048 (1930).
420. Luther and v. Friedolsheim, U. S. Patent 1,993,375 '1935).
421. Elbel, U. S. Patent 2,081,865 (1937).
422. Engelmann, U. S. Patent 2,199,398 (1940).
423. Chemische Fabrik Stockhausen & Cie., Brit. Patent 418,139 (1934).
424. I. G. Farbenind. A.-G., Ger. Patent 657,357 (1938).
425. Baldwin and Piggott, Brit. Patent 435,039 (1935
426. Mauersberger, U. S. Patent 2,042,952 (1936).
427. Bertsch, U. S. Patent 2,264,737 (1941).
428. Waldmann and Chwala, Austrian Patent 158,406 (1940).
429. J. R. Geigy A.-G., Swiss Patents 167,024–7 (1934).
430. Martin, U. S. Patent 2,156,996 (1939).
431. Allen, *J. Org. Chem.*, **7**, 23 (1942).
432. Graves, U. S. Patents 2,037,717–8 (1936).
433. Deutsche Hydrierwerke A.-G., Ger. Patent 566,027 (1930).
434. Werntz, U. S. Patent 2,070,634 (1937).
435. Soc. pour l'ind. chim. à Bâle, Swiss Patent 213,554 (1941).
436. J. R. Geigy A.-G., Swiss Patents 163,000–3 (1933).
437. Imperial Chemical Industries Ltd. and Baldwin, Brit. Patent 437,285 (1935).
438. J. R. Geigy A.-G., Swiss Patent 191,011 (1937).
439. Nicolet and Bate, *J. Am. Chem. Soc.*, **49**, 2064 (1927).
440. Jerchel, *Ber.*, **76B**, 600 (1943).
441. Hibbert, *ibid.*, **39**, 160 (1906).

X

THE FATTY ACID ANHYDRIDES, ACID CHLORIDES, ALDEHYDES, KETONES, AND RELATED COMPOUNDS

THE FATTY ACID ANHYDRIDES

The anhydrides of the lower aliphatic carboxylic acids, acetic, propionic, and butyric, are well-known compounds. Those of the higher acids, however, have attracted little scientific and technical interest. Although the lower anhydrides are liquids which readily dissolve in water with the formation of the related acids, the anhydrides of the higher acids are stable solids which are comparatively insoluble in water and are hydrolyzed only with some difficulty. An interesting feature concerning the aliphatic anhydrides is that whereas the lower anhydrides possess melting points appreciably below those of the corresponding acids, the higher anhydrides show melting points somewhat above those of the related acids. Since the aliphatic anhydrides contain two acyl groups, they are represented by two types of compounds; namely, the symmetrical or simple anhydrides, $(RCO)_2O$, in which the R groups are alike, and the unsymmetrical or mixed anhydrides, $(RCO)(R'CO)O$, in which they differ. Mixed anhydrides of the fatty acids and various inorganic acids have also been synthesized and described.

Several procedures are available for the preparation of the symmetrical anhydrides of the higher fatty acids. The most direct of these methods consists of the removal of a molecule of water from two molecules of acid by the action of strong dehydrating agents such as acetic anhydride. A procedure first proposed by Albitskiĭ [1] consists of heating the free acids with acetic anhydride under pressure in a glass tube at 150–160°. This method is satisfactory for the preparation of anhydrides of both saturated and unsaturated carboxylic acids; [2,3] for example, a 73% yield of linoleic anhydride

794

is obtained [4] by heating linoleic acid with acetic anhydride in a sealed tube at 140–150° for four hours. Holde and Wilke [5] have reported an 84.5% yield of erucic anhydride from erucic acid by this procedure. The method of purification generally consists of the removal by vacuum distillation of the excess acetic anhydride together with the acetic acid formed during the reaction. The residue is then dissolved in petroleum ether and the solution washed with dilute sodium carbonate solution to remove any traces of acetic acid or unreacted higher acid. After being washed with alcohol, the petroleum ether solution is dried and the ether removed by distillation. Holde and Tacke [6] reported a 94% yield of oleic anhydride from oleic acid, employing this method of purifying the reaction mixture. The higher anhydrides may readily be obtained simply by refluxing the respective acids with an excess of acetic anhydride. Palmitic anhydride and stearic anhydride, for example, have been prepared from palmitic and stearic acids by this method,[7] and Holde and Gentner [8] have obtained the anhydrides of the even acids from caprylic to stearic inclusive by its use. The reaction mixture is refluxed over an oil bath for four to seven hours, the excess of acetic anhydride and the acetic acid are removed under a vacuum, and the anhydride is purified through its petroleum ether solution. In several instances yields as high as 91.5% are obtained. The application of this method to the preparation of the lower symmetrical anhydrides, such as caproic anhydride, has also been described.[9] For the synthesis of anhydrides of unsaturated acids, Holde and Gentner [10] have recommended that the reaction be conducted in the presence of carbon dioxide. Thus, linoleic anhydride is prepared by heating the acid under a reflux condenser with three times the calculated amount of acetic anhydride for 4.5 hours at 150–170° in an atmosphere of carbon dioxide, a 91% yield of the anhydride being obtained. Dehydration of fatty acids by means of acetic anhydride is facilitated by the continuous removal of the acetic acid resulting from the reaction.[11] It has been proposed to introduce the vapors of the lower anhydride below the surface of the heated acid and to remove continuously the excess of lower anhydride and the acid from the reaction zone.[12] It has recently been stated [13] that small amounts of sulfuric acid are catalytic for anhydride formation by this method.

Although acetic anhydride is the most commonly employed dehydrating agent for the conversion of the higher fatty acids into their respective anhydrides, a number of other dehydrating agents have been investigated. The monobasic acids yield a mixture of anhydrides and ketones when heated with phosphorus pentoxide, and approximately 80% yields of palmitic anhydride and stearic anhydride are obtained by subjecting the respective acids in benzene solution to the action of phosphorus pentoxide formed *in situ* from phosphorus and air.[14] Acetyl chloride may be employed as the dehydrating agent, an example being the preparation of caproic anhydride by the action of acetyl chloride on caproic acid.[15] It has been stated [16] that if the saturated fatty acids are treated in dilute ether solution with acetyl chloride, the higher acids lauric, myristic, palmitic, and stearic yield the corresponding simple anhydrides, whereas the lower acids caproic, caprylic, and capric yield mixed anhydrides. This statement has not been verified, although it has been proposed to separate the higher from the lower fatty acids by recourse to this procedure.

The sodium salts of the higher acids are frequently used as starting points for the preparation of anhydrides. Foremost among such methods is that first introduced by Gerhardt,[17] which consists of heating the anhydrous sodium soap with its corresponding acid chloride, the reaction proceeding as follows:

$$RCO_2Na + RCOCl \rightarrow (RCO)_2O + NaCl$$

Among the first to adapt this reaction to the preparation of higher aliphatic anhydrides was Villier,[18] who obtained palmitic anhydride by the action at 150° of palmitoyl chloride on sodium palmitate. Enanthic, caprylic, pelargonic, lauric, myristic, and palmitic anhydrides have been synthesized [19] by the action of their acid chlorides on the corresponding sodium salts. The sodium soaps also yield the corresponding symmetrical anhydrides when heated in a sealed tube with acetic anhydride, Michael [20] having described the preparation of caproic anhydride by heating sodium caproate with acetic anhydride. Whitby [21] has prepared a number of anhydrides of saturated acids by heating their silver salts with their respective acid chlorides.

One of the earlier methods for the preparation of anhydrides consists of treating the anhydrous sodium soaps with phosgene,[22] the reaction proceeding as follows.

$$2RCO_2Na + COCl_2 \rightarrow (RCO)_2O + CO_2 + 2NaCl$$

Anhydrides of the fatty acids of tall oil have been obtained [23] by treating suspensions of their sodium soaps in benzene with phosgene. Anhydrides result from the action of pyrosulfates on the anhydrous soaps of fatty acids,[24] or from treatment of soaps in the presence of inert diluents with sulfur dioxide dissolved in sulfuric acid.[25] An early patent [26] proposes the preparation of higher anhydrides by the action of sulfur monochloride on the soaps of fatty acids, and it has also been suggested [27] to prepare such anhydrides by treating the sodium soaps with sulfur and chlorine. Sulfur monochloride and thionyl chloride react with some metal salts of the fatty acids to give compounds of the formulas $(RCO_2)_2S_2$ and $(RCO_2)_2SO$ respectively, which yield anhydrides when heated above their decomposition points.[28] Thus, silver palmitate and sulfur monochloride yield the so-called thiosulfite $(C_{15}H_{31}CO_2)_2S_2$, which is converted into palmitic anhydride on heating. The metallic soaps yield the corresponding anhydrides when treated with phosphorus oxychloride, an example being the preparation of caproic anhydride by the action of phosphorus oxychloride on barium caproate.[29]

The reaction of ketene with the higher acids first yields a mixed acetic anhydride, thus: [30]

$$RCO_2H + CH_2{=}C{=}O \rightarrow RCO_2COCH_3$$

When these mixed anhydrides are distilled at relatively high temperatures they are generally transformed into the two symmetrical anhydrides. The use of two moles of fatty acid and one mole of ketene yields the symmetrical anhydride and acetic acid. The action of ketene on caproic acid at low temperatures, followed by fractional distillation of the resulting product, produces caproic anhydride. The preparation has been described in detail,[31] and yields of 80–87% of the theoretical amount have been reported. The overall reaction is as follows:

$$2C_5H_{11}CO_2H + CH_2{=}C{=}O \rightarrow (C_5H_{11}CO)_2O + CH_3CO_2H$$

The preparation of ketene has been described by Williams and Hurd.[32]

When two moles of an aromatic carboxylic acid are treated with one mole of oxalyl chloride in benzene solution, a high yield of the aromatic acid anhydride is obtained; [33] however, when the same procedure is applied to the preparation of aliphatic anhydrides, the yields are much lower.[34] The resulting product contains appreciable amounts of unchanged acid and also of acid chloride, thus indicating that aliphatic anhydrides are more readily converted to acid chlorides by this reagent than are aromatic anhydrides. Higher yields of aliphatic anhydrides are obtained by the action of oxalyl chloride on the sodium salts of the acids. It was postulated that the simple anhydride may be formed through a double anhydride of the acid and oxalic acid, thus:

$$2RCO_2H + (COCl)_2 \rightarrow (RCO_2CO)_2 \rightarrow (RCO)_2O + CO_2 + CO$$

The reaction of the sodium salts with oxalyl chloride may proceed either through the above mechanism or by the direct formation of the anhydrides, thus:

$$2RCO_2Na + (COCl)_2 \rightarrow (RCO)_2O + CO_2 + CO + 2NaCl$$

The following yields of anhydrides have been obtained by the action of oxalyl chloride on the respective sodium salts: butanoic, 79%; pentanoic, 91%; and dodecanoic, 80%.

The oxidation of paraffin by blowing with air has repeatedly been stated to yield anhydrides, Holde [35] having verified the presence of small amounts of anhydrides in such products.

The anhydrides of the low molecular weight acids possess melting points which are distinctly lower than those of the acids from which they are derived. Myristic acid and its anhydride have essentially similar melting points, and the anhydrides higher than myristic melt several degrees above the corresponding acids. Only the lower anhydrides can be distilled without decomposition, and the higher members cannot be distilled even under high vacuum. The higher anhydrides are insoluble in water and in polar organic solvents. They are soluble in ether, chlorinated hydrocarbons, petroleum ether, and many other organic solvents.

Physical constants for the higher symmetrical anhydrides have been reported by a number of investigators,[7, 8, 21, 36, 37, 38] the values for the symmetrical anhydrides from butyric to stearic inclusive being shown in Table I.

A plot of the melting points of the symmetrical anhydrides against the number of carbon atoms in the parent acids shows that the alternation is the reverse of that exhibited by the acids, the anhydrides of the odd acids melting above those of the even acids.[38] This alternation is quite marked with the anhydrides of the lower acids from valeric acid downward. The average of the melting points of the anhydrides from enanthic to stearic is 1.2° above that of the corresponding acids.

The physical constants of several of the anhydrides higher than stearic have been reported [36] to be as follows: (anhydride, m.p.,

TABLE I

Physical Constants of Symmetrical Aliphatic Anhydrides

Anhydride	B.P., °C.	M.P., °C.	d_4^t	n_D^t
Butyric	198	-75	0.9946^{20}	1.4143^{18}
	$85-86_{18}$			
Valeric	215	-56.1	0.929^{20}	......
Caproic	241–243	-40.6	0.9279^{11}	......
Enanthic	258	-10.8	0.932^{20}	1.4312^{20}
	164.5_{15}			
Caprylic	280–290	0.9 ± 0.1	$0.9065^{17.5}$	$1.4358^{17.5}$
Pelargonic	207_{15}	14.8	......	......
Capric	......	24.7 ± 0.2	0.8596^{70}	1.4234^{70}
Undecanoic	......	36.7	......	......
Lauric	......	42.1 ± 0.1	0.8552^{70}	1.4292^{70}
Tridecanoic	......	49.9 ± 0.2	......	......
Myristic	......	53.5 ± 0.1	0.8502^{70}	1.4335^{70}
Pentadecanoic	......	60.6	......	......
Palmitic	......	63.9 ± 0.1	0.847^{70}	1.4357^{70}
Margaric	......	67.6	......	......
Stearic	......	70.7	0.8443^{70}	1.4379^{70}

d_4^{100}, n_D^{100}) eicosanoic, 77.5–77.7°, 0.8225, 1.4301; docosanoic, 81.7–81.9°, 0.8206, 1.4320; tetracosanoic, 86.0–86.3°, 0.8196, 1.4329; hexacosanoic, 89.3–89.5°, 0.8188, 1.4337; octacosanoic, 92.7–92.9°, 0.8183, 1.4345; and triacontanoic, 94.6–94.7°, —, 1.4352.

A number of anhydrides of the ethylenic acids have been prepared and their properties described. These include 10-undecenoic anhydride, m.p. 13–13.5°, obtained by the action of 10-undecenoyl chloride on sodium 10-undecenoate;[39] oleic anhydride,[40] m.p. 22–22.2°, d_4^{20} 0.8982, n_D^{20} 1.4630; elaidic anhydride, m.p. 46.2–46.4°, d_4^{100} 0.8338, n_D^{100} 1.4339; and erucic anhydride,[5] m.p. 46.0–46.5°. Brassidic anhydride, m.p. 64°, d_4^{70} 0.835, has been prepared by rearrangement of erucic anhydride by means of nitrous acid.[23] Linoleic anhydride, which solidifies at $-18°$ and melts at $-4°$ to $-3°$, has been obtained [10,41] by the action of acetic anhydride on linoleic acid in an atmosphere of carbon dioxide.

The anhydrides of the higher dicarboxylic acids may exist either as monomeric rings or as linear or cyclic polymers. Those of succinic and glutaric acids are monomeric rings which contain five and six atoms, respectively. Adipic anhydride was first prepared by Voerman [42] by the action of acetyl chloride on adipic acid; the product so obtained was a solid which melted at 98°. Later,

Farmer and Kracovski [43] reported adipic anhydride to be monomeric and to melt at 97°. Hill [44] subsequently showed that this anhydride is a linear polymer which cannot be distilled, inasmuch as it breaks down at 200° into a monomeric anhydride freezing at about 20° and boiling at about 100° at 0.1 mm. The monomeric anhydride reacts readily with aniline to yield the monoanilide, thus being distinguished from the polymeric anhydride. It is readily hydrolyzed in water to yield adipic acid. On heating at 100° or on standing, it is converted into a polymer melting at 80–85°, which can again be converted into the monomer on distillation. Blanc [45] has reported that when adipic or pimelic anhydride is distilled at ordinary pressures carbon dioxide is evolved and high yields of the corresponding ketones result. Hill and Carothers [46] have extended these studies to include sebacic anhydride and have shown that the linear polymer (α-anhydride) which first forms is converted by molecular distillation into a polyanhydride of high molecular weight (ω-anhydride) and a depolymerized crystalline product (β-anhydride) which was shown to be a twenty-two-membered cyclic dimer.

Very few mixed anhydrides of the aliphatic acids have been described. Verkade [47] has prepared several mixed anhydrides of the lower acids by the action of acid chlorides on anhydrous sodium soaps, and this process is adaptable to the synthesis of the higher mixed anhydrides. Acetic-propionic anhydride has been obtained by the action of acetyl chloride on propionic acid in ether solution in the presence of pyridine.[48] The mixed anhydrides decompose slowly upon distillation to yield simple anhydrides,[49] and as a consequence, no reliable boiling point data concerning them are available. Mixed acetic anhydrides can be obtained by the action of ketene on aliphatic acids. The preparation of acetic-butyric anhydride by this procedure has been described,[30] and the method is probably adaptable to the preparation of the higher mixed acetic anhydrides.

Ralston and Reck [50] have recently synthesized several mixed aliphatic anhydrides containing eighteen carbon atoms, in which the length of the longest chain varies from ten to sixteen carbon atoms. The thermal constants of these mixed anhydrides, the parent long-chain acid, and its symmetrical anhydride are shown in Table II.

The melting points of the four isomeric, mixed anhydrides contained in Table II show that these values differ over a wide range

TABLE II

THERMAL CONSTANTS OF MIXED ANHYDRIDES, ACIDS, AND SYMMETRICAL
ANHYDRIDES

Mixed Anhydride	M.P., °C.	Acid	F.P., °C.[51]	Symmetrical Anhydride	M.P., °C.[38]
C_{16}—C_2	62.5	C_{16}	62.41	C_{16}—C_{16}	63.9
C_{14}—C_4	52.7	C_{14}	53.78	C_{14}—C_{14}	53.5
C_{12}—C_6	42.4	C_{12}	43.86	C_{12}—C_{12}	42.1
C_{10}—C_8	16.0	C_{10}	30.92	C_{10}—C_{10}	24.7

and decrease progressively with decrease in the length of the longest chain. Thus, the melting point of an unsymmetrical anhydride is more dependent upon the length of the longest hydrocarbon chain contained therein than upon the total number of carbon atoms in the molecule. There is only a small difference between the melting point of a mixed anhydride containing a C_{12}, C_{14}, or C_{16} chain and that of the corresponding long-chain acid or that of the symmetrical anhydride of this acid. This correlation, however, disappears with the mixed C_{10}—C_8 anhydride and the C_{10}—C_{10} anhydride, both of which melt considerably lower than the C_{10} acid. The unsymmetrical anhydrides undergo disproportionation reactions in polar solvents, and this characteristic is especially marked when the difference in chain lengths is appreciable, such as with acetic-palmitic anhydride. Mixed anhydrides may be crystallized from non-polar organic solvents, although acetic-palmitic anhydride forms some acetic anhydride and palmitic anhydride upon prolonged heating in petroleum ether. The unsymmetrical anhydrides are soluble in both polar and non-polar solvents. They are readily hydrolyzed by water, the rate of hydrolysis apparently increasing with increasing difference in the chain lengths.

Mixed anhydrides of the higher aliphatic acids and silicic acid have been prepared by heating carboxylic acids with silicon halides,[52] and mixed anhydrides of the aliphatic acids and boric acid have also been obtained [53] by condensing the acids with boric acid in the presence of an acid chloride or acid anhydride. The high molecular weight acid chlorides react with monosilver phosphate to yield mixed anhydrides, palmitic-phosphoric anhydride and stearic-phosphoric anhydride having been synthesized recently by this method.[54]

The higher symmetrical anhydrides are not easily hydrolyzed by water at ordinary temperatures and can be kept under atmospheric conditions for indefinite periods without undergoing material change. Holde and Gentner [55] have reported that palmitic anhydride, when allowed to stand for eight months in a flask loosely stoppered with cotton, undergoes no detectable change. Myristic anhydride is unchanged after six months under a water-vapor pressure of 4.3 mm., and only 1 to 3% is converted into myristic acid after six months' exposure to an atmosphere saturated with water vapor. The lower anhydrides are rapidly hydrolyzed by treatment with alkaline hydroxide solution, the higher anhydrides much more slowly. A study [55] of the rate of hydrolysis of the higher anhydrides in petroleum ether solution upon shaking with a 5% aqueous solution of sodium carbonate showed that the amount hydrolyzed is dependent upon the time of contact, 2.2 to 3.25% of palmitic anhydride being hydrolyzed after ten minutes and 7.3% after fifty minutes.

The higher anhydrides are slowly hydrogenated in the presence of palladium and hydrochloric acid to yield polymerized aldehydes. [56] For example, lauric anhydride yields a polymerized lauraldehyde, m.p. 57°, and some didodecyl ether together with other products when hydrogenated in the presence of palladium black and hydrochloric acid in decalin solution. Saturated hydrocarbons are obtained when the higher anhydrides are hydrogenated at high temperatures and pressures in the presence of mixed oxide catalysts such as copper chromite. [57]

The higher anhydrides are converted into acid chlorides under approximately the same conditions and by the same reagents employed for the preparation of acid chlorides from the corresponding acids.

The anhydrides function as acylating agents in the presence of Friedel-Crafts catalysts, one mole of anhydride requiring two moles of aluminum chloride or similar halide to effect the acylation. [58, 59] An example of the above reaction is the synthesis of phenyl propyl ketone by the condensation of benzene and butyric anhydride in the presence of two moles of aluminum chloride. [60]

Several interesting uses have been suggested for the higher anhydrides. They have been stated to impart a high degree of water repellency when incorporated into cellulose acetate rayon, [61] and aqueous dispersions of the higher anhydrides may be used for waterproofing textiles and allied materials. [62] The sulfonation of mixed anhydrides containing hydroxyl groups or ethylenic bonds has been investigated for the preparation of wetting agents. [63]

Holde and Smelkus [2] have stated that anhydrides of the higher acids are absorbed in the intestines and may be employed as substitutes for edible glycerides.

THE HIGH MOLECULAR WEIGHT FATTY ACID HALIDES

The fatty acid halides, RCOX, are derived from the fatty acids by replacement of the hydroxyl group by halogen. The higher fatty acid chlorides, RCOCl, are well-known compounds.* Although the acid bromides of several of the higher acids have been described, the iodides and fluorides are essentially unknown. The fatty acid chlorides are intermediate compounds for the synthesis of many types of fatty acid derivatives, their great importance residing almost solely in their use as synthetic agents. Their use as acylating agents for the preparation of esters and ketones, their reaction with ammonia or amines for the synthesis of amides, and their use in the preparation of acid anhydrides are reactions with which all chemists are quite familiar.

The higher fatty acid chlorides are liquids which can be distilled under reduced pressures without decomposition. The chlorides of the acids higher than stearic are solids which melt slightly above room temperature. All the acid chlorides are characterized by their high chemical activity. Since they are readily hydrolyzed to the corresponding acids by water or water vapor, care must be exercised to protect them from moisture.

Preparation of the Fatty Acid Halides

The fatty acid chlorides are generally prepared by the action of chlorinating agents on the fatty acids or their sodium salts, in either the presence or the absence of solvents. Those inorganic chlorides or oxychlorides which readily exchange their chlorine atoms for hydroxyl groups are generally capable of converting the carboxylic acids into their corresponding acid chlorides. These include phosphorus pentachloride and trichloride, thionyl chloride,

---

* The termination "oyl" is customarily applied to designate the acid chlorides, and names such as "dodecanoyl chloride" or "octadecanoyl chloride" are generally preferable to the common names which are frequently employed. When designating the fatty acid chlorides by their common names we have followed the recommendation proposed by *Chemical Abstracts*, in that those members of the series which contain ten or less carbon atoms terminate in "yl" and the higher members in "oyl."

silicon tetrachloride, and allied compounds. The preparation of the higher acid chlorides by the action of such reagents on the acids has been the subject of many investigations. Certain organic chlorine compounds, notable examples of which are oxalyl chloride and carbonyl chloride, are also employed for the conversion of the higher acids into their respective acid chlorides. In spite of the apparent simplicity of the reactions involved in their formation, the higher fatty acid chlorides are not easily prepared and purified. Very often side reactions are encountered which greatly reduce the yield of acid chloride, and consequently the proper choice of a reagent and of the reaction conditions is essential in order to obtain satisfactory yields.

One of the first reagents investigated for the conversion of acids into their acid chlorides was phosphorus pentachloride. Although several individual higher acid chlorides were previously prepared by the action of phosphorus pentachloride on the acids or their soaps [18, 64, 65] the first comprehensive study of their preparation by the use of this reagent was reported in 1884 by Krafft and Bürger.[66] Lauroyl, myristoyl, palmitoyl, and stearoyl chlorides were prepared by warming a mixture of equal amounts of the respective acids and phosphorus pentachloride and removing the resulting phosphoryl chloride by distillation under vacuum. Later, the preparation of undecenoyl chloride, oleoyl chloride, and elaidoyl chloride by the action of phosphorus pentachloride on the respective acids was accomplished.[39] The action of phosphorus pentachloride on the higher acids has since been employed for the preparation of the acid chloride of a number of saturated and unsaturated acids.[67, 68, 69] Although phosphorus pentachloride is, in many instances, a satisfactory reagent for the synthesis of the higher acid chlorides, its use sometimes presents certain difficulties which argue in favor of the employment of other reagents. Its extremely high chemical activity often brings about secondary reactions not encountered with other agents, and it is frequently very difficult to separate the resulting phosphoryl chloride completely from the acid chloride.

Phosphorus trichloride is one of the most useful reagents for both the laboratory and the commercial preparation of the higher acid chlorides. Its advantage lies in the fact that all three chlorine atoms are available, the trichloride being hydrolyzed to phosphorous acid. Since phosphorous acid is insoluble in the higher acid chlorides, it sinks to the bottom of the reaction vessel and is easily removed as a separate layer. The conversion of an acid to an acid chloride in the presence of this reagent takes place at ordinary temperatures and only slight warming is necessary to complete the reaction. The use of an inert solvent, such as carbon tetrachloride, is indicated for the conversion of those acids which are solid at ordinary temperatures. However, solvents are not necessary when the liquid acids are involved. The preparation of linoleoyl chloride by the action of phosphorus trichloride on linoleic acid has been studied by McCutcheon,[70] and the purification of oleoyl chloride prepared by this method has been described in detail.[67] Although the removal of phosphorous acid can be readily accomplished because of its insolubility, the separation of the excess phosphorus halide is frequently difficult. This excess can often be removed by heating the product under a vacuum; however, it has recently been suggested [71] that the removal may be effected by heating the reaction product at temperatures in excess of 100° under atmospheric pressure. Since phosphorus trichloride is very readily hydrolyzed, whereas the higher acid chlorides hydrolyze comparatively slowly, a convenient method for the removal of the excess of the former consists of adding a small amount of water to the reaction mixture. The excess of phosphorus trichloride is then removed as phosphorous acid. Examples have been given [72] of the preparation of lauroyl chloride, stearoyl chloride, and linoleoyl chloride by the action of phosphorus trichloride on the respective acids, followed by removal of the excess of phosphorus chloride by hydrolysis with water.

Thionyl chloride readily converts both saturated and unsaturated acids and also halo-substituted acids to their corresponding acid chlorides. High yields are generally realized by the use of this reagent, but it is quite necessary that it be pure since the presence of sulfuryl chloride greatly reduces the yields. Owing to the fact that the products of hydrolysis of thionyl chloride are both gaseous, the purification of the acid chlorides so obtained is generally accomplished readily. Sulzberger [73] reported comparable yields of oleoyl chloride by the action of either thionyl chloride or phosphorus pentachloride on oleic acid. An 82% yield of oleoyl chloride was reported [74] by the action of thionyl chloride on oleic acid, and recently Verkade [75] has stated that the yield may be increased by using thionyl chloride which has been previously refluxed over quinoline and linseed oil. Bardan [76] has reported a theoretical yield of caproyl chloride by the action of thionyl chloride on caproic acid. The chlorides of the even saturated acids from caprylic to stearic inclusive have been obtained by this procedure.[77] The preparation of stearoyl chloride by the action of thionyl chloride on stearic acid has been described [78] as follows:

> Stearic acid (586 g., 2 moles), m.p. 67–70°, was placed in a three-necked flask fitted with a dropping funnel, reflux condenser, mechanical stirrer, and thermometer. Thionyl chloride (285.5 g., 2.4 moles) was then added over a period of two and one-half hours and the mixture heated at 75° for two hours. The temperature was then increased to 90° and the heating continued for an additional two hours. The excess thionyl chloride was then removed under a vacuum and the product fractionally distilled. An 81% yield of stearoyl chloride boiling at 200–215° at 13–15 mm. was obtained.

Iodo fatty acids yield the corresponding acid chlorides when treated with this reagent,[79] an example being the preparation of diiodoelaidoyl chloride by the action of thionyl chloride on diiodo-elaidic acid.[80] 9,10,12,13-Tetrabromostearic acid is converted into its acid chloride by the action of thionyl chloride at 120°.[81] Mc-Master and Ahmann [82] have studied the action of thionyl chloride on the dibasic acids and have reported that succinic and glutaric acids yield anhydrides whereas malonic, suberic, and sebacic acids yield the dichlorides. An 80% yield of sebacyl dichloride has been obtained [83] by the action of thionyl chloride on sebacic acid. The action of sulfur and chlorine on the anhydrous soaps of the fatty acids has been stated to yield the corresponding acid chlorides.[84]

Silicon tetrachloride has been investigated as a reagent for the conversion of some of the lower acids to their acid chlorides, but its action with the higher acids has not been studied. Rauter [85] obtained butyryl chloride by heating butyric acid with silicon tetrachloride in a sealed tube at 150–160°, and more recently Montonna [86] prepared the acid chlorides of several of the lower aliphatic acids by reaction with this reagent in an inert solvent at 50°. It was suggested that a mixed anhydride of silicic acid and the aliphatic acid is first formed, which then reacts with more silicon tetrachloride to yield the acid chloride and silica.

The preparation of acid chlorides of the lower acids by passing the acid vapors mixed with phosgene over charcoal or other contact substances at elevated temperatures was patented in 1913 by Hochstetter.[87] In a subsequent patent [88] it was shown that acid chlorides are also obtained by the reaction of the sodium salts of the lower acids with phosgene in a closed vessel. Chlorides of the higher fatty acids may be prepared by passing the acid vapors mixed with phosgene over charcoal at 150°.[89] The reaction may be accomplished by passing phosgene through the acid at 100° in the presence of a small amount of a tertiary amine.[90] Prat and Étienne [91] reported 85–90% yields of lauroyl chloride by the action of phosgene on lauric acid. Yields of 70–75% of palmitoyl and stearoyl chlorides are also obtained by this method. The optimum temperature was reported to be 140–150°, and the reaction rate was found to be dependent upon the rate of addition of the phosgene. Somewhat lower yields of acid chloride are obtained from oleic acid at 160° and from sodium oleate at 140°. In the latter instance it was postulated that the reaction proceeds with the initial formation of an anhydride.

Excellent yields of the higher acid chlorides are obtained by treating the acids or their sodium salts with oxalyl chloride, the reaction taking place almost quantitatively in the presence or absence of a solvent.[34] The reaction requires the use of 2.5 moles of oxalyl chloride per mole of acid, the anhydride which first forms being rapidly converted into the acid chloride. When the sodium salt of the acid is used, an amount of oxalyl chloride slightly in excess of an equimolar proportion is required. The sodium salt is suspended in benzene and the oxalyl chloride added gradually to this suspension. Caproyl, capryl, lauroyl, myristoyl, and stearoyl chlorides have been prepared by the action of oxalyl chloride on the respective acids.[92] Acid anhydrides are readily converted into the corresponding acid chlorides by treatment with oxalyl chloride. Acid bromides may be prepared by treating acids, anhydrides, or sodium soaps with oxalyl bromide under substantially the same conditions as those employed for the preparation of acid chlorides. Oxalyl chloride has been found to be an excellent reagent for the preparation of acid chlorides of the unsaturated acids.[93] Oleoyl, elaidoyl, linoleoyl, and linolenoyl chlorides have been synthesized by this method, the preparation of linoleoyl chloride having been described as follows:

Linoleic acid (16.5 g., 0.06 mole) was refluxed at 65 to 70° with 22.4 g. (0.18 mole) of oxalyl chloride (Eastman Kodak Company) for four hours in an all glass still. The excess oxalyl chloride was removed by warming the mixture to 100° *in vacuo*. The acid chloride was distilled under 2 to 3 mm. pressure. The yield was 14.5 g. (82% of the calculated amount) of water-white linoleyl chloride.

Bauer [94] has recently compared the efficiencies of a number of reagents in the presence and absence of solvents for the preparation of acid chlorides of both the higher saturated and unsaturated acids. A method of analysis of the products based upon the conversion of the acid chlorides to anilides was also proposed.

From the foregoing it is evident that a number of procedures have been suggested and investigated for the preparation of the higher fatty acid chlorides. The choice of a particular method is, therefore, somewhat optional. Purification of the higher acid chlorides by distillation, however, is frequently attended by excessive decomposition which results in large residues attended by low yields of the desired acid chlorides. The acid chlorides, when heated for a substantial period of time in an inert atmosphere at temperatures above 210°, lose hydrogen chloride and yield dark, undistillable products. It has been suggested [95] that such a decomposition proceeds with the initial formation of a ketene which rapidly polymerizes. Although care is necessary in the distillation of the higher acid chlorides, it is felt that most of the difficulties encountered are due to incomplete conversion of the reaction mixture to acid chloride. The presence of residual acid or of an excessive amount of chlorinating agent results in anhydride formation and other reactions during the distillation process. It is consequently necessary to choose reaction conditions which bring about an essentially complete conversion of acid to acid chloride, if high yields of distilled acid chlorides are to be obtained.

Physical Properties of the Fatty Acid Halides

The acid chlorides of the saturated acids below stearic acid are liquids at ordinary temperature. Only the lower members of the series can be distilled under atmospheric pressure without undergoing excessive decomposition. The fatty acid halides are soluble in most organic solvents, but they react readily with those solvents which contain replaceable hydrogens. They are hydrolyzed by water, the lower members with great rapidity, the higher members much more slowly. The physical constants of the acyl chlorides from butanoyl chloride to octadecanoyl chloride inclusive are shown in Table III.

Physical constants have been reported for only a few of the unsaturated acyl chlorides. These include oleoyl chloride,[75] $b_{0.05}$ 158–159°; elaidoyl chloride, b_{13} 216°; linoleoyl chloride, $b_{2.3}$ 167–168°; and 10-undecenoyl chloride,[39] b_{14} 128.5°. 2-Bromocaproyl chloride, prepared by bromination of the acid chloride,[76] boils at 106–107° at 31 mm., and 2-bromocaprylyl chloride, similarly prepared, boils at 129–133° under 25–26 mm. Hopwood [96] has prepared 2-bromononanoyl chloride, b_9 118–120°; 2-bromolauroyl chloride, b_{16} 170°; and 2-bromopalmitoyl chloride, b_{26} 215° (decomp.), by the action of phosphorus pentachloride on the respective 2-bromo acids. Kirrmann [97] has reported the following

TABLE III

PHYSICAL CONSTANTS OF ACYL CHLORIDES

Acyl Chloride	Common Name	F.P., °C.	B.P., °C.	d_4^t	n_D^t
Butanoyl	Butyryl	−89.0	101–102	1.0277^{20}	1.41209^{20}
Pentanoyl	Valeryl	−110.0	107–110	1.0155^{15}	
Hexanoyl	Caproyl	−87.3	138–140	....	
Heptanoyl	Enanthyl	−83.8	175.2	0.95219^{30}	
Octanoyl	Caprylyl	−61.0	195.55 83_{15}	0.94000^{30}	
Nonanoyl	Pelargonyl	−60.5	215.35 98_{15}	0.93353^{30}	
Decanoyl	Capryl	−34.5	232.3 $104–105_9$		
Dodecanoyl	Lauroyl	−17	150_{22}		
Tetradecanoyl	Myristoyl	−1	168_{15} $134_{2.5}$		
Pentadecanoyl	....	....	157_5		
Hexadecanoyl	Palmitoyl	12	192.5_{15}		
Octadecanoyl	Stearoyl	23	198–200_{15} $165_{0.4}$		

constants for heptanoyl bromide: b_{12} 80°, d_4^{18} 1.211, and n_D^{18} 1.4605. Several 2-bromo acid bromides have been described;[98] namely, 2-bromovaleryl bromide, b 190°; 2-bromocaproyl bromide, $b_{12–13}$ 95–96°; and 2-bromoenanthyl bromide, b_9 101–102°.

Chemical Properties of the Fatty Acid Halides

The extensive use of the higher acid chlorides as intermediates in the syntheses of many high molecular weight aliphatic compounds testifies to their high chemical activity. Their reaction with alcohols or alkoxides to yield esters has previously been discussed in detail. When treated with ammonia or amines they yield amides or substituted amides, the preparation of which has already been considered. They function as acylating agents in the presence of Friedel-Crafts catalysts and have been employed for the preparation of many higher alkyl aryl ketones and related compounds.

The replacement of the chlorine atom of acyl chlorides by hydrogen yields the corresponding aldehydes. This may be accomplished by hydrogenation in the presence of metallic platinum or palladium, a procedure first successfully employed by Rosenmund.[99] The catalytic activities of nickel and of platinum oxide for the hydrogenation of acid chlorides to aldehydes have been compared,[100] the optimum temperature for the former being 300°. Low yields of valeraldehyde and caproaldehyde are obtained by hydrogenation of valeryl and caproyl chlorides in the presence of platinum oxide at 225°. The hydrogenation of lauroyl chloride at 300–320° under 170–180 mm. pressure in the presence of metallic platinum gives a product which consists largely of undecane; however, at 50 mm. pressure and a temperature of 200–205° an appreciable amount of lauraldehyde results.[101] Capryl chloride yields some capryl aldehyde when similarly treated. Myristoyl chloride, however, gives only a small amount of myristaldehyde, the main product apparently being an aldehyde polymer. The higher acyl chlorides do not yield aldehydes when hydrogenated at 160° under 50 mm. pressure in the presence of metallic nickel. Sebacyl dichloride has been stated [83] to yield the corresponding dialdehyde when hydrogenated in the presence of 2% of a Pd-CaCO$_3$ catalyst. A variety of products result when the dichlorides of the dibasic acids are reduced by sodium amalgam or by catalytic methods.[102]

The higher acyl chlorides react smoothly with sodium in boiling ether to yield the corresponding esters of the unsaturated diols, the reaction proceeding through the diketone as follows: [78]

$$2RC\overset{\displaystyle O}{\underset{\displaystyle Cl}{\big<}} \xrightarrow{2Na} RC{-}CR \xrightarrow{2Na} RC{=}CR \xrightarrow{2RCOCl} RC{=}CR$$

$$\qquad\qquad\quad \underset{O\ \ O}{\|\ \ \|} \qquad \underset{ONa\ ONa}{|\ \ \ |} \qquad \underset{RCO_2\ O_2CR}{|\ \ \ \ |}$$

The dilaurate of 12-tetracosene-12,13-diol, the dimyristate of 14-octacosene-14,15-diol, the dipalmitate of 16-dotriacontene-16,17-diol, and the distearate of 18-hexatriacontene-18,19-diol are obtained in approximately 70% yields by this procedure.

High molecular weight ketenes have been stated [103] to be formed by the removal of hydrogen chloride from the higher acyl chlorides, through the action of tertiary amines in the presence of inert solvents in which the hydrochlorides of the base are insoluble.

A study [95] of the decomposition of pelargonyl, lauroyl, and palmitoyl chlorides when heated at 250° in a current of carbon dioxide indicated that ketenes are first formed by the removal of hydrogen chloride. The residues were considered to be polymerized ketenes.

Fatty acid peroxides are formed by the action of alkali or alkaline earth peroxides on the higher acyl chlorides; [104] for example, bis(monoethyl adipyl) peroxide has been prepared in a 73% yield by the action of barium peroxide on monoethyl adipyl chloride.[105]

Mailhe [106] has described the direct transformation of acid chlorides into nitriles by passing the vapors of the former, mixed with ammonia, over aluminum oxide heated to 490–500°. Such a reaction undoubtedly proceeds with the initial formation of the amide, which is subsequently dehydrated to the nitrile.

Reaction of the higher acyl chlorides with amino acids or various protein degradation products yields a variety of substances which are of both biological and industrial interest.[107] Abderhalden and Funk [108] have investigated the products obtained by the reaction of the higher acyl chlorides with glycine, d-alanine, l-tyrosine, and allied substances, and have identified many of the products so obtained. Diiodoelaidoylglycine, diiodoelaidoylalanine, and similar compounds have been synthesized and their physiological activities investigated.[80] A number of products formed by condensation of amino acids with the higher α-bromo acyl chlorides have been synthesized by Hopwood and Weizmann.[96] Amorphous powders soluble in ethanol, chloroform, benzene, and acetone result by treating alkaline solutions of peptones with ether solutions of the higher acyl chlorides.[109] Wetting agents suitable for treating textiles have been prepared by the action of higher acyl chlorides on hydrolyzed proteins, such as hydrolyzed leather or hide cuttings.[110, 111] The hydrolyzed products from albumen have been treated with the higher acyl chlorides in the presence of alkalies to yield products which function as dispersing agents.[112] Hydrolyzed casein, gelatin, horn, and allied substances react with the higher acyl chlorides to yield water-dispersible products.[113] Acylation was assumed to take place at the nitrogen-containing group.

Acylated derivatives of the sugars are obtained by the action of the higher acyl chlorides on sugars in the presence of pyridine or other acid-accepting agents. For example, Hess and Messmer [114] have prepared α-pentapalmitoylglucose in good yields by the reaction at −10° of 1.89 g. of glucose in 20 cc. of pyridine with 14 g. of palmitoyl chloride in 20 cc. of chloroform. α-Pentastearoylglucose, β-monostearoyltetraacetylglucose, octapalmitoylsucrose, m.p. 54–55°, octastearoylsucrose, hendecapalmitoylraffinose, m.p. 39°, and hendecastearoylraffinose, m.p. 63°, were similarly prepared.

The higher fatty acid chlorides have been employed as intermediates in the preparation of many chemicals which possess wetting and detergent properties, and the many specific examples which appear in the patent literature are too numerous to discuss in detail. One of the most important types of such derivatives results from the treatment of aromatic, cycloaliphatic, or aliphatic sulfonic acids which contain hydroxyl or other groups with the higher acyl chlorides. Examples have been given of the preparation of wetting agents by the action of oleoyl chloride on sodium hydroxycyclohexanesulfonate,[115] or on sodium hydroxyethylenesulfonate.[116] Wetting agents are obtained by the action of the higher acyl chlorides with sodium 1,2-dihydroxybutanesulfonate, resorcinoldisulfonic acid, and allied substances.[117] Aromatic amines containing a nuclear sulfonic acid group react with the higher acyl chlorides to form water-soluble products which possess wetting properties.[118] Condensation products of the acid chloride of chaulmoogric or dihydrochaulmoogric acid with aromatic amino sulfonic acids [119] and with halophenols [120] have been investigated as therapeutic agents for the treatment of leprosy. Reaction products of the higher acyl chlorides with naphthalene or petroleum oil fractions have been suggested as addends to lubricating oils.[121]

THE HIGH MOLECULAR WEIGHT ALIPHATIC ALDEHYDES

Much significance has repeatedly been placed upon the fact that the aldehydes represent a series of compounds intermediate between the carboxylic acids and the alcohols. This great emphasis is somewhat unfortunate, since frequently we fail to realize that the aldehydes are, in their own right, one of the most interesting and potentially important groups of aliphatic compounds. It is true, of course, that an aldehyde is an intervening product in the oxidation of an alcohol to a carboxylic acid or in the reduction of the latter to the former, and that this is of importance in establishing their structure and in formulating many of the methods for their synthesis. It is equally true, however, that the aldehydes bear little resemblance in chemical properties to either the alcohols or the acids. Actually they possess many characteristic physical and chemical properties which establish them as one of the most distinctive series of aliphatic derivatives. The aliphatic aldehydes, irrespective of their chain length, are extremely reactive chemically. They are very readily polymerized, they enter into many condensation and addition reactions, and they are strong reducing agents. Owing to the rapidity with which they polymerize, the aldehydes are extremely difficult to purify. They are very unstable in the presence of oxidizing agents and are slowly oxidized in the air at room temperature. In spite of the facts that many of the higher aldehydes are found in natural products in small amounts and that their synthesis has been the subject of a large number of investigations, they are still among the lesser known of the major derivatives of the fatty acids. Much is yet to be learned concerning both their physical and their chemical properties.

The higher aldehydes have been isolated in small amounts from a number of plant oils, and they undoubtedly contribute to the characteristic odors of many of the floral oils. Octanal and nonanal are present in the essential oils of many plants; decanal has been isolated in significant amounts from coriander oil; [122] and dodecanal occurs in the oil from lily of the valley.[123] An aldoalcohol containing eighteen carbon atoms has been obtained by the extraction of olive pulp.[124] Many of the floral oils owe their characteristic odors to the presence of unsaturated, aliphatic aldehydes. For example, violet leaf oil has been shown [125] to contain 2,6-nonadienal, $CH_3CH_2CH:CHCH_2CH_2CH:CHCHO$, the structure of the naturally occurring aldehyde having been determined by oxidative and synthetic procedures.[126] Because of their characteristically pleasant odors and their ability to modify more volatile odors, the higher aldehydes have been extensively used in perfumery. The floral odor of the aldehydes increases from pentanal to undecanal. However, each aldehyde possesses a characteristic odor which distinguishes it from its homologs and which largely determines its ability to modify the natural floral odors.[127] Aldehydes as high as hexadecanal are used in lavender, honeysuckle, and iris perfumes.

Preparation of the Higher Aliphatic Aldehydes

The synthesis of higher aldehydes from fatty acids or their various derivatives has been studied for many years. These investigations have resulted in the development of a number of methods for their preparation, many of which give reasonably satisfactory yields. Perhaps more synthetic procedures are available for the higher aldehydes than for any other of the major fatty acid derivatives. In spite of this, the higher aldehydes are not readily available, possibly owing to the fact that none of the proposed syntheses is adaptable to large-scale preparation. The low yields frequently encountered during the synthesis of higher aldehydes are generally due to difficulties in separating the aldehydes from the reaction mixture.

One of the oldest and best-known methods for the preparation of the higher aldehydes consists of heating the calcium or barium soap of a fatty acid with calcium or barium formate, the reaction proceeding as follows:

$$Ca(O_2CR)_2 + Ca(O_2CH)_2 \rightarrow 2RCHO + 2CaCO_3$$

Krafft [128] has described the preparation of dodecanal, tetradecanal, hexadecanal, and octadecanal by the dry distillation of the calcium soaps of the respective acids with calcium formate, a large excess of the latter being employed to retard ketone formation. The reacting components were mixed with calcium carbonate to prevent excessive sintering and the heating was done under vacuum to facilitate the escape of the aldehydes. Although this procedure is satisfactory for the preparation of the lower aldehydes, the apparently inherent difficulties result in very small yields of the higher homologs. It has been stated [129] that higher yields are obtained if the calcium soaps are treated with calcium formate in an autoclave under pressure in the presence of an inert solvent. Zaar [130] has studied the preparation of dodecanal by heating barium laurate with barium formate and has reported that 1-dodecanol, resulting from the further reduction of dodecanal, is among the reaction products. The mechanism by which aldehydes are formed in this reaction is somewhat in doubt; however, they probably result from the reducing action of decomposition products of the formate. Speculations as to the mechanism of aldehyde formation by this method have undoubtedly provided one of the motivating influences behind many of the subsequently proposed procedures for the synthesis of the higher aldehydes. The corresponding aldehydes are formed when the higher aliphatic acids, mixed with formic acid, are passed in the vapor state over decarboxylating catalysts.[131] For example, a 30% yield of dodecanal results from passing the vapors of lauric and formic acids over manganous oxide at 355–360°,[132] and pelargonic acid gives a 50–55% yield of nonanal when similarly treated.[133] Yields of 70–75%

of decanal have been obtained from the reaction of capric and formic acids under these conditions.[134] Unsaturated aldehydes such as oleic aldehyde can be prepared similarly.[135] The higher aldehydes result when the aliphatic acids or their esters are passed with formaldehyde over oxidizing catalysts,[136] and aldehydes are also formed when the soaps of the fatty acids are treated at high temperatures with formaldehyde.[137]

The controlled oxidation of the higher alcohols yields the corresponding aldehydes. Such oxidations are generally accomplished by passing the alcohols in the vapor phase over silver catalysts in the presence of a limited amount of air. The reaction is decidedly exothermic and the yields are dependent upon the rate of passage of the vapors over the catalyst and upon the ratio of reactants. The vapors of the alcohol, mixed with somewhat less than the theoretical amount of air, may be passed over a finely divided silver catalyst at 230–300°.[138] In those instances in which the reaction is too intense, it has been recommended that it be conducted in two stages. Aleksandrova [139] has stated that 96% of the theoretical yield of octanal is obtained by passing 1-octanol and a limited amount of air over a silver catalyst at a temperature of 300°. Yields as high as 82% were reported for the higher aldehydes. The preparation of nonanal by the catalytic oxidation of 1-nonanol has been studied,[140] and Bruylants [141] has reported a 70% yield of hexanal by the catalytic oxidation of 1-hexanol. The preparation of higher aldehydes by passing vapors of alcohols mixed with air over a silver-containing catalyst at high temperatures (400° or higher) has been patented.[142]

The liquid-phase dehydrogenation of higher alcohols to the corresponding aldehydes may be accomplished by heating the former at carefully regulated temperatures in the presence of metallic nickel. For example, a 20% yield of dodecanal results [143] from heating 1-dodecanol for two hours at 250° in the presence of 5% of metallic nickel. Higher temperatures and longer times result in reduced yields. It was stated that satisfactory yields of aldehydes can be obtained by this method from alcohols as high as 1-octadecanol. Lazier [144] has reported that long-chain alcohols can be dehydrogenated to the corresponding aldehydes by passing their vapors at elevated temperatures over a catalyst consisting of zinc, copper, or aluminum mixed with chromic oxide.

Aldehydes result from the decomposition of ozonides, the classical example being the formation of nonanal and 9-aldononanoic acid by hydrolysis of the ozonide of oleic acid. Since, under such conditions, the aldehydes are formed in a highly oxidizing environment, their formation and oxidation to carboxylic acids frequently occur simultaneously. An immediate oxidation takes place, for example, if the cleavage is conducted in a highly alkaline medium. Nonanal has been obtained in 20% yield by passing ozonized air into a suspension of oleic acid in an aqueous solution of sodium bisulfite containing a small amount of decalin.[145] Higher yields of aldehydes are obtained by catalytic hydrogenation of the ozonides, it having been observed that even highly polymerized ozonides can be hydrogenated to aldehydes under high hydrogen pressure. Fischer and others [146] have employed this procedure for the degradation of an aldehyde to its next lower homolog, the aldehyde first being converted to a secondary alcohol by reaction with phenylmagnesium bromide. This alcohol is then dehydrated to an olefin, the ozonolysis and hydrogenation of which yield the lower aldehyde. The general reactions are as follows:

$$RCH_2CHO \xrightarrow{C_6H_5MgBr} \underset{\underset{OH}{|}}{RCH_2CHC_6H_5} \rightarrow RCH{:}CHC_6H_5 \xrightarrow[H_2]{O_3}$$

$$RCHO + C_6H_5CHO$$

A 65% yield of octanal from nonanal is obtained by this method. Acids yield the next lower aldehyde when similarly treated, the preparation of the tertiary alcohol requiring three moles of phenylmagnesium bromide.

Chemical reduction of ozonides to aldehydes predates their catalytic reduction. Harries [147] proposed the use of potassium ferrocyanide in the presence or absence of acids for the reduction of ozonides to aldehydes, and described the preparation of nonanal from oleic acid ozonide by use of this reagent. Nonanal and 9-aldononanoic acid have been obtained in small yields by reduction of oleic acid ozonide with zinc and acetic acid in ethyl acetate solution.[148] In all such reactions, resin formation due to polymerization of the aldehydes is a disturbing factor.

An alternate and more satisfactory method for the preparation of aldehydes from unsaturated acids consists of the oxidative cleavage of the corresponding polyhydroxy acids. Thus, 9,10-dihydroxystearic acid, obtained by the oxidation of oleic acid with potassium permanganate, undergoes oxidative cleavage when treated for twenty-four hours with lead tetraacetate in glacial acetic acid solution.[149] An approximately 85% yield of nonanal and 9-aldononanoic acid, isolated as their semicarbazones, results from

the above reaction. A similar treatment in benzene solution of
9,10,12-trihydroxystearic acid, obtained by the oxidation of ricinoleic acid, yields 9-aldononanoic acid. Bergmann [150] has reported
the successful preparation of nonanal from oleic acid by this
method. The oxidation of methyl 9,10-dihydroxystearate by
minium (Pb_3O_4) results in an approximately 50% yield of nonanal
and 9-aldononanoic acid.[145] An interesting modification of this
method has been proposed for the synthesis of aldehydes from the
saturated acids, the reactions involved being illustrated by the
conversion of stearic acid to octadecanal.[151] The reaction of
stearoyl chloride with diazomethane gives 1-diazononadecan-2-
one, $C_{17}H_{35}COCHN_2$, which when treated with acetic acid yields
2-ketononadecyl acetate, $C_{17}H_{35}COCH_2OCOCH_3$, the reduction
of which results in nonadecane-1,2-diol, $C_{17}H_{35}CH(OH)CH_2OH$.
Oxidation of this glycol with lead tetraacetate yields octad̃ nal
and formaldehyde. The application of this method to the pr̃
tion of aldehydes from oleic and elaidic acids and from oth
saturated acids has also been described. Hershberg [152] has s̃ed
the preparation of aldehydes by oxidation of several lower m̃ c-
ular weight glycols with lead tetraacetate.

The pyrolysis of ricinoleic acid under high vacuum yields heptanal and 10-undecenoic acid [153,154] together with a mixture of
dienoic acids. Small yields, approximately 15%, of heptanal have
been obtained by passing castor oil under high vacuum through a
copper tube heated to 550°.[155] The destructive distillation of castor
oil for the production of heptanal and 10-undecenoic acid has been
described in the patent literature.[156,157]

The higher α-hydroxy acids when heated above their decomposition points yield not only the corresponding lactides but also
appreciable amounts of aldehydes which contain one carbon atom
less than the original acids. The aldehydes result from the cleavage
of a molecule of formic acid from the α-hydroxy acid the reaction
being as follows:

$$RCH(OH)CO_2H \rightarrow RCHO + HCO_2H$$

Le Sueur [158] has observed that the decomposition of 2-hydroxy-
stearic acid begins at 200° and proceeds rapidly at 270°, to give a
50–60% yield of heptadecanal. The contention of Blaise [159] that
the aldehyde is formed through the lactide rather than the hydroxy
acid was shown not to hold for the higher acids, since the lactides
are more resistant to decomposition than the hydroxy acids.

Bagard [160] has prepared nonanal and decanal by this method, and the synthesis of tridecanal, tetradecanal, pentadecanal, and hexadecanal by heating the next higher α-hydroxy acid has been described in detail by Le Sueur.[161] Several modifications of this method of preparing aldehydes have been proposed. The degradation of α-hydroxy acids through their acetyl derivatives has been accomplished successfully.[162] Heating α-methoxy acids in the presence of copper has been observed to give almost theoretical yields of aldehydes,[163] and the α-methoxy derivatives of enanthic, lauric, and stearic acids were converted to aldehydes by this procedure. The synthesis of α,α-dimethyl aldehydes has been accomplished by the decomposition of glycidic esters.[164] Such rearrangements, however, take place only with the higher molecular weight esters.[165] The preparation of 2-methylundecanal by the condensation of 2-undecanone with ethyl chloroacetate, followed by saponification of the resulting glycidate, has been described.[166] Grignard reagents yield acetals when treated with ethyl orthoformate, $CH(OC_2H_5)_3$, the hydrolysis of which gives the corresponding aldehydes. A 45–50% yield of hexanal has been reported by the reaction of pentylmagnesium bromide with ethyl orthoformate, followed by hydrolysis of the resulting acetal.[167]

It has been stated by Stephen [168] that nitriles can be quantitatively converted into aldehydes, and this procedure is extremely interesting in view of the ease of preparation and purification of the higher aliphatic nitriles. The method consists of converting the nitrile into an imino chloride and reducing this with stannous chloride to a stannic aldimonium chloride, the hydrolysis of which yields the corresponding aldehyde. The following is a description of the method:

An ether suspension of dry stannous chloride (1.5 moles) is saturated with dry hydrogen chloride until the mixture separates into two layers. The nitrile (1 mole) is then added with vigorous shaking, forming crystalline stannic aldimonium chloride. The double salt is then separated by filtration and hydrolyzed by warm water. The aldehyde is separated either by steam distillation or by solvent extraction.

The reactions involved are as follows:

$$RCN + HCl \rightarrow RCCl{:}NH \xrightarrow{SnCl_2 + 2HCl} (RCH{:}NH \cdot HCl)_2SnCl_4$$

$$RCH{:}NH \cdot HCl \xrightarrow{HOH} RCHO$$

Details were given for the synthesis of octanal, tetradecanal, hexadecanal, and octadecanal from the corresponding nitriles, and it was stated that the method is satisfactory for the preparation of both aliphatic and aromatic aldehydes. Recently, some doubt has been cast upon the applicability of this method for the synthesis of the aliphatic aldehydes. Williams [169] has reported only a 31% yield of isocaproaldehyde from the nitrile after seven days reaction, and a similar treatment of α-hydroxy propionitrile gives none of the expected aldehyde. The author has also experienced some difficulty in the application of this method to the preparation of the higher aldehydes, and it is evident that future work is required for its complete evaluation.

Physical Properties of the Aliphatic Aldehydes

No precise study has ever been made of the physical constants of the higher aliphatic aldehydes. Since even the higher members of the series undergo polymerization, the aldehydes are generally isolated as stable derivatives such as the bisulfite addition compounds, oximes, or semicarbazones. It is quite possible that the aldehydes may exist in two or more polymorphic forms, although this question has not been settled.

The aliphatic aldehydes have lower melting and boiling points than the corresponding acids. The liquid aldehydes possess characteristic fruitlike odors, whereas the higher aldehydes are odorless when solid and have a paraffin-like odor when melted. A consideration of the melting points of the higher saturated aldehydes shows a perfect example of how erroneous values for an entire series of compounds can be accepted for many years, largely owing to failure to consider the physical state of the compounds in question. When Krafft [128] first prepared the higher aldehydes he reported that their melting points were very close to those of the parent acids. Dodecanal, for example, was stated to have a melting point differing only a fraction of a degree from that of lauric acid. On the other hand, Krafft found the boiling points of the aldehydes to be decidedly lower than those of the acids. It was not until a number of years later that Le Sueur [158] showed that this abnormality was due to partial polymerization and that previously reported melting points were not those of a monomeric aldehyde, but rather those of a polymer. Le Sueur observed that heptadecanal, prepared from α-hydroxystearic acid, melts at 35–36°; however, a solution of this aldehyde in hot absolute ethanol deposits crystals which melt at 52°. The aldehyde slowly polymerizes in the solid state. For example, a specimen kept for six weeks melted at 55°, and the recrystallization of this solid yielded crystals which melted at

77–78°.   Later, Le Sueur [161] showed that the aldehyde polymers are trimolecular. Whereas the monomeric aldehydes are readily soluble in most organic solvents, readily form oximes and semicarbazones, and reduce solutions of potassium permanganate, the polymers are relatively insoluble, do not form oximes or semicarbazones, and will not reduce potassium permanganate solution even on boiling. When distilled under a vacuum these polymers are quantitatively reconverted into the monomeric aldehydes. The higher aldehydes are very soluble in cold ether, chloroform, benzene, and petroleum ether and are soluble in hot ethanol, acetone, and ethyl acetate.

The higher aldehydes are generally identified as their semicarbazones, $RCH{=}NNHCONH_2$, or oximes, $RCH{=}NOH$, both of which are well-crystallized, easily purified derivatives. The semicarbazones are obtained by addition of the aldehydes to an alcoholic solution of semicarbazide hydrochloride containing potassium acetate. They are insoluble in most organic solvents in the cold. The oximes are prepared by heating the aldehydes with an alcoholic solution of hydroxylamine over a water bath for one hour and allowing the mixture to stand for several hours. The higher aldoximes are soluble in ether and chloroform and are difficultly soluble in cold acetone, benzene, and petroleum ether. They can easily be crystallized from ethanol and possess well-defined melting points. The p-nitrophenylhydrazones and the 2,4-dinitrophenylhydrazones of the higher aldehydes are yellow crystalline solids and are frequently employed for their identification.

The physical constants of the saturated aldehydes from pentanal to octadecanal inclusive, together with the melting points of their semicarbazones and oximes, are shown in Table IV.

The α,α-dimethyl-substituted aldehydes possess lower melting points than the unsubstituted aldehydes. For example, 2,2-dimethylstearaldehyde melts at 14.5° and 2,2-dimethyllauraldehyde is a liquid, b_{13} 140°.[165]

The polymers of the higher aldehydes have been shown to be trimolecular [161] and to possess sharp melting points, which have been reported to be as follows: C_{13}, 61.5°; C_{14}, 65.5°; C_{15}, 69–70°; C_{16}, 73°; and C_{17}, 77–78°.

Several unsaturated aldehydes have been prepared and their properties described. These include oleyl aldehyde, $b_{0.001}$ 108–110°, d_4^{20} 0.8509, n_D^{20} 1.4558, 2,4-dinitrophenylhydrazone, m.p. 67–

TABLE IV

PHYSICAL CONSTANTS OF SATURATED ALIPHATIC ALDEHYDES

Aldehyde	Common Name	M.P., °C.	B.P., °C.	d_4^{20}	n_D^{20}	Semicarbazone M.P., °C.	Oxime M.P., °C.
Pentanal	Valeraldehyde	−91.5	103.4	0.8095	1.3944	......	52
Hexanal	Caproaldehyde	.....	131 28_{12}	0.8335	......	106	51
Heptanal	Enanthaldehyde	−43.3	152.8 44.4_9	0.8495	1.4257	109	57–58
Octanal	Caprylaldehyde	.....	163.4 65_{11}	0.821	1.4217	98	60
Nonanal	Pelargonaldehyde	.....	$90–91_{20}$	0.860^{15}	1.4240	100	64
Decanal	Capraldehyde	.....	208–209 92_{10}	0.828^{15}	1.4298^{15}	102	69
Undecanal		−4	117_{18}	0.8251^{23}	1.4322^{23}	103	72
Dodecanal	Lauraldehyde	11.1 *	$103–104_4$ $98–99_{2.5}$	0.8352^{15}	1.4350	......	73
Tridecanal		14	156_{23}			106	80.5
Tetradecanal	Myristaldehyde	23.5	155_{10}			106.5	82.5
Pentadecanal		24–25				106.5	86
Hexadecanal	Palmitaldehyde	34	$192–193_{22}$			107	88
Heptadecanal	Margaraldehyde	35–36	$203–204_{26}$			107–108	89.5
Octadecanal	Stearaldehyde	38	......			108–109	89

* Denotes freezing point.

68°; 10-undecenal, b_{10} 101–103°, d_4^{18} 0.8609, n_D^{18} 1.4491, 2,4-dinitrophenylhydrazone, m.p. 91°; and elaidyl aldehyde, semicarbazone, m.p. 92°, 2,4-dinitrophenylhydrazone, m.p. 90°.

A large number of identifying derivatives have been proposed for the aliphatic aldehydes. Among the most frequently employed, in addition to the semicarbazones and oximes, are the 2,4-dinitrophenylhydrazones and the p-nitrophenylhydrazones. The p-nitrophenylhydrazones of tetradecanal, hexadecanal, and octadecanal are yellow crystalline solids which melt at 95°, 96.5°, and 101°, respectively. The phenylsemicarbazones, prepared by condensing the aldehydes with phenylsemicarbazide, possess relatively high melting points and are apparently satisfactory derivatives for distinguishing between the various members of the series.[170] 3,5-Dinitrobenzohydrazide has been stated [171] to be preferable to 2,4-dinitrophenylhydrazine for the identification of aldehydes, although only the members of the series from C_2 to C_{10} were prepared. Other reagents which have been suggested for the identification of the aliphatic aldehydes are: p-tolylsemicarbazide,[172] o-tolylsemicarbazide,[173] p-nitrobenzohydrazide,[174] o-chlorobenzohydrazide,[175] o-nitrobenzohydrazide,[176] phenylsemioxamazide,[177] β-naphthylhydrazine,[178] o-bromobenzohydrazide,[179] and α-naphthylsemicarbazide.[180]

The absorption spectra of the vapors of the saturated aldehydes from ethanal to heptanal inclusive have been investigated by Eastwood and Snow.[181]

Chemical Properties of the Aliphatic Aldehydes

Aldehydes in general are characterized by high chemical activity, and the higher aliphatic aldehydes as a group are among the most reactive of the fatty acid derivatives. They are readily oxidized to the corresponding acids and are easily reduced by chemical or catalytic methods. The aldehydes undergo many addition and condensation reactions. Although few comparisons of the relative reaction rates of the lower and higher aliphatic aldehydes have been made, it has been shown that, in general, the higher aliphatic aldehydes undergo all the reactions which characterize their lower homologs.

The higher aldehydes polymerize, even at room temperature, and polymerization must be considered to be competitive with any of the reactions which involve aldehydes. In many instances low yields of a desired reaction product are obtained because of the formation of aldehyde polymers, which are much less reactive than the aldehydes themselves. The early confusion which existed, because of the failure to appreciate the rapidity with which the higher aldehydes polymerize, has been discussed previously. Bruylants [182] observed that pentanal polymerizes rapidly in ether solution in the presence of potassium carbonate to give a crystalline polymer which melts at 83–84°. Heptanal rapidly polymerizes under similar conditions to yield a product melting at 51–52°, and its higher homologs behave in a similar manner. When heated in the presence of catalysts, aldehydes undergo a reaction known as the aldol condensation, two molecules of aldehyde combining to yield a hydroxy aldehyde as follows:

$$RCH_2CHO + RCH_2CHO \rightarrow RCH_2CH(OH)CHRCHO$$

Upon further treatment, the aldols are either dehydrated to unsaturated aldehydes or further condensed to higher polymers. The reactions of aldehydes in the presence of metals has been studied by v. Braun and Manz,[183] who postulated that such reactions proceed through the metal enolates, $RCH:CHOM$, to the aldols, $RCH_2CH(OM)CHRCHO$. At low temperatures the aldol yields the metal hydroxide and an unsaturated aldehyde. Higher temperatures, however, result in the formation of glycol esters,

$$RCH_2 \cdot CH-OM$$
$$| \qquad\qquad O$$
$$RCHCH_2OC$$
$$\qquad\qquad CH_2R$$

The glycol ester from enanthal may be saponified to enanthic acid and 6-hydroxymethyl-7-tridecanol. When heated with metallic magnesium or aluminum, the higher aldehydes rapidly undergo an aldol condensation, followed by dehydration to the unsaturated aldehydes.[184] For example, octanal, when heated with a small amount of magnesium, yields 2-hexyl-2-decenal as follows:

$$C_7H_{15}CHO + C_7H_{15}CHO \xrightarrow{\text{Mg}} C_7H_{15}CH(OH)CH(C_6H_{13})CHO \xrightarrow{-H_2O}$$
$$C_7H_{15}CH{=}C(C_6H_{13})CHO$$

The higher aldehydes undergo aldol condensations with ketones to yield hydroxy ketones. Thus, butanal is easily condensed with acetone in the presence of alkalies to 4-hydroxy-2-heptanone, the reaction being as follows:

$$C_3H_7CHO + CH_3CCH_3 \rightarrow C_3H_7CHCH_2CCH_3$$
$$\qquad\qquad\quad ||\qquad\qquad\qquad |\qquad\quad ||$$
$$\qquad\qquad\quad O\qquad\qquad\qquad OH\quad O$$

The condensation of 2-ethylhexanal with acetone yields 4-hydroxy-5-ethyl-2-nonanone, the dehydration of which yields an unsaturated ketone.[185] The reaction of 2-ethylhexanal with 5-ethyl-3-nonen-2-one has been described.[186] The condensation of aldehydes in the presence of catalysts followed by catalytic hydrogenation of the resulting products has been studied.[187]

Practically all oxidizing agents convert the higher aldehydes to acids, and in many instances such oxidations proceed quite rapidly. Chromic acid, for example, vigorously oxidizes heptanal or its polymers to heptanoic acid,[188] and peracetic acid also brings about a quantitative oxidation of this aldehyde.[189] The higher aldehydes are slowly oxidized upon exposure to air, the reaction probably proceeding with the initial formation of a peroxide. The oxidative action of air on the aldehydes is catalyzed by the presence of heavy metals or their salts, those of silver and iron being the most effective. The oxidation of liquid aldehydes in the presence of soluble copper compounds gives high yields of the corresponding acids.[190] Potassium permanganate readily oxidizes the aldehydes of both monobasic and dibasic acids to the corresponding acids,[191] the oxidation of heptadecanal with powdered potassium permanganate in acetone giving a quantitative yield of heptadecanoic acid.[158] The oxidation of hexadecanal, pentadecanal, tetradecanal, and tridecanal with potassium permanganate has been described in detail.[161] In their study of the oxidation of the higher aldehydes, v. Braun and Keller [192] observed that they readily undergo autoxidation in the presence of manganese dioxide, the amount of catalyst required being between 1/4000 to 1/1000 mole per mole of aldehyde oxidized. The aldehydes have been reported to form addition products with hydrogen peroxide which are slowly converted to acids. When oxidized with nitric acid, the aliphatic aldehydes yield carboxylic acids together with various nitrogen-containing compounds.[193] Silver oxide or ammoniacal silver nitrate solutions rapidly oxidize the higher aldehydes to acids,[194] the reaction being one of the standard tests for the presence of aldehydes.

The higher aldehydes are easily reduced to alcohols by either chemical or catalytic methods. For example, tetradecanal yields 1-tetradecanol when reduced with zinc and hydrochloric acid or with sodium in ethanol.[195] The reduction of aldoximes yields primary amines, an example being the reduction of tetradecanal-doxime to tetradecylamine by sodium amalgam in ethanol. Aluminum or the aluminates in isopropyl alcohol are frequently employed for the reduction of unsaturated aldehydes to the corresponding unsaturated alcohols.[196] Catalytic hydrogenation of the higher aldehydes, especially under high pressures and at high temperatures, frequently yields products other than the corresponding alcohols. Thus enanthal, when hydrogenated at high pressures in the presence of metallic nickel, yields not only 1-heptanol but also appreciable amounts of a secondary alcohol with double the number of carbon atoms.[197] The hydrogenation of decanal also gives a higher alcohol, $C_{20}H_{41}OH$, in addition to 1-decanol. Since the former yields an isomer of eicosane upon further hydrogenation, it has been suggested [183] that the higher alcohol results from the hydrogenation of an aldol which is formed in the initial stage of the reaction. It has also been observed [198] that 1-hexene is among the products formed during the hydrogenation of heptanal in the presence of nickel, and the assumption has been made that this results from pyrolysis of the resulting 1-heptanol into 1-hexene and methanol.

The aliphatic aldehydes are converted into the corresponding thioaldehydes by treatment with hydrogen sulfide. Thiopentanal, so prepared, has been described as a white crystalline solid, m.p. 69°, which possesses a very disagreeable, persistent odor.[199] Selenopentanal, obtained by the action of hydrogen selenide on pentanal, forms white crystals, m.p. 56.5°.

The higher aldehydes undergo a wide variety of additive reactions. Such reactions usually involve the double-bonded, terminal oxygen atom, which is generally converted into a hydroxy group by the addition of a hydrogen atom, thus permitting the addition of another group to the aldehydo carbon atom. The higher aldehydes form crystalline derivatives with sodium bisulfite, which are generally prepared by shaking an ethereal or alcoholic solution of the aldehyde with a saturated aqueous solution of sodium bisulfite, the addition product precipitating as a white crystalline solid. The bisulfite addition products are readily decomposed by treatment with alkalies or acids. For example, heptadecanal is obtained from its bisulfite addition product by boiling the latter with a 15% aqueous sodium carbonate solution.[158] Some polymerization of the higher aldehydes may be encountered during the formation and decomposition of their bisulfite addition compounds. Advantage is often taken of this additive reaction for the separation of aldehydes from mixtures. The bisulfite addition products undergo many of the typical reactions of the aldehydes themselves, the free aldehyde probably being formed during the course of the reaction.

Hydrogen cyanide adds directly to an aldehyde group to form a cyanohydrin, the reaction being as follows:

$$RCHO + HCN \rightarrow RCH\begin{subarray}{l} OH \\ CN \end{subarray}$$

The higher alkyl cyanohydrins are crystalline compounds which are soluble in ethanol, ether, chloroform, benzene, and petroleum ether and may be crystallized from any of these solvents. They possess higher melting points than the aldehydes from which they are derived. The reported melting points [158, 161] for several of the 2-hydroxyalkanenitriles are as follows: -tetradecanenitrile, 44.5°; -pentadecanenitrile, 50.5°; -hexadecanenitrile, 52.5–53.5°; -heptadecanenitrile, 60–61°; and -octadecanenitrile, 61.5–62.5°. The cyanohydrins may also be obtained by the action of hydrogen cyanide on the bisulfite addition products of the aldehydes.[200, 201] Kobata [148] has described the preparation of 2-hydroxydecanenitrile by this latter method. Hydrolysis of the cyanohydrins by warming with concentrated hydrochloric acid first yields 2-hydroxy amides, the further hydrolysis of which yields 2-hydroxy acids. Thus, the hydrolysis of 2-hydroxyoctadecanenitrile yields 2-hydroxystearamide, m.p. 148–148.5°, which when boiled with aqueous potassium hydroxide yields 2-hydroxystearic acid, m.p. 91–92°.[158] 2-Hydroxymyristamide, m.p. 150°; 2-hydroxypentadecanamide, m.p. 149–150°; 2-hydroxypalmitamide, m.p. 149.5°; and 2-hydroxyheptadecanamide, m.p. 148.5°, have also been prepared by this method. The hydrolysis of these hydroxy amides yields 2-hydroxymyristic acid, m.p. 81.5–82°; 2-hydroxypentadecanoic acid, m.p. 84.5°; 2-hydroxypalmitic acid, m.p. 86.5–87°; and 2-hydroxyheptadecanoic acid, m.p. 89°. 2-Hydroxycapric acid has been obtained by hydrolysis of the cyanohydrin of nonanal.[148] The cyanohydrins yield α-ethylenic nitriles when treated with strong dehydrating agents, an example being the synthesis of 2-heptenenitrile, $CH_3(CH_2)_3CH:CHCN$, by the action of phosphoric acid on 2-hydroxyheptanenitrile.[141]

The higher aldehydes react with ammonia to yield addition compounds which are probably α-hydroxy amines, and Kobata [148] has described the preparation of 2-hydroxynonylamine by the action of an alcoholic solution of ammonia on nonanal. Such hydroxy amines yield α-amino nitriles when treated with hydrocyanic acid, the hydrolysis of which results in α-amino acids. The preparation of a number of addition products of the higher aldehydes has been described in the patent literature.[202]

The aliphatic aldehydes combine with malonic acid or its esters in the presence of bases to yield β-hydroxy-α,α-dicarboxylic acids, the dehydration and partial decarboxylation of which yields α-ethylenic acids. It has been reported that β-unsaturated acids result if such degradations take place in the presence of primary or secondary bases, whereas α-unsaturated acids are formed in the presence of tertiary bases. Zaar [203] has studied the condensation of several of the higher aldehydes with malonic acid in the presence of piperidine and has reported the preparation of 2-nonenoic acid from heptanal, 2-decenoic acid from octanal, 2-dodecenoic acid from decanal, and 2-tridecenoic acid from undecanal. 9-Aldononanoic acid when refluxed with malonic acid in the presence of a small amount of piperidine gives a 24% yield of 2-undecenedioic acid.[150]

Condensation reactions involving the higher aldehydes have been employed for the synthesis of α-amino acids. The aliphatic aldehydes condense with hydantoin to yield products the reduction of which gives hydantoins of α-amino acids, which are readily hydrolyzed to the free α-amino acids. Johnson [204] has described the preparation of 2-aminopelargonic acid by condensing heptanal with hydantoin to give 5-heptylidenehydantoin,

$$CH_3(CH_2)_5CH = C \begin{matrix} CO-NH \\ | \quad\quad\quad > CO \\ NH \end{matrix}$$

the reduction of which yields the hydantoin of 2-aminopelargonic acid,

$$CH_3(CH_2)_6CH-NH \begin{matrix} CO-NH \\ | \quad\quad > CO \\ \end{matrix}$$

which when hydrolyzed gives the free amino acid.

Aldehydes condense with alcohols to yield acetals, $RCH(OR')_2$, which may be considered as ethers of the hypothetical glycol, $RCH(OH)_2$. A number of the acetals of the higher aliphatic aldehydes have been prepared and their properties described. The ease of formation of an acetal is dependent upon the specific alcohol and aliphatic aldehyde employed, and apparently the higher aldehydes form acetals more readily than their lower homologs. Acetal formation is catalyzed by the presence of acids, the reaction representing an equilibrium, since the aldehydes are reformed upon

boiling the acetals with dilute solutions of mineral acids. Kirrmann [97] has described the preparation of the dimethyl acetals of
the aldehydes from butanal to heptanal. Equimolar mixtures of
the higher aldehydes and alcohols react exothermally with the
formation of condensation products which are apparently hemiacetals, RCH(OH)(OR'). Hemiacetals prepared from the following
pairs have been described: [205] 1-heptanol, heptanal, m.p. 2°;
1-octanol, octanal, m.p. 7°; 1-nonanol, nonanal, m.p. 19°; 1-dec-
anol, decanal, m.p. 31°; 1-undecanol, undecanal, m.p. 35°; and
1-decanol, octanal, m.p. 13°. Zaar [130] has prepared the addition
products of 1-dodecanol and dodecanal, m.p. 44.5–45.5°, and 1-
decanol and dodecanal, m.p. 35.5°. Cyclic acetals have been
obtained [206] by the interaction of the higher aldehydes with 1-
halo-2,3-epoxypropanes in inert solvents in the presence of catalysts such as stannic chloride. A series of α-alkoxy acetals has
been synthesized by condensation of the alkoxides of higher alcohols with bromoacetaldehyde.[207]

The reaction of halogens or certain halogen compounds with the
higher aldehydes forms the starting point for the synthesis of
many interesting derivatives. The action of the phosphorus
halides and allied compounds on the aliphatic aldehydes proceeds
with a replacement of the aldehydo oxygen atom by halogens, thus
yielding 1,1-dihalohydrocarbons. Acetylenic hydrocarbons result
when such compounds are treated with alcoholic potassium hydroxide. 1-Pentyne and 1-heptyne have been prepared from pentanal
and heptanal respectively by this series of reactions.[208] 1-Octyne
has been similarly prepared from octanal.[209] More recently, hep-
tynylsodium has been prepared by the action of metallic sodium
on 1-heptyne obtained from heptanal.[210] The action of carbon
dioxide on 1-heptynylsodium yields 2-octynoic acid.

The higher aldehydes readily yield the highly reactive α-bromo
aldehydes when treated with moist bromine. Thus, the bromination of pentanal followed by treatment of the product with absolute
ethanol gives the α-bromo acetal, from which the α-hydroxy aldehyde may be obtained by reaction with potassium hydroxide.[211]
Kirrmann [97] has described the preparation of a number of α-bromo
aldehydes by treatment of the methyl acetals with bromine in the
presence of phosphorus trichloride. All the liquid α-bromo aldehydes are strong lachrymators.

The reaction of the α-bromo aldehydes with Grignard reagents
has been investigated,[212] such reactions generally yielding sub-

stantial amounts of olefins because of the dehydration of the resulting alcohols. In his studies of the reactions of α-bromo aldehydes,
Kirrmann [213] has stated that certain reagents apparently remove
hydrogen bromide from the α-bromo aldehydes, yielding a ketene
as an intermediate. The bromine atom may readily be replaced
by a hydroxyl group.

Those hydroxy aldehydes which contain the hydroxyl group
remote from the carbonyl group constitute an extremely interesting group of aliphatic derivatives. Such compounds are stable
chiefly in the cyclic form; for example, 5-hydroxyhexanal readily
assumes the cyclic form 2-methyl-6-hydroxytetrahydropyran.[214]
4-Hydroxynonadecanal has been stated to exist largely as a mixture
of the linear and cyclic forms.[215] The ω-hydroxy aldehydes likewise
readily assume the cyclic form, 9-hydroxynonanal yielding the
cyclic acetal

$$\begin{array}{l} (CH_2)_7CHOCH_3 \\ \quad | \qquad\quad | \\ \quad CH_2{-}O \end{array}$$

when treated with methanol in the presence of hydrochloric acid.[216]
The similarity which exists between the chemical properties of the
higher hydroxy aldehydes and those of the sugars is of interest.

Because of their relative unavailability, not many uses have
been proposed for the higher aldehydes other than in perfumery or
the field of chemical intermediates. They have been suggested as
fungicides, especially in admixture with other known fungicidal
agents.[217] Cadwell [218] has proposed their use as accelerating agents
in the vulcanization of rubber. Octanal and nonanal have been
stated to possess high germicidal activities.[219]

THE HIGH MOLECULAR WEIGHT KETONES

Ketones possess the general formula RCOR'. Owing to the
presence of the carbonyl group, the ketones have many chemical
properties in common with the aldehydes. They are, however,
decidedly less reactive and, in contrast to the aldehydes, are one
of the most stable groups of fatty acid derivatives. Those ketones
which are related to the higher fatty acids are characterized by
the presence of at least one long hydrocarbon radical. They fall
into two general groups, the dialkyl ketones and the alkyl aryl
ketones. In the former both R groups are aliphatic, whereas in
the latter one is aliphatic and the other aromatic. Although these

two types of ketones possess many similarities, their methods of synthesis and many of their physical properties show some characteristic differences. The alkyl aryl ketones do not occur in natural products.

THE DIALKYL KETONES

These constitute a well-known and important class of fatty acid derivatives, and many representatives of this type of compound have been synthesized and studied. Such compounds fall naturally into two groups: the symmetrical ketones, in which the R groups are alike, and the unsymmetrical ketones, in which the R groups differ. Several methods of naming these ketones may be employed. In the chemical literature they are most frequently named by designating the two R groups and the keto group; for example, diundecyl ketone, $C_{11}H_{25}COC_{11}H_{25}$, or methyl undecyl ketone, $CH_3COC_{11}H_{25}$. This method has the advantage of permitting a rapid visualization of the structure of the compound and has been generally employed in our discussion. The nomenclature employed by the International Union of Chemistry designates the ketone as a straight chain of carbon atoms. The compound is thus named as if it were a hydrocarbon with the exception that the suffix "one" is added. The position of the keto group is indicated by a numerical prefix. For example, diundecyl ketone is correctly named 12-tricosanone, and methyl undecyl ketone is 2-tridecanone. This method has the advantage of enabling the clear indication of the position of other functional groups; thus $CH_3CH(OH)(CH_2)_9$-$CO(CH_2)_9CH(OH)CH_3$ is designated as 2,22-dihydroxy-12-tricosanone. Quite frequently those symmetrical ketones which are derived from the better-known aliphatic acids retain the common name of the acid; thus diundecyl ketone is termed laurone; ditridecyl ketone, myristone; and diheptadecyl ketone, stearone. The disadvantages of such a nomenclature are obvious, although it is improbable that names such as acetone will ever fall into disuse.

Dialkyl ketones are found in certain oils, a notable example being the presence of methyl alkyl ketones in oil of rue. Both methyl heptyl ketone and methyl nonyl ketone have been isolated from this oil,[220] and more recently methyl octyl ketone has also been identified as a component.[221] Palmitone and d-10-hydroxypalmitone have been isolated from the unsaponifiable portion of the wax of sandal leaves,[222] and myristone has been identified as a component of alfalfa wax.[223] The methyl ketones present in the natural oils probably result from the β-oxidation of saturated acids followed by the splitting out of carbon dioxide. The occurrence in natural products of ketones with an even number of carbon atoms, such as methyl octyl ketone, is of biological interest, since if they are formed by the above process the parent acid must contain an uneven number of carbon atoms.

Ketones are present in the products formed by the action of bacteria or molds on fats, their formation being attributed to decarboxylation of the β-keto acids which are intermediates in the biological oxidation of fats or fatty acids.[224] Highly oxidizing conditions are, therefore, unfavorable to ketone formation, since they result in the further oxidation of the keto acids. Small amounts of ketones are produced by the action of either bacteria or molds on media containing oleic acid.[225] The so-called ketonic rancidity of fats has been attributed to the presence of methyl alkyl ketones.[226] Methyl alkyl ketones have been isolated from coconut or palm oils, their fatty acids, or their ammonium soaps which have been exposed to the action of molds in the presence of various nitrogenous media. Factors such as pH exert a decided influence upon the formation of ketones by the action of molds on fats.[227] In many instances, the size of the fat molecule appears to be of importance. In general, the acids of higher molecular weight, myristic acid and its higher homologs, appear to be more resistant to the action of molds than acids of intermediate molecular weight. Unsaturation, on the other hand, appears to be without a decided influence. The fatty acids become ketonic upon exposure to light, the reaction taking place in the presence or absence of oxygen. It has been reported [228] that ketone formation proceeds rapidly upon heating the fatty acids, the amount formed first increasing then decreasing with continued heating. This latter finding, however, has been shown [229] to be incorrect since the ketones are very thermostable. It is quite evident that the problem of the ketonic rancidity of fats presents many interesting aspects which await further exploration.

Preparation of the Higher Dialkyl Ketones

A number of methods are available for the synthesis of the higher molecular weight dialkyl ketones. Perhaps the best known of these procedures consists of heating a metallic soap or a mixture

of metallic soaps above the decomposition point, decarboxylation
ensuing with the formation of a ketone, thus:

$$(RCO_2)_2Ca \rightarrow RCOR + CaCO_3$$

The mechanism of this reaction has been the subject of many
studies, and the principles involved have been incorporated into
several of the proposed methods for the preparation of the high
molecular weight dialkyl ketones. Most of the known symmetrical dialkyl ketones have been synthesized by this procedure.
Schmidt [230] has obtained high yields of the ketones up to and including dihexyl ketone by dry distillation of the barium salts of
the respective acids, and Krafft [231] has prepared laurone, myristone,
palmitone, and stearone by heating the barium salts of the acids
under vacuum. When this method is applied to the higher alkyl
ketones, however, the yields are generally small owing to the high
temperatures involved. The yields may be increased by conducting the reaction slowly at lower temperatures under a vacuum,
substantial yields of oleone having been obtained by heating calcium oleate at 130–170° under 15 mm. pressure,[232] and of didecenyl
ketone by heating calcium undecenoate at 90–120° under 20 mm.
pressure. The influence of the molecular weight of the acid upon
the yield of ketone has been studied by Araki.[233] The preparation
of ketones by such processes is not limited to the calcium or
barium soaps, since most of the heavy metal soaps of the fatty
acids yield ketones upon decarboxylation. Both magnesium and
manganese soaps form ketones when heated above 300°; however,
zinc salts give only hydrocarbons and are therefore not satisfactory
for the preparation of ketones.[234] The lead salts appear to be quite
adaptable to ketone formation, an 80% yield each of laurone and
stearone having been obtained from lead laurate and lead stearate,
respectively.[235] This yield compares favorably with those obtained from lead salts of the lower acids. The use of soaps other
than the calcium or barium soaps for ketone formation has been
proposed in the patent literature.[236] It has been shown [237] that the
presence of an α-hydrogen atom is necessary for ketone formation,
which suggests that the reaction proceeds through the initial formation of a keto acid or its salt, the decarboxylation of which yields
the ketone. This decomposition may proceed through the keto
or the enol form, the presence of water or acid being necessary in
the latter instance. It has been shown that the temperature of

ketone formation is lowered and side reactions are minimized if traces of water are present.

Substantial yields of ketones result when the higher fatty acids or esters are heated in the presence of metals or their oxides, such substances evidently exerting a catalytic effect. The yields of ketones are generally larger than those resulting from decarboxylation of the soaps. A variety of catalytic materials have been investigated for ketone formation from fatty acids. Stearic acid, for example, yields stearone together with hydrocarbons when distilled in the presence of powdered magnesium.[238] Metallic iron exerts a powerful catalytic effect, stearic, oleic, brassidic, erucic, and other higher fatty acids yielding the corresponding ketones when heated to 370° in the presence of 10% of iron filings.[239] The yields are apparently higher than those obtained by decarboxylation of the corresponding ferrous salts. Metals such as aluminum or manganese exert a catalytic effect comparable to that of iron; however, when the higher acids are heated with zinc, the products consist largely of hydrocarbons. The addition of heavy metal soaps to the reaction mixture prevents violent frothing.[234] Grün and coworkers [240] have studied the effect of various catalysts on the conversion of stearic acid into stearone, yields of 6–7% being obtained when the acid is heated for six hours at 300° in the presence of SiO_2, CuO, ZnO, TiO_2, or ThO_2; 13%, in the presence of CdO; and 17–24%, in the presence of iron oxides, aluminum oxide, or magnesium oxide on kieselguhr. It was reported that nearly quantitative yields of ketones are formed when either palmitic acid or stearic acid is heated in an iron vessel at approximately 300° for a period of several hours. The catalytic effect of iron or magnesium has been reported [241] to be superior to that of other metals, the ease of ketone formation in the presence of magnesium increasing with the molecular weight of the acid. Tin exerts only a slight catalytic effect. The hydrogenation of palmitic or stearic acid at 300–400° in the presence of a nickel-copper oxide catalyst forms large amounts of unsaponifiable matter which consists largely of ketones.[242] Ketones result when the higher acids are heated above their decomposition points in the presence of strong dehydrating agents, an example being the preparation of laurone or myristone by heating lauric or myristic acid with phosphorus pentoxide.[243] Ketone formation from unsaturated fatty acids is facilitated if the reaction is conducted in the presence of an inert gas.[244]

The catalytic transformation of fatty acids into ketones is best accomplished by passing the vapors of the acids over decarboxylating catalysts, which generally consist of metallic oxides or their mixtures. For example, the fatty acids are converted into ketones when passed at high temperatures in the vapor phase over alkaline earth oxides.[245] Thoria and ceria are extremely effective catalysts for the vapor-phase formation of ketones from higher acids, and the preparation of a thoria-gel catalyst for this purpose has been described in detail.[246] The ethyl esters are rapidly converted into ketones when passed over this catalyst, ethyl laurate giving a 92.5% yield of laurone, and ethyl undecenoate an 86% yield of didecenyl ketone at 300°.[247] Catalysts consisting of manganese chromite or zinc chromite are also highly effective for the vapor-phase conversion of fatty acids into ketones.[248]

The unsymmetrical dialkyl ketones may be prepared by any of the procedures described. Whereas the distillation of barium stearate yields only diheptadecyl ketone, the distillation of a mixture of barium stearate and barium acetate yields the unsymmetrical ketone, methyl heptadecyl ketone, together with the two symmetrical ketones, diheptadecyl ketone and acetone. Since in the above example the methyl heptadecyl ketone is the desired product, it is necessary to employ a large molecular excess of barium acetate in order to minimize the formation of diheptadecyl ketone. The reaction product, under these conditions, consists essentially of methyl heptadecyl ketone and acetone, which are easily separated. Thus, Krafft[249] heated barium palmitate or barium stearate with equal weight amounts of barium acetate for the preparation of methyl pentadecyl or methyl heptadecyl ketone. Morgan and Holmes[250] have prepared a series of methyl alkyl ketones by heating the barium salts of the fatty acids from caprylic to arachidic acid inclusive with three moles of barium acetate and have also described the synthesis of methyl heneicosyl ketone by the reaction of barium behenate with an excess of barium acetate.[251] Propyl hexyl ketone has been obtained by heating a mixture of potassium butyrate and potassium heptanoate,[252] and the preparation of this and many other mixed ketones by heating mixtures of the calcium soaps has been described in the patent literature.[253]

The same principles apply when unsymmetrical ketones in which the R groups have markedly different chain lengths are formed by heating acid mixtures in either the vapor or the liquid phase. Thus, in the formation of methyl alkyl ketones from acetic acid and a higher acid, an excess of the lower acid is always employed, favoring the formation of the unsymmetrical ketone at the expense of the higher symmetrical ketone. Methyl tridecyl ketone and methyl pentadecyl ketone have been prepared by passing the vapors of myristic and palmitic acids mixed with an excess of acetic acid over thorium oxide at 400°.[254] Ruzicka and coworkers [255] have described the preparation of a number of methyl alkyl ketones by heating the vapors of the higher acids with acetic acid. Unsaturated ketones, such as methyl heptadecenyl ketone, have been obtained by passing the vapors of oleic or other acids and acetic acid, acetic anhydride, or acetyl chloride over decarboxylating catalysts at high temperatures.[256, 257] Disproportionation reactions probably are not involved in the formation of unsymmetrical ketones, the mixed ketone being a primary reaction product.[258] Unsymmetrical ketones are formed when mixed glycerides are thermally decomposed in the presence of decarboxylating catalysts.[259]

Cyclic ketones result from the decarboxylation of dibasic acids, their anhydrides, or their alkaline earth or other salts. An early patent [260] on this subject discloses the preparation of cyclic ketones by heating adipic acid or its homologs under reduced pressure in the presence of decarboxylating catalysts, and states that suberone is obtained in good yields by heating suberic acid in the presence of 5% of iron filings. Aschan [261] later showed that cyclic ketones are formed only in small amounts by heating dicarboxylic acids; however, it was subsequently observed [262] that the yield of cyclic ketones is materially greater if the calcium salts of the dibasic acids are subjected to pyrolysis. In 1928, Vogel [263] studied the conversion of a mixture of suberic and azelaic acids to suberone, and obtained high yields by the dry distillation of the acids mixed with an equal weight of iron filings and 5% of barium hydroxide. The reaction evidently proceeds in two stages, the first of which is the formation of a cyclic anhydride which is converted to the ketone by loss of carbon dioxide. This mechanism receives support from the fact that Blanc [264] had previously shown that high yields of cyclic ketones can be obtained by heating adipic and pimelic acids with acetic anhydride at 220–250°, the reaction apparently proceeding with the initial formation of a cyclic anhydride. Ruzicka and coworkers [265, 266, 267, 268, 269, 270] have made many extensive investigations of the preparation of cyclic ketones by the decarboxylation both of the dicarboxylic acids themselves and of their various salts. The highest yields of cyclic ketones result from decomposition of the cerium or thorium salts of the dicarboxylic acids, or from passage of the acids in the vapor phase over either cerium or thorium oxide. Cyclic ketones containing from nine to thirty carbon atoms have been prepared by this method. Cyclization may result in the formation of either mono- or diketones, with the former generally present in much the larger amount. The thorium salt of azelaic acid yields cyclooctanone in addition to cyclohexanone, thus indicating a rather abnormal behavior. Harries and Tank [271] had previously shown that the dry distillation of calcium azelate yields a mixture of cyclic ketones. The preparation of cyclic ketones by dry distillation of the cerium or thorium salts of the dibasic acids has been patented by Ruzicka,[272] an example being the preparation of cyclopentadecanone by the distillation of the cerium or thorium salts of hexadecanedioic acid. In carrying out this process, the dicarboxylic acid may be mixed with cerium or thorium oxide and heated above 400° under vacuum, or the vapors of the dicarboxylic acid may be passed over either of these oxides.[273] Alternate procedures are to heat the acids with acetic anhydride and to heat the anhydrides of the acids in the presence or absence of catalysts.

Although the pyrogenic reactions which we have discussed have been found to be satisfactory for the preparation of many of the dialkyl ketones, several other methods have been suggested and employed. Some of these procedures offer distinct advantages, since they are not accompanied by the excessive decomposition occasioned by the high temperatures involved in decarboxylation reactions. In several of these methods the yields are satisfactorily high and the resulting ketones are easily purified, and some of the reactions are well adapted to the laboratory preparation of pure ketones.

The Dakin synthesis, in which the ammonium or alkali metal salts of the fatty acids are oxidized by hydrogen peroxide to yield methyl alkyl ketones, is of only theoretical interest when applied to the higher fatty acids. In 1908, Dakin [274] stated that acetone is obtained from the oxidation of ammonium butyrate with hydrogen peroxide, and in a later article [275] he showed that the ammonium salts of the higher fatty acids are oxidized by hydrogen peroxide to β-keto acids, decarboxylation of which yields methyl alkyl ketones. Thus, a solution of ammonium caprylate when warmed with an excess of hydrogen peroxide yields methyl pentyl ketone, the caprate yields methyl heptyl ketone, and the stearate gives methyl pentadecyl ketone. However, the yields progressively decrease with increasing chain length.[276] Acids above caproic give yields of less than 10% of the desired ketones when subjected to this procedure.

Acid chlorides yield ketones when treated with alkylzincs or related compounds, the addition product which is first formed being decomposed by a second molecule of the acid chloride. Bertrand [277] has synthesized ethyl pentadecyl ketone and propyl pentadecyl ketone by the action of diethylzinc and dipropylzinc, respectively, on palmitoyl chloride. The reaction in the former case is as follows:

$$C_{15}H_{31}COCl + Zn(C_2H_5)_2 \rightarrow C_{15}H_{31}COCl \cdot Zn(C_2H_5)_2 \xrightarrow{C_{15}H_{31}COCl} 2C_{15}H_{31}\underset{\underset{O}{\|}}{C}C_2H_5 + ZnCl_2$$

A number of keto acids have been synthesized [278] by the action of alkylzinc iodides on the acid chlorides of the monoesters of dicarboxylic acids, $ClOC(CH_2)_xCO_2R$. Blaise and Koehler [279] have also described the preparation of a series of diketones by the action of alkylzinc iodides on the acid chlorides of the dicarboxylic acids.

Both nitriles and amides react readily with Grignard reagents to yield addition products which hydrolyze to give ketones. The Grignard method has proved to be an extremely satisfactory procedure for the laboratory preparation of both symmetrical and unsymmetrical dialkyl ketones, and also alkyl aryl ketones. This method is especially adaptable to the synthesis of pure unsymmetrical dialkyl ketones, such as the preparation of methyl heptadecyl ketone from stearonitrile and methylmagnesium iodide.[280] Two moles of the alkylmagnesium halide are required for the conversion of amides to ketones, an example being the synthesis of ethyl 9-decenyl ketone by the action of 10-undecenamide and ethylmagnesium bromide.[281] Esters yield tertiary alcohols when treated with Grignard reagents, ethyl laurate and butylmagnesium chloride, for example, yielding 5-butyl-5-hexadecanol. The esters of higher fatty acids, however, react in an abnormal manner with tert-butylmagnesium chloride, this reagent exerting a condensation action with the formation of unsymmetrical ketones.[282] Thus, when ethyl laurate is heated with tert-butylmagnesium chloride in xylene for five hours at 110–120° and the product is hydrolyzed with hydrogen chloride, a 35% yield of laurone is obtained. Ethyl palmitate yields palmitone when similarly treated.

The acetoacetic ester condensation of higher esters, followed by hydrolysis of the resulting β-keto esters, offers an excellent method for the preparation of higher symmetrical dialkyl ketones. Mc-Elvain [283] has shown that ethyl 2-propionylpropionate and ethyl 2-butyrylbutyrate are obtained in high yields by the acetoacetic ester condensation of ethyl propionate and ethyl butyrate, respectively, in the presence of sodium ethoxide, the reaction being as follows:

$$2RCH_2CO_2C_2H_5 + NaOC_2H_5 \rightarrow RCH_2C(ONa){=}C(R)CO_2C_2H_5 + 2C_2H_5OH$$

Later, Briese and McElvain [284] prepared a series of β-keto esters of higher fatty acids by condensation of the ethyl esters in the presence of sodium ethoxide, the yields varying from 74 to 84%. Hydrolysis of these keto esters by refluxing for several hours with a 5% solution of potassium hydroxide in 90% ethanol yields the corresponding symmetrical ketones. The dialkyl ketones from valerone to myristone were prepared in high yields by this method. Recently, caprione, laurone, myristone, palmitone, and stearone have been synthesized by condensation of the respective ethyl esters in the presence of sodium ethoxide.[285] The preparation of stearone by the alkaline hydrolysis of ethyl 2-stearoylstearate has been described by Spielman and Schmidt.[286]

The oxidation of secondary alcohols yields ketones, although such procedures are rarely employed for the preparation of the higher dialkyl ketones. A catalyst consisting of 60% copper, 38.5% zinc, and 1.5% tin has been suggested for the vapor-phase oxidation of secondary alcohols to ketones.[287] Unsaturated ketones result from the oxidation of disubstituted acetylenes, 6-dodecyne, $C_5H_{11}C{\equiv}CC_5H_{11}$, yielding 6-dodecyn-5-one by air oxidation. Other disubstituted acetylenes react in a similar manner.[288]

The so-called acyloins or keto alcohols, RCHOHCOR, are readily obtained by the action of sodium on ether or benzene solutions of aliphatic esters. This reaction was first proposed by Bouveault and Locquin,[289] and proceeds as follows:

$$2RCO_2R' + 4Na \rightarrow \begin{array}{c} RC{-}ONa \\ \| \\ RC{-}ONa \end{array} (+ 2R'ONa) \xrightarrow{H_2O} \begin{array}{c} RC{-}OH \\ \| \\ RC{-}OH \end{array} \rightarrow \begin{array}{c} RCHOH \\ | \\ RC{=}O \end{array}$$

In a later investigation, Corson, Benson, and Goodwin [290] prepared the aliphatic acyloins up to and including capronoin by heating the respective ethyl esters with sodium in ether, the acyloins resulting in approximately 50% yields. The higher esters, ethyl laurate and myristate, were found to react only incompletely under these conditions. In the preparation of acyloins, it has been noted that substantial amounts of diketones are present in the reaction product, their formation being ascribed to an oxidation of the salt of the dienolate.[290, 291] Snell and McElvain [292] have held that the formation of a diketone is an intermediate step in the condensation of the esters in the presence of sodium, the diketone probably appearing as a sodium alkoxide addition product. The high molecular weight acyloins from butyroin to stearoin have been prepared by Hansley [293] in 80–95% yields, by reaction of the methyl esters in xylene with sodium at a temperature above the melting point of sodium (105°). The following melting points were reported for the acyloins so prepared: butyroin, −10°; capronoin, 9°; capryloin, 39°; nonanoin, 45°; caprinoin, 51–52°; lauroin, 61–62°; myristoin, 71–72°; palmitoin, 77–78°; and stearoin, 82–83°. Hydrogenation of the acyloins yields symmetrically substituted ethylene glycols, RCHOHCHOHR, which melt as follows: (R group, m.p.) C_7H_{15}, 129–130°; $C_{12}H_{25}$, 125–126°; $C_{13}H_{27}$, 124°; and $C_{17}H_{35}$, 123–124°. Oxidation of the acyloins yields diketones, RCOCOR, lauroin giving 12,13-tetracosanedione (bright yellow solid, m.p. 71–71.5°) when treated with Wijs solution.

Physical Properties of the Higher Dialkyl Ketones

Much is yet to be learned concerning the physical properties and behavior of the dialkyl ketones. The symmetrical dialkyl ketones, including dihexyl ketone and its higher homologs, are crystalline solids, whereas the still higher molecular weight ketones assume waxlike properties and resemble paraffin in appearance. The lower members of the series possess distinctly pleasant odors; however, this odor progressively decreases with increase in molecular weight, the higher members being odorless. The physical properties of the higher symmetrical dialkyl ketones from dipentyl ketone to diheptadecyl ketone are shown in Table V.

The ketones, like the aldehydes, react with hydroxylamine, phenylhydrazine, semicarbazide, p-nitrophenylhydrazine, and 2,4- or 2,5-dinitrophenylhydrazine to form identifying derivatives. Many of these derivatives, however, possess lower melting points than the ketones themselves; for example, the ketoximes of laurone, myristone, palmitone, and stearone melt at 39–40°, 51°, 59°, and 62–63°, respectively. [294]

Oximes of the symmetrical ketones do not exist in isomeric forms; however, those of the unsymmetrical dialkyl ketones exist in two stereoisomeric forms:

$$\begin{matrix} RCR' & & RCR' \\ \| & \rightleftarrows & \| \\ HON & & NOH \end{matrix}$$

Thus, ethyl pentadecyl ketone gives two oximes, m.p. 58–59° and 44–45°, rearrangement of which yields isomeric amides, one of which gives pentadecylamine and the other palmitic acid upon

TABLE V

PHYSICAL PROPERTIES OF SYMMETRICAL DIALKYL KETONES

Ketone	Common Name	M.P.,°C.	B.P.,°C.	d_4^t
Dipentyl	Caprone	14–15	226	0.8262^{20}
Dihexyl	Enanthone	30–31	255	0.825^{30}
		29.7 *		
Diheptyl	Caprylone	41–42	......	......
		39.25 *		
Dioctyl	Pelargonone	53	......	......
Dinonyl	Caprione	58–59	......	......
		57.8 *		
Diundecyl	Laurone	68–69	......	$0.7888^{90.9}$
		69.3 *		
Ditridecyl	Myristone	78–79	......	0.7986^{81}
		77.2 *		
Dipentadecyl	Palmitone	83.7 *		
Diheptadecyl	Stearone	88–89		
		88.7 *		
Di-9-decenyl		43		
Di-cis-8-heptadecenyl	Oleone	59.5		
Di-trans-8-heptadecenyl	Elaidone	70		

* Denotes freezing point.

saponification.[295] Ethyl heptadecyl ketone likewise yields two oximes, m.p. 64–65° and 52.5–53.5°, which yield isomeric amides upon rearrangement, saponifications of which yield heptadecylamine and stearic acid. Propyl pentadecyl ketone behaves similarly. After rearrangement and saponification, dipentadecyl ketoxime yields pentadecylamine with only traces of palmitic acid. Houben [220] has made an extensive investigation of the rearrangement of the methyl nonyl ketoximes to the substituted amides.

The unsymmetrical dialkyl ketones possess somewhat lower melting points than the corresponding symmetrical ketones containing the same number of carbon atoms. For example, methyl pentadecyl ketone melts at 48°,[254] whereas its symmetrical isomer dioctyl ketone melts at 53°. A study of the influence of the position of the carbonyl group upon the freezing points of the members of two series of isomeric ketones, $C_{17}H_{34}O$ and $C_{18}H_{36}O$, has indicated that the higher freezing points occur when the polar group is adjacent to a terminal methyl group or symmetrically placed in the middle of the chain.[296, 297] This suggests that the activation energy of melting is supplied by a torsional oscillation of the chains about the carbonyl group.

The methyl alkyl ketones are the best known of the unsymmetrical dialkyl ketones, many of the members of this group having been described.[249, 250, 251, 254, 298, 299] The lower members of this series are pleasant-smelling liquids; the higher homologs are odorless solids. The following physical constants have been reported for the higher methyl alkyl ketones: (R group, m.p., b.p., d_4^{15}) hexyl, −20.9° (f.p.), 173.5°, 0.82332 (ketoxime, −6.4° (f.p.), 114.6$_{13}$°, 0.88966); heptyl, −8.20° (f.p.), 195.3°, 0.82605 (ketoxime, 16.1°, 131.0$_{15}$°, —); octyl, 14°, 209°, 0.8248^{20} (semicarbazone, 124°, —, —); nonyl, 13° (f.p.), 120$_{20}$°, — (semicarbazone, 115°, —, —); decyl, 20°, —, —; undecyl, 27.5°, —, — (semicarbazone, 115–117°, —, —); dodecyl, 33°, —, —; tridecyl, 37°, 184$_{20}$°, —; tetradecyl, 43°, —, — (semicarbazone, 126.5°, —, —); pentadecyl, 48°, 197$_{12}$°, — (semicarbazone, 125.5°, —, —); hexadecyl, 52°, —, —; heptadecyl, 55°, —, — (semicarbazone, 117–119°, —, —); octadecyl, 58°, —, —; nonadecyl, 61°, —, —; eicosyl, 63.5°, —, —; and heneicosyl, 66.5°, —, —.

The higher ethyl alkyl and propyl alkyl ketones possess melting points comparable to or somewhat lower than those of their isomeric methyl alkyl ketones. For example, ethyl pentadecyl ketone melts at 53° and propyl pentadecyl ketone at 50.5°.[277] 12-Pentacosanone (undecyl tridecyl ketone) has been reported to melt at 59°.[259]

The symmetrical and unsymmetrical dialkyl ketones are soluble in all organic solvents, the solubility decreasing with increasing molecular weight of the ketone and with increasing polarity of the solvent. In general, the unsymmetrical dialkyl ketones are somewhat more soluble than their symmetrical isomers. The solubilities of several of the higher molecular weight symmetrical dialkyl ketones have recently been determined [285] in benzene, cyclohexane, tetrachloromethane, ethyl acetate, butyl acetate, acetone, 2-

butanone, methanol, 95% ethanol, 2-propanol, 1-butanol, nitroethane, and acetonitrile, and the results reported illustrate the
general solubility behavior of the dialkyl ketones in organic solvents. In the non-polar solvents benzene, cyclohexane, and tetrachloromethane, the ketones are most soluble in benzene and least
soluble in cyclohexane. They form eutectics with benzene and
cyclohexane. 10-Nonadecanone forms a eutectic with benzene at
3.9° which contains 10% of ketone, and with cyclohexane at 5.1°
which contains 10% of ketone. 12-Tricosanone forms a eutectic
with benzene at 5.4° containing 0.4% of ketone, and with cyclohexane at 6.3° containing 1.2% of ketone. Eutectics with the
higher ketones occur at much lower concentrations. The solubilities of several symmetrical ketones in benzene are shown in
Table VI.

TABLE VI

SOLUBILITIES OF SYMMETRICAL KETONES IN BENZENE

No. of C Atoms	Grams per 100 g. Benzene			
	10.0°	30.0°	50.0°	80.1°
19	13.8	67.5	510	∞
23	1.2	20.3	142	∞
27	0.3	6.3	64.7	∞
31	≈0.1	1.7	27.7	1200
35	<0.1	0.6	12.7	383

The ketones, in general, tend to be less soluble in the more
polar solvents, being less soluble in ethyl acetate and butyl acetate
than in the previously mentioned non-polar solvents. They are
more soluble in 2-butanone than in acetone and are much less
soluble in methanol than in the higher alcohols. Their solubilities
in methanol and 95% ethanol are shown in Tables VII and VIII,
respectively.

TABLE VII

SOLUBILITIES OF SYMMETRICAL KETONES IN METHANOL

No. of C Atoms	Grams per 100 g. Methanol			
	10.0°	30.0°	50.0°	64.7°
19	0.6	1.5	69.5	∞
23	≈0.1	0.5	1.7	≈23
27	...	≈0.1	0.4	1.9
31	...	...	≈0.1	0.9
35	...	...	...	0.3

TABLE VIII

SOLUBILITIES OF SYMMETRICAL KETONES IN 95% ETHANOL

Grams per 100 g. 95% Ethanol

No. of C Atoms	10.0°	30.0°	50.0°	65.0°	78.5°
19	1.2	3.2	194	∞	∞
23	0.2	0.6	6.0	900	∞
27	<0.1	≈0.1	0.8	13.8	∞
31	...	...	0.2	2.7	69.5
35	...	...	<0.1	0.4	4.9

The higher ketones show a considerable range of immiscibility in the liquid state in methanol, and the liquid ketones are immiscible with acetonitrile over a large range of concentration.

The solubility behavior of the ketones may be influenced by intermolecular association, since they possess appreciable polarities.[300, 301, 302] Cole,[303] however, has stated that the ebullioscopic behavior of 14-heptacosanone and 16-hentriacontanone in hexane, cyclohexane, and benzene cannot be explained simply by the association of these compounds in solution. The physical behavior of the higher ketones suggests a continuous chain of carbon atoms, x-ray studies showing a structure closely similar to that of the corresponding paraffins.[296] The contribution of the dipole layers to the heats of fusion of the unsymmetrical and symmetrical ketones approximates 3.2 and 5.3 kg. cal./mole, respectively. The Raman frequency of the $C:O$ group has been stated [304] to be independent of the length of the chains constituting the R groups.

Chemical Properties of the Higher Dialkyl Ketones

The ketones show many of the reactions characteristic of the aldehydes, with the notable exception that although they enter into condensation reactions they do not readily polymerize. Because of this difference, reactions involving the higher ketones generally proceed smoothly and do not give the polymerized products of undetermined composition which are often encountered when an aldehyde is one of the reacting components.

Reduction of the ketones, either by chemical or by catalytic means, yields secondary alcohols, the further reduction of which gives hydrocarbons. The preparation of secondary alcohols by reduction of ketones may readily be accomplished by treatment of the ketones with sodium and an alcohol, Thoms and Mannich [305] having described the reduction of methyl nonyl ketone to 2-undec-anol by the action of sodium in absolute ethanol. Such reactions are conducted by dissolving the ketone in excess ethanol, adding somewhat more than the theoretical amount of sodium, and, after the initial reaction has subsided, heating the mixture on a water bath until completion. Cooling may be necessary in the early stages of the reaction. Although the method is of general application, the higher dialkyl ketones are frequently somewhat difficult to reduce. Caprone when reduced by sodium in ethanol gives a high yield of 6-undecanol, m.p. 16°, b_{754} 235°.[306] Pickard and Kenyon [254, 307] have employed this procedure for the reduction of a number of methyl alkyl ketones, examples being the reduction of methyl tridecyl ketone to 2-pentadecanol, m.p. 38–39°, b_9 181–183°, and of methyl pentadecyl ketone to 2-heptadecanol, m.p. 46°, b_{16} 230°. Reduction of the higher ketones may easily be accomplished by treatment with sodium and a higher alcohol, Easterfield and Taylor [239] having described the reduction of stearone to 18-pentatriacontanol, m.p. 89.5°, by the action of sodium and 1-pentanol. Sodium alkoxides reduce ketones to the corresponding carbinols, the action of sodium isopropoxide on methyl nonyl ketone giving a 92% yield of 2-undecanol.[308] Grün and associates [240] have described the conversion of a number of high ketones to carbinols by treatment with sodium ethoxide in aqueous ethanol at 300° for six to eight hours. Diundecyl, dipentadecyl, and diheptadecyl ketones were reduced to the respective carbinols by this procedure.

The reduction of the higher ketones by the use of amalgamated zinc and hydrochloric acid [309] yields hydrocarbons. For example, the reduction of either dipentyl ketone or methyl nonyl ketone by this method gives undecane.[306] Heptahexacontane, $C_{67}H_{136}$, m.p. 104.1°, has been obtained by the reduction of ditritriacontyl ketone, $(C_{33}H_{67})_2CO$, m.p. 109–110°, by this method.[310] Dehydration of higher molecular weight secondary alcohols yields olefins, 18-pentatriacontanol yielding 17-pentatriacontene when treated with thionyl chloride. Hydrogenation of this olefin yields the saturated hydrocarbon pentatriacontane, $C_{35}H_{72}$.[240] Saturated hydrocarbons may also be obtained from the higher ketones by treatment with phosphorus pentachloride or allied agents, followed by reduction of the dichlorohydrocarbon with hydrogen iodide and phosphorus. Krafft [311] has described the preparation of saturated hydrocarbons from laurone and several of its higher homologs by this method.

Catalytic hydrogenation of the higher ketones in the presence of metallic nickel or other catalyst yields the corresponding secondary alcohols together with hydrocarbons.[312, 313, 314] When high temperatures are employed during the catalytic hydrogenation of ketones, the yields of secondary alcohols are generally very small, since hydrocarbons and polymerized materials constitute the greater proportion of the reaction product. Thus, Haller and Lassieur[315] obtained largely hydrocarbons and their polymerization products by the hydrogenation of methyl nonyl ketone at 300° over metallic nickel. The catalytic-nickel hydrogenation of a number of ketones to secondary alcohols at temperatures from 75° to 200° has been described in the patent literature.[316] Blumenfeld[317] has called attention to the favorable influence of alkali metal alkoxides during the catalytic hydrogenation of ketones to secondary alcohols. The hydrogenation of unsaturated to saturated ketones in the presence of metallic nickel has been described.[318] The hydrogenation of unsaturated ketones yields either saturated ketones or secondary alcohols, the latter of which have been proposed as starting materials for the preparation of wetting agents.[319, 320]

Catalytic hydrogenation of the higher ketones under high hydrogen pressure in the presence of ammonia or amines yields the corresponding amines. Such reactions probably proceed with the initial formation of a secondary alcohol which then condenses with the ammonia or amine. The preparation of higher amines by this method has been described in the patent literature.[321, 322]

Oxidation of the higher ketones results in a rupture of the chain at the carbonyl group with the formation of carboxylic acids. In such oxidations, the carbonyl group generally remains attached to the smaller alkyl group. For example, the products of the oxidation of methyl pentadecyl ketone with potassium dichromate are pentadecanoic acid and acetic acid. Ethyl pentadecyl ketone and propyl pentadecyl ketone both yield pentadecanoic acid as one of their oxidation products,[277] and methyl heneicosyl ketone gives heneicosanoic acid. Morgan and Holmes[251] have described the oxidation of a number of the methyl alkyl ketones by sodium dichromate and sulfuric acid. Methyl nonyl ketone yields pelargonic and acetic acids when oxidized with sodium hypochlorite. The mechanism and rate of oxidation of a number of dialkyl ketones have recently been the subject of an investigation in which the latter was shown to be dependent upon the rate of enolization.[323]

The higher dialkyl ketones are very resistant to thermal decomposition. Carbon monoxide, saturated and unsaturated hydrocarbons, and small quantities of hydrogen and carbon dioxide are the chief products of pyrolysis of the higher dialkyl ketones. Stearone and oleone give small amounts of carbon monoxide when heated to 300–350°, the amount increasing with increase in the temperature.[324] Stearone yields 48.0% of the theoretical amount of carbon monoxide when heated for one hour at 550°, and oleone gives 66.7% when heated at 600° for a similar period.

The reaction of ketones with Grignard reagents parallels that of aldehydes, the addition product yielding a tertiary alcohol upon hydrolysis. Such reactions are frequently employed for the preparation of high molecular weight tertiary alcohols and alkyl-substituted hydrocarbons. Stearone forms an addition product with ethylmagnesium iodide which hydrolyzes to give 18-ethyl-18-pentatriacontanol, which in turn yields 18-ethylpentatriacontane when reduced with hydrogen iodide and phosphorus.[325]

The higher ketones undergo condensation reactions with the formation of keto alcohols, the reaction being similar to an aldol condensation. Strong acids or alkalies function as condensation catalysts for such reactions. Grignard and Colonge [326] obtained small yields of keto alcohols by condensation of the ketones in the presence of acids. Condensation of the methyl alkyl ketones in the presence of aminomagnesium halides, $RR'NMgX$, gives high yields of keto alcohols, the condensation of methyl nonyl ketone in the presence of such reagents yielding 10-methyl-12-keto-10-heneicosanol, m.p. 23°, in 70% yield, the condensation proceeding as follows:

$$C_9H_{19}COCH_3 + CH_3COC_9H_{19} \rightarrow C_9H_{19}\overset{\overset{\displaystyle CH_3}{|}}{\underset{\underset{\displaystyle OH}{|}}{C}}-CH_2COC_9H_{19}$$

Ketones likewise condense with aldehydes to yield keto alcohols, which are easily dehydrated to unsaturated ketones.

Ketones condense with ethylene oxide to yield ether alcohols, the sulfonation of which gives water-soluble compounds.[327] Such condensations probably proceed through the enol form of the ketones.

The higher ketones add hydrogen cyanide with the formation of cyanohydrins, the reaction being similar to that of the aldehydes with this reagent. Hydrolysis of these cyanohydrins yields substituted glycolic acids. Maehlmann [328] has described the preparation of methylhexyl-, m.p. 36°; methylheptyl-, m.p. 38°; methyloctyl-, m.p. 41°; and methylnonylglycolic acids, m.p. 46°, by the action of hydrogen cyanide on the corresponding methyl alkyl ketones, followed by hydrolysis of the resulting cyanohydrins. These substituted glycolic acids have been resolved into their optical isomerides through their strychnine salts.

The dialkyl ketones yield thioketones when treated with phosphorus pentasulfide; however, the higher alkyl thioketones have never been prepared in a state of high purity. The lower molecular weight thioketones are reddish yellow liquids which are readily soluble in organic solvents.

The action of sulfating and sulfonating agents on both saturated and unsaturated ketones has been described in a number of patents. Unsaturated ketones such as oleone, when treated with concentrated sulfuric acid, yield sulfates whose hydrolysis gives hydroxy ketones which have been proposed as substitutes for the natural waxes.[329] Three isomeric bis(hydroxyheptadecyl) ketones have been described, the melting points being 86°, 89°, and 90°.[232] The treatment of saturated dialkyl ketones with strong sulfonating agents for the preparation of water-soluble or water-dispersible compounds has been described in several patents.[330, 331, 332, 333] The preparation of wetting agents from higher ketones has been accomplished by chlorination followed by complete or partial substitution of the halogen atoms by water-solubilizing groups.[334]

THE ALKYL ARYL KETONES

The high molecular weight alkyl aryl ketones possess many of the chemical and physical properties of the higher dialkyl ketones. They are, however, distinguished from the latter in that the presence of an aromatic radical imparts to them characteristic aromatic properties which are not encountered with the dialkyl ketones. Both their chemical and physical properties are greatly influenced by their unsymmetrical structures. Several procedures for the preparation of the higher ketones may be applied with equal success to both dialkyl and alkyl aryl ketones, whereas other methods are specific for the synthesis of one or the other type.

Preparation of the Alkyl Aryl Ketones

Acylation reactions constitute by far the most important method for the synthesis of the higher alkyl aryl ketones, and the

Friedel-Crafts reaction finds one of its most interesting applications in the preparation of these compounds. This reaction and its several modifications are of essentially universal application for the synthesis of the alkyl aryl ketones. The procedure generally employed consists of treating an aromatic compound with a higher acyl chloride in the presence of at least one molecular equivalent of aluminum chloride, an example being the preparation of phenyl pentadecyl ketone [335] by the reaction of palmitoyl chloride with an excess of benzene, which proceeds as follows:

$$C_{15}H_{31}COCl + C_6H_6 \xrightarrow{AlCl_3} C_{15}H_{31}COC_6H_5 + HCl$$

The application of this method to the preparation of the higher alkyl aryl ketones was first extensively studied by Krafft,[336] who described the synthesis of p-tolyl pentadecyl ketone, p-tolyl heptadecyl ketone, m-xylyl pentadecyl ketone, p-methoxyphenyl pentadecyl ketone, p-ethoxyphenyl pentadecyl ketone, and 1,3-dimethoxyphenyl pentadecyl ketone by reaction of the respective acid chlorides and aromatic compounds in the presence of aluminum chloride. Later, Claus and Häfelin [337] obtained phenyl heptadecyl ketone, p-xylyl heptadecyl ketone, m-xylyl heptadecyl ketone, p-tolyl pentadecyl ketone, and mesityl pentadecyl ketone by a similar procedure.

Friedel-Crafts reactions of acylation are essentially catalytic reactions which involve the formation of metallic complexes. Many halides other than aluminum chloride have been shown to be catalytic in such reactions. These include ferric chloride, zinc chloride, stannic chloride, titanium tetrachloride, boron trichloride, and zirconium tetrachloride, and the following decreasing order of activity has been proposed [338] for the more commonly employed halides: $AlCl_3$, $FeCl_3$, $ZnCl_2$, $SnCl_4$, $TiCl_4$, $ZrCl_4$. That such reactions proceed through the formation of metallic complexes was first shown by Perrier [339] and later confirmed by Kohler [340] and by Boeseken,[341] who showed that the acid chloride forms a complex with aluminum chloride, $RCOCl \cdot AlCl_3$, and that this complex acts as an acylating agent. The ketone also forms a complex with the aluminum chloride, $RCOR' \cdot AlCl_3$, which is incapable of promoting further acylation.[342, 343] Hydrolysis of this ketone-aluminum chloride complex yields the desired ketone. Acylation reactions thus involve several steps, as follows:

$$RCOCl + C_6H_6 + AlCl_3 \rightarrow RCOCl \cdot AlCl_3 + C_6H_6 \rightarrow$$

$$RCOC_6H_5 \cdot AlCl_3 + HCl$$

Such reactions differ decidedly from those of alkylation, since in the latter only catalytic amounts of aluminum chloride are necessary, whereas in acylation reactions at least a molecular equivalent of catalyst is required to complete the reaction. Anhydrides and fatty acids also function as acylating agents in the presence of Friedel-Crafts catalysts, the former requiring two moles [343, 344] and the latter three moles [345, 346] of condensing agent. This suggests that such reactions proceed with the initial formation of an acyl chloride, which results from the action of the aluminum chloride or other halide on the anhydride or acid.

When the hydrocarbon to be acylated is a liquid, such as benzene, toluene, or xylene, it is customary to employ an excess of this hydrocarbon as the solvent for the acylation reaction. This is not feasible, however, when the hydrocarbon is a solid at the reaction temperature. In such instances an inert solvent is used, the most common being carbon disulfide or petroleum ether. In many cases reactive solvents may be employed if their activity is below that of the compound to be acylated.

A large number of high molecular weight alkyl aryl ketones have been prepared by Ralston and Christensen,[347] and the synthesis of xenyl heptadecyl ketone by the Friedel-Crafts reaction may be taken as typifying the preparation of such compounds by this method:

A 15.4-gram (0.1 mole) sample of biphenyl was dissolved in 200 cc. carbon disulfide and 30.2 grams (0.1 mole) stearoyl chloride added. This mixture was cooled in ice to approximately 10°C., and 13.3 grams (0.1 mole) aluminum chloride was added slowly over a period of one-half hour with constant stirring. The mixture was then refluxed until no further evolution of hydrochloric acid was observed, and was finally poured upon a mixture of ice and dilute hydrochloric acid to hydrolyze the complex aluminum compound formed. The hydrolyzed mixture was steam-distilled to remove carbon disulfide and complete the hydrolysis, after which the ketone was separated from the water layer by decantation. The ketone was recrystallized from benzene to constant melting point.

This procedure was employed by Ford [348] for the preparation of several xenyl alkyl ketones. It is apparently unsatisfactory for the preparation of alkyl aryl ketones from the higher acyl chlorides and naphthalene or anthracene, the reactions yielding only oily products from which no pure compounds can be isolated.[347] Frequently with Friedel-Crafts reactions involving high molecular

weight acid chlorides and aromatics it will be found that the final
ketone complex is resistant to hydrolysis. In such instances it has
been proposed [349] to conduct the hydrolysis in the presence of a
wetting agent, such as a salt of a high molecular weight amine.
This procedure generally results in rapid and complete hydrolysis
of the ketone complex.

The preparation of the higher alkyl aryl ketones from phenol or
other hydroxy aromatic compounds presents a specific type of
reaction which holds many points of interest. Two general procedures are available for the synthesis of such compounds. Phenol
may be treated directly with an acid chloride and aluminum chloride by a standard Friedel-Crafts procedure; or a phenyl or other
ester may be subjected to a Fries [350] rearrangement, which involves
treating the ester with an active metal halide, the presence of
which transforms the ester into the isomeric alkyl hydroxyaryl
ketone. These two reactions have much in common, it having
been stated that the Friedel-Crafts synthesis involving phenols
often proceeds with the initial formation of phenyl esters. [351] It
has also been suggested [352, 353] that the mechanism of the Fries
rearrangement is a scission of the ester to yield the acyl chloride
followed by acylation of the phenol.

In the acylation of phenol or other substituted aromatics, the
formation of two or more isomeric ketones is theoretically possible.
Thus, when phenol is acylated, *ortho-*, *para-*, or *meta-*hydroxyphenyl
ketones may result. Actually, *meta-*hydroxyphenyl ketones are
not formed, so that the reaction mixture which results either by
the Friedel-Crafts acylation of phenol with acid chlorides or by
the Fries rearrangement of phenyl esters consists of a mixture of
ortho- and *para-*hydroxyphenyl alkyl ketones. A number of studies
have been made of the effect of various factors upon orientation in
the acylation of phenol with the higher acid chlorides and in the
rearrangements of phenyl esters, and these investigations have contributed materially to our understanding of such reactions.

Sandulesco and Girard [354] have shown that phenol reacts with
aluminum chloride to form phenoxyaluminum chloride, C_6H_5O-
$AlCl_2$, and that this reacts with an acid chloride to form ketones.
Since, however, the acid chloride can also form a complex with
aluminum chloride, it is evident that the reaction mechanism is
influenced by the mole proportion of aluminum chloride employed.
In an extensive study of the acylation of phenol with caprylyl

chloride, Ralston, McCorkle, and Bauer [355] showed that the relative yields of o- and p-isomers are quite dependent upon the mole proportion of aluminum chloride. The use of one mole of aluminum chloride, the amount sufficient to form only the $C_6H_5OAlCl_2$ complex, gives a p/o ratio less than unity, whereas the use of two moles, the amount sufficient to form both complexes, gives a p/o ratio much greater than unity. The order of addition of the reactants does not affect the orientation if both complexes are present; however, low temperatures (below 50°) give an orientation characteristic of that complex originally present. In a subsequent study [356] of the rearrangement of phenyl caprylate in the presence of aluminum chloride, it was shown that the products of this reaction are also influenced by the quantity of aluminum chloride employed. Rearrangements in which one mole of aluminum chloride is used involve the initial formation of an ester-aluminum chloride complex, the reaction proceeding as follows:

$$C_6H_5OCC_7H_{15} \rightarrow C_6H_5OAlCl_2 + C_7H_{15}COCl \rightarrow Cl_2AlOC_6H_4COC_7H_{15} + HCl$$
$$\underset{\underset{AlCl_3}{|}}{\overset{\|}{O}}$$

A study of the intermediate stages of this rearrangement showed that an *ortho* orientation is favored in the early stages of the reaction and a *para* orientation in the latter, the p/o ratio increasing as the reaction progresses. Esters may be rearranged by aluminum chloride complexes of ketones or hydroxy ketones, and consequently the molecular amount of ester rearranged is greater than the molecular equivalent of aluminum chloride employed, if the amount of aluminum chloride is less than a molecular proportion. When substantially more than one equivalent of aluminum chloride is used, the p/o ratio is much greater than unity, the following reaction mechanism having been proposed:

$$C_6H_5OCC_7H_{15} + AlCl_3 \rightarrow C_6H_5OAlCl_2 + C_7H_{15}COCl \cdot AlCl_3$$
$$\overset{\|}{O} \cdot AlCl_3$$

The reaction then follows one of two courses:
(I) The phenoxyaluminum dichloride may be acylated, thus:

$$C_6H_5OAlCl_2 + C_7H_{15}COCl \cdot AlCl_3 \rightarrow Cl_2AlOC_6H_4CC_7H_{15} + HCl$$
$$\overset{\|}{O} \cdot AlCl_3$$

(II) The ester may be acylated and this product react with phenoxyaluminum dichloride, thus:

$$C_6H_5OCC_7H_{15} + C_7H_{15}CCl \cdot AlCl_3 \rightarrow C_7H_{15}CC_6H_4OCC_7H_{15} \cdot AlCl_3 + HCl$$

$$C_7H_{15}CC_6H_4OCC_7H_{15} \cdot AlCl_3 + C_6H_5OAlCl_2 \rightarrow 2C_7H_{15}CC_6H_4OAlCl_2 + HCl$$

The ratio of *p*- to *o*-hydroxy ketones obtained during either a Friedel-Crafts acylation of phenol or a rearrangement of phenyl esters is greatly influenced by the solvent and by the acylating agent employed. Of the four solvents which have been investigated [357] (carbon disulfide, nitrobenzene, tetrachloroethane, and petroleum ether), the lowest ratio of *para*- to *ortho*-hydroxy ketones was obtained with carbon disulfide, and the highest with nitrobenzene. The activity of ferric chloride is comparable to that of aluminum chloride in the rearrangement of phenyl esters, and *para*-hydroxy ketone formation is decidedly favored in the presence of this catalyst.[358] Titanium tetrachloride is decidedly less active than ferric chloride, and stannic and zinc chlorides are only weakly catalytic. The chain length does not appear to exert a decided influence upon orientation in the acylation of phenol.[356, 359]

The Grignard method offers a very satisfactory procedure for the synthesis of many of the higher alkyl aryl ketones. Ketones such as α-naphthyl heptadecyl ketone, which are quite difficult to synthesize by acylation reactions, may be obtained in high yields by this procedure. In the application of this method to the synthesis of higher alkyl aryl ketones, either an amide or a nitrile of a higher acid is treated with the magnesium halide of the aromatic hydrocarbon, the resulting complex then being hydrolyzed to obtain the ketone. When the amide is used as the starting material, two moles of the arylmagnesium halide are required, the reaction proceeding by the following steps:

(I) $\quad RCONH_2 + R'MgX \rightarrow RCONHMgX + R'H$

(II) $\quad RCONHMgX + R'MgX \rightarrow \underset{R'}{\overset{R}{>}}C\underset{NHMgX}{\overset{OMgX}{<}} \xrightarrow{2H_2O}$

$$RR'CO + Mg(OH)_2 + MgX_2 + NH_3$$

The preparation of several higher alkyl aryl ketones by the action of Grignard reagents on amides has been described by Ryan and Nolan,[360] who obtained α-naphthyl heptadecyl ketone from stearamide, and phenyl, α-naphthyl, and p-tolyl pentadecyl ketones from palmitamide, by this method. Nitriles require only one mole of arylmagnesium halide, the ketimine which forms yielding a ketone upon acid hydrolysis. The synthesis of a number of higher alkyl aryl ketones by the action of arylmagnesium halides on nitriles has been described,[347] an example being the synthesis of phenoxyphenyl heptadecyl ketone by the action of stearonitrile on phenoxyphenylmagnesium bromide.

Physical Properties of Alkyl Aryl Ketones

With the exception of those alkyl aryl ketones which are liquid at room temperature, the alkyl aryl ketones are waxy solids, retaining their waxlike characteristics even after extensive purification. Many representatives of this class of compounds have been described both in the academic [298, 335, 336, 337, 348, 360, 361, 362, 363, 364] and in the patent literature. The latter group includes phenoxyphenyl alkyl ketones,[365] xenyl alkyl ketones,[366] furyl and dibenzofuryl alkyl ketones,[367] carbazole alkyl ketones,[368] thienyl alkyl ketones,[369] and mixed xylyl heptadecyl ketones.[370]

The reported melting points of a number of the higher alkyl aryl ketones are shown in Table IX.

The higher alkyl aryl ketones are insoluble in water and glycerol. They are very soluble in organic solvents, in some of which they form stiff gels. The solubilities of xenyl heptadecyl ketone in a number of organic solvents [347] are shown in Table X.

The melting points of the p-hydroxyphenones are substantially higher than those of their ortho isomers. Such compounds can readily be identified as their 2,4-dinitrophenylhydrazones. Table XI shows the melting points of some isomeric hydroxyphenones together with the melting points and appearances of their 2,4-dinitrophenylhydrazones.[359]

The o- and p-hydroxyphenones are separated by the preferential solubility of the p-isomers in aqueous alcoholic sodium hydroxide solution.[371] The p-isomers give intense colorations with ferric chloride, whereas the o-isomers give no coloration when treated with this reagent. Ketones have been prepared from the homologs of phenol and also from the di- and trihydroxybenzenes. Klarmann [372] has described the preparation of the higher alkyl aryl ketones from resorcinol, and Karrer and Rosenfeld [361] have prepared several of the higher alkyl ketones of resorcinol and phloroglucinol. The preparation of chaulmoogroylresorcinol [373] and

TABLE IX

Melting Points of Alkyl Aryl Ketones

Ketone	M.P.,°C.	Other Constants
Phenyl heptyl	16.4	b 283.0, d_4^{20} 0.95155
Phenyl undecyl	46	
Phenyl pentadecyl	59 *	b_{15} 250.5–251
Phenyl heptadecyl	59	
Xenyl undecyl	97–98	
Xenyl tridecyl	102–103	
Xenyl pentadecyl	103–104	
Xenyl heptadecyl	108–109	d_{20}^{20} 0.9384
Phenoxyphenyl undecyl	45–46	
Phenoxyphenyl tridecyl	53.5–54.5	
Phenoxyphenyl heptadecyl	68	
m-Xylyl heptadecyl	39	
p-Xylyl heptadecyl	57	
m-Xylyl pentadecyl	37	b_{15} 268–269
p-Methoxyphenyl undecyl	60	
p-Methoxyphenyl pentadecyl	70.5	b_{15} 279–280
p-Methoxyphenyl heptadecyl	76	
p-Ethoxyphenyl pentadecyl	69	
p-Methylxenyl heptadecyl	105–106	
p-Chloroxenyl heptadecyl	96–97	
p-Methylphenoxyphenyl heptadecyl	77–78	
p-Tolyl pentadecyl	60	
p-Tolyl heptadecyl	67	
2-Furyl undecyl	....	b_5 165–166
2-Furyl heptadecyl	56–57	
5-Methyl-2-furyl heptadecyl	68–69	
2-Dibenzofuryl undecyl	74–75	
2-Dibenzofuryl heptadecyl	83–84	
2-Lauroylcarbazole	101–102	
2-Stearoylcarbazole	105–106	
2,8-Dilauroylcarbazole	176	
2,8-Dimyristoylcarbazole	169	
2,8-Dipalmitoylcarbazole	162	
2,8-Distearoylcarbazole	161–162	
2-Lauroylthiophene	....	b_4 190–195, n_D^{25} 1.5019, d_{25}^{25} 0.9632
2-Myristoylthiophene	....	b_4 205–210, n_D^{25} 1.4961, d_{25}^{25} 0.9506
2-Stearoylthiophene	48–49	
3-Stearoyldibenzothiophene	69–70	
α-Naphthyl undecyl	....	b_5 240–245
α-Naphthyl heptadecyl	53–54	

* Probably high.

TABLE X

SOLUBILITIES OF XENYL HEPTADECYL KETONE

Solvent	Temp.,°C.	Solubility g./100 cc.
Ethanol	27.0	0.082
Glycerol	50.0	0.000
Acetone	15.0	0.202
	24.0	0.400
1-Butanol	9.0	0.40
	45.0	1.00
	70.5	8.00
Benzene	26.0	4.00
	50.5	24.02
	61.0	80.04
Toluene	31.0	4.00
	48.0	20.00
	65.5	80.00
Carbon tetrachloride	24.0	4.01
	52.0	30.02
	80.0	80.00
Chloroform	20.0	8.0
	43.0	32.0
	54.0	64.0
Kerosene	30.0	1.0
	47.5	4.0
	75.0	48.0
Turpentine	22.0	1.0
	41.5	4.0
	73.5	60.0

TABLE XI

MELTING POINTS OF HYDROXYPHENONES

Phenone	M.P.,°C.	2,4-Dinitrophenyl-hydrazone Color, M.P.,°C.
o-Hydroxycaprylo	b1 97–99	Orange, 140–141
p-Hydroxycaprylo	62.5–63.5	Red, 176–178
o-Hydroxylauro	44–45.5	Orange, 92–93
p-Hydroxylauro	71–72	Dark red, 150–151
o-Hydroxymyristo	52–55	Orange, 92–92.5
p-Hydroxymyristo	78–80	Dark red, 142–143
o-Hydroxypalmito	54–56	Yellowish orange, 94–95
p-Hydroxypalmito	84.5–85	Dark red, 141–142
o-Hydroxystearo	64–66	Yellow, 96–97
p-Hydroxystearo	87–89	Dark red, 139.5–140

hexanoylresorcinol [374] has been described. The acylation of styrene,[375] indene,[376] coumarones,[377] and various coal-tar distillates [378, 379] has been described in the patent literature, and the use of such products as modifying agents for resins has been studied.[380, 381] The acylation of a number of dyes with high molecular weight acyl chlorides in the presence of aluminum chloride or other Friedel-Crafts catalysts yields oil-soluble products.[382]

Both the high molecular weight dialkyl ketones and the alkyl aryl ketones form monomolecular films on water, and such films show a marked correlation between the structure of the ketone and the type of film formed. Films of methyl heptadecyl ketone are less compressible than those of stearone. A comparison of the films of xenyl heptadecyl ketone and phenoxyphenyl heptadecyl ketone shows that the areas occupied by the latter are much greater at low compressions, owing to the hydrophylic nature of the ether oxygen. At higher compressions, the areas occupied by these two ketones become approximately identical.[280]

Chemical Properties of Alkyl Aryl Ketones

The higher alkyl aryl ketones possess chemical properties very similar to those previously described for the dialkyl ketones. Clemmensen reduction yields alkyl aryl hydrocarbons, the reduction of laurophenone, for example, giving dodecylbenzene, m.p. −7°, b_{13} 179–180°,[383] and the reduction of p-hydroxylaurophenone yielding p-dodecylphenol.[363] Mikeska and Cohen [364] have recently prepared a number of high molecular weight alkyl aryl hydrocarbons by reduction of the corresponding alkyl aryl ketones. Phenyl heneicosyl ketone, m.p. 73–76°, gives docosylbenzene when reduced by the Clemmensen method. Heneicosyl naphthyl ketone, m.p. 67–69°, yields docosylnaphthalene, m.p. 56–58°, when similarly treated.

The action of alkyl aryl ketones with Grignard reagents yields tertiary carbinols, the reduction of which gives hydrocarbons. Thus, stearophenone and butylmagnesium chloride yield 5-phenyl-5-docosanol,[384] the reduction of which gives 5-phenyldocosane.

The alkyl phenyl ketones are split by treatment with yellow ammonium sulfide to yield amides, the reaction being accomplished by heating the ketones with a solution of yellow ammonium sulfide under pressure at 200–220° for five or six hours. The yield of amide decreases with increase in the length of the alkyl group, phenyl methyl ketone giving a 49.6% yield of phenylacetamide and 13.5% of phenylacetic acid, whereas phenyl pentadecyl ketone gives no amide or acid of the same carbon content as the original ketone.[385]

Advantage has been taken of the presence of the aryl group in the alkyl aryl ketones for the preparation of many types of derivatives. The aryl group may easily be sulfonated for the preparation of water-soluble compounds.[386, 387] Amino ketones are obtained by the action of ammonia or amines on halo-substituted ketones, p-chlorostearophenone yielding p-dimethylaminostearophenone when treated with dimethylamine.[388, 389] Treatment of p-dimethylaminostearophenone with dimethyl sulfate yields p-stearoylphenyltrimethylammonium methosulfate.

Many uses have been suggested for the higher alkyl aryl ketones and allied compounds. Hydroxyphenyl alkyl ketones and related compounds have been suggested as disinfecting agents.[390] The higher alkyl aryl ketones have been added to lubricating oils,[391, 392, 393] and chlorinated alkyl aryl ketones have been proposed as lubricating oil addends.[394] The higher alkyl aryl ketones are useful in waxing and polishing compositions,[395] and have been proposed as insulating and dielectric materials for electrical apparatus.[396]

References

1. Albitskiĭ, *J. Russ. Phys. Chem. Soc.*, **31**, 103 (1899).
2. Holde and Smelkus, *Ber.*, **53B**, 1889 (1920).
3. Hólde and Tacke, *ibid.*, **53B**, 1898 (1920).
4. Grün and Schönfeld, *Z. angew. Chem.*, **29**, 37 (1916).
5. Holde and Wilke, *ibid.*, **35**, 105 (1922).
6. Holde and Tacke, *Chem.-Ztg.*, **45**, 949 (1921).
7. Holde, Ripper, and Zadek, *Ber.*, **57B**, 103 (1924).
8. Holde and Gentner, *ibid.*, **58B**, 1418 (1925).
9. Autenrieth, *ibid.*, **34**, 168 (1901).
10. Holde and Gentner, *ibid.*, **58B**, 1067 (1925).
11. Deutsche Gold- und Silber-Scheideanstalt vorm. Roessler, Fr. Patent 784,458 (1935).
12. Oxley and Thomas, U. S. Patent 2,246,599 (1941).
13. Malm and Fisher, U. S. Patent 2,221,026 (1940).
14. Rankov, *Ann. univ. Sofia, II, Livre Faculté phys.-math.* 2, **33**, 221 (1937) [*C.A.*, **32**, 3335 (1938)].
15. Fournier, *Bull. soc. chim.* [4], **5**, 920 (1909).
16. Gsell, *Chem.-Ztg.*, **31**, 100 (1907).
17. Gerhardt, *Ann.*, **87**, 57 (1853).
18. Villier, *Ber.*, **9**, 1932 (1876).
19. Krafft and Rosiny, *ibid.*, **33**, 3576 (1900).

20. Michael, *ibid.*, **34**, 918 (1901).
21. Whitby, *J. Chem. Soc.*, 1458 (1926).
22. Hentschel, *Ber.*, **17**, 1284 (1884).
23. Holde and Schmidt, *Z. angew. Chem.*, **35**, 502 (1922).
24. Dreyfus, Fr. Patent 478,951 (1916).
25. Dreyfus, Fr. Patent 20,261 (1917).
26. Kessler, Ger. Patent 132,605 (1900).
27. Goldschmidt, Brit. Patent 25,433 (1908).
28. Denham and Woodhouse, *J. Chem. Soc.*, **103**, 1861 (1913).
29. Chiozza, *Ann.*, **86**, 259 (1853).
30. Hurd and Dull, *J. Am. Chem. Soc.*, **54**, 3427 (1932).
31. Williams and Krynitsky, *Organic Syntheses*, **21**, 13 (1941).
32. Williams and Hurd, *J. Org. Chem.*, **5**, 122 (1940).
33. Adams, Wirth, and French, *J. Am. Chem. Soc.*, **40**, 424 (1918).
34. Adams and Ulich, *ibid.*, **42**, 599 (1920).
35. Holde, *Chem.-Ztg.*, **44**, 477 (1920).
36. Bleyberg and Ulrich, *Ber.*, **64B**, 2504 (1931).
37. Lewis, *J. Chem. Soc.*, 32 (1940).
38. Wallace and Copenhaver, *J. Am. Chem. Soc.*, **63**, 699 (1941).
39. Krafft and Tritschler, *Ber.*, **33**, 3580 (1900).
40. Holde and Rietz, *ibid.*, **57B**, 99 (1924).
41. Holde and Weill, *Chem. Umschau*, **30**, 205 (1923).
42. Voerman, *Rec. trav. chim.*, **23**, 265 (1904).
43. Farmer and Kracovski, *J. Chem. Soc.*, 680 (1927).
44. Hill, *J. Am. Chem. Soc.*, **52**, 4110 (1930).
45. Blanc, *Compt. rend.*, **144**, 1356 (1907).
46. Hill and Carothers, *J. Am. Chem. Soc.*, **54**, 1569 (1932).
47. Verkade, *Rec. trav. chim.*, **35**, 299 (1915).
48. Kilpatrick and Kilpatrick, *J. Am. Chem. Soc.*, **52**, 1418 (1930).
49. Béhal, *Ann. chim. phys.* [7], **19**, 274 (1900).
50. Ralston and Reck, *J. Org. Chem.*, **11**, 624 (1946).
51. Ralston and Hoerr, *ibid.*, **7**, 546 (1942).
52. Henkel & Cie. G.m.b.H., Fr. Patent 751,571 (1933).
53. Henkel & Cie. G.m.b.H., Brit. Patent 398,064 (1933).
54. Lehninger, *J. Biol. Chem.*, **162**, 333 (1946).
55. Holde and Gentner, *Ber.*, **58B**, 1424 (1925).
56. Mannich and Nadelmann, *ibid.*, **63B**, 796 (1930).
57. Henkel & Cie. G.m.b.H., Ger. Patent 622,649 (1935).
58. Rubidge and Qua, *J. Am. Chem. Soc.*, **36**, 732 (1914).
59. Hill, *ibid.*, **54**, 4105 (1932).
60. Noller with Adams, *ibid.*, **46**, 1889 (1924).
61. Deutsche Kunstseiden-Studienges. G.m.b.H., Ger. Patent 623,276 (1935).
62. I. G. Farbenind. A.-G., Brit. Patent 451,300 (1936).
63. Farb- und Gerbstoff-Werke Carl Flesch, Jr., Fr. Patent 721,070 (1931).
64. Krafft and Stauffer, *Ber.*, **15**, 1728 (1882).
65. Krafft, *ibid.*, **16**, 3018 (1883).
66. Krafft and Bürger, *ibid.*, **17**, 1378 (1884).
67. Täufel and Künkele, *Fettchem. Umschau*, **42**, 27 (1935).
68. Bömer and Stather, *Fette u. Seifen*, **44**, 29 (1937).

69. Börner and Kappeller, *ibid.*, **44**, 340 (1937).
70. McCutcheon, *Can. J. Research*, **16B**, 158 (1938).
71. Cahn, U. S. Patent 2,282,320 (1942).
72. Ralston, McCorkle, and Vander Wal, U. S. Patent 2,262,431 (1941).
73. Sulzberger, *Z. angew. Chem.*, **27**, 40 (1914).
74. Noller and Dannerot, *J. Am. Chem. Soc.*, **56**, 1563 (1934).
75. Verkade, *Rec. trav. chim.*, **62**, 393 (1943).
76. Bardan, *Bull. soc. chim.* [5], **1**, 141 (1934).
77. Daubert, Fricke, and Longenecker, *J. Am. Chem. Soc.*, **65**, 2142 (1943).
78. Ralston and Selby, *ibid.*, **61**, 1019 (1939).
79. Hoffmann-La Roche & Co., Ger. Patent 232,459 (1910).
80. Abderhalden and Hirsch, *Z. physiol. Chem.*, **75**, 38 (1911).
81. Black and Overley, *J. Am. Chem. Soc.*, **61**, 3051 (1939).
82. McMaster and Ahmann, *ibid.*, **50**, 145 (1928).
83. Waser, *Helv. Chim. Acta*, **8**, 117 (1925).
84. Durrans and Boake, Roberts & Co., Brit. Patent 128,270 (1917).
85. Rauter, *Ann.*, **270**, 235 (1892).
86. Montonna, *J. Am. Chem. Soc.*, **49**, 2114 (1927).
87. Hochstetter, Ger. Patent 283,896 (1913).
88. Hochstetter, Ger. Patent 284,617 (1913).
89. I. G. Farbenind. A.-G., Brit. Patent 515,963 (1939); Ger. Patent 687,670 (1940).
90. Soc. pour l'ind. chim. à Bâle, Brit. Patent 540,096 (1941).
91. Prat and Étienne, *Bull. soc. chim.* [5], **11**, 30 (1944).
92. Averill, Roche, and King, *J. Am. Chem. Soc.*, **51**, 866 (1929).
93. Wood, Jackson, Baldwin, and Longenecker, *ibid.*, **66**, 287 (1944).
94. Bauer, *Oil & Soap*, **23**, 1 (1946).
95. Bistrzycki and Landtwing, *Ber.*, **42**, 4720 (1909).
96. Hopwood and Weizmann, *Proc. Chem. Soc.*, **26**, 69 (1910); **27**, 55 (1911); *J. Chem. Soc.*, **99**, 571 (1911); Hopwood, *Proc. Chem. Soc.*, **29**, 345 (1913).
97. Kirrmann, *Ann. chim.* [10], **11**, 223 (1929).
98. v. Auwers and Wegener, *J. prakt. Chem.* [2], **106**, 226 (1923).
99. Rosenmund, *Ber.*, **51**, 585 (1918).
100. Grignard and Mingasson, *Compt. rend.*, **185**, 1173 (1927).
101. Escourrou, *Bull. soc. chim.* [5], **6**, 1173 (1939).
102. Fröschl and Maier, *Monatsh.*, **59**, 256 (1932).
103. Deutsche Hydrierwerke A.-G., Brit. Patent 522,033 (1940).
104. Stoddard and Kokatnur, U. S. Patent 1,718,609 (1929).
105. Fichter and Buess, *Helv. Chim. Acta*, **18**, 445 (1935).
106. Mailhe, *Bull. soc. chim.* [4], **23**, 380 (1918).
107. Bondi and Eissler, *Biochem. Z.*, **23**, 499 (1910).
108. Abderhalden and Funk, *Z. physiol. Chem.*, **65**, 61 (1910).
109. Izar and Di Zuattro, *Biochem. Z.*, **59**, 226 (1914).
110. I. G. Farbenind. A.-G., Brit. Patent 435,481 (1935).
111. Orthner and Meyer, U. S. Patent 2,041,265 (1936).
112. Sommer, U. S. Patent 2,015,912 (1935).
113. Chemische Fabrik Grünau Landshoff & Meyer A.-G., Brit. Patent 413,016 (1934).
114. Hess and Messmer, *Ber.*, **54B**, 499 (1921).

115. I. G. Farbenind. A.-G., Fr. Patent 39,893 (1931).
116. I. G. Farbenind. A.-G., Ger. Patent 652,410 (1937).
117. Steindorff, Daimler, and Platz, U. S. Patent 1,916,776 (1933).
118. I. G. Farbenind. A.-G., Ger. Patent 673,731 (1939).
119. Wrenshall, U. S. Patent 1,926,506 (1933).
120. Santillan and West, *Philippine J. Sci.*, **40**, 493 (1929).
121. Lieber, U. S. Patent 2,268,409 (1941).
122. Shorygin and Osipova, *Sintezy Dushistykh Veshchestv, Sbornik Statei*, 246 (1939); Bryusova, Shagalova, and Novikova, *ibid.*, 247 (1939) [*C.A.*, **36**, 3781 (1942)].
123. Hannemann, *Deutsche Parfümerie-Ztg.*, **9**, No. 7/8, 7 (1923); *Chimie & industrie*, **11**, 941 (1924).
124. Marcelet, *Compt. rend.*, **206**, 529 (1938).
125. Späth and Kesztler, *Ber.*, **67B**, 1496 (1934).
126. Ruzicka and Schinz, *Helv. Chim. Acta*, **17**, 1592 (1934).
127. Clemente, *Ind. sapon.*, **27**, 51 (1927) [*C.A.*, **21**, 2355 (1927)].
128. Krafft, *Ber.*, **13**, 1413 (1880).
129. H. Th. Böhme A.-G., Brit. Patent 382,929 (1932).
130. Zaar, *J. prakt. Chem.* [2], **132**, 163, 169 (1932).
131. I. G. Farbenind. A.-G., Brit. Patent 414,148 (1934).
132. Nametkin and Khol'mer, *Sintezy Dushistykh Veshchestv, Sbornik Statei*, 55 (1939) [*C.A.*, **36**, 3629 (1942)].
133. Nametkin and Shagalova, *ibid.*, 274 (1939) [*C.A.*, **36**, 3781 (1942)].
134. Osipova, *Masloboino Zhirovoe Delo*, **11**, 378 (1935).
135. I. G. Farbenind. A.-G., Fr. Patent 750,467 (1933); Ger. Patent 660,735 (1938).
136. Ralston and Jackson, U. S. Patent 2,033,539 (1936).
137. Ralston and Vander Wal, Brit. Patent 509,203 (1939); U. S. Patent 2,145,801 (1939).
138. Moureu and Mignonac, *Compt. rend.*, **170**, 258 (1920).
139. Aleksandrova, *J. Applied Chem. (U.S.S.R.)*, **10**, 105 (1937).
140. Shagalova, *Masloboino Zhirovoe Delo*, **11**, 452 (1935).
141. Bruylants, *Bull. soc. chim. Belg.*, **41**, 333 (1932).
142. Babcock and Werntz, U. S. Patent 2,123,520 (1938).
143. Halasz, *Compt. rend.*, **209**, 1000 (1939).
144. Lazier, U. S. Patent 2,178,761 (1939).
145. Isikawa and Miyata, *Science Repts. Tokyo Bunrika Daigaku*, **A3**, 257, (1939) [*C.A.*, **34**, 981 (1940)].
146. Fischer, Düll, and Ertel, *Ber.*, **65B**, 1467 (1932).
147. Harries, Ger. Patent 321,567 (1918).
148. Kobata, *J. Agr. Chem. Soc. Japan*, **11**, 709 (1935).
149. Hsing and Chang, *J. Am. Chem. Soc.*, **61**, 3589 (1939).
150. Bergmann, *ibid.*, **62**, 3255 (1940).
151. Grundmann, Bär, and Trischmann, *Ann.*, **524**, 31 (1936).
152. Hershberg, *Helv. Chim. Acta*, **17**, 351 (1934).
153. Bussy, *J. Pharm. Chim.* [3], **8**, 321 (1845).
154. Krafft, *Ber.*, **10**, 2034 (1877).
155. Nametkin and Shagalova, *Sintezy Dushistykh Veshchestv, Sbornik Statei*, 261 (1939) [*C.A.*, **36**, 3782 (1942)].

156. Fanto, U. S. Patent 1,886,538 (1932).
157. Bruson and Robinson, U. S. Patent 1,889,348 (1932).
158. Le Sueur, *J. Chem. Soc.*, **85**, 827 (1904).
159. Blaise, *Compt. rend.*, **138**, 697 (1904); *Bull. soc. chim.* [3], **31**, 483 (1904).
160. Bagard, *Bull. soc. chim.* [4], **1**, 346 (1907).
161. Le Sueur, *J. Chem. Soc.*, **87**, 1888 (1905).
162. Bagard, *Bull. soc. chim.* [4], **1**, 307 (1907).
163. Darzens and Lévy, *Compt. rend.*, **196**, 348 (1933).
164. Darzens, *ibid.*, **195**, 884 (1932).
165. Darzens and Lévy, *ibid.*, **196**, 184 (1933).
166. Smol'yaninova, *Sintezy Dushistykh Veshchestv, Sbornik Statei*, 81 (1939) [*C.A.*, **36**, 3782 (1942)].
167. Bachman, *Organic Syntheses*, Coll. Vol. 2, Blatt, editor, p. 323, John Wiley & Sons, New York (1943).
168. Stephen, *J. Chem. Soc.*, **127**, 1874 (1925).
169. Williams, *J. Am. Chem. Soc.*, **61**, 2248 (1939).
170. Sah and Ma, *J. Chinese Chem. Soc.*, **2.** 32 (1934).
171. Sah and Ma, *ibid.*, **2**, 40 (1934).
172. Sah and Lei, *ibid.*, **2**, 167 (1934).
173. Lei, Sah, and Shih, *ibid.*, **3**, 246 (1935).
174. Chen, *ibid.*, **3**, 251 (1935).
175. Sun and Sah, *Science Repts. Natl. Tsing Hua Univ.* [A], **2**, 359 (1934) [*C.A.*, **29**, 466 (1935)].
176. Sah and Kao, *ibid.* [A], **3**, 461 (1936) [*C.A.*, **31**, 3825 (1937)].
177. Sah and Han, *ibid.* [A], **3**, 469 (1936) [*C.A.*, **31**, 3825 (1937)].
178. Chen and Sah, *J. Chinese Chem. Soc.*, **4**, 62 (1936).
179. Kao, Tao, Kao, and Sah, *ibid.*, **4**, 69 (1936).
180. Sah and Chiang, *ibid.*, **4**, 496 (1936).
181. Eastwood and Snow, *Proc. Roy. Soc. (London)*, **149A**, 434 (1935).
182. Bruylants, *Ber.*, **8**, 414 (1875).
183. v. Braun and Manz, *ibid.*, **67B**, 1696 (1934).
184. Shorigin, Issaguljanz, and Gussewa, *ibid.*, **66B**, 1431 (1933).
185. Carbide & Carbon Chemicals Corp., Fr. Patent 786,734 (1935).
186. Carbide & Carbon Chemicals Corp., Fr. Patent 789,406 (1935).
187. I. G. Farbenind. A.-G., Fr. Patent 776,517 (1935).
188. Perkin, *Ber.*, **16**, 210 (1883).
189. D'Ans and Kneip, *ibid.*, **48**, 1136 (1915).
190. Toussaint, Can. Patent 383,687 (1939).
191. Baeyer, *Ber.*, **30**, 1962 (1897).
192. v. Braun and Keller, *ibid.*, **66B**, 215 (1933).
193. Ponzio, *J. prakt. Chem.* [2], **53**, 431 (1896).
194. Delépine and Bonnet, *Compt. rend.*, **149**, 39 (1909).
195. Krafft, *Ber.*, **23**, 2360 (1890).
196. Reichstein, Ammann, and Trivelli, *Helv. Chim. Acta*, **15,** 261 (1932).
197. v. Braun and Kochendörfer, *Ber.*, **56B**, 2172 (1923).
198. van Beresteyn, *Bull. soc. chim. Belg.*, **25**, 293 (1911).
199. Schröder, *Ber.*, **4**, 400 (1871).
200. Bucherer and Grolée, *ibid.*, **39,** 1224 (1906).
201. Albert, *ibid.*, **49**, 1382 (1916).

202. I. G. Farbenind. A.-G., Fr. Patent 755,143 (1933).
203. Zaar, *Ber. Schimmel & Co. A.-G.*, 299 (1929) [*C.A.*, **24**, 2107 (1930)].
204. Johnson, *J. Am. Chem. Soc.*, **61**, 2485 (1939).
205. Anon., *Ann. Rept. Essential Oils, Synthetic Perfumes, &c., Schimmel & Co.*, 71 (1933) [*C.A.*, **30**, 3774 (1936)].
206. Willfang, *Ber.*, **74B**, 145 (1941).
207. Rotbart, *Ann. chim.* [11], **1**, 439 (1934).
208. Bruylants, *Ber.*, **8**, 406 (1875).
209. Béhal, *Bull. soc. chim.* [2], **47**, 33 (1887).
210. Nametkin, Isagulyants, and Eliseeva, *Sintezy Dushistykh Veshchestv, Sbornik Statei*, 281 (1939) [*C.A.*, **36**, 3783 (1942)].
211. Dworzak and Enenkel, *Monatsh.*, **50**, 449 (1928).
212. Kirrmann, *Compt. rend.*, **184**, 1463 (1927).
213. Kirrmann, *ibid.*, **185**, 1482 (1927).
214. Helferich and Malkomes, *Ber.*, **55B**, 702 (1922).
215. Helferich and Köster, *ibid.*, **56B**, 2088 (1923).
216. Helferich and Schäfer, *ibid.*, **57B**, 1911 (1924).
217. I. G. Farbenind. A.-G., Ger. Patent 624,899 (1936).
218. Cadwell, U. S. Patent 1,988,438 (1935).
219. Penfold and Grant, *J. Proc. Roy. Soc. N.S. Wales*, **60**, 167 (1926).
220. Houben, *Ber.*, **35**, 3587 (1902).
221. St. Pfau, *Helv. Chim. Acta*, **15**, 1267 (1932).
222. Chibnall, Piper, el Mangouri, Williams, and Iyengar, *Biochem. J.*, **31**, 1981 (1937).
223. Jacobson, *J. Am. Chem. Soc.*, **33**, 2048 (1911).
224. Derx, *Verslag Akad. Wetenschappen Amsterdam*, **33**, 545 (1925).
225. Reynolds and Hopkins, *Oil & Soap*, **15**, 310 (1938).
226. Stärkle, *Biochem. Z.*, **151**, 371 (1924).
227. Täufel, Thaler, and Löweneck, *Fettchem. Umschau*, **43**, 1 (1936).
228. Täufel, Thaler, and Martinez, *Margarine Ind.*, **26**, 37 (1933).
229. Schmalfuss, Werner, and Gehrke, *ibid.*, **26**, 87 (1933).
230. Schmidt, *Ber.*, **5**, 597 (1872).
231. Krafft, *ibid.*, **15**, 1711 (1882).
232. Breuer and Weinmann, *Monatsh.*, **67**, 42 (1936).
233. Araki, *Mem. Coll. Sci. Kyoto Imp. Univ.* [A], **16**, 137 (1933) [*C.A.*, **27**, 4212 (1933)].
234. Kino, *J. Soc. Chem. Ind., Japan*, **40**, S.b. 437 (1937).
235. Kenner and Morton, *Ber.*, **72B**, 452 (1939).
236. H. Th. Böhme A.-G., Brit. Patent 385,551 (1932).
237. Neunhoeffer and Paschke, *Ber.*, **72B**, 919 (1939).
238. Hébert, *Bull. soc. chim.* [3], **29**, 316 (1903).
239. Easterfield and Taylor, *J. Chem. Soc.*, **99**, 2298 (1911).
240. Grün, Ulbrich, and Krczil, *Z. angew. Chem.*, **39**, 421 (1926).
241. Kino, *J. Soc. Chem. Ind., Japan*, **40**, S.b. 194, 311 (1937).
242. Tanaka, Kobayashi, and Fukushima, *ibid.*, **36**, S.b. 311 (1933).
243. Kipping, *J. Chem. Soc.*, **57**, 532, 980 (1890); **63**, 452 (1893).
244. Tressler, U. S. Patent 1,941,640 (1934).
245. Giordani and Negro, *Atti congr. intern. chim.*, *10th Congr., Rome*, **3**, 189 (1939).

246. Kistler, Swann, and Appel, *Ind. Eng. Chem.*, **26**, 388 (1934).
247. Swann, Appel, and Kistler, *ibid.*, **26**, 1014 (1934).
248. Wortz, U. S. Patent 2,108,156 (1938).
249. Krafft, *Ber.*, **12**, 1668 (1879).
250. Morgan and Holmes, *J. Soc. Chem. Ind.*, **44**, 108T (1925).
251. Morgan and Holmes, *ibid.*, **44**, 491T (1925).
252. Popoff, *Ber.*, **8**, 1683 (1875).
253. Naldi, Fr. Patent 847,753 (1939).
254. Pickard and Kenyon, *Proc. Chem. Soc.*, **27**, 312 (1911).
255. Ruzicka, Stoll, and Schinz, *Helv. Chim. Acta*, **11**, 670 (1928).
256. I. G. Farbenind. A.-G., Fr. Patent 740,494 (1932).
257. Schmidt and Huttner, U. S. Patent 1,988,021 (1935).
258. Dosios and Leucaditis, *Compt. rend.*, **184**, 1458 (1927).
259. Holleman and Koolhaas, *Rec. trav. chim.*, **58**, 666 (1939).
260. Bayer & Co., Ger. Patent 256,622 (1911).
261. Aschan, *Ber.*, **45**, 1603 (1912).
262. Day, Kon, and Stevenson, *J. Chem. Soc.*, **117**, 639 (1920).
263. Vogel, *ibid.*, 2032 (1928).
264. Blanc, *Bull. soc. chim.* [4], **3**, 778 (1908).
265. Ruzicka and Brugger, *Helv. Chim. Acta*, **9**, 389 (1926).
266. Ruzicka, Brugger, Pfeiffer, Schinz, and Stoll, *ibid.*, **9**, 499 (1926).
267. Ruzicka, *ibid.*, **9**, 715 (1926).
268. Ruzicka, Brugger, Seidel, and Schinz, *ibid.*, **11**, 496 (1928).
269. Ruzicka, Stoll, and Schinz, *ibid.*, **11**, 670 (1928).
270. Ruzicka, Stoll, Scherrer, Schinz, and Seidel, *ibid.*, **15**, 1459 (1932).
271. Harries and Tank, *Ber.*, **40**, 4555 (1907).
272. Ruzicka, U. S. Patent 1,673,093 (1928).
273. M. Naef et Cie., Brit. Patents 235,540 (1924); 251,188 (1925).
274. Dakin, *J. Biol. Chem.*, **4**, 77, 91 (1908).
275. Dakin, *ibid.*, **4**, 227 (1908).
276. Dakin, *Am. Chem. J.*, **44**, 41 (1910).
277. Bertrand, *Bull. soc. chim.* [3], **15**, 764 (1896).
278. Blaise and Koehler, *Compt. rend.*, **148**, 489 (1909).
279. Blaise and Koehler, *Bull. soc. chim.* [4], **5**, 681 (1909).
280. Hoffman, Ralston, and Ziegler, *J. Phys. Chem.*, **43**, 301 (1939).
281. Lévy and Wellisch, *Bull. soc. chim.* [4], **45**, 930 (1929).
282. Petrov, Karasev, and Cheltzova, *Compt. rend. acad. sci. U.R.S.S.* [N.S.], **4**, 31 (1935); *Bull. soc. chim.* [5], **3**, 169 (1936).
283. McElvain, *J. Am. Chem. Soc.*, **51**, 3124 (1929).
284. Briese and McElvain, *ibid.*, **55**, 1697 (1933).
285. Garland, Hoerr, Pool, and Ralston, *J. Org. Chem.*, **8**, 344 (1943).
286. Spielman and Schmidt, *J. Am. Chem. Soc.*, **59**, 2009 (1937).
287. Archibald and Beamer, U. S. Patent 2,028,267 (1936).
288. Murray and Cleveland, *J. Am. Chem. Soc.*, **63**, 1363 (1941).
289. Bouveault and Locquin, *Bull. soc. chim.* [3], **35**, 629 (1906).
290. Corson, Benson, and Goodwin, *J. Am. Chem. Soc.*, **52**, 3988 (1930).
291. Scheibler and Emden, *Ann.*, **434**, 265 (1923).
292. Snell and McElvain, *J. Am. Chem. Soc.*, **53**, 750 (1931).
293. Hansley, *ibid.*, **57**, 2303 (1935).

294. Kipping, *J. Chem. Soc.*, **57**, 980 (1890).
295. Furukawa, *Sci. Papers Inst. Phys. Chem. Research Tokyo*, **20**, 71 (1933).
296. Ubbelohde and Oldham, *Nature*, **42**, 74 (1938).
297. Oldham and Ubbelohde, *Trans. Faraday Soc.*, **35**, 328 (1939).
298. Deffet, *Bull. soc. chim. Belg.*, **40**, 385 (1931).
299. Cowan, Jeffery, and Vogel, *J. Chem. Soc.*, 171 (1940).
300. Wolf and Lederle, *Physik. Z.*, **29**, 948 (1928).
301. Müller, *Proc. Roy. Soc. (London)*, **A158**, 403 (1937).
302. Morgan and Yager, *Ind. Eng. Chem.*, **32**, 1519 (1940).
303. Cole, *J. Chem. Phys.*, **9**, 251 (1941).
304. Milone, *Gazz. chim. ital.*, **64**, 876 (1934).
305. Thoms and Mannich, *Ber.*, **36**, 2544 (1903).
306. Hess and Bappert, *Ann.*, **441**, 151 (1925).
307. Pickard and Kenyon, *J. Chem. Soc.*, **99**, 45 (1911); **103**, 1923 (1913).
308. Verley, *Bull. soc. chim.* [4], **37**, 871 (1925).
309. Clemmensen, *Ber.*, **46**, 1837 (1913); **47**, 51, 681 (1914).
310. Francis, King, and Willis, *J. Chem. Soc.*, 999 (1937).
311. Krafft, *Ber.*, **15**, 1711 (1882).
312. Sabatier and Senderens, *Compt. rend.*, **137**, 301, 1025 (1903).
313. Mailhe, *Bull. soc. chim.* [4], **15**, 327 (1914).
314. Grün, *Z. angew. Chem.*, **39**, 1037 (1926).
315. Haller and Lassieur, *Compt. rend.*, **150**, 1013 (1910).
316. McCall, U. S. Patent 2,108,133 (1938).
317. Blumenfeld, U. S. Patent 2,158,040 (1939).
318. Tressler, U. S. Patent 1,979,586 (1934).
319. Carbide & Carbon Chemicals Corp., Fr. Patents 789,967, 799,037 (1936).
320. Wickert, U. S. Patent 2,088,016 (1937).
321. I. G. Farbenind. A.-G., Brit. Patent 384,314 (1932).
322. Lommel and Schröter, U. S. Patent 1,989,325 (1935).
323. Mel'nikov and Rokitskaya, *J. Gen. Chem. (U.S.S.R.)*, **10**, 1713 (1940).
324. Sato, *J. Soc. Chem. Ind., Japan*, **30**, S.b. 74 (1927); Sato and Ito, *ibid.*, **30**, S.b. 75 (1927).
325. Staudinger and Kern, *Ber.*, **66B**, 373 (1933).
326. Grignard and Colonge, *Bull. soc. chim. Romania*, **15**, 5 (1933).
327. v. Reibnitz and Neber, U. S. Patent 2,265,194 (1941).
328. Maehlmann, *Arb. Pharm. Inst. Univ. Berlin*, **11**, 107 (1914).
329. Tressler and Schade, U. S. Patent 1,941,639 (1934).
330. Guenther and Holsten, U. S. Patent 2,037,974 (1936).
331. Oranienburger Chemische Fabrik A.-G., Ger. Patent 658,650 (1938).
332. Keppler and Schroeter, U. S. Patent 2,195,088 (1940).
333. Schowalter, Haussmann, Neber, Keppler, and Schroeter, U. S. Patent 2,218,660 (1940).
334. Compagnie nationale de matières colorantes et manufactures de produits chimiques du nord réunies établissement Kuhlmann, Fr. Patent 785,561 (1935).
335. Krafft, *Ber.*, **19**, 2982 (1886).
336. Krafft, *ibid.*, **21**, 2265 (1888).
337. Claus and Häfelin, *J. prakt. Chem.* [2], **54**, 391 (1896).
338. Calloway, *Chem. Rev.*, **17**, 327 (1935).

339. Perrier, *Ber.*, **33**, 815 (1900).
340. Kohler, *Am. Chem. J.*, **24**, 385 (1900).
341. Boeseken, *Rec. trav. chim.*, **39**, 623 (1920).
342. Olivier, *Chem. Weekblad*, **11**, 372 (1914); *Rec. trav. chim.*, **45**, 817 (1926).
343. Groggins, *Ind. Eng. Chem.*, **23**, 152 (1931).
344. Riddell and Noller, *J. Am. Chem. Soc.*, **52**, 1905 (1930).
345. Groggins, Nagel, and Stirton, *Ind. Eng. Chem.*, **26**, 1317 (1934).
346. Groggins and Nagel, U. S. Patent 1,997,213 (1935).
347. Ralston and Christensen, *Ind. Eng. Chem.*, **29**, 194 (1937).
348. Ford, *Iowa State Coll. J. Sci.*, **12**, 121 (1937).
349. Ralston and Vander Wal, U. S. Patent 2,189,383 (1940).
350. Fries and Finck, *Ber.*, **41**, 4271 (1908).
351. Rosenmund and Schnurr, *Ann.*, **460**, 56 (1928).
352. Skraup and Poller, *Ber.*, **57B**, 2033 (1924).
353. Cox, *J. Am. Chem. Soc.*, **52**, 352 (1930).
354. Sandulesco and Girard, *Bull. soc. chim.* [4], **47**, 1300 (1930).
355. Ralston, McCorkle, and Bauer, *J. Org. Chem.*, **5**, 645 (1940).
356. Ralston, McCorkle, and Segebrecht, *ibid.*, **6**, 750 (1941).
357. Ralston, Ingle, and McCorkle, *ibid.*, **7**, 457 (1942).
358. Ralston, Segebrecht, and McCorkle, *ibid.*, **7**, 522 (1942).
359. Ralston and Bauer, *ibid.*, **5**, 165 (1940).
360. Ryan and Nolan, *Proc. Roy. Irish Acad.*, **30B**, 1 (1912).
361. Karrer and Rosenfeld, *Helv. Chim. Acta*, **4**, 707 (1921).
362. Nishimura, *Science Repts. Tôhoku Imp. Univ.* [1], **20**, 97 (1931).
363. Bell and Driver, *J. Chem. Soc.*, 835 (1940).
364. Mikeska and Cohen, *J. Org. Chem.*, **6**, 787 (1941).
365. Ralston and Christensen, U. S. Patent 2,033,540 (1936).
366. Ralston and Christensen, U. S. Patent 2,033,541 (1936).
367. Ralston and Christensen, U. S. Patents 2,033,542, 2,033,548 (1936).
368. Ralston and Christensen, U. S. Patent 2,101,559 (1937).
369. Ralston, U. S. Patent 2,101,560 (1937).
370. Ralston and Christensen, U. S. Patent 2,075,765 (1937).
371. Baltzly and Bass, *J. Am. Chem. Soc.*, **55**, 4292 (1933).
372. Klarmann, *ibid.*, **48**, 2358 (1926).
373. Hinegardner and Johnson, *ibid.*, **51**, 1503 (1929).
374. Dohme, U. S. Patent 1,649,669 (1928).
375. Ralston and Vander Wal, U. S. Patent 2,197,709 (1940).
376. Ralston, Vander Wal, and Bauer, U. S. Patent 2,197,710 (1940).
377. Ralston, Vander Wal, and Segebrecht, U. S. Patent 2,197,711 (1940).
378. Ralston, Christensen, and Bauer, U. S. Patent 2,033,545 (1936).
379. Ralston, U. S. Patent 2,033,547 (1936).
380. Ralston, *Oil & Soap*, **16**, 215 (1939).
381. Ralston, Vander Wal, Bauer, and Segebrecht, *Ind. Eng. Chem.*, **32**, 99 (1940).
382. Ralston and Vander Wal, U. S. Patent 2,209,902 (1940).
383. Petrov and Lapteva, *J. Gen. Chem. (U.S.S.R.)*, **8**, 207 (1938).
384. Mikeska, Smith, and Lieber, *J. Org. Chem.*, **2**, 499 (1938).
385. Willgerodt and Merk, *J. prakt. Chem.* [2], **80**, 192 (1909).
386. Ralston, U. S. Patent 2,089,154 (1937).

387. Engel and Pfaehler, U. S. Patent 2,199,789 (1940).
388. J. R. Geigy A.-G., Swiss Patents 202,160–2 (1939); Fr. Patent 840,734 (1939).
389. Martin and Hirt, U. S. Patent 2,205,728 (1940).
390. Henkel & Cie. G.m.b.H., Brit. Patent 468,832 (1937); Fr. Patents 816,843, 816,889 (1937).
391. Ralston and Christensen, U. S. Patent 2,033,543 (1936).
392. Ralston, Christensen, and Selby, U. S. Patent 2,033,546 (1936).
393. Ralston and Hoffman, U. S. Patents 2,197,712–3 (1940).
394. Ralston and Christensen, U. S. Patent 2,107,905 (1938).
395. Ralston and Christensen, U. S. Patent 2,033,544 (1936).
396. Ralston and Christensen, U. S. Patent 2,039,837 (1936).

XI

THE ALIPHATIC HYDROCARBONS AND METALLIC SOAPS

THE ALIPHATIC HYDROCARBONS

Fatty acids are frequently employed as starting materials for the synthesis of pure aliphatic hydrocarbons or of alkyl aryl hydrocarbons. No discussion of the fatty acid derivatives would be complete without reference to the several procedures which have been proposed for the preparation of hydrocarbons from the fatty acids. Although such reactions are not of present commercial significance, the fact that they offer a means of obtaining many hydrocarbons in a state of high purity has contributed materially to our knowledge of the physical and chemical properties of such compounds. Obviously, this discussion of the hydrocarbons must be confined to those obtainable from the fatty acids or their simple derivatives, and by reason of such limitation this treatment of the hydrocarbons cannot be considered as exhaustive or complete.

Small amounts of hydrocarbons are present in many of the naturally occurring fats and waxes. They have been isolated in significant amounts from candelilla wax,[1] carnauba wax,[2] beeswax,[3] and other vegetable and insect waxes. Hata [4] has separated large amounts of hydrocarbons from the unsaponifiable matter of Formosan beeswax, among which was identified hentriacontane, $C_{31}H_{64}$, together with smaller amounts of pentacosane, $C_{25}H_{52}$, heptacosane, $C_{27}H_{56}$, and nonacosane, $C_{29}H_{60}$. The higher unsaturated hydrocarbon squalene, $C_{30}H_{50}$, has been identified in yeast fat [5] and in the unsaponifiable fractions of wheat germ oil and olive oil.[6] Marcelet [7] has isolated small amounts of hydrocarbons from the unsaponifiable matter of peanut oil and has stated that their presence is largely responsible for the characteristic odor and taste of the raw oil. The hydrocarbons present in natural oils are removed by the deodorization process and are thereby concentrated in the distillate. A study [8] of the products removed from olive oil and peanut oil by the deodorization process has shown that they contain a large number of unsaturated hydrocarbons and that such hydrocarbons contribute materially to the odor and taste of these oils. Highly unsaturated hydrocarbons have been isolated from shark liver oil,[9] and a saturated hydrocarbon, $C_{18}H_{38}$, has been separated from this oil in significant amounts.[10] The presence of hydrocarbons in the various naturally occurring fats and waxes presents an interesting biological problem which merits further investigation.

Preparation of Hydrocarbons from Fatty Acids

The preparation of hydrocarbons from the fatty acids or their derivatives possibly has very wide implications, since there are those who hold that the fatty acids, particularly those of marine origin, constitute one of the mother substances of petroleum. That hydrocarbons are one of the major products of the pyrogenic decarboxylation of the fatty acids or their soaps has been known for many years. In 1846, Gottlieb [11] obtained hydrocarbons by the destructive distillation of olive oil, and it has also been observed [12, 13] that hydrocarbons result from the pyrolysis of sodium oleate. The destructive distillation of stearic acid yields both solid and liquid hydrocarbons,[14, 15] and lower fatty acids and hydrocarbons have been isolated from the products of pyrolysis of fatty acid mixtures.[16] In the memorable researches of Engler,[17] it was shown that hydrocarbons result from the destructive distillation of fish oils and other glycerides, and it was suggested that such reactions may be involved in the formation of petroleum. Since this work, many investigators have studied the pyrogenic decomposition of the fats, fatty acids, or soaps and have commented upon the similarity of the resulting products to some of the natural petroleums. Mailhe,[18] for example, obtained complex petroleum-like mixtures when the vapors of linseed oil were passed at 600–650° over a catalyst consisting of magnesium oxide and copper, and later it was shown [19] that saturated and unsaturated hydrocarbons result when linseed oil is heated at about 300° in the presence of inert catalysts such as kieselguhr. The decomposition of cottonseed oil in a closed vessel at 450° in the presence of hydrogen proceeds through the loss of oxygen as carbon dioxide, carbon monoxide, and water, yielding hydrocarbons many of which boil within the gasoline range.[20] Egloff and associates [21] have studied the production of motor fuels by the cracking of fish oils and of cottonseed oil.

The cracking of menhaden oil gave 37.5 to 47.5% of distillate boiling within the gasoline range. The treatment of this distillate with dilute sodium hydroxide gave a water-white product which had only a slight fishy odor. The cracking of cottonseed oil under pressure gave a 54% yield of refined gasoline. A Russian patent [22] issued in 1924 discloses the preparation of lubricating oils by passing the vapors of fatty acids, obtained from either animal or vegetable oils, over iron oxide at 250–400°. The type of hydrocarbons which result by cracking either fatty acids or fats is largely dependent upon the conditions employed in the cracking process, since high temperatures or continued heating yields low-boiling products as a result of secondary reactions.

The decomposition of the alkali or alkaline earth soaps of the higher fatty acids generally gives better yields of hydrocarbons than are obtained by pyrolysis of the corresponding fatty acids or fats. Both liquid and solid paraffins have been stated [23] to result from the destructive distillation of sodium stearate, and sodium oleate yields olefins when similarly treated. The pyrolysis of calcium stearate gives a mixture of paraffins and oil, whereas calcium oleate yields unsaturated products. [24] It has been suggested that such processes may account for the presence of paraffinic hydrocarbons in petroleum, but that naphthenic hydrocarbons are probably formed from the resinous, terpene-like substances found in plants. The preparation of hydrocarbons from the calcium soaps probably proceeds with the initial formation of ketones. [25] Grün and Wirth [26] obtained only unsaturated hydrocarbons from the decomposition of sodium stearate, and they believed that the saturated hydrocarbons are not primary decomposition products. Yields of hydrocarbons as high as 70–80% of the fatty acids have been obtained by the pyrolysis of alkali or alkaline earth soaps, [27] and the dry distillation of the soaps resulting from the refining of fish oils has been suggested as a source of petroleum-like hydrocarbons. [28] The decomposition of palmitic, stearic, and oleic acids in the presence of aluminum chloride yields small amounts of liquid products which resemble paraffin oil in appearance. [29] The similarity of the products resulting from the decomposition of the fatty acid soaps to many of the petroleum hydrocarbons is certainly not merely coincidental. Many who have studied this problem believe that the conversion of fatty substances into soaps, followed by the high-temperature decomposition of these products, accounts for the formation of certain types of naturally occurring petroleums.

In the previous discussion of the preparation of alcohols by the catalytic hydrogenation of fatty acids or their esters, it was pointed out that hydrocarbons constitute the end products of such reactions. Mixtures of alcohols and hydrocarbons are obtained, for example, when esters of the higher acids are hydrogenated at 250–350° under 100 atmospheres pressure, in the presence of various catalysts.[30] The alcohols and esters formed during the hydrogenation of soybean oil in the presence of a copper chromite catalyst are completely reduced to hydrocarbons if the process is conducted at 390°, and above this temperature cracking is encountered with the formation of lower-boiling hydrocarbons.[31] Ueno [32] has described the preparation of a number of saturated hydrocarbons by the high-pressure hydrogenation of fish oils at very high temperatures. Such processes, however, are not frequently employed for the synthesis of hydrocarbons because of the extreme conditions involved.

Many methods have been employed for the preparation of pure hydrocarbons from the fatty acids. One of the earliest of these procedures consists of the direct reduction of the acids themselves by the action of hydrogen iodide and red phosphorus, Krafft [33] having described the preparation of undecane, dodecane, tridecane, tetradecane, pentadecane, hexadecane, heptadecane, and octadecane by the reduction of the respective acids with these reagents at about 240°. This method is not frequently employed for the synthesis of pure hydrocarbons owing to the small yields which are obtained. A somewhat allied procedure, which has proved to be reasonably satisfactory, consists of the conversion of fatty acids to ketones and the reduction of these ketones to the corresponding hydrocarbons. The early applications of this method were likewise described by Krafft [33, 34] and consisted of the conversion of the ketone to the dichlorohydrocarbon followed by reduction of the product with hydrogen iodide and phosphorus, the reaction proceeding as follows:

$$\underset{R'}{\overset{R}{>}}CO \xrightarrow{PCl_5} \underset{R'}{\overset{R}{>}}C\underset{Cl}{\overset{Cl}{<}} \xrightarrow{HI + P} \underset{R'}{\overset{R}{>}}CH_2$$

This procedure differs from the direct reduction of the acids in that the resulting hydrocarbons contain more carbon atoms than the starting acids. Thus, tridecane may be prepared by the conversion of lauric acid into 2-tridecanone followed by reduction. It is, therefore, possible to synthesize a number of hydrocarbons from a specific acid, since the acid may be converted into a number of different ketones. Krafft,[33, 34] for example, has studied the preparation of pentadecane from 2-pentadecanone, of heptadecane from 2-heptadecanone, and of several higher hydrocarbons, such as heptacosane from myristone and pentatriacontane from stearone. The preparation of docosane from 7-docosanone, and of tetracosane from 7-tetracosanone, has also been described.

The synthesis of hydrocarbons from ketones received a material impetus by the advent of the Clemmensen method of reduction, and this procedure with its various modifications has been used frequently as a source of pure hydrocarbons. The method consists of heating the ketone with amalgamated zinc and hydrochloric acid and is applicable to the reduction of both the higher dialkyl ketones and the higher alkyl aryl ketones. In an initial paper upon this subject, Clemmensen [35] described the reduction of propyl phenyl ketone to butylbenzene, of 2-undecanone to undecane, of 2-nonadecanone to nonadecane, and of diheptadecyl ketone to pentatriacontane, and he stated that the method is of general application for the reduction of such ketones. The Clemmensen reduction of either caprone or 2-undecanone gives high yields of undecane.[36] The application of this method to the reduction of the higher dialkyl ketones may be illustrated by the reduction of 22-tritetracontanone to tritetracontane,[37] $C_{43}H_{88}$, or of 34-heptahexacontanone to heptahexacontane,[38] $C_{67}H_{136}$. The Clemmensen reduction of a number of symmetrical and unsymmetrical ketones has been employed by Müller and Saville [39] for the preparation of the hydrocarbons from heptadecane to pentatriacontane inclusive. The method has since been used for the preparation of a number of pure hydrocarbons for physico-chemical studies.[40, 41] Aliphatic aldehydes such as heptanal are also reduced to the corresponding hydrocarbons by this procedure.

The reduction of the higher alkyl aryl ketones proceeds quite slowly owing to solubility factors, and a modification of the Clemmensen method, adaptable to such compounds, has been proposed.[42] This modified procedure is illustrated by the reduction of stearophenone to octadecylbenzene, the method being described as follows:

About a three-inch layer of mossy zinc amalgamated according to Clemmensen's directions with 5% mercuric chloride was placed in a two-liter Erlenmeyer flask, provided with an inlet tube for hydrogen chloride, and a return condenser. Two hundred fifty grams of stearophenone dissolved in 750 cc. of xylol was then added, followed by just enough concentrated hydrochloric acid to cover only about half of the zinc amalgam. This left the xylol solution of the stearophenone in direct contact with the other half of the zinc amalgam. The mixture was then heated to boiling. During refluxing, hydrogen chloride was passed into the reaction mixture to replace the hydrochloric acid consumed. After a contact time of seven hours, the product was isolated, and was distilled under 5 mm. pressure. The product distilled at 220–235° and weighed 228 g. The residue consisted of 30 g. of heavy oil. The distillate was redissolved in xylol and placed in contact with zinc-mercury amalgam as before for 7 hours. On isolation and distillation under 4 mm. pressure, 190 g. of a product boiling at 195–205° and melting at 33° was obtained.

The reduction of heptadecyl xenyl ketone to octadecylbiphenyl and of heptadecyl tetrahydronaphthyl ketone to octadecyltetrahydronaphthalene by this procedure was likewise accomplished. A later paper [43] described the reduction of heneicosyl phenyl ketone to docosylbenzene, of heneicosyl naphthyl ketone to docosylnaphthalene, and of heneicosyl xenyl ketone to docosylbiphenyl.

Hydrocarbons may be obtained by the catalytic reduction of ketones, the preparation of dodecylbenzene by the catalytic hydrogenation of laurophenone having been described.[44] Schmidt and Grosser [45] have prepared a series of α,ω-diphenylalkanes by conversion with aluminum isopropoxide of α,ω-dibenzoylalkanes to the corresponding diols, followed by dehydrogenation of the diols to dienes and hydrogenation of the latter to the saturated hydrocarbons in the presence of a $Pd\text{-}BaSO_4$ catalyst.

The haloalkanes are the most frequently employed intermediates for the synthesis of pure hydrocarbons from the fatty acids, and a number of procedures have been described for the preparation of hydrocarbons from these compounds. Such processes include the replacement of the halogen by hydrogen either by chemical reduction or by catalytic hydrogenation, the condensation of two alkyl radicals by the well-known Wurtz reaction, the formation and hydrolysis of alkylmagnesium halides, and the reaction of haloalkanes with Grignard reagents followed by hydrolysis of the resulting complex.

Reduction of the higher haloalkanes may be accomplished by treatment with zinc and hydrochloric acid, and Levene and others [46] have prepared the saturated hydrocarbons from $C_{16}H_{34}$ to $C_{32}H_{66}$ by reduction of the corresponding iodo compounds with zinc and hydrochloric acid. This method is a modification of that previously employed for the preparation of hexadecane from 1-iodohexadecane.[47] Carey and Smith [48] have reported that 1-iodohexadecane is quantitatively converted to hexadecane by boiling its acetic acid solution for three hours with zinc dust; however, it was suggested that propionic acid be substituted for acetic acid for the reduction of the higher iodoalkanes. When 1-bromohexadecane is treated for ten hours with acetic acid and zinc the reduction is still incomplete, the product containing 7.8% of bromine, and 1-chlorohexadecane is not materially reduced after twenty hours. This indicates that the method is not satisfactory when applied to the higher bromo- or chloroalkanes. The reduction of 1-iodohexadecane with a zinc-copper couple gives a 90% yield of hexadecane, and a similar yield is obtained by the catalytic hydrogenation of an iodo compound in the presence of a $Pd-CaCO_3$ catalyst.

Iodoalkanes are reduced to the corresponding hydrocarbons by reaction with sodium amalgam in absolute ethanol. The application of this method has been described by Gascard,[49] who reduced 1-iodohexadecane, 1-iodoöctadecane, and other iodoalkanes to the corresponding hydrocarbons.

The well-known Wurtz reaction is probably the most frequently employed method for the synthesis of higher hydrocarbons. The reaction consists of treating the haloalkanes in an inert solvent with sodium or potassium, the resulting hydrocarbons thus containing twice the number of carbon atoms present in the original halo compound. When two halo derivatives of different chain lengths are employed, the product consists of a mixture of the three theoretically possible hydrocarbons. The reaction is, therefore, adaptable to the synthesis of a large number of both aliphatic and alkyl aryl hydrocarbons from the fatty acids. In his initial disclosure of this reaction, Wurtz [50] described the synthesis of 2,5-dimethylhexane from 2-methyl-1-iodopropane and sodium and of several other hydrocarbons by the action of iodoalkanes with this metal. Later, Schorlemmer [51] accomplished the synthesis of octane by the action of sodium with 1-iodobutane, the reaction proceeding as follows:

$$2C_4H_9I + 2Na \rightarrow C_8H_{18} + 2NaI$$

It was several years before this reaction was applied to the preparation of the higher hydrocarbons. Dotriacontane was synthesized in 1884–1885 by the reaction of sodium on 1-iodohexa-

decane,[47, 52] and in 1886 Krafft [53] described the synthesis of tetradecane, hexadecane, octadecane, and eicosane by the reaction of
haloalkanes with sodium. Triacontane, $C_{30}H_{62}$, is obtained from
1-iodopentadecane by treatment for ten hours with sodium in
boiling xylene.[54] Yields of 55 to 65% of pure decane have been
obtained [55] by the action of sodium upon 1-bromopentane. The
preparation of dotriacontane, $C_{32}H_{66}$, by treating 1-iodohexa-
decane with sodium in boiling ether has been described in detail.[56]
In his study of the synthesis of the higher hydrocarbons from 1-
iodoalkanes, Gascard [49] observed that potassium is more satisfactory than sodium.

The application of the Wurtz reaction to the preparation of the
alkyl aryl hydrocarbons was first described by Fittig and König.[57]
The method was successfully used by Schweinitz,[58] who obtained
octylbenzene by the action of sodium on a mixture of bromoben-
zene and 1-bromoöctane in ether, and also by Krafft,[59] who prepared hexadecylbenzene and octadecylbenzene by the action of
sodium on iodobenzene and the respective 1-iodoalkanes. A
recent description of the Wurtz-Fittig reaction has been given by
Gilman and Turck,[60] who prepared octadecylbenzene by the action
of sodium on iodobenzene and 1-iodoöctadecane.

The mechanism of the Wurtz reaction has been the subject of
several investigations.[61, 62] Bachmann and Clarke [63] have postulated a mechanism based upon the production of free radicals.
That the reaction is not a simple one is shown by the investigation
of these authors upon the action of sodium with 1-bromoheptane.
In addition to tetradecane, the reaction mixture contains heptane,
heptene, a heneicosane, and higher hydrocarbons. In their study
of the influence of various factors upon the preparation of octane
from 1-bromobutane and sodium, Lewis and others [64] arrived at
the following conclusions: (1) optimum yields are obtained when
the sodium is used in excess (not greater than 50 mole per cent);
(2) a volume of ether 2.5 times the volume of 1-bromobutane is
necessary; (3) low temperatures favor the formation of octane,
whereas higher temperatures give greater yields of unsaturated
hydrocarbons; (4) finely divided sodium should be employed; (5)
traces of moisture greatly reduce the yield; and (6) agitation materially increases the reaction rate. These authors have published
the following directions for the preparation of octane from 1-bromo-
butane (butyl bromide):

. . . Twenty moles (1480 g.) of ether, dried over calcium chloride and distilled over sodium, is placed in a five liter round-bottomed flask equipped with an addition tube, a four foot reflux condenser and an agitator. Sodium cut thin with a sodium knife is added to the amount of 12.1 moles (278 g.) and then 8.3 moles (1137 g.) of dry butyl bromide run in over fifteen minutes. The mixture is refluxed with agitation for ten hours and then the excess sodium destroyed by slowly adding water to the contents of the flask. The layers are separated; the ether layer is dried with calcium chloride and fractionally distilled.

A 68% yield was obtained, on the basis of the 1-bromobutane used.

High yields of octane are also obtained by dropping 1-bromobutane upon metallic sodium and removing the reaction product at the reflux temperature.[64, 65]

The action of sodium with the α,ω-dihaloparaffins yields a mixture of saturated hydrocarbons. For example, sodium and 1,10-dibromodecane, $Br(CH_2)_{10}Br$, give a mixture of paraffins of the general formula $H[(CH_2)_{10}]_x H$, eicosane, triacontane, tetracontane, pentacontane, hexacontane, and heptacontane having been isolated from the reaction mixture.[66]

The Grignard method offers one of the most versatile procedures for the preparation of hydrocarbons from haloalkanes. Hydrocarbons with the same number of carbon atoms as the starting halo compounds are obtained by the formation of the alkylmagnesium halide followed by its hydrolysis. The reaction proceeds as follows:

$$RX + Mg \rightarrow RMgX$$

$$RMgX + HOH \xrightarrow{HX} RH + MgXOH$$

A recent example of the application of this procedure is the synthesis of 9-octadecene by the action of magnesium on 1-bromo-9-octadecene, followed by decomposition of the resulting 9-octadecenylmagnesium bromide with 5% hydrochloric acid containing some ammonium chloride.[67]

Magnesium, like sodium, can function as a condensing agent, the resulting hydrocarbons containing twice the number of carbon atoms present in the original haloalkanes. The overall reaction may be represented as follows:

$$2RBr + Mg \rightarrow RR + MgBr_2$$

Grignard,[68] for example, synthesized several hydrocarbons by the action of magnesium on bromoalkanes, and the condensing action of magnesium was later studied by Houben,[69] who postulated that the reaction proceeds with the initial formation of an alkylmagnesium bromide which then reacts with a second molecule of haloalkane, thus:

$$RMgBr + RBr \rightarrow RR + MgBr_2$$

The presence of an excess of haloalkane favors the condensation reaction, so that this condition is avoided when high yields of the alkylmagnesium halide are desired. Such reactions do not take place readily with the lower haloalkanes, but an increase in chain length apparently favors condensation. The preparation of several higher hydrocarbons by the condensation action of magnesium on iodoalkanes has been described.[46]

Grignard reagents readily form complexes with organic halo compounds, the hydrolysis of which yields hydrocarbons. Such reactions offer the major contribution of the Grignard reagents to those syntheses of hydrocarbons which involve the higher haloalkanes. Many unsaturated and branched-chain hydrocarbons, which would be extremely difficult to prepare by other methods, have been obtained by recourse to this procedure. The application of this method to the synthesis of 1-alkenes may be illustrated by the action of the higher alkylmagnesium halides with 3-bromopropene, a reaction which has been investigated extensively.[70, 71, 72, 73] This procedure has recently been employed [74] for the preparation of a number of 1-alkenes, the synthesis of 1-pentadecene from dodecylmagnesium bromide and 3-bromopropene proceeding as follows:

$$C_{12}H_{25}MgBr + BrCH_2CH:CH_2 \rightarrow C_{12}H_{25}CH_2CH:CH_2 + MgBr_2$$

1-Nonene, 1-decene, 1-undecene, 1-dodecene, 1-tridecene, 1-heptadecene, and 1-heneicosene are similarly obtained. The hydrogenation of these olefins in the presence of platinum oxide yields the corresponding saturated hydrocarbons. Waterman and de Kok [75] have described the synthesis of 1-heptene by the action of 3-bromopropene on butylmagnesium bromide, and the preparation of several higher molecular weight alkenes by a similar procedure has been published by Kozacik and Reid.[76]

High molecular weight unsaturated alkyl aryl hydrocarbons have been obtained by dehydration of the tertiary alcohols resulting from the action of Grignard reagents on ketones.[42, 43] For example, the reaction of stearophenone with butylmagnesium bromide yields 5-phenyl-5-docosanol, which, when heated with oxalic acid, is dehydrated to the unsaturated hydrocarbon 5-phenyl-5-docosene. The hydrogenation of this hydrocarbon in the presence of platinum oxide and glacial acetic acid yields the saturated hydrocarbon 5-phenyldocosane. This method has been employed for the synthesis of a number of high molecular weight branched-chain alkyl aryl hydrocarbons.

The electrolysis of aqueous alcoholic solutions of alkali metal soaps yields hydrocarbons, and recourse to this method, which was initially proposed by Kolbe,[77] is frequently taken for their synthesis. The reaction was first used for the preparation of the higher hydrocarbons by Petersen,[78] who observed that electrolysis of the salts of saturated fatty acids yields saturated hydrocarbons together with olefins, esters, and small amounts of alcohols. Petersen [79] has proposed the following equations for the changes which take place during the electrolysis of undecenoic acid:

(I) $2C_{10}H_{19}CO_2H \rightarrow 2C_{10}H_{19}CO_2 + H_2$

(II) $2C_{10}H_{19}CO_2 + H_2O \rightarrow 2C_{10}H_{19}CO_2H + (O)$

(III) $2C_{10}H_{19}CO_2 \rightarrow (C_{10}H_{19})_2 + 2CO_2$

(IV) $2C_{10}H_{19}CO_2 \rightarrow C_{10}H_{18} + C_{10}H_{19}CO_2H + CO_2$

(V) $C_{10}H_{18} + H_2O \rightarrow C_{10}H_{19}OH$

The main reaction is expressed by equation (III). Thus, the major product formed by the electrolysis of undecenoic acid is the unsaturated hydrocarbon $(C_{10}H_{19})_2$, which results from a combination of two alkenyl groups initially present in the starting acid. Small amounts of an alcohol are always present in the final product. In a more recent study of the mechanism of the electrolysis of potassium caproate, Fichter and Zumbrunn [80] have stated that the decomposition of the primary electrolysis product, $(C_5H_{11}CO_2)_2$, is due to evolution of heat at the cathode. They suggest that two main decompositions are involved, one of which proceeds through the Kolbe synthesis and the other through the intermediate formation of percaproic acid, thus:

(I) $2C_5H_{11}CO_2H \rightarrow (C_5H_{11}CO_2)_2 \rightarrow C_{10}H_{22} + 2CO_2$

(II) $(C_5H_{11}CO_2)_2 + H_2O \rightarrow C_5H_{11}CO_3H + C_5H_{11}CO_2H$

$C_5H_{11}CO_3H \rightarrow C_5H_{11}OH + CO_2$

Some of the alcohol formed under these conditions yields an unsaturated hydrocarbon by dehydration, in addition to a small amount of ester which results from esterification with the acid present. Dover and Helmers [81] have published a detailed preparation of 9,25-tetratriacontadiene, $C_{34}H_{66}$, by the electrolysis of potassium oleate. Fifteen grams of oleic acid were dissolved in 75 cc. of ethanol and neutralized with an aqueous solution of potassium carbonate. Five more grams of oleic acid were added and the solution electrolyzed at 50–60° between platinum electrodes in a narrow 300-cc. beaker. The electrodes were of such a size as to permit a current density of about 5.5 amperes per sq. dm. when a current of 1.25 amperes was passed through the solution. It was stated that the best results were obtained by electrolyzing the solution for a period of twenty-five to thirty hours, with the addition of 4.5 grams of oleic acid (dissolved in 30 to 50 cc. of warm ethanol) every three hours to replace that used in the reaction. In a study of the electrolysis of sodium stearate, Rhodes [82] obtained only small amounts of hydrocarbons after 14 hours at 0.3 ampere. Electrolysis of an alcoholic solution of potassium myristate at 55–60° and 0.96 ampere gives a 60% yield of hexacosane, and potassium palmitate at 70° and 0.98 ampere gives a similar yield of triacontane.[74] Hexahexacontane, $C_{66}H_{134}$, has been prepared by the electrolysis of potassium tetratriacontanoate [38] in aqueous ethanol at 70°; however, only small quantities were prepared at a time owing to the limited solubility of the soap in ethanol.

The higher alkyl aryl hydrocarbons may be prepared by the Friedel-Crafts alkylation of aromatic compounds, although such reactions have not been extensively investigated. It has been reported that alkylations with halopropanes,[83] halobutanes,[84, 85, 86] and halopentanes [87, 88] involve appreciable branching of the alkyl groups, and Calloway [89] has stated that it is virtually impossible to introduce a normal alkyl chain with more than two carbon atoms. Gilman and Turck,[60] however, have reported a 50% yield of octadecylbenzene by the Friedel-Crafts alkylation of benzene with 1-bromoöctadecane, thus indicating that no significant rearrangement takes place under the conditions employed. The alkylation of phenol with high molecular weight haloalkanes or haloalkenes, followed by sulfonation of the resulting compounds, has been proposed for the preparation of wetting agents.[90]

The synthesis of unsaturated hydrocarbons by the dehydration of alcohols or the dehydrohalogenation of haloalkanes is discussed in previous chapters. Consequently, reference is made in this present chapter only to a few specific examples of such reactions.

The former of these procedures may be accomplished either by catalytic means or by heating with dehydrating agents such as concentrated sulfuric acid or phosphoric anhydride. The action of phosphoric anhydride on the alcohols is one of the earliest methods employed for the preparation of the higher olefins, Dumas and Péligot [91] having prepared 1-hexadecene by the dehydration of 1-hexadecanol with this reagent.

Olefin mixtures result from the pyrolysis of haloalkanes, the dehydrochlorination of 1-chlorohexadecane having been stated to yield mainly 1-hexadecene.[92] Generally, dehydrohalogenations are accomplished by treatment of haloalkanes with alcoholic potassium hydroxide, an example being the action of this reagent with 1-iodohexane to yield 1-hexene. An isomeric hexene is obtained when the hydrogen iodide is removed by means of quinoline.[93] The dehydroiodination of 3-iodononane with alcoholic potassium hydroxide yields a nonene, the catalytic reduction of which gives nonane.[94]

Reactions of dehydrohalogenation have been advantageously employed for the preparation of acetylenic hydrocarbons from the corresponding olefins. For example, 1-dodecyne has been synthesized from 1-dodecene by brominating the latter in carbon disulfide solution followed by autoclaving the resulting dibromide with alcoholic potassium hydroxide for five hours at 150°.[95] The preparation of 1-tetradecyne, 1-hexadecyne, and 1-octadecyne was accomplished by a similar procedure.[95, 96] Hill and Tyson [97] have studied the preparation of 1-heptyne by the dehydrochlorination of 1,1-dichloroheptane over soda-lime, and have reported that, owing to molecular rearrangement occasioned by the high temperatures involved, very small yields of the acetylene are obtained. It was observed that when alkaline solutions are employed, the dehydrochlorination is incomplete below 360°, and above 420° extensive rearrangement is encountered. Yields of approximately 30% result at the lower temperature. Very small yields, on the order of 2%, are obtained by the dehydrohalogenation of this compound in the presence of aluminum silicate at 470°.

The foregoing procedures constitute the main reactions which have been employed for the preparation of higher hydrocarbons from fatty acids or their simple derivatives. There are, however, several additional methods which have been investigated and are worthy of mention.

The pyrolysis of esters of higher alcohols and higher aliphatic acids yields a mixture of fatty acids and olefins. This reaction was initially proposed by Smith,[98] who observed that the decomposition of hexadecyl palmitate yields hexadecene and palmitic acid, the reaction proceeding as follows:

$$C_{16}H_{33}O_2CC_{15}H_{31} \rightarrow C_{15}H_{31}CO_2H + C_{16}H_{32}$$

Krafft [99] employed this reaction for the preparation of dodecene, tetradecene, hexadecene, and octadecene, and showed that it is of general application for the preparation of the higher olefins. The pyrolysis is generally accomplished by distilling the esters under slightly reduced pressures (300–400 mm.).[100] The application of this method to the preparation of the higher olefins has been described by Pummerer and Kranz,[101] who obtained from the distillation of myricyl palmitate a product which was probably a mixture of triacontene and dotriacontene. High molecular weight hydrocarbons may be prepared by decarboxylation of higher alkyl-substituted malonic acids, several of the higher saturated hydrocarbons having been synthesized by this procedure.[37, 102]

An interesting synthesis of higher olefins has recently been accomplished by Niemann and Wagner,[103] the procedure resulting in the conversion of a 1-bromoalkane, RCH_2Br, into a 1-alkene of the general formula $RCH_2CH{=}CH_2$. The process consists of converting the 1-bromoalkane into the α-alkyl-β-bromoethyl ethyl ether, the treatment of which with zinc and 1-butanol results in a simultaneous removal of the ethoxy group and the bromine atom,[104] yielding an olefin. The synthesis of 1-hexadecene from 1-bromotetradecane is represented by the following series of equations:

$$C_{14}H_{29}Br + Mg \rightarrow C_{14}H_{29}MgBr$$

$$C_{14}H_{29}MgBr + CH_2BrCHBrOC_2H_5 \rightarrow CH_2BrCH(C_{14}H_{29})OC_2H_5 + MgBr_2$$

$$CH_2BrCH(C_{14}H_{29})OC_2H_5 + Zn \rightarrow C_{14}H_{29}CH{=}CH_2 + Zn(OC_2H_5)Br$$

This method is adaptable to the synthesis of many of the higher olefins. Its use for this purpose has been studied in detail by Boord and coworkers,[105, 106, 107, 108] who applied it and closely allied procedures to the synthesis of pentenes, heptenes, and other unsaturated hydrocarbons.

The higher molecular weight olefins may be prepared by pyrolysis of salts of the higher aliphatic secondary amines, the method having been described in the patent literature.[109]

In the preparation of olefins by any of the procedures described in this chapter, it should be borne in mind that migration of the ethylenic bond is frequently encountered and that the resulting product is often a mixture of two or more isomeric olefins. Failure to realize this point has frequently resulted in erroneous assumptions with reference to the homogeneity of the final products.

Physical Properties of the Aliphatic Hydrocarbons

The melting and boiling points of the higher saturated hydrocarbons are substantially lower than those of the fatty acids and other fatty derivatives of similar carbon content. In 1941, Deanesly and Carleton [110] made a very critical study of the physical constants which have been reported for the normal paraffinic hydrocarbons from C_5 to C_{18} inclusive, and, by a process of selecting certain reference points and smoothing the reported values, established quite accurate values. The freezing and boiling points, densities, and refractive indices of the saturated hydrocarbons from C_5 to C_{18} inclusive as reported by these authors are shown in Table I.

TABLE I

PHYSICAL CONSTANTS OF THE NORMAL PARAFFINS

No. of C Atoms	F.P.,°C., at 760 mm.	B.P.,°C., at 760 mm.	d_4^{20}	n_D^{20}
5	−129.7	36.1	0.62633	1.35772
6	−95.3	68.7	0.65940	1.37503
7	−90.6	98.4	0.68370	1.38770
8	−56.8	125.6	0.70255	1.39752
9	−53.7	150.7	0.71757	1.40535
10	−29.7	174.0	0.72984	1.41174
11	−25.6	195.8	0.74006	1.41707
12	−9.60	216.2	0.74872	1.42158
13	−6.0	235.5	0.75616	1.42547
14	5.5	253.6	0.76263	1.42886
15	10.0	270.6	0.76832	1.43184
16	18.145 ± 0.003	286.5	0.77336	1.43448
17	22.0	301.4	0.77785	1.43684
18	28.0	315.3	0.78188	1.43896

Although the higher hydrocarbons have not been so extensively studied as their lower homologs, many of the physical constants *

* For a complete tabulation of the physical constants of hydrocarbons the reader is referred to Doss, *Physical Constants of the Principal Hydrocarbons*, 4th ed., The Texas Company, New York (1943).

which have been reported for these compounds are undoubtedly reliable. The following are the melting and boiling points which have been reported [38, 39, 41, 46, 56, 66, 111] for the higher normal saturated hydrocarbons: nonadecane, $C_{19}H_{40}$, 32°, —; eicosane, $C_{20}H_{42}$, 38°, $b_{0.5}$ 148°; heneicosane, $C_{21}H_{44}$, 40.3–40.5°, $b_{2.5}$ 172–172.5°; docosane, $C_{22}H_{46}$, 47°, —; tricosane, $C_{23}H_{48}$, 47.25–47.4°, —; tetracosane, $C_{24}H_{50}$, 51°, —; hexacosane, $C_{26}H_{54}$, 59.60°, $b_{0.4}$ 199°; heptacosane, $C_{27}H_{56}$, 59.5°, —; octacosane, $C_{28}H_{58}$, 64–65°, $b_{1.1}$ 224°; triacontane, $C_{30}H_{62}$, 68–70°, $b_{1.0}$ 235°; hentriacontane, $C_{31}H_{64}$, 69°, —; dotriacontane, $C_{32}H_{66}$, 70.16°, $b_{1.5}$ 245°; tetratriacontane, $C_{34}H_{70}$, 76–76.5°, $b_{1.0}$ 255°; hexatriacontane, $C_{36}H_{74}$, 78.5°, $b_{1.0}$ 265°; tetracontane, $C_{40}H_{82}$, 80.5–81°, —; pentacontane, $C_{50}H_{102}$, 91.9–92.3°, —; tetrapentacontane, $C_{54}H_{110}$, 95°, —; hexacontane, $C_{60}H_{122}$, 98.5–99°, —; dohexacontane, $C_{62}H_{126}$, 100.5°, —; heptacontane, $C_{70}H_{142}$, 105–105.5°, —.

The polymorphic behavior of the normal saturated hydrocarbons presents an interesting study, and although certain aspects of this subject have been discussed previously, they can well bear repetition. The polymorphism exhibited by the hydrocarbons is quite similar to that observed for the ethyl esters of the saturated acids, the relative stabilities of the polymorphic forms being dependent upon chain length. The higher saturated hydrocarbons exist in at least two polymorphic forms, one of which is stable only in the vicinity of the melting points. The polymorphism of the hydrocarbons was probably first recognized by Müller and Saville,[39] who observed that the long crystal spacings of the hydrocarbons as shown by x-rays exhibit a constant increment of 1.3 Å per carbon atom. It was noted, however, that octadecane and eicosane upon being held for any appreciable period of time exhibit two long spacings, one of which disappears completely upon further standing. Octadecane shows the two spacings 23.9 Å and 25.9 Å, the latter of which relates to the transparent α-form and the former to the opaque β-form. Eicosane shows the two spacings 26.2 Å and 28.0 Å. These observations indicate that these hydrocarbons possess at least two forms, which are stable within certain temperature intervals.

For those hydrocarbons which contain more than eighteen carbon atoms, the transparent α-form is stable at the melting points, and a plot of these melting points against the number of carbon atoms is a straight line. The reversible transition $\alpha \rightarrow \beta$ takes place several degrees below the melting point. The thermal properties of the polymorphic forms of several higher hydrocarbons from docosane to tetratriacontane, as determined by Garner and associates,[112] are tabulated in Table XXVIII, Chapter V. The heats of transition vary from 6.90 to 11.48 kg. cal./mole. Upon cooling from the molten state, such hydrocarbons crystallize in transparent, glasslike crystals (α-form) which rapidly change to white, opaque solids (β-form) upon further cooling. The relative stabilities of the α- and β-forms of triacontane have been investigated by Schoon,[113] who observed that the α-form is stable at higher temperatures. Binary systems of such hydrocarbons have been investigated by Piper and others [40] and were reported to yield continuous series of solid solutions without maxima or minima. For the even-carbon-membered hydrocarbons which contain eighteen or less carbon atoms, the α-form melts lower than the β-form. Carey and Smith [114] have determined the melting point of the transparent form of octadecane to be 27.1°, and that of the opaque form, 27.9–28.0°.

The transparent α-form possesses a vertical chain, and the opaque β-form of the even hydrocarbons possesses a tilted chain. The odd hydrocarbons above undecane do not crystallize in forms containing tilted chains. Upon cooling, such hydrocarbons first crystallize in a vertical, rotating form which changes into a vertical, non-rotating form upon further cooling.[115] The reverse change occurs upon heating. Hexacosane and its higher even homologs have been stated [40] to possess a third modification, the angle of tilt of this form being greater than that of the β-modification.

In a study of the binary system hexadecane-octadecane, Smith [116] observed that the addition of either homolog stabilizes the transparent, metastable form of the other, so that such mixtures remain metastable for appreciable periods of time. Near either end of the concentration range, however, the transition is so rapid that only the higher-melting form is obtainable, the melting point of the metastable form being determined only by extrapolation. The fact that at least 5% of a homolog is required to stabilize the metastable forms of hexadecane and octadecane accounts for the observation of Phillips and Mumford [117] that there is no halt in the cooling curves of these hydrocarbons from their freezing points to −10°. The system hexadecane-octadecane as determined by Smith is shown in Fig. 1. Similar systems were obtained for hexadecane-heptadecane and for heptadecane-octadecane.[114]

The solubilities of saturated hydrocarbons[111] in polar solvents differ decidedly from those of polar compounds, since they are practically immiscible with such solvents as methanol, ethanol, nitromethane, and acetonitrile. Their solubility behaviors in non-polar and slightly polar solvents, however, are qualitatively similar to those of polar aliphatic compounds of corresponding chain lengths. They form eutectics with benzene, cyclohexane,

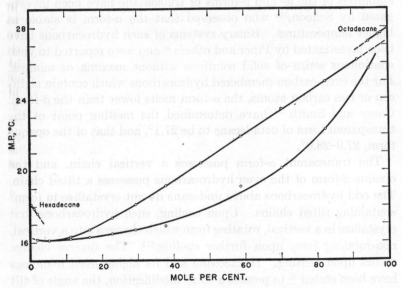

FIG. 1. The system: hexadecane–octadecane.

tetrachloromethane, and chloroform, the compositions and temperatures of which are shown in Table II.

The solubilities of hexadecane,[111] shown in Table III, may be taken as representative of the solubility behavior of the higher saturated hydrocarbons.

The presence of ethylenic bonds in the hydrocarbon chain is attended by a lowering of the melting and boiling points, the degree of the effect being dependent upon the length of the chain and the position of the ethylenic bond or bonds. Considerable disagreement is to be found in the literature relative to the physical constants of the ethylenic hydrocarbons. For example, the following values have been reported for the boiling point of 1-hexene: 67.0°,[118] 67.7–68.1°,[119] 60.5–61.5°,[71] and 63.35°.[120] This is partially occasioned by the fact that many of the reactions considered satisfac-

TABLE II

EUTECTICS FORMED BY HYDROCARBONS

Solvent	8	12	16	17	32
Benzene					
Wt. % solute	91.8	65.1	32.4	37.2	...
Temp.,°C.	−58.4	−17.9	−1.3	−1.9	...
Cyclohexane					
Wt. % solute	39.1	28.5	17.6	17.5	0.5
Temp.,°C.	−71.6	−32.9	−12.5	−10.8	6.5
Tetrachloromethane					
Wt. % solute	39.1	9.9	3.5	3.3	...
Temp.,°C.	−66.3	−34.2	−26.2	−25.6	...
Chloroform					
Wt. % solute	25.3	0.3	....	....	...
Temp.,°C.	−67.8	−63.6	....	....	...

Number of C Atoms heads columns 8, 12, 16, 17, 32.

TABLE III

SOLUBILITIES OF HEXADECANE *

Grams per 100 g. Solvent

Solvent	−30.0°	−20.0°	−10.0°	0.0°	10.0°	15.0 °
Benzene	...	....	....	....	360	1440
Cyclohexane	...	....	....	....	430	1440
Tetrachloromethane	...	5.5	15.1	56	245	790
Chloroform	0.4	2.2	8.1	32.4	214	1020
Ethyl ether	1.4	5.4	16.3	64	302	1200
Ethyl acetate	...	....	≈0.1	3.0	50	840
Butyl acetate	...	≈0.2	1.6	9.9	138	1090
Acetone †	...	....	<0.1	1.2	5.3	13.0
2-Butanone	...	....	0.3	2.6	17.6	830
2-Propanol	...	<0.1	0.4	1.7	7.5	21.2
1-Butanol	...	0.3	1.2	4.1	16.7	≈50

* ∞ above 18.2° with solvents listed, except acetone.
† ∞ above 35.8°.

tory for the synthesis of such compounds involve the possibility of isomerization. Very reliable constants for many of the higher 1-alkenes have recently been reported,[74, 76, 103] and the observed values are shown in Table IV.

Cis-9-octadecene, obtained from the bromoalkane derived from oleic acid,[67] melts at −2° to 0°. The excellent work of Board and

TABLE IV

Physical Constants of 1-Alkenes

1-Alkene	M.P.,°C.	b_{11}	d_4^{20}	n_D^{20}
1-Nonene	−88.0	33.5	0.7296	1.4169
1-Decene	−66.3	52	0.7396	1.4220
1-Undecene	−49.5	74.8	0.7506	1.4270
1-Dodecene	−33.6	89–89.5	0.7582	1.4308
1-Tridecene	−22.2	104	0.7658	1.4340
1-Pentadecene	−4	135.2	0.7769	1.4394
1-Hexadecene	+4.0 *	122–122.5	......	1.4410
1-Heptadecene	11	157	0.7854	1.4438
1-Octadecene	17.5 *	144–146$_3$	......	1.4448
1-Nonadecene	21.7	177$_{10}$	0.7858^{35}	......
1-Eicosene	28.5	151$_{1.5}$	......	1.4440^{30}
1-Heneicosene	35.5	134$_{0.04}$	0.7985	1.4510

* Denotes freezing point.

associates [105,106,107,108] has served to furnish reliable data for the lower molecular weight 1-olefins and to enable a comparison of these values with those of isomeric compounds. The influence of unsaturation and isomerization upon the boiling points of the C_5 hydrocarbons is illustrated by the following values: (hydrocarbon, boiling point) $CH_3(CH_2)_3CH_3$, 36.3°; CH_3CH=$CHCH_2CH_3$, 36.4°; CH_2=$CHCH_2CH_2CH_3$, 30.2°; CH_2=$CHCH_2CH$=CH_2, 29–30°; $CH_3CH_2CH(CH_3)_2$, 27.95°; CH_2=$CHCH(CH_3)_2$, 20.5–20.7°. The following values have been reported for the boiling points of the C_6 hydrocarbons: $CH_3(CH_2)_4CH_3$, 68.95°; CH_3-CH=$CHCH_2CH_2CH_3$, 68.0–68.2°; CH_2=$CHCH_2CH_2CH_2CH_3$, 63.35°; and CH_2=$CHCH_2CH_2CH$=CH_2, 59.57°. The influence of the position of the ethylenic bond is further illustrated by the physical constants of the following isomeric heptenes: (hydrocarbon, b.p., d_4^{20}, n_D^{20}) CH_2=$CH(CH_2)_4CH_3$, 94.9°, 0.6993, 1.3999; CH_3CH=$CH(CH_2)_3CH_3$, 98.1–98.4°, 0.7034, 1.4041; and CH_3-CH_2CH=$CH(CH_2)_2CH_3$, 95.8–96.1°, 0.7043, 1.4090. Thermal data for a number of the saturated and unsaturated aliphatic hydrocarbons have been reported by Parks, Huffman, and Thomas.[121]

Only a few reliable constants are available for the higher alkyl aryl hydrocarbons. A few years ago Mikeska and others [42,43] prepared some representatives of this type of compound, the list including octadecylbenzene, m.p. 33°; octadecylcyclohexane, m.p.

40°; docosylcyclohexane, m.p. 49–50°; octadecylbiphenyl, m.p. 79–81°; docosylbiphenyl, m.p. 82–84.5°; octadecyldecahydronaphthalene, m.p. 43–47°; docosylnaphthalene, m.p. 56–58°; and docosyldecahydronaphthalene, m.p. 53–54°. Octadecylbenzene had previously been synthesized by Krafft,[59] who reported m.p. 36° and b_{15} 249°. He also observed hexadecylbenzene to melt at 27°, and boil at 230° at 15 mm. A series of isomeric phenyldodecanes has recently been prepared by Schmidt and Grosser,[122] who have reported the following physical constants of these compounds: 2-phenyldodecane, $b_{1.8}$ 143°, n_D^{20} 1.4849, d_4^{30} 0.8488; 3-phenyl-, $b_{0.8}$ 127°, n_D^{20} 1.4829, d_4^{30} 0.8466; 4-phenyl-, $b_{0.6}$ 140–142°, n_D^{20} 1.4850, d_4^{30} 0.8489; 5-phenyl-, $b_{0.4}$ 113°, n_D^{20} 1.4850, d_4^{30} 0.8485; 6-phenyl-, $b_{0.4}$ 108°, n_D^{20} 1.4852, d_4^{30} 0.8477. These authors have also prepared [45] 1,10-diphenyldecane, $b_{0.03}$ 169–170°, m.p. 17.5°, n_D^{20} 1.5282, d_4^{30} 0.9232; 1,10-dicyclohexyldecane, $b_{0.3}$ 158°, m.p. 33.5–34.5°, n_D^{30} 1.4724, d_4^{50} 0.8452; and 1,18-diphenyloctadecane, m.p. 93°.

The chemical reactions of the higher hydrocarbons constitute so broad a subject that its treatment is far beyond the limitations of this present writing. Their oxidation to fatty acids,[123, 124, 125, 126] for example, is a subject with which all chemists are generally familiar. The sulfonation of higher unsaturated hydrocarbons, derived from fatty acids, for the preparation of wetting agents has been described in the patent literature.[127, 128]

THE METALLIC SOAPS OF THE FATTY ACIDS

The general properties of the alkali metal soaps and possibly of the ammonium soaps are familiar to all chemists, and their preparation, properties, and uses are extensively treated in the chemical literature. The alkaline earth and heavy metal soaps of the higher fatty acids, on the other hand, are not so widely known, and it is the chief purpose of this writing to compile certain of the existing information relative to this latter type of derivative. Before considering the alkaline earth and heavy metal soaps, however, a brief discussion of the structure and general properties of the more common alkali metal and ammonium soaps appears to be in order.

The alkali metal soaps may be obtained either by saponification of glycerides or other esters or by neutralization of the fatty acids themselves with alkali hydroxides, carbonates, or other salts. The ammonium soaps are generally prepared by neutralization of the fatty acids with ammonia or ammonium hydroxide, either in aqueous solution or in organic solvents. Certain phases of the saponification process for the preparation of sodium or potassium soaps are discussed elsewhere in this book, and it suffices to say here that such processes constitute a major industry, the many aspects of which comprise a large subject in themselves.

The sodium and potassium soaps may exist as the normal salts, RCO_2M, or as the acid salts, $RCO_2M \cdot RCO_2H$. These two series of soaps possess markedly different solubilities in water and organic solvents and are characterized by differences in their crystal spacings and other physical properties. The normal soaps result from the usual saponification processes, or from the complete neutralization of the fatty acids with alkali hydroxides, carbonates, or allied compounds. The acid soaps, on the other hand, result from partial hydrolysis of the normal soaps or partial neutralization of the fatty acids in alcoholic solution. Since the fatty acids are monobasic, true acid soaps cannot theoretically exist, the term actually referring to an equimolar compound of neutral soap and free acid. In 1929, Ekwall and Mylius [129] suggested the existence of acid soaps containing other than equimolar ratios of the salts and acid and claimed the isolation not only of equimolar compounds but also of compounds such as 2 sodium palmitate·1 palmitic acid or 1 sodium palmitate·2 palmitic acid. The next year, Malkin [130] investigated the acid potassium and sodium salts of a number of the higher fatty acids and showed that only the neutral soaps and equimolar compounds are true chemical individuals. The non-equimolar compositions previously described were shown to be mixtures of the acid soaps with either the neutral soaps or the acids. An x-ray examination [131] of both normal and acid potassium soaps of the acids from formic to tetracosanoic acid inclusive showed that both types of soap exist in double molecules with the polar groups in contact, the long crystal spacing thus relating to twice the length of a single molecule. Plots of the long spacings of both neutral and acid soaps against the number of carbon atoms lie on straight lines, the spacings of the acid soaps being substantially greater than those of the neutral. Some of the values observed for the long crystal spacings of the normal and acid soaps are as follows: K laurate, 30.2 Å; acid K laurate, 35.53 Å; K myristate, 33.95 Å; acid K myristate, 40.45 Å; K palmitate, 37.9 Å; acid K palmitate, 45.29 Å; K stearate, 42 Å; acid K stearate, 50.47 Å. The values for the normal soaps correspond to a chain inclined at 54°54′, whereas those for the acid soaps approximate a vertical chain.

The acid potassium salts of a number of saturated acids have been synthesized by Levi,[132] who has studied their conversion to normal soaps, and also the relative solubilities of the two types in ethanol. Acid K butyrate, m.p. 85–140°, acid K valerate, m.p. 55–120°, and acid K caprylate, m.p. 80–140°, are transformed into neutral soaps and free acids upon adding ether to their alcoholic solutions. The acid soaps of the higher acids are not changed by this treatment, acid K undecanoate being transformed in boiling benzene into the free acid and the neutral salt, the acid salt again being formed upon cooling the solution. Acid K laurate, m.p. 80–150°, acid K myristate, m.p. 95–160°, acid K palmitate, m.p. 100–160°, and acid K stearate, m.p. 100–160°, are less soluble in 99.8% ethanol than the corresponding neutral soaps, the solubilities of the acid and neutral potassium soaps of stearic acid at 13.5°, for example, being 0.113 and 0.1896 g. per 100 g., respectively, in this solvent. The solubility in ethanol of acid potassium oleate, originally prepared by McBain and Stewart,[133] is greater (6.5% at 13.5°) than that of the neutral salt (4.313% at 13.5°). Neutral soaps of the higher acids can form mixed acid salts with acids of different chain length. Such mixed acid salts can be separated from the neutral salts by fractional crystallization from ethanol.

Upon heating, the higher fatty acid soaps of the alkali metals apparently go through a number of characteristic transitions before becoming isotropic liquids.[134] Such a phenomenon is occasioned by the fact that the hydrocarbon portion of the molecule, owing to oscillation energy, easily assumes the liquid state, with a consequent disruption of the crystal lattice. Complete melting is only accomplished when the alkali metal ion enters the liquid-crystalline or the liquid state. As a consequence, such a compound exhibits a series of transitions before the true melting point is reached.[135] The extreme difficulties encountered in obtaining completely anhydrous alkali metal soaps raise the question as to whether some of the values which have been observed for these transitions actually characterize the behavior of anhydrous soaps. To the writer's knowledge, none of the directions described for the preparation of anhydrous alkali metal soaps of the higher fatty acids is completely reliable. A study of the thermal behavior of the soaps is also rendered quite difficult owing to the high temperatures involved.

The alkali soaps of the fatty acids are water soluble, the solubility decreasing rapidly with increasing length of the hydrocarbon chain. Aqueous solutions of the higher soaps, beyond a certain critical concentration, consist essentially of associated ions and associated molecules, the presence of which is responsible for the characteristic behavior of such solutions. The many studies which have been made upon the osmotic, electrical, and other properties of aqueous soap solutions form much of the basis of our present-day knowledge of colloidal electrolytes. The reader is referred to the many original contributions of McBain, Hartley, and others upon various aspects of this subject.[136]

The ammonium soaps of the fatty acids are represented by both neutral salts, RCO_2NH_4, and the acid salts, $RCO_2NH_4 \cdot RCO_2H$, the latter of which are the more stable. The neutral ammonium soaps readily lose ammonia upon exposure to the air, being converted to the acid soaps which are only decomposed at higher temperatures. Because of the relative instabilities of the neutral salts, many of the constants reported for these compounds undoubtedly refer to mixtures of neutral salts, acid salts, and free acids.

Although the ammonium soaps of the higher fatty acids had been known for many years, the first complete description of their preparation and general properties was published in 1910 by Falciola,[137] who prepared many ammonium soaps of both saturated and unsaturated acids by treatment of alcoholic solutions of the acids with concentrated aqueous ammonia. The great differences between the solubilities of the ammonium soaps of saturated and unsaturated acids led to the suggestion that they be employed for the separation of oleic acid from a mixture of oleic, palmitic, and stearic acids. These salts were described as melting over a very appreciable temperature range with considerable decomposition. Currie [138] has obtained a number of the neutral ammonium salts of the higher fatty acids by passing dry ammonia into a benzene solution of the acids, and somewhat later McMaster and Magill [139] prepared the neutral salts by the action of dry ammonia on ether solutions of the acids. Ammonium myristate was described as readily soluble in ethanol, methanol, and acetic acid, and insoluble in ether, benzene, acetone, and chloroform. It is stable in dry air at ordinary temperatures, but decomposes at 50°. In 1939, Kench and Malkin [140] published the results of their investigation of both neutral and acid ammonium soaps of the fatty acids from heptanoic to stearic acid inclusive. It was found that the neutral salts result from the action of ammonia on alcoholic solutions of the acids, but that the acid salts are formed when ether solutions are treated with dry ammonia. The salts obtained from ethanol showed two spacings upon x-ray examination, the shorter relating to the neutral salt and the longer to the acid salt. In both neutral and acid salts the spacings correspond to double molecules, the neutral salts being inclined at an angle of 45°40′ to the reflecting planes whereas the acid salts possess vertical chains. The melting points of the acid ammonium soaps, when plotted against the number of carbon atoms in the acid, form a continuous curve, distinguishing them from the neutral salts for which widely varying and discordant values have been reported. Table V shows the melting

TABLE V

MELTING POINTS OF ACID AMMONIUM SALTS OF THE FATTY ACIDS

C Atoms in Acid	Melting Point, °C.	C Atoms in Acid	Melting Point, °C.
7	45	14	84
8	54	15	86
10	68	16	89
11	72	17	91
12	77	18	93
13	81		

points of the acid ammonium salts as reported by Kench and Malkin.[140]

The melting points which have been reported for the neutral ammonium soaps are undoubtedly much in error, since the true values are probably higher than those of the corresponding acid salts. When heated in a sealed capillary tube to avoid decomposition, ammonium laurate was observed to melt at 130°, a value much higher than any of those previously reported for this compound.

The lithium salts of the higher acids are sparingly soluble in water and somewhat more soluble in ethanol. The solubilities in both solvents decrease rapidly with increase in molecular weight of the acids.[141] Jacobson and Holmes [142] have prepared the lithium salts of lauric, myristic, palmitic, and stearic acids by adding the calculated amount of lithium acetate to ethanol solutions of the respective fatty acids and have determined the solubilities of these soaps in a number of solvents. The following melting points were reported for the lithium salts: laurate, 229.2–229.8°; myristate, 223.6–224.2°; palmitate, 224–225°; stearate, 220.5–221.5°. The solubilities of the lithium salts in water in grams per 100 g. at 25°

are as follows: laurate, 0.187; myristate, 0.036; palmitate, 0.015; stearate, 0.01. These salts are moderately soluble in methanol, less soluble in ethanol, and very slightly soluble in ether, 1-pentanol, chloroform, pentyl acetate, methyl acetate, and acetone.

The alkaline earth salts of the fatty acids may be prepared by saponification of glycerides or other esters with alkaline earth oxides or hydroxides, or by double decomposition reactions between the soluble alkali soaps and the alkaline earth salts. Both calcium and magnesium soaps of the higher acids possess very limited solubilities in water, and their formation is immediately observable when the soluble alkali soaps are added to the so-called hard waters. The calcium soaps of the higher acids are extensively used commercially, their biggest use being as emulsifying agents in the manufacture of solid lubricants and other greases. Certain magnesium soaps, particularly magnesium oleate, have been rather generally used in dry-cleaning compositions, in which they increase the electrical conductivity of the solvent and thus prevent the accumulation of static charges.

The calcium soaps are somewhat soluble in organic solvents, but their solubilities are greatly reduced by traces of water.[143] Anhydrous calcium oleate is appreciably soluble in benzene.[144] The calcium soaps sinter before melting and melt with considerable decomposition, calcium palmitate and calcium stearate having been reported [145] to melt at 153–156° and 150–154°, respectively. When heated to higher temperatures, such salts yield ketones and hydrocarbons, the decomposition of calcium soaps having been suggested as one of the processes involved in the formation of petroleum.[24]

Many uses have been suggested for the calcium soaps of the higher acids. Among these may be mentioned their use in the waterproofing of paper,[146,147] and their incorporation in waxes,[148] varnishes,[149] paints,[150] and cleansing compositions.[151]

The magnesium salts are very similar in their chemical and physical properties to those of calcium. Magnesium laurate, myristate, palmitate, and stearate have been obtained by adding a slight excess of magnesium acetate to warm ethanol solutions of the respective acids.[142] The magnesium salts possess somewhat lower melting points than the corresponding calcium salts, the following values having been reported: magnesium laurate, 150.4°; myristate, 131.6°; palmitate, 121–122°; and stearate, 132°.

Like the calcium salts, the magnesium salts possess very limited solubilities in water and organic solvents. They are more soluble in methanol than in water and are practically insoluble in ether and the higher alcohols at low temperatures. Unsaturation is attended by a slight increase in solubility in all solvents.[150] The solubilities of magnesium salts are comparable to, but generally somewhat higher than, those of the corresponding calcium salts.[153] The presence of salts such as sodium chloride materially increases the water solubilities of both calcium and magnesium soaps of the higher acids.[154] The emulsifying action of magnesium oleate on a mixture of benzene and water has been studied,[155] those emulsions containing more than 70% of water being water continuous. Gels formed from magnesium oleate and alcohol together with combustible materials have been suggested for use as solid fuels.[156] The use of magnesium soaps in various coating compositions has been proposed.[157] Several bromine derivatives of calcium and magnesium soaps, such as calcium mono- and dibromobehenate and magnesium monobromobehenate, have been investigated as therapeutic agents.[158]

The barium soaps of the higher aliphatic acids may be obtained by adding an ethanol solution of barium hydroxide to ethanol solutions of the acids.[142] Their solubilities in water are comparable to those of the corresponding calcium and magnesium soaps. The barium soaps are practically insoluble in methanol, ethanol, ether, acetone, and other organic solvents. Barium oleate has been described as a white, amorphous powder which is insoluble in water and slightly soluble in hot benzene.[159] The barium salts of chlorinated acids are appreciably soluble in ether and may be separated from those of the saturated acids by the use of this solvent.[160]

The strontium soaps generally resemble the barium soaps, those of the brominated acids being appreciably soluble in organic solvents.[161] The strontium soaps have been suggested as ingredients of pyrotechnic compositions.[162]

Very little is known concerning the beryllium soaps of the higher aliphatic acids. Lacombe [163] has prepared the beryllium soaps of several of the lower acids. The structure of the beryllium soaps of the higher acids has not been determined.

Aluminum salts of the fatty acids are best prepared by treating ammonium soaps with soluble aluminum salts. A number of patents have been issued covering various methods of preparing aluminum salts of the higher acids, including processes such as heating solutions of the fatty acids in organic solvents with aluminum alkoxides,[164] or with aluminum hydroxide in the presence of alkaline catalysts.[165]   A so-called pseudo aluminum stearate has been stated [166] to result by the action of aluminum hydroxide on stearic acid.   The preparation of aluminum oleate by the action of aluminum hydroxide on ammonium oleate has been described in detail.[167]   The aluminum soaps are generally obtained as jelly-like masses which are extremely difficult to purify.   They are slightly soluble in water and moderately soluble in organic solvents. Solutions of aluminum soaps in organic solvents possess quite high viscosities and frequently set to stable gels.   Because of this property the aluminum soaps are often used as thickeners for oils and as components of various solid lubricating compositions.   A rather recent patent [168] discloses the addition of both aluminum and magnesium oleates to a lubricating oil for the preparation of a solid lubricant.   Aluminum soaps are frequently used as waterproofing agents and for treating textiles.[169]   Many other uses have been suggested for the aluminum soaps, a few of which are: as an ingredient of stencil paper,[170] as a soundproofer in wall board,[171] as a wire-drawing lubricant,[172] and as a dewaxing agent for lubricating oils.[173]

Although the thallium soaps of the fatty acids are not of commercial importance, the great solubility differences which exist between the thallium salts of saturated and unsaturated acids, and also their mesomorphic behavior on melting, make them one of the most interesting series of fatty acid soaps.   Meigen and Neuberger [174] have claimed a practically quantitative separation of stearic from oleic acid by utilization of the difference in solubility of their thallium salts in 96% ethanol.

Thallium salts of the higher acids have been prepared by the neutralization of their ethanol solutions with an $N/10$ aqueous solution of thallium hydroxide, using phenolphthalein as the indicator, followed by crystallization from or washing with 96% ethanol.   Thallous stearate, m.p. 119°, thallous palmitate, m.p. 115–117°, and thallous oleate, m.p. 83°, have been prepared by this method.[175]   These salts were described as white powders which crystallize from ethanol in small needles.   They possess limited solubilities in water, the oleate being the most soluble and the stearate the least.   In 96% ethanol, however, the solubility of the oleate is many times that of the stearate or palmitate, as shown in Fig. 2.

Thallous laurate, m.p. 125–126°, and thallous myristate, m.p. 120–123°, were subsequently prepared by Holde and Takehara,[176] by the procedure employed for the higher members. Thallous

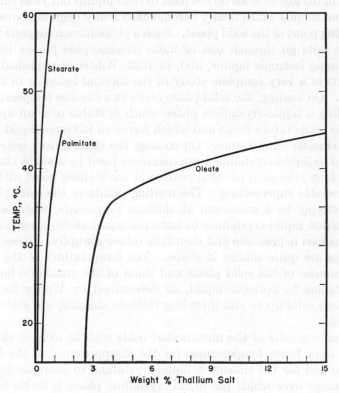

FIG. 2.   Solubilities of thallium soaps in 96% ethanol.

valerate, m.p. 145–147°, has been stated [177] to be very soluble in water, ethanol, and hot benzene, and sparingly soluble in ether.

A procedure for the separation of saturated from unsaturated acids by means of their thallous salts has been described by Holde and coworkers,[178] who have reported the following solubilities for thallous oleate: 2.254 g. in 100 g. 96% ethanol at 15°; 0.924 g. in 100 g. 50% ethanol at 15°; 0.0461 g. in 100 g. water at 15°; and 0.3034 g. in 100 g. water at 80°. The solubilities of thallous laurate, myristate, palmitate, and stearate in ether have been reported,[179] and it was observed that the solubility of thallous palmitate represents a minimum for the series in this solvent.

The thallium salts of the lower acids formic, acetic, and propionic sinter below their melting points and melt to clear isotropic liquids. It was reported, however, by Holde and others that the thallous salts of the higher acids do not melt to clear liquids but yield turbid, viscous liquids which finally become clear many degrees above the melting point of the solid phase. Such a phenomenon suggests that these salts go through one or more mesomorphic phases before becoming isotropic liquids, and, in 1926, Walter [180] published the results of a very complete study of the thermal behavior of these salts. On heating, the solid phase melts at a definite temperature, yielding a liquid-crystalline phase which is stable over an appreciable temperature range and which forms an isotropic liquid at a reproducible temperature. On cooling, the change from isotropic liquid to liquid-crystalline form manifests itself by a slight change in volume, the solid phase appearing at the melting point without appreciable supercooling. The melting points of the solid phase rise steeply to a maximum at thallous propionate, whereas the transition liquid-crystalline to isotropic liquid shows a maximum at thallous heptanoate and then falls rather abruptly. These two curves are quite similar in shape. The temperatures of the disappearance of the solid phase and those of the transition liquid-crystalline to isotropic liquid, as determined by Walter for the thallous salts up to and including thallous stearate, are shown in Fig. 3.

Thallous salts of the unsaturated acids such as oleic or elaidic acid show lower temperatures for the disappearance of the solid phase and for the transition liquid-crystalline to isotropic liquid, the range over which the liquid-crystalline phase is stable being approximately the same as that for the saturated soaps.

This behavior of the thallous salts on heating probably finds its counterpart in many of the soaps of the higher acids, as indicated by more recent work on the soaps of the alkali metals. [181, 182, 183, 184] The thallous soaps, because of their stabilities and relatively low melting points, offer an excellent opportunity for the study of this phenomenon.

Many of the heavy metal soaps of the fatty acids have been important industrial chemicals for generations, and it is unfortunate that more is not known concerning the physical and chemical properties of this interesting class of chemical compounds. The industrial uses to which the heavy metal soaps have been adapted are many and varied. The manganese, lead, and cobalt soaps of the higher unsaturated acids have long been employed as drying agents in paints; those of copper and mercury are extensively used as algicides in marine paints;[185] copper, mercury, and other soaps are employed as ingredients in various fungicidal sprays;[186,187]

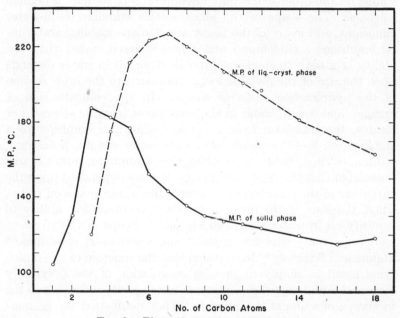

Fig. 3.   Phase changes in thallium soaps.

mercury soaps are used in salves and ointments;[188] and those of zinc have long been employed as dusting and drying powders.[189] Many of the heavy metal soaps are used for treating leather and various fabrics. They have been employed as mordants for dyes, and as coloring agents in varnishes and other coatings and in the paper and rubber industries. Mercuric stearate has been proposed as a bactericide for paper money and other surfaces.[190] Salts such as zinc undecanoate have been suggested as ingredients of cosmetics and allied substances.[191] The soaps of catalytic metals such as nickel have been proposed as hydrogenating catalysts.[192,193,194] Considerable interest has been evidenced within recent years in the addition of heavy metal soaps to lubricants; lead oleate[195,196] chromium oleate,[197] nickel and chromium oleates,[198] mixtures of nickel and magnesium soaps,[199] and mixtures of chromium oleate, tin oleate, and lead compounds [200] having been suggested for this purpose. Several of the metallic soaps, particularly the lead soaps, are used extensively in the analytical separation of mixtures of the fatty acids.

Most of the heavy metal soaps possess limited solubilities in water; on the other hand, they are appreciably soluble in organic solvents. The soaps of the alkali metals stabilize oil-in-water emulsions, and many of the heavy metal soaps stabilize water-in-oil emulsions. Hildebrand and others [201] have stated that the ability of a soap to emulsify water in oil or oil in water depends upon the size of the metallic ion as compared to the cross section of the hydrocarbon chain or chains. In the emulsification of organic liquids with water in the presence of metallic stearates or oleates, the transition from a stable oil-in-water emulsion to a stable water-in-oil emulsion follows the order cesium, potassium, sodium, calcium, silver, magnesium, zinc, aluminum, iron. It was postulated that the emulsifying properties are dependent upon the curvature of the adsorbed film towards the water or the oil phase. Thus, the salts of the divalent metals have much less ability to emulsify oil in water than water in oil.[202] Soaps of the trivalent metals are quite effective in stabilizing water-in-oil emulsions.[203] Stamm and Kraemer [204] have stated that the function of an emulsifying agent is simply to prevent coagulation of the previously dispersed liquid particles, a function which is dependent upon the formation of a film at the interface. They doubt that the geometrical shape or size of the emulsifying agent is determinative as regards this function. Adsorbed films at such interfaces are probably monomolecular.[205, 206]

The heavy metal soaps of the fatty acids are generally prepared by one of two procedures. Either the free acid dissolved in an organic solvent is treated with a solution of a metallic salt,[142] or an aqueous solution of an alkali metal soap is treated with an aqueous solution of a heavy metal salt.[207, 208, 209] In the latter procedure a small amount of ethanol is generally added to the reaction mixture in order to retain the alkali metal soap in solution. Because of the insolubility of most of the heavy metal soaps in water, the latter method is generally employed, although certain of the heavy metal soaps are frequently very difficult to purify and show a tendency to occlude the more soluble alkali soaps. The heavy metal soaps are generally amorphous solids which can be obtained in crystalline form from the appropriate solvent. The preparation and chemical and physical behavior of some of the more important heavy metal soaps are briefly discussed in the following. The lead salts of the fatty acids are white, amorphous powders which melt without appreciable decomposition. They have been prepared by addition of an ethanol solution of lead acetate to ethanol solutions of the acids,[142] or by addition of aqueous solutions of lead salts to aqueous solutions of the alkali metal soaps.[209] The melting points which have been reported [142, 209, 210, 211] for the lead salts of many of the higher fatty acids are shown in Table VI.

TABLE VI

MELTING POINTS OF LEAD SOAPS

Acid	Melting Point, °C.
Caproic	95
Enanthic	85
Caprylic	100
Pelargonic	95–100
Undecanoic	90–92
Lauric	104.6–104.8
Myristic	108.6–108.8
Palmitic	112.2–112.4
Stearic	115.6–115.8
Oleic	≈50
Hydnocarpic	77–78
Chaulmoogric	83

The lead soaps of the higher saturated acids possess limited solubilities in water and organic solvents. The fact that these soaps are practically insoluble in ether and petroleum ether, whereas those of the unsaturated acids are quite soluble in these solvents, has long been used as the basis for the analytical separation of saturated from unsaturated acids.[212]

The silver salts of the fatty acids have been obtained by addition of an ammoniacal solution of silver nitrate to alcoholic solutions of the acids [142, 213] or by addition of silver nitrate to aqueous solutions of the alkali soaps.[209] They have been described as white, fluffy powders which melt with considerable decomposition above 200°. The following melting points have been reported: [142] silver laurate, 212–213°; myristate, 211°; palmitate, 209°; and stearate, 209°. The silver salts are very slightly soluble in water, ethanol, methanol, and ether. They yield reversible gels in toluene or xylene and in various chlorinated solvents.[214] Silver oleate gives a gel with benzene, but the silver salts of the saturated acids do not yield gels with this solvent.

The cadmium salts of the lower fatty acids butyric to caproic acid inclusive, are readily soluble in water; those of the higher acids are almost completely insoluble.[215] Cadmium oleate has been described [216] as a yellow, waxy solid which is soluble in most organic solvents, with many of which it forms gels. Cadmium stearate yields a clear solution with toluene which on cooling to 60° forms a white gel.[217] This gel becomes crystalline upon further cooling. The cadmium soaps of mixed acids form gels when dissolved in paraffin oil.[218]

Several examples of mercurous and mercuric soaps have been described,[208] the latter being the better known. Mercuric soaps of the higher saturated acids are white powders which melt sharply without decomposition. The following melting points have been reported for the mercuric soaps: [209] laurate, 100°; palmitate, 105°; stearate, 112.2°. Mercuric oleate is a plastic solid which is unstable, yielding metallic mercury and oleic acid upon standing. It is extremely difficult to purify owing to its tendency to hold water. Mercuric enanthate,[219] m.p. 106.5°, is a white solid slightly soluble in water and soluble in ethanol, methanol, ether, and chloroform.

Interest in the bismuth salts of the higher acids has largely centered around their therapeutic use. Lauter, Jurist, and Christiansen [220] have described the preparation of bismuth laurate, myristate, palmitate, and oleate, and have determined their toxicities by intramuscular injections into albino rats. Emulsions of bismuth salts, suitable for injection, have been prepared by dissolving the salts in volatile organic solvents, adding the solutions to neutral oils, and evaporating the solvents.[221] Assimilable bismuth salts of mixed acids, such as bismuth oleate-salicylate, have been synthesized.[222] Stable solutions of bismuth salts in vegetable oils have been proposed as therapeutic agents.[223] Antimony oleate, which is soluble in organic solvents, vegetable oils, and similar solvents, has been prepared both by the action of antimony oxide on oleic acid [224] and by double decomposition reactions.[225]

Zinc stearate is by far the most important of the zinc salts of the higher acids, being extensively used in medicine and the arts. The "zinc stearate" of commerce is actually a mixture of the zinc salts of palmitic and stearic acids and is prepared by the action of zinc oxide on a mixture of these acids. The zinc salts of the higher saturated acids are white, fluffy powders with a talclike feel. They melt without decomposition and upon cooling form translucent, glassy, brittle masses which are easily powdered.[209] The following melting points have been reported for the zinc salts: stearate, 130°; palmitate, 129°; laurate, 128°. Zinc oleate is a cream-colored, waxlike, amorphous mass, which melts at approximately 70°. It is soluble in benzene, and is apparently not associated in this solvent.[226]

Both the cuprous and the cupric salts of the fatty acids have been described. The former have been prepared either by the reduction of cupric soaps or by the action of alkali soaps on moist cuprous chloride.[208] The latter may easily be obtained by double decomposition reactions. Cupric laurate is a light-blue powder, m.p. 111–113°; the palmitate melts at 120° to yield a clear, blue liquid; and the stearate melts at 125° to a blue liquid which sets to a brittle, opaque mass on cooling. The oleate, m.p. about 100°, is an amorphous, bluish mass which is soluble in ether and other organic solvents. A solution of cupric oleate in xylene passes through a number of color changes when heated.[227]

Several of the nickel and cobalt salts of the higher fatty acids have been synthesized and described. Nickel oleate is a bluish green oil which is appreciably soluble in water. The laurate, palmitate, and stearate of nickel melt at 44°, 80°, and 100°, respectively. The stearate undergoes some decomposition on melting. Cobalt palmitate and cobalt stearate melt at 70–75° and 73–75°, respectively.[207]

The manganous, chromous, and chromic salts of oleic and stearic acids have been described.[208, 228, 229] Chromic oleate is very soluble in benzene, and the heating of its solutions produces a series of color changes which have been attributed to solvation effects.[230] Chromium palmitate forms an elastic gel when heated in xylene.[231]

Ferric salts of unsaturated acids are very soluble in organic solvents and offer a source of soluble iron compounds of medical interest. Solutions of ferric oleate in cod liver oil have been stated to possess therapeutic value,[232] and the iron salts of iodo fatty acids have been proposed as medicants.[233] Both the ferrous and the ferric salts of linolenic acid are extremely soluble in organic solvents, solutions of the former being rapidly oxidized.[234] Dyer[235] has utilized the preferential solubilities of ferric salts in ether and water as a means for the colorimetric identification of saturated fatty acids. Very few of the iron salts of the higher acids have been obtained in a pure state. Klimont [236] has described ferric palmitate as an amorphous powder which melts at 182°.

A basic stannic stearate of the probable formula $Sn(C_{17}H_{35}CO_2)_4 \cdot SnO(C_{17}H_{35}CO_2)_2$ has been described by Koenig [207] as a yellowish solid which melts at about 50°. This salt was prepared by the addition of stannic chloride to a solution of cupric stearate in benzene, cupric chloride being precipitated immediately and the stannic soap being obtained by evaporation of the benzene. The stannous and stannic soaps are very easily hydrolyzed.

Fatty acid soaps of titanium, zirconium, and thorium, and also mixed metallic soaps containing these metals, have been described in the patent literature. [237]

To the writer's knowledge no pure silicon soaps of the fatty acids have been prepared. So-called silicon carboxylates have been described, the method of preparation being to heat a mixed silicic anhydride, such as silicic-acetic anhydride, with a higher fatty acid. [238] The addition of silicon tetrachloride to a benzene solution of cupric stearate gives a precipitate of cupric chloride, the colorless filtrate yielding a gelatin-like solid upon evaporation of the solvent. [207]

Stoddart and Hill [239] have investigated the separation of the rare earth metals from one another by the fractional precipitation of their stearates, the method being based upon the differences which exist in the basicity of the rare earths. When an alcoholic solution of potassium stearate is added to a neutral solution of the rare earth nitrates, the potassium ion of the soap removes the nitrate ion from the most basic of the earths, thus leaving the earth metal free to form an insoluble stearate. By adding only a portion of the amount of potassium stearate required for complete precipitation, an effective separation of certain of the rare earths can be accomplished by this procedure. Gadolinium and europium were also separated from their ores, and the process was shown to be adaptable to the purification of the rare earths of the cerium group.

The solubility behaviors of the palmitates and stearates of copper, chromium, cobalt, nickel, manganese, and tin in a large number of organic solvents have been investigated by Koenig. [207] Solutions of such salts, particularly in non-polar solvents, set to gels upon cooling, thus indicating a high degree of solvation. All these soaps are very soluble in pyridine, with which they form crystalline addition products, the composition and melting points of which are

shown in Table VII.   These addition products undergo a number
of color changes upon heating.

TABLE VII

ADDITION PRODUCTS OF METALLIC SOAPS WITH PYRIDINE

Addition Compound	M.P.,°C.
$Cu(C_{17}H_{35}CO_2)_2 \cdot C_5H_5N$	87.0
$Cu(C_{15}H_{31}CO_2)_2 \cdot C_5H_5N$	86.6
$Co(C_{17}H_{35}CO_2)_2 \cdot 2C_5H_5N$	70.4
$Co(C_{15}H_{31}CO_2)_2 \cdot 2C_5H_5N$	64.0
$Ni(C_{17}H_{35}CO_2)_2 \cdot C_5H_5N$	85.4

Solutions of the heavy metal soaps in organic solvents offer many
interesting problems which merit further investigation.   Such solutions can take part in many double decomposition reactions which
Kahlenberg [240] considered to be non-ionic reactions.   However, a
subsequent study [241] of the conductivity effects attending such
reactions has conclusively shown them to be ionic.   Solutions of
the heavy metal soaps in paraffin oil readily form gels, the structures of which have been the subject of an extensive investigation.[242]

In spite of the fact that the heavy metal soaps of the fatty acids
have been known for years, it is clearly evident that our present
knowledge of their chemical and physical behavior is largely
empirical.   This situation will undoubtedly be remedied by future
investigations.

References

1. Fraps and Rather, *J. Ind. Eng. Chem.*, **2**, 454 (1910).
2. Stürcke, *Ann.*, **223**, 283 (1884).
3. Brodie, *ibid.*, **67**, 180 (1848); **71**, 144 (1849).
4. Hata, *J. Chem. Soc. Japan*, **58**, 1188 (1937).
5. Täufel, Thaler, and Schreyegg, *Fettchem. Umschau*, **43**, 26 (1936).
6. Täufel, Heinisch, and Heimann, *Biochem. Z.*, **303**, 324 (1940).
7. Marcelet, *Bull. soc. chim.* [5], **3**, 2055 (1936).
8. Marcelet, *J. pharm. chim.*, **24**, 213 (1936); *Compt. rend.*, **202**, 867 (1936).
9. Tsujimoto, *J. Ind. Eng. Chem.*, **8**, 889 (1916); *J. Soc. Chem. Ind.*, *Japan*, **19**, 277 (1916); **20**, 1069 (1917).
10. Tsujimoto, *ibid.*, **20**, 1099 (1917); Toyama, *Chem. Umschau*, **30**, 181 (1923).
11. Gottlieb, *Ann.*, **57**, 33 (1846).
12. Bolley, *Dinglers Polytech. J.* [4], **179**, 463 (1866).

13. Berthelot, *Compt. rend.*, **89**, 336 (1879).
14. Heintz, *Ann. Phys. Chem.*, **94**, 272 (1855).
15. Thorpe and Young, *Ber.*, **5**, 556 (1872).
16. Johnston, *ibid.*, **8**, 1465 (1875).
17. Engler, *ibid.*, **21**, 1816 (1888); Engler and Singer, *ibid.*, **26**, 1449 (1893).
18. Mailhe, *Ann. chim.* [9], **17**, 304 (1922).
19. Marcusson and Bauerschäfer, *Chem.-Ztg.*, **49**, 1045 (1925).
20. Waterman and Perquin, *Proc. Acad. Sci. Amsterdam*, **27**, 83 (1924).
21. Faragher, Egloff, and Morrell, *Ind. Eng. Chem.*, **24**, 440 (1932); Egloff and Morrell, *ibid.*, **24**, 1426 (1932).
22. Stadnikov, Gavrilov, and Vinogradov, Russ. Patent 1,245 (1924).
23. Pictet and Potok, *Helv. Chim. Acta*, **2**, 501 (1919).
24. Künkler and Schwedhelm, *Seifensieder-Ztg.*, **35**, 1285 (1908).
25. Inouye, *J. Chem. Soc. Japan*, **42**, 1065 (1921).
26. Grün and Wirth, *Ber.*, **53B**, 1301 (1920).
27. Shimizu and the Nippon Glycerine Kôgyô Kabushiki Kaisha, Japan. Patent 40,210 (1921).
28. Hirose and Yamada, *J. Soc. Chem. Ind.*, *Japan*, **25**, 1428 (1922).
29. Zelinsky and Lawrowsky, *Ber.*, **61B**, 1054 (1928).
30. Deutsche Hydrierwerke A.-G., Ger. Patent 629,244 (1936).
31. Sinozaki and Kubo, *J. Soc. Chem. Ind.*, *Japan*, **38**, S.b. 21 (1935).
32. Ueno, *ibid.*, **33**, S.b. 264 (1930).
33. Krafft, *Ber.*, **15**, 1687 (1882).
34. Krafft, *ibid.*, **15**, 1711 (1882).
35. Clemmensen, *ibid.*, **46**, 1837 (1913).
36. Hess and Bappert, *Ann.*, **441**, 151 (1925).
37. Backer and Strating, *Rec. trav. chim.*, **59**, 933 (1940).
38. Francis, King, and Willis, *J. Chem. Soc.*, 999 (1937).
39. Müller and Saville, *ibid.*, **127**, 599 (1925).
40. Piper, Chibnall, Hopkins, Pollard, Smith, and Williams, *Biochem. J.*, **25**, 2072 (1931).
41. Strating and Backer, *Rec. trav. chim.*, **55**, 903 (1936).
42. Mikeska, Smith, and Lieber, *J. Org. Chem.*, **2**, 499 (1938)
43. Mikeska and Cohen, *ibid.*, **6**, 787 (1941).
44. I. G. Farbenind. A.-G., Brit. Patent 453,778 (1936).
45. Schmidt and Grosser, *Ber.*, **75B**, 826 (1942).
46. Levene, West, and van der Scheer, *J. Biol. Chem.*, **20**, 521 (1915).
47. Sorabji, *J. Chem. Soc.*, **47**, 37 (1885).
48. Carey and Smith, *ibid.*, 346 (1933).
49. Gascard, *Ann. chim.* [9], **15**, 332 (1921).
50. Wurtz, *Ann. chim. phys.* [3], **44**, 275 (1855); *Ann.*, **96**, 364 (1855).
51. Schorlemmer, *ibid.*, **161**, 263 (1872).
52. Lebedew, *J. Russ. Phys. Chem. Soc.*, **16**, 299 (1884).
53. Krafft, *Ber.*, **19**, 2218 (1886).
54. Gascard, *Compt. rend.*, **153**, 1484 (1911).
55. Lewis and Tryon, *J. Chem. Education*, **7**, 2712 (1930).
56. Delcourt, *Bull. soc. chim. Belg.*, **40**, 284 (1931).
57. Fittig and König, *Ann.*, **144**, 277 (1867).
58. Schweinitz, *Ber.*, **19**, 640 (1886).

59. Krafft, *ibid.*, **19**, 2982 (1886).
60. Gilman and Turck, *J. Am. Chem. Soc.*, **61**, 478 (1939).
61. Schlubach and Goes, *Ber.*, **55B**, 2889 (1922).
62. Goldschmidt and Schön, *ibid.*, **59B**, 948 (1926).
63. Bachmann and Clarke, *J. Am. Chem. Soc.*, **49**, 2089 (1927).
64. Lewis, Hendricks, and Yohe, *ibid.*, **50**, 1993 (1928).
65. Lewis and Yohe, *Proc. Iowa Acad. Sci.*, **32**, 327 (1925).
66. Carothers, Hill, Kirby, and Jacobson, *J. Am. Chem. Soc.*, **52**, 5279 (1930).
67. Deatherage and Olcott, *ibid.*, **61**, 630 (1939).
68. Grignard, *Ann. chim. phys.* [7], **24**, 433 (1901).
69. Houben, *Ber.*, **36**, 3083 (1903).
70. Braun, Deutsch, and Schmatloch, *ibid.*, **45**, 1246 (1912).
71. Brooks and Humphrey, *J. Am. Chem. Soc.*, **40**, 822 (1918).
72. Kirrmann, *Bull. soc. chim.* [4], **39**, 988 (1926).
73. Wilkinson, *J. Chem. Soc.*, 3057 (1931).
74. Schmidt, Schoeller, and Eberlein, *Ber.*, **74B**, 1313 (1941).
75. Waterman and de Kok, *Rec. trav. chim.*, **52**, 298 (1933).
76. Kozacik and Reid, *J. Am. Chem. Soc.*, **60**, 2436 (1938).
77. Kolbe, *Ann.*, **69**, 257 (1849).
78. Petersen, *Z. Elektrochem.*, **12**, 141 (1906).
79. Petersen, *Oversigt. K. Danske Vidensk. Selsk. Forh.*, No. 1 (1912) [*C.A.*, **6**, 3269 (1912)].
80. Fichter and Zumbrunn, *Helv. Chim. Acta*, **10**, 869 (1927).
81. Dover and Helmers, *Ind. Eng. Chem.*, **27**, 455 (1935).
82. Rhodes, *Chem. News*, **108**, 201 (1913).
83. Wertyporoch and Firla, *Ann.*, **500**, 287 (1933).
84. Bialobrzeski and Nencki, *Ber.*, **30**, 1776 (1897).
85. Gurewitsch, *ibid.*, **30**, 2424 (1899).
86. Gustavson, *J. prakt. Chem.* [2], **68**, 209 (1903).
87. Friedel and Crafts, *Compt. rend.*, **84**, 1392 (1877).
88. Gilman and Calloway, *J. Am. Chem. Soc.*, **55**, 4197 (1933).
89. Calloway, *Chem. Rev.*, **17**, 327 (1935).
90. Flett, U. S. Patents 2,134,711-2 (1938).
91. Dumas and Péligot, *Ann. chim. phys.* [2], **62**, 5 (1836).
92. Tüttschew, *Jahresber. Fortschr. Chem.*, 405 (1860).
93. Zelinskii and Przheval'skii, *J. Russ. Phys. Chem. Soc.*, **39**, 1168 (1907).
94. Clarke and Adams, *J. Am. Chem. Soc.*, **37**, 2536 (1915).
95. Krafft, *Ber.*, **17**, 1371 (1884).
96. Krafft and Reuter, *ibid.*, **25**, 2243 (1892).
97. Hill and Tyson, *J. Am. Chem. Soc.*, **50**, 172 (1928).
98. Smith, *Ann. chim. phys.* [3], **6**, 40 (1842).
99. Krafft, *Ber.*, **16**, 3018 (1883).
100. Messer, *Chem. News*, **138**, 292 (1929).
101. Pummerer and Kranz, *Ber.*, **62B**, 2620 (1929).
102. Brigl, *Z. physiol. Chem.*, **95**, 161 (1915).
103. Niemann and Wagner, *J. Org. Chem.*, **7**, 227 (1942).
104. Gladstone and Tribe, *J. Chem. Soc.*, **27**, 406 (1874).
105. Swallen and Boord, *J. Am. Chem. Soc.*, **52**, 651 (1930).
106. Dykstra, Lewis, and Boord, *ibid.*, **52**, 3396 (1930).

107. Shoemaker and Boord, *ibid.*, **53**, 1505 (1931).
108. Soday and Boord, *ibid.*, **55**, 3293 (1933).
109. H. Th. Böhme A.-G., Fr. Patent 785,005 (1935); Brit. Patent 436,345 (1935).
110. Deanesly and Carleton, *J. Phys. Chem.*, **45**, 1104 (1941).
111. Ralston, Hoerr, and Crews, *J. Org. Chem.*, **9**, 319 (1944).
112. Garner, Van Bibber, and King, *J. Chem. Soc.*, 1533 (1931).
113. Schoon, *Ber.*, **72B**, 1821 (1939).
114. Carey and Smith, *J. Chem. Soc.*, 1348 (1933).
115. Müller, *Proc. Roy. Soc.* (*London*), **120A**, 437 (1928); **127A**, 417 (1930); **138A**, 514 (1932).
116. Smith, *J. Chem. Soc.*, 737 (1932).
117. Phillips and Mumford, *ibid.*, 1732 (1931).
118. Brochet, *Bull. soc. chim.* [3], **7**, 566 (1892).
119. Van Beresteyn, *Bull. soc. chim. Belg.*, **25**, 293 (1911).
120. Van Risseghem, *ibid.*, **35**, 328 (1926).
121. Parks, Huffman, and Thomas, *J. Am. Chem. Soc.*, **52**, 1032 (1930).
122. Schmidt and Grosser, *Ber.*, **75B**, 829 (1942).
123. Pardubitzer Fabrik der Akt.-Ges. für Mineralöl-Ind. vorm. D. Fanto & Co., Brit. Patents 131,301–3 (1919).
124. Fischer and Schneider, *Ber.*, **53B**, 922 (1920).
125. Francis and Wood, *J. Chem. Soc.*, 1897 (1927).
126. Landa, *Compt. rend.*, **187**, 948 (1928).
127. H. Th. Böhme A.-G., Brit. Patent 360,602 (1930).
128. Bertsch, U. S. Patent 2,027,896 (1936).
129. Ekwall and Mylius, *Ber.*, **62B**, 1080 (1929).
130. Malkin, *ibid.*, **63B**, 1807 (1930).
131. Piper, *J. Chem. Soc.*, 234 (1929).
132. Levi, *Gazz. chim. ital.*, **62**, 709 (1932).
133. McBain and Stewart, *J. Chem. Soc.*, 1392 (1927).
134. Thiessen, v. Kleck, Gockowiack, and Stauff, *Z. physik. Chem.*, **174A**, 335 (1935).
135. Gallay and Puddington, *Can. J. Research*, **21B**, 202 (1943).
136. McBain, *Trans. Faraday Soc.*, **9**, 99 (1913); McBain, Laing, and Titley, *J. Chem. Soc.*, **115**, 1279 (1919); Laing and McBain, *ibid.*, **117**, 1506 (1920); Darke, McBain, and Salmon, *Proc. Roy. Soc.* (*London*), **98A**, 395 (1921); McBain and Martin, *J. Chem. Soc.*, **119**, 1369 (1921); McBain and Jenkins, *ibid.*, **121**, 2325 (1922); McBain and Bowden, *ibid.*, **123**, 2417 (1923); Thiessen and Triebel, *Z. physik. Chem.*, **156A**, 309 (1931); Thiessen, *ibid.*, **156A**, 457 (1931); Ekwall and Otterström, *ibid.*, **161A**, 195 (1932); Hartley, *Aqueous Solutions of Paraffin-Chain Salts*, Hermann et Cie., Paris (1936); Hess and Gundermann, *Ber.*, **70B**, 1800 (1937); Hess, Philippoff, and Kiessig, *Kolloid-Z.*, **88**, 40 (1939); Harkins, Mattoon, and Corrin, *J. Am. Chem. Soc.*, **68**, 220 (1946); Ralston, *Ann. N. Y. Acad. Sci.*, **46**, 351 (1946).
137. Falciola, *Gazz. chim. ital.*, **40**, II, 217, 425 (1910).
138. Currie, *J. Agr. Research*, **2**, 1 (1914).
139. McMaster and Magill, *J. Am. Chem. Soc.*, **38**, 1785 (1916).
140. Kench and Malkin, *J. Chem. Soc.*, 230 (1939).

141. Partheil and Ferié, *Arch. Pharm.*, **241**, 545 (1903).
142. Jacobson and Holmes, *J. Biol. Chem.*, **25**, 29 (1916).
143. Harrison, *Biochem. J.*, **18**, 1222 (1924).
144. Pink, *J. Chem. Soc.*, 619 (1939).
145. Faber, *Centr. Mineral. Geol.*, **1933A**, 191 [*C.A.*, **27**, 3914 (1933)].
146. Clapp, U. S. Patent 1,345,470 (1920).
147. Hoskins, U. S. Patents 1,370,650 (1921); 1,424,306 (1922).
148. Flaxman, U. S. Patent 2,010,297 (1935).
149. Schaefer, U. S. Patent 2,108,616 (1938).
150. Blenio, U. S. Patent 1,382,617 (1921).
151. Neidig, U. S. Patent 1,613,620 (1927).
152. Kemp and Fish, *Virginia J. Sci.*, **1**, 127 (1940).
153. Blitz and Röhrs, *Z. angew. Chem.*, **36**, 609 (1923).
154. Haupt, *ibid.*, **27**, I, 535 (1914).
155. Pink, *J. Chem. Soc.*, 211 (1940).
156. Epstein, U. S. Patent 1,888,820 (1932).
157. Collings, U. S. Patent 1,428,272 (1922).
158. Fischer, U. S. Patents 848,230, 850,111 (1907); 917,758 (1909)
159. Farnsteiner, *Z. Untersuch. Nahr.- u. Genussm.*, **4**, 63 (1901).
160. Escher, *Helv. Chim. Acta*, **12**, 103 (1929).
161. Almoradie and West, *Philippine J. Sci.*, **33**, No. 3, 257 (1927).
162. Hale, U. S. Patent 2,131,041 (1938).
163. Lacombe, *Compt. rend.*, **134**, 772 (1902).
164. I. G. Farbenind. A.-G., Ger. Patent 569,946 (1933).
165. Boner, U. S. Patent 2,267,148 (1941).
166. Eigenberger and Eigenberger-Bittner, *Kolloid-Z.*, **91**, 287 (1940).
167. Stich, *Pharm. Zentralhalle*, **63**, 261 (1922).
168. Freuler, U. S. Patent 2,266,544 (1941).
169. Pomeranz, *Z. ges. Textil-Ind.*, **25**, 277 (1921).
170. Carr, U. S. Patent 1,916,203 (1933).
171. New, U. S. Patent 1,946,914 (1934).
172. Elder, U. S. Patent 1,963,298 (1934).
173. Bennett, U. S. Patent 1,993,396 (1935).
174. Meigen and Neuberger, *Chem. Umschau*, **29**, 337 (1922).
175. Holde and Selim, *Ber.*, **58B**, 523 (1925).
176. Holde and Takehara, *ibid.*, **58B**, 1788 (1925).
177. Menzies and Wilkins, *J. Chem. Soc.*, **125**, 1148 (1924).
178. Holde, Selim, and Bleyberg, *Z. deut. Oel-Fett-Ind.*, **44**, 277, 298 (1924).
179. Canneri and Bigalli, *Ann. chim. applicata*, **26**, 430 (1936).
180. Walter, *Ber.*, **59B**, 962 (1926).
181. Vold, Rosevear, and Ferguson, *Oil & Soap*, **16**, 48 (1939).
182. Vold and Vold, *J. Am. Chem. Soc.*, **61**, 808 (1939).
183. Vold, *ibid.*, **63**, 160 (1941).
184. Vold, Macomber, and Vold, *ibid.*, **63**, 168 (1941).
185. Lopez, *Quím. e ind.*, **68**, 222 (1929) [*C.A.*, **24**, 250 (1930)].
186. Vermorel and Dantony, *Compt. rend.*, **152**, 1263 (1911).
187. Kalusowski, U. S. Patent 1,481,012 (1924).
188. Friedländer, *Apoth. Ztg.*, **44**, 167 (1929).
189. Farrell and Coogan, U. S. Patent 1,463,881 (1923).

190. Kohn and Gruschka, U. S. Patent 1,864,073 (1932).
191. I. G. Farbenind. A.-G., Brit. Patent 433,142 (1935).
192. Hausamann, U. S. Patent 1,145,480 (1915).
193. Ellis, U. S. Patent 1,217,118, 1,251,201 (1917); 1,378,336–8 (1921); 1,390,683, 1,390,687 (1922); 1,476,330, 1,482,740 (1924).
194. Williams and McAllister, U. S. Patent 2,067,368 (1937).
195. Dimmig, Can. Patent 280,036 (1928).
196. van Gundy and Dimmig, Can. Patent 280,037 (1928).
197. Griffith and Helmore, Brit. Patent 423,441 (1935).
198. C. C. Wakefield & Co., Ltd., and Evans, Brit. Patent 474,156 (1937).
199. Standard Oil Development Co., Brit. Patent 535,777 (1941).
200. C. C. Wakefield & Co., Ltd., Fr. Patent 780,448 (1935).
201. Finkle, Draper, and Hildebrand, *J. Am. Chem. Soc.*, **45**, 2780 (1923).
202. Newman, *J. Phys. Chem.*, **18**, 34 (1914).
203. Bhatnagar, *J. Chem. Soc.*, **119**, 61, 1760 (1921).
204. Stamm and Kraemer, *J. Phys. Chem.*, **30**, 992 (1926).
205. Griffin, *J. Am. Chem. Soc.*, **45**, 1648 (1923).
206. Fischer and Harkins, *J. Phys. Chem.*, **36**, 98 (1932).
207. Koenig, *J. Am. Chem. Soc.*, **36**, 951 (1914).
208. Albuquerque, *Rev. chim. pura applicada* [2], **1**, reprint, 8 pp. (1916) [*C.A.*, **14**, 2174 (1920)].
209. Whitmore and Lauro, *Ind. Eng. Chem.*, **22**, 646 (1930).
210. Kenner and Morton, *Ber.*, **72B**, 452 (1939).
211. Cole, *Philippine J. Sci.*, **47**, No. 3, 351 (1932).
212. Neave, *Analyst*, **37**, 399 (1912).
213. Whitby, *Trans. Roy. Soc. Can.* [3], **13**, Sect. III, 257 (1919).
214. Whitby, *Science*, **53**, 580 (1921).
215. Paal and Amberger, *Z. Untersuch. Nahr.- u. Genussm.*, **17**, 23 (1909).
216. Braun, *Chem.-Ztg.*, **53**, 913 (1929).
217. Fischer and Hooker, *Kolloid-Z.*, **51**, 39 (1930).
218. Boner, *Ind. Eng. Chem.*, **29**, 58 (1937).
219. Bornwater, *Rec. trav. chim.*, **26**, 413 (1907).
220. Lauter, Jurist, and Christiansen, *J. Am. Pharm. Assoc.*, **21**, 1277 (1932).
221. Hoffmann-La Roche & Co., Brit. Patent 206,487 (1923).
222. Gardner, Brit. Patent 443,860 (1936).
223. Société des usines chimiques Rhône-Poulenc, Fr. Patent 752,768 (1933).
224. I. G. Farbenind. A.-G., Brit. Patent 478,587 (1938).
225. Schmidt, U. S. Patent 2,229,992 (1941).
226. Bhatnagar, Kapur, and Hussain, *Proc. Indian Acad. Sci.*, **9A**, 143 (1939).
227. von Veimarn, *J. Russ. Phys. Chem. Soc.*, **48**, 705 Proc., (1916).
228. Fay and Hamilton, *8th Intern. Congr. Applied Chem.*, II, Sect. Vd, 7 (1912).
229. von Veimarn, Morozov, and Anosov, *J. Russ. Phys. Chem. Soc.*, **48**, 703 Proc. (1916).
230. von Veimarn, *J. Russ. Phys. Chem. Soc.*, **48**, 532 (1916).
231. McBain and McClatchie, *J. Phys. Chem.*, **36**, 2567 (1932).
232. Feist and Auernhammer, *Arch. Pharm.*, **248**, 520 (1910).
233. Hoffmann-La Roche & Co., Ger. Patent 249,720 (1911).
234. Salvaterra, *Z. angew. Chem.*, **43**, 620 (1930).

235. Dyer, *J. Biol. Chem.*, **28**, 445 (1917).
236. Klimont, *J. prakt. Chem.* [2], **109**, 265 (1925).
237. Titanium Pigment Co., Inc., Brit. Patent 395,406 (1933).
238. Hintermaier, U. S. Patent 2,017,000 (1935).
239. Stoddart and Hill, *J. Am. Chem. Soc.*, **33**, 1076 (1911).
240. Kahlenberg, *J. Phys. Chem.*, **6**, 1 (1902).
241. Cady and Lichtenwalter, *J. Am. Chem. Soc.*, **35**, 1434 (1913).
242. Lawrence, *Trans. Faraday Soc.*, **34**, 660 (1938).

XII

ADDENDUM

If one writes of ancient peoples or of events long past one can complete the manuscript with a feeling of confidence. This satisfaction is denied to those whose subject embraces current happenings and changing concepts. This addendum has been motivated by the many recent contributions to the subjects treated in the foregoing chapters. The number and importance of these contributions testify to the present active interest in the fatty acids and their various derivatives. In writing this addendum the author has endeavored to present the material in a sequence comparable with that previously employed, in the belief that the reader is thus better enabled to integrate these later contributions with those previously discussed. In several instances the work of cooperating or contemporary investigators upon a specific subject has been quite voluminous. Where this has occurred the author has incorporated some of the earlier portions of this work into this addendum.

The Saturated Acids

Our knowledge of the saturated fatty acids has been materially advanced during the past several years by the synthesis and study of a number of branched-chain fatty acids. These acids may be conveniently prepared by the Clemmensen reduction of branched-chain keto esters followed by hydrolysis of the reduction product. The synthesis of the intermediate keto esters by the reaction of dialkylcadmiums with ω-carbethoxyalkanoyl chlorides has been investigated by Cason and associates,[1] who have prepared the following acids: 17-methyloctadecanoic, m.p. 67.3–67.8°; 16-methyloctadecanoic, m.p. 49.9–50.6°; 15-methyloctadecanoic, m.p. 41.0–43.5°; 10-methyltetracosanoic, m.p. 50.5–51.5°; and 14-methyltetracosanoic, m.p. 57.9–58.5°.

Attempts to identify the C_{11} acid resulting from the oxidation of phthioic acid have led to the syntheses of the monomethyldecanoic acids,[2,3] the reported boiling points of the acids and the melting points of their p-bromophenacyl esters being: 2-methyl-decanoic, b_4 135–137°, 66–67°; 3-methyl-, b_{12} 155–157°, 39–40°; 4-methyl-, b_{10} 152–153°, 45–46°; 5-methyl-, b_2 117–119°, 48–49°; 6-methyl-, b_{17} 160–164°, 51–51.5°; 7-methyl-, b_{15} 161–162°, 56°; 9-methyl-, b_2 122–124°, 65–65.5°. Polgar and Robinson accomplished the synthesis of 3,13,19-trimethyltricosanoic acid, the properties of which correspond to those of phthioic acid. The proposed structure of phthioic acid as ethyldecyldodecylacetic acid [4] had been previously shown [5] to be incorrect by a comparison of the synthetic with the natural acid. The value of the long crystal spacing of barium phthioate, 35 Å, is much lower than that of the barium salt of the normal acid of comparable chain length, which indicates that the former must correspond to a tilted chain. Studies of the monolayers of methylated acids [6] show them to occupy larger areas at the point of collapse than normal acids. Such observations indicate a difference in crystal structure between the branched-chain and normal acids and support the recent work on the structure of phthioic acid. Several high molecular weight acids containing a methyl group in the 2- or 10-position have been described by Schneider and Spielman,[7] who reported the following melting points for these acids and their corresponding amides: 2-methylstearic, 54.5°, 104.5°; 2-methyleicosanoic, 61.5–62.0°, 108°; 2-methyldocosanoic, 67.0–67.5°, 109–109.5°; 2-methyltetracosanoic, 72.0–72.5°, 111.5°; 2-methylhexacosanoic, 75.5–76.0°, 113.0°; 10-methyldocosanoic, 45.5–46.0°, 78–78.5°; 10-methyltetracosanoic, 51.0°, 79–79.5°; 10-methylhexacosanoic, 54.0–55.0°, 81–81.5°. 2,2-Dimethyllauric acid, m.p. 4°, and 2,2-dimethylstearic acid, m.p. 42°, have been described by Birch and Robinson.[8]

A comparison of the crystal spacings of tuberculostearamide and d,l-10-methylstearamide [9] are consistent with the hypothesis that tuberculostearic acid is optically active and support the previously proposed structure, d- or l-10-methylstearic acid. The branched-chain fatty acids present in the lipides of tubercle bacilli have been the subject of several recent investigations,[10] and a levorotatory acid termed mycocerosic acid, melting at 27–28° and corresponding to the formula $C_{30}H_{60}O_2$, has been isolated.

The Olefinic Acids

The literature on the occurrence, preparation, and synthesis of the olefinic and polyolefinic acids has been enlarged by several recent noteworthy investigations. The high linoleic acid content of corn oil has been confirmed by Baur and Brown,[11] who have reported 56.3% of this acid present in a specimen of corn oil. Knight, Jordan, and Swern [12] have shown that the octadecadienoic and octadecatrienoic acids present in beef tallow are cis,cis-9,12-linoleic and cis,cis,cis-9,12,15-linolenic acids, respectively, and are identical with those previously found in vegetable oils. The presence of tetradecenoic and hexadecenoic acids and also of small amounts of arachidonic acid in human depot fats has been reported.[13] Studies of fat metabolism with the aid of deuterium [14] support the contention that the highly unsaturated acids are not synthesized by the animal body but are derived from the diet. Brown and coworkers [15] have investigated the absorption spectra of arachidonic acid and its alkali-isomerization product and have stated that a study of the oxidation products of arachidonic acid shows it to be 5,8,11,14-eicosatetraenoic acid. This structure has been confirmed by Arcus and Smedley-Maclean.[16]

Recent studies [17] of the preparation of fatty acids from the natural fats have indicated that fractional distillation followed by low-temperature solvent crystallization is a satisfactory procedure for preparing oleic acid from unsaturated fats. Selective hydrogenation to remove polyolefinic acids, followed by removal of the saturated acids by solvent crystallization and distillation of the liquid fraction, has been proposed [18] for the preparation of purified oleic acid from animal fats. A method for the separation of erucic acid from rape seed oil has been described,[19] the reported yields being 25–30%.

The list of known octadecenoic acids has been increased by the syntheses of 16- and 17-octadecenoic acids,[20] which melt at 62.8–63.5° and 55–55.5°, respectively.

Miscellaneous Acids

Although nonane- and decane-α,ω-dicarboxylic acids have been known for some time, no satisfactory procedure had been proposed for their preparation. This situation has been improved by the work of Hall and Reid,[21] who have reported that high yields of these acids can be obtained by the nitric acid oxidation of 12-hydroxystearic acid, which is easily obtained by the catalytic hydrogenation of ricinoleic acid. The attending monobasic acids are separated by steam distillation and the dicarboxylic acids then separated by distillation of their methyl esters. Houston [22] has prepared 4-ketopalmitic acid by the action of 3-carbomethoxypropionyl chloride and didodecylcadmium. Reduction of the keto acid gives 4-palmitolactone, m.p. 40.7–41.3°, which can easily be converted to 4-hydroxypalmitic acid, m.p. 79.0–79.6°. The hydroxy acid is slowly reconverted to the lactone at its melting point.

Recent interest in the surface active properties of organic acids has necessitated the synthesis of various acids containing interrupted chains. Examples of such acids are the ω-alkylmercapto acids of the general formula $CH_3(CH_2)_xS(CH_2)_yCO_2H$, recently synthesized by Rapoport, Smith, and Newman.[23] Oxidation of these ω-alkylmercapto acids with 30% hydrogen peroxide gives the corresponding ω-alkylsulfonyl acids in excellent yields. The ω-aurothio acids, $AuS(CH_2)_xCO_2H$, have been prepared [24] by the action of gold salts upon ω-carboxyalkylisothioureas. The sodium salt of ω-aurothioundecanoic acid melts at 265–275° and yields a turbid, soapy solution. 6-Aminocaproic acid has been prepared [25] in high yield by the ammonolysis under pressure of the corresponding lactone.

Separation of the Fatty Acids

No studies are more vital to the entire field of the fatty acid derivatives than those concerned with the separation of individual fatty acids from their naturally occurring mixtures. It is for this reason that contributions to this aspect of the subject assume an added significance and should be followed with interest.

Chromatographic adsorption as a means for analysis and separation of fatty acid mixtures is receiving considerable present attention. The value of this technique as an analytical tool is undeniable; its importance as a separation procedure can be evaluated only by future experimentation. When one is faced with the removal of a small amount of an impurity from a fatty acid or a derivative this method should certainly be considered. In general, the process consists in passing the mixture dissolved in a suitable solvent through a column containing a solid adsorbent which is insoluble in the solution. The method is based upon the principle that an adsorbed substance can be replaced by a more strongly adsorbed substance, so that, if a solution containing a plurality of substances is passed through a column containing an adsorbent, zones of varying concentration will result depending upon the relative affinities of the components for the solid surfaces. Thus, the more strongly adsorbed substances will concentrate at the top of the column, and the less strongly adsorbed will be displaced downward.

The application of these principles to separation processes is relatively old. Pioneer work upon this subject [26] was done as early as 1906 by the Russian botanist, M. Tswett, who showed that plant pigments could be separated and purified by chromatographic adsorption. Many years elapsed before Tswett's work received the attention which it merited. The possibilities inherent in Tswett's work were ably reviewed by Cassidy,[27] and subsequent events have evidenced an increased interest in this method. In 1940, Cassidy [28] studied the adsorption isotherms of lauric, myristic, palmitic, and stearic acids and observed that these acids differ markedly in their adsorption behaviors toward carbons, aluminas, magnesium oxide, activated clay, and silica gel. A study of the adsorption of a mixture of lauric and stearic acids showed that each exerts an effect upon the adsorbability of the other, so that the ability to separate a mixture cannot be predicted solely by a comparison of the adsorption isotherms of the pure components. In the same year, Wilson [29] developed a theory of chromatographic analysis based on the assumption that the equilibrium between solution and adsorbent is established instantaneously and that diffusion effects are negligible. A subsequent study by Cassidy and Wood [30] in which they used a solution of lauric acid in petroleum ether with carbon as the adsorbent gave results in essential agreement with this theory. Cassidy [31] then showed that even complex mixtures of fatty acids could be separated provided the proper adsorbent was employed. Prior to this work, it had been shown [32] that oleic acid can be separated from palmitic and stearic acids by chromatographic adsorption, and incomplete separations of palmitic acid from stearic acid had also been obtained.[33] Kaufmann [34] employed alumina or silica gel as the adsorbent and obtained comparatively satisfactory separations of both saturated and unsaturated fatty acid mixtures. Recent applications of chromatographic adsorption techniques to fatty acid chemistry include the separation of methyl linoleate from the methyl esters of cottonseed oil acids by adsorption upon alumina,[35] the separation of stearic acid from hydrogenated tall oil by the use of carbon,[36] and the separation of mixtures of oleic and stearic acids by means of several commercially available adsorbents.[37] The application of a highly sensitive differential refractometer by which changes in refractive indices can be accurately followed during adsorption has been suggested by Tiselius.[38]

In connection with the general problem of the separation of fatty acids, mention should be made of the work of Vilbrandt and associates [39] upon the separation of tall oil fatty acids from resin acids by selective sulfonation. Burr and associates [40] have determined the heats of polymerization of unsaturated fatty acids and have stated that acids containing up to three double bonds are fairly resistant to the heat treatment involved in a vacuum fractional distillation.

Physical Properties of the Fatty Acids

Studies of the ultraviolet absorption spectra of the saturated fatty acids and of oleic, linoleic, linolenic, and arachidonic acids have been extended to 2100 Å by Burr and associates.[41] Since none of the unsaturated acids reaches a peak at 2100 Å these studies were later extended to the extreme ultraviolet and many interesting observations noted.[42] A comparison of the absorption spectra of myristic acid dissolved in ethanol, isoöctane, and heptane shows that the polar solvent, ethanol, shifts the absorption maximum to a lower wave length and gives lower absolute values for the extinction coefficients. All the saturated acids have a broad band with the maximum at about 2050 Å and an intense absorption between 1850 Å and 1730 Å. Unsaturation in the fatty acids produces absorption similar to that of the unsaturated hydrocarbons. Elaidinization of oleic acid shifts the absorption curve toward the visible end of the spectrum. The available spectroscopic data on the fats, fatty acids, and their esters have recently been compiled.[43]

Striking differences have been noted [44] in the x-ray diffraction patterns of the two polymorphic forms of oleic acid. The lower-melting form, m.p. 13°, has a long spacing of 40.5 Å and a side spacing of 4.19 Å, being somewhat similar to the B and C spacings of stearic acid. The higher-melting form, m.p. 16°, has a long spacing of 42.2 Å and short spacings of 4.65 and 3.67 Å, and differs from the other long-chain monocarboxylic acids so far examined.

A recent study of monolayers of oxidized and heat-bodied linseed oil [45] shows that oxidation of the double bonds increases the attraction of the hydrocarbon chain for the water, thus causing the molecule to occupy a larger area, a limiting area being reached with the addition of three oxygen atoms to the glyceride molecule. Polymerization has little effect upon the force-area curves. A comparison of the monolayers of dilauryl maleate and dilauryl fumarate [46] shows that the cis isomer tends to form stable monolayers of the expanded type, and the *trans* isomer less stable mono-layers of the condensed type. The normal fatty acids apparently are adsorbed upon nickel or platinum surfaces to form monolayers similar to those formed upon a water surface.[47] Stearic acid dis-solves in sulfuric acid to form solutions which yield bubble films of great stability.[48] It has been estimated that such films can attain a minimum thickness of two molecules before collapse.

Physico-chemical studies of the complexes formed between pro-teins, starches, and allied compounds and the fatty acids have attracted considerable interest. Starches adsorb palmitic acid from its methanol solution,[49] indicating that the fatty acids asso-ciated with starch are probably adsorbed. It has been stated,[50] however, that the presence of fatty acids interferes with the forma-tion of the amylose-iodine complex, and a more recent study [51] has shown that the fatty acids form molecular complexes with amylose.

Electrophoretic studies [52] indicate that both native and heat-denatured egg albumins form complexes with the alkylbenzene-sulfonates, which can combine with a maximum of three times their weight of reactive protein. Part of the sulfonate is reversibly bound, since dissociation occurs during electrophoresis. When the surface active agent is present in substantial amount the complexes exhibit the electrophoretic behavior of completely denatured pro-tein. Complex formation occurs on both the acid and the alkaline sides of the isoelectric point.[53] An electrophoretic study of the system horse serum-sodium dodecyl sulfate [54] indicates a stoichio-metric combination of surface active ions with basic protein groups. Free detergent is not present below a detergent-protein ratio of 1:1. Experiments with the lower sodium alkyl sulfates indicate a dependency of anion activity upon chain length, the concentration of sodium octyl sulfate required for complete pre-cipitation being several times that of sodium decyl sulfate. Studies of mixed monolayers of egg albumin and sodium dodecyl sulfate [55] and of β-lactoglobulin and sodium dodecyl sulfate [56] indicate the formation of definite complexes between protein and detergent molecules. Palmer [57] has postulated a structure for denatured egg albumin-detergent complex which consists of a polar protein monolayer with the detergent molecules adsorbed on one side only and with the long axis of the detergent molecules perpendicular to the protein layers. The presence of fatty acid anions brings about increased thermal stabilities of both human and bovine serum albumins.[58] Where low concentrations of acid are present the protective action increases with increase in chain length of the fatty acid up to twelve carbon atoms; however, at higher concentrations the maximum stabilization is obtained with the seven- or eight-carbon-membered acids. Further studies [59] indicated that the fatty acid anions combine with both the positive groups and the non-polar portions of the albumin. Higher fatty acid derivatives of the proteins have been prepared by acylation in the presence of aqueous alkali, and the physical properties of these derivatives have been reported.[60]

Oxidation, Halogenation, Polymerization, and Miscellaneous Reactions Not Involving the Carboxyl Group

No phase of fatty acid chemistry has attracted more attention within recent years than that concerned with the reactions of the hydrocarbon portion of the molecule. These studies have resulted in many noteworthy contributions, several of which are of exceptional interest.

A number of these studies have been concerned with the mechanism and products of the oxidation of unsaturated acids. Burr and associates [61] have employed spectrophotometric methods in their studies of the oxidation of oleic and elaidic acids and of ethyl oleate. Mild oxidation brings about a slight increase in the absorption of these compounds; however, marked changes are observed upon prolonged oxidation. The absorption shows an inflection at 2750 Å and a maximum at 2300 Å. It was suggested that the increased absorption is, in part, due to the formation of conjugated unsaturated systems containing carbonyl groups or to conjugated polymers formed by the enolization of such systems. The increase in absorption is not directly occasioned by peroxide formation. The autoxidation of linoleic acid [62] yields products which are not spectroscopically similar to those obtained from oleic acid, the oxidation being accompanied by an increase in the absorption at 2750 Å. The autoxidation of 10,12-linoleic acid is accompanied by a substantial reduction in the absorption at 2300 Å. The oxidation of non-conjugated trienes is attended by an increased absorption [63] and the production of maxima at 2350 Å and 2750 Å. Oxidation of conjugated trienes brings about a decreased absorption between 2600 Å and 2800 Å and an increased absorption at 2300 Å and above 3200 Å. It was concluded that the changes in absorption which take place upon autoxidation are due to oxygen-containing chromophores. The color produced by the treatment of oxidized acids with alcoholic alkali probably results from unsaturated carbonyl compounds produced during the oxidation.[64] A comparison [65] of the rate of oxidation with the rate of formation of chromophores absorbing at 2325 Å indicates the formation of a conjugated monohydroperoxide. It was stated that color development cannot be taken as a measure of oxygen uptake unless the composition of the fatty acid mixture is known. Spectrophotometric studies [66] of the rate of the oxidation of β-eleostearic acid indicate that the initial oxidation results in a dimerization with the formation of some carbon-to-carbon bonds. Continued oxidation yields dibasic acids which may be dimers of the original acids.

The oxidation of oleic acid under various pressures of oxygen has been studied by Henderson and Young,[67] the evidence indicating the initial formation of peroxides followed by the destruction of the double bond. A comparison [68] of the oxidation of methyl oleate by oxygen at 20° and 120° showed that the oxidation at 20° takes place at the —CH_2— groups adjacent to the double bond; however, at 120° the oxygen appears to combine directly with the double bond. The oxidation of methyl oleate at temperatures above 80° appears to differ in character from oxidations at lower temperatures.[69] Conjugated diene formation reaches a maximum and then declines during the autoxidation of methyl linoleate, the presence of the group —CH:CHCH$_2$CH:CH— causing a marked increase in the ease of oxidation. The relative rates of autoxidation of methyl oleate, linoleate, and linolenate at 20° are 1:12:ca. 25. The autoxidation of methyl oleate is greatly accelerated by the presence of small amounts of methyl linoleate.[70] It has been suggested that hydroperoxide formation is preceded by the direct addition of oxygen to the double bond; however, Sutton [71] has stated that when methyl oleate or methyl elaidate is oxidized at 35° in the presence of ultraviolet light the primary product is the ester hydroperoxide. The hydroperoxides of methyl oleate have been isolated by low-temperature fractional crystallization from acetone [72] and have been subjected to hydrogenation, oxidative fission, and reduction with hydrogen iodide. Swern and associates [73] have molecularly distilled the polymers formed by the autoxidation of methyl oleate and have stated that the polymers are apparently oxygen-linked. Secondary reactions result in a scission of the chain. Faith and Rollins [74] have ascertained the optimum conditions for the catalytic, vapor-phase oxidation of fatty oils.

A study of the biological oxidation [75] of octanoic acid containing C^{13} in the carboxyl group showed that such oxidations proceed by a mechanism which involves a splitting into two-carbon fragments followed by condensation of these fragments to ketone bodies. A later study [76] indicated that butyric acid is converted to ketone bodies mainly by fission into two-carbon units and subsequent recombination.

The oxidation of unsaturated fatty acids by chemical oxidizing agents has been the subject of several recent investigations. Swern and associates [77] have studied the production of epoxy compounds by the mild oxidation of unsaturated acids and allied compounds with both perbenzoic acid and peracetic acid. 9,10-Epoxyoctadecanol, m.p. 54–54.5°, can be readily obtained by the action of perbenzoic acid on oleyl alcohol. It readily forms a mixture of 9,10- and 10,9-chlorohydroxyoctadecanols, m.p. 61–62°, when it reacts with hydrogen chloride. The initial action of peracetic acid on ethylenic compounds is similar to that of perbenzoic acid; however, the epoxide ring is opened in the presence of acetic acid to give hydroxyacetoxy compounds. The rate of ring opening of 9,10-epoxystearic acid, m.p. 59.5° (from oleic acid), by acetic acid is only about 1% per hour at 25°; however, at 65° to 100° the reaction is complete in one to four hours. The 9,10-epoxystearic acid, m.p. 55.5° (from elaidic acid), is much more stable in the presence of acetic acid. No epoxy compounds can be isolated when oleic acid is oxidized with performic acid,[78] the reaction apparently yielding dihydroxy acids as the primary product. The oxidation of 1-olefins with performic acid gives high yields of glycols, the following having been obtained by this method: 1,2-octanediol, m.p. 30–30.5°; 1,2-decanediol, m.p. 48–49°; 1,2-dodecanediol, m.p. 60–61°; 1,2-tetradecanediol, m.p. 75–76°; and 1,2-octadecanediol, m.p. 80–81°. The 1-olefins react slowly with peracetic acid to give the corresponding 1,2-epoxides. A modification of the Criegee reaction [79] has been proposed [80] in which the lead tetraacetate is not isolated. Quantitative conversion to scission products of such compounds as cis-9,10-dihydroxystearic acid is obtained by the use of this reagent. Two 9,10,12-trihydroxystearic acids, α, m.p. 112°, and β, m.p. 138°, result from the oxidation of ricinoleic acid with alkaline potassium permanganate or of ricinelaidic acid with peracetic acid.[81] The isomeric 9,10,12-trihydroxystearic acids, γ, m.p. 87°, and δ, m.p. 110°, result when ricinoleic acid is oxidized with peracetic acid or ricinelaidic acid with alkaline potassium permanganate. The formation of peroxides by the oxidation of aldehydes and aldehydo acids has been studied by King.[82] Such peroxides readily undergo reversible dissociation into the free aldehydes and hydrogen peroxide. The oxidation of thioethers to sulfoxides is strongly catalyzed by the presence of unsaturated acids,[83] the actual catalyst probably being the peroxide of the fatty acid.

Studies of the antioxidative properties of compounds and the search for effective antioxidants will probably continue for many years. Several recent contributions to this subject are worthy of mention. Golumbic[84] has studied the antioxygenic action of hydroxycoumarones, tocopherols, and related compounds on animal fats and has also investigated[85] the natural antioxidants present in the vegetable oils. The synergistic action of ascorbic acid and quinone has been studied by Calkins and Mattill.[86] The synergistic action of traces of phosphoric acid upon the quinones and quinols has been ascribed to its ability to form a complex and to its ease of reduction.[87] A new antioxidant, nordihydroguaiaretic acid,

$$\text{HO} \qquad\qquad\qquad\qquad\qquad\qquad \text{OH}$$
$$\text{HO}\!\!\diagup\!\!\diagdown\,\text{CH}_2\text{CH}(\text{CH}_3)\text{CH}(\text{CH}_3)\text{CH}_2\!\!\diagup\!\!\diagdown\,\text{OH}$$

has recently been studied by Burr and associates.[88] This compound is a white, crystalline solid, m.p. 184–185°, which is slightly soluble in water and quite soluble in most organic solvents. Its effectiveness is increased by the presence of ascorbic acid.

The nitric acid oxidation of the monohydroxy acids which result from the sulfation and subsequent hydrolysis of oleic acid shows[89] that sulfation followed by hydrolysis is attended by a migration of the hydroxyl groups and that 9- and 10-monohydroxy acids are not formed exclusively during this process.

The chlorination of methyl caprylate, laurate, myristate, and stearate by dry chlorine in the presence of various catalysts has been studied by Guest and Goddard.[90] The formation of polychloro esters was found to preclude high yields of the desired 2-chloro esters. These authors have also described the preparation of 2-chlorostearic acid by the action of thionyl chloride on 2-hydroxystearic acid. The products of the reaction of chloro acids with sodium acetate in acetic acid solution[91] are largely dependent upon the position of the chlorine atoms. The reagent yields acetoxy acids with 2-, 4-, or 5-chloro acids, but it yields 2-olefinic acids with 3-chloro acids. Cheronis and associates[92] have studied the formation of amino acids by the action of both aqueous and anhydrous ammonia on 2-chloro acids.

The isomerizing action of alkali metal hydroxides on unconjugated fatty acids has been shown to proceed in aqueous media provided sufficiently high temperatures are employed.[93] A catalyst consisting of reduced nickel upon kieselguhr has been found to be effective for the isomerization of vegetable oils.[94]

The thermal polymerization of methyl 10-undecenoate [95] proceeds largely by addition to the terminal olefinic group to give a straight-chain ester of the formula $CH_3CO_2(CH_2)_7CH{=}CH-CH_2(CH_2)_{10}CO_2CH_3$, the remaining double bond shifting from the 10- to the 9-position. It has been observed [96] that the polymerization of undecenoic acid in the presence of boron trifluoride is attended by esterification of the carboxyl group by the double bond. Super polymers have been prepared by the esterification of dilinoleic acid with ethylene glycol,[97] and it has been observed [98] that such products can be cured with sulfur or allied reagents.

Sheppard and Burton [99] have recently investigated the effects of radioactivity on the fatty acids and have subjected lauric and palmitic acids to alpha-particle bombardment. Both these acids gave liquid products, one of the main results being decarboxylation, which proceeds according to the equation

$$C_{15}H_{31}CO_2H \xrightarrow[\text{bombardment}]{\text{Alpha}} C_{15}H_{32} + CO_2$$

Several processes are involved in the decomposition of the fatty acids under these conditions. These processes include (1) dehydrogenation, (2) decarboxylation, (3) formation of low molecular weight water-soluble acids, (4) formation of methane and higher hydrocarbons, (5) production of carbon monoxide and water. Evidence was obtained that dehydrogenation does not occur in the same molecule as decarboxylation since the unsaponifiable fractions appeared to be saturated. This study is of exceptional interest since it has been suggested [100, 101, 102] that radioactive processes may be involved in petroleum formation.

Esters of the Fatty Acids

The acid-catalyzed esterification of the fatty acids in dry methanol has been further studied by Smith and Reichardt,[103] who concluded that the constant r in the Goldschmidt equation (see page 495) is independent of the nature of the acid or its concentration. It was also stated that the activation energy is constant for the normal acids and has a value of approximately 10,000 cal. per mole. The latter statement is contrary to previous beliefs.[104] A determination of the parachor values of tricaprin, trilaurin, trimyristin, tripalmitin, and tristearin [105] showed the differences between alternate members to be less than the calculated differences. This indicates that the two outer chains continue along parallel paths, and supports the contention that the triglycerides possess a tuning-fork structure.

A series of alkyl esters of the fatty acids has been prepared by Hoback and associates,[106] who have described the following esters which had not been previously synthesized (see Table IV, Chapter VII): (ester, b_{20} °C., m.p. °C., n_D^{25}, d_4^{25}) nonyl caproate, 173.3, −22.3, 1.4318, 0.8582; undecyl caproate, 198.4, −10.5, 1.4365, 0.8569; dodecyl caproate, 221.3, −4.6, 1.4382, 0.8562; tridecyl caproate, decomp., 6.9, 1.4396, 0.8550; tetradecyl caproate, decomp., 2.0, 1.4414, 0.8543; pentadecyl caproate, decomp., 16.3, 1.4422, 0.8536; propyl pelargonate, 120–122, −36.0, 1.4236, 0.8540; butyl pelargonate, 122–124, −38.0, 1.4262, 0.8520; pentyl pelargonate, 130–132, −27.0, 1.4318, 0.8506. The glycidyl esters, $CH_2CHCH_2CO_2R$, of the higher acids have been prepared by the
$\diagdown O \diagup$

reaction of the sodium soaps with epichlorohydrin.[107] These esters have been proposed as plasticizers and are of current interest in view of the ready availability of epichlorohydrin. They are either liquids or low-melting solids, the following physical constants having been reported: (glycidyl ester, b_1 °C., m.p. °C., n_D^{60}) laurate, 126, 21, 1.4310; myristate, 146, 33.5–34.5, 1.4345; palmitate, 170, 44.5–45.0, 1.4363; stearate, 193, 50.5–51.3, 1.4387; oleate, 185, −1, 1.4469. The furfuryl esters of several higher aliphatic acids have been prepared [108] by alcoholysis of their alkyl esters with furfuryl alcohol in the presence of sodium. The fatty acid monoesters of l-ascorbic acid and d-isoascorbic acid have been prepared by Swern and associates,[109] who have reported the following melting points: (l-ascorbyl ester, m.p. °C.) laurate, 105.5–106.5; myristate, 110.5–111.5; palmitate, 116–117; stearate, 117.5–118; (d-isoascorbyl ester, m.p. °C.) laurate, 78–79; myristate, 84–85; palmitate, 88.5–89.5; stearate, 91.5–92.5. When tested as antioxidants,[110] these esters showed a marked synergistic effect with α-tocopherol. A series of esters of the polyhydric alcohol xylitol has been prepared by Carson and Maclay,[111] who observed the following melting points: (xylityl ester, m.p. °C.) pentalaurate, 33.5–35; pentamyristate, 45.5–47; pentapalmitate, 56–58; and pentastearate, 66–68. The esters of 9,10-dihydroxystearic acids, m.p. 95° and 130°, are white, crystalline solids which are insoluble in water and soluble in most organic solvents. The melting points of these esters [112] are shown in Table I.

TABLE I

MELTING POINTS OF ESTERS OF 9,10-DIHYDROXYSTEARIC ACIDS

Ester	M.P., °C., of Ester of 95° M.P. Acid	M.P., °C., of Ester of 130° M.P. Acid
Propyl	57.5–58	92.5–93.5
Butyl	53 –54	89 –90
Pentyl	58.5–59.5	86.5–88
Hexyl	64.5–65.5	87 –87.5
Octyl	73 –74	88 –89
Decyl	72.5–73	89.5–90.5
Dodecyl	70 –72	91 –92
Tetradecyl	71.5–72	92 –93
Hexadecyl	73 –74	94 –95.5
Octadecyl	76 –77	94 –95

The allyl, methallyl, β-chloroallyl, furfuryl, cinnamyl, oleyl, and elaidyl esters of the dihydroxystearic acids, m.p. 95° and 130°, have also been described by Swern and associates.[113] Ethyl 6-bromo-caproate, b_{14} 120–125°, n_D^{21} 1.4566, has been prepared [114] by esterification of the product of the action of hydrobromic acid on the lactone of 6-hydroxycaproic acid, obtained by the oxidation of cyclohexanone. Front and Daubert [115] have described cholesteryl linoleate, m.p. 42.5°, in connection with the development of a spectrophotometric method for the determination of linoleic acid in small quantities of blood. Connor and Wright [116] have studied the rates of methoxymercuration of the esters of oleic and elaidic acids. The rapidity of reaction of the esters of oleic acid when compared with those of elaidic acid indicates that this reaction may be employed for differentiating between esters of *cis* and *trans* acids.

The polyesters of dibasic acids and trimethylene glycol [117] increase in melting point with increase in chain length of the dicarboxylic acid. Fiber patterns indicate the crystalline regions to contain planar, zigzag-chain molecules inclined to the fiber axis; the amorphous regions to contain disordered, kinked chains; and the mesomorphic regions to possess disordered groups of parallel chains. The dielectric properties of polyesters [118] indicate the presence of small oscillating units in the chains.

Several recent investigations have been concerned with the preparation of synthetic drying oils by the esterification of highly unsaturated fatty acids with polyhydric alcohols or with unsaturated alcohols. For example, varnish oils have been obtained by the esterification of linseed fatty acids with sorbitol [119] or with polypentaerythritols.[120] Teeter and Cowan [121] have prepared the allyl, β-methallyl, and β-chloroallyl esters of polymeric soybean acids by direct esterification, and similar esters of dilinoleic acid by alcoholysis of methyl dilinoleate.

Nitrogen-Containing Derivatives of the Fatty Acids

In view of their interesting properties and relative ease of synthesis the nitrogen-containing derivatives of the fatty acids will be subjects of interest for many years to come.

The lachrymatory properties and pungency of the 4-acylamido-ω-chloroacetophenones and the 3-acylamido-ω-chloroacetophenones have been investigated by Waters,[122] who observed that, unlike the acylvanillylamides, these properties decrease progressively with increase in the chain length. Several N^4-acylsulfanilamides have been prepared by Bergmann and Haskelberg,[123] who reported the following melting points: (acyl group, m.p. °C.) undecanoyl, 205 (decomp.); undecenoyl, 194–196; stearoyl, 245; oleoyl, 204; stearoloyl, 189. The N-xanthyl derivatives have been proposed [124] for characterization of the unsubstituted amides, N-xanthylpalmitamide melting at 140–142° and N-xanthylstearamide at 139–141°. An equimolar mixture of these amides melts at 133–135°. Houston [125] has observed that the melting points of the p-bromoanilides of certain fatty acids differ from those previously reported,[126, 127] the values as determined by this author being: (acid, m.p. °C. of p-bromoanilide) capric, 101.9; lauric, 106.7; myristic, 110.2; palmitic, 113.2; and stearic, 115.2.

When the dimeric acids, for example dilinoleic acid, are treated with diamines, such as ethylenediamine and its higher homologs, a series of interesting polyamides results. These polyamides have been the subject of an appreciable amount of research by Cowan and associates [128] and have been proposed as coating materials for paper and other surfaces. The dielectric properties of several polyamides have been investigated by Baker and Yager,[129] who reported that such substances show quite steep temperature coefficients.

Compounds which possess CONH linkages when irradiated as monolayers undergo photolysis; for example, stearanilide when so treated is split into stearic acid and aniline.[130] This observation has been confirmed by Carpenter,[131] who irradiated monolayers of stearanilide, N-benzylstearamide, $C_{17}H_{35}CONHCH_2C_6H_5$, and N-(2-phenylethyl)stearamide, $C_{17}H_{35}CONH(CH_2)_2C_6H_5$, at 2483 Å and 2537 Å and observed them to undergo photolysis at the CONH linkage. Since this is a characteristic linkage of protein molecules this observation explains why irradiation of proteins increases the number of free amino groups.

The methyl esters of alkanoylglycines and -polyglycines have been prepared by the action of acid chlorides on aqueous alkaline solutions of glycine or polyglycines followed by esterification.[132] These esters can be converted to the corresponding amides by the action of ammonia. Both the esters and the amides are high-melting solids. The successful synthesis of N-alkylethylenediamines has been accomplished [133] by the action of alkyl chlorides or bromides on ethylenediamine. Previous attempts to synthesize these derivatives by the use of alkyl iodides [134] were unsuccessful. The salts of the N-alkylethylenediamines function as cationic colloidal electrolytes. The free bases are low-melting, white, waxy solids which are insoluble in water but soluble in organic solvents. N-octyl-, N-dodecyl-, and N-hexadecylpiperidine have been synthesized [135] by the refluxing of aqueous piperidine with the respective alkyl iodides and the gradual addition of an excess of potassium hydroxide. The long-chain N-alkylpiperidines are weak bases. 2-Octyl nitrite has recently been synthesized [136] by the addition of nitrosyl chloride to 2-octanol in pyridine solution and also by the reaction of sodium nitrite and sulfuric acid with 2-octanol. This compound was observed to decompose at room temperature. Nitrite esters have previously been reported [137] to be unstable. Baltzly, Ide, and Buck [138] have described the synthesis of several chaulmoogryltrialkyl quaternary ammonium compounds, conventional methods having been employed for their preparation.

The relationship between the structures of the quaternary ammonium compounds and their bactericidal activities has been studied by Shelton and associates,[139] who prepared a large number of higher alkyl quaternary ammonium compounds during the course of their investigations. The alkyltrimethylammonium bromides were described as white, nearly odorless, high-melting crystals. Hexadecyltriethylammonium bromide melts at 145–155° and the corresponding iodide at 175–177°. In general, the higher alkyl quaternary ammonium halides are soluble in acetone, alcohol, and water, but insoluble in ether and benzene. Little germicidal activity was observed when the long alkyl chain contained less than eight carbon atoms, the activity increasing with increase in chain length and reaching a maximum with hexadecyltrimethyl-ammonium bromide. The substitution of a benzyl for a methyl group in hexadecyltrimethylammonium bromide did not result in an increase in activity. Substitution of dihydroxypropyl groups for methyl groups lowers the activity. The replacement of methyl groups by carbethoxymethyl or 2-acetoxyethyl groups enhanced the activities of N-dodecyl compounds but reduced those of the N-hexadecyl compounds. In the unsaturated cyclic series the peak of activity was observed with the hexadecylpyridinium salts, and in the saturated series with hexadecylpiperidinium bromide. Long-chain quaternary ammonium compounds were prepared from a number of cyclic amines such as pyridine, picoline, lutidine, quinoline, piperidine, pipicoline, and morpholine.

The Alcohols

The occurrence, synthesis, and properties of the higher aliphatic alcohols have been the subject of many recent studies. The dihydric ether alcohols, chimyl, batyl, and selachyl alcohols (see page 714), the occurrence of which was previously supposed to be confined to marine oils, have been found to occur in small amounts in many of the animal fats. Holmes and associates [140] have isolated batyl alcohol from the yellow bone marrow of cattle; Ruzicka and associates [141] have obtained it from the fat of pig spleens and of arteriosclerotic aortas of human beings. Baer and Fischer [142] have found that the optical rotations of natural batyl and chimyl alcohols are identical with those of similar structure synthesized from l-acetone glycerol and, consequently, the natural alcohols belong to the d series. A later comparison of natural selachyl alcohol with d-, l-, and racemic selachyl alcohols,[143] prepared by the condensation of oleyl p-toluenesulfonate with the sodium salts of d-, l-, and racemic acetone glycerols, showed selachyl alcohol like-wise to belong to the d series. The synthetic selachyl alcohols were obtained as crystalline solids; d- and l-selachyl alcohols melt at 48.5–49.5°, and d,l-selachyl alcohol at 46.5–47.5°. An improved method for the synthesis of batyl alcohol [144] consists of the reaction of sodium alloxide, $CH_2{=}CHCH_2ONa$, with octadecyl iodide followed by hydroxylation of the ethylenic bond of the resulting allyl octadecyl ether.

The identity of the higher alcohols present in carnauba wax has long been a controversial subject. Further light has been thrown upon these alcohols by Koonce and Brown,[145] who have reported that they can be distilled under high vacuum without undergoing appreciable decomposition. Distillation of the unsaponifiable fraction of carnauba wax followed by crystallization showed the presence of normal C_{28}, C_{30}, and C_{32} alcohols in this wax and indicated the presence of the C_{34} alcohol and its higher homologs. The occurrence of hexadecyl palmitate in corals has been reported.[146]

The higher aliphatic alcohols may be intermediates in fat metabolism. Deuterium-labeled hexadecyl and octadecyl acetates have been fed to rats, it being observed that both are readily assimilated and converted into saturated acids of the same chain lengths as the original alcohols.[147] When deuterium-labeled palmitic acid was fed, evidence was obtained which indicated its partial transformation into hexadecanol.

The synthesis of the higher aliphatic alcohols by the sodium reduction of fatty acid esters has been reviewed and greatly expanded in a very comprehensive article by Hansley.[148] It was pointed out that this reduction proceeds through the soluble sodium ester ketals, the mechanism of the reduction of ethyl palmitate being:

$$\text{(I)} \qquad C_{15}H_{31}\overset{\displaystyle O}{\underset{\displaystyle \|}{C}}OC_2H_5 + 2Na \;\rightarrow\; C_{15}H_{31}\overset{\displaystyle ONa}{\underset{\displaystyle Na}{C}}\!{-}OC_2H_5$$

$$\text{(II)} \qquad C_{15}H_{31}\overset{\displaystyle ONa}{\underset{\displaystyle Na}{C}}\!{-}OC_2H_5 + C_2H_5OH \;\rightarrow\; C_{15}H_{31}\overset{\displaystyle ONa}{\underset{\displaystyle H}{C}}\!{-}OC_2H_5 + C_2H_5ONa$$

$$\text{(III)} \qquad C_{15}H_{31}\overset{\displaystyle ONa}{\underset{\displaystyle H}{C}}\!{-}OC_2H_5 \;\rightarrow\; C_{15}H_{31}\overset{\displaystyle }{\underset{\displaystyle O}{C}}\!H + C_2H_5ONa$$

The aldehyde then forms a sodium ketal which immediately reacts with the alcohol to give the sodium alkoxide of the higher alcohol, thus:

(IV)

$$C_{15}H_{31}CH \underset{\underset{O}{\|}}{} + 2Na \rightarrow C_{15}H_{31}\underset{\underset{Na}{|}}{\overset{\overset{ONa}{|}}{C}}H$$

(V)

$$C_{15}H_{31}\underset{\underset{Na}{|}}{\overset{\overset{ONa}{|}}{C}}H + C_2H_5OH \rightarrow C_{15}H_{31}CH_2ONa + C_2H_5ONa$$

Hydrolysis then yields the free alcohol, as follows:

(VI) $C_{15}H_{31}CH_2ONa + HOH \rightarrow C_{15}H_{31}CH_2OH + NaOH$

A study of the above mechanism shows that any hydrogen formed by direct reaction of the sodium with the reducing alcohol does not take part in the reduction. A reducing alcohol is required which reacts with the sodium intermediate but not to any appreciable extent with the reducing alcohol. It was stated by Hansley that primary alcohols react rapidly with the sodium, whereas tertiary alcohols decompose the intermediate sodium ketals too slowly. The use of secondary alcohols was, therefore, suggested. The recommended procedure consists in adding the ester, mixed with the reducing alcohol and sufficient solvent to keep the reaction mixture fluid, to the sodium contained in the reaction vessel. Glycerides are much more readily reduced than alkyl esters, the difference being attributed to the greater solubility of trisodium glycerate as compared with sodium methoxide or its homologs. Examples were given of the preparation of saturated alcohols from the glycerides of saturated acids, of 9-octadecenol from olive oil, and of 9,12-octadecadienol and 9,12,15-octadecatrienol from their respective glycerides.

Hass and associates [149] have studied the oxidation of hexadecane with air under 2000 lb. pressure at temperatures from 190° to 300°. Hydrogenation of the oxidation product gave a mixture which contained alcohols with molecular weights as high as 165.

During the past few years a number of alcohols have been synthesized which had not been described previously. These include the 1-alkylcyclopentanols,[150] the density curves of which show a decided break at 1-heptylcyclopentanol. This has been attributed to the relationship in size between the alkyl group and the cyclopentyl ring. Above heptyl, the alkyl group is determinative as regards the crystal packing. The density curves of the 1-alkyl-cyclohexanols show a similar break at 1-hexylcyclohexanol.[151] The synthesis of the allergenic principle of poison ivy, 3-pentadecyl-catechol, m.p. 58–59°, from 2,3-dimethoxybenzaldehyde has been described.[152] Its prior synthesis from o-veratraldehyde has been claimed,[153] and its use as a standard agent for the determination of hypersensitiveness to poison ivy has been described.[154]

The o-alkyl derivatives of saccharin [155] have been prepared by heating pseudo-saccharin chloride [156] with the higher alcohols, and have been proposed as characterizing derivatives. The melting points of the saccharin derivatives of the aliphatic alcohols are shown in Table II.

TABLE II

MELTING POINTS OF o-ALKYL DERIVATIVES OF SACCHARIN

Alkyl	Melting Point, °C.	Alkyl	Melting Point, °C.
Propyl	124.5	Dodecyl	54
Butyl	96	Tridecyl	66
Pentyl	62	Tetradecyl	62
Hexyl	60	Pentadecyl	72
Heptyl	55	Hexadecyl	69.5
Octyl	46	Heptadecyl	76
Nonyl	49	Octadecyl	74.5
Decyl	47.5	Nonadecyl	80.5
Undecyl	58.5		

Mixed melting points with adjacent members showed considerable depressions; for example, undecyl-dodecyl, 48–52°, dodecyl-tridecyl, 52–58°, and heptadecyl-octadecyl, 54–67°. Ward and Jenkins [157] have proposed the alkyl esters of p-nitrophenylacetic acid as characterizing derivatives for the higher alcohols.

The catalytic dehydration of the higher alcohols has been the subject of several recent studies. The vapor-phase dehydration of heptanol over activated alumina at 380–400° yields 1-heptene as the principal product.[158] Hexanol and octanol when similarly treated [159] yield 1-hexene and 1-octene, respectively. The products obtained by the liquid-phase dehydration of the higher alcohols in the presence of metallic nickel [160] are quite dependent upon the temperature employed. Dehydrogenation with the formation of the corresponding aldehydes occurs at 140°; higher temperatures,

250°, result in the formation of olefins by the splitting of carbon monoxide and hydrogen from the aldehydes. Some saturated hydrocarbons are also produced by hydrogenation of the olefins with the liberated hydrogen. Dehydration of the alcohols to the corresponding olefins apparently does not occur under these conditions. When the primary alcohols are heated at 380–400° in the presence of vanadium pentoxide, saturated hydrocarbons which contain the same number of carbon atoms as the alcohol are formed.[161] Vanadium oxide-aluminum oxide catalysts increase the yield of paraffinic hydrocarbons. The dehydrogenation of the alcohols to aldehydes over copper-chromium oxide catalysts becomes more difficult with increase in the chain length of the alcohol.[162] The dehydrogenation of heptane over chromia-alumina catalysts yields both olefinic and aromatic hydrocarbons,[163] hexene and toluene being the principal products formed. High temperatures or long contact times favor aromatic formation. The addition of water vapor, on the other hand, retards the formation of toluene.

The use of primary alcohols as metal-cutting fluids has been studied by Shaw,[164] who reported that those alcohols which contain an uneven number of carbon atoms require lower cutting forces than those which contain an even number.

Esters of the Higher Alcohols

The recent contributions to our knowledge of the esters of the higher aliphatic alcohols have been extensive and important. Many new esters have been prepared and their properties described. The alkyl esters of nicotinic acid [165] are either liquids or low-melting solids. Dodecyl nicotinate freezes at 22.7° and tetradecyl, hexadecyl, and octadecyl nicotinates melt at 40.2–40.8°, 46.7–47.0°, and 55.3–55.8°, respectively. The corresponding amides increase in melting point with increase in the length of the alkyl chain, dodecylnicotinamide melting at 77.6–77.8° and octadecylnicotinamide at 91.7–92.0°. The alkyl esters of gallic acid have been obtained by the esterification of the tribenzyl ether of gallic acid followed by debenzylation of the resulting esters.[166] The melting points range from 93.5° for hexyl gallate to 104.5° for octadecyl gallate. Cowan and associates [167] have described the preparation of octadecyl, octadecenyl, and octadecadienyl esters of orthosilicic acid. Several alkyl selenocyanates have been prepared [168] by refluxing alkyl bromides with potassium selenocyanate in ethanol. These compounds possess disgusting odors which prohibit their use as fungicides. The alkyl acrylates having from two to sixteen carbon atoms in the alkyl group have been prepared by alcoholysis of methyl acrylate.[169] These esters are easily polymerized, the higher esters yielding waxlike polymers. The higher alkyl salicylates [170] are low-melting solids; dodecyl salicylate melts at 25° and octadecyl salicylate at 53°.

The dialkyl adipates, up to and including dinonyl adipate, are colorless liquids; those above dinonyl adipate are white, waxy solids.[171] The melting points of these esters are: (ester, m.p. °C.) dipentyl, -14; dihexyl, -9 to -7; diheptyl, 3.8–4.5; dioctyl, 9.5–9.8; dinonyl, 21.6; didecyl, 27.4; diundecyl, 34.7; didodecyl, 39.3; ditridecyl, 45.9; ditetradecyl, 49.4; dipentadecyl, 55.0; dihexadecyl, 57.3; diheptadecyl, 61.8; dioctadecyl, 63.4; dinonadecyl, 66.7; dieicosyl, 65.2. The non-catalytic esterification of octanol with polybasic acids has been claimed [172] to result in higher yields of esters than when catalysts are employed. End-group analyses, viscosity measurements, and the solution behaviors of the linear polymers of 11-hydroxyundecanoic acid indicate a coupling action of separate sections within a given chain.[173]

The physical constants of highly purified alkyl chlorides, bromides, and iodides have been determined by Vogel,[174] the recorded values representing a considerable revision of and addition to those previously reported (see Chapter IX). The following constants were determined by Vogel: (number of C atoms, b.p. °C., d_4^{20}, n_D^{20}) chlorides: 6, 134_{759}, 0.8784, 1.41991; 7, 159.5_{769}, 0.8766, 1.42571; 8, 181.5_{765}, 0.8748, 1.43058; 9, 202_{760}, 0.8704, 1.43400; 10, $222-223_{760}$, 0.8683, 1.43731; 11, $240-241_{772}$, 0.8677, 1.44003; 12, 116.5_5, 0.8673, 1.44255; bromides: 6, 153.5_{740}, 1.1748, 1.44781; 7, 177.5_{758}, 1.1401, 1.45052; 8, 200_{768}, 1.1124, 1.45267; 9, 219.5_{745}, 1.0901, 1.45417; 10, $102.5_{5.9}$, 1.0658, 1.45527; 11, 114_5, 1.0541, 1.45697; 12, $130.0_{5.7}$, 1.0382, 1.45807; iodides: 6, 180_{774}, 1.4367, 1.49264; 7, 202_{774}, 1.3734, 1.48974; 8, $221-221.5_{752}$, 1.3297, 1.48892. The dielectric properties of several of the higher alkyl iodides have been investigated,[175] and it has been observed that the dipole moment undergoes a small decrement, 0.01 D. per carbon atom, from butyl iodide to hexadecyl iodide.

The rate of hydrolysis of both soluble and insoluble proteins is markedly accelerated by the presence of strong monobasic acids containing long-chain alkyl groups.[176] In the presence of certain of these compounds the rate of hydrolysis of the amide, $RCONH_2$, and the peptide, RCONHR', bonds is approximately one hundred times as fast as in the presence of hydrochloric acid. Among the more effective hydrolyzing agents are the half esters of sulfuric acid. The relative effectiveness of these esters in accelerating the hydrolysis of wool is shown in Table III.

TABLE III

RELATIVE EFFECTIVENESS OF SULFATE HALF ESTERS IN ACCELERATING THE ACID HYDROLYSIS OF WOOL AT 65° *

Sulfate Half Ester	Amide Hydrolysis, Time Required to Liberate 0.3 Millimole Ammonia per Gram	Peptide Hydrolysis, Time Required to Liberate 1.0 Millimole of Non-ammonia Nitrogen per Gram
	Hours	*Hours*
Octyl	45.2	100
Decyl	11.4	26
Dodecyl	9.8	17
Tetradecyl	9.3	15
Hexadecyl	10.3	21
Octadecyl	12.2	29

* All solutions contained 0.05M HCl and 0.05M Na salt of the half ester.

Similar results were obtained with the soluble protein (egg albumin), although the rate of hydrolysis of soluble proteins is enormously less with the sulfonates or sulfates than with pepsin.

The High Molecular Weight Aliphatic Ethers

The ethers of *p*-hydroxybenzoic acid have been proposed as identifying derivatives for the alkyl halides.[177] Reid and Wilson [178] have prepared both the mono- and the diethers of stilbesterol and have reported that the estrogenic activity decreases as the length of the alkyl group increases in each series. Grummitt and Hall [179] have synthesized pure 2,3-dihydroxypropyl dodecyl ether, which is a waxlike solid melting at about 20°.

The Sulfur-Containing Derivatives of the Fatty Acids

The alkyl xenyl sulfides from hexyl xenyl sulfide to heptadecyl xenyl sulfide have been prepared [180] by the direct addition of 4-mercaptobiphenyl to olefins. The melting points of these sulfides do not vary greatly from member to member, hexyl xenyl sulfide melting at 75.1–75.7° and heptadecyl xenyl sulfide at 99.7–100.6°. The identity of these sulfides was established by mixed-melting-point determinations with sulfides obtained by the reaction of alkyl bromides with 4-mercaptobiphenyl. Hall and Reid [181] have prepared the α,ω-dimercaptans from 1,2-ethanedithiol to 1,12-dodecanedithiol. The physical constants which were reported are shown in Table IV.

TABLE IV

PROPERTIES OF α,ω-DIMERCAPTANS

No. of C Atoms	Melting Point, °C.	Boiling Point, °C.	d_4^{25}	n_D^{25}
2	−41.2	146.0	1.1192	1.5558
3	−79.0	172.9	1.0775	1.5371
4	−53.9	195.6	1.0395	1.5265
5	−72.5	217.3	1.0158	1.5194
6	−21.0	237.1	0.9886	1.5077
7	−38.1	252.2	0.9707	1.4950
8	0.9	269.3	0.9620	1.5009
9	−17.5	284.0	0.9510	1.4940
10	17.8	297.1	0.9432	1.4950
11	− 5.4	308.8	0.9368	1.4931
12	28.4	319.3	0.9270^{30}	......

Pure sodium 1-dodecanesulfinate has been prepared, and its reaction with mercuric chloride to give dodecylmercuric chloride has been studied.[182] The effect of chain length of the aliphatic mercaptans upon their regulatory action during the emulsion polymerization of styrene and butadiene has been investigated,[183] and it has been found that the rate of diffusion through the aqueous phase is a determining factor in their regulatory action.

The Fatty Acid Halides

The fatty acid halides are important intermediates in the synthesis of many fatty acid derivatives. Their preparation will, therefore, continue to be a subject of considerable importance. It is well known that the chlorides of the highly unsaturated acids are difficult to prepare and purify, and many attempts have been made to obtain satisfactory yields of these compounds. The use of oxalyl chloride as the chlorinating agent, originally suggested by Adams and Ulich,[184] has been reinvestigated,[185] and high yields of oleoyl, elaidoyl, linoleoyl, and linolenoyl chlorides have been obtained from their respective acids. Spectrophotometric studies showed that the reaction is not accompanied by rearrangement of the double bonds to produce conjugated systems. The purification of thionyl chloride, one of the important chlorinating agents, has been accomplished [186] by reflux with sulfur followed by distillation. The sulfur converts the contaminate, sulfuryl chloride, to sulfur dioxide and sulfur chlorides.

The Rosenmund reduction of undecenoyl chloride with a palladium-barium sulfate catalyst in boiling xylene gives a 55% yield of unsaturated aldehydes.[187] The reaction is accompanied by almost complete rearrangement of the double bond from the original 10-position to the 8- and 9-positions. Bromination of the double bond prior to reduction, followed by debromination of the reduction product, permits the reduction of the acid chloride group without migration of the unsaturated linkage.

The High Molecular Weight Aliphatic Aldehydes

Aldehydes of an average chain length of sixteen to eighteen carbon atoms have been isolated from animal tissues by means of their p-carboxyphenylhydrazones and carboxymethoximes.[188] The yields of crude aldehydes correspond to 0.05–0.2% of the tissue used. The behavior of the higher aliphatic aldehydes and their derivatives in the fuchsin test has been studied,[189] and it was observed that with the acetals as standards the tests must be conducted at a temperature of at least 37°. Since the naturally occurring aldehyde complexes develop color at a much lower temperature, some doubt is cast on the belief that the aldehydes are present in tissues as their glyceryl acetals. The 2,4-dinitrophenylhydrazone of pentanal has been reported [190] to crystallize from methanol in fine needles melting at 107.6°.

The preparation of higher aldehydes by the hydrolysis of olefin ozonides has been investigated,[191] and reasonable yields of aldehydes have been obtained by the decomposition of such ozonides by catalytic hydrogenation.[192] A study has been made [193] of the catalytic, liquid-phase dehydrogenation of the higher alcohols to aldehydes and ketones in which ethylene under pressure was used as the hydrogen acceptor. A 33% yield of dodecanal from dodecanol was obtained by the use of this procedure.

The catalytic hydrogenation of heptanal in the presence of nickel at 250° under atmospheric pressure has been shown [194] to yield n-hexane as the principal product together with some 1-heptanol. A further study [195] of the decomposition of heptanal in the presence of nickel and in the absence of added hydrogen showed that 1-hexene is a primary product. This indicates that the hexane obtained under hydrogenating conditions may result from the hydrogenation of 1-hexene.

The High Molecular Weight Ketones

An important reaction of ketones, the Willgerodt reaction [196] (see page 856), formerly considered to take place only with alkyl aryl ketones, has been shown [197, 198] to occur with dialkyl ketones and with a wide variety of other types of aliphatic compounds. Methyl propyl ketone, dipropyl ketone, and dibutyl ketone give valeramide, enanthamide, and pelargonamide, the yields being 49, 9, and 1%, respectively.[199] The decrease in yield with increase in chain length is similar to that observed with the alkyl aryl ketones. If mercaptans are intermediates they should also yield amides, and it was observed that 2-propanethiol, 3-pentanethiol, 4-heptanethiol, and 5-nonanethiol give propionamide, valeramide, enanthamide, and pelargonamide, respectively. Olefins were likewise observed to yield amides, 3-pentene, 4-heptene, and 5-nonene giving the respective amides. 3-Pentanol, 4-heptanol, and 5-nonanol did not yield amides when similarly treated. Since it was postulated that the reaction proceeds through the olefin it is evident that, under mild conditions, the olefin must result from the dehydrosulfidation of a mercaptan. Alcohols, however, were observed to be reactive at higher temperatures (200°). Thus, it is evident that the reactivity of an alcohol in this reaction must be a function of its ease of dehydration. It is evident, therefore, that either an alcohol or a thiol can be the parent substance of the intermediate olefin, the former requiring higher temperatures. The higher olefins 1-octene, 1-decene, and 1-tetradecene also yield the corresponding amides when heated with ammonium polysulfide at 200°. In view of the proposed mechanism, ketone → thioketone → mercaptan → olefin, etc., any mercaptan should yield an amide when subjected to this reaction. The mercaptans from ethanethiol to dodecanethiol were found to give varying yields of amides, octanethiol, decanethiol, and dodecanethiol giving yields of 6, 8, and 62%, respectively.

The Aliphatic Hydrocarbons

A recent study [200] of the densities and transition points of the higher saturated hydrocarbons has, in general, supported previous opinions concerning their structures. A plot of the densities against temperature shows that the lines are parallel for the liquid state, indicating an orderly arrangement of the molecules. This arrangement disappears as the temperature approaches the boiling point. The densities of the solid state indicate that the manner of crystal packing is the same for all the normal hydrocarbons which contain an even number of carbon atoms. The transition points of the C_{18}, C_{20}, and C_{22} hydrocarbons are observed only on cooling, whereas those of the C_{24} to C_{34} hydrocarbons are observed upon both cooling and heating. Melting points for a number of the normal hydrocarbons were compiled, and the values were observed to fit the equation $\log (N - 2) = a + bt$, developed by Moullin,[201] if discontinuities were assumed at the C_{16} and C_{33} hydrocarbons. The values of the constants a and b are: $C_6 \rightarrow C_{16}$ (even), 1.051, 0.00481; $C_7 \rightarrow C_{15}$ (odd), 1.067, 0.00410; $C_{16} \rightarrow C_{34}$, 1.02, 0.0065; $C_{33} \rightarrow C_{70}$, 0.08, 0.0006. Some of the reported values for the melting points of the higher hydrocarbons are: (number of C atoms, m.p. °C.) 25, 53.3; 29, 63.3; 33, 72.0; 35, 75.0; 37, 74.4; 38, 77.6; 39, 78.8; 41, 81.7; 42, 82.9; 43, 83.8; 44, 86.4. The parachors and molecular refractivities of the pure hydrocarbons from pentane to hexadecane have been determined by Vogel,[202] who reported the following values for the parachor: (number of C atoms, parachor value) 5, 231.8; 6, 270.9; 7, 312.0; 8, 350.5; 9, 390.7; 10, 429.9; 11, 470.6; 12, 510.0; 13, 550.5; 14, 591.4; 15, 631.3; 16, 671.3. The heats of combustion of a number of the higher hydrocarbons have recently been reported,[203, 204] and the heats of formation, $-\Delta H_f^0$, of these compounds from the elements have been calculated. The following are some of the representative values: (hydrocarbon, $-\Delta H_f^0$ in kcal. mole^{-1}) octadecane, 135.92; 11-phenylheneicosane, 120.83; 13-phenylpentacosane, 164.71; 11-decylheneicosane, 201.72; and dotriacontane, 231.82. The heat capacity and heat of fusion of 11-decylheneicosane have recently been determined,[205] the average molal heat of fusion being 17017.7 ± 6.0 cal. per mole. The compressibility of liquid octane has been determined [206] at 25° intervals from 100° to 275°, the pressures ranging from 1 to 300 atmospheres. The specific volumes vary from 1.574 cc. per gram at 100° to 2.518 cc. per gram at 275°.

Eicosane and 1-phenyleicosane, m.p. 43.5°, have been prepared [207] by reduction of the corresponding heptadecyl ketones obtained by the condensation of stearoyl chloride with the appropriate dialkylcadmiums. The higher hydrocarbons 1-phenyleicosane, 1-cyclohexyleicosane, and 1-cyclopentyleicosane have also been obtained [208] by heating the appropriate heptadecyl ketone with sodium methoxide, excess hydrazine hydrate, and a lower anhydrous alcohol. The ketones were prepared by the action of Grignard reagents upon stearonitrile.

Friedel-Crafts alkylations generally involve rearrangement of the alkyl group, the formation of octadecylbenzene from octadecyl bromide being one of the reported exceptions.[209] A further study [210] of alkylations with the higher alkyl bromides showed that under mild conditions benzene reacts with normal alkyl bromides in the presence of aluminum chloride to give a mixture of phenylalkanes, thus indicating that the phenyl group can attach itself to any of the carbon atoms of the alkyl residue. These studies confirmed the previous observation that such reactions proceed without appreciable branching of the chain. No apparent reaction occurs when aluminum bromide is mixed with hexane or heptane in the absence of promoters; [211] however, if hydrogen bromide is added, cracking, isomerization, and alkylation occur with the formation of branched-chain hydrocarbons.

The recent preparation of many of the higher acetylenic hydrocarbons [212] has given us more precise physical constants for these compounds than were previously available. The hydrocarbons were prepared by the condensation of alkyl bromides or sulfates with sodium acetylides.[213] The dialkylacetylenes were prepared either by the action of alkyl halides with disodium acetylene or by a two-step process consisting of the alkylation of the sodium derivative of a monoalkylacetylene. The physical constants of the higher acetylenic hydrocarbons prepared by Henne and Greenlee are shown in Table V.

TABLE V

PHYSICAL CONSTANTS OF ACETYLENIC HYDROCARBONS

Hydrocarbon	Freezing Point, °C.	Boiling Point, °C.	d_4^{20}	n_D^{20}
1-Pentyne	−106.07	40.25	0.6908	1.3852
1-Hexyne	−132.09	71.4	.7156	1.3990
1-Heptyne	−80.93	99.78	.7325	1.4088
1-Octyne	−79.48	126.25	.7460	1.4159
2-Pentyne	−109.33	56.07	.7104	1.4039
3-Hexyne	−105.53	81.0	.....	1.4115
2-Octyne	−61.6	138.00	.7596	1.4278
3-Octyne	−103.9	133.14	.7522	1.4250
4-Octyne	−102.55	131.57	.7509	1.4248
1,6-Heptadiyne	−84.84	111.5	.8051	1.4423
1,8-Nonadiyne	−27.28	161.98	.8158	1.4490
2,7-Nonadiyne	4.30	180.0	.8332	1.4674

Hennion and Banigan [214] have recently called attention to the fact that the calculated and observed values of the molecular refractivities of the acetylenic hydrocarbons are in disagreement. A method of calculation based upon the average contributions of various types of atoms in the molecules was proposed.

The reduction of the monoalkylacetylenes with sodium in liquid ammonia [215] gives high yields of 1-alkenes. A comparison of the isomeric hexenes and octenes showed that the 1-alkenes have the lowest boiling points, densities, and refractive indices. These values are at a maximum with the 2-alkenes and then progressively decrease as the double bond moves toward the middle of the chain.

The Metallic Soaps

The anhydrous ammonium soaps of the aliphatic acids are quite hygroscopic, and exposure to moisture brings about a decided lowering of their melting points. In general, however, hygroscopicity decreases with increase in molecular weight. Zuffanti [216] has described a process whereby the ammonium soaps may be prepared and their melting points determined without contact with atmospheric moisture. The following melting points were reported for several of the ammonium soaps of the fatty acids: (ammonium soap, m.p. °C.) valerate, 108; caproate, 108; enanthate, 112; caprylate, 114; and pelargonate, 115. The acid sodium stearates have recently been prepared by Ryer,[217] who obtained evidence for the existence of stearates of the compositions, $1NaSt \cdot 1HSt$, $2NaSt \cdot 3HSt$, and $1NaSt \cdot 2HSt$, but not of $2NaSt \cdot 1HSt$. X-ray diffraction studies [218] of pure calcium, barium, and magnesium stearates have indicated the non-existence of basic and mixed acid salts of these metals. Studies of the crystal structures [219] of aluminum dilaurate and aluminum distearate indicate that the acid radicals attached to the aluminum atom lie side by side, the crystal structure being similar to that of the sodium soaps.

High Molecular Weight Organometallic Compounds

Until comparatively recently, the high molecular weight organometallic compounds have received scant attention. In a search for suitable identifying derivatives of the higher aliphatic acids, Meals [220] has described the preparation of a number of organometallic compounds of sodium, potassium, calcium, lithium, mercury, tin, and lead. Many of these compounds are low-melting solids; for example, didodecylmercury melts at 44–44.5°, ditetradecyl-mercury at 53–54°, dihexadecylmercury at 61–62°, and diocta-decylmercury at 66.5–67°. Tetratetradecyl- and tetrahexadecyl-lead melt at 31° and 42°, respectively. A mixed melting point of tetrahexadecyllead with tetrahexadecyltin, m.p. 41.5–42.5°, showed no depression. A number of alkylmetal halides were also prepared and described during the course of this investigation. Octylsodium and decylsodium have been prepared [221] from their respective chlorides by the action of sodium in petroleum ether. The properties of these compounds are similar to those of pentyl-sodium; [222] the petroleum ether solutions are pink in color in con-trast to the blue colorations of butylsodium and its lower homologs. Their solutions exhibit a decided tendency to form gels. Organo-sodium compounds are intermediates in the Wurtz reaction,[223] which proceeds with the initial formation of an alkylsodium fol-lowed by its reaction with an alkyl halide.

The organosilicon compounds have attracted much recent atten-tion, and a number of higher alkylsilicon derivatives have been described. Whitmore and associates [224] have synthesized the higher alkyltrimethyl- and alkyltriethylsilicons by the reaction of alkyl-magnesium bromides with silicon tetrachloride to form the alkyl-silicon trichlorides, followed by the reaction of these compounds with methyl- or ethylmagnesium bromide. An alternate procedure comprises the reaction of a higher alkylmagnesium bromide with trimethyl- or triethylsilicon chloride. The silicon compounds have lower boiling points and higher densities and refractive indices than the trimethyl- or triethylalkanes of corresponding molecular weight. The recent synthesis [225] of octylsilicon trichloride by the peroxide-catalyzed addition of 1-octene to trichlorosilane, $SiHCl_3$, presents a very interesting method for the preparation of many higher alkylsilicon derivatives.

References

1. Cason, J. Am. Chem. Soc., **64**, 1106 (1942); Cason and Prout, ibid., **66**, 46 (1944); Cason, Adams, Bennett, and Register, ibid., **66**, 1764 (1944); Cason, ibid., **68**, 2078 (1946).
2. Polgar and Robinson, J. Chem. Soc., 389 (1945).
3. Wilson, J. Am. Chem. Soc., **67**, 2161 (1945).
4. Stenhagen and Ställberg, J. Biol. Chem., **139**, 345 (1941).
5. Polgar and Robinson, J. Chem. Soc., 615 (1943).
6. Ställberg-Stenhagen and Stenhagen, J. Biol. Chem., **148**, 685 (1943).
7. Schneider and Spielman, ibid., **142**, 345 (1942).

8. Birch and Robinson, *J. Chem. Soc.*, **488** (1942).
9. Velick, *J. Biol. Chem.*, **154**, 497 (1944).
10. Ginger and Anderson, *ibid.*, **156**, 443 (1944); Ginger, *ibid.*, **156**, 453 (1944); Ginger and Anderson, *ibid.*, **157**, 203 (1945).
11. Baur and Brown, *J. Am. Chem. Soc.*, **67**, 1899 (1945).
12. Knight, Jordan, and Swern, *J. Biol. Chem.*, **164**, 477 (1946).
13. Cramer and Brown, *ibid.*, **151**, 427 (1943).
14. Bernhard and Schoenheimer, *ibid.*, **133**, 707 (1940).
15. Mowry, Brode, and Brown, *ibid.*, **142**, 671, 679 (1942).
16. Arcus and Smedley-Maclean, *Biochem. J.*, **37**, 1 (1943).
17. Swern, Knight, and Findley, *Oil & Soap*, **21**, 133 (1944).
18. Swern, Scanlan, and Roe, *ibid.*, **23**, 128 (1946).
19. Dorée and Pepper, *J. Chem. Soc.*, **477** (1942).
20. Kapp and Knoll, *J. Am. Chem. Soc.*, **65**, 2062 (1943).
21. Hall and Reid, *ibid.*, **65**, 1468 (1943).
22. Houston, *ibid.*, **69**, 517 (1947).
23. Rapoport, Smith, and Newman, *ibid.*, **69**, 693 (1947).
24. Moore and Rapala, *ibid.*, **69**, 266 (1947).
25. Galat and Mallin, *ibid.*, **68**, 2729 (1946).
26. Tswett, *Ber. deut. botan. Ges.*, **24**, 316, 384 (1906).
27. Cassidy, *J. Chem. Education*, **16**, 88 (1939).
28. Cassidy, *J. Am. Chem. Soc.*, **62**, 3073, 3076 (1940).
29. Wilson, *ibid.*, **62**, 1583 (1940).
30. Cassidy and Wood, *ibid.*, **63**, 2628 (1941).
31. Cassidy, *ibid.*, **63**, 2735 (1941).
32. Kondo, *J. Pharm. Soc. Japan*, **57**, 218 (1937).
33. Manunta, *Helv. Chim. Acta*, **22**, 1156 (1939).
34. Kaufmann, *Fette u. Seifen*, **46**, 268 (1939); *Angew. Chem.*, **53**, 98 (1940).
35. Swift, Rose, and Jamieson, *Oil & Soap*, **20**, 249 (1943).
36. Papps and Othmer, *Ind. Eng. Chem.*, **36**, 430 (1944).
37. Dutton, *J. Phys. Chem.*, **48**, 179 (1944).
38. Tiselius and Claesson, *Arkiv Kemi, Mineral. Geol.*, **15B**, 1 (1942) [*C.A.*, **38**, 35 (1944)].
39. Vilbrandt, Chapman, and Crockin, *Ind. Eng. Chem.*, **33**, 197 (1941).
40. Norris, Rusoff, Miller, and Burr, *J. Biol. Chem.*, **147**, 273 (1943).
41. Barnes, Rusoff, Miller, and Burr, *Ind. Eng. Chem., Anal. Ed.*, **16**, 385 (1944).
42. Rusoff, Platt, Klevens, and Burr, *J. Am. Chem. Soc.*, **67**, 673 (1945).
43. Rusoff, Holman, and Burr, *Oil & Soap*, **22**, 290 (1945).
44. Lutton, *ibid.*, **23**, 265 (1946).
45. Lichtenwalner, Adams, and Powers, *J. Phys. Chem.*, **49**, 511 (1945).
46. Shereshefsky and Wall, *J. Am. Chem. Soc.*, **66**, 1072 (1944).
47. Smith and Fuzek, *ibid.*, **68**, 229 (1946).
48. McCulloch, *ibid.*, **68**, 2735 (1946).
49. Lehrman, *ibid.*, **64**, 2144 (1942).
50. Schoch and Williams, *ibid.*, **66**, 1232 (1944).
51. Mikus, Hixon, and Rundle, *ibid.*, **68**, 1115 (1946).
52. Lundgren, Elam, and O'Connell, *J. Biol. Chem.*, **149**, 183 (1943).
53. Putnam and Neurath, *ibid.*, **150**, 263 (1943).

54. Putnam and Neurath, *ibid.*, **159**, 195 (1945).
55. Bull, *J. Am. Chem. Soc.*, **67**, 10 (1945).
56. Bull, *ibid.*, **68**, 747 (1946).
57. Palmer, *J. Phys. Chem.*, **48**, 12 (1944).
58. Boyer, Lum, Ballou, Luck, and Rice, *J. Biol. Chem.*, **162**, 181 (1946).
59. Boyer, Ballou, and Luck, *ibid.*, **162**, 199 (1946).
60. Gordon, Brown, and Jackson, *Ind. Eng. Chem.*, **38**, 1239 (1946); Gordon, Brown, McGrory, and Gall, *ibid.*, **38**, 1243 (1946).
61. Holman, Lundberg, Lauer, and Burr, *J. Am. Chem. Soc.*, **67**, 1285 (1945).
62. Holman, Lundberg, and Burr, *ibid.*, **67**, 1386 (1945).
63. Holman, Lundberg, and Burr, *ibid.*, **67**, 1390 (1945).
64. Holman, Lundberg, and Burr, *ibid.*, **67**, 1669 (1945).
65. Holman and Burr, *ibid.*, **68**, 562 (1946).
66. Brauer and Steadman, *ibid.*, **66**, 563 (1944).
67. Henderson and Young, *J. Phys. Chem.*, **46**, 670 (1942).
68. Atherton and Hilditch, *J. Chem. Soc.*, 105 (1944).
69. Gunstone and Hilditch, *ibid.*, 836 (1945).
70. Gunstone and Hilditch, *ibid.*, 1022 (1946).
71. Sutton, *ibid.*, 242 (1944).
72. Swift, Dollear, and O'Connor, *Oil & Soap*, **23**, 355 (1946).
73. Swern, Knight, Scanlan, and Ault, *J. Am. Chem. Soc.*, **67**, 1132 (1945).
74. Faith and Rollins, *Ind. Eng. Chem.*, **36**, 91 (1944).
75. Weinhouse, Medes, and Floyd, *J. Biol. Chem.*, **153**, 689 (1944); *ibid.*, **155**, 143 (1944).
76. Medes, Weinhouse, and Floyd, *ibid.*, **157**, 35 (1945).
77. Swern, Findley, and Scanlan, *J. Am. Chem. Soc.*, **66**, 1925 (1944); Findley, Swern, and Scanlan, *ibid.*, **67**, 412 (1945).
78. Swern, Billen, Findley, and Scanlan, *ibid.*, **67**, 1786 (1946).
79. Criegee, *Ber.*, **64B**, 260 (1931); *Ann.*, **495**, 211 (1933); Criegee, Kraft, and Rank, *ibid.*, **507**, 159 (1933).
80. Scanlan and Swern, *J. Am. Chem. Soc.*, **62**, 2305, 2309 (1940).
81. Kass and Radlove, *ibid.*, **64**, 2253 (1942).
82. King, *J. Chem. Soc.*, 218 (1942).
83. Robertson, Hartwell, and Kornberg, *J. Am. Chem. Soc.*, **66**, 1894 (1944).
84. Golumbic, *ibid.*, **63**, 1142 (1941).
85. Golumbic, *ibid.*, **64**, 2337 (1942).
86. Calkins and Mattill, *ibid.*, **66**, 239 (1944).
87. Calkins, *ibid.*, **69**, 384 (1947).
88. Lundberg, Halvorson, and Burr, *Oil & Soap*, **21**, 33 (1944).
89. Schaeffer, Roe, Dixon, and Ault, *J. Am. Chem. Soc.*, **66**, 1924 (1944).
90. Guest and Goddard, *ibid.*, **66**, 2074 (1944).
91. Guest, *ibid.*, **69**, 300 (1947).
92. Cheronis and Spitzmueller, *J. Org. Chem.*, **6**, 349 (1941); Sisler and Cheronis, *ibid.*, **6**, 467 (1941).
93. Bradley and Richardson, *Ind. Eng. Chem.*, **34**, 237 (1942).
94. Radlove, Teeter, Bond, Cowan, and Kass, *ibid.*, **38**, 997 (1946).
95. Ross, Gebhart, and Gerecht, *J. Am. Chem. Soc.*, **67**, 1275 (1945).
96. Cann and Amstutz, *ibid.*, **66**, 839 (1944).
97. Cowan and Wheeler, *ibid.*, **66**, 84 (1944).

98. Cowan, Ault, and Teeter, *Ind. Eng. Chem.*, **38**, 1138 (1946).
99. Sheppard and Burton, *J. Am. Chem. Soc.*, **68**, 1636 (1946).
100. Lind, Bardwell, and Perry, *ibid.*, **48**, 1556 (1926).
101. Bell, Goodman, and Whitehead, *Bull. Am. Assoc. Petroleum Geol.*, **24**, 1529 (1940).
102. Tiratsoo, *Petroleum*, **4**, 58 (1941).
103. Smith and Reichardt, *J. Am. Chem. Soc.*, **63**, 605 (1941).
104. Fairclough and Hinshelwood, *J. Chem. Soc.*, 593 (1939).
105. Gibling, *ibid.*, 299 (1941).
106. Hoback, Parsons, and Bartlett, *J. Am. Chem. Soc.*, **65**, 1606 (1943).
107. Kester, Gaiser, and Lazar, *J. Org. Chem.*, **8**, 550 (1943).
108. Norris and Terry, *Oil & Soap*, **21**, 193 (1944).
109. Swern, Stirton, Turer, and Wells, *ibid.*, **20**, 224 (1943).
110. Riemenschneider, Turer, Wells, and Ault, *ibid.*, **21**, 47 (1944).
111. Carson and Maclay, *J. Am. Chem. Soc.*, **66**, 1609 (1944).
112. Swern and Jordan, *ibid.*, **67**, 902 (1945).
113. Swern, Jordan, and Knight, *ibid.*, **68**, 1673 (1946).
114. Brown and Partridge, *ibid.*, **66**, 839 (1944).
115. Front and Daubert, *ibid.*, **67**, 1509 (1945).
116. Connor and Wright, *ibid.*, **68**, 256 (1946).
117. Fuller, Frosch, and Pape, *ibid.*, **64**, 154 (1942).
118. Yager and Baker, *ibid.*, **64**, 2164 (1942).
119. Brandner, Hunter, Brewster, and Bonner, *Ind. Eng. Chem.*, **37**, 809 (1945).
120. Burrell, *ibid.*, **37**, 86 (1945).
121. Teeter and Cowan, *Oil & Soap*, **22**, 177 (1945).
122. Waters, *J. Chem. Soc.*, 966 (1946).
123. Bergmann and Haskelberg, *J. Am. Chem. Soc.*, **63**, 2243 (1941).
124. Phillips and Pitt, *ibid.*, **65**, 1355 (1943).
125. Houston, *ibid.*, **62**, 1303 (1940).
126. Robertson, *J. Chem. Soc.*, **115**, 1210 (1919).
127. Acree and LaForge, *J. Org. Chem.*, **2**, 308 (1937).
128. Cowan, Lewis, and Falkenburg, *Oil & Soap*, **21**, 101 (1944); Falkenburg, Teeter, Skell, and Cowan, *ibid.*, **22**, 143 (1945).
129. Baker and Yager, *J. Am. Chem. Soc.*, **64**, 2171 (1942).
130. Rideal and Mitchell, *Proc. Roy. Soc. (London)*, **159A**, 206 (1937).
131. Carpenter, *J. Am. Chem. Soc.*, **62**, 289 (1940).
132. Koebner, *J. Chem. Soc.*, 564 (1941).
133. Linsker and Evans, *J. Am. Chem. Soc.*, **67**, 1581 (1945).
134. Schneider, *Ber.*, **28**, 3072 (1895).
135. Stross and Evans, *J. Am. Chem. Soc.*, **64**, 2511 (1942).
136. Kornblum and Oliveto, *ibid.*, **69**, 465 (1947).
137. Horswell and Silverman, *Ind. Eng. Chem., Anal. Ed.*, **13**, 555 (1941).
138. Baltzly, Ide, and Buck, *J. Am. Chem. Soc.*, **64**, 2514 (1942).
139. Shelton, Van Campen, Tilford, Lang, Nisonger, Bandelin, and Rubenkoenig, *ibid.*, **68**, 753, 755, 757 (1946).
140. Holmes, Corbet, Geiger, Kornblum, and Alexander, *ibid.*, **63**, 2607 (1941).
141. Hardegger, Ruzicka, and Tagmann, *Helv. Chim. Acta*, **26**, 2205 (1943); Prelog, Ruzicka, and Stern, *ibid.*, **26**, 222 (1943).
142. Baer and Fischer, *J. Biol. Chem.*, **140**, 397 (1941).

143. Baer, Rubin, and Fischer, *ibid.*, **155**, 447 (1944).
144. Kornblum and Holmes, *J. Am. Chem. Soc.*, **64**, 3045 (1942).
145. Koonce and Brown, *Oil & Soap*, **21**, 231 (1944).
146. Lester and Bergmann, *J. Org. Chem.*, **6**, 120 (1941).
147. Stetten and Schoenheimer, *J. Biol. Chem.*, **133**, 347 (1940).
148. Hansley, *Ind. Eng. Chem.*, **39**, 55 (1947).
149. Hass, McBee, and Churchill, *ibid.*, **37**, 445 (1945).
150. McLellan and Edwards, *J. Am. Chem. Soc.*, **66**, 409 (1944).
151. Williams and Edwards, *ibid.*, **69**, 336 (1947).
152. Mason, *ibid.*, **67**, 1538 (1945).
153. Dawson, Wasserman, and Keil, *ibid.*, **68**, 534 (1946).
154. Keil, Wasserman, and Dawson, *J. Exptl. Med.*, **80**, 275 (1944).
155. Meadoe and Reid, *J. Am. Chem. Soc.*, **65**, 457 (1943).
156. Jesurun, *Ber.*, **26**, 2286 (1893).
157. Ward and Jenkins, *J. Org. Chem.*, **10**, 371 (1945).
158. Appleby, Dobratz, and Kapranos, *J. Am. Chem. Soc.*, **66**, 1938 (1944).
159. Komarewsky, Uhlick, and Murray, *ibid.*, **67**, 557 (1945).
160. Badin, *ibid.*, **65**, 1809 (1943).
161. Komarewsky, Price, and Coley, *ibid.*, **69**, 238 (1947).
162. Dunbar and Arnold, *J. Org. Chem.*, **10**, 501 (1945).
163. Mattox, *J. Am. Chem. Soc.*, **66**, 2059 (1944).
164. Shaw, *ibid.*, **66**, 2057 (1944).
165. Badgett, Provost, Ogg, and Woodward, *ibid.*, **67**, 1135 (1945).
166. Morris and Riemenschneider, *ibid.*, **68**, 500 (1946).
167. Falkenburg, Teeter, and Cowan, *ibid.*, **69**, 486 (1947).
168. Weaver and Whaley, *ibid.*, **68**, 2115 (1946).
169. Rehberg and Fisher, *ibid.*, **66**, 1203 (1944).
170. McMillan, *ibid.*, **67**, 2271 (1945).
171. Feagan and Copenhaver, *ibid.*, **62**, 869 (1940).
172. Gordon and Aronowitz, *Ind. Eng. Chem.*, **37**, 780 (1945).
173. Baker, Fuller, and Heiss, *J. Am. Chem. Soc.*, **63**, 2142 (1941).
174. Vogel, *J. Chem. Soc.*, 636 (1943).
175. Audsley and Goss, *ibid.*, 358 (1942).
176. Steinhardt and Fugitt, *J. Research Natl. Bur. Standards*, **29**, 315 (1942).
177. Lauer, Sanders, Leekley, and Ungnade, *J. Am. Chem. Soc.*, **61**, 3050 (1939).
178. Reid and Wilson, *ibid.*, **64**, 1625 (1942).
179. Grummitt and Hall, *ibid.*, **66**, 1229 (1944).
180. Lester, Rodgers, and Reid, *ibid.*, **66**, 1674 (1944).
181. Hall and Reid, *ibid.*, **65**, 1466 (1943).
182. Marvel, Adams, and Johnson, *ibid.*, **68**, 2735 (1946).
183. Smith, *ibid.*, **68**, 2064 (1946).
184. Adams and Ulich, *ibid.*, **42**, 599 (1920).
185. Wood, Jackson, Baldwin, and Longenecker, *ibid.*, **66**, 287 (1944).
186. Cottle, *ibid.*, **68**, 1380 (1946).
187. English and Velick, *ibid.*, **67**, 1413 (1945).
188. Anchel and Waelsch, *J. Biol. Chem.*, **145**, 605 (1942).
189. Anchel and Waelsch, *ibid.*, **152**, 501 (1944).
190. Airs, Firth, and Garner, *J. Chem. Soc.*, 1089 (1946).

191. Henne and Hill, *J. Am. Chem. Soc.*, **65**, 752 (1943).
192. Henne and Perilstein, *ibid.*, **65**, 2183 (1943).
193. Reeve and Adkins, *ibid.*, **62**, 2874 (1940).
194. Suen and Fan, *ibid.*, **64**, 1460 (1942).
195. Suen and Fan, *ibid.*, **65**, 1243 (1943).
196. Willgerodt, *Ber.*, **20**, 2467 (1887); *ibid.*, **21**, 534 (1888).
197. Cavalieri, Pattison, and Carmack, *J. Am. Chem. Soc.*, **67**, 1783 (1945).
198. King and McMillan, *ibid.*, **68**, 525, 632 (1946).
199. King and McMillan, *ibid.*, **68**, 1369 (1946).
200. Seyer, Patterson, and Keays, *ibid.*, **66**, 179 (1944).
201. Moullin, *Proc. Cambridge Phil. Soc.*, **34**, 459 (1938).
202. Vogel, *J. Chem. Soc.*, 133 (1946).
203. Knowlton and Huffman, *J. Am. Chem. Soc.*, **66**, 1492 (1944).
204. Parks, West, Naylor, Fujii, and McClaine, *ibid.*, **68**, 2524 (1946).
205. Fischl, Naylor, Ziemer, Parks, and Aston, *ibid.*, **67**, 2075 (1945).
206. Felsing and Watson, *ibid.*, **64**, 1822 (1942).
207. Sherk, Augur, and Soffer, *ibid.*, **67**, 2239 (1945).
208. Whitmore, Herr, Clarke, Rowland, and Schiessler, *ibid.*, **67**, 2059 (1945).
209. Gilman and Turck, *ibid.*, **61**, 478 (1939).
210. Gilman and Meals, *J. Org. Chem.*, **8**, 126 (1943).
211. Grummitt, Sensel, Smith, Burk, and Lankelma, *J. Am. Chem. Soc.*, **67**, 910 (1945).
212. Henne and Greenlee, *ibid.*, **67**, 484 (1945).
213. Vaughn, Hennion, Vogt, and Nieuwland, *J. Org. Chem.*, **2**, 1 (1937).
214. Hennion and Banigan, *J. Am. Chem. Soc.*, **68**, 1381 (1946).
215. Campbell and Eby, *ibid.*, **63**, 2683 (1941).
216. Zuffanti, *ibid.*, **63**, 3123 (1941).
217. Ryer, *Oil & Soap*, **23**, 310 (1946).
218. Smith and Ross, *ibid.*, **23**, 77 (1946).
219. Ross and McBain, *ibid.*, **23**, 214 (1946).
220. Meals, *J. Org. Chem.*, **9**, 211 (1944).
221. Morton, Davidson, and Best, *J. Am. Chem. Soc.*, **64**, 2239 (1942).
222. Morton, Richardson, and Hallowell, *ibid.*, **63**, 327 (1941).
223. Morton and Richardson, *ibid.*, **62**, 123 (1940).
224. Whitmore, Sommer, Di Giorgio, Strong, Van Strien, Bailey, Hall, Pietrusza, and Kerr, *ibid.*, **68**, 475 (1946).
225. Sommer, Pietrusza, and Whitmore, *ibid.*, **69**, 188 (1947).

INDEX

DATE DUE